Mathematical Excursions

Custom Edition for Pasadena City College

Second Edition

Richard N. Aufmann | Joanne S. Lockwood | Richard D. Nation |
Daniel K. Clegg

CENGAGE
Learning™

Australia • Brazil • Japan • Korea • Mexico • Singapore • Spain • United Kingdom • United States

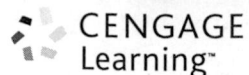
CENGAGE
Learning™

**Mathematical Excursionse: Custom Edition
for Pasadena City College, Second Edition**

Executive Editors:
Maureen Staudt
Michael Stranz

Senior Project Development Manager:
Linda deStefano

Marketing Specialist:
Courtney Sheldon

Senior Production/Manufacturing Manager:
Donna M. Brown

PreMedia Manager:
Joel Brennecke

Sr. Rights Acquisition Account Manager:
Todd Osborne

Cover Image:
Getty Images*

*Unless otherwise noted, all cover images used by Custom
Solutions, a part of Cengage Learning, have been supplied
courtesy of Getty Images with the exception of the Earthview
cover image, which has been supplied by the National
Aeronautics and Space Administration (NASA).

Mathematical Excursions, 2nd Edition
Richard N. Aufmann | Joanne S. Lockwood | Richard D. Nation | Daniel K. Clegg

For product information and technology assistance, contact us at
Cengage Learning Customer & Sales Support, 1-800-354-9706

For permission to use material from this text or product,
submit all requests online at **cengage.com/permissions**
Further permissions questions can be emailed to
permissionrequest@cengage.com

This book contains select works from existing Cengage Learning resources and
was produced by Cengage Learning Custom Solutions for collegiate use. As such,
those adopting and/or contributing to this work are responsible for editorial
content accuracy, continuity and completeness.

Compilation © 2011 Cengage Learning

ISBN-13: 978-1-133-62044-0

ISBN-10: 1-133-62044-2

Cengage Learning
5191 Natorp Boulevard
Mason, Ohio 45040
USA

Cengage Learning is a leading provider of customized learning solutions with
office locations around the globe, including Singapore, the United Kingdom,
Australia, Mexico, Brazil, and Japan. Locate your local office at:
international.cengage.com/region.

Cengage Learning products are represented in Canada by Nelson Education, Ltd.
For your lifelong learning solutions, visit **www.cengage.com/custom.**
Visit our corporate website at **www.cengage.com.**

Custom Brief Contents

SPECIAL FEATURES Created by Jessica Valentine:

- Managing Your Time
- Calculating How Busy You Are: A Reality Check

CONTENTS

CHAPTER

Problem Solving *1*

CHAPTER

Sets *52*

CHAPTER

Logic *113*

CHAPTER

Numeration Systems and Number Theory *177*

CHAPTER

Applications of Equations *245*

CHAPTER

Applications of Functions   *327*

CHAPTER

Mathematical Systems   *407*

CHAPTER

The Mathematics of Finance *641*

CHAPTER

Combinatorics and Probability *719*

Mathematical Excursions is about mathematics as a system of knowing or understanding our surroundings. It is similar to an English literature textbook, an Introduction to Philosophy textbook, or perhaps an Introductory Psychology textbook. Each of those books provide glimpses into the thoughts and perceptions of some of the world's greatest writers, philosophers, and psychologists. Reading and studying their thoughts enables us to better understand the world we inhabit.

In a similar way, Mathematical Excursions provides glimpses into the nature of mathematics and how it is used to understand our world. This understanding, in conjunction with other disciplines, contributes to a more complete portrait of our world. Our contention is that ancient Greek architecture is quite dramatic but even more so when the "Golden Ratio" is considered. That I. M. Pei's work becomes even more interesting with a knowledge of elliptical shapes. That the challenges of sending information across the Internet is better understood by examining prime numbers. That the perils of radioactive waste take on new meaning with a knowledge of exponential functions. That generally, a knowledge of mathematics strengthens the way we know, perceive, and understand our surroundings.

The central purpose of Mathematical Excursions is to explore those facets of mathematics that will strengthen your quantitative understandings of our environs. We hope you enjoy the journey.

New to This Edition

- Reading and interpreting graphs has been expanded to allow students more practice with this important topic.

- Chapter 8, Geometry, has been expanded to include the Pythagorean Theorem and congruent triangles.

- An introduction to right triangle trigonometry has been added to Chapter 8, Geometry.

- Chapter 10, Finance, has expanded coverage of stocks, bonds, and annuities.

- There is an Algebra Review Appendix that can be downloaded from the web as a PDF.

- All the exercise sets have been reviewed and new, contemporary problems have been added.

page 252

Interactive Method

An Interactive Approach

Mathematical Excursions, Second Edition, is written in a style that encourages the student to interact with the textbook. Each section contains a variety of worked examples. Each example is given a title so that the student can see at a glance the type of problem that is being solved. Most examples include annotations that assist the student in moving from step to step, and the final answer is in color in order to be readily identifiable.

Check Your Progress Exercises

Following each worked example is a Check Your Progress exercise for the student to work. By solving this exercise, the student actively practices concepts as they are presented in the text. For each Check Your Progress exercise, there is a detailed solution in the Solutions appendix.

Question/Answer Feature

At various places throughout the text, a Question is posed about the topic that is being developed. This question encourages students to pause, think about the current discussion, and answer the question. Students can immediately check their understanding by referring to the Answer to the question provided in a footnote on the same page. This feature creates another opportunity for the student to interact with the textbook.

page 450

Interactive Method, *continued*

Excursions

Each section ends with an Excursion along with corresponding Excursion Exercises. These activities engage students in the mathematics of the section. Some Excursions are designed as in-class cooperative learning activities that lend themselves to a hands-on approach. They can also be assigned as projects or extra credit assignments. The Excursions are a unique and important feature of this text. They provide opportunities for students to take an active role in the learning process.

---

774   Chapter 11 • Combinatorics and Probability

Excursion

Sharing Birthdays

Have you ever been introduced to someone at a party or other social gathering and discovered that you share the same birthday? It seems like an amazing coincidence when it occurs. In fact, how rare is this?

As an example, suppose four people have gathered for a dinner party. We can determine the probability that at least two of the guests have the same birthday. (For simplicity, we will ignore the February 29th birthday from leap years.) Let E be the event that at least two people share a birthday. It is easier to look at the complement E^c, the event that no one shares the same birthday.

If we start with one of the guests, then the second guest cannot share the same birthday, so that person has 364 possible dates for his or her birthday from a total of 365. Thus the conditional probability that the second guest has a different birthday, given that we know the first person's birthday, is $\frac{364}{365}$. Similarly, the third person has 363 possible birthday dates that do not coincide with those of the first two guests. So the conditional probability that the third person does not share a birthday with either of the first two guests, given that we know the birthdays of the first two people, is $\frac{363}{365}$. The probability of the fourth guest having a distinct birthday is, similarly, $\frac{362}{365}$. We can use the Product Rule for Probabilities to find the probability that all of these conditions are met; that is, none of the four guests share a birthday.

$$P(E^c) = \frac{364}{365} \cdot \frac{363}{365} \cdot \frac{362}{365} \approx 0.984$$

Then $P(E) = 1 - P(E^c) \approx 0.016$, so there is about a 1.6% chance that in a group of four people, two or more have the same birthday.

It would require 366 people gathered together to *guarantee* that two people in the group will have the same birthday. But how many people would be required to guarantee that the chance that at least two of them share the same birthday is at least 50/50? Make a guess before you proceed through the exercises. The results may surprise you!

Excursion Exercises

1. If eight people are present at a meeting, find the probability that at least two share a common birthday.

2. Compute the probability that at least two people among a group of 15 have the same birthday.

3. If 23 people are in attendance at a party, what is the probability that at least two share a birthday?

4. In a group of 40 people, what would you estimate to be the probability that at least two people share a birthday? If you have the patience, compute the probability to check your guess.

page 774

AIM for Success Student Preface

This 'how to use this text' preface explains what is required of a student to be successful and how this text has been designed to foster student success. AIM for Success can be used as a lesson on the first day of class or as a project for students to complete to strengthen their study skills.

AIM FOR SUCCESS

Welcome to *Mathematical Excursions*, second edition. As you begin this course we know two important facts: (1) You want to succeed. (2) We want you to succeed. In order to accomplish these goals, an effort is required from each of us. For the next few pages, we are going to show you what is required of you to achieve your goal and how we have designed this text to help you succeed.

✓ **TAKE NOTE**

Motivation alone will not lead to success. For instance, suppose a person who cannot swim is placed in a boat, taken out to the middle of a lake, and then thrown overboard. That person has a lot of motivation to swim but there is a high likelihood that the person will drown without some help. Motivation gives us the desire to learn but is not the same as learning.

Motivation

One of the most important keys to success is motivation. We can try to motivate you by offering interesting or important ways that you can benefit from mathematics. But, in the end, the motivation must come from you. On the first day of class it is easy to be motivated. Eight weeks into the term, it is harder to keep that motivation.

To stay motivated, there must be outcomes from this course that are worth your time, money, and energy. List some reasons you are taking this course. Do not make a mental list—actually write them out. Do this now.

Although we hope that one of the reasons you listed was an interest in mathematics, we know that many of you are taking this course because it is required to graduate, it is a prerequisite for a course you must take, or because it is required for your major. Although you may not agree that this course should be necessary, it is! If you are motivated to graduate or complete the requirements for your major, then use that motivation to succeed in this course. Do not become distracted from your goal to complete your education!

Commitment

To be successful, you must make a commitment to succeed. This means devoting time to math so that you achieve a better understanding of the subject.

List some activities (sports, hobbies, talents such as dance, art, or music) that you enjoy and at which you would like to become better. Do this now.

Next to these activities, put the number of hours each week that you spend practicing these activities.

Whether you listed surfing or sailing, aerobics or restoring cars, or any other activity you enjoy, note how many hours a week you spend on each activity. To succeed in math, you must be willing to commit the same amount of time. Success requires some sacrifice.

The "I Can't Do Math" Syndrome

There may be things you cannot do, for instance, lift a two-ton boulder. You can, however, do math. It is much easier to learn than lifting the two-ton boulder. When you first learned the activities you listed above, you probably could not do them well. With practice, you got better. With practice, you will be better at math. Stay focused, motivated, and committed to success.

xix

page xix

Math Matters and Margin Notes

page 366

Math Matters

This feature of the text typically contains an interesting sidelight about mathematics, its history, or its applications.

Historical Note

These margin notes provide historical background information related to the concept under discussion or vignettes of individuals who were responsible for major advancements in their fields of expertise.

Point of Interest

These notes provide interesting information related to the topics under discussion. Many of these are of a contemporary nature and, as such, they provide students with the needed motivation for studying concepts that may at first seem abstract and obscure without this information.

Take Note

These notes alert students to a point requiring special attention or are used to amplify the concepts that are currently being developed. Some Take Notes, identified by ⊙, reference the student CD. A student who needs to review a prerequisite skill or concept can find the needed material on this CD.

Calculator Note

These notes provide information about how to use the various features of a calculator.

page 475

Exercises

Exercise Sets

The exercise sets were carefully written to provide a wide variety of exercises that range from drill and practice to interesting challenges. Exercise sets emphasize skill building, skill maintenance, concepts, and applications, when they are appropriate. Icons are used to identify various types of exercise.

Writing exercises

Data analysis exercises

Graphing calculator exercises

Internet exercises

page 388

Extensions

Extension exercises are placed at the end of each exercise set. These exercises are designed to extend concepts. In most cases these exercises are more challenging and require more time and effort than the preceding exercises. The Extension exercises always include at least two of the following types of exercises:

Critical Thinking
Cooperative Learning
Explorations

Some Critical Thinking exercises require the application of two or more procedures or concepts.

The Cooperative Learning exercises are designed for small groups of 2 to 4 students.

Many of the Exploration exercises require students to search on the Internet or through reference materials in a library.

page 756

End of Chapter

Chapter Summary

At the end of each chapter there is a Chapter Summary that includes *Key Terms* and *Essential Concepts* that were covered in the chapter. These chapter summaries provide a single point of reference as the student prepares for an examination. Each key word references the page number where the word was first introduced.

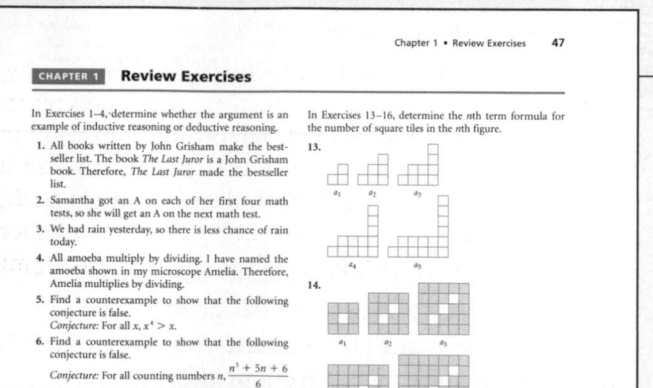

page 46

Chapter Review Exercises

Review exercises are found near the end of each chapter. These exercises were selected to help the student integrate the major topics presented in the chapter. The answers to all the Chapter Review Exercises appear in the answer section along with a section reference for each exercise. These section references indicate the section or sections where a student can locate the concepts needed to solve each exercise.

page 47

Chapter Test

The Chapter Test exercises are designed to emulate a possible test of the material in the chapter. The answers to all the Chapter Test exercises appear in the answer section along with a section reference for each exercise. The section references indicate the section or sections where a student can locate the concepts needed to solve each exercise.

page 566

Supplements for the Instructor

Mathematical Excursions, Second Edition, has an extensive support package for the instructor that includes:

Instructor's Annotated Edition (IAE): The *Instructor's Annotated Edition* is an exact replica of the student textbook with the following additional text-specific items for the instructor: answers to *all* of the end-of-section and end-of-chapter exercises, answers to *all* Excursion and Exploration exercises, Instructor Notes, Suggested Assignments, and 🅟 icons denoting tables and art that appear in PowerPoint® slides. (The files can be downloaded from our website at **www.cengage.com/math**).

Online Teaching Center: This free companion website contains an abundance of instructor resources such as solutions to all exercises in the text, digital art and tables, suggested course syllabi, Chapter Tests, Graphing Calculator Guide, and Microsoft® Excel spreadsheets. Visit **www.cengage.com/math** and choose *Mathematical Excursions,* 2/e, from the list provided on the site.

Online Instructor's Solutions Manual: The *Online Instructor's Solutions Manual* offers worked-out solutions to *all* of the exercises in each exercise set as well as solutions to the Excursion and Exploration exercises.

CL ClassPrep™ with Diploma Testing CD-ROM (powered by Diploma™): This CD-ROM is a combination of two course management tools.

- *Diploma Testing* (powered by *Diploma*) offers instructors a flexible and powerful tool for test generation and test management. Now supported by the Brownstone Research Group's market-leading *Diploma* software, this new version of *Diploma Testing* significantly improves on functionality and ease of use by offering all the tools needed to create, author, deliver, and customize multiple types of tests—including authoring and editing algorithmic questions. *Diploma* is currently in use at thousands of college and university campuses throughout the United States and Canada.

- CL ClassPrep also features the same text-specific resources for the instructor that are available on the Online Teaching Center.

Supplements for the Student

Mathematical Excursions, Second Edition, has an extensive support package for the student that includes:

Student Solutions Manual: The *Student Solutions Manual* contains complete, worked-out solutions to *all* odd-numbered exercises and *all* of the solutions to the Chapter Reviews and Chapter Tests in the text.

Online Study Center: This free companion website contains an abundance of student resources such as binary cards, Graphing Calculator Guide, and Microsoft® Excel spreadsheets.

Online CLAST Preparation Guide: The CLAST Preparation Guide is a competency-based study guide that reviews and offers preparatory material for the CLAST (College Level Academic Skills Test) objectives required by the State of Florida for mathematics. The guide includes a correlation of the CLAST objectives to the *Mathematical Excursions*, Second Edition, text, worked-out examples, practice examples, cumulative reviews, and sample diagnostic tests with grading sheets.

Online Study Center® Student Tutorial CD ROM ⊚ : This tutorial provides opportunities for self-paced review and practice with algorithmically generated exercises and step-by-step solutions.

Cengage Learning Instructional DVDs: These text-specific DVDs, professionally produced by Dana Mosely, provide explanations of key concepts, examples, and exercises in a lecture-based format. They offer students a valuable resource for further instruction and review. They also provide support for students in online courses.

Acknowledgments

The authors would like to thank the people who have reviewed this manuscript and provided many valuable suggestions.

Brenda Alberico, *College of DuPage*

Beverly R. Broomell, *Suffolk County Community College*

Henjin Chi, *Indiana State University*

Ivette Chuca, *El Paso Community College*

Marcella Cremer, *Richland Community College*

Kenny Fister, *Murray State University*

Luke Foster, *Northeastern State University*

Rita Fox, *Kalamazoo Valley Community College*

Sue Grapevine, *Northwest Iowa Community College*

Shane Griffith, *Lee University*

Dr. Nancy R. Johnson, *Manatee Community College*

Dr. Vernon Kays, *Richland Community College*

Dr. Suda Kunyosying, *Shepherd College*

Kathryn Lavelle, *Westchester Community College*

Roger Marty, *Cleveland State University*

Eric Matsuoka, *Leeward Community College*

Beverly Meyers, *Jefferson College*

Dr. Alec Mihailovs, *Shepherd University*

Bette Nelson, *Alvin Community College*

Kathleen Offenholley, *Brookdale Community College*

Kathy Pinchback, *University of Memphis*

Michael Polley, *Southeastern Community College*

Dr. Anne Quinn, *Edinboro University of Pennsylvania*

Brenda Reed, *Navarro College*

Marc Renault, *Shippensburg University*

Chistopher Rider, *North Greenville College*

Sharon M. Saxton, *Cascadia Community College*

Mary Lee Seitz, *Erie Community College—City Campus*

Dr. Sue Stokley, *Spartanburg Technical College*

Dr. Julie M. Theoret, *Lyndon State College*

Walter Jacob Theurer, *Fulton Montgomery Community College*

Jamie Thomas, *University of Wisconsin Colleges—Manitowoc*

William Twentyman, *ECPI College of Technology*

Denise A. Widup, *University of Wisconsin—Parkside*

Nancy Wilson, *Marshall University*

Jane-Marie Wright, *Suffolk Community College*

Welcome to *Mathematical Excursions,* Second Edition. As you begin this course, we know two important facts: (1) You want to succeed. (2) We want you to succeed. In order to accomplish these goals, an effort is required from each of us. For the next few pages, we are going to show you what is required of you to achieve your goal and how we have designed this text to help you succeed.

Motivation

One of the most important keys to success is motivation. We can try to motivate you by offering interesting or important ways that you can benefit from mathematics. But, in the end, the motivation must come from you. On the first day of class it is easy to be motivated. Eight weeks into the term, it is harder to keep that motivation.

To stay motivated, there must be outcomes from this course that are worth your time, money, and energy. List some reasons you are taking this course. Do not make a mental list—actually write them out. Do this now.

Although we hope that one of the reasons you listed was an interest in mathematics, we know that many of you are taking this course because it is required to graduate, it is a prerequisite for a course you must take, or because it is required for your major. Although you may not agree that this course should be necessary, it is! If you are motivated to graduate or complete the requirements for your major, then use that motivation to succeed in this course. Do not become distracted from your goal to complete your education!

Commitment

To be successful, you must make a commitment to succeed. This means devoting time to math so that you achieve a better understanding of the subject.

List some activities (sports, hobbies, talents such as dance, art, or music) that you enjoy and at which you would like to become better. Do this now.

Next to these activities, put the number of hours each week that you spend practicing these activities.

Whether you listed surfing or sailing, aerobics or restoring cars, or any other activity you enjoy, note how many hours a week you spend on each activity. To succeed in math, you must be willing to commit the same amount of time. Success requires some sacrifice.

The "I Can't Do Math" Syndrome

There may be things you cannot do, for instance, lift a two-ton boulder. You can, however, do math. It is much easier than lifting the two-ton boulder. When you first learned the activities you listed above, you probably could not do them well. With practice, you got better. With practice, you will be better at math. Stay focused, motivated, and committed to success.

✔ TAKE NOTE

Motivation alone will not lead to success. For instance, suppose a person who cannot swim is placed in a boat, taken out to the middle of a lake, and then thrown overboard. That person has a lot of motivation to swim but there is a high likelihood the person will drown without some help. Motivation gives us the desire to learn but is not the same as learning.

It is difficult for us to emphasize how important it is to overcome the "I Can't Do Math Syndrome." If you listen to interviews of very successful athletes after a particularly bad performance, you will note that they focus on the positive aspect of what they did, not the negative. Sports psychologists encourage athletes to always be positive—to have a "Can Do" attitude. You need to develop this attitude toward math.

Strategies for Success

Know the Course Requirements   To do your best in this course, you must know exactly what your instructor requires. Course requirements may be stated in a *syllabus,* which is a printed outline of the main topics of the course, or they may be presented orally. When they are listed in a syllabus or on other printed pages, keep them in a safe place. When they are presented orally, make sure to take complete notes. In either case, it is important that you understand them completely and follow them exactly. Be sure you know the answer to each of the following questions.

1. What is your instructor's name?

2. Where is your instructor's office?

3. At what times does your instructor hold office hours?

4. Besides the textbook, what other materials does your instructor require?

5. What is your instructor's attendance policy?

6. If you must be absent from a class meeting, what should you do before returning to class? What should you do when you return to class?

7. What is the instructor's policy regarding collection or grading of homework assignments?

8. What options are available if you are having difficulty with an assignment? Is there a math tutoring center?

9. If there is a math lab at your school, where is it located? What hours is it open?

10. What is the instructor's policy if you miss a quiz?

11. What is the instructor's policy if you miss an exam?

12. Where can you get help when studying for an exam?

Remember: Your instructor wants to see you succeed. If you need help, ask! Do not fall behind. If you were running a race and fell behind by 100 yards, you may be able to catch up but it will require more effort than had you not fallen behind.

Time Management   We know that there are demands on your time. Family, work, friends, and entertainment all compete for your time. We do not want to see you receive poor job evaluations because you are studying math. However, it is also true that we do not want to see you receive poor math test scores because you devoted too much time to work. When several competing and important tasks require your time and energy, the only way to manage the stress of being successful at both is to manage your time efficiently.

Instructors often advise students to spend twice the amount of time outside of class studying as they spend in the classroom. Time management is important if you are to accomplish this goal and succeed in school. The following activity is intended to help you structure your time more efficiently.

✔ **TAKE NOTE**

Besides time management, there must be realistic ideas of how much time is available. There are very few people who can *successfully* work full-time and go to school full-time. If you work 40 hours a week, take 15 units, spend the recommended study time given at the right, and sleep 8 hours a day, you will use over 80% of the available hours in a week. That leaves less than 20% of the hours in a week for family, friends, eating, recreation, and other activities.

Take out a sheet of paper and list the names of each course you are taking this term, the number of class hours each course meets, and the number of hours you should spend outside of class studying course materials. Now create a weekly calendar with the days of the week across the top and each hour of the day in a vertical column. Fill in the calendar with the hours you are in class, the hours you spend at work, and other commitments such as sports practice, music lessons, or committee meetings. Then fill in the hours that are more flexible, for example, study time, recreation, and meal times.

	Monday	Tuesday	Wednesday	Thursday	Friday	Saturday	Sunday
10–11 a.m.	History	Rev Spanish	History	Rev Span Vocab	History	Jazz Band	
11–12 p.m.	Rev History	Spanish	Study group	Spanish	Math tutor	Jazz Band	
12–1 p.m.	Math		Math		Math		Soccer

We know that many of you must work. If that is the case, realize that working 10 hours a week at a part-time job is equivalent to taking a three-unit class. If you must work, consider letting your education progress at a slower rate to allow you to be successful at both work and school. There is no rule that says you must finish school in a certain time frame.

Schedule Study Time   As we encouraged you to do by filling out the time management form, schedule a certain time to study. You should think of this time like being at work or class. Reasons for "missing study time" should be as compelling as reasons for missing work or class. "I just didn't feel like it" is not a good reason to miss your scheduled study time. Although this may seem like an obvious exercise, list a few reasons you might want to study. Do this now.

Of course we have no way of knowing the reasons you listed, but from our experience one reason given quite frequently is "To pass the course." There is nothing wrong with that reason. If that is the most important reason for you to study, then use it to stay focused.

One method of keeping to a study schedule is to form a ***study group***. Look for people who are committed to learning, who pay attention in class, and who are punctual. Ask them to join your group. Choose people with similar educational goals but different methods of learning. You can gain from seeing the material from a new perspective. Limit groups to four or five people; larger groups are unwieldy.

There are many ways to conduct a study group. Begin with the following suggestions and see what works best for your group.

1. Test each other by asking questions. Each group member might bring two or three sample test questions to each meeting.

2. Practice teaching each other. Many of us who are teachers learned a lot about our subject when we had to explain it to someone else.

3. Compare class notes. You might ask other students about material in your notes that is difficult for you to understand.

4. Brainstorm test questions.

5. Set an agenda for each meeting. Set approximate time limits for each agenda item and determine a quitting time.

And now, probably the most important aspect of studying is that it should be done in relatively small chunks. If you can only study three hours a week for this course (probably not enough for most people), do it in blocks of one hour on three separate days, preferably after class. Three hours of studying on a Sunday is not as productive as three hours of paced study.

Features of This Text That Promote Success

Preparing for Class   Before the class meeting in which your professor begins a new section, you should read the title of each section. Next, browse through the chapter material, being sure to note each word in bold type. These words indicate important concepts that you must know to learn the material. Do not worry about trying to understand all the material. Your professor is there to assist you with that endeavor. The purpose of browsing through the material is so that your brain will be prepared to accept and organize the new information when it is presented to you. Turn to page 794. Write down the title of Section 12.1.

Write down the words in the section that are in bold print. It is not necessary for you to understand the meaning of these words. You are in this class to learn their meaning.

Math is Not a Spectator Sport   To learn mathematics you must be an active participant. Listening and watching your professor do mathematics is not enough. Mathematics requires that you interact with the lesson you are studying. If you have been writing down the things we have asked you to do, you were being interactive. There are other ways this textbook has been designed so that you can be an active learner.

Check Your Progress   One of the key instructional features of this text is a completely worked-out example followed by a *Check Your Progress*.

✔ **TAKE NOTE**

If you have difficulty with a particular algebra topic, there is a computer tutorial that accompanies this text that can be used to refresh your skills. You will see references to this tutorial as you go through this text.

11.2 • Permutations and Combinations   **733**

EXAMPLE 3 ■ Counting Permutations

 In 2004, the Kentucky Derby had 18 horses entered in the race. How many different finishes of first, second, third, and fourth place were possible?

Solution

Because the order in which the horses finish the race is important, the number of possible finishes of first, second, third, and fourth place is $P(18, 4)$.

$$P(18, 4) = \frac{18!}{(18 - 4)!} = \frac{18!}{14!} = \frac{18 \cdot 17 \cdot 16 \cdot 15 \cdot 14!}{14!}$$
$$= 18 \cdot 17 \cdot 16 \cdot 15 = 73{,}440$$

There were 73,440 possible finishes of first, second, third, and fourth places.

CHECK YOUR PROGRESS 3   There were 42 cars entered in the 2004 Daytona 500 NASCAR race. How many different ways could first, second, and third place prizes be awarded?

Solution   See page S42.

page 733

Note that each Example is completely worked out and the *Check Your Progress* following the example is not. Study the worked-out example carefully by working through each step. Your should do this with paper and pencil.

Now work the *Check Your Progress*. If you get stuck, refer to the page number following the word *Solution* which directs you to the page on which the *Check Your Progress* is solved—a complete worked-out solution is provided. Try to use the given solution to get a hint for the step you are stuck on. Then try to complete your solution.

When you have completed the solution, check your work against the solution we provide.

CHECK YOUR PROGRESS 3, *page 733*

The order in which the cars finish is important, so the number of ways to place first, second, and third is

$$P(42, 3) = \frac{42!}{(42-3)!} = \frac{42 \cdot 41 \cdot 40 \cdot 39!}{39!} = 68,880$$

There are 68,880 different ways to award the first, second, and third place prizes.

---

page S42

Be aware that frequently there is more than one way to solve a problem. Your answer, however, should be the same as the given answer. If you have any question as to whether your method will "always work," check with your instructor or with someone in the math center.

Browse through the textbook and write down the page numbers where two other paired example features occur.

Remember: Be an active participant in your learning process. When you are sitting in class watching and listening to an explanation, you may think that you understand. However, until you actually try to do it, you will have no confirmation of the new knowledge or skill. Most of us have had the experience of sitting in class thinking we knew how to do something only to get home and realize we didn't.

Rule Boxes   Pay special attention to rules placed in boxes. These rules give you the reasons certain types of problems are solved the way they are. When you see a rule, try to rewrite the rule in your own words.

Simple Interest Formula

The simple interest formula is

$$I = Prt$$

where I is the interest, P is the principal, r is the interest rate, and t is the time period.

---

page 642

Chapter Exercises   When you have completed studying a section, do the section exercises. Math is a subject that needs to be learned in small sections and practiced continually in order to be mastered. Doing the exercises in each exercise set will help you master the problem-solving techniques necessary for success. As you work through the exercises, check your answers to the odd-numbered exercises with those in the back of the book.

Preparing for a Test   There are important features of this text that can be used to prepare for a test.

- Chapter Summary
- Chapter Review Exercises
- Chapter Test

After completing a chapter, read the Chapter Summary. (See page 109 for the Chapter 2 Summary.) This summary highlights the important topics covered in the chapter. The page number following each topic refers you to the page in the text on which you can find more information about the concept.

Following the Chapter Summary are Chapter Review Exercises (see page 110). Doing the review exercises is an important way of testing your understanding of the chapter. The answer to each review exercise is given at the back of the book, along with, in brackets, the section reference from which the question was taken (see page A3). After checking your answers, restudy any section from which a question you missed was taken. It may be helpful to retry some of the exercises for that section to reinforce your problem-solving techniques.

Each chapter ends with a Chapter Test (see page 112). This test should be used to prepare for an exam. We suggest that you try the Chapter Test a few days before your actual exam. Take the test in a quiet place and try to complete the test in the same amount of time you will be allowed for your exam. When taking the Chapter Test, practice the strategies of successful test takers: 1) scan the entire test to get a feel for the questions; 2) read the directions carefully; 3) work the problems that are easiest for you first; and perhaps most importantly, 4) try to stay calm.

When you have completed the Chapter Test, check your answers (see page A7). Next to each answer is, in brackets, the reference to the section from which the question was taken. If you missed a question, review the material in that section and rework some of the exercises from that section. This will strengthen your ability to perform the skills in that section.

Your career goal goes here. →

Is it difficult to be successful? YES! Successful music groups, artists, professional athletes, teachers, sociologist, chefs, and _____ have to work very hard to achieve their goals. They focus on their goals and ignore distractions. The things we ask you to do to achieve success take time and commitment. We are confident that if you follow our suggestions, you will succeed.

1 Problem Solving

1.1	Inductive and Deductive Reasoning
1.2	Problem Solving with Patterns
1.3	Problem-Solving Strategies

Most occupations require good problem-solving skills. For instance, architects and engineers must solve many complicated problems as they design and construct modern buildings that are aesthetically pleasing, functional, and that meet stringent safety requirements. Two goals of this chapter are to help you become a better problem solver and to demonstrate that problem solving can be an enjoyable experience.

One problem that many have enjoyed is the Monty Hall (host of the game show *Let's Make a Deal*) problem, which is stated as follows. The grand prize in *Let's Make a Deal* is behind one of three curtains. Less desirable prizes (for instance, a goat and a box of candy) are behind the other two curtains. You select one of the curtains, say curtain A. Monty Hall reveals one of the less desirable prizes behind one of the other curtains. You are then given the opportunity either to stay with your original choice or to choose the remaining closed curtain.

| Curtain A | Curtain B | Curtain C |

Marilyn vos Savant, author of the "Ask Marilyn" column featured in *Parade Magazine,* analyzed this problem,[1] claiming that you *double* your chances of winning the grand prize by switching to the other closed curtain. Many readers, including some mathematicians, responded with arguments that contradicted Marilyn's analysis.

What do you think? Do you have a better chance of winning the grand prize by switching to the other closed curtain or staying with your original choice?

Of course there is also the possibility that it does not matter, if the chances of winning are the same with either strategy.

Discuss the Monty Hall problem with some of your friends and classmates. Is everyone in agreement? Additional information on this problem is given in Exploration Exercise 56 on page 15.

 For online student resources, visit this textbook's website at **www.cengage.com/math.**

---

1. "Ask Marilyn," *Parade Magazine,* September 9, 1990, p. 15.

Inductive Reasoning

The type of reasoning that forms a conclusion based on the examination of specific examples is called *inductive reasoning*. The conclusion formed by using inductive reasoning is often called a **conjecture,** since it may or may not be correct.

> **Inductive reasoning** is the process of reaching a general conclusion by examining specific examples.

When you examine a list of numbers and predict the next number in the list according to some pattern you have observed, you are using inductive reasoning.

EXAMPLE 1 ■ Use Inductive Reasoning to Predict a Number

Use inductive reasoning to predict the most probable next number in each of the following lists.

a. 3, 6, 9, 12, 15, ?   **b.** 1, 3, 6, 10, 15, ?

Solution
a. Each successive number is 3 larger than the preceding number. Thus we predict that the most probable next number in the list is 3 larger than 15, which is 18.
b. The first two numbers differ by 2. The second and the third numbers differ by 3. It appears that the difference between any two numbers is always 1 more than the preceding difference. Since 10 and 15 differ by 5, we predict that the next number in the list will be 6 larger than 15, which is 21.

CHECK YOUR PROGRESS 1   Use inductive reasoning to predict the most probable next number in the following lists.

a. 5, 10, 15, 20, 25, ?   **b.** 2, 5, 10, 17, 26, ?

Solution   See page S1.

Inductive reasoning is not used just to predict the next number in a list. In Example 2 we use inductive reasoning to make a conjecture about an arithmetic procedure.

EXAMPLE 2 ■ Use Inductive Reasoning to Make a Conjecture

Consider the following procedure: Pick a number. Multiply the number by 8, add 6 to the product, divide the sum by 2, and subtract 3.

Complete the above procedure for several different numbers. Use inductive reasoning to make a conjecture about the relationship between the size of the resulting number and the size of the original number.

Solution

Suppose we pick 5 as our original number. Then the procedure would produce the following results:

Original number:	5
Multiply by 8:	$8 \times 5 = 40$
Add 6:	$40 + 6 = 46$
Divide by 2:	$46 \div 2 = 23$
Subtract 3:	$23 - 3 = 20$

We started with 5 and followed the procedure to produce 20. Starting with 6 as our original number produces a final result of 24. Starting with 10 produces a final result of 40. Starting with 100 produces a final result of 400. In each of these cases the resulting number is four times the original number. We *conjecture* that following the given procedure will produce a resulting number that is four times the original number.

CHECK YOUR PROGRESS 2   Consider the following procedure: Pick a number. Multiply the number by 9, add 15 to the product, divide the sum by 3, and subtract 5.

Complete the above procedure for several different numbers. Use inductive reasoning to make a conjecture about the relationship between the size of the resulting number and the size of the original number.

Solution   *See page S1.*

historical note

Galileo Galilei
(găl′-ə-lā′ē′) entered the University of Pisa to study medicine at the age of 17, but he soon realized that he was more interested in the study of astronomy and the physical sciences. Galileo's study of pendulums assisted in the development of pendulum clocks. ∎

Scientists often use inductive reasoning. For instance, Galileo Galilei (1564–1642) used inductive reasoning to discover that the time required for a pendulum to complete one swing, called the *period* of the pendulum, depends on the length of the pendulum. Galileo did not have a clock, so he measured the periods of pendulums in "heartbeats." The following table shows some results obtained for pendulums of various lengths. For the sake of convenience, a length of 10 inches has been designated as 1 unit.

Length of pendulum, in units	Period of pendulum, in heartbeats
1	1
4	2
9	3
16	4

The period of a pendulum is the time it takes for the pendulum to swing from left to right and back to its original position.

EXAMPLE 3 ■ Use Inductive Reasoning to Solve an Application

Use the data in the table and inductive reasoning to answer each of the following.

a. If a pendulum has a length of 25 units, what is its period?

b. If the length of a pendulum is quadrupled, what happens to its period?

Solution

a. In the table on the previous page, each pendulum has a period that is the square root of its length. Thus we conjecture that a pendulum with a length of 25 units will have a period of 5 heartbeats.

b. In the table, a pendulum with a length of 4 units has a period that is twice that of a pendulum with a length of 1 unit. A pendulum with a length of 16 units has a period that is twice that of a pendulum with a length of 4 units. It appears that quadrupling the length of a pendulum doubles its period.

Height of tsunami, in feet	Velocity of tsunami, in feet per second
4	6
9	9
16	12
25	15
36	18
49	21
64	24

CHECK YOUR PROGRESS 3   A tsunami is a sea wave produced by an underwater earthquake. The velocity of a tsunami as it approaches land depends on the height of the tsunami. Use the table at the left and inductive reasoning to answer each of the following questions.

a. What happens to the height of a tsunami when its velocity is doubled?

b. What should be the height of a tsunami if its velocity is 30 feet per second?

Solution   *See page S1.*

Conclusions based on inductive reasoning may be incorrect. As an illustration, consider the circles shown below. For each circle, all possible line segments have been drawn to connect each dot on the circle with all the other dots on the circle.

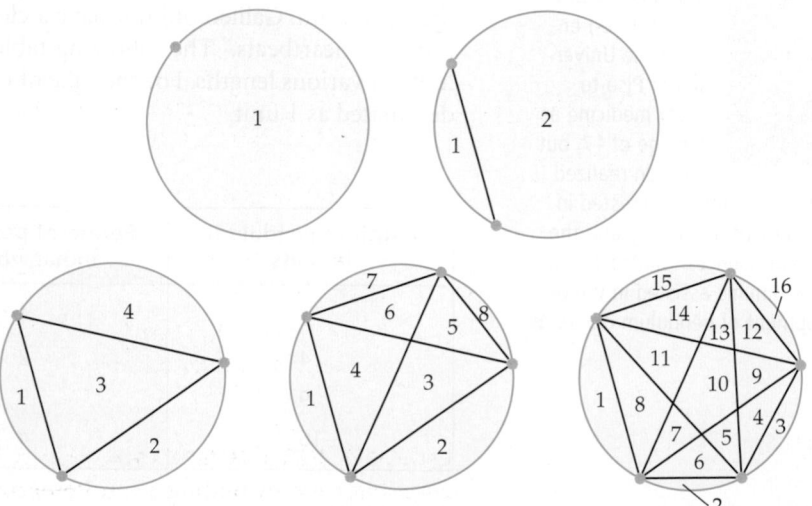

The maximum numbers of regions formed by connecting dots on a circle

For each circle, count the number of regions formed by the line segments that connect the dots on the circle. Your results should agree with the results in the following table.

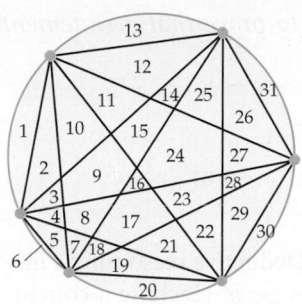

The line segments connecting six dots on a circle yield a maximum of 31 regions.

Number of dots	1	2	3	4	5	6
Maximum number of regions	1	2	4	8	16	?

There appears to be a pattern. Each additional dot seems to double the number of regions. Guess the maximum number of regions you expect for a circle with six dots. Check your guess by counting the maximum number of regions formed by the line segments that connect six dots on a *large* circle. Your drawing will show that for six dots, the maximum number of regions is 31 (see the figure at the left), not 32 as you may have guessed. With seven dots the maximum number of regions is 57. This is a good example to keep in mind. Just because a pattern holds true for a few cases, it does not mean the pattern will continue. When you use inductive reasoning, you have no guarantee that your conclusion is correct.

Counterexamples

A statement is a true statement if and only if it is true in all cases. If you can find *one case* for which a statement is not true, called a **counterexample,** then the statement is a false statement. In Example 4 we verify that each statement is a false statement by finding a counterexample for each.

EXAMPLE 4 ■ Find a Counterexample

Verify that each of the following statements is a false statement by finding a counterexample.
For all x:

a. $|x| > 0$ **b.** $x^2 > x$ **c.** $\sqrt{x^2} = x$

Solution
A statement may have many counterexamples, but we need only find one counterexample to verify that the statement is false.

a. Let $x = 0$. Then $|0| = 0$. Because 0 is not greater than 0, we have found a counterexample. Thus "for all x, $|x| > 0$" is a false statement.

b. For $x = 1$ we have $1^2 = 1$. Since 1 is not greater than 1, we have found a counterexample. Thus "for all x, $x^2 > x$" is a false statement.

c. Consider $x = -3$. Then $\sqrt{(-3)^2} = \sqrt{9} = 3$. Since 3 is not equal to -3, we have found a counterexample. Thus "for all x, $\sqrt{x^2} = x$" is a false statement.

CHECK YOUR PROGRESS 4
Verify that each of the following statements is a false statement by finding a counterexample for each.
For all x:

a. $\dfrac{x}{x} = 1$ **b.** $\dfrac{x+3}{3} = x + 1$ **c.** $\sqrt{x^2 + 16} = x + 4$

Solution   *See page S1.*

QUESTION   *How many counterexamples are needed to prove that a statement is false?*

Deductive Reasoning

Another type of reasoning is called *deductive reasoning*. Deductive reasoning is distinguished from inductive reasoning in that it is the process of reaching a conclusion by applying general principles and procedures.

> **Deductive reasoning** is the process of reaching a conclusion by applying general assumptions, procedures, or principles.

EXAMPLE 5 ■ Use Deductive Reasoning to Establish a Conjecture

Use deductive reasoning to show that the following procedure produces a number that is four times the original number.

    Procedure: Pick a number. Multiply the number by 8, add 6 to the product, divide the sum by 2, and subtract 3.

Solution

Let *n* represent the original number.

    Multiply the number by 8: $8n$

    Add 6 to the product: $8n + 6$

    Divide the sum by 2: $\dfrac{8n + 6}{2} = 4n + 3$

    Subtract 3: $4n + 3 - 3 = 4n$

We started with *n* and ended with 4*n*. The procedure given in this example produces a number that is four times the original number.

CHECK YOUR PROGRESS 5   Use deductive reasoning to show that the following procedure produces a number that is three times the original number.

    Procedure: Pick a number. Multiply the number by 6, add 10 to the product, divide the sum by 2, and subtract 5. *Hint:* Let *n* represent the original number.

Solution   *See page S1.*

ANSWER   *One*

Math Matters The MYST® Adventure Games and Inductive Reasoning

Most games have several rules, and the players are required to use a combination of deductive and inductive reasoning to play the game. However, the MYST® computer/video adventure games have no specific rules. Thus your only option is to explore and make use of inductive reasoning to discover the clues needed to solve the game.

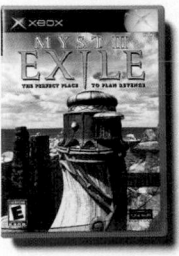

MYST® III: *EXILE*

Inductive Reasoning vs. Deductive Reasoning

In Example 6 we analyze arguments to determine whether they use inductive or deductive reasoning.

EXAMPLE 6 ■ Determine Types of Reasoning

Determine whether each of the following arguments is an example of inductive reasoning or deductive reasoning.

a. During the past 10 years, a tree has produced plums every other year. Last year the tree did not produce plums, so this year the tree will produce plums.

b. All home improvements cost more than the estimate. The contractor estimated my home improvement will cost $35,000. Thus my home improvement will cost more than $35,000.

Solution

a. This argument reaches a conclusion based on specific examples, so it is an example of inductive reasoning.

b. Because the conclusion is a specific case of a general assumption, this argument is an example of deductive reasoning.

CHECK YOUR PROGRESS 6 Determine whether each of the following arguments is an example of inductive reasoning or deductive reasoning.

a. All Janet Evanovich novels are worth reading. The novel *To the Nines* is a Janet Evanovich novel. Thus *To the Nines* is worth reading.

b. I know I will win a jackpot on this slot machine in the next 10 tries, because it has not paid out any money during the last 45 tries.

Solution See page S1.

Some logic puzzles, similar to the one in Example 7, can be solved by using deductive reasoning and a chart that enables us to display the given information in a visual manner.

EXAMPLE 7 ■ Solve a Logic Puzzle

Each of four neighbors, Sean, Maria, Sarah, and Brian, has a different occupation (editor, banker, chef, or dentist). From the following clues, determine the occupation of each neighbor.

1. Maria gets home from work after the banker but before the dentist.
2. Sarah, who is the last to get home from work, is not the editor.
3. The dentist and Sarah leave for work at the same time.
4. The banker lives next door to Brian.

Solution

From clue 1, Maria is not the banker or the dentist. In the following chart, write X1 (which stands for "ruled out by clue 1") in the Banker and the Dentist columns of Maria's row.

	Editor	Banker	Chef	Dentist
Sean				
Maria		X1		X1
Sarah				
Brian				

From clue 2, Sarah is not the editor. Write X2 (ruled out by clue 2) in the Editor column of Sarah's row. We know from clue 1 that the banker is not the last to get home, and we know from clue 2 that Sarah is the last to get home; therefore, Sarah is not the banker. Write X2 in the Banker column of Sarah's row.

	Editor	Banker	Chef	Dentist
Sean				
Maria		X1		X1
Sarah	X2	X2		
Brian				

From clue 3, Sarah is not the dentist. Write X3 for this condition. There are now X's for three of the four occupations in Sarah's row; therefore, Sarah must be the chef. Place a $\sqrt{}$ in that box. Since Sarah is the chef, none of the other three people can be the chef. Write X3 for these conditions. There are now X's for three of the four occupations in Maria's row; therefore, Maria must be the editor. Insert a $\sqrt{}$ to indicate that Maria is the editor, and write X3 twice to indicate that neither Sean nor Brian is the editor.

	Editor	Banker	Chef	Dentist
Sean	X3		X3	
Maria	$\sqrt{}$	X1	X3	X1
Sarah	X2	X2	$\sqrt{}$	X3
Brian	X3		X3	

From clue 4, Brian is not the banker. Write X4 for this condition. Since there are three X's in the Banker column, Sean must be the banker. Place a $\sqrt{}$ in that box. Thus Sean cannot be the dentist. Write X4 in that box. Since there are 3 X's in the Dentist column, Brian must be the dentist. Place a $\sqrt{}$ in that box.

	Editor	Banker	Chef	Dentist
Sean	X3	$\sqrt{}$	X3	X4
Maria	$\sqrt{}$	X1	X3	X1
Sarah	X2	X2	$\sqrt{}$	X3
Brian	X3	X4	X3	$\sqrt{}$

Sean is the banker, Maria is the editor, Sarah is the chef, and Brian is the dentist.

CHECK YOUR PROGRESS 7   Brianna, Ryan, Tyler, and Ashley were recently elected as the new class officers (president, vice president, secretary, treasurer) of the sophomore class at Summit College. From the following clues, determine which position each holds.

1. Ashley is younger than the president but older than the treasurer.
2. Brianna and the secretary are both the same age, and they are the youngest members of the group.
3. Tyler and the secretary are next door neighbors.

Solution   *See page S1.*

Excursion

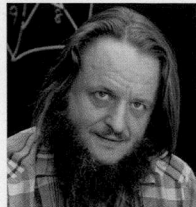

John H. Conway
Princeton University

A spot with 3 lives.

A spot with 2 lives.

A spot with 1 life.

A dead spot.

The status of a
spot in the game
of *Sprouts*

The Game of *Sprouts* by John H. Conway

The mathematician John H. Conway has created several games that are easy to play but complex enough to provide plenty of mental stimulation. For instance, in 1967 Conway, along with Michael Paterson, created the two-person, paper-and-pencil game of *Sprouts*. After more than three decades, the game of *Sprouts* has not been completely analyzed. Here are the rules for *Sprouts*.

Rules for Sprouts

1. A few spots (dots) are drawn on a piece of paper.

2. The players alternate turns. A turn (move) consists of drawing a curve between two spots or drawing a curve that starts at a spot and ends at the same spot. The active player then places a new spot on the new curve. **No curve may pass through a previously drawn spot. No curve may cross itself or a previously drawn curve.**

3. A spot with no rays emanating from it has 3 lives. A spot with one ray emanating from it has 2 lives. A spot with two rays emanating from it has 1 life. A spot is dead and cannot be used when it has three rays that emanate from it. See the figure at the left.

4. The winner is the last player who is able to draw a curve.

Here is an example of a game of *2-Spot Sprouts*.

A Game of 2-Spot Sprouts

Start

A B

First Move

The first player connects *A* with *B* and draws spot *C*.

Second Move

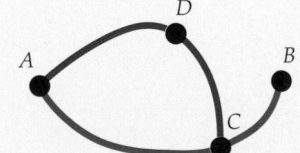

The second player connects *A* with *C* and draws spot *D*.

Third Move

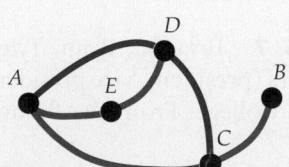

The first player connects *D* with *A* and draws spot *E*.

Fourth Move

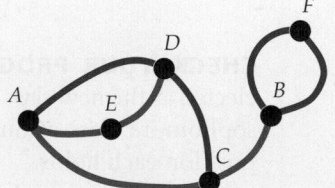

The second player connects *B* to itself and draws spot *F*. The second player is the winner because the first player cannot draw another curve.

(continued)

Note in the previous game that the spots *E* and *F* both have one life, but they cannot be connected because no curve can cross a previously drawn curve.

Excursion Exercises

1. Play a game of *1-Spot Sprouts*. Explain how you know that it is not possible for the first player to win a game of 1-Spot Sprouts.

2. Every *n-Spot Sprouts* game has a maximum of $3n - 1$ moves. To verify this, we use the following deductive argument.

   At the start of a game, each spot has three lives. Thus an *n-Spot Sprouts* game starts with $3n$ lives. Each time a move is completed, two lives are killed and one life is created. Thus each move decreases the number of lives by one. The game cannot continue when only one life remains. Thus the maximum number of moves is $3n - 1$.

   It can also be shown that an *n-Spot Sprouts* game must have at least $2n$ turns. Play several *2-Spot Sprouts* games. Did each *2-Spot Sprouts* game you played have at least $2(2) = 4$ moves and at most $3(2) - 1 = 5$ moves?

3. Play several *3-Spot Sprouts* games. Did each *3-Spot Sprouts* game you played have at least $2(3) = 6$ moves and at most $3(3) - 1 = 8$ moves?

The first move in a game of *2-Spot Sprouts*

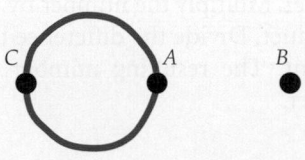

4. In a *2-Spot Sprouts* game, the second player can always play in a manner that will guarantee a win. In the following exercises, you are asked to illustrate a winning strategy for the second player in three situations.

   a. In a *2-Spot Sprouts* game, the first player makes the first move as shown at the left. What move can the second player make to guarantee a win? Explain how you know this move will guarantee that the second player will win.

   b. In a *2-Spot Sprouts* game, the first player makes the first move as shown at the left. What move can the second player make to guarantee a win? Explain how you know this move will guarantee that the second player will win.

The first move in a game of *2-Spot Sprouts*

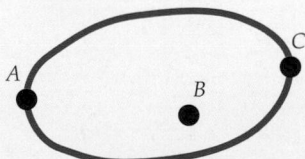

   c. In a *2-Spot Sprouts* game, the first player draws a curve from *A* to *B* and the second player draws a curve from *B* back to *A* as shown at the right.

The first two moves in a game of *2-Spot Sprouts*

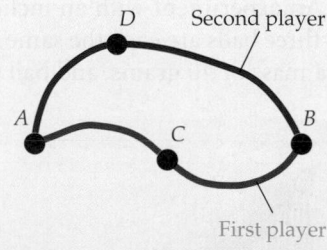

   At this point, the game can progress in several different ways. However, it is possible to show that regardless of how the first player responds on the third move, the second player can win the game on the fourth move. Choose, *at random,* a next move for the first player and demonstrate how the second player can win the game on the fourth move.

5. In 1990, David Applegate, Daniel Sleator, and Guy Jacobson used a computer program to try to analyze the game of *n-Spot Sprouts*. From their work, they *conjectured* that the first player has a winning strategy when the number of spots divided by six leaves a remainder of three, four, or five. Assuming that this conjecture is correct, determine in which *n-Spot Sprouts* games, with $1 \leq n \leq 11$, the first player has a winning strategy.

Exercise Set 1.1

In Exercises 1–10, use inductive reasoning to predict the most probable next number in each list.

1. 4, 8, 12, 16, 20, 24, ?

2. 5, 11, 17, 23, 29, 35, ?

3. 3, 5, 9, 15, 23, 33, ?

4. 1, 8, 27, 64, 125, ?

5. 1, 4, 9, 16, 25, 36, 49, ?

6. 80, 70, 61, 53, 46, 40, ?

7. $\dfrac{3}{5}, \dfrac{5}{7}, \dfrac{7}{9}, \dfrac{9}{11}, \dfrac{11}{13}, \dfrac{13}{15}$, ?

8. $\dfrac{1}{2}, \dfrac{2}{3}, \dfrac{3}{4}, \dfrac{4}{5}, \dfrac{5}{6}, \dfrac{6}{7}$, ?

9. 2, 7, −3, 2, −8, −3, −13, −8, −18, ?

10. 1, 5, 12, 22, 35, ?

In Exercises 11–16, use inductive reasoning to decide whether the conclusion for each argument is correct. *Note:* The numbers 1, 2, 3, 4, ... are called **natural numbers** or **counting numbers**. The numbers ..., −3, −2, −1, 0, 1, 2, 3, ... are called **integers**.

11. The sum of any two even numbers is an even number.

12. If a number with three or more digits is divisible by 4, then the number formed by the last two digits of the number is divisible by 4.

13. The product of an odd integer and an even integer is always an even number.

14. The cube of an odd integer is always an odd number.

15. Pick any counting number. Multiply the number by 6. Add 8 to the product. Divide the sum by 2. Subtract 4 from the quotient. The resulting number is twice the original number.

16. Pick any counting number. Multiply the number by 8. Subtract 4 from the product. Divide the difference by 4. Add 1 to the quotient. The resulting number is twice the original number.

Experimental Data Galileo used inclines similar to the one shown below to measure the distance balls of various weights would travel in equal time intervals. The conclusions that Galileo reached from these experiments were contrary to the prevailing Aristotelian theories on the subject, and he lost his post at the University of Pisa because of them.

An experiment with an incline and three balls produced the following results. The three balls are each the same size; however, ball A has a mass of 20 grams, ball B has a mass of 40 grams, and ball C has a mass of 80 grams.

Time, in seconds	Distance traveled, in inches		
	Ball A (20 grams)	Ball B (40 grams)	Ball C (80 grams)
1	6	6	6
2	24	24	24
3	54	54	54
4	96	96	96

In Exercises 17–24, use the above table and inductive reasoning to answer each question.

17. If the weight of a ball is doubled, what effect does this have on the distance it rolls in a given time interval?

18. If the weight of a ball is quadrupled, what effect does this have on the distance it rolls in a given time interval?

19. How far will ball A travel in 5 seconds?

20. How far will ball A travel in 6 seconds?

21. If a particular time is doubled, what effect does this have on the distance a ball travels?

22. If a particular time is tripled, what effect does this have on the distance a ball travels?

23. How much time is required for one of the balls to travel 1.5 inches?

24. How far will one of the balls travel in 1.5 seconds?

In Exercises 25–32, determine whether the argument is an example of inductive reasoning or deductive reasoning.

25. Andrea enjoyed reading the Dark Tower series by Stephen King, so I know she will like his next novel.

26. All pentagons have exactly five sides. Figure A is a pentagon. Therefore, Figure A has exactly five sides.

27. Every English setter likes to hunt. Duke is an English setter, so Duke likes to hunt.

28. Cats don't eat tomatoes. Scat is a cat. Therefore, Scat does not eat tomatoes.

29. A number is a "neat" number if the sum of the cubes of its digits equals the number. Therefore, 153 is a "neat" number.

30. The Atlanta Braves have won five games in a row. Therefore, the Atlanta Braves will win their next game.

31. Since

$$11 \times (1)(101) = 1111$$
$$11 \times (2)(101) = 2222$$
$$11 \times (3)(101) = 3333$$
$$11 \times (4)(101) = 4444$$
$$11 \times (5)(101) = 5555$$

we know that the product of 11 and a multiple of 101 is a number in which every digit is the same.

32. The following equations show that $n^2 - n + 11$ is a prime number for all counting numbers $n = 1, 2, 3, 4, \ldots$.

$$(1)^2 - 1 + 11 = 11 \qquad n = 1$$
$$(2)^2 - 2 + 11 = 13 \qquad n = 2$$
$$(3)^2 - 3 + 11 = 17 \qquad n = 3$$
$$(4)^2 - 4 + 11 = 23 \qquad n = 4$$

Note: A **prime number** is a counting number greater than 1 that has no counting number factors other than itself and 1. The first 15 prime numbers are 2, 3, 5, 7, 11, 13, 17, 19, 23, 29, 31, 37, 41, 43, and 47.

In Exercises 33–42, find a counterexample to show that the statement is false.

33. $x > \dfrac{1}{x}$

34. $x + x > x$

35. $x^3 \geq x$

36. $|x + y| = |x| + |y|$

37. $-x < x$

38. $\dfrac{(x + 1)(x - 1)}{(x - 1)} = x + 1$ *Hint:* Division by zero is undefined.

39. If the sum of two natural numbers is even, then the product of the two natural numbers is even.

40. If the product of two natural numbers is even, then both of the numbers are even numbers.

41. Pick any three-digit counting number. Reverse the digits of the original number. The difference of these two numbers has a tens digit of 9.

42. If a counting number with two or more digits remains the same with its digits reversed, then the counting number is a multiple of 11.

43. Use deductive reasoning to show that the following procedure always produces a number that is equal to the original number.
Procedure: Pick a number. Multiply the number by 6 and add 8. Divide the sum by 2, subtract twice the original number, and subtract 4.

44. Use deductive reasoning to show that the following procedure always produces the number 5.
Procedure: Pick a number. Add 4 to the number and multiply the sum by 3. Subtract 7 and then decrease this difference by the triple of the original number.

45. **Stocks** Each of four siblings (Anita, Tony, Maria, and Jose) is given \$5000 to invest in the stock market. Each chooses a different stock. One chooses a utility stock, another an automotive stock, another a technology stock, and the other an oil stock. From the following clues, determine which sibling bought which stock.

  a. Anita and the owner of the utility stock purchased their shares through an online brokerage, whereas Tony and the owner of the automotive stock did not.

  b. The gain in value of Maria's stock is twice the gain in value of the automotive stock.

  c. The technology stock is traded on NASDAQ, whereas the stock that Tony bought is traded on the New York Stock Exchange.

46. Gourmet Chefs The Changs, Steinbergs, Ontkeans, and Gonzaleses were winners in the All-State Cooking Contest. There was a winner in each of four categories: soup, entrée, salad, and dessert. From the following clues, determine in which category each family was the winner.

a. The soups were judged before the Ontkeans' winning entry.

b. This year's contest was the first for the Steinbergs and for the winner in the dessert category. The Changs and the winner of the soup category entered last year's contest.

c. The winning entrée took 2 hours to cook, whereas the Steinberg's entrée required no cooking at all.

47. Collectibles The cities of Atlanta, Chicago, Philadelphia, and Seattle held conventions this summer for collectors of coins, stamps, comic books, and baseball cards. From the following clues, determine which collectors met in which city.

a. The comic book collectors convention was in August, as was the convention held in Chicago.

b. The baseball card collectors did not meet in Philadelphia, and the coin collectors did not meet in Seattle or Chicago.

c. The convention in Atlanta was held during the week of July 4, whereas the coin collectors convention was held the week after that.

d. The convention in Chicago had more collectors attending it than did the stamp collectors convention.

48. Map Coloring The map shows eight states in the central time zone of the United States. Four colors have been used to color the states such that no two bordering states are the same color.

a. Can this map be colored, using only three colors, such that no two bordering states are the same color? Explain.

b. Can this map be colored, using only two colors, such that no two bordering states are the same color? Explain.

49. Driving Time You need to buy groceries at the supermarket, deposit a check at the credit union, and purchase a book at the bookstore. You can complete the errands in any order, however, you must start and end at your home. The driving time, in minutes, between each of these locations is given in the following figure.

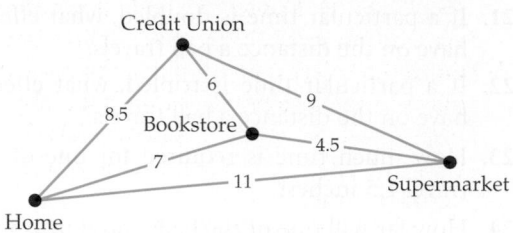

Find a route whose total driving time is less than 30 minutes.

50. Driving Time Suppose, in Exercise 49, that you need to go to the supermarket after you have completed the other two errands. What route should you take to minimize your travel time?

Extensions

CRITICAL THINKING

51. Use inductive reasoning to predict the next letter in the following list.

$$O, T, T, F, F, S, S, E, \ldots$$

Hint: Look for a pattern that involves letters from words used for counting.

52. Use inductive reasoning to predict the next symbol in the following list.

Ϻ, ♎, 8, ℳ, �750, ...

Hint: Look for a pattern that involves counting numbers and symmetry about a line.

53. The Foucault Pendulum For the World's Fair in 1850, the French physicist Jean Bernard Foucault (*foo-ko*) installed a pendulum in the Pantheon in Paris. Foucault's pendulum had a period of about 16.4 seconds. If a pendulum with a length of 0.25 meter has a period of 1 second, determine which of the following lengths best approximates the length of Foucault's pendulum. *Hint:* Use the results of Example 3b.

a. 7 meters   **b.** 27 meters

c. 47 meters   **d.** 67 meters

54. Counterexamples Find a counterexample to prove that the inductive argument in

a. Exercise 31 is incorrect.

b. Exercise 32 is incorrect.

EXPLORATIONS

55. **The Game of Life** The Game of Life was invented by the mathematician John H. Conway in 1970. It is not really a game in that there are no players, and no one wins or loses. The game starts by placing "pieces" on a grid. Once the "pieces" are in place, the rules determine everything that happens. It may sound like a boring game, but many people have found it to be an intriguing game that is full of surprises! Write a short essay that explains how the Game of Life is played and some of the reasons why it continues to be such a popular game.

Many websites have applets that allow you to play the Game of Life. Use one of these applets to play the Game of Life before you write your essay. (*Note:* Conway's Game of Life is not the same game as the Game of Life board game with the pink and blue babies in the back seat of a plastic car.)

56. **The Monty Hall Problem Redux** You can use the Internet to perform an experiment to determine the best strategy for playing the Monty Hall problem, which was stated in the Chapter 1 opener on page 1. Here is the procedure.

a. Use a search engine to find a website that provides a simulation of the Monty Hall problem. This problem is also known as the three-door problem, so search under both of these titles. Once you locate a site that provides a simulation, play the simulation 30 times using the strategy of not switching. Record the number of times you win the grand prize. Now play the simulation 30 times using the strategy of switching. How many times did you win the grand prize by not switching? How many times did you win the grand prize by switching?

b. On the basis of this experiment, which strategy seems to be the best strategy for winning the grand prize? What type of reasoning have you used?

| SECTION 1.2 | **Problem Solving with Patterns**

Terms of a Sequence

An ordered list of numbers such as

$$5, 14, 27, 44, 65, \ldots$$

is called a **sequence.** The numbers in a sequence that are separated by commas are the **terms** of the sequence. In the above sequence, 5 is the first term, 14 is the second term, 27 is the third term, 44 is the fourth term, and 65 is the fifth term. The three dots "..." indicate that the sequence continues beyond 65, which is the last written term. It is customary to use the subscript notation a_n to designate the *n*th **term of a sequence.** That is,

a_1 represents the first term of a sequence.

a_2 represents the second term of a sequence.

a_3 represents the third term of a sequence.

$$\vdots$$

a_n represents the *n*th term of a sequence.

In the sequence 2, 6, 12, 20, 30, ..., $n^2 + n$, ...

$a_1 = 2$, $a_2 = 6$, $a_3 = 12$, $a_4 = 20$, $a_5 = 30$, and $a_n = n^2 + n$.

When we examine a sequence, it is natural to ask:

- What is the next term?
- What formula or rule can be used to generate the terms?

To answer these questions we often construct a **difference table,** which shows the differences between successive terms of the sequence. The following table is a difference table for the sequence 2, 5, 8, 11, 14, ...

Each of the numbers in row (1) of the table is the difference between the two closest numbers just above it (upper right number minus upper left number). The differences in row (1) are called the **first differences** of the sequence. In this case the first differences are all the same. Thus, if we use the above difference table to predict the next number in the sequence, we predict that $14 + 3 = 17$ is the next term of the sequence. This prediction might be wrong; however, the pattern shown by the first differences seems to indicate that each successive term is 3 larger than the preceding term.

The following table is a difference table for the sequence 5, 14, 27, 44, 65, ...

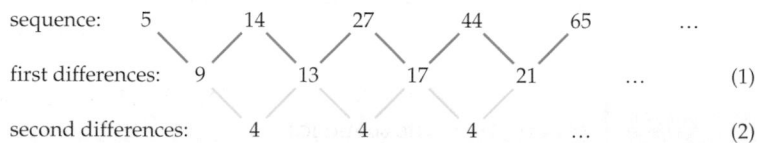

In this table the first differences are *not* all the same. In such a situation it is often helpful to compute the successive differences of the first differences. These are shown in row (2). These differences of the first differences are called the **second differences.** The differences of the second differences are called the **third differences.**

To predict the next term of a sequence, we often look for a pattern in a row of differences. For instance, in the following table, the second differences shown in blue are all the same constant, namely 4. If the pattern continues, then a 4 would also be the next second difference, and we can extend the table to the right as shown.

Now we work upward. That is, we add 4 to the first difference 21 to produce the next first difference, 25. We then add this difference to the fifth term, 65, to predict that 90 is the next term in the sequence. This process can be repeated to predict additional terms of the sequence.

second differences: 4   4   4   4   ...   (2)

EXAMPLE 1 ■ Predict the Next Term of a Sequence

Use a difference table to predict the next term in the sequence.

2, 7, 24, 59, 118, 207, . . .

Solution
Construct a difference table as shown below.

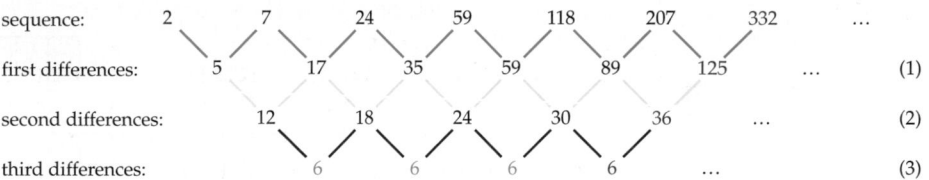

The third differences, shown in blue, are all the same constant, 6. Extending this row so that it includes an additional 6 enables us to predict that the next second difference will be 36. Adding 36 to the first difference 89 gives us the next first difference, 125. Adding 125 to the sixth term 207 yields 332. Using the method of extending the difference table, we predict that 332 is the next term in the sequence.

CHECK YOUR PROGRESS 1   Use a difference table to predict the next term in the sequence.

1, 14, 51, 124, 245, 426, . . .

Solution   *See page S2.*

QUESTION   *Must the fifth term of the sequence 2, 4, 6, 8, . . . be 10?*

nth Term Formula for a Sequence

In Example 1 we used a difference table to predict the next term of a sequence. In some cases we can use patterns to predict a formula, called an ***n*th term formula,** that generates the terms of a sequence. As an example, consider the formula $a_n = 3n^2 + n$. This formula defines a sequence and provides a method for finding any term of the sequence. For instance, if we replace n with 1, 2, 3, 4, 5, and 6, then

✔ **TAKE NOTE**

Recall that the numbers 1, 2, 3, 4, . . . are called *natural numbers* or *counting numbers.* We will often use the letter n to represent an arbitrary natural number.

ANSWER   *No. The fifth term could be any number. However, if you used the method shown in Example 1, then you would predict that the fifth term is 10.*

the formula $a_n = 3n^2 + n$ generates the sequence 4, 14, 30, 52, 80, 114. To find the 40th term, replace each n with 40.

$$a_{40} = 3(40)^2 + 40 = 4840$$

In Example 2 we make use of patterns to determine an nth term formula for a sequence given by geometric figures.

EXAMPLE 2 ■ Find an nth Term Formula

Assume the pattern shown by the square tiles in the following figures continues.

a. What is the nth term formula for the number of tiles in the nth figure of the sequence?

b. How many tiles are in the eighth figure of the sequence?

c. Which figure will consist of exactly 320 tiles?

a_1 a_2 a_3 a_4

Solution

a. Examine the figures for patterns. Note that the second figure has two tiles on each of the horizontal sections and one tile between the horizontal sections. The third figure has three tiles on each horizontal section and two tiles between the horizontal sections. The fourth figure has four tiles on each horizontal section and three tiles between the horizontal sections.

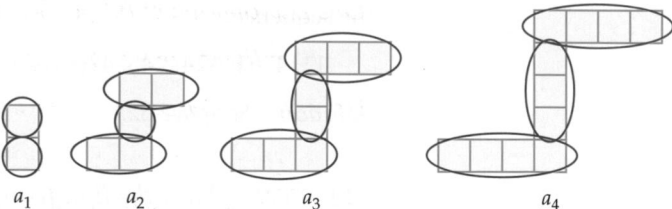

a_1 a_2 a_3 a_4

Thus the number of tiles in the nth figure is given by two groups of n plus a group of n less one. That is,

$$a_n = 2n + (n - 1)$$
$$a_n = 3n - 1$$

b. The number of tiles in the eighth figure of the sequence is $3(8) - 1 = 23$.

c. To determine which figure in the sequence will have 320 tiles, we solve the equation $3n - 1 = 320$.

$$3n - 1 = 320$$
$$3n = 321$$
$$n = 107$$

The 107th figure is composed of 320 tiles.

TAKE NOTE

The method of grouping used in Example 2a is not unique. Do you see a different way to group the tiles? Does your method of grouping still produce the nth term formula $a_n = 3n - 1$?

CHECK YOUR PROGRESS 2   Assume the pattern shown by the square tiles in the following figure continues.

a. What is the *n*th term formula for the number of tiles in the *n*th figure of the sequence?

b. How many tiles are in the tenth figure of the sequence?

c. Which figure will consist of exactly 419 tiles?

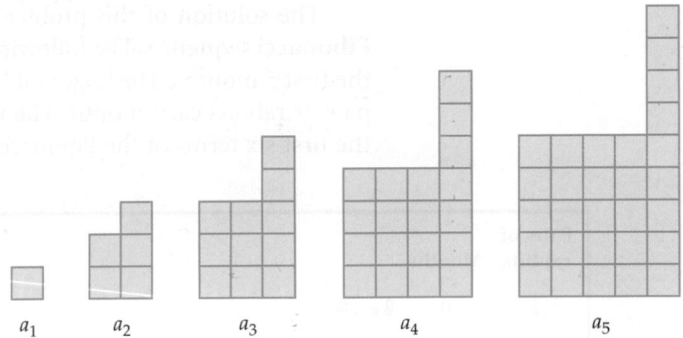

a_1 a_2 a_3 a_4 a_5

Solution   *See page S2.*

Math Matters   Sequences on the Internet

If you find it difficult to determine how the terms of a sequence are being generated, you might be able to find a solution on the Internet. One resource is *Sloane's On-Line Encyclopedia of Integer Sequences*© at:

http://www.research.att.com/~njas/sequences/

Here are two sequences from Sloane's website.

■ 1, 2, 3, 5, 9, 12, 21, 22, 23, 25, 29, 31, 32, 33, 35, 39, 41, 42, 43, 45, 49, 51, 52, . . .
*n*th term formula: *The natural numbers whose names, in English, end with vowels.*

■ 5, 5, 5, 3, 4, 4, 4, 2, 5, 5, 5, 3, 6, 6, 6, 5, 10, 10, 10, 8, . . .
*n*th term formula: *Beethoven's Fifth Symphony;* 1 stands for the first note in the C minor scale, and so on.

The Fibonacci Sequence

Leonardo of Pisa, also known as Fibonacci (fē′bə-nä′chē) (c. 1170–1250), is one of the best-known mathematicians of medieval Europe. In 1202, after a trip that took him to several Arab and Eastern countries, Fibonacci wrote the book *Liber Abaci*. In this book Fibonacci explained why the Hindu-Arabic numeration system that he had learned about during his travels was a more sophisticated and efficient system than the Roman numeration system. This book also contains a

Fibonacci

problem created by Fibonacci that concerns the birth rate of rabbits. Here is a statement of Fibonacci's rabbit problem.

> At the beginning of a month, you are given a pair of newborn rabbits. After a month the rabbits have produced no offspring; however, every month thereafter, the pair of rabbits produces another pair of rabbits. The offspring reproduce in exactly the same manner. If none of the rabbits dies, how many pairs of rabbits will there be at the start of each succeeding month?

The solution of this problem is a sequence of numbers that we now call the **Fibonacci sequence.** The following figure shows the numbers of pairs of rabbits for the first 5 months. The larger rabbits represent mature rabbits that produce another pair of rabbits each month. The numbers in the blue region—1, 1, 2, 3, 5, 8—are the first six terms of the Fibonacci sequence.

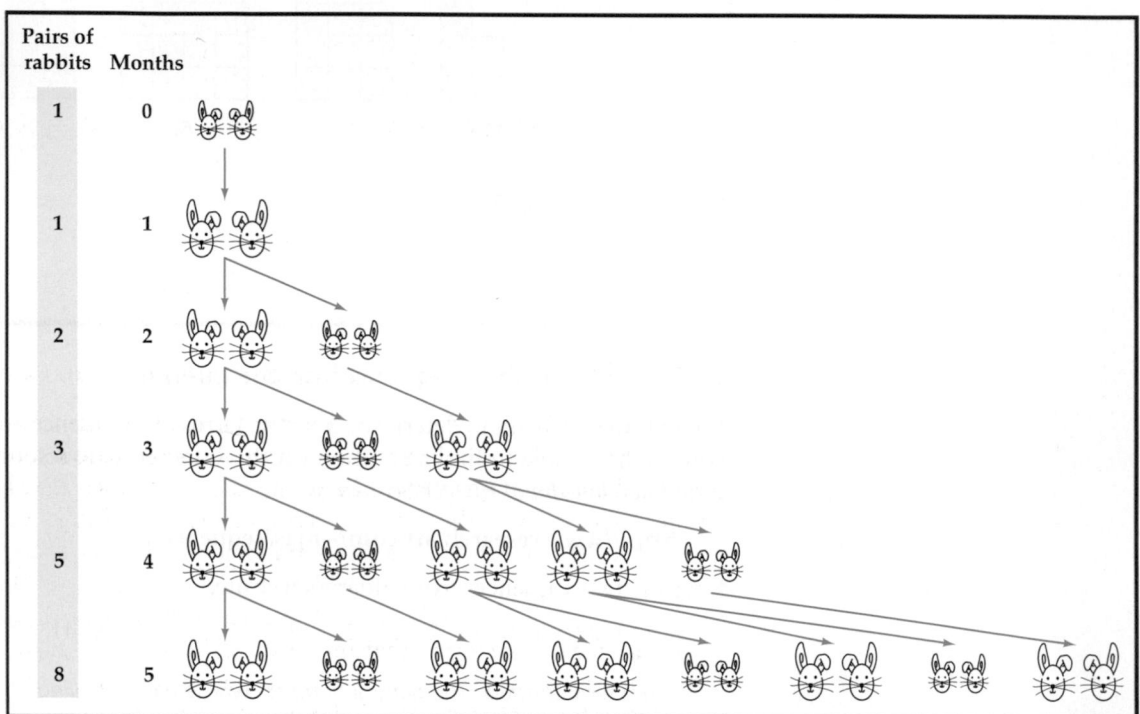

Fibonacci discovered that the number of pairs of rabbits for any month after the first two months can be determined by adding the numbers of pairs of rabbits in each of the *two previous* months. For instance, the number of pairs after 5 months is $3 + 5 = 8$.

A **recursive definition** for a sequence is one in which each successive term of the sequence is defined by using some of the preceding terms. If we use the mathematical notation F_n to represent the nth Fibonacci number, then the numbers in the Fibonacci sequence are given by the following recursive definition.

The Fibonacci Numbers

$F_1 = 1$, $F_2 = 1$,   and $F_n = F_{n-1} + F_{n-2}$ for $n \geq 3$

EXAMPLE 3 ■ Find a Fibonacci Number

Use the definition of Fibonacci numbers to find the seventh and eighth Fibonacci numbers.

Solution

The first six Fibonacci numbers are 1, 1, 2, 3, 5, and 8. The seventh Fibonacci number is the sum of the two previous Fibonacci numbers. Thus,

$$F_7 = F_6 + F_5$$
$$= 8 + 5$$
$$= 13$$

The eighth Fibonacci number is

$$F_8 = F_7 + F_6$$
$$= 13 + 8$$
$$= 21$$

CHECK YOUR PROGRESS 3   Use the definition of Fibonacci numbers to find the ninth Fibonacci number.

Solution   *See page S2.*

Math Matters   Fibonacci Numbers: Cropping Up Everywhere!

Fibonacci's rabbit problem is not a very realistic model of the population growth rate of rabbits; however, the numbers in the Fibonacci sequence often occur in nature. For instance, the seeds on a sunflower are arranged in spirals that curve both clockwise and counterclockwise from the center of the sunflower's head to its outer edge. In many sunflowers, the number of clockwise spirals and the number of counterclockwise spirals are consecutive Fibonacci numbers. In the sunflower shown at the left, the number of clockwise spirals is 34 and the number of counterclockwise spirals is 55.

It has been conjectured that the seeds on a sunflower grow in spirals that involve Fibonacci numbers because this arrangement forms a uniform packing. At any stage in the sunflower's development, its seeds are packed so that they are not too crowded in the center and not too sparse at the edges.

Pineapples have spirals formed by their hexagonal nubs. The nubs on many pineapples form 8 spirals that rotate diagonally upward to the left and 13 spirals that rotate diagonally upward to the right. The numbers 8 and 13 are consecutive Fibonacci numbers.

The nubs on many small pine cones exhibit a pattern of 5 spirals in one direction and 8 spirals in the other. The numbers 5 and 8 are also consecutive Fibonacci numbers.

Much additional information about the occurrence of Fibonacci numbers in nature can be found on the World Wide Web. For instance, the website **http://www.mcs.surrey.ac.uk/Personal/R.Knott/Fibonacci/fibnat.html#refs** has a wealth of information about the occurrence of Fibonacci numbers in nature, and it includes several links to websites with additional information on this topic.

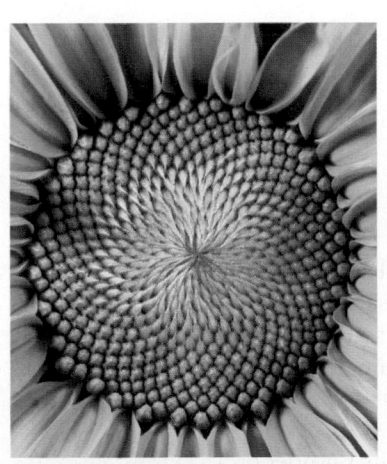

The seeds on this sunflower form 34 clockwise spirals and 55 counterclockwise spirals. The numbers 34 and 55 are consecutive Fibonacci numbers.

We can find any term after the second term of the Fibonacci sequence by computing the sum of the previous two terms. However, this procedure of adding the previous two terms can be tedious. For instance, what is the 100th term or the 1000th term of the Fibonacci sequence? To find the 100th term, we need to know the 98th and 99th terms. To find the 1000th term, we need to know the 998th and 999th terms. Many mathematicians tried to find a nonrecursive nth term formula for the Fibonacci sequence without success, until a formula was discovered by Jacques Binet in 1843. Binet's Formula is given in Exercise 23 of this section.

QUESTION   *What happens if you try to use a difference table to determine Fibonacci numbers?*

EXAMPLE 4 ■ Determine Properties of Fibonacci Numbers

Determine whether each of the following statements about Fibonacci numbers is true or false. *Note:* The first 10 terms of the Fibonacci sequence are 1, 1, 2, 3, 5, 8, 13, 21, 34, and 55.

a. If n is even, then F_n is an odd number.   **b.** $2F_n - F_{n-2} = F_{n+1}$ for $n \geq 3$

Solution

a. An examination of Fibonacci numbers shows that the second Fibonacci number, 1, is odd and the fourth Fibonacci number, 3, is odd, but the sixth Fibonacci number, 8, is even. Thus the statement "If n is even, then F_n is an odd number" is false.

b. Experiment to see whether $2F_n - F_{n-2} = F_{n+1}$ for several values of n. For instance, for $n = 7$, we get

$$2F_n - F_{n-2} = F_{n+1}$$
$$2F_7 - F_{7-2} = F_{7+1}$$
$$2F_7 - F_5 = F_8$$
$$2(13) - 5 = 21$$
$$26 - 5 = 21$$
$$21 = 21$$

which is true. Evaluating $2F_n - F_{n-2}$ for several additional values of n, $n \geq 3$, we find that in each case $2F_n - F_{n-2} = F_{n+1}$. Thus, by inductive reasoning, we conjecture $2F_n - F_{n-2} = F_{n+1}$ for $n \geq 3$ is a true statement. *Note:* This property of Fibonacci numbers can also be established using deductive reasoning. See Exercise 36 of this section.

> ✔ **TAKE NOTE**
>
> Pick any Fibonacci number larger than 1. The equation
>
> $$2F_n - F_{n-2} = F_{n+1}$$
>
> merely states that for numbers in the Fibonacci sequence
>
> 1, 1, 2, 3, 5, 8, 13, 21, …
>
> the double of a Fibonacci number, F_n, less the Fibonacci number two to its left, is the Fibonacci number just to the right of F_n.

CHECK YOUR PROGRESS 4   Determine whether each of the following statements about Fibonacci numbers is true or false.

a. $2F_n > F_{n+1}$ for $n \geq 3$ **b.** $2F_n + 3 = F_{n+2}$

Solution   See page S2.

ANSWER   *The difference table for the numbers in the Fibonacci sequence does not contain a row of differences that are all the same constant.*

Excursion

historical note

Pythagoras
(c. 580 B.C.–520 B.C.)
The ancient Greek
philosopher and
mathematician
Pythagoras
(pĭ-thăg′ər-əs)
formed a secret brotherhood that
investigated topics in music, astronomy, philosophy, and mathematics. The Pythagoreans
believed that the nature of the
universe was directly related to
mathematics and that whole
numbers and the ratios formed
by whole numbers could be used
to describe and represent all natural events.

The Pythagoreans were
particularly intrigued by the number 5 and the shape of a pentagon. They used the following
figure, which is a five-pointed
star inside a regular pentagon, as
a secret symbol that could be
used to identify other members
of the brotherhood. ∎

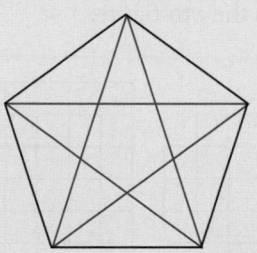

Polygonal Numbers

The ancient Greek mathematicians were interested in the geometric shapes associated with numbers. For instance, they noticed that triangles can be constructed using 1, 3, 6, 10, or 15 dots, as shown in Figure 1.1. They called the numbers 1, 3, 6, 10, 15, . . . the *triangular numbers*. The Greeks called the numbers 1, 4, 9, 16, 25, . . . the *square numbers* and the numbers 1, 5, 12, 22, 35, . . . the *pentagonal numbers*.

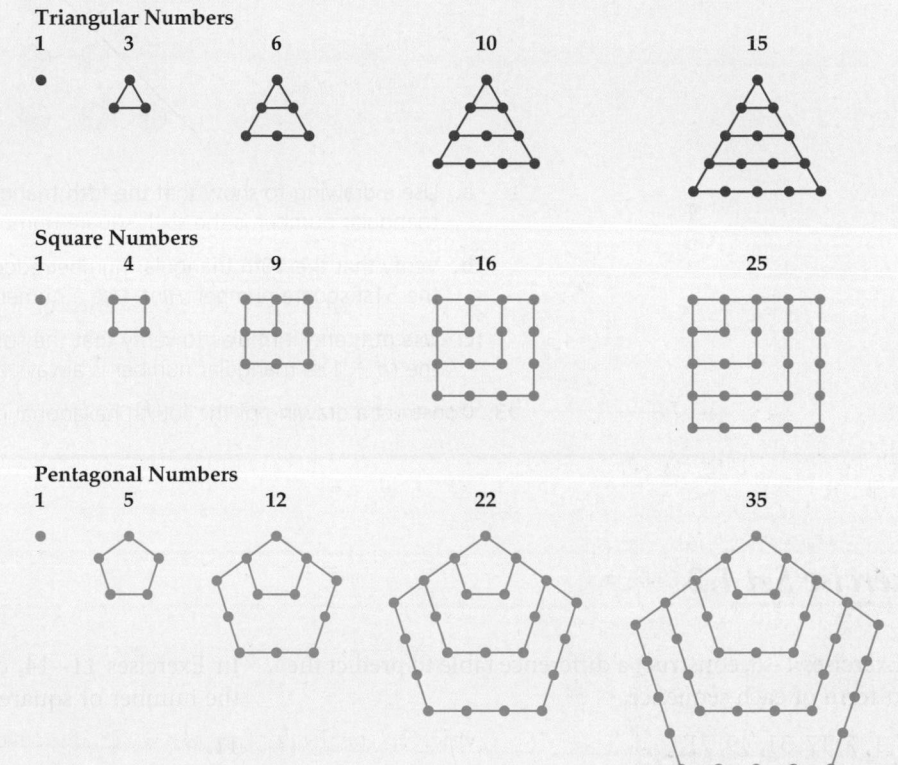

Figure 1.1

An *n*th term for the triangular numbers is:

$$Triangular_n = \frac{n(n+1)}{2}$$

The square numbers have an *n*th term formula of $Square_n = n^2$. The *n*th term formula for the pentagonal numbers is

$$Pentagonal_n = \frac{n(3n-1)}{2}$$

(continued)

Excursion Exercises

1. Extend Figure 1.1, page 23, by constructing drawings of the sixth triangular number, the sixth square number, and the sixth pentagonal number.

2. The figure below shows that the fourth triangular number, 10, added to the fifth triangular number, 15, produces the fifth square number, 25.

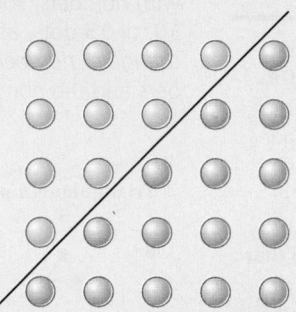

   a. Use a drawing to show that the fifth triangular number added to the sixth triangular number is the sixth square number.

   b. Verify that the 50th triangular number added to the 51st triangular number is the 51st square number. *Hint:* Use a numerical approach; don't use a drawing.

   c. Use nth term formulas to verify that the sum of the nth triangular number and the $(n + 1)$st triangular number is always the square number $(n + 1)^2$.

3. Construct a drawing of the fourth hexagonal number.

Exercise Set 1.2

In Exercises 1–6, construct a difference table to predict the next term of each sequence.

1. $1, 7, 17, 31, 49, 71, \ldots$

2. $10, 10, 12, 16, 22, 30, \ldots$

3. $-1, 4, 21, 56, 115, 204, \ldots$

4. $0, 10, 24, 56, 112, 190, \ldots$

5. $9, 4, 3, 12, 37, 84, \ldots$

6. $17, 15, 25, 53, 105, 187, \ldots$

In Exercises 7–10, use the given nth term formula to compute the first five terms of the sequence.

7. $a_n = \dfrac{n(2n + 1)}{2}$

8. $a_n = \dfrac{n}{n + 1}$

9. $a_n = 5n^2 - 3n$

10. $a_n = 2n^3 - n^2$

In Exercises 11–14, determine the nth term formula for the number of square tiles in the nth figure.

11.

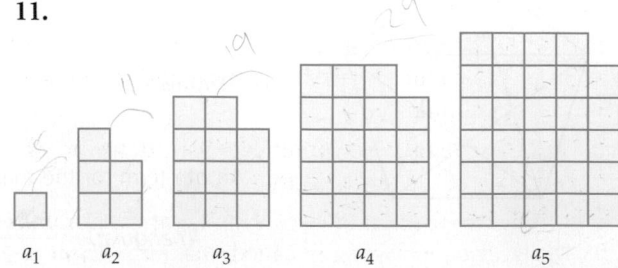

$a_1 \qquad a_2 \qquad a_3 \qquad a_4 \qquad a_5$

12.

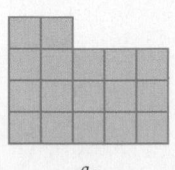

$a_1 \qquad a_2 \qquad a_3 \qquad a_4 \qquad a_5$

13.

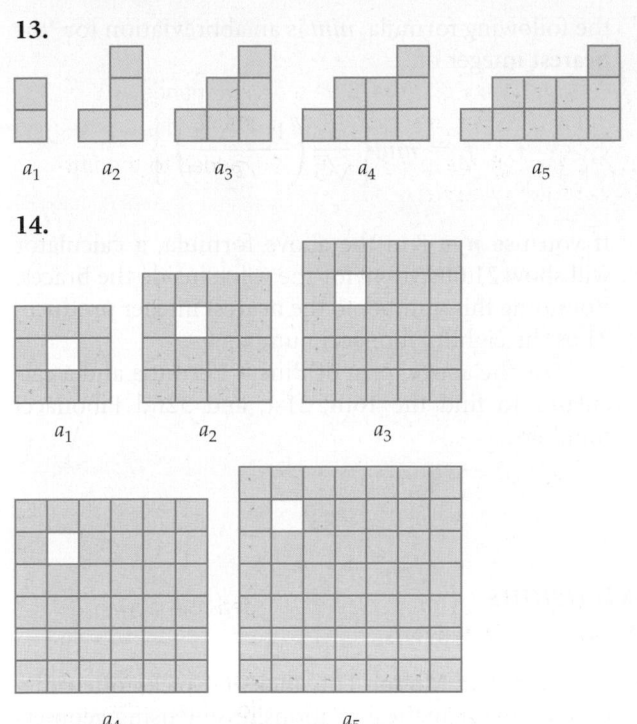

14.

a_1 a_2 a_3

a_4 a_5

Cannonballs can be stacked to form a pyramid with a triangular base. Five of these pyramids are shown below. Use these figures in Exercises 15 and 16.

$a_1 = 1$ $a_2 = 4$ $a_3 = 10$ $a_4 = 20$ $a_5 = 35$

15. a. Use a difference table to predict the number of cannonballs in the sixth pyramid and in the seventh pyramid.

 b. Write a few sentences that describe the eighth pyramid in the sequence.

16. The sequence formed by the numbers of cannonballs in the above pyramids is called the *tetrahedral sequence*. The nth term formula for the tetrahedral sequence is

$$tet_n = \frac{1}{6}n(n + 1)(n + 2)$$

Find tet_{10}.

17. Pieces vs. Cuts One cut of a stick of licorice produces two pieces. Two cuts produce three pieces. Three cuts produce four pieces.

 a. How many pieces are produced by five cuts and by six cuts? Assume the cuts are made in the manner shown above.

 b. Predict the nth term formula for the number of pieces of licorice that are produced by n cuts, made in the manner shown above, of a stick of licorice.

18. Pieces vs. Cuts One straight cut across a pizza produces two pieces. Two cuts can produce a maximum of four pieces. Three cuts can produce a maximum of seven pieces. Four cuts can produce a maximum of 11 pieces.

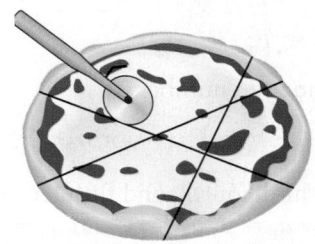

 a. Use a difference table to predict the maximum number of pieces that can be produced with seven cuts.

 b. How are the pizza-slicing numbers related to the triangular numbers, which are defined by

$$Triangular_n = \frac{n(n + 1)}{2}?$$

19. Pieces vs. Cuts One straight cut through a thick piece of cheese produces two pieces. Two straight cuts can produce a maximum of four pieces. Three straight cuts can produce a maximum of eight pieces. You might be inclined to think that every additional cut doubles the previous number of pieces. However, for four straight cuts, you will find that you get a maximum of 15 pieces. An nth term formula for the maximum number of pieces, P, that can be produced by n straight cuts is

$$P(n) = \frac{n^3 + 5n + 6}{6}$$

a. Use the formula at the bottom right of the previous page to determine the maximum number of pieces that can be produced by five straight cuts.

b. What is the fewest number of straight cuts that you can use if you wish to produce at least 60 pieces? *Hint:* Use the formula and experiment with larger and larger values of n.

20. Fibonacci Properties The Fibonacci sequence has many unusual properties. Experiment to decide which of the following properties are valid. *Note:* F_n represents the nth Fibonacci number.

a. $3F_n - F_{n-2} = F_{n+2}$ for $n \geq 3$

b. $F_n F_{n+3} = F_{n+1} F_{n+2}$

c. F_{3n} is an even number.

d. $5F_n - 2F_{n-2} = F_{n+3}$ for $n \geq 3$

21. Find the third, fourth, and fifth terms of the sequence defined by $a_1 = 3$, $a_2 = 5$, and $a_n = 2a_{n-1} - a_{n-2}$ for $n \geq 3$.

22. Find the third, fourth, and fifth terms of the sequence defined by $a_1 = 2$, $a_2 = 3$, and $a_n = (-1)^n a_{n-1} + a_{n-2}$ for $n \geq 3$.

23. **Binet's Formula** The following formula is known as *Binet's Formula* for the nth Fibonacci number.

$$F_n = \frac{1}{\sqrt{5}} \left[\left(\frac{1 + \sqrt{5}}{2} \right)^n - \left(\frac{1 - \sqrt{5}}{2} \right)^n \right]$$

The advantage of this formula over the recursive formula $F_n = F_{n-1} + F_{n-2}$ is that you can determine the nth Fibonacci number without finding the two preceding Fibonacci numbers.
　　Use Binet's Formula and a calculator to find the 20th, 30th, and 40th Fibonacci numbers.

24. **Binet's Formula Simplified** Binet's Formula (see Exercise 23) can be simplified if you round your calculator results to the nearest integer. In the following formula, *nint* is an abbreviation for "the nearest integer of."

$$f_n = nint\left\{ \frac{1}{\sqrt{5}} \left(\frac{1 + \sqrt{5}}{2} \right)^n \right\}$$

If you use $n = 8$ in the above formula, a calculator will show 21.00951949 for the value inside the braces. Rounding this number to the nearest integer produces 21 as the eighth Fibonacci number.
　　Use the above form of Binet's Formula and a calculator to find the 16th, 21st, and 32nd Fibonacci numbers.

Extensions
CRITICAL THINKING

25. **A Geometric Model** The ancient Greeks often discovered mathematical relationships by using geometric drawings. Study the accompanying drawing to determine what needs to be put in place of the question mark to make the equation a true statement.

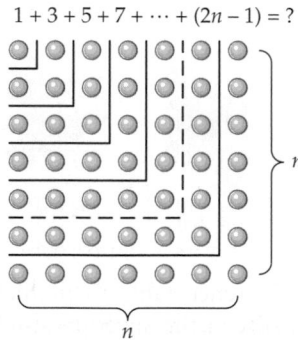

$$1 + 3 + 5 + 7 + \cdots + (2n - 1) = ?$$

26. The nth term formula

$$a_n = \frac{n(n-1)(n-2)(n-3)(n-4)}{4 \cdot 3 \cdot 2 \cdot 1} + 2n$$

generates 2, 4, 6, 8, 15 for $n = 1, 2, 3, 4, 5$. Make minor changes to the above formula to produce an nth term formula that will generate the following finite sequences.

a. 2, 4, 6, 8, 20

b. 2, 4, 6, 8, 30

COOPERATIVE LEARNING

Bode's Rule Near the end of the eighteenth century, the German astronomers J. Daniel Titus and John Ehlert Bode discovered a pattern concerning the distances of the planets from the sun. This pattern is now known as *Bode's rule*. To understand Bode's rule, examine the following table, which shows the *average* distances from the sun of planets Mercury, Venus, Earth, Mars, Jupiter, and Saturn. In the 1770s these were the only known planets. The distances are measured in astronomical units (AU), where 1 AU is the average distance of Earth from the sun. Bode noticed that he could approximate these distances by the following rule.

Start with the numbers 0 and 0.3, and then continue to double 0.3 to produce the sequence 0, 0.3, 0.6, 1.2, 2.4, 4.8, 9.6, 19.2. To each of these numbers add 0.4. This produces Bode's numbers: 0.4, 0.7, 1.0, 1.6, 2.8, 5.2, 10.0, 19.6. Most astronomers did not pay much attention to Bode's numbers until Uranus was discovered in 1781. The average distance from Uranus to the sun is 19.18 AU. The fact that this distance is close to Bode's eighth number inspired astronomers to search for a planet with an orbit between the orbits of Mars and Jupiter. No such planet has ever been discovered; however, in 1801, the asteroid Ceres, with a diameter of 480 miles, was discovered in this vicinity.

The sun and nine known planets of our solar system. The distances from the sun are not drawn to scale.

	1	2	3	4	5	6	7	8	9	10
Planets/Asteroid	Mercury	Venus	Earth	Mars	Ceres	Jupiter	Saturn	Uranus	Neptune	Pluto
Average distance from the sun (AU)	0.38	0.72	1.00	1.52	2.99	5.20	9.54	19.18	30.60	39.52
Bode's numbers	0.4	0.7	1.0	1.6	2.8	5.2	10.0	19.6	?	?

27. The next planet after Uranus is Neptune.

   a. Use Bode's ninth number to predict the average distance from the sun to Neptune.

   b. How does your answer in part a compare to Neptune's average distance from the sun, which is 30.60 AU? *Note:* Some people think that Bode's ninth number does not produce accurate results for Neptune because Pluto's orbit is such that Pluto is sometimes closer to the sun than Neptune.

28. The next planet after Neptune is Pluto. How does Bode's 10th number compare to Pluto's average distance from the sun of 39.52 AU?

A drawing of Pluto, Its Satellite Charon, and the Pluto-Kuiper Express

NASA has scheduled the Pluto-Kuiper Express for a robotic mission to Pluto in the year 2010.

29. On November 14, 2003, astronomers at California's Mount Palomar Observatory discovered the most distant object yet found that orbits the sun. There is some debate about whether this object, named Sedna, qualifies as a true planet, but some astronomers have indicated that this discovery redefines our solar system. Sedna orbits the sun in an extreme elliptical path. Sedna's minimum distance from the sun is about 90 AU, and its maximum distance from the sun is about 880 AU.

   a. According to Bode's eleventh number, the next planet after Pluto would have what average distance from the sun?

   b. Is Bode's eleventh number in the interval 90 AU to 880 AU?

30. In 1995, three planets were discovered that orbit the pulsating star known as PSR B1257+12. The planets have orbits that measure 0.19 AU, 0.36 AU, and 0.47 AU.

   a. If the largest orbit of 0.47 AU is thought of as 1 unit, then determine the sizes, in units, of the smaller orbits. Round to the nearest hundredth.

   b. How do the results in part a compare with Bode's first two numbers?

c. On the basis of the results in part b, can we conclude that there is a universal mechanism for the placement of planets around stars and that Bode's rule is an accurate model for this mechanism?

31. Fibonacci Sums Make a conjecture for each of the following sums, where F_n represents the nth Fibonacci number.

a. $F_n + 2F_{n+1} + F_{n+2} = ?$

b. $F_n + F_{n+1} + F_{n+3} = ?$

32. Fibonacci Sums Make a conjecture for each of the following sums, where F_n represents the nth Fibonacci number.

a. $F_1 + F_2 + F_3 + F_4 + \cdots + F_n = ?$

b. $F_2 + F_4 + F_6 + \cdots + F_{2n} = ?$

The following information is needed to solve Exercises 33 and 34.

The Golden Ratio, Φ The irrational number pi (π) is the ratio of the circumference of a circle to its diameter. Phi (Φ) is another important irrational number that is defined by a geometric ratio.

Divide a line segment, with length c, into two segments with lengths a and $c - a$ such that $\dfrac{c}{a}$ is equal to $\dfrac{a}{c - a}$. See the following figure.

By definition, phi is the value of each of the ratios $\dfrac{c}{a}$ and $\dfrac{a}{c - a}$. The equation $\dfrac{c}{a} = \dfrac{a}{c - a}$ can be rewritten as $c^2 - ac = a^2$ or $c^2 - ac - a^2 = 0$. Using the quadratic formula (See Section 5.4.), we find

$$c = \left(\frac{1 + \sqrt{5}}{2}\right)a \quad \text{and}$$

$$\Phi = \frac{c}{a} = \frac{1 + \sqrt{5}}{2} \approx 1.618033989$$

What makes phi (which is also called the **golden ratio,** the **golden mean,** and the **divine proportion**) such a special number is that it "shows up" in many diverse situations. Surprisingly, there is even a relationship between the ratio of consecutive Fibonacci numbers and phi. Here is the specific relationship.

As n increases without bound, $\dfrac{F_n}{F_{n-1}}$ approaches Φ.

Visit **http://goldennumber.net/neophite.htm** for an interesting and comprehensive overview of phi.

33. Compute each of the following ratios.

$$\frac{F_8}{F_7}, \frac{F_{10}}{F_9}, \frac{F_{12}}{F_{11}}, \text{ and } \frac{F_{14}}{F_{13}}$$

Round each ratio to the nearest millionth. Make a conjecture about the relationship between the ratio $\dfrac{F_n}{F_{n-1}}$ and Φ, where n is any *even* number.

34. Compute each of the following ratios.

$$\frac{F_9}{F_8}, \frac{F_{11}}{F_{10}}, \frac{F_{13}}{F_{12}}, \text{ and } \frac{F_{15}}{F_{14}}$$

Round each ratio to the nearest millionth. Make a conjecture about the relationship between the ratio $\dfrac{F_n}{F_{n-1}}$ and Φ, where n is any *odd* number.

EXPLORATIONS

35. A Puzzle The *Tower of Hanoi* is a puzzle invented by Edouard Lucas in 1883. The puzzle consists of three pegs and a number of disks of distinct diameters stacked on one of the pegs such that the largest disk is on the bottom, the next largest is placed on the largest disk, and so on as shown by the figure below.

The object of the puzzle is to transfer the tower to one of the other pegs. The rules require that *only one disk be moved at a time* and that *a larger disk may not be placed on a smaller disk*. All pegs may be used.

Determine the *minimum* number of moves required to transfer all of the disks to another peg for each of the following situations.

a. You start with only one disk.

b. You start with two disks.

c. You start with three disks. (*Note:* You can use a stack of various size coins to simulate the puzzle, or you can use one of the many websites that provide a JavaScript simulation of the puzzle.)

d. You start with four disks.

e. You start with five disks.

f. You start with *n* disks.

g. Lucas included with the Tower puzzle a legend about a tower that had 64 gold disks on one of three diamond needles. A group of priests had the task of transferring the 64 disks to one of the other needles using the same rules as the Tower of Hanoi puzzle. When they had completed the transfer, the tower would crumble and the universe would cease to exist. Assuming that the priests could transfer one disk to another needle every second, how many years would it take them to transfer all of the 64 disks to one of the other needles?

36. Use the recursive definition for Fibonacci numbers and *deductive* reasoning to verify that, for Fibonacci numbers, $2F_n - F_{n-2} = F_{n+1}$ for $n \geq 3$. *Hint:* By definition, $F_{n+1} = F_n + F_{n-1}$ and $F_n = F_{n-1} + F_{n-2}$.

| # Problem-Solving Strategies

historical note

George Polya
After a brief stay at Brown University, George Polya (pōl′yə) moved to Stanford University in 1942 and taught there until his retirement. While at Stanford, he published 10 books and a number of articles for mathematics journals. Of the books Polya published, *How to Solve it* (1945) is one of his best known. In this book, Polya outlines a strategy for solving problems from virtually any discipline.

   "A great discovery solves a great problem but there is a grain of discovery in the solution of any problem. Your problem may be modest; but if it challenges your curiosity and brings into play your inventive faculties, and if you solve it by your own means, you may experience the tension and enjoy the triumph of discovery." ∎

Polya's Problem-Solving Strategy

Ancient mathematicians such as Euclid and Pappus were interested in solving mathematical problems, but they were also interested in *heuristics*, the study of the methods and rules of discovery and invention. In the seventeenth century, the mathematician and philosopher René Descartes (1596–1650) contributed to the field of heuristics. He tried to develop a universal problem-solving method. Although he did not achieve this goal, he did publish some of his ideas in *Rules for the Direction of the Mind* and his better-known work *Discourse de la Methode*.

   Another mathematician and philosopher, Gottfried Wilhelm Leibnitz (1646–1716), planned to write a book on heuristics titled *Art of Invention*. Of the problem-solving process, Leibnitz wrote, "Nothing is more important than to see the sources of invention which are, in my opinion, more interesting than the inventions themselves."

   One of the foremost recent mathematicians to make a study of problem solving was George Polya (1887–1985). He was born in Hungary and moved to the United States in 1940. The basic problem-solving strategy that Polya advocated consisted of the following four steps.

Polya's Four-Step Problem-Solving Strategy
1. Understand the problem.
2. Devise a plan.
3. Carry out the plan.
4. Review the solution.

Polya's four steps are deceptively simple. To become a good problem solver, it helps to examine each of these steps and determine what is involved.

Understand the Problem This part of Polya's four-step strategy is often over-looked. You must have a clear understanding of the problem. To help you focus on understanding the problem, consider the following questions.

- Can you restate the problem in your own words?
- Can you determine what is known about these types of problems?
- Is there missing information that, if known, would allow you to solve the problem?
- Is there extraneous information that is not needed to solve the problem?
- What is the goal?

Devise a Plan Successful problem solvers use a variety of techniques when they attempt to solve a problem. Here are some frequently-used procedures.

- Make a list of the known information.
- Make a list of information that is needed.
- Draw a diagram.
- Make an organized list that shows all the possibilities.
- Make a table or a chart.
- Work backwards.
- Try to solve a similar but simpler problem.
- Look for a pattern.
- Write an equation. If necessary, define what each variable represents.
- Perform an experiment.
- Guess at a solution and then check your result.
- Use indirect reasoning.

Carry Out the Plan Once you have devised a plan, you must carry it out.

- Work carefully.
- Keep an accurate and neat record of all your attempts.
- Realize that some of your initial plans will not work and that you may have to devise another plan or modify your existing plan.

Review the Solution Once you have found a solution, check the solution.

- Ensure that the solution is consistent with the facts of the problem.
- Interpret the solution in the context of the problem.
- Ask yourself whether there are generalizations of the solution that could apply to other problems.

In Example 1 we apply Polya's four-step problem-solving strategy to solve a problem involving the number of routes between two points.

EXAMPLE 1 ■ Apply Polya's Strategy *(Solve a Similar but Simpler Problem)*

Consider the map shown in Figure 1.2. Allison wishes to walk along the streets from point A to point B. How many direct routes can Allison take?

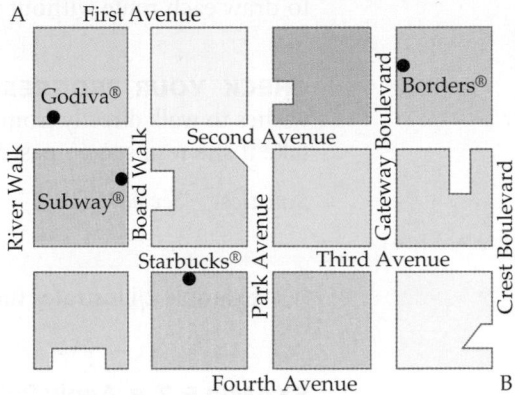

Figure 1.2 *City Map*

Solution

Understand the Problem We would not be able to answer the question if Allison retraced her path or traveled away from point B. Thus we assume that on a direct route, she always travels along a street in a direction that gets her closer to point B.

Devise a Plan The map in Figure 1.2 has many extraneous details. Thus we make a diagram that allows us to concentrate on the essential information. See the figure at the left.

Because there are many routes, we consider the similar but simpler diagrams shown below. The number at each street intersection represents the number of routes from point A to that particular intersection.

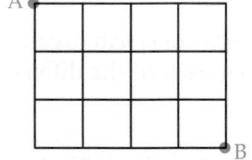

A simple diagram of the street map in Figure 1.2

Simple Street Diagrams

Look for patterns. It appears that the number of routes to an intersection is the *sum* of the number of routes to the adjacent intersection to its left and the number of routes to the intersection directly above. For instance, the number of routes to the intersection labeled 6 is the sum of the number of routes to the intersection to its left, which is three, and the number of routes to the intersection directly above, which is also three.

✔ **TAKE NOTE**

The strategy of working a similar but simpler problem is an important problem-solving strategy that can be used to solve many problems.

A street diagram with the number of routes to each intersection labeled

Carry Out the Plan Using the pattern discovered on the previous page, we see from the figure at the left that the number of routes from point A to point B is $20 + 15 = 35$.

Review the Solution Ask yourself whether a result of 35 seems reasonable. If you were required to draw each route, could you devise a scheme that would enable you to draw each route without missing a route or duplicating a route?

CHECK YOUR PROGRESS 1 Consider the street map in Figure 1.2. Allison wishes to walk directly from point A to point B. How many different routes can she take if she wants to go past Starbucks on Third Avenue?

Solution *See page S2.*

Example 2 illustrates the technique of using an organized list.

EXAMPLE 2 ■ Apply Polya's Strategy *(Make an Organized List)*

A baseball team won two out of their last four games. In how many different orders could they have two wins and two losses in four games?

Solution

Understand the Problem There are many different orders. The team may have won two straight games and lost the last two (WWLL). Or maybe they lost the first two games and won the last two (LLWW). Of course there are other possibilities, such as WLWL.

Devise a Plan We will make an *organized list* of all the possible orders. An organized list is a list that is produced using a system that ensures that each of the different orders will be listed once and only once.

Carry Out the Plan Each entry in our list must contain two W's and two L's. We will use a strategy that makes sure each order is considered, with no duplications. One such strategy is to always write a W unless doing so will produce too many W's or a duplicate of one of the previous orders. If it is not possible to write a W, then and only then do we write an L. This strategy produces the six different orders shown below.

1. WWLL (Start with two wins)
2. WLWL (Start with one win)
3. WLLW
4. LWWL (Start with one loss)
5. LWLW
6. LLWW (Start with two losses)

Review the Solution We have made an organized list. The list has no duplicates and the list considers all possibilities, so we are confident that there are six different orders in which a baseball team can win exactly two out of four games.

CHECK YOUR PROGRESS 2   A true-false quiz contains five questions. In how many ways can a student answer the questions if the student answers two of the questions with "false" and the other three with "true"?

Solution   *See page S3.*

In Example 3 we make use of several problem-solving strategies to solve a problem involving the total number of games to be played.

EXAMPLE 3 ■ Apply Polya's Strategy   *(Solve a Similar but Simpler Problem)*

In a basketball league consisting of 10 teams, each team plays each of the other teams exactly three times. How many league games will be played?

Solution

Understand the Problem   There are 10 teams in the league and each team plays exactly three games against each of the other teams. The problem is to determine the total number of league games that will be played.

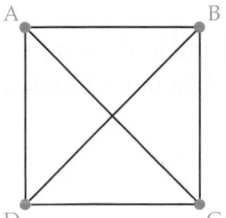

The possible pairings of a league with only four teams

Devise a Plan   Try the strategy of working a similar but simpler problem. Consider a league with only four teams (denoted by A, B, C, and D) in which each team plays each of the other teams only once. The diagram at the left illustrates that the games can be represented by line segments that connect the points A, B, C, and D.

   Since each of the four teams will play a game against each of the other three, we might conclude that this would result in $4 \cdot 3 = 12$ games. However, the diagram shows only six line segments. It appears that our procedure has counted each game twice. For instance, when team A plays team B, team B also plays team A. To produce the correct result, we must divide our previous result, 12, by 2. Hence, four teams can play each other once in $\frac{4 \cdot 3}{2} = 6$ games.

Carry Out the Plan   Using the process developed above, we see that 10 teams can play each other *once* in a total of $\frac{10 \cdot 9}{2} = 45$ games. Since each team plays each opponent exactly three times, the total number of games is $45 \cdot 3 = 135$.

AB AC AD AE AF AG AH AI AJ
BC BD BE BF BG BH BI BJ
CD CE CF CG CH CI CJ
DE DF DG DH DI DJ
EF EG EH EI EJ
FG FH FI FJ
GH GI GJ
HI HJ
IJ

An organized list of all possible games

Review the Solution   We could check our work by making a diagram that includes all 10 teams represented by dots labeled A, B, C, D, E, F, G, H, I, and J. Because this diagram would be somewhat complicated, let's try the method of making an organized list. The figure at the left shows an organized list in which the notation BC represents a game between team B and team C. The notation CB is not shown because it also represents a game between team B and team C. This list shows that 45 games are required for each team to play each of the other teams once. Also notice that the first row has nine items, the second row has eight items, the third row has seven items, and so on. Thus 10 teams require

$$9 + 8 + 7 + 6 + 5 + 4 + 3 + 2 + 1 = 45$$

games if each team plays every other team once and $45 \cdot 3 = 135$ games if each team plays exactly three games against each opponent.

CHECK YOUR PROGRESS 3   If six people greet each other at a meeting by shaking hands with one another, how many handshakes will take place?

Solution   *See page S3.*

In Example 4 we make use of a table to solve a problem.

EXAMPLE 4 ■ **Apply Polya's Strategy**   *(Make a Table and Look for a Pattern)*

Determine the digit 100 places to the right of the decimal point in the decimal representation $\frac{7}{27}$.

Solution

Understand the Problem   Express the fraction $\frac{7}{27}$ as a decimal and look for a pattern that will enable us to determine the digit 100 places to the right of the decimal point.

Devise a Plan   Dividing 27 into 7 by long division or by using a calculator produces the decimal 0.259259259.... Since the decimal representation repeats the digits 259 over and over forever, we know that the digit located 100 places to the right of the decimal point is either a 2, a 5, or a 9. A table may help us to see a pattern and enable us to determine which one of these digits is in the 100th place. Since the decimal digits repeat every three digits, we use a table with three columns.

The first 15 decimal digits of $\frac{7}{27}$

Column 1		Column 2		Column 3	
Location	Digit	Location	Digit	Location	Digit
1st	2	2nd	5	3rd	9
4th	2	5th	5	6th	9
7th	2	8th	5	9th	9
10th	2	11th	5	12th	9
13th	2	14th	5	15th	9
⋮		⋮		⋮	

Carry Out the Plan   Only in column 3 is each of the decimal digit *locations* evenly divisible by 3. From this pattern we can tell that the 99th decimal digit (because 99 is evenly divisible by 3) must be a 9. Since a 2 always follows a 9 in the pattern, the 100th decimal digit must be a 2.

Review the Solution   The above table illustrates additional patterns. For instance, if each of the location numbers in column 1 is divided by 3, a remainder of 1 is produced. If each of the location numbers in column 2 is divided by 3, a remainder of 2 is produced. Thus we can find the decimal digit in any location by dividing the

CALCULATOR NOTE

Some calculators display $\frac{7}{27}$ as 0.25925925926. However, the last digit 6 is not correct. It is a result of the rounding process. The actual decimal representation of $\frac{7}{27}$ is the decimal 0.259259... or $0.\overline{259}$, in which the digits continue to repeat the 259 pattern forever.

location number by 3 and examining the remainder. For instance, to find the digit in the 3200th decimal place of $\frac{7}{27}$, merely divide 3200 by 3 and examine the remainder, which is 2. Thus, the digit 3200 places to the right of the decimal point is a 5.

CHECK YOUR PROGRESS 4   Determine the ones digit of 4^{200}.

Solution   *See page S3.*

Example 5 illustrates the method of working backwards. In problems in which you know a final result, this method may require the least effort.

EXAMPLE 5 ■ **Apply Polya's Strategy**   *(Work Backwards)*

In consecutive turns of a Monopoly game, Stacy first paid $800 for a hotel. She then lost half her money when she landed on Boardwalk. Next, she collected $200 for passing GO. She then lost half her remaining money when she landed on Illinois Avenue. Stacy now has $2500. How much did she have just before she purchased the hotel?

Solution

Understand the Problem   We need to determine the number of dollars that Stacy had just prior to her $800 hotel purchase.

Devise a Plan   We could guess and check, but we might need to make several guesses before we found the correct solution. An algebraic method might work, but setting up the necessary equation could be a challenge. Since we know the end result, let's try the method of working backwards.

Carry Out the Plan   Stacy must have had $5000 just before she landed on Illinois Avenue; $4800 just before she passed GO; and $9600 prior to landing on Boardwalk. This means she had $10,400 just before she purchased the hotel.

Review the Solution   To check our solution we start with $10,400 and proceed through each of the transactions. $10,400 less $800 is $9600. Half of $9600 is $4800. $4800 increased by $200 is $5000. Half of $5000 is $2500.

CHECK YOUR PROGRESS 5   Melody picks a number. She doubles the number, squares the result, divides the square by 3, subtracts 30 from the quotient, and gets 18. What are the possible numbers that Melody could have picked? What operation does Melody perform that prevents us from knowing with 100% certainty which number she picked?

Solution   *See page S3.*

Some problems can be solved by making guesses and checking. Your first few guesses may not produce a solution, but quite often they will provide additional information that will lead to a solution.

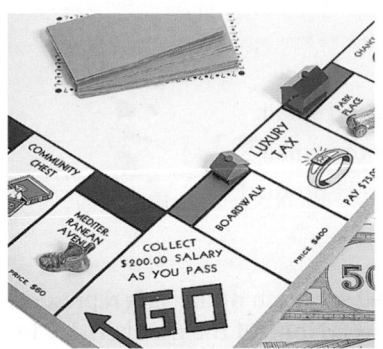

✔ **TAKE NOTE**

Example 5 can also be worked by using algebra. Let A be the amount of money Stacy had just before she purchased the hotel. Then

$$\frac{1}{2}\left[\frac{1}{2}(A - 800) + 200\right] = 2500$$

$$\frac{1}{2}(A - 800) + 200 = 5000$$

$$A - 800 + 400 = 10{,}000$$

$$A - 400 = 10{,}000$$

$$A = 10{,}400$$

Which do you prefer, the algebraic method or the method of working backwards?

EXAMPLE 6 ■ Apply Polya's Strategy *(Guess and Check)*

The product of the ages, in years, of three teenagers is 4590. None of the teens are the same age. What are the ages of the teenagers?

Solution

Understand the Problem We need to determine three distinct whole numbers, from the list 13, 14, 15, 16, 17, 18, and 19, that have a product of 4590.

Devise a Plan If we represent the ages by x, y, and z, then $xyz = 4590$. We are unable to solve this equation, but we notice that 4590 ends in a zero. Hence, 4590 has a factor of 2 and a factor of 5, which means that at least one of the numbers we seek must be an even number and at least one number must have 5 as a factor. The only number in our list that has 5 as a factor is 15. Thus 15 is one of the numbers and at least one of the other numbers must be an even number. At this point we try to solve by *guessing and checking*.

Carry Out the Plan

$15 \cdot 16 \cdot 18 = 4320$ • No. This product is too small.

$15 \cdot 16 \cdot 19 = 4560$ • No. This product is too small.

$15 \cdot 17 \cdot 18 = 4590$ • Yes. This is the correct product.

The ages of the teenagers are 15, 17, and 18.

Review the Solution Because $15 \cdot 17 \cdot 18 = 4590$ and each of the ages represents the age of a teenager, we know our solution is correct. None of the numbers 13, 14, 16, and 19 is a factor (divisor) of 4590, so there are no other solutions.

CHECK YOUR PROGRESS 6 Nothing is known about the personal life of the ancient Greek mathematician Diophantus except for the information in the following epigram. "Diophantus passed $\frac{1}{6}$ of his life in childhood, $\frac{1}{12}$ in youth, and $\frac{1}{7}$ more as a bachelor. Five years after his marriage was born a son who died four years before his father, at $\frac{1}{2}$ his father's (final) age."

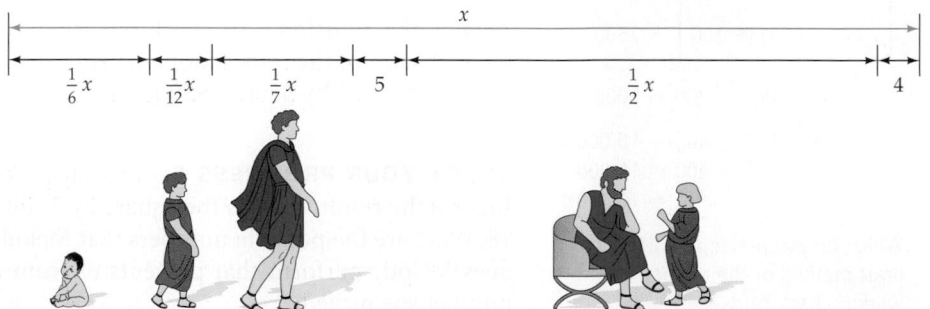

A diagram of the data, where x represents the age of Diophantus when he died

How old was Diophantus when he died? (*Hint:* Although an equation can be used to solve this problem, the method of guessing and checking will probably require less effort. Also assume that his age, when he died, is a natural number.)

Solution   See page S4.

QUESTION   *Is the process of guessing at a solution and checking your result one of Polya's problem-solving strategies?*

Math Matters   A Mathematical Prodigy

Karl Friedrich Gauss (gous) was a German scientist and mathematician. His work encompassed several disciplines, including number theory, differential geometry, analysis, astronomy, geodesy, and optics. He is often called the "Prince of Mathematicians" and is known for having shown remarkable mathematical prowess as early as age three. It is reported that soon after Gauss entered elementary school, his teacher assigned an arithmetic problem designed to keep the students occupied for a lengthy period of time. The problem consisted of finding the sum of the first 100 natural numbers. Gauss was able to determine the correct sum in a matter of a few seconds. The following solution shows the thought process that Gauss applied as he solved the problem.

Understand the Problem   The sum of the first 100 natural numbers is represented by

$$1 + 2 + 3 + \cdots + 98 + 99 + 100$$

Devise a Plan   Adding the first 100 natural numbers from left to right would produce the desired sum, but would be time consuming and laborious. Gauss considered another method. He added 1 and 100 to produce 101. He noticed that 2 and 99 have a sum of 101, and that 3 and 98 have a sum of 101. Thus the 100 numbers could be thought of as 50 pairs, each with a sum of 101.

Carry Out the Plan   To find the sum of the 50 pairs, each with a sum of 101, Gauss computed 50 · 101 and arrived at 5050 as the solution.

Review the Solution   Because the addends in an addition problem can be placed in any order without changing the sum, Gauss was confident that he had the correct solution.

An Extension   The solution of one problem often leads to solutions of additional problems. For instance, the sum $1 + 2 + 3 + \cdots + (n - 2) + (n - 1) + n$ can be found by using the following formula.

A summation formula for the first *n* natural numbers:

$$1 + 2 + 3 + \cdots + (n - 2) + (n - 1) + n = \frac{n(n + 1)}{2}$$

ANSWER   *Yes*

Karl Friedrich Gauss
(1777–1855)

Some problems are deceptive. After reading one of these problems, you may think that the solution is obvious or impossible. These deceptive problems generally require that you carefully read the problem several times and that you check your solution to make sure it satisfies all the conditions of the problem.

EXAMPLE 7 ■ Solve a Deceptive Problem

A hat and a jacket together cost $100. The jacket costs $90 more than the hat. What are the cost of the hat and the cost of the jacket?

Solution

Understand the Problem   After reading the problem for the first time, you may think that the jacket costs $90 and the hat costs $10. The sum of these costs is $100, but the cost of the jacket is only $80 more than the cost of the hat. We need to find two dollar amounts that differ by $90 and whose sum is $100.

Devise a Plan   Write an equation using h for the cost of the hat and $h + 90$ for the cost of the jacket.

$$h + h + 90 = 100$$

Carry Out the Plan   Solve the above equation for h.

$2h + 90 = 100$ • Collect like terms.
$2h = 10$ • Solve for h.
$h = 5$

The cost of the hat is $5 and the cost of the jacket is $90 + $5 = $95.

Review the Solution   The sum of the costs is $5 + $95 = $100 and the cost of the jacket is $90 more than the cost of the hat. This check confirms that the hat costs $5 and the jacket costs $95.

CHECK YOUR PROGRESS 7   Two U.S. coins have a total value of 35¢. One of the coins is not a quarter. What are the two coins?

Solution   See page S4.

Reading and Interpreting Graphs

Graphs are often used to display numerical information in a visual format that allows the reader to see pertinent relationships and trends quickly. Three of the most common types of graphs are the *bar graph*, the *circle graph*, and the *broken-line graph*.

Figure 1.3 is a bar graph that displays the average U.S. movie theatre ticket prices for the years from 1996 to 2003. The years are displayed on the horizontal axis. Each vertical bar is used to display the average ticket price for a given year. The higher the bar, the greater the average ticket price for that year.

Figure 1.3 *Average U.S. Movie Theatre Ticket Prices*

Source: National Association of Theatre Owners

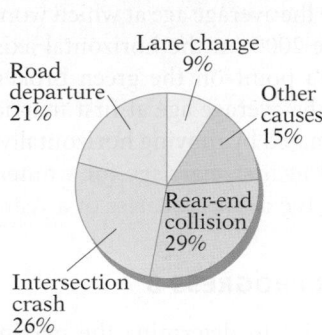

Figure 1.4 *Types of Automobile Accidents in Twin Falls in 2005*

Figure 1.5 *U.S. Average Age at First Marriage*

Source: Bureau of the Census

Figure 1.4 is a circle graph that uses circular sectors to display the percent of automobile accidents of a particular type that occurred in the city of Twin Falls in 2005. The size of a particular sector is proportional to the percent of accidents that occurred in that category.

Figure 1.5 shows two broken-line graphs. The maroon broken-line graph displays the average age at first marriage for men for selected years from 1960 to 2000. The green broken-line graph displays the average age at first marriage for women for selected years during this same time period. The $\wr$ symbol on the vertical axis indicates that the ages between 0 and 20 are not displayed. This break in the vertical axis allows the graph to be displayed in a compact form. The line segments that connect points on the graph indicate trends. Increasing trends are indicated by line segments that rise as they move to the right, and decreasing trends are indicated by line segments that fall as they move to the right. The blue arrows in Figure 1.5 show that the average age at which men married for the first time in the year 1990 was about 26 years, rounded to the nearest quarter of a year.

EXAMPLE 8 ■ Use Graphs to Solve Problems

a. Use Figure 1.3 to determine the minimum average U.S. movie theatre ticket price for the years from 1996 to 2003.

b. Use Figure 1.4 to estimate the number of rear-end collisions that occurred in Twin Falls in the year 2005. *Note:* The total number of accidents in Twin Falls for the year 2005 was 4300.

c. Use Figure 1.5 to estimate the average age at which women married for the first time in the year 2000. Round to the nearest quarter of a year.

Solution

a. The minimum of the average ticket prices is displayed by the shortest vertical bar in Figure 1.3. Thus the minimum average U.S. movie theatre ticket price for the years from 1996 to 2003 was $4.42, in the year 1996.

b. Figure 1.4 indicates that in 2005, 29% of the 4300 automobile accidents in Twin Falls were rear-end collisions. Thus $0.29 \cdot 4300 = 1247$ of the accidents were accidents involving rear-end collisions.

c. To estimate the average age at which women married for the first time in the year 2000, locate 2000 on the horizontal axis of Figure 1.5 and then move directly upward to a point on the green broken-line graph. The height of this point represents the average age at first marriage for women in the year 2000, and it can be estimated by moving horizontally to the vertical axis on the left. Thus the average age at first marriage for women in the year 2000 was about 25 years, rounded to the nearest quarter of a year.

CHECK YOUR PROGRESS 8

a. Use Figure 1.3 to determine the maximum average U.S. movie theatre ticket price for the years from 1996 to 2003.

b. Use Figure 1.4 to determine the number of lane change accidents that occurred in Twin Falls in the year 2005.

c. Use Figure 1.5 to estimate the average age at first marriage for men and for women in the year 1975. Round to the nearest quarter of a year.

Solution   *See page S4.*

Excursion

Routes on a Probability Demonstrator

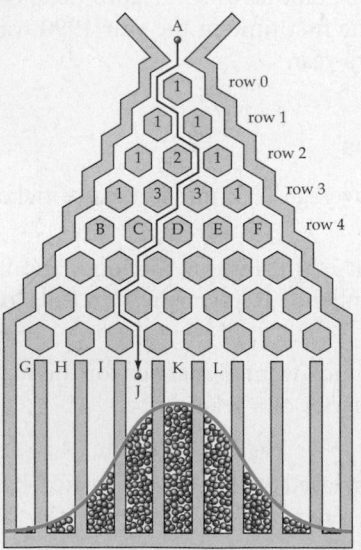

The object shown at the left is called a *Galton board*. It was invented by the English statistician Francis Galton (1822–1911). This particular board has 256 small red balls that are released so that they fall through an array of hexagons. The board is designed such that when a ball falls on a vertex of one of the hexagons, it is equally likely to fall to the left or to the right. As the ball continues its downward path, it strikes a vertex of a hexagon in the next row, where the process of falling to the left or to the right is repeated. After the ball passes through all the rows of hexagons, it falls into one of the bins at the bottom. In most cases the balls will form a *bell shape*, as shown by the green curve. Examine the numbers displayed in the hexagons in rows 0 through 3. Each number indicates the number of different routes a ball can take from point A to the top of that particular hexagon.

Excursion Exercises

1. How many routes can a ball take as it travels from point A to point B, from A to C, from A to D, from A to E, and from A to F? *Hint:* This problem is similar to Example 1 on page 31.

2. How many routes can a ball take as it travels from point A to points G, H, I, J, and K?

3. Explain how you know that the number of routes from point A to point J is the same as the number of routes from point A to point L.

4. Explain why the greatest number of balls tend to fall into the center bin.

Exercise Set 1.3

Use Polya's four-step problem-solving strategy and the problem-solving procedures presented in this lesson to solve each of the following exercises.

1. **Number of Girls** There are 364 first-grade students in Park Elementary School. If there are 26 more girls than boys, how many girls are there?

2. **Heights of Ladders** If two ladders are placed end to end, their combined height is 31.5 feet. One ladder is 6.5 feet shorter than the other ladder. What are the heights of the two ladders?

3. How many squares are in the following figure?

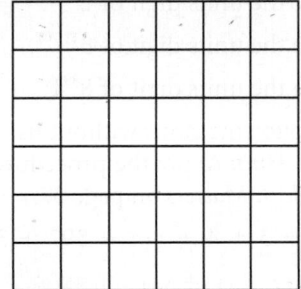

4. What is the 44th decimal digit in the decimal representation of $\frac{1}{11}$?

$$\frac{1}{11} = 0.09090909\ldots$$

5. **Cost of a Shirt** A shirt and a tie together cost $50. The shirt costs $30 more than the tie. What is the cost of the shirt?

6. **Number of Games** In a basketball league consisting of 12 teams, each team plays each of the other teams exactly twice. How many league games will be played?

7. **Number of Routes** Consider the following map. Tyler wishes to walk along the streets from point A to point B. How many direct routes (no backtracking) can Tyler take?

8. **Number of Routes** Use the map in Exercise 7 to answer each of the following.
   a. How many direct routes are there from A to B if you want to pass by Starbucks?
   b. How many direct routes are there from A to B if you want to stop at Subway for a sandwich?
   c. How many direct routes are there from A to B if you want to stop at Starbucks and at Subway?

9. **True-False Test** In how many ways can you answer a 12-question true-false test if you answer each question with either a "true" or a "false"?

10. **A Puzzle** A frog is at the bottom of a 17-foot well. Each time the frog leaps it moves up 3 feet. If the frog has not reached the top of the well, then the frog slides back 1 foot before it is ready to make another leap. How many leaps will the frog need to escape the well?

11. **Probability Demonstrator** Consider the following probability demonstrator. Note that this probability demonstrator has one additional row of hexagons compared with the probability demonstrator on page 40.

   a. How many routes can a ball take from point A to points B, C, D, E, F, G, and H?
   b. Explain why the number of routes from A to F is the same as the number from A to G.

12. **Pascal's Triangle** The triangular pattern shown on the following page is known as **Pascal's triangle**. Pascal's triangle has intrigued mathematicians for hundreds of years. Although it is named after the

mathematician Blaise Pascal (1623–1662), there is evidence that it was first developed in China in the 1300s. The numbers in Pascal's triangle are created in the following manner. Each row begins and ends with the number 1. Any other number in a row is the sum of the two closest numbers above it. For instance, the first 10 in row 5 is the sum of the first 4 and the 6 above it in row 4.

```
                    1                     row 0
                 1     1                  row 1
              1     2     1               row 2
           1     3     3     1            row 3
        1     4     6     4     1         row 4
     1     5    10    10     5     1      row 5
```

Pascal's Triangle

There are many patterns that can be discovered in Pascal's triangle.

a. Find the sum of the numbers in each row of the portion of Pascal's triangle shown above. What pattern do you observe concerning these sums? Predict the sum of the numbers in row 9 of Pascal's triangle.

b. ✎ How are the numbers in Pascal's triangle related to the number of routes found for the probability demonstrator in Exercise 11?

c. The numbers $1, 3, 6, 10, 15, \ldots, \dfrac{n(n+1)}{2}, \ldots$ are called *triangular numbers*. Where do the triangular numbers appear in Pascal's triangle?

13. **Number of Handshakes** If eight people greet each other at a meeting by shaking hands with one another, how many handshakes take place?

14. **Number of Line Segments** Twenty-four points are placed around a circle. A line segment is drawn between each pair of points. How many line segments are drawn?

15. **Number of Pigs** The number of ducks and pigs in a field totals 35. The total number of legs among them is 98. Assuming each duck has exactly two legs and each pig has exactly four legs, determine how many ducks and how many pigs are in the field.

16. ✎ **Racing Strategies** Carla and Allison are sisters. They are on their way from school to home. Carla runs half the time and walks half the time. Allison runs half the distance and walks half the distance. If Carla and Allison walk at the same speed and run at the same speed, which one arrives home first? Explain.

17. **Change for a Quarter** How many ways can you make change for 25¢ using dimes, nickels, and/or pennies?

18. **Carpet for a Room** A room measures 12 feet by 15 feet. How many 3-foot by 3-foot squares of carpet are needed to cover the floor of this room?

19. Determine the units digit of 4^{7022}.

20. Determine the units digit of 2^{6543}.

21. Determine the units digit of $3^{11,707}$.

22. Determine the units digit of 8^{8985}.

23. Find the following sums without using a calculator or a formula. *Hint:* Apply the procedure used by Gauss. (See the *Math Matters* on page 37.)

a. $1 + 2 + 3 + 4 + \cdots + 397 + 398 + 399 + 400$

b. $1 + 2 + 3 + 4 + \cdots + 547 + 548 + 549 + 550$

c. $2 + 4 + 6 + 8 + \cdots + 80 + 82 + 84 + 86$

24. ✎ Explain how you could modify the procedure used by Gauss (see the *Math Matters* on page 37) to find the following sum.

$$1 + 2 + 3 + 4 + \cdots + 62 + 63 + 64 + 65$$

25. **Palindromic Numbers** A **palindromic number** is a whole number that remains unchanged when its digits are written in reverse order. Find all palindromic numbers that have exactly

a. three-digits and are the square of a natural number.

b. four-digits and are the cube of a natural number.

26. **Speed of a Car** A car has an odometer reading of 15951 miles, which is a palindromic number. (See Exercise 25.) After 2 hours of continuous driving at a constant speed, the odometer reading is the next palindromic number. How fast, in miles per hour, was the car being driven during these 2 hours?

27. **A Puzzle** Three volumes of the series *Mathematics: Its Content, Methods, and Meaning* are on a shelf with no space between the volumes. Each volume is 1 inch thick without its covers. Each cover is $\frac{1}{8}$ inch thick. See

the following figure. A bookworm bores horizontally from the first page of Volume 1 to the last page of Volume III. How far does the bookworm travel?

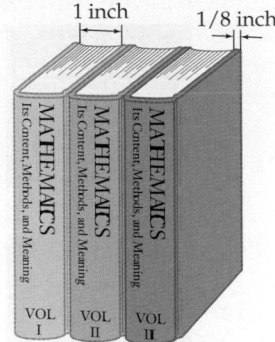

1 inch   1/8 inch

28. **Connect the Dots** Nine dots are arranged as shown. Is it possible to connect the nine dots with exactly four lines if you are not allowed to retrace any part of a line and you are not allowed to remove your pencil from the paper? If it can be done, demonstrate with a drawing.

29. **Admissions** The following bar graph shows the number of U.S. movie theatre admissions for the years from 1994 to 2003.

U.S. Movie Theatre Admissions

Source: National Association of Theatre Owners

a. Estimate the number of admissions for the years 1996, 2001, and 2003. Round each estimate to the nearest tenth of a billion.

b. Which year had the least number of admissions?

c. Which year had the greatest number of admissions?

d. For which two consecutive years did the greatest increase in admissions occur?

30. **Revenues** The following circle graph shows the percentage of refreshment revenues that a movie theatre complex received from various types of refreshments on a given day.

Total Revenues from Refreshments: $3910.25

a. Determine the revenue the theatre earned from candy sales for the given day.

b. By how much did the popcorn revenue exceed the soda revenue for the given day?

31. **Box Office Grosses** The following broken-line graph shows the U.S. box office grosses, in billions of dollars, for the years from 1994 to 2003.

U.S. Movie Theatre Box Office Grosses

Source: National Association of Theatre Owners

a. Which year had the least box office gross?

b. Which year had the greatest box office gross?

c. Movie theatre box office grosses declined from 2002 to 2003, even though the average ticket price increased from $5.80 in 2002 to $6.03 in 2003. Explain how this is possible. *Hint:* See Exercise 29.

32. **Votes in an Election** In a school election, one candidate for class president received more than 94%, but less than 100%, of the votes cast. What is the least possible number of votes cast?

33. **Floor Design** A square floor is tiled with congruent square tiles. The tiles on the two diagonals of the floor are blue. The rest of the tiles are green. If 101 blue tiles are used, find the total number of tiles on the floor.

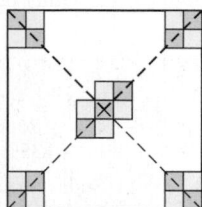

34. **Number of Children** How many children are there in a family wherein each girl has as many brothers as sisters, but each boy has twice as many sisters as brothers?

35. **Brothers and Sisters** I have two more sisters than brothers. Each of my sisters has two more sisters than brothers. How many more sisters than brothers does my youngest brother have?

36. **A Coin Problem** If you take 22 pennies from a pile of 57 pennies, how many pennies do you have?

37. **Bacterial Growth** The bacteria in a petri dish grow in a manner such that each day, the number of bacteria doubles. On what day will the number of bacteria be half of the number present on the 12th day?

38. **Number of River Crossings** Four people on one side of a river need to cross the river in a boat that can carry a maximum load of 180 pounds. The weights of the people are 80, 100, 150, and 170 pounds.

    a. Explain how the people can use the boat to get every one to the opposite side of the river.

    b. What is the minimum number of crossings that must be made by the boat?

39. **Examination Scores** On three examinations Dana received scores of 82, 91, and 76. What score does Dana need on the fourth examination to raise his average to 85?

40. **Puzzle from a Movie** In the movie *Die Hard: With A Vengeance*, Bruce Willis and Samuel L. Jackson are given a 5-gallon jug and a 3-gallon jug and they must put *exactly* 4 gallons of water on a scale to keep a bomb from exploding. Explain how they could accomplish this feat. Take your time, you have 2 minutes.

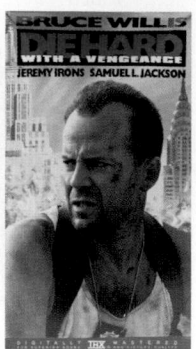

41. **Find the Fake Coin** You have eight coins. They all look identical, but one is a fake and is slightly lighter than the others. Explain how you can use a balance scale to determine which coin is the fake in exactly

    a. three weighings.

    b. two weighings.

Problems from the Mensa Workout Mensa is a society that welcomes people from every walk of life whose IQ is in the top 2% of the population. The multiple-choice Exercises 42–45 are from the *Mensa Workout*, which is posted on the Internet at

http://www.mensa.org/info.php

42. If it were two hours later, it would be half as long until midnight as it would be if it were an hour later. What time is it now?

    a. 18:30   b. 20:00   c. 21:00
    d. 22:00   e. 23:30

43. Sally likes 225 but not 224; she likes 900 but not 800; she likes 144 but not 145. Which of the following does she like?

    a. 1600   b. 1700

44. There are 1200 elephants in a herd. Some have pink and green stripes, some are all pink, and some are all blue. One third are pure pink. Is it true that 400 elephants are definitely blue?

    a. Yes   **b.** No

45. Following the pattern shown in the number sequence below, what is the missing number?

$$1 \quad 8 \quad 27 \quad ? \quad 125 \quad 216$$

    a. 36   **b.** 45   **c.** 46

    d. 64   **e.** 99

Extensions

CRITICAL THINKING

46. Compare Exponential Expressions

    a. How many times as large is $3^{(3^3)}$ than $(3^3)^3$?

    b. How many times as large is $(4^4)^4$ than $4^{(4^4)}$? *Note:* Most calculators will not display the answer to this problem because it is too large. However, the answer can be determined in exponential form by applying the following properties of exponents.

$$(a^m)^n = a^{mn} \quad \text{and} \quad \frac{a^m}{a^n} = a^{m-n}$$

47. A Famous Puzzle The mathematician Augustus De Morgan once wrote that he had the distinction of being x years old in the year x^2. He was 43 in the year 1849.

    a. Explain why people born in the year 1980 might share the distinction of being x years old in the year x^2. *Note:* Assume x is a natural number.

    b. What is the next year after 1980 for which people born in that year might be x years old in the year x^2?

48. Verify a Procedure Select a two-digit number between 50 and 100. Add 83 to your number. From this number form a new number by adding the digit in the hundreds place to the number formed by the other two digits (the digits in the tens place and the ones place). Now subtract this newly formed number from your original number. Your final result is 16. Use a deductive approach to show that the final result is always 16 regardless of which number you start with.

49. Numbering Pages How many digits does it take in total to number a book from page 1 to page 240?

50. Cover a Checkerboard Consider a checkerboard with two red squares on opposite corners removed, as shown in the accompanying figure. Determine whether it is possible to completely cover the checkerboard with 31 dominoes if each domino is placed horizontally or vertically and each domino covers exactly two squares. If it is possible, show how to do it. If it is not possible, explain why it cannot be done.

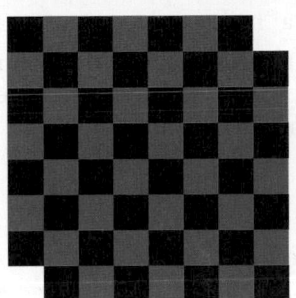

COOPERATIVE LEARNING

51. The 4 Fours Problem The object of this exercise is to create mathematical expressions that use exactly four 4's and that simplify to a counting number from 1 to 20, inclusive. You are allowed to use the following mathematical symbols: $+, -, \times, \div, \sqrt{}, ($, and $)$. For example,

$$\frac{4}{4} + \frac{4}{4} = 2, \quad 4^{(4-4)} + 4 = 5, \quad \text{and}$$
$$4 - \sqrt{4} + 4 \times 4 = 18$$

52. A Cryptarithm The following puzzle is a famous *cryptarithm*.

Each letter in the cryptarithm represents one of the digits 0 through 9. The leading digits, represented by S and M, are not zero. Determine which digit is represented by each of the letters so that the addition is correct. *Note:* A letter that is used more than once, such as M, represents the same digit in each position in which it appears.

EXPLORATIONS

53. 🌐 **The Collatz Problem** There are many unsolved problems in mathematics. One famous unsolved problem is known as the *Collatz problem,* or the $3n + 1$ problem. This problem was created by L. Collatz in 1937. Although the procedures in the Collatz problem are easy to understand, the problem remains unsolved. Search the Internet or a library to find information on the Collatz problem.

    a. ✎ Write a short report that explains the Collatz problem. In your report, explain the meaning of a "hailstone" sequence.

    b. Show that for each of the natural numbers 2, 3, 4, ..., 10, the Collatz procedure does generate a sequence that "returns" to 1.

54. ✎ **Paul Erdos** Paul Erdos (1913–1996) was a mathematician known for his elegant solutions of problems in number theory, combinatorics, discrete mathematics, and graph theory. He loved to solve mathematical problems, and for those problems he could not solve, he offered financial rewards, up to $10,000, to the person who could provide a solution.

    Write a report on the life of Paul Erdos. In your report, include information about the type of problem that Erdos considered the most interesting. What did Erdos have to say about the Collatz problem mentioned in Exploration Exercise 53?

CHAPTER 1   Summary

Key Terms

Binet's Formula [p. 26]
Bode's Rule [p. 27]
Collatz problem [p. 46]
counterexample [p. 5]
counting number [p. 12]
difference table [p. 16]
first, second, and third differences [p. 16]
integer [p. 12]
natural number [p. 12]
nth term formula [p. 17]
nth term of a sequence [p. 15]
palindromic number [p. 42]
Pascal's Triangle [p. 41]
phi, the golden ratio [p. 28]
polygonal numbers [p. 23]
prime number [p. 13]
recursive definition [p. 20]
sequence [p. 15]
term of a sequence [p. 15]

Essential Concepts

■ *Inductive reasoning* is the process of reaching a general conclusion by examining specific examples. A conclusion based on inductive reasoning is called a *conjecture*. A conjecture may or may not be correct.

■ *Deductive reasoning* is the process of reaching a conclusion by applying general assumptions, procedures, or principles.

■ A statement is a *true statement* provided it is true in all cases. If you can find one case in which a statement is not true, called a *counterexample*, then the statement is a *false statement*.

■ The terms of the *Fibonacci sequence* 1, 1, 2, 3, 5, 8, 13, 21, ... can be determined by using the *recursive definition*

$$F_1 = 1, F_2 = 1, \text{ and } F_n = F_{n-1} + F_{n-2} \quad \text{for } n \geq 3$$

■ Many problems can be solved by applying *Polya's problem-solving strategy:*

    1. Understand the problem.

    2. Devise a plan.

    3. Carry out the plan.

    4. Review your solution.

■ A summation formula for the first n natural numbers:

$$1 + 2 + 3 + \cdots + (n - 2) + (n - 1) + n = \frac{n(n + 1)}{2}$$

CHAPTER 1 **Review Exercises**

In Exercises 1–4, determine whether the argument is an example of inductive reasoning or deductive reasoning.

1. All books written by John Grisham make the best-seller list. The book *The Last Juror* is a John Grisham book. Therefore, *The Last Juror* made the bestseller list.

2. Samantha got an A on each of her first four math tests, so she will get an A on the next math test.

3. We had rain yesterday, so there is less chance of rain today.

4. All amoeba multiply by dividing. I have named the amoeba shown in my microscope Amelia. Therefore, Amelia multiplies by dividing.

5. Find a counterexample to show that the following conjecture is false.
Conjecture: For all x, $x^4 > x$.

6. Find a counterexample to show that the following conjecture is false.

Conjecture: For all counting numbers n, $\dfrac{n^3 + 5n + 6}{6}$ is an even number.

7. Find a counterexample to show that the following conjecture is false.
Conjecture: For all x, $(x + 4)^2 = x^2 + 16$.

8. Find a counterexample to show that the following conjecture is false.
Conjecture: For numbers a and b, $(a + b)^3 = a^3 + b^3$.

9. Use a difference table to predict the next term of each sequence.
   a. $-2, 2, 12, 28, 50, 78, ?$
   b. $-4, -1, 14, 47, 104, 191, 314, ?$

10. Use a difference table to predict the next term of each sequence.
   a. $5, 6, 3, -4, -15, -30, -49, ?$
   b. $2, 0, -18, -64, -150, -288, -490, ?$

11. A sequence has an nth term formula of
$$a_n = 4n^2 - n - 2$$
Use the nth term formula to determine the first five terms of the sequence and the 20th term of the sequence.

12. A sequence has an nth term formula of
$$a_n = -2n^3 + 5n$$
Use the nth term formula to determine the first five terms of the sequence and the 25th term of the sequence.

In Exercises 13–16, determine the nth term formula for the number of square tiles in the nth figure.

13.

14.

15.

16.
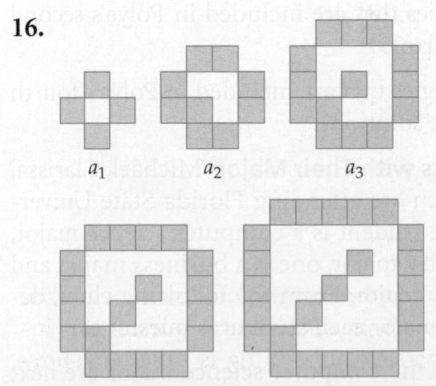

Polya's Problem-Solving Strategy In Exercises 17–22, solve each problem using Polya's four-step problem-solving strategy. Label your work so that each of Polya's four steps is identified.

17. A rancher decides to enclose a rectangular region by using an existing fence along one side of the region and 2240 feet of new fence on the other three sides. The rancher wants the length of the rectangular region to be five times as long as its width. What will be the dimensions of the rectangular region?

18. In how many ways can you answer a 15-question test if you answer each question with either a "true," a "false," or an "always false"?

19. The skyboxes at a large sports arena are equally spaced, around a circle. The 11th skybox is directly opposite the 35th skybox. How many skyboxes are there in the sports arena?

20. A rancher needs to get a dog, a rabbit, and a basket of carrots across a river. The rancher has a small boat that will only stay afloat carrying the rancher and one of the critters or the rancher and the carrots. The rancher cannot leave the dog alone with the rabbit because the dog will eat the rabbit. The rancher cannot leave the rabbit alone with the carrots because the rabbit will eat the carrots. How can the rancher get across the river with the critters and the carrots?

21. An investor bought 20 shares of stock for a total cost of $1200 and then sold all the shares for $1400. A few months later the investor bought 25 shares of the same stock for a total cost of $1800 and then sold all the shares for $1900. How much money did the investor earn on these investments?

22. If 15 people greet each other at a meeting by shaking hands with one another, how many handshakes will take place?

23. List five strategies that are included in Polya's second step (devise a plan).

24. List three strategies that are included in Polya's fourth step (review the solution).

25. **Match Students with Their Major** Michael, Clarissa, Reggie, and Ellen are attending Florida State University (FSU). One student is a computer science major, one is a chemistry major, one is a business major, and one is a biology major. From the following clues, determine which major each student is pursuing.

   a. Michael and the computer science major are next door neighbors.

   b. Clarissa and the chemistry major have attended FSU for 2 years. Reggie has attended FSU for 3 years, and the biology major has attended FSU for 4 years.

   c. Ellen has attended FSU for fewer years than Michael.

   d. The business major has attended FSU for 2 years.

26. **Little League Baseball** Each of the Little League teams in a small rural community is sponsored by a different local business. The names of the teams are the Dodgers, the Pirates, the Tigers, and the Giants. The businesses that sponsor the teams are the bank, the supermarket, the service station, and the drug store. From the following clues, determine which business sponsors each team.

   a. The Tigers and the team sponsored by the service station have winning records this season.

   b. The Pirates and the team sponsored by the bank are coached by parents of the players, whereas the Giants and the team sponsored by the drug store are coached by the director of the Community Center.

   c. Jake is the pitcher for the team sponsored by the supermarket and coached by his father.

   d. The game between the Tigers and the team sponsored by the drug store was rained out yesterday.

27. **Map Coloring** The following map shows seven countries in the Indian subcontinent. Four colors have been used to color the countries such that no two bordering countries are the same color.

   a. Can this map be colored using only three colors, such that no two bordering countries are the same color? Explain.

   b. Can this map be colored using only two colors, such that no two bordering countries are the same color? Explain.

28. Find a Route The following map shows the 10 bridges and 3 islands between the suburbs of North Bay and South Bay.

   a. During your morning workout, you decide to jog over each bridge exactly once. Draw a route that you can take. Assume that you want to start from North Bay and that your workout concludes after you jog over the 10th bridge.

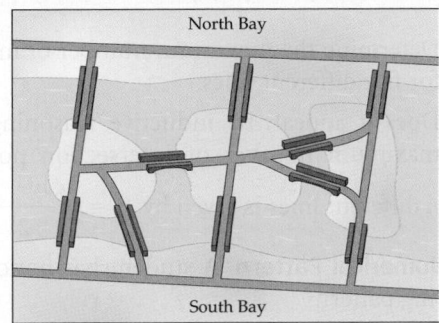

   b. Assume you want to start your jog from South Bay. Can you find a route that crosses each bridge exactly once?

29. Areas of Rectangles Two perpendicular line segments partition the interior of a rectangle into four smaller rectangles. The areas of these smaller rectangles are x, 2, 5, and 10 square inches. Find all possible values of x.

30. Consider the following figures.

   Figure a_1 consists of two line segments and figure a_2 consists of four line segments. If the pattern of adding a smaller line segment to each end of the shortest line segments continues, how many line segments will be in

   a. figure a_{10}?   **b.** figure a_{30}?

31. A Cryptarithm In the following addition problem, each letter represents one of the digits 0, 1, 2, 3, 4, 5, 6, 7, 8, or 9. The leading digits represented by A and B are nonzero digits. What digit is represented by each letter?

$$
\begin{array}{r}
A \\
+\,B\,B \\
\hline
A\,D\,D
\end{array}
$$

32. Make Change In how many different ways can change be made for a dollar using only quarters and/or nickels?

33. Counting Problem In how many different orders can a basketball team win exactly three out of their last five games?

34. What is the units digit of 7^{56}?

35. What is the units digit of 23^{85}?

36. Verify a Conjecture Use deductive reasoning to show that the following procedure always produces a number that is twice the original number.
Procedure: Pick a number. Multiply the number by 4, add 12 to the product, divide the sum by 2, and subtract 6.

37. Explain why 2004 nickels are worth more than 100 dollars.

38. College Graduates The following bar graph shows the percent of the U.S. population, age 25 and over, who have attained a bachelor's degree, or higher, for selected years from 1940 to 2000.

Percent of U.S. Population, Age 25 and Over, with a Bachelor's Degree or Higher

Source: U.S. Census Bureau

   a. During which 10-year period did the percent of bachelor degree recipients, or higher, increase the most?

   b. What was the amount of that increase?

39. The Film Industry The following circle graph categorizes, by their ratings, the 655 films released during a recent year.

Ratings of Films Released

Source: MPA Worldwide Market Research

   a. How many times as many PG-13 films were released than NC-17 films?

   b. How many times as many R-rated films were released than NC-17 films?

40. SAT Scores The following broken-line graphs show the average SAT math scores and the average SAT verbal scores for the years from 1999 to 2004.

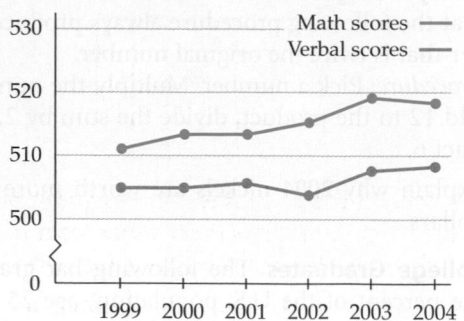

Average SAT Scores

Source: The College Board

a. In which year did the math scores increase and the verbal scores decrease, from the previous year?

b. In which year did the verbal scores increase and the math scores decrease, from the previous year.

41. Palindromic Numbers Recall that palindromic numbers read the same from left to right as they read from right to left. For instance, 37,573 is a palindromic number. Find the smallest palindromic number larger than 1000 that is a multiple of 5.

42. Narcissistic Numbers A **narcissistic number** is a two-digit natural number that is equal to the sum of the squares of its digits. Find all narcissistic numbers.

43. Number of Intersections Two different lines can intersect in at most one point. Three different lines can intersect in at most three points, and four different lines can intersect in at most six points.

a. Determine the maximum number of intersections for five different lines.

b. Does it appear, by inductive reasoning, that the maximum number of intersection points I_n for n different lines is given by $I_n = \dfrac{n(n-1)}{2}$?

44. A Numerical Pattern A student has noticed the following pattern.

$$9^1 = 9 \text{ has one digit.}$$
$$9^2 = 81 \text{ has two digits.}$$
$$9^3 = 729 \text{ has three digits.}$$
$$\vdots$$
$$9^{10} = 3,486,784,401 \text{ has ten digits.}$$

a. Find a natural number n such that the number of digits in the decimal expansion of 9^n is *not* equal to n.

b. A professor indicates that you can receive five extra-credit points if you write all of the digits in the decimal expansion of $9^{(9^9)}$. Is this a worthwhile project? Explain.

CHAPTER 1   **Test**

In Exercises 1–4, determine whether the problem is an example of inductive reasoning or deductive reasoning.

1. All novels by Sidney Sheldon are gruesome. The novel *Are You Afraid of the Dark?* was written by Sidney Sheldon. Therefore, *Are You Afraid of the Dark?* is a gruesome novel.

2. Ashlee Simpson's last album made the top-ten list, so her next album will also make the top-ten list.

3. **A Bubble Sort vs. a Shell Sort** Two computer programs, a *bubble sort* and a *shell sort*, are used to sort data. In each of 50 experiments, the shell sort program took less time to sort the data than did the bubble sort program. Thus the shell sort program is the faster of the two sorting programs.

4. **Geometry** If a figure is a rectangle, then it is a parallelogram. Figure A is a rectangle. Therefore, Figure A is a parallelogram.

5. Use a difference table to predict the next term in the sequence $-1, 0, 9, 32, 75, 144, 245, \dots$.

6. List the first 10 terms of the Fibonacci sequence.

7. In each of the following, determine the nth term formula for the number of square tiles in the nth figure.

a.

b.

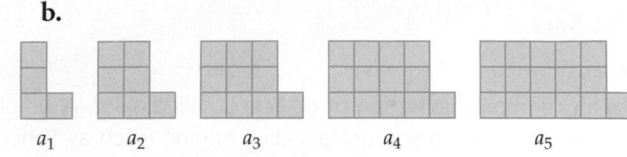

8. A sequence has an nth term formula of

$$a_n = (-1)^n \left(\frac{n(n-1)}{2} \right)$$

Use the nth term formula to determine the first five terms and the 105th term in the sequence.

9. In the following sequence, each term after the second term is the sum of the two preceding terms.

$$2, 5, 7, 12, 19, 31, 50, 81, \ldots$$

Find the next three terms of the sequence.

10. State the four steps of Polya's four-step problem-solving strategy.

11. **Make Change** How many different ways can change be made for a dollar using only half-dollars, quarters, and/or dimes?

12. **Counting Problem** In how many different orders can a basketball team win exactly four out of their last six games?

13. What is the units digit of 3^{4513}?

14. **Vacation Money** Shelly has saved some money for a vacation. Shelly spends half of her vacation money on an airline ticket; she then spends $50 for sunglasses, $22 for a taxi, and one-third of her remaining money for a room with a view. After her sister repays her a loan of $150, Shelly finds that she has $326. How much vacation money did Shelly have at the start of her vacation?

15. **Number of Different Routes** How many different direct routes are there from point A to point B in the following figure?

16. **Number of League Games** In a league of nine football teams, each team plays every other team in the league exactly once. How many league games will take place?

17. **Ages of Children** The four children in the Rivera family are Reynaldo, Ramiro, Shakira, and Sasha. The ages of the two teenagers are 13 and 15. The ages of the younger children are 5 and 7. From the following clues, determine the age of each of the children.

a. Reynaldo is older than Ramiro.

b. Sasha is younger than Shakira.

c. Sasha is 2 years older than Ramiro.

d. Shakira is older than Reynaldo.

18. **Palindromic Numbers** Find the smallest palindromic number larger than 600 that is a multiple of 3.

19. Find a counterexample to show that the following conjecture is false.

Conjecture: For all x, $\dfrac{(x-4)(x+3)}{x-4} = x + 3$.

20. **Navigation Systems** The following bar graph shows the number of new vehicles sold with navigation systems.

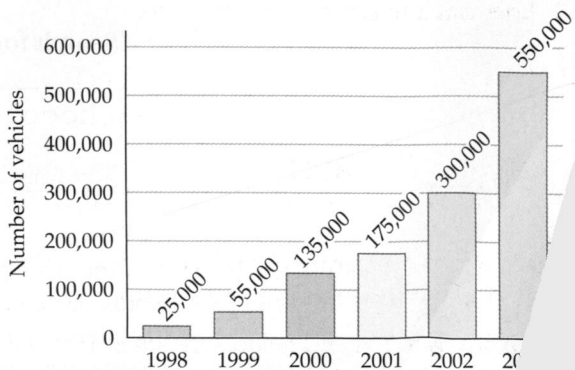

New Vehicles Sold with Navigation System

Source: J. D. Power and Associates

a. Between which two years did the number vehicles sold with navigation systems in most?

b. What was the amount of that increase?

Sets

2

In mathematics any group or collection of objects is called a *set*. A simple application of sets occurs when you use a search engine (such as Yahoo, AltaVista, Google, or Lycos) to find a topic on the Internet. You merely enter a few words describing what you are searching for and click the "Search" button. The search engine then creates a list (set) of websites that contain a match for the words you submitted.

For instance, suppose you wish to make a dessert. You decide to search the Internet for a chocolate cake recipe. You search for the words "chocolate cake" and you obtain a set containing 300,108 matches. This is a very large number, so you narrow your search. One method of narrowing your search is to use the AND option found in the Advanced Search link of some search engines. An AND search is an all-words search. That is, an AND search finds only those sites that contain all of the words submitted. An AND search for "chocolate cake" produces a set containing 74,400 matches. This is a more reasonable number, but it is still quite large.

Search for:

chocolate cake|

Search

Advanced Search

You attempt to narrow the search even further by using an AND search for the words "chocolate cake recipe." This search returns 17,945 matches. An AND search for "flourless chocolate cake recipe" returns only 913 matches. The second of these sites provides you with a recipe and states that it is fabulous and foolproof.

Sometimes it is helpful to perform a search using the OR option. An OR search is an any-words search. That is, an OR search finds all those sites that contain any of the words you submitted.

Many additional applications of sets are given in this chapter.

| **Basic Properties of Sets**

Sets

The constellation Scorpius is a set of stars.

In an attempt to better understand the universe, ancient astronomers classified certain groups of stars as constellations. Today we still find it extremely helpful to classify items into groups that enable us to find order and meaning in our complicated world.

Any group or collection of objects is called a **set.** The objects that belong in a set are the **elements,** or **members,** of the set. For example, the set consisting of the four seasons has spring, summer, fall and winter as its elements.

The following two methods are often used to designate a set.

- Describe the set using words.

- List the elements of the set inside a pair of braces, { }. This method is called the **roster method.** Commas are used to separate the elements.

For instance, let's use S to represent the set consisting of the four seasons. Using the roster method we would write

$S = \{$spring, summer, fall, winter$\}$

The order in which the elements of a set are listed is not important. Thus the set consisting of the four seasons can also be written as

$S = \{$winter, spring, fall, summer$\}$

The following table gives two examples of sets, where each set is designated by a word description and also by using the roster method.

✔ TAKE NOTE

Sets can also be designated by using *set-builder notation.* This method is described on page 56.

▼ point of interest

Paper currency in denominations of $500, $1000, $5000, and $10,000 has been in circulation, but production of these bills ended in 1945. If you just happen to have some of these bills, you can still cash them for their face value.

Table 2.1 *Define Sets by Using a Word Description and the Roster Method*

Description	Roster Method
The set of denominations of U.S. paper currency in production at this time	{$1, $2, $5, $10, $20, $50, $100}
The set of states in the United States that border the Pacific Ocean.	{California, Oregon, Washington, Alaska, Hawaii}

EXAMPLE 1 ■ Use The Roster Method to Represent a Set

Use the roster method to represent the set of the days in a week.

Solution   {Sunday, Monday, Tuesday, Wednesday, Thursday, Friday, Saturday}

CHECK YOUR PROGRESS 1   Use the roster method to represent the set of months that start with the letter A.

Solution   *See page S4.*

TAKE NOTE

Some sets can be described in more than one way. For instance, {Sunday, Saturday} can be described as the days of the week that begin with the letter *S*, as the days of the week that occur in a weekend, or as the first and last days of a week.

TAKE NOTE

In this chapter the letters *N, W, I, Q, 𝒥*, and *R* will often be used to represent the basic number sets defined at the right.

EXAMPLE 2 ■ Use a Word Description to Represent a Set

Write a word description for the set

$A = \{a, b, c, d, e, f, g, h, i, j, k, l, m, n, o, p, q, r, s, t, u, v, w, x, y, z\}$

Solution Set *A* is the set of letters of the English alphabet.

CHECK YOUR PROGRESS 2 Write a word description for the set {March, May}.

Solution See page S4.

The following sets of numbers are used extensively in many areas of mathematics.

Basic Number Sets

Natural Numbers or Counting Numbers $N = \{1, 2, 3, 4, 5, \ldots\}$

Whole Numbers $W = \{0, 1, 2, 3, 4, 5, \ldots\}$

Integers $I = \{\ldots, -4, -3, -2, -1, 0, 1, 2, 3, 4, \ldots\}$

Rational Numbers $Q = $ the set of all terminating or repeating decimals

Irrational Numbers $\mathcal{J} = $ the set of all nonterminating, nonrepeating decimals

Real Numbers $R = $ the set of all rational or irrational numbers

The set of natural numbers is also called the set of counting numbers. The three dots ... are called an **ellipsis** and indicate that the elements of the set continue in a manner suggested by the elements that are listed.

The integers $\ldots, -4, -3, -2, -1$ are **negative integers.** The integers $1, 2, 3, 4, \ldots$ are **positive integers.** Note that the natural numbers and the positive integers are the same set of numbers. The integer zero is neither a positive nor a negative integer.

If a number in decimal form terminates or repeats a block of digits, then the number is a rational number. Rational numbers can also be written in the form $\frac{p}{q}$, where *p* and *q* are integers and $q \neq 0$. For example,

$$\frac{1}{4} = 0.25 \quad \text{and} \quad \frac{3}{11} = 0.\overline{27}$$

are rational numbers. The bar over the 27 means that the block of digits 27 repeats without end; that is, $0.\overline{27} = 0.27272727\ldots$.

A decimal that neither terminates nor repeats is an **irrational number.** For instance, $0.35335333533335\ldots$ is a nonterminating, nonrepeating decimal and thus is an irrational number.

Every real number is either a rational number or an irrational number.

EXAMPLE 3 ■ Use The Roster Method to Represent a Set of Numbers

Use the roster method to write each of the given sets.

a. The set of natural numbers less than 5

b. The solution set of $x + 5 = -1$

c. The set of negative integers greater than -4

Solution

a. The set of natural numbers is given by {1, 2, 3, 4, 5, 6, 7, ...}. The natural numbers less than 5 are 1, 2, 3, and 4. Using the roster method, we write this set as {1, 2, 3, 4}.

b. Adding −5 to each side of the equation produces $x = -6$. The solution set of $x + 5 = -1$ is {−6}.

c. The set of negative integers greater than −4 is {−3, −2, −1}.

CHECK YOUR PROGRESS 3   Use the roster method to write each of the given sets.

a. The set of whole numbers less than 4

b. The set of counting numbers larger than 11 and less than or equal to 19

c. The set of negative integers between −5 and 7

Solution   See page S4.

Definitions Regarding Sets

A set is **well defined** if it is possible to determine whether any given item is an element of the set. For instance, the set of letters of the English alphabet is well defined. The set of *great songs* is not a well-defined set. It is not possible to determine whether any given song is an element of the set or is not an element of the set because there is no standard method for making such a judgment.

The statement "4 is an element of the set of natural numbers" can be written using mathematical notation as $4 \in N$. The symbol $\in$ is read "is an element of." To state that "−3 is not an element of the set of natural numbers," we use the "is not an element of" symbol, $\notin$, and write $-3 \notin N$.

✔ **TAKE NOTE**

Recall that *N* denotes the set of natural numbers, *I* denotes the set of integers, and *W* denotes the set of whole numbers.

EXAMPLE 4 ■ True or False

Determine whether each statement is true or false.

a. $4 \in \{2, 3, 4, 7\}$ b. $-5 \in N$ c. $\frac{1}{2} \notin I$

d. The set of nice cars is a well-defined set.

Solution

a. Since 4 is an element of the given set, the statement is true.

b. There are no negative natural numbers, so the statement is false.

c. Since $\frac{1}{2}$ is not an integer, the statement is true.

d. The word *nice* is not precise, so the statement is false.

CHECK YOUR PROGRESS 4   Determine whether each statement is true or false.

a. $5.2 \in \{1, 2, 3, 4, 5, 6\}$ b. $-101 \in I$ c. $2.5 \notin W$

d. The set of all integers larger than π is a well-defined set.

Solution   See page S4.

The **empty set,** or **null set,** is the set that contains no elements. The symbol ∅ or { } is used to represent the empty set. As an example of the empty set, consider the set of natural numbers that are negative integers.

Another method of representing a set is **set-builder notation.** Set-builder notation is especially useful when describing infinite sets. For instance, in set-builder notation, the set of natural numbers greater than 7 is written as follows:

membership conditions

$\{x \mid x \in N \text{ and } x > 7\}$

the set | of all elements x | such that | x is an element of the set of natural numbers | and x is greater than 7

The above set-builder notation is read as "the set of all elements x such that x is an element of the set of natural numbers and x is greater than 7." It is impossible to list all the elements of the set, but set-builder notation defines the set by describing its elements.

EXAMPLE 5 ■ Set-Builder Notation

Use set-builder notation to write the following sets.

a. The set of integers greater than -3

b. The set of whole numbers less than 1000

Solution

a. $\{x \mid x \in I \text{ and } x > -3\}$ **b.** $\{x \mid x \in W \text{ and } x < 1000\}$

CHECK YOUR PROGRESS 5   Use set-builder notation to write the following sets.

a. The set of integers less than 9

b. The set of natural numbers greater than 4

Solution   See page S4.

A set is **finite** if the number of elements in the set is a whole number. The **cardinal number** of a finite set is the number of elements in the set. The cardinal number of a finite set A is denoted by the notation $n(A)$. For instance, if $A = \{1, 4, 6, 9\}$, then $n(A) = 4$. In this case, A has a cardinal number of 4, which is sometimes stated as "A has a *cardinality* of 4."

EXAMPLE 6 ■ The Cardinality of a Set

Find the cardinality of each of the following sets.

a. $J = \{2, 5\}$ **b.** $S = \{3, 4, 5, 6, 7, \ldots, 31\}$ **c.** $T = \{3, 3, 7, 51\}$

Solution

a. Set J contains exactly two elements, so J has a cardinality of 2. Using mathematical notation we state this as $n(J) = 2$.

b. Only a few elements are actually listed. The number of natural numbers from 1 to 31 is 31. If we omit the numbers 1 and 2, then the number of natural numbers from 3 to 31 must be $31 - 2 = 29$. Thus $n(S) = 29$.

c. Elements that are listed more than once are counted only once. Thus $n(T) = 3$.

CHECK YOUR PROGRESS 6   Find the cardinality of the following sets.

a. $C = \{-1, 5, 4, 11, 13\}$ **b.** $D = \{0\}$ **c.** $E = \varnothing$

Solution   See page S4.

The following definitions play an important role in our work with sets.

Definition of Equal Sets

Set A is **equal** to set B, denoted by $A = B$, if and only if A and B have exactly the same elements.

For instance $\{d, e, f\} = \{e, f, d\}$.

Definition of Equivalent Sets

Set A is **equivalent** to set B, denoted by $A \sim B$, if and only if A and B have the same number of elements.

QUESTION   *If two sets are equal, must they also be equivalent?*

EXAMPLE 7 ■ Equal Sets and Equivalent Sets

State whether each of the following pairs of sets are equal, equivalent, both, or neither.

a. $\{a, e, i, o, u\}, \{3, 7, 11, 15, 19\}$ **b.** $\{4, -2, 7\}, \{3, 4, 7, 9\}$

Solution
a. The sets are not equal. However, each set has exactly five elements, so the sets are equivalent.
b. The first set has three elements and the second set has four elements, so the sets are not equal and are not equivalent.

CHECK YOUR PROGRESS 7   State whether each of the following pairs of sets are equal, equivalent, both, or neither.

a. $\{x \mid x \in W \text{ and } x \leq 5\}, \{\alpha, \beta, \Gamma, \Delta, \delta, \varepsilon\}$
b. $\{5, 10, 15, 20, 25, 30, \ldots, 80\}, \{x \mid x \in N \text{ and } x < 17\}$

Solution   See page S4.

ANSWER   *Yes. If the sets are equal, then they have exactly the same elements; therefore, they also have the same number of elements.*

Math Matters   Georg Cantor

Georg Cantor

Georg Cantor (kăn'tər) (1845–1918) was a German mathematician who developed many new concepts regarding the theory of sets. Cantor studied under the famous mathematicians Karl Weirstrass and Leopold Kronecker at the University of Berlin. Although Cantor demonstrated a talent for mathematics, his professors were unaware that Cantor would produce extraordinary results that would cause a major stir in the mathematical community.

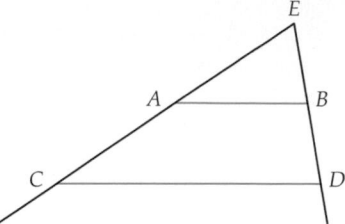

Cantor never achieved his lifelong goal of a professorship at the University of Berlin. Instead he spent his active career at the undistinguished University of Halle. It was during this period, when Cantor was between the ages of 29 and 39, that he produced his best work. Much of this work was of a controversial nature. One of the simplest of the controversial concepts concerned points on a line segment. For instance, consider the line segment $\overline{AB}$ and the line segment $\overline{CD}$ in the figure above. Which of these two line segments do you think contains the most points? Cantor was able to prove that they both contain the same number of points. In fact, he was able to prove that any line segment, no matter how short, contains the same number of points as a line, or a plane, or all of three-dimensional space. We will take a closer look at some of the mathematics developed by Cantor in the last section of this chapter.

Excursion

Fuzzy Sets

In traditional set theory, an element either belongs to a set or does not belong to the set. For instance, let $A = \{x \mid x \text{ is an even integer}\}$. Given $x = 8$, we have $x \in A$. However, if $x = 11$, then $x \notin A$. For any given integer, we can decide whether x belongs to A.

Now consider the set $B = \{x \mid x \text{ is a number close to } 10\}$. Does 8 belong to this set? Does 9.9 belong to the set? Does 10.001 belong to the set? Does 10 belong to the set? Does -50 belong to the set? Given the imprecision of the words "close to," it is impossible to know which numbers belong to set B.

In 1965, Lotfi A. Zadeh of the University of California, Berkeley, published a paper titled *Fuzzy Sets* in which he described the mathematics of fuzzy set theory. This theory proposed that "to some degree," many of the numbers 8, 9.9, 10.001, 10 and -50 belong to set B defined in the previous paragraph. Zadeh proposed giving each element of a set a *membership grade* or *membership value*. This value is a number from 0 to 1. The closer the membership value is to 1, the greater the certainty that an element belongs to the set. The closer the membership value is to 0, the less the certainty that an element

(continued)

historical note

Lotfi Zadeh
Lotfi Zadeh's work in the area of fuzzy sets has led to a new area of mathematics called *soft computing*. On the topic of soft computing, Zadeh stated, "The essence of soft computing is that unlike the traditional, hard computing, soft computing is aimed at an accommodation with the pervasive imprecision of the real world. Thus the guiding principle of soft computing is: Exploit the tolerance for imprecision, uncertainty and partial truth to achieve tractability, robustness, low solution cost and better rapport with reality. In the final analysis, the role model for soft computing is the human mind." ∎

belongs to the set. Elements of fuzzy sets are written in the form (element, membership value). Here is an example of a fuzzy set.

$$C = \{(8, 0.4), (9.9, 0.9), (10.001, 0.999), (10, 1), (-50, 0)\}$$

An examination of the membership values suggests that we are certain that 10 belongs to C (membership value is 1) and we are certain that -50 does not belong to C (membership value is 0). Every other element belongs to the set "to some degree."

The concept of a fuzzy set has been used in many real-world applications. Here are a few examples.

- Control of heating and air conditioning systems
- Compensation against vibrations in camcorders
- Voice recognition by computers
- Control of valves and dam gates at power plants
- Control of robots
- Control of subway trains
- Automatic camera focusing

A Fuzzy Heating System

Typical heating systems are controlled by a thermostat that turns a furnace on when the room temperature drops below a set point and turns the furnace off when the room temperature exceeds the set point. The furnace either runs at full force or it shuts down completely. This type of heating system is inefficient, and the frequent off and on changes can be annoying. A fuzzy heating system makes use of "fuzzy" definitions such as cold, warm, and hot to direct the furnace to run at low, medium, or full force. This results in a more efficient heating system and fewer temperature fluctuations.

Excursion Exercises

1. Mark, Erica, Larry, and Jennifer have each defined a fuzzy set to describe what they feel is a "good" grade. Each person paired the letter grades A, B, C, D, and F with a membership value. The results are as follows.

   Mark: $M = \{(A, 1), (B, 0.75), (C, 0.5), (D, 0.5), (F, 0)\}$

   Erica: $E = \{(A, 1), (B, 0), (C, 0), (D, 0), (F, 0)\}$

   Larry: $L = \{(A, 1), (B, 1), (C, 1), (D, 1), (F, 0)\}$

   Jennifer: $J = \{(A, 1), (B, 0.8), (C, 0.6), (D, 0.1), (F, 0)\}$

   a. Which of the four people considers an A grade to be the only good grade?
   b. Which of the four people is most likely to be satisfied with a grade of D or better?
   c. Write a fuzzy set that you would use to describe the set of good grades. Consider only the letter grades A, B, C, D, and F.

(continued)

2. In some fuzzy sets, membership values are given by a *membership graph* or by a *formula*. For instance, the following figure is a graph of the membership values of the fuzzy set *OLD*.

Use the membership graph of *OLD* to determine the membership value of each of the following.
   a. $x = 15$ **b.** $x = 50$ **c.** $x = 65$
   d. Use the graph of *OLD* to determine the age x with a membership value of 0.25.

An ordered pair (x, y) of a fuzzy set is a **crossover point** if its membership value is 0.5.
   e. Find the crossover point for *OLD*.

3. The following membership graph provides a definition of real numbers x that are "about" 4.

Use the graph of *ABOUTFOUR* to determine the membership value of:
   a. $x = 2$ **b.** $x = 3.5$ **c.** $x = 7$
   d. Use the graph of *ABOUTFOUR* to determine its crossover points.

4. The membership graphs in the following figure provide definitions of the fuzzy sets *COLD* and *WARM*.

(continued)

The point (35, 0.5) on the membership graph of *COLD* indicates that the membership value for $x = 35$ is 0.5. Thus, by this definition, 35°F is 50% cold. Use the above graphs to estimate

 a. the *WARM* membership value for $x = 40$.
 b. the *WARM* membership value for $x = 50$.
 c. the crossover points of *WARM*.

5. The membership graph in Excursion Exercise 2 shows one person's idea of what ages are "old." Use a grid similar to the following to draw a membership graph that you feel defines the concept of being "young" in terms of a person's age in years.

Show your membership graph to a few of your friends. Do they concur with your definition of "young?"

Exercise Set 2.1

In Exercises 1–12, use the roster method to write each of the given sets. For some exercises you may need to consult a reference, such as the Internet or an encyclopedia.

 1. The set of U.S. coins with a value of less than 50¢

 2. The set of months of the year with a name that ends with the letter y

 3. The set of planets in our solar system with a name that starts with the letter M

 4. The set of the seven dwarfs

 5. The set of U.S. presidents who have served after Jimmy Carter

 6. The set of months with exactly 30 days

 7. The set of negative integers greater than -6

 8. The set of whole numbers less than 8

 9. The set of integers x that satisfy $x - 4 = 3$

 10. The set of integers x that satisfy $2x - 1 = -11$

 11. The set of natural numbers x that satisfy $x + 4 = 1$

 12. The set of whole numbers x that satisfy $x - 1 < 4$

In Exercises 13–20, write a description of each set. There may be more than one correct description.

 13. {Tuesday, Thursday}   **14.** {Libra, Leo}

 15. {Mercury, Venus}   **16.** {penny, nickel, dime}

 17. $\{1, 2, 3, 4, 5, 6, 7, 8, 9\}$ **18.** $\{2, 4, 6, 8\}$

 19. $\{x \,|\, x \in N \text{ and } x \leq 7\}$

 20. $\{x \,|\, x \in W \text{ and } x < 5\}$

In Exercises 21–30, determine whether each statement is true or false. If the statement is false, give the reason.

 21. $b \in \{a, b, c\}$ **22.** $0 \notin N$

 23. $\{b\} \in \{a, b, c\}$ **24.** $\{1, 5, 9\} \sim \{\Psi, \Pi, \Sigma\}$

 25. $\{0\} \sim \varnothing$

 26. The set of large numbers is a well-defined set.

 27. The set of good teachers is a well-defined set.

 28. The set $\{x \,|\, 2 \leq x \leq 3\}$ is a well-defined set.

 29. $\{x^2 \,|\, x \in I\} = \{x^2 \,|\, x \in N\}$

 30. $0 \in \varnothing$

In Exercises 31–40, use set-builder notation to write each of the following sets.

31. {1, 2, 3, 4, 5, 6, 7, 8, 9, 10, 11, 12}

32. {45, 55, 65, 75}

33. {5, 10, 15}

34. {1, 4, 9, 16, 25, 36, 49, 64, 81}

35. {January, March, May, July, August, October, December}

36. {Iowa, Ohio, Utah}

37. {Arizona, Alabama, Arkansas, Alaska}

38. {Mexico, Canada}

39. {spring, summer}

40. {1900, 1901, 1902, 1903, 1904, ..., 1999}

Charter Schools During recent years, the number of U.S. charter schools has increased dramatically. The following horizontal bar graph shows the eight states with the greatest percent of U.S. charter schools in the fall of 2004.

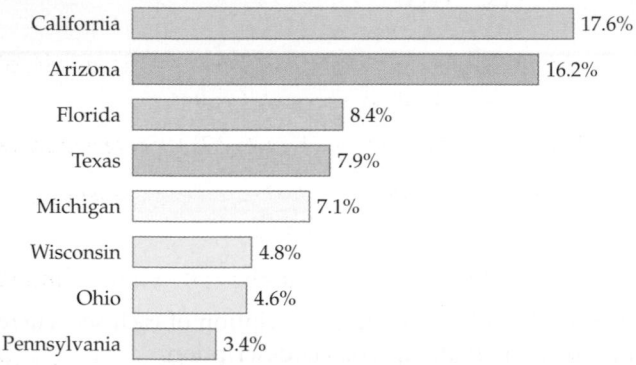

States with the Greatest Percent of Charter Schools

Source: U.S. Charter Schools webpage, **http://www.uscharterschools.org**

Use the data in the above graph and the roster method to represent each of the sets in Exercises 41–44.

41. The set of states in which more than 15% of the schools are charter schools

42. The set of states in which between 5% and 10% of the schools are charter schools

43. $\{x \mid x$ is one of the four states with the greatest percent of charter schools$\}$

44. $\{x \mid x$ is a state in which between 4% and 5% of the schools are charter schools$\}$

Affordability of Housing The following bar graph shows the monthly principal and interest payment needed to purchase an average-priced existing home in the United States for the years from 1997 to 2004.

Monthly Principal and Interest Payment for an Average-Priced Existing Home

Source: National Association of REALTORS® as reported in the World Almanac, 2005, p. 483

Use the data in the above graph and the roster method to represent each of the sets in Exercises 45–48.

45. The set of years in which the monthly principal and interest payment, for an average-priced existing home, exceeded $800

46. The set of years in which the monthly principal and interest payment, for an average-priced existing home, was between $700 and $800

47. $\{x \mid x$ is a year in which the monthly principal and interest payment, for an average-priced existing home, was between $600 and 700\}$

48. $\{x \mid x$ is a year in which the monthly principal and interest payment, for an average-priced existing home, was more than 750\}$

Gasoline Prices The following graph shows the average cost for a gallon of regular unleaded gasoline in California and in the nation on the first day of each month in 2004.

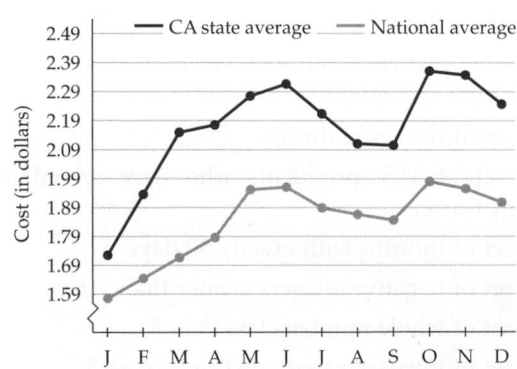

Average Cost of Gallon of Regular Unleaded Gasoline on the First Day of Each Month in 2004

Source: AAA's Media site for retail gasoline prices, **http://198.6.95.31/CAavg.asp**

Use the information in the previous graph and the roster method to represent each of the sets in Exercises 49 and 50.

49. The set of months for which the average cost for a gallon of regular unleaded gasoline was more than $2.29 in the state of California on the first day of the month

50. The set of months for which the national average cost for a gallon of regular unleaded gasoline was less than $1.69 on the first day of the month

Ticket Prices The following table shows the average U.S. movie theatre ticket prices for the years from 1985 to 2004.

Average U.S. Movie Theatre Ticket Prices

Year	Price	Year	Price
1985	$3.55	1995	$4.35
1986	3.71	1996	4.42
1987	3.91	1997	4.59
1988	4.11	1998	4.69
1989	3.99	1999	5.06
1990	4.22	2000	5.39
1991	4.21	2001	5.65
1992	4.15	2002	5.80
1993	4.14	2003	6.03
1994	4.08	2004	6.21

Source: National Association of Theatre Owners, **http://www.natoonline.org/statisticstickets.htm**

Use the information in the table and the roster method to represent each of the sets in Exercises 51–54.

51. $\{x \mid x$ is a year in the table for which the average ticket price was less than $4.00\}$

52. $\{x \mid x$ is a year in the table for which the average ticket price was greater than $5.20\}$

53. $\{x \mid x$ is a year in the table for which the average ticket price was greater than $4.10 but less than $4.50\}$

54. $\{x \mid x$ is a year in the table for which the average ticket price was greater than $4.25 but less than $6.00\}$

In Exercises 55–64, find the cardinality of each of the following sets. For some exercises you may need to consult a reference, such as the Internet or an encyclopedia.

55. $A = \{2, 4, 6, 8, 10, 12, 14, 16, 18, 20, 22\}$

56. $B = \{7, 14, 21, 28, 35, 42, 49, 56\}$

57. $D = $ the set of all dogs that can spell "elephant"

58. $S = $ the set of all states in the United States

59. $J = $ the set of all states of the United States that border Minnesota

60. $T = $ the set of all stripes on the U.S. flag

61. $N = $ the set of all baseball teams in the National League

62. $C = $ the set of all chess pieces on a chess board at the start of a chess game

63. $\{3, 6, 9, 12, 15, \ldots, 363\}$

64. $\{7, 11, 15, 19, 23, 27, \ldots, 407\}$

In Exercises 65–72, state whether each of the given pairs of sets are equal, equivalent, both, or neither.

65. The set of U.S. senators; the set of U.S. representatives

66. The set of single-digit natural numbers; the set of pins used in a regulation bowling game

67. The set of positive whole numbers; the set of counting numbers

68. The set of single-digit natural numbers; the set of single-digit integers

69. $\{1, 2, 3\}; \{I, II, III\}$

70. $\{6, 8, 10, 12\}; \{1, 2, 3, 4\}$

71. $\{2, 5\}; \{0, 1\}$

72. $\{ \}; \{0\}$

In Exercises 73–84, determine whether each of the sets is a well-defined set.

73. The set of good foods

74. The set of the six most heavily populated cities in the United States

75. The set of tall buildings in the city of Chicago

76. The set of states that border Colorado

77. The set of even integers

78. The set of rational numbers of the form $\frac{1}{p}$, where p is a counting number

79. The set of former presidents of the United States who are alive at the present time

80. The set of real numbers larger than 89,000

81. The set of small countries

82. The set of great cities in which to live

83. The set consisting of the best soda drinks

84. The set of fine wines

Extensions

CRITICAL THINKING

In Exercises 85–88, determine whether the given sets are equal. Recall that W represents the set of whole numbers and N represents the set of natural numbers.

85. $A = \{2n + 1 \mid n \in W\}$
    $B = \{2n - 1 \mid n \in N\}$

86. $A = \left\{16\left(\frac{1}{2}\right)^{n-1} \middle| n \in N\right\}$
    $B = \left\{16\left(\frac{1}{2}\right)^{n} \middle| n \in W\right\}$

87. $A = \{2n - 1 \mid n \in N\}$
    $B = \left\{\frac{n(n + 1)}{2} \middle| n \in N\right\}$

88. $A = \{3n + 1 \mid n \in W\}$
    $B = \{3n - 2 \mid n \in N\}$

89. Give an example of a set that cannot be written using the roster method.

EXPLORATIONS

90. In this section we have introduced the concept of *cardinal numbers*. Use the Internet or a mathematical textbook to find information about *ordinal numbers* and *nominal numbers*. Write a few sentences that explain the differences between these three types of numbers.

SECTION 2.2 | Complements, Subsets, and Venn Diagrams

The Universal Set and the Complement of a Set

In complex problem-solving situations and even in routine daily activities, we need to understand the set of all elements that are under consideration. For instance, when an instructor assigns letter grades, the possible choices may include A, B, C, D, F, and I. In this case the letter H is not a consideration. When you place a telephone call, you know that the area code is given by a natural number with three digits. In this instance a rational number such as $\frac{2}{3}$ is not a consideration. The set of all elements that are being considered is called the **universal set.** We will use the letter U to denote the universal set.

The Complement of a Set

The **complement** of a set A, denoted by A', is the set of all elements of the universal set U that are not elements of A.

To determine the complement of a set A you must know the elements of A as well as the elements of the universal set, U, that is being used.

EXAMPLE 1 ■ **Find the Complement of a Set**

Let $U = \{1, 2, 3, 4, 5, 6, 7, 8, 9, 10\}$, $S = \{2, 4, 6, 7\}$, and $T = \{x \mid x < 10 \text{ and } x \in \text{the odd counting numbers}\}$. Find

a. S' **b.** T'

Solution

a. The elements of the universal set are 1, 2, 3, 4, 5, 6, 7, 8, 9, and 10. From these elements we wish to exclude the elements of S, which are 2, 4, 6, and 7. Therefore $S' = \{1, 3, 5, 8, 9, 10\}$.

b. $T = \{1, 3, 5, 7, 9\}$. Excluding the elements of T from U gives us $T' = \{2, 4, 6, 8, 10\}$.

CHECK YOUR PROGRESS 1   Let $U = \{0, 2, 3, 4, 6, 7, 17\}$, $M = \{0, 4, 6, 17\}$, and $P = \{x \mid x < 7 \text{ and } x \in \text{the even natural numbers}\}$. Find

a. M' **b.** P'

Solution   *See page S5.*

There are two fundamental results concerning the universal set and the empty set. Because the universal set contains all elements under consideration, the complement of the universal set is the empty set. Conversely, the complement of the empty set is the universal set, because the empty set has no elements and the universal set contains all the elements under consideration. Using mathematical notation, we state these fundamental results as follows:

The Complement of the Universal Set and the Complement of the Empty Set

$U' = \varnothing$ and $\varnothing' = U$

Subsets

Consider the set of letters in the alphabet and the set of vowels $\{a, e, i, o, u\}$. Every element of the set of vowels is an element of the set of letters in the alphabet. The set of vowels is said to be a *subset* of the set of letters in the alphabet. We will often find it useful to examine subsets of a given set.

A Subset of a Set

Set A is a **subset** of set B, denoted by $A \subseteq B$, if and only if every element of A is also an element of B.

Here are two fundamental subset relationships.

Subset Relationships

$A \subseteq A$, for any set A

$\varnothing \subseteq A$, for any set A

To convince yourself that the empty set is a subset of any set, consider the following. We know that a set is a subset of a second set provided every element of the first set is an element of the second set. Pick an arbitrary set A. Because every element of the empty set (*there are none*) is an element of A, we know that $\varnothing \subseteq A$.

The notation $A \not\subseteq B$ is used to denote that A is *not* a subset of B. To show that A is not a subset of B, it is necessary to find at least one element of A that is not an element of B.

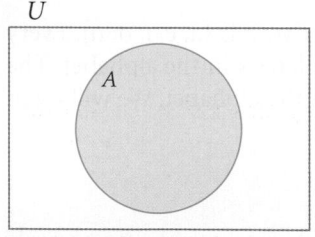

✓ **TAKE NOTE**

Recall that W represents the set of whole numbers and N represents the set of natural numbers.

EXAMPLE 2 ■ True or False

Determine whether each statement is true or false.

a. $\{5, 10, 15, 20\} \subseteq \{0, 5, 10, 15, 20, 25, 30\}$

b. $W \subseteq N$

c. $\{2, 4, 6\} \subseteq \{2, 4, 6\}$

d. $\varnothing \subseteq \{1, 2, 3\}$

Solution

a. True; every element of the first set is an element of the second set.

b. False; 0 is a whole number, but 0 is not a natural number.

c. True; every set is a subset of itself.

d. True; the empty set is a subset of every set.

CHECK YOUR PROGRESS 2　Determine whether each statement is true or false.

a. $\{1, 3, 5\} \subseteq \{1, 5, 9\}$

b. The set of counting numbers is a subset of the set of natural numbers.

c. $\varnothing \subseteq U$

d. $\{-6, 0, 11\} \subseteq I$

Solution　*See page S5.*

U

A

A Venn diagram

The English logician John Venn (1834–1923) developed diagrams, which we now refer to as *Venn diagrams,* that can be used to illustrate sets and relationships between sets. In a **Venn diagram,** the universal set is represented by a rectangular region and subsets of the universal set are generally represented by oval or circular regions drawn inside the rectangle. The Venn diagram at the left shows a universal set and one of its subsets, labeled as set A. The size of the circle is not a concern. The region outside of the circle, but inside of the rectangle, represents the set A'.

QUESTION　*What set is represented by $(A')'$?*

ANSWER　*The set A' contains the elements of U that are not in A. By definition the set $(A')'$ contains only the elements of U that are elements of A. Thus $(A')' = A$.*

Proper Subsets of a Set

> **Proper Subset**
>
> Set A is a **proper subset** of set B, denoted by $A \subset B$, if every element of A is an element of B, and $A \neq B$.

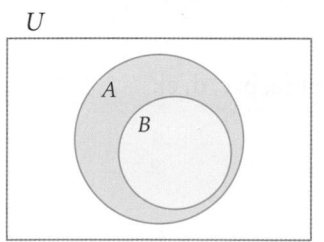

U

A

B

B is a proper subset of *A*.

To illustrate the difference between subsets and proper subsets, consider the following two examples.

1. Let $R =$ {Mars, Venus} and $S =$ {Mars, Venus, Mercury}. The first set R is a subset of the second set S, because every element of R is an element of S. In addition, R is also a proper subset of S, because $R \neq S$.

2. Let $T =$ {Europe, Africa} and $V =$ {Africa, Europe}. The first set T is a subset of the second set V; however, T is *not* a proper subset of V because $T = V$.

Venn diagrams can be used to represent proper subset relationships. For instance, if a set B is a proper subset of a set A, then we illustrate this relationship in a Venn diagram by drawing a circle labeled B inside of a circle labeled A. See the Venn diagram at the left.

EXAMPLE 3 ■ Proper Subsets

For each of the following, determine whether the first set is a proper subset of the second set.

a. {a, e, i, o, u}, {e, i, o, u, a}   **b.** N, I

Solution

a. Because the sets are equal, the first set is not a proper subset of the second set.

b. Every natural number is an integer, so the set of natural numbers is a subset of the set of integers. The set of integers contains elements that are not natural numbers, such as -3. Thus the set of natural numbers is a proper subset of the set of integers.

CHECK YOUR PROGRESS 3   For each of the following, determine whether the first set is a proper subset of the second set.

a. N, W **b.** {1, 4, 5}, {5, 1, 4}

Solution   *See page S5.*

Some counting problems in the study of probability require that we find all of the subsets of a given set. One way to find all the subsets of a given set is to use the method of making an organized list. First list the empty set, which has no elements. Next list all the sets that have exactly one element, followed by all the sets that contain exactly two elements, followed by all the sets that contain exactly three elements, and so on. This process is illustrated in the following example.

EXAMPLE 4 ■ List all the Subsets of a Set

List all the subsets of {1, 2, 3, 4}.

Solution

An organized list produces the following subsets.

{ }	• Subsets with 0 elements
{1}, {2}, {3}, {4}	• Subsets with 1 element
{1, 2}, {1, 3}, {1, 4}, {2, 3}, {2, 4}, {3, 4}	• Subsets with 2 elements
{1, 2, 3}, {1, 2, 4}, {1, 3, 4}, {2, 3, 4}	• Subsets with 3 elements
{1, 2, 3, 4}	• Subsets with 4 elements

CHECK YOUR PROGRESS 4   List all of the subsets of {a, b, c, d, e}.

Solution   See page S5.

Number of Subsets of a Set

The counting techniques developed in Section 1.3 can be used to produce the following result.

> **The Number of Subsets of a Set**
>
> A set with n elements has 2^n subsets.

EXAMPLE 5 ■ The Number of Subsets of a Set

Find the number of subsets of each set.

a. {1, 2, 3, 4, 5, 6}

b. {4, 5, 6, 7, 8, ..., 15}

c. ∅

Solution

a. {1, 2, 3, 4, 5, 6} has six elements. It has $2^6 = 64$ subsets.

b. {4, 5, 6, 7, 8, ..., 15} has 12 elements. It has $2^{12} = 4096$ subsets.

c. The empty set has zero elements. It has only one subset ($2^0 = 1$), itself.

CHECK YOUR PROGRESS 5   Find the number of subsets of each set.

a. {Mars, Jupiter, Pluto}

b. $\{x \mid x \le 15, x \in N\}$

c. {2, 3, 4, 5, ..., 11}

Solution   See page S5.

CALCULATOR NOTE

A calculator can be used to compute powers of 2. The following results were produced on a TI-84 calculator.

```
2^6
                    64
2^12
                  4096
2^0
                     1
```

Math Matters   The Barber's Paradox

Some problems that concern sets have led to paradoxes. For instance, in 1902, the mathematician Bertrand Russell developed the following paradox. "Is the set A of all sets that are not elements of themselves an element of itself?" Both the assumption that A is an element of A and the assumption that A is not an element of A lead to a contradiction. Russell's paradox has been popularized as follows.

> The town barber shaves all males who do not shave themselves, and he shaves only those males. The town barber is a male who shaves. Who shaves the barber?

The assumption that the barber shaves himself leads to a contradiction, and the assumption that the barber does not shave himself also leads to a contradiction.

Excursion

Subsets and Complements of Fuzzy Sets

TAKE NOTE

A set such as {3, 5, 9} is called a *crisp set,* to distinguish it from a fuzzy set.

This excursion extends the concept of fuzzy sets that was developed in the Excursion in Section 2.1. Recall that the elements of a fuzzy set are ordered pairs. For any ordered pair (x, y) of a fuzzy set, the membership value y is a real number such that $0 \leq y \leq 1$.

The set of all x-values that are being considered is called the **universal set for the fuzzy set** and it is denoted by X.

Definition of a Fuzzy Subset

If the fuzzy sets $A = \{(x_1, a_1), (x_2, a_2), (x_3, a_3), \ldots\}$ and
$B = \{(x_1, b_1), (x_2, b_2), (x_3, b_3), \ldots\}$ are both defined on the universal set
$X = \{x_1, x_2, x_3, \ldots\}$, then $A \subseteq B$ if and only if $a_i \leq b_i$ for all i.

A fuzzy set A is a **subset** of a fuzzy set B if and only if the membership value of each element of A *is less than or equal to* its corresponding membership value in set B. For instance, in Excursion Exercise 1 in Section 2.1, Mark and Erica used fuzzy sets to describe the set of good grades as follows:

Mark: $M = \{(A, 1), (B, 0.75), (C, 0.5), (D, 0.5), (F, 0)\}$

Erica: $E = \{(A, 1), (B, 0), (C, 0), (D, 0), (F, 0)\}$

In this case fuzzy set E is a subset of fuzzy set M because each membership value of set E *is less than or equal to* its corresponding membership value in set M.

Definition of the Complement of a Fuzzy Set

Let A be the fuzzy set $\{(x_1, a_1), (x_2, a_2), (x_3, a_3), \ldots\}$ defined on the universal set
$X = \{x_1, x_2, x_3, \ldots\}$. **Then the complement** of A is the fuzzy set
$A' = \{(x_1, b_1), (x_2, b_2), (x_3, b_3), \ldots\}$, where each $b_i = 1 - a_i$.

(continued)

Each element of the fuzzy set A' has a membership value that is 1 minus its membership value in the fuzzy set A. For example, the complement of

$$S = \{(\text{math}, 0.8), (\text{history}, 0.4), (\text{biology}, 0.3), (\text{art}, 0.1), (\text{music}, 0.7)\}$$

is the fuzzy set

$$S' = \{(\text{math}, 0.2), (\text{history}, 0.6), (\text{biology}, 0.7), (\text{art}, 0.9), (\text{music}, 0.3)\}.$$

The membership values in S' were calculated by subtracting the corresponding membership values in S from 1. For instance, the membership value of math in set S is 0.8. Thus the membership value of math in set S' is $1 - 0.8 = 0.2$.

Excursion Exercises

1. Let $K = \{(1, 0.4), (2, 0.6), (3, 0.8), (4, 1)\}$ and
   $J = \{(1, 0.3), (2, 0.6), (3, 0.5), (4, 0.1)\}$ be fuzzy sets defined on $X = \{1, 2, 3, 4\}$. Is
   $J \subseteq K$? Explain.

2. Consider the following membership graphs of *YOUNG* and *ADOLESCENT* defined
   on $X = \{x \mid 0 \leq x \leq 50\}$, where x is age in years.

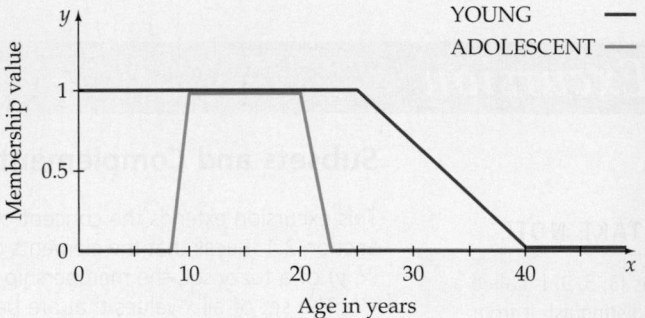

   Is the fuzzy set *ADOLESCENT* a subset of the fuzzy set *YOUNG*? Explain.

3. Let the universal set be $\{A, B, C, D, F\}$ and let

   $$G = \{(A, 1), (B, 0.7), (C, 0.4), (D, 0.1), (F, 0)\}$$

   be a fuzzy set defined by Greg to describe what he feels is a good grade.
   Determine G'.

4. Let $C = \{(\text{Ferrari}, 0.9), (\text{Ford Mustang}, 0.6), (\text{Dodge Neon}, 0.5), (\text{Hummer}, 0.7)\}$ be
   a fuzzy set defined on the universal set {Ferrari, Ford Mustang, Dodge Neon,
   Hummer}. Determine C'.

Consider the following membership graph.

(continued)

The membership graph of *WARM'* can be drawn by *reflecting* the graph of *WARM* about the graph of the line $y = 0.5$, as shown in the following figure.

Temperature in degrees Fahrenheit

Note that when the membership graph of *WARM* is at a height of 0, the membership graph of *WARM'* is at a height of 1, and vice versa. In general, for any point (x, a) on the graph of *WARM*, there is a corresponding point $(x, 1 - a)$ on the graph of *WARM'*.

5. Use the following membership graph of *COLD* to draw the membership graph of *COLD'*.

Temperature in degrees Fahrenheit

Exercise Set 2.2

In Exercises 1–8, find the complement of the set given that $U = \{0, 1, 2, 3, 4, 5, 6, 7, 8\}$.

1. $\{2, 4, 6, 7\}$ **2.** $\{3, 6\}$

3. $\varnothing$ **4.** $\{4, 5, 6, 7, 8\}$

5. $\{x \mid x < 7 \text{ and } x \in N\}$

6. $\{x \mid x < 6 \text{ and } x \in W\}$

7. The set of odd counting numbers less than 8

8. The set of even counting numbers less than 10

In Exercises 9–18, insert either $\subseteq$ or $\nsubseteq$ in the blank space between the sets to make a true statement.

9. $\{a, b, c, d\}$ $\{a, b, c, d, e, f, g\}$

10. $\{3, 5, 7\}$ $\{3, 4, 5, 6\}$

11. $\{big, small, little\}$ $\{large, petite, short\}$

12. $\{red, white, blue\}$ $\{the colors in the American flag\}$

13. the set of integers   the set of rational numbers

14. the set of real numbers   the set of integers

15. $\varnothing$ {a, e, i, o, u}

16. {all sandwiches}   {all hamburgers}

17. {2, 4, 6, ..., 5000}   the set of even whole numbers

18. $\{x \mid x < 10 \text{ and } x \in Q\}$ the set of integers

In Exercises 19–36, let $U = \{p, q, r, s, t\}$, $D = \{p, r, s, t\}$, $E = \{q, s\}$, $F = \{p, t\}$, and $G = \{s\}$. Determine whether each statement is true or false.

19. $F \subseteq D$ 20. $D \subseteq F$

21. $F \subset D$ 22. $E \subset F$

23. $G \subset E$ 24. $E \subset D$

25. $G' \subset D$ 26. $E = F'$

27. $\varnothing \subset D$ 28. $\varnothing \subset \varnothing$

29. $D' \subset E$ 30. $G \in E$

31. $F \in D$ 32. $G \not\subset F$

33. D has exactly eight subsets and seven proper subsets.

34. U has exactly 32 subsets.

35. F and F' each have exactly four subsets.

36. $\{0\} = \varnothing$

37. ▦ A class of 16 students has 2^{16} subsets. Use a calculator to determine how long (to the nearest hour) it would take you to write all the subsets, assuming you can write each subset in 1 second.

38. ▦ A class of 32 students has 2^{32} subsets. Use a calculator to determine how long (to the nearest year) it would take you to write all the subsets, assuming you can write each subset in 1 second.

In Exercises 39–42, list all subsets of the given set.

39. $\{\alpha, \beta\}$ 40. $\{\alpha, \beta, \Gamma, \Delta\}$

41. {I, II, III}   42. $\varnothing$

In Exercises 43–50, find the number of subsets of the given set.

43. {2, 5}   44. {1, 7, 11}

45. $\{x \mid x \text{ is an even counting number between 7 and 21}\}$

46. $\{x \mid x \text{ is an odd integer between } -4 \text{ and } 8\}$

47. The set of eleven players on a football team

48. The set of all letters of our alphabet

49. The set of all negative whole numbers

50. The set of all single-digit natural numbers

51. Suppose you have a nickel, two dimes, and a quarter. One of the dimes was minted in 1976, and the other one was minted in 1992.

a. Assuming you choose at least one coin, how many different sets of coins can you form?

b. Assuming you choose at least one coin, how many different sums of money can you produce?

c. Explain why the answers in part a and part b are not the same.

52. ▦ The number of subsets of a set with n elements is 2^n.

a. Use a calculator to find the exact value of 2^{18}, 2^{19}, and 2^{20}.

b. What is the largest integer power of 2 for which your calculator will display the exact value?

53. **Attribute Pieces** Elementary school teachers use plastic pieces called *attribute pieces* to illustrate subset concepts and to determine whether a student has learned to distinguish among different shapes, sizes, and colors. The following figure shows 12 attribute pieces.

A set of 12 attribute pieces

A student has been asked to form the following sets. Determine the number of elements the student should have in each set.

a. The set of red attribute pieces

b. The set of red squares

c. The set of hexagons

d. The set of large blue triangles

54. **Sandwich Choices** A delicatessen makes a roast-beef-on-sour-dough sandwich for which you can choose from eight condiments.

a. How many different types of roast-beef-on-sour-dough sandwiches can the delicatessen prepare?

b. What is the minimum number of condiments the delicatessen must have available if it wished to offer at least 2000 different types of roast-beef-on-sour-dough sandwiches?

55. Omelet Choices A restaurant provides a brunch where the omelets are individually prepared. Each guest is allowed to choose from 10 different ingredients.

a. How many different types of omelets can the restaurant prepare?

b. What is the minimum number of ingredients that must be available if the restaurant wants to advertise that it offers over 4000 different omelets?

56. Truck Options A truck company makes a pickup truck with 12 upgrade options. Some of the options are air conditioning, chrome wheels, and a CD player.

a. How many different versions of this truck can the company produce?

b. What is the minimum number of upgrade options the company must be able to provide if it wishes to offer at least 14,000 different versions of this truck?

Extensions

57. a. Explain why $\{2\} \notin \{1, 2, 3\}$.

  b. Explain why $1 \not\subseteq \{1, 2, 3\}$.

  c. Consider the set $\{1, \{1\}\}$. Does this set have one or two elements? Explain.

58. a. A set has 1024 subsets. How many elements are in the set?

b. A set has 255 proper subsets. How many elements are in the set?

c. Is it possible for a set to have an odd number of subsets? Explain.

59. Voting Coalitions Five people, designated A, B, C, D, and E, serve on a committee. To pass a motion, at least three of the committee members must vote for the motion. In such a situation any set of three or more voters is called a **winning coalition** because if this set of people votes for a motion, the motion will pass. Any nonempty set of two or fewer voters is called a losing coalition.

a. List all the winning coalitions.

b. List all the losing coalitions.

EXPLORATIONS

60. Subsets and Pascal's Triangle Following is a list of all the subsets of $\{a, b, c, d\}$.
Subsets with

  0 elements: $\{\ \}$

  1 element: $\{a\}, \{b\}, \{c\}, \{d\}$

  2 elements: $\{a, b\}, \{a, c\}, \{a, d\}, \{b, c\}, \{b, d\}, \{c, d\}$

  3 elements: $\{a, b, c\}, \{a, b, d\}, \{a, c, d\}, \{b, c, d\}$

  4 elements: $\{a, b, c, d\}$

There is 1 subset with zero elements, and there are 4 subsets with exactly one element, 6 subsets with exactly two elements, 4 subsets with exactly three elements, and 1 subset with exactly four elements. Note that the numbers 1, 4, 6, 4, 1 are the numbers in row 4 of Pascal's triangle, which is shown below. Recall that the numbers in Pascal's triangle are created in the following manner. Each row begins and ends with the number 1. Any other number in a row is the sum of the two closest numbers above it. For instance, the first 10 in row 5 is the sum of the first 4 and the 6 in row 4.

```
            1                  row 0
          1   1                row 1
        1   2   1              row 2
      1   3   3   1            row 3
    1   4   6   4   1          row 4
  1   5  10  10   5   1        row 5
```

Pascal's triangle

a. Use Pascal's triangle to make a conjecture about the numbers of subsets of {a, b, c, d, e} that have: zero elements, exactly one element, exactly two elements, exactly three elements, exactly four elements, and exactly five elements. Use your work from Check Your Progress 4 on page 68 to verify that your conjecture is correct.

b. Extend Pascal's triangle to show row 6. Use row 6 of Pascal's triangle to make a conjecture about the number of subsets of {a, b, c, d, e, f} that have exactly three elements. Make a list of all the subsets of {a, b, c, d, e, f} that have exactly three elements to verify that your conjecture is correct.

SECTION 2.3 | **Set Operations**

Intersection and Union of Sets

In Section 2.2 we defined the operation of finding the complement of a set. In this section we define the set operations *intersection* and *union*. In everyday usage, the word "intersection" refers to the *common region* where two streets cross. See the figure at the left. The intersection of two sets is defined in a similar manner.

> **Intersection of Sets**
>
> The **intersection** of sets A and B, denoted by $A \cap B$, is the set of elements common to both A and B.
>
> $$A \cap B = \{x \mid x \in A \quad \text{and} \quad x \in B\}$$

In the figure at the left, the region shown in blue represents the intersection of sets A and B.

U

$A \cap B$

EXAMPLE 1 ■ Find Intersections

Let $A = \{1, 4, 5, 7\}$, $B = \{2, 3, 4, 5, 6\}$, and $C = \{3, 6, 9\}$. Find

a. $A \cap B$ **b.** $A \cap C$

Solution

a. The elements common to both sets are 4 and 5.

$$A \cap B = \{1, 4, 5, 7\} \cap \{2, 3, 4, 5, 6\}$$
$$= \{4, 5\}$$

b. Sets A and C have no common elements. Thus $A \cap C = \varnothing$.

CHECK YOUR PROGRESS 1   Let $D = \{0, 3, 8, 9\}$, $E = \{3, 4, 8, 9, 11\}$, and $F = \{0, 2, 6, 8\}$. Find

a. $D \cap E$ **b.** $D \cap F$

Solution   See page S5.

> **✔ TAKE NOTE**
>
> It is a mistake to write
>
> $\{1, 5, 9\} \cap \{3, 5, 9\} = 5, 9$
>
> The intersection of two sets is a set. Thus
>
> $\{1, 5, 9\} \cap \{3, 5, 9\} = \{5, 9\}$

U

$A \cap C = \varnothing$

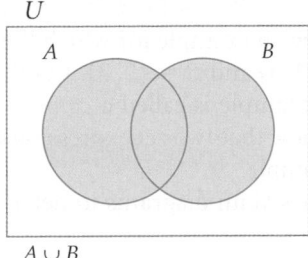

U

$A \cup B$

Two sets are **disjoint** if their intersection is the empty set. The sets A and C in Example 1b are disjoint. The Venn diagram at the left illustrates two disjoint sets.

In everyday usage, the word "union" refers to the act of uniting or joining together. The union of two sets has a similar meaning.

Union of Sets

The **union** of sets A and B, denoted by $A \cup B$, is the set that contains all the elements that belong to A or to B or to both.

$$A \cup B = \{x \mid x \in A \quad \text{or} \quad x \in B\}$$

In the figure at the left, the region shown in blue represents the union of sets A and B.

EXAMPLE 2 ■ Find Unions

Let $A = \{1, 4, 5, 7\}$, $B = \{2, 3, 4, 5, 6\}$, and $C = \{3, 6, 9\}$. Find

a. $A \cup B$　　**b.** $A \cup C$

Solution

a. List all the elements of set A, which are 1, 4, 5, and 7. Then add to your list the elements of set B that have not already been listed—in this case 2, 3, and 6. Enclose all elements with a pair of braces. Thus

$A \cup B = \{1, 4, 5, 7\} \cup \{2, 3, 4, 5, 6\}$
$= \{1, 2, 3, 4, 5, 6, 7\}$

b. $A \cup C = \{1, 4, 5, 7\} \cup \{3, 6, 9\}$
$= \{1, 3, 4, 5, 6, 7, 9\}$

CHECK YOUR PROGRESS 2　Let $D = \{0, 4, 8, 9\}$, $E = \{1, 4, 5, 7\}$, and $F = \{2, 6, 8\}$. Find

a. $D \cup E$　　**b.** $D \cup F$

Solution　*See page S5.*

In mathematical problems that involve sets, the word "and" is interpreted to mean *intersection*. For instance, the phrase "the elements of A and B" means the elements of $A \cap B$. Similarly, the word "or" is interpreted to mean *union*. The phrase "the elements of A or B" means the elements of $A \cup B$.

EXAMPLE 3 ■ Describe Sets

Write a sentence that describes the set.

a. $A \cup (B \cap C)$　　**b.** $J \cap K'$

Solution

a. The set $A \cup (B \cap C)$ can be described as "the set of all elements that are in A, or are in B and C."

b. The set $J \cap K'$ can be described as "the set of all elements that are in J and are not in K."

TAKE NOTE

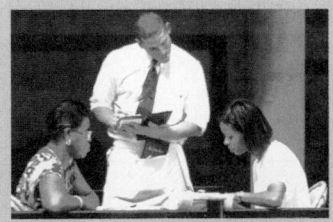

Would you like soup or salad?

In a sentence, the word "or" can mean one or the other, but not both. For instance, if a menu states that you can have soup or salad with your meal, this generally means that you can have either soup or salad for the price of the meal, but not both. In this case the word "or" is said to be an *exclusive or*. In the mathematical statement "A or B," the "or" is an *inclusive or*. It means A or B, or both.

CHECK YOUR PROGRESS 3 Write a sentence that describes the set.

a. $D \cap (E' \cup F)$ **b.** $L' \cup M$

Solution   *See page S5.*

Venn Diagrams and Equality of Sets

The equality $A \cup B = A \cap B$ is true for some sets A and B, but not for all sets A and B. For instance, if $A = \{1, 2\}$ and $B = \{1, 2\}$, then $A \cup B = A \cap B$. However, we can prove that, in general, $A \cup B \neq A \cap B$ by finding an example for which the expressions are not equal. One such example is $A = \{1, 2, 3\}$ and $B = \{2, 3\}$. In this case $A \cup B = \{1, 2, 3\}$, whereas $A \cap B = \{2, 3\}$. This example is called a *counterexample*. The point to remember is that if you wish to show that two set expressions are *not equal,* then you need to find just one counterexample.

In the next example, we present a technique that uses Venn diagrams to determine whether two set expressions are equal.

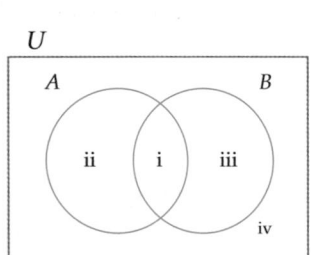

EXAMPLE 4 ■ Equality of Sets

Use Venn diagrams to determine whether $(A \cup B)' = A' \cap B'$ for all sets A and B.

Solution

Draw a Venn diagram that shows the two sets A and B, as in the figure at the left. Label the four regions as shown. To determine what region(s) represents $(A \cup B)'$, first note that $A \cup B$ consists of regions i, ii, and iii. Thus $(A \cup B)'$ is represented by region iv. See Figure 2.1.

Draw a second Venn diagram. To determine what region(s) represents $A' \cap B'$, we shade A' (regions iii and iv) with a diagonal up pattern and we shade B' (regions ii and iv) with a diagonal down pattern. The intersection of these shaded regions, which is region iv, represents $A' \cap B'$. See Figure 2.2.

Figure 2.1

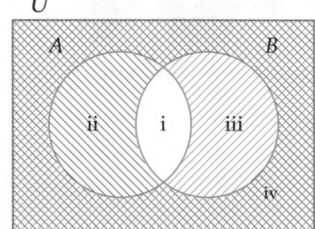

Figure 2.2

Because both $(A \cup B)'$ and $A' \cap B'$ are represented by the same region, we know that $(A \cup B)' = A' \cap B'$ for all sets A and B.

CHECK YOUR PROGRESS 4 Use Venn diagrams to determine whether $(A \cap B)' = A' \cup B'$ for all sets A and B.

Solution   *See page S5.*

The properties that were verified in Example 4 and Check Your Progress 4 are known as **De Morgan's laws.**

De Morgan's Laws

For all sets A and B,

$$(A \cup B)' = A' \cap B' \quad \text{and} \quad (A \cap B)' = A' \cup B'$$

De Morgan's law $(A \cup B)' = A' \cap B'$ can be stated as "the complement of the union of two sets is the intersection of the complements of the sets. De Morgan's law $(A \cap B)' = A' \cup B'$ can be stated as "the complement of the intersection of two sets is the union of the complements of the sets."

Math Matters   The Cantor Set

Consider the set of points formed by a line segment with a length of 1 unit. Remove the middle third of the line segment. Remove the middle third of each of the remaining two line segments. Remove the middle third of each of the remaining four line segments. Remove the middle third of each of the remaining eight line segments. Remove the middle third of each of the remaining sixteen line segments.

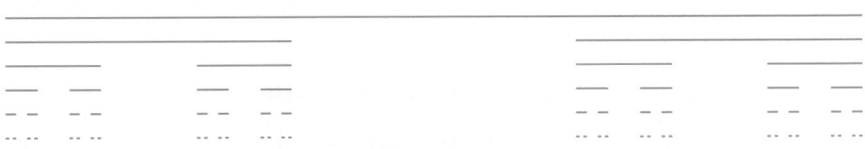

The first five steps in the formation of the Cantor set.

The **Cantor set,** also known as **Cantor's Dust,** is the set of points that *remain* after the above process is repeated infinitely many times. You might conjecture that there are no points in the Cantor set, but it can be shown that there are just as many points in the Cantor set as in the original line segment! This is remarkable because it can also be shown that the sum of the lengths of the *removed* line segments equals 1 unit, which is the length of the original line segment. You can find additional information about the remarkable properties of the Cantor set on the Internet.

Venn Diagrams Involving Three Sets

In the next example, we extend the Venn diagram procedure illustrated in the previous examples to expressions that involve three sets.

U

Figure 2.3

U

Figure 2.4

U

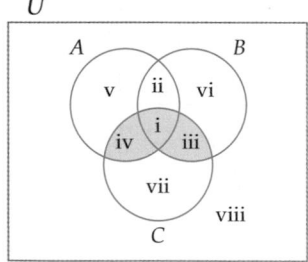

Figure 2.5

EXAMPLE 5 ■ Equality of Set Expressions

Use Venn diagrams to determine whether $A \cup (B \cap C) = (A \cup B) \cap C$ for all sets A, B, and C.

Solution
Draw a Venn diagram that shows the sets A, B, and C and the eight regions they form. See Figure 2.3. To determine what region(s) represents $A \cup (B \cap C)$, we first consider $(B \cap C)$, represented by regions i and iii, because it is in parentheses. Set A is represented by the regions i, ii, iv, and v. Thus $A \cup (B \cap C)$ is represented by all of the listed regions (namely i, ii, iii, iv, and v), as shown in Figure 2.4.

Draw a second Venn diagram showing the three sets A, B, and C, as in Figure 2.3. To determine what region(s) represents $(A \cup B) \cap C$, we first consider $(A \cup B)$ (regions i, ii, iii, iv, v, and vi) because it is in parentheses. Set C is represented by regions i, iii, iv, and vii. Therefore, the intersection of $(A \cup B)$ and C is represented by the overlap, or regions i, iii, and iv. See Figure 2.5.

Because the sets $A \cup (B \cap C)$ and $(A \cup B) \cap C$ are represented by different regions, we conclude that $A \cup (B \cap C) \neq (A \cup B) \cap C$.

CHECK YOUR PROGRESS 5 Use Venn diagrams to determine whether $A \cup (B \cap C) = (A \cup B) \cap (A \cup C)$ for all sets A, B, and C.

Solution   *See page S5.*

Venn diagrams can be used to verify each of the following properties.

Properties of Sets

For all sets A and B,
  Commutative Properties
    $A \cap B = B \cap A$ Commutative property of intersection
    $A \cup B = B \cup A$ Commutative property of union

For all sets A, B, and C,
  Associative Properties
    $(A \cap B) \cap C = A \cap (B \cap C)$ Associative property of intersection
    $(A \cup B) \cup C = A \cup (B \cup C)$ Associative property of union
  Distributive Properties
    $A \cap (B \cup C) = (A \cap B) \cup (A \cap C)$ Distributive property of intersection over union
    $A \cup (B \cap C) = (A \cup B) \cap (A \cup C)$ Distributive property of union over intersection

QUESTION   Does $(B \cup C) \cap A = (A \cap B) \cup (A \cap C)$?

ANSWER   *Yes. The commutative property of intersection allows us to write $(B \cup C) \cap A$ as $A \cap (B \cup C)$, and $A \cap (B \cup C) = (A \cap B) \cup (A \cap C)$ by the distributive property of intersection over union.*

Application: Blood Groups and Blood Types

historical note

The Nobel Prize is an award granted to people who have made significant contributions to society. Nobel Prizes are awarded annually for achievements in physics, chemistry, physiology or medicine, literature, peace, and economics. The prizes were first established in 1901 by the Swedish industrialist Alfred Nobel, who invented dynamite. ■

Karl Landsteiner won a Nobel Prize in 1930 for his discovery of the four different human blood groups. He discovered that the blood of each individual contains exactly one of the following combinations of antigens.

- Only A antigens (blood group A)
- Only B antigens (blood group B)
- Both A and B antigens (blood group AB)
- No A antigens and no B antigens (blood group O)

These four blood groups are represented by the Venn diagram at the left below.

In 1941, Landsteiner and Alexander Wiener discovered that human blood may or may not contain an Rh, or rhesus, factor. Blood with this factor is called Rh-positive and denoted by Rh+. Blood without this factor is called Rh-negative and is denoted by Rh−.

The Venn diagram in Figure 2.6 illustrates the eight blood types (A+, B+, AB+, O+, A−, B−, AB−, O−) that are possible if we consider antigens and the Rh factor.

The four blood groups

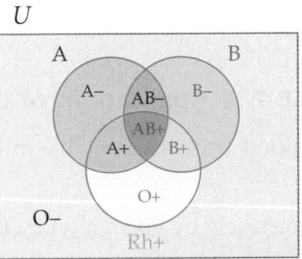

Figure 2.6 The eight blood types

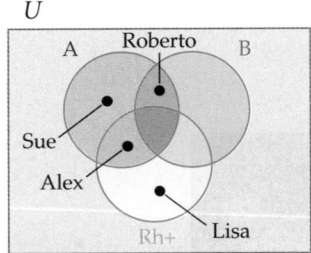

Figure 2.7

EXAMPLE 6 ■ **Venn Diagrams and Blood Type**

Use the Venn diagrams in Figures 2.6 and 2.7 to determine the blood type of each of the following people.

a. Sue   **b.** Lisa

Solution
a. Because Sue is in blood group A, not in blood group B, and not Rh+, her blood type is A−.
b. Lisa is in blood group O and she is Rh+, so her blood type is O+.

CHECK YOUR PROGRESS 6   Use the Venn diagrams in Figures 2.6 and 2.7 to determine the blood type of each of the following people.

a. Alex   **b.** Roberto

Solution   *See page S6.*

The following table shows the blood types that can safely be given during a blood transfusion to persons of each of the eight blood types.

Blood Transfusion Table

Recipient Blood Type	Donor Blood Type
A+	A+, A−, O+, O−
B+	B+, B−, O+, O−
AB+	A+, A−, B+, B−, AB+, AB−, O+, O−
O+	O+, O−
A−	A−, O−
B−	B−, O−
AB−	A−, B−, AB−, O−
O−	O−

Source: American Red Cross

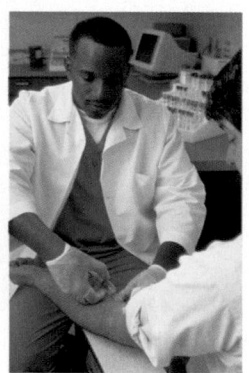

EXAMPLE 7 ■ Applications of the Blood Transfusion Table

Use the blood transfusion table and Figures 2.6 and 2.7 to answer the following questions.

a. Can Sue safely be given a type O+ blood transfusion?

b. Why is a person with type O− blood called a *universal donor?*

Solution

a. Sue's blood type is A−. The blood transfusion table shows that she can safely receive blood only if it is type A− or type O−. Thus it is not safe for Sue to receive type O+ blood in a blood transfusion.

b. The blood transfusion table shows that all eight blood types can safely receive type O− blood. Thus a person with type O− blood is said to be a universal donor.

CHECK YOUR PROGRESS 7   Use the blood transfusion table and Figures 2.6 and 2.7 to answer the following questions.

a. Is it safe for Alex to receive type A− blood in a blood transfusion?

b. What blood type do you have if you are classified as a *universal recipient?*

Solution   See page S6.

Excursion

Union and Intersection of Fuzzy Sets

This Excursion extends the concepts of fuzzy sets that were developed in Sections 2.1 and 2.2.

There are a number of ways in which the *union of two fuzzy sets* and the *intersection of two fuzzy sets* can be defined. The definitions we will use are called the **standard union operator** and the **standard intersection operator.** These standard operators preserve many of the set relations that exist in standard set theory.

Union and Intersection of Two Fuzzy Sets

Let $A = \{(x_1, a_1), (x_2, a_2), (x_3, a_3), \ldots\}$ and $B = \{(x_1, b_1), (x_2, b_2), (x_3, b_3), \ldots\}$ Then

$$A \cup B = \{(x_1, c_1), (x_2, c_2), (x_3, c_3), \ldots\}$$

where c_i is the *maximum* of the two numbers a_i and b_i and

$$A \cap B = \{(x_1, c_1), (x_2, c_2), (x_3, c_3), \ldots\}$$

where c_i is the *minimum* of the two numbers a_i and b_i.

Each element of the fuzzy set $A \cup B$ has a membership value that is the *maximum* of its membership value in the fuzzy set A and its membership value in the fuzzy set B. Each element of the fuzzy set $A \cap B$ has a membership value that is the *minimum* of its membership value in fuzzy set A and its membership value in fuzzy set B. In the following example, we form the union and intersection of two fuzzy sets. Let P and S be defined as follows.

Paul: $P = \{(\text{math}, 0.2), (\text{history}, 0.5), (\text{biology}, 0.7), (\text{art}, 0.8), (\text{music}, 0.9)\}$

Sally: $S = \{(\text{math}, 0.8), (\text{history}, 0.4), (\text{biology}, 0.3), (\text{art}, 0.1), (\text{music}, 0.7)\}$

Then

the maximum membership values for each of the given elements math, history, biology, art, and music

$P \cup S = \{(\text{math}, 0.8), (\text{history}, 0.5), (\text{biology}, 0.7), (\text{art}, 0.8), (\text{music}, 0.9)\}$

$P \cap S = \{(\text{math}, 0.2), (\text{history}, 0.4), (\text{biology}, 0.3), (\text{art}, 0.1), (\text{music}, 0.7)\}$

the minimum membership values for each of the given elements math, history, biology, art, and music

Excursion Exercises

In Excursion Exercise 1 of Section 2.1, we defined the following fuzzy sets.

Mark: $M = \{(A, 1), (B, 0.75), (C, 0.5), (D, 0.5), (F, 0)\}$

Erica: $E = \{(A, 1), (B, 0), (C, 0), (D, 0), (F, 0)\}$

Larry: $L = \{(A, 1), (B, 1), (C, 1), (D, 1), (F, 0)\}$

Jennifer: $J = \{(A, 1), (B, 0.8), (C, 0.6), (D, 0.1), (F, 0)\}$

(continued)

Use these fuzzy sets to find each of the following.

1. $M \cup J$ **2.** $M \cap J$ **3.** $E \cup J'$ **4.** $J \cap L'$ **5.** $J \cap (M' \cup L')$

Consider the following membership graphs.

The membership graph of $COLD \cup WARM$ is shown in purple in the following figure. The membership graph of $COLD \cup WARM$ lies on either the membership graph of $COLD$ or

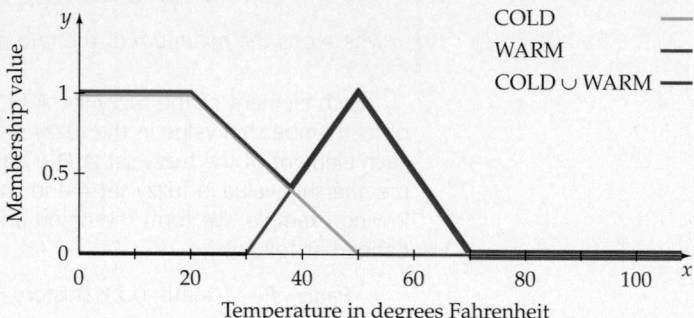

the membership graph of $WARM$, depending on which of these graphs is *higher* at any given temperature x.

The membership graph of $COLD \cap WARM$ is shown in green in the following figure. The membership graph of $COLD \cap WARM$ lies on either the membership graph of $COLD$

or the membership graph of $WARM$, depending on which of these graphs is *lower* at any given temperature x.

(continued)

6. Use the following graphs to draw the membership graph of *WARM* ∪ *HOT*.

7. Let $X = \{a, b, c, d, e\}$ be the universal set. Determine whether De Morgan's Law $(A \cap B)' = A' \cup B'$ holds true for the fuzzy sets
$A = \{(a, 0.3), (b, 0.8), (c, 1), (d, 0.2), (e, 0.75)\}$ and
$B = \{(a, 0.5), (b, 0.4), (c, 0.9), (d, 0.7), (e, 0.45)\}$.

Exercise Set 2.3

In Exercises 1–20, let $U = \{1, 2, 3, 4, 5, 6, 7, 8\}$, $A = \{2, 4, 6\}$, $B = \{1, 2, 5, 8\}$, and $C = \{1, 3, 7\}$. Find each of the following.

1. $A \cup B$
2. $A \cap B$
3. $A \cap B'$
4. $B \cap C'$
5. $(A \cup B)'$
6. $(A' \cap B)'$
7. $A \cup (B \cup C)$
8. $A \cap (B \cup C)$
9. $A \cap (B \cap C)$
10. $A' \cup (B \cap C)$
11. $B \cap (B \cup C)$
12. $A \cap A'$
13. $B \cup B'$
14. $(A \cap (B \cup C))'$
15. $(A \cup C') \cap (B \cup A')$
16. $(A \cup C') \cup (B \cup A')$
17. $(C \cup B') \cup \varnothing$
18. $(A' \cup B) \cap \varnothing$
19. $(A \cup B) \cap (B \cap C')$
20. $(B \cap A') \cup (B' \cup C)$

In Exercises 21–28, write a sentence that describes the given mathematical expression.

21. $L' \cup T$
22. $J' \cap K$
23. $A \cup (B' \cap C)$
24. $(A \cup B) \cap C'$
25. $T \cap (J \cup K')$
26. $(A \cap B) \cup C$
27. $(W \cap V) \cup (W \cap Z)$
28. $D \cap (E \cup F)'$

In Exercises 29–36, draw a Venn diagram to show each of the following sets.

29. $A \cap B'$
30. $(A \cap B)'$
31. $(A \cup B)'$
32. $(A' \cap B) \cup B'$
33. $A \cap (B \cup C')$
34. $A \cap (B' \cap C)$
35. $(A \cup C) \cap (B \cup C')$
36. $(A' \cap B) \cup (A \cap C')$

In Exercises 37–40, draw two Venn diagrams to determine whether the following expressions are equal for all sets A and B.

37. $A \cap B'; A' \cup B$
38. $A' \cap B; A \cup B'$
39. $A \cup (A' \cap B); A \cup B$
40. $A' \cap (B \cup B'); A' \cup (B \cap B')$

In Exercises 41–46, draw two Venn diagrams to determine whether the following expressions are equal for all sets A, B, and C.

41. $(A \cup C) \cap B'; A' \cup (B \cup C)$
42. $A' \cap (B \cap C), (A \cup B') \cap C$
43. $(A' \cap B) \cup C, (A' \cap C) \cap (A' \cap B)$
44. $A' \cup (B' \cap C), (A' \cup B') \cap (A' \cup C)$
45. $((A \cup B) \cap C)', (A' \cap B') \cup C'$
46. $(A \cap B) \cap C, (A \cup B \cup C)'$

Computers and televisions make use of *additive color mixing*. The following figure shows that when the *primary colors* red R, green G, and blue B are mixed together using additive color mixing, they produce white, W. Using set notation, we state this as $R \cap B \cap G = W$. The colors yellow Y, cyan C, and magenta M are called *secondary colors*. A secondary color is produced by mixing exactly two of the primary colors.

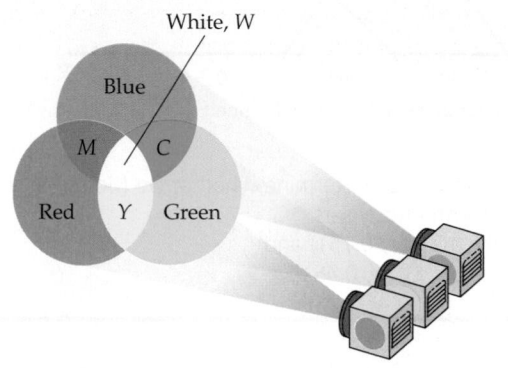

White, W
Blue
M C
Red Y Green

Additive Color Mixing In Exercises 47–49, determine which color is represented by each of the following. Assume the colors are being mixed using additive color mixing. (Use R for red, G for green, and B for blue.)

47. $R \cap G \cap B'$ **48.** $R \cap G' \cap B$

49. $R' \cap G \cap B$

Artists that paint with pigments use *subtractive color mixing* to produce different colors. In a subtractive color mixing system, the primary colors are cyan C, magenta M, and yellow Y. The following figure shows that when the three primary colors are mixed in equal amounts, using subtractive color mixing, they form black, K. Using set notation, we state this as $C \cap M \cap Y = K$. In subtractive color mixing the colors red R, blue B, and green G are the secondary colors. As mentioned previously, a secondary color is produced by mixing equal amounts of exactly two of the primary colors.

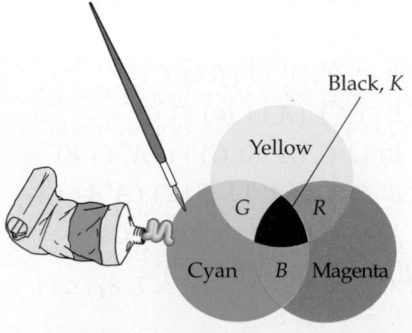

Black, K
Yellow
G R
Cyan B Magenta

Subtractive Color Mixing In Exercises 50–52, determine which color is represented by each of the following. Assume the colors are being mixed using subtractive color mixing. (Use C for cyan, M for magenta, and Y for yellow.)

50. $C \cap M \cap Y'$ **51.** $C' \cap M \cap Y$

52. $C \cap M' \cap Y$

In Exercises 53–62, use set notation to describe the shaded region. You may use any of the following symbols: A, B, C, $\cap$, $\cup$, and $'$. Keep in mind that each shaded region has more than one set description.

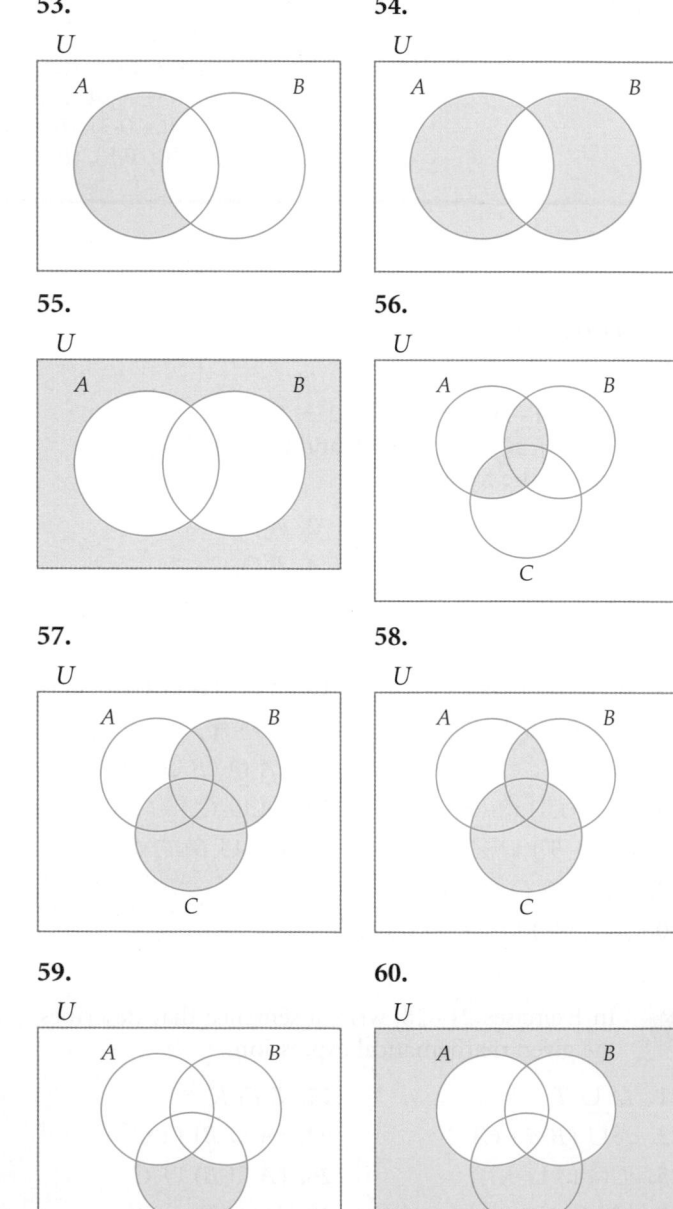

53.
U
A B

54.
U
A B

55.
U
A B

56.
U
A B
C

57.
U
A B
C

58.
U
A B
C

59.
U
A B
C

60.
U
A B
C

61. **62.**

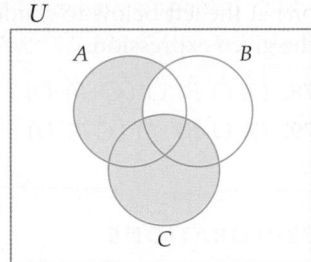

63. A Survey A special interest group plans to conduct a survey of households concerning a ban on hand guns. The special-interest group has decided to use the following Venn diagram to help illustrate the results of the survey. *Note:* A rifle is a gun, but it is not a hand gun.

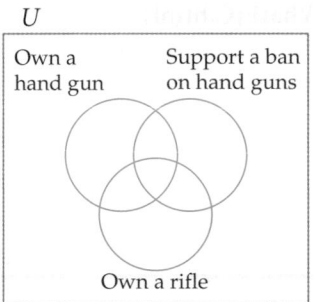

a. Shade in the regions that represent households that own a hand gun and do not support the ban on hand guns.

b. Shade in the region that represents households that own only a rifle and support the ban on hand guns.

c. Shade in the region that represents households that do not own a gun and do not support the ban on hand guns.

64. A Music Survey The administrators of an Internet music site plan to conduct a survey of college students to determine how the students acquire music. The administrators have decided to use the following Venn diagram to help tabulate the results of the survey.

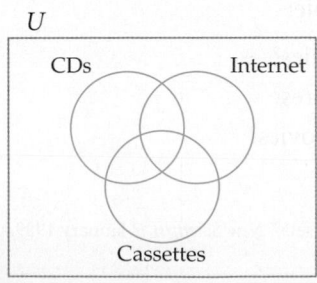

a. Shade in the region that represents students who acquire music from CDs and the Internet, but not from cassettes.

b. Shade in the regions that represent students who acquire music from CDs or the Internet.

c. Shade in the regions that represent students who acquire music from both CDs and cassettes.

In Exercises 65–68, draw a Venn diagram with each of the given elements placed in the correct region.

65. $U = \{-1, 0, 1, 2, 3, 4, 5, 6, 7, 8, 9\}$
$A = \{1, 3, 5\}$
$B = \{3, 5, 7, 8\}$
$C = \{-1, 8, 9\}$

66. $U = \{2, 4, 6, 8, 10, 12, 14\}$
$A = \{2, 10, 12\}$
$B = \{4, 8\}$
$C = \{6, 8, 10\}$

67. $U = \{$Sue, Bob, Al, Jo, Ann, Herb, Eric, Mike, Sal$\}$
$A = \{$Sue, Herb$\}$
$B = \{$Sue, Eric, Jo, Ann$\}$
$Rh+ = \{$Eric, Sal, Al, Herb$\}$

68. $U = \{$Hal, Marie, Rob, Armando, Joel, Juan, Melody$\}$
$A = \{$Marie, Armando, Melody$\}$
$B = \{$Rob, Juan, Hal$\}$
$Rh+ = \{$Hal, Marie, Rob, Joel, Juan, Melody$\}$

In Exercises 69 and 70, use two Venn diagrams to verify the following properties for all sets A, B, and C.

69. The associative property of intersection

$$(A \cap B) \cap C = A \cap (B \cap C)$$

70. The distributive property of intersection over union

$$A \cap (B \cup C) = (A \cap B) \cup (A \cap C)$$

Extensions
CRITICAL THINKING

Difference of Sets Another operation that can be defined on sets A and B is the **difference of the sets,** denoted by $A - B$. Here is a formal definition of the difference of sets A and B.

$$A - B = \{x \,|\, x \in A \quad \text{and} \quad x \notin B\}$$

Thus $A - B$ is the set of elements that belong to A but not to B. For instance, let $A = \{1, 2, 3, 7, 8\}$ and $B = \{2, 7, 11\}$. Then $A - B = \{1, 3, 8\}$.

In Exercises 71–76, determine each difference, given that $U = \{1, 2, 3, 4, 5, 6, 7, 8, 9\}$, $A = \{2, 4, 6, 8\}$, and $B = \{2, 3, 8, 9\}$.

71. $B - A$ **72.** $A - B$

73. $A - B'$ **74.** $B' - A$

75. $A' - B'$ **76.** $A' - B$

77. 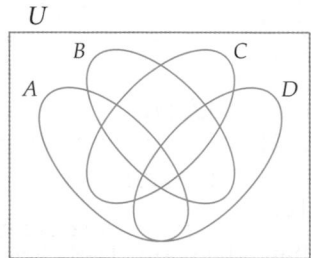 **John Venn** Write a few paragraphs about the life of John Venn and his work in the area of mathematics.

The following Venn diagram illustrates that four sets can partition the universal set into 16 different regions.

In Exercises 78 and 79, use a Venn diagram similar to the one at the left below to shade in the region represented by the given expression.

78. $(A \cap B) \cup (C' \cap D)$

79. $(A \cup B)' \cap (C \cap D)$

EXPLORATIONS

80. In an article in *New Scientist* magazine, Anthony W. F. Edwards illustrated how to construct Venn diagrams that involve many sets.[1] Search the Internet to find Edwards's method of constructing a Venn diagram for five sets and a Venn diagram for six sets. Use drawings to illustrate Edwards's method of constructing a Venn diagram for five sets and a Venn diagram for six sets. (*Source:* **http://www.combinatorics.org/Surveys/ds5/VennWhatEJC.html**)

| **Applications of Sets**

Surveys: An Application of Sets

Counting problems occur in many areas of applied mathematics. To solve these counting problems, we often make use of a Venn diagram and the inclusion-exclusion principle, which will be presented in this section.

EXAMPLE 1 ■ A Survey of Preferences

A movie company is making plans for future movies it wishes to produce. The company has done a random survey of 1000 people. The results of the survey are shown below.

   695 people like action adventures.

   340 people like comedies.

   180 people like both action adventures and comedies.

Of the people surveyed, how many people:

a. like action adventures but not comedies?

b. like comedies but not action adventures?

c. do not like either of these types of movies?

---

1. Anthony W. F. Edwards, "Venn diagrams for many sets," *New Scientist*, 7 January 1989, pp. 51–56.

Solution

A Venn diagram can be used to illustrate the results of the survey. We use two overlapping circles (see Figure 2.8). One circle represents the set of people who like action adventures and the other represents the set of people who like comedies. The region i where the circles intersect represents the set of people who like both types of movies.

We start with the information that 180 people like both types of movies and write 180 in region i. See Figure 2.9.

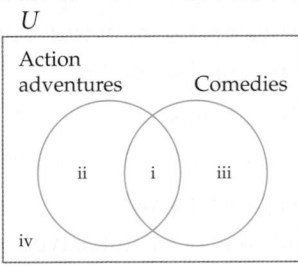

Figure 2.8   Figure 2.9

a. Regions i and ii have a total of 695 people. So far we have accounted for 180 of these people in region i. Thus the number of people in region ii, which is the set of people who like action adventures but do not like comedies, is $695 - 180 = 515$.

b. Regions i and iii have a total of 340 people. Thus the number of people in region iii, which is the set of people who like comedies but do not like action adventures, is $340 - 180 = 160$.

c. The number of people who do not like action adventure movies or comedies is represented by region iv. The number of people in region iv must be the total number of people, which is 1000, less the number of people accounted for in regions i, ii, and iii, which is 855. Thus the number of people who do not like either type of movie is $1000 - 855 = 145$.

CHECK YOUR PROGRESS 1   The athletic director of a school has surveyed 200 students. The survey results are shown below.

   140 students like volleyball.

   120 students like basketball.

   85 students like both volleyball and basketball.

Of the students surveyed, how many students:

a. like volleyball but not basketball?

b. like basketball but not volleyball?

c. do not like either of these sports?

Solution   *See page S6.*

In the next example we consider a more complicated survey that involves three types of music.

EXAMPLE 2 ■ A Music Survey

A music teacher has surveyed 495 students. The results of the survey are listed below.

320 students like rap music.

395 students like rock music.

295 students like heavy metal music.

280 students like both rap music and rock music.

190 students like both rap music and heavy metal music.

245 students like both rock music and heavy metal music.

160 students like all three.

How many students:

a. like exactly two of the three types of music?

b. like only rock music?

c. like only one of the three types of music?

Solution

The Venn diagram at the left shows three overlapping circles. Region i represents the set of students who like all three types of music. Each of the regions v, vi, and vii represent the students who like only one type of music.

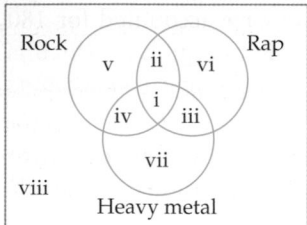

a. The survey shows that 245 students like rock and heavy metal music, so the numbers we place in regions i and iv must have a sum of 245. Since region i has 160 students, we see that region iv must have 245 − 160 = 85 students. In a similar manner, we can determine that region ii has 120 students and region iii has 30 students. Thus 85 + 120 + 30 = 235 students like exactly two of the three types of music.

b. The sum of the students represented by regions i, ii, iv, and v must be 395. The number of students in region v must be the difference between this total and the sum of the numbers of students in region i, ii, and iv. Thus the number of students who like only rock music is 395 − (160 + 120 + 85) = 30. See the Venn diagram at the left.

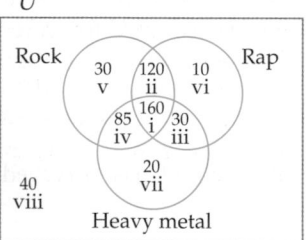

c. Using the same reasoning as in part b, we find that region vi has 10 students and region vii has 20 students. To find the number of students who like only one type of music, find the sum of the numbers of students in regions v, vi, and vii, which is 30 + 10 + 20 = 60. See the Venn diagram at the left.

CHECK YOUR PROGRESS 2 An activities director for a cruise ship has surveyed 240 passengers. Of the 240 passengers,

135 like swimming. 80 like swimming and dancing.

150 like dancing. 40 like swimming and games.

65 like games. 25 like dancing and games.

15 like all three activities.

How many passengers:

a. like exactly two of the three types of activities?

b. like only swimming?

c. like none of these activities?

Solution See page S6.

Grace Chisholm Young

Math Matters   Grace Chisholm Young (1868–1944)

Grace Chisholm Young studied mathematics at Girton College, which is part of Cambridge University. In England at that time, women were not allowed to earn a university degree, so she decided to continue her mathematical studies at the University of Göttingen in Germany, where her advisor was the renowned mathematician Felix Klein. She excelled while at Göttingen and at the age of 27 earned her doctorate in mathematics, magna cum laude. She was the first woman officially to earn a doctorate degree from a German university. Shortly after her graduation she married the mathematician William Young. Together they published several mathematical papers and books, one of which was the first textbook on set theory.

✔ **TAKE NOTE**

Recall that $n(A)$ represents the number of elements in set A.

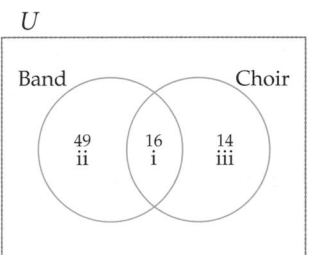

The Inclusion-Exclusion Principle

A music director wishes to take the band and the choir on a field trip. There are 65 students in the band and 30 students in the choir. The number of students in both the band and the choir is 16. How many students should the music director plan on taking on the field trip?

Using the process developed in the previous examples, we find that the number of students that are in only the band is $65 - 16 = 49$. The number of students that are in only the choir is $30 - 16 = 14$. See the Venn diagram at the left. Adding the numbers of students in regions i, ii, and iii gives us a total of $49 + 16 + 14 = 79$ students that might go on the field trip.

Although we can use Venn diagrams to solve counting problems, it is more convenient to make use of the following technique. First add the number of students in the band to the number of students in the choir. Then subtract the number of students who are in both the band and the choir. This technique gives us a total of $(65 + 30) - 16 = 79$ students, the same result as above. The reason we subtract the 16 students is that we have counted each of them twice. Note that first we include the students that are in both the band and the choir twice, and then we exclude them once. This procedure leads us to the following result.

The Inclusion-Exclusion Principle

For all finite sets A and B.

$$n(A \cup B) = n(A) + n(B) - n(A \cap B)$$

QUESTION   *What must be true of the finite sets A and B if*
$n(A \cup B) = n(A) + n(B)$?

ANSWER   *A and B must be disjoint sets.*

EXAMPLE 3 ■ **An Application of the Inclusion-Exclusion Principle**

A school finds that 430 of its students are registered in chemistry, 560 are registered in mathematics, and 225 are registered in both chemistry and mathematics. How many students are registered in chemistry or mathematics?

Solution

Let $C = \{$students registered in chemistry$\}$ and let
$M = \{$students registered in mathematics$\}$.

$$n(C \cup M) = n(C) + n(M) - n(C \cap M)$$
$$= 430 + 560 - 225$$
$$= 765$$

Using the inclusion-exclusion principle, we see that 765 students are registered in chemistry or mathematics.

CHECK YOUR PROGRESS 3   A high school has 80 athletes who play basketball, 60 athletes who play soccer, and 24 athletes who play both basketball and soccer. How many athletes play either basketball or soccer?

Solution   See page S6.

The inclusion-exclusion principle can be used provided we know the number of elements in any three of the four sets in the formula.

EXAMPLE 4 ■ **An Application of the Inclusion-Exclusion Principle**

Given $n(A) = 15$, $n(B) = 32$, and $n(A \cup B) = 41$, find $n(A \cap B)$.

Solution

Substitute the given information in the inclusion-exclusion formula and solve for the unknown.

$$n(A \cup B) = n(A) + n(B) - n(A \cap B)$$
$$41 = 15 + 32 - n(A \cap B)$$
$$41 = 47 - n(A \cap B)$$

Thus

$$n(A \cap B) = 47 - 41$$
$$n(A \cap B) = 6$$

CHECK YOUR PROGRESS 4   Given $n(A) = 785$, $n(B) = 162$, and $n(A \cup B) = 852$, find $n(A \cap B)$.

Solution   See page S6.

The inclusion-exclusion formula can be adjusted and applied to problems that involve percents. In the following formula we denote "the percent in set A" by the notation $p(A)$.

The Percent Inclusion-Exclusion Formula

For all finite sets A and B,

$$p(A \cup B) = p(A) + p(B) - p(A \cap B).$$

AB+
3%

AB− B−
1% 2%

B+
9%   A−
6%

O+
38%

A+
34%

O−
7%

Percentage of U.S. Population with Each Blood Type

Source: American Association of Blood Banks,
http://www.aabb.org/ All_About_Blood/FAQs/ aabb_faqs.htm

EXAMPLE 5 ■ An Application of the Percent Inclusion-Exclusion Formula

 The American Association of Blood Banks reports that about

44% of the U.S. population has the A antigen.

15% of the U.S. population has the B antigen.

4% of the U.S. population has both the A and the B antigen.

Use the percent inclusion-exclusion formula to estimate the percent of the U.S. population that has the A antigen or the B antigen.

Solution

We are given $p(A) = 44\%$, $p(B) = 15\%$, and $p(A \cap B) = 4\%$. Substituting in the percent inclusion-exclusion formula gives

$$p(A \cup B) = p(A) + p(B) - p(A \cap B)$$
$$= 44\% + 15\% - 4\%$$
$$= 55\%$$

Thus about 55% of the U.S. population has the A antigen or the B antigen. **Notice** that this result checks with the data given in the pie chart at the left (1% + 3% + 2% + 9% + 6% + 34% = 55%).

CHECK YOUR PROGRESS 5 The American Association of Blood Banks reports that about

44% of the U.S. population has the A antigen.

84% of the U.S. population is Rh+.

91% of the U.S. population either has the A antigen or is Rh+.

Use the percent inclusion-exclusion formula to estimate the percent of the U.S. population that has the A antigen *and* is Rh+.

Solution *See page S6.*

In the next example the data are provided in a table. The number in column G and row M represents the number of elements in $G \cap M$. The sum of all the numbers in column G and column L represents the number of elements in $G \cup L$.

EXAMPLE 6 ■ A Survey Presented in Tabular Form

A survey of men M, women W, and children C concerning the use of the Internet search engines Google G, Yahoo! Y, and Lycos L yielded the following results.

	Google (G)	Yahoo! (Y)	Lycos (L)
Men (M)	440	310	275
Women (W)	390	280	325
Children (C)	140	410	40

Use the data in the table to find each of the following.

a. $n(W \cap Y)$ **b.** $n(G \cap C')$ **c.** $n(M \cap (G \cup L))$

Solution

a. The table shows that 280 of the women surveyed use Yahoo! as a search engine. Thus, $n(W \cap Y) = 280$.

b. The set $G \cap C'$ is the set of surveyed Google users who are men or women. The number in this set is $440 + 390 = 830$.

c. The number of men in the survey that use either Google or Lycos is $440 + 275 = 715$.

CHECK YOUR PROGRESS 6   Use the table in Example 6 to find each of the following.

a. $n(Y \cap C)$ **b.** $n(L \cap M')$ **c.** $n((G \cap M) \cup (G \cap W))$

Solution   See page S6.

Excursion

Voting Systems

There are many types of voting systems. When people are asked to vote for or against a resolution, a one-person, one-vote *majority system* is often used to decide the outcome. In this type of voting, each voter receives one vote, and the resolution passes only if it receives *most* of the votes.

In any voting system, the number of votes that is required to pass a resolution is called the **quota**. A **coalition** is a set of voters each of whom votes the same way, either for or against a resolution. A **winning coalition** is a set of voters the sum of whose votes is greater than or equal to the quota. A **losing coalition** is a set of voters the sum of whose votes is less than the quota.

Sometimes you can find all the winning coalitions in a voting process by making an organized list. For instance, consider the committee consisting of Alice, Barry, Cheryl, and

(continued)

An ostrakon

In ancient Greece, the citizens of Athens adopted a procedure that allowed them to vote for the expulsion of any prominent person. The purpose of this procedure, known as an *ostracism*, was to limit the political power that any one person could attain.

In an ostracism, each voter turned in a *potsherd*, a piece of pottery fragment, on which was inscribed the name of the person the voter wished to ostracize. The pottery fragments used in the voting process became known as *ostrakon*.

The person who received the majority of the votes, above some set minimum, was exiled from Athens for a period of 10 years. ■

Dylan. To decide on any issues, they use a one-person, one-vote majority voting system. Since each of the four voters has a single vote, the quota for this majority voting system is 3. The winning coalitions consist of all subsets of the voters that have three or more people. We list these winning coalitions in the table at the left below, where A represents Alice, B represents Barry, C represents Cheryl, and D represents Dylan.

A **weighted voting system** is one in which some voters' votes carry more weight regarding the outcome of an election. As an example, consider a selection committee that consists of four people designated by A, B, C, and D. Voter A's vote has a weight of 2, and the vote of each other member of the committee has a weight of 1. The quota for this weighted voting system is 3. A winning coalition must have a weighted voting sum of at least 3. The winning coalitions are listed in the table at the right below.

Winning Coalition	Sum of the Votes
{A, B, C}	3
{A, B, D}	3
{A, C, D}	3
{B, C, D}	3
{A, B, C, D}	4

Winning Coalition	Sum of the Weighted Votes
{A, B}	3
{A, C}	3
{A, D}	3
{B, C, D}	3
{A, B, C}	4
{A, B, D}	4
{A, C, D}	4
{A, B, C, D}	5

A **minimal winning coalition** is a winning coalition that has no proper subset that is a winning coalition. In a minimal winning coalition each voter is said to be a **critical voter,** because if any of the voters leaves the coalition, the coalition will then become a losing coalition. In the table at the right above, the minimal winning coalitions are {A, B}, {A, C}, {A, D}, and {B, C, D}. If any single voter leaves one of these coalitions, then the coalition will become a losing coalition. The coalition {A, B, C, D} is not a minimal winning coalition, because it contains at least one proper subset, for instance {A, B, C}, that is a winning coalition.

Excursion Exercises

1. A selection committee consists of Ryan, Susan, and Trevor. To decide on issues, they use a one-person, one-vote majority voting system.
   a. Find all winning coalitions.
   b. Find all losing coalitions.

2. A selection committee consists of three people designated by M, N, and P. M's vote has a weight of 3, N's vote has a weight of 2, and P's vote has a weight of 1. The quota for this weighted voting system is 4. Find all winning coalitions.

3. Determine the minimal winning coalitions for the voting system in Excursion Exercise 2.

Additional information on the applications of mathematics to voting systems is given in Chapter 13.

Exercise Set 2.4

In Exercises 1–8, let U = {English, French, History, Math, Physics, Chemistry, Psychology, Drama},
A = {English, History, Psychology, Drama},
B = {Math, Physics, Chemistry, Psychology, Drama}, and
C = {French, History, Chemistry}.
Find each of the following.

1. $n(B \cup C)$

2. $n(A \cup B)$

3. $n(B) + n(C)$

4. $n(A) + n(B)$

5. $n(A \cup B \cup C)$

6. $n(A \cap B)$

7. $n(A) + n(B) + n(C)$

8. $n(A \cap B \cap C)$

9. Verify that for A and B as defined in Exercises 1–8, $n(A \cup B) = n(A) + n(B) - n(A \cap B)$.

10. Verify that for A and C as defined in Exercises 1–8, $n(A \cup C) = n(A) + n(C) - n(A \cap C)$.

11. Given $n(J) = 245$, $n(K) = 178$, and $n(J \cup K) = 310$, find $n(J \cap K)$.

12. Given $n(L) = 780$, $n(M) = 240$, and $n(L \cap M) = 50$, find $n(L \cup M)$.

13. Given $n(A) = 1500$, $n(A \cup B) = 2250$, and $n(A \cap B) = 310$, find $n(B)$.

14. Given $n(A) = 640$, $n(B) = 280$, and $n(A \cup B) = 765$, find $n(A \cap B)$.

In Exercises 15 and 16, use the given information to find the number of elements in each of the regions labeled with a question mark.

15. $n(A) = 28$, $n(B) = 31$, $n(C) = 40$, $n(A \cap B) = 15$, $n(U) = 75$

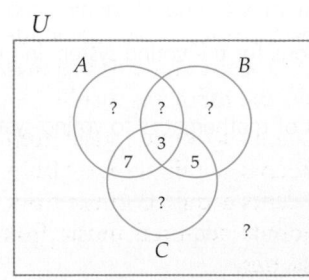

16. $n(A) = 610$, $n(B) = 440$, $n(C) = 1000$, $n(U) = 2900$

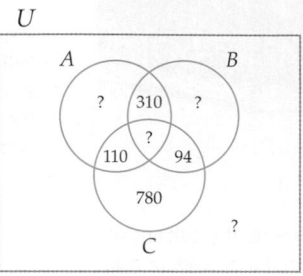

17. **A Survey** In a survey of 600 investors, it was reported that 380 had invested in stocks, 325 had invested in bonds, and 75 had not invested in either stocks or bonds.

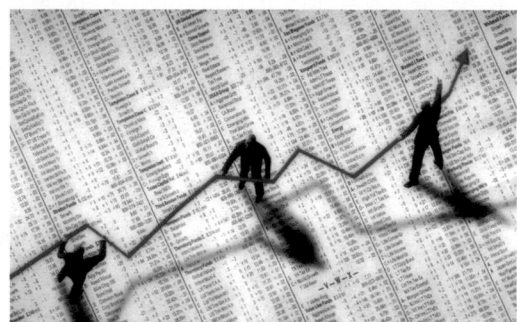

   a. How many investors had invested in both stocks and bonds?

   b. How many investors had invested only in stocks?

18. **A Survey** A survey of 1500 commuters in New York City showed that 1140 take the subway, 680 take the bus, and 120 do not take either the bus or the subway.

   a. How many commuters take both the bus and the subway?

   b. How many commuters take only the subway?

19. **A Survey** A team physician has determined that of all the athletes who were treated for minor back pain, 72% responded to an analgesic, 59% responded to a muscle relaxant, and 44% responded to both forms of treatment.

   a. What percent of the athletes who were treated responded to the muscle relaxant but not to the analgesic?

   b. What percent of the athletes who were treated did not respond to either form of treatment?

20. A Survey The management of a hotel conducted a survey. It found that of the 2560 guests who were surveyed,

>1785 tip the wait staff.
>1219 tip the luggage handlers.
>831 tip the maids.
>275 tip the maids and the luggage handlers.
>700 tip the wait staff and the maids.
>755 tip the wait staff and the luggage handlers.
>245 tip all three services.
>210 do not tip these services.

How many of the surveyed guests tip:

a. exactly two of the three services?

b. only the wait staff?

c. only one of the three services?

21. A Survey A computer company advertises its computers in *PC World*, in *PC Magazine,* and on television. A survey of 770 customers finds that the numbers of customers who are familiar with the company's computers because of the different forms of advertising are as follows:

>305, *PC World*
>290, *PC Magazine*
>390, television
>110, *PC World* and *PC Magazine*
>135, *PC Magazine* and television
>150, *PC World* and television
>85, all three sources

How many of the surveyed customers know about the computers because of:

a. exactly one of these forms of advertising?

b. exactly two of these forms of advertising?

c. *BYTE* magazine and neither of the other two forms of advertising?

22. **Blood Types** A report from the American Association of Blood Banks shows that in the United States:

>44% of the population has the A antigen.
>15% of the population has the B antigen.
>84% of the population has the Rh+ factor.
>34% of the population is blood type A+.
>9% of the population is blood type B+.
>4% of the population has the A antigen and the B antigen.
>3% of the population is blood type AB+.

(*Source:* **http://www.aabb.org/All_About_Blood/ FAQs/aabb_faqs.htm.**)

Find the percent of the U.S. population that is:

a. A−   **b.** O+   **c.** O−

23. A Survey A special-interest group has conducted a survey concerning a ban on hand guns. *Note:* A rifle is a gun, but it is not a hand gun. The survey yielded the following results for the 1000 households that responded.

>271 own a hand gun.
>437 own a rifle.
>497 supported the ban on hand guns.
>140 own both a hand gun and a rifle.
>202 own a rifle but no hand gun and do not support the ban on hand guns.
>74 own a hand gun and support the ban on hand guns.
>52 own both a hand gun and a rifle and also support the ban on hand guns.

How many of the surveyed households:

a. only own a hand gun and do not support the ban on hand guns?

b. do not own a gun and support the ban on hand guns?

c. do not own a gun and do not support the ban on hand guns?

24. A Survey A survey of college students was taken to determine how the students acquired music. The survey showed the following results.

>365 students acquired music from CDs.
>298 students acquired music from the Internet.
>268 students acquired music from cassettes.
>212 students acquired music from both CDs and cassettes.

155 students acquired music from both CDs and the Internet.

36 students acquired music from cassettes, but not from CDs or the Internet.

98 students acquired music from CDs, cassettes, and the Internet.

Of those surveyed,

a. how many acquired music from CDs, but not from the Internet or cassettes?

b. how many acquired music from the Internet, but not from CDs or cassettes?

c. how many acquired music from CDs or the Internet?

d. how many acquired music from the Internet and cassettes?

25. Diets A survey was completed by individuals who were currently on the Atkins diet (A), the South Beach diet (S), or the Weight Watchers diet (W). All persons surveyed were also asked whether they were currently in an exercise program (E), taking diet pills (P), or under medical supervision (M). The following table shows the results of the survey.

		Supplements			
		E	**P**	**M**	**Totals**
Diet	**A**	124	82	65	271
	S	101	66	51	218
	W	133	41	48	222
	Totals	358	189	164	711

Find the number of surveyed people in each of the following sets.

a. $S \cap E$

b. $A \cup M$

c. $S' \cap (E \cup P)$

d. $(A \cup S) \cap (M')$

e. $W' \cap (P \cup M)'$

f. $W' \cup P$

26. Financial Assistance A college study categorized its seniors (S), juniors (J), and sophomores (M) who are currently receiving financial assistance. The types of financial assistance consist of full scholarships (F), partial scholarships (P), and government loans (G). The following table shows the results of the survey.

		Financial Assistance			
		F	**P**	**G**	**Totals**
Year	**S**	210	175	190	575
	J	180	162	110	452
	M	114	126	86	326
	Totals	504	463	386	1353

Find the number of students who are currently receiving financial assistance in each of the following sets.

a. $S \cap P$

b. $J \cup G$

c. $M \cup F'$

d. $S \cap (F \cup P)$

e. $J \cap (F \cup P)'$

f. $(S \cup J) \cap (F \cup P)$

Extensions

CRITICAL THINKING

27. Given that set A has 47 elements and set B has 25 elements, determine each of the following.

a. The maximum possible number of elements in $A \cup B$.

b. The minimum possible number of elements in $A \cup B$.

c. The maximum possible number of elements in $A \cap B$.

d. The minimum possible number of elements in $A \cap B$.

28. Given that set A has 16 elements, set B has 12 elements, and set C has 7 elements, determine each of the following.

a. The maximum possible number of elements in $A \cup B \cup C$.

b. The minimum possible number of elements in $A \cup B \cup C$.

c. The maximum possible number of elements in $A \cap (B \cup C)$.

d. The minimum possible number of elements in $A \cap (B \cup C)$.

29. A Survey The following Venn diagram displays U parceled into 16 distinct regions by four sets.

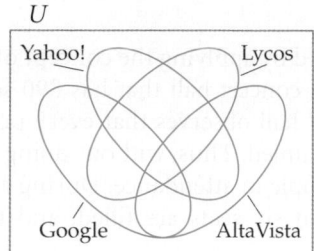

Use the above Venn diagram and the information in the column at right to answer the questions that follow.

A survey of 1250 Internet users shows the following results concerning the use of the search engines Google, AltaVista, Yahoo!, and Lycos.

585 use Google.
620 use Yahoo!.
560 use Lycos.
450 use AltaVista.
100 use only Google, Yahoo!, and Lycos.
41 use only Google, Yahoo!, and AltaVista.
50 use only Google, Lycos, and AltaVista.
80 use only Yahoo!, Lycos, and AltaVista.
55 use only Google and Yahoo!.
34 use only Google and Lycos.
45 use only Google and AltaVista.
50 use only Yahoo! and Lycos.
30 use only Yahoo! and AltaVista.
45 use only Lycos and AltaVista.
60 use all four.

How many of the Internet users:

a. use only Google?
b. use exactly three of the four search engines?
c. do not use any of the four search engines?

30. An Inclusion–Exclusion Formula for Three Sets Exactly one of the following equations is a valid inclusion-exclusion formula for the union of three finite sets. Which equation do you think is the valid formula? *Hint:* Use the data in Example 2 on page 88 to check your choice.

a. $n(A \cup B \cup C) = n(A) + n(B) + n(C)$
b. $n(A \cup B \cup C) = n(A) + n(B) + n(C) - n(A \cap B \cap C)$
c. $n(A \cup B \cup C) = n(A) + n(B) + n(C) - n(A \cap B) - n(A \cap C) - n(B \cap C)$
d. $n(A \cup B \cup C) = n(A) + n(B) + n(C) - n(A \cap B) - n(A \cap C) - n(B \cap C) + n(A \cap B \cap C)$

SECTION 2.5 | Infinite Sets

One-To-One Correspondences

Much of Georg Cantor's work with sets concerned infinite sets. Some of Cantor's work with infinite sets was so revolutionary that it was not readily accepted by his contemporaries. Today, however, his work is generally accepted, and it provides unifying ideas in several diverse areas of mathematics.

Much of Cantor's set theory is based on the simple concept of a *one-to-one correspondence.*

One-to-One Correspondence

A **one-to-one correspondence** (or $1-1$ correspondence) between two sets A and B is a rule or procedure that pairs each element of A with exactly one element of B and each element of B with exactly one element of A.

Many practical problems can be solved by applying the concept of a one-to-one correspondence. For instance, consider a concert hall that has 890 seats. During a performance the manager of the concert hall observes that every person occupies exactly one seat and that every seat is occupied. Thus, without doing any counting, the manager knows that there are 890 people in attendance. During a different performance the manager notes that all but six seats are filled, and thus there are $890 - 6 = 884$ people in attendance.

Recall that two sets are equivalent if and only if they have the same number of elements. One method of showing that two sets are equivalent is to establish a one-to-one correspondence between the elements of the sets.

One-to-One Correspondence and Equivalent Sets

Two sets A and B are equivalent, denoted by $A \sim B$, if and only if A and B can be placed in a one-to-one correspondence.

Set $\{a, b, c, d, e\}$ is equivalent to set $\{1, 2, 3, 4, 5\}$ because we can show that the elements of each set can be placed in a one-to-one correspondence. One method of establishing this one-to-one correspondence is shown in the following figure.

$$\{a, \quad b, \quad c, \quad d, \quad e\}$$
$$\updownarrow \quad \updownarrow \quad \updownarrow \quad \updownarrow \quad \updownarrow$$
$$\{1, \quad 2, \quad 3, \quad 4, \quad 5\}$$

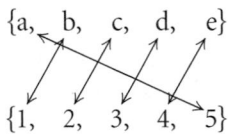

Each element of $\{a, b, c, d, e\}$ has been paired with exactly one element of $\{1, 2, 3, 4, 5\}$, and each element of $\{1, 2, 3, 4, 5\}$ has been paired with exactly one element of $\{a, b, c, d, e\}$. This is not the only one-to-one correspondence that we can establish. The figure at the left shows another one-to-one correspondence between the sets. In any case, we know that both sets have the same number of elements because we have established a one-to-one correspondence between the sets.

Sometimes a set is defined by including a general element. For instance, in the set $\{3, 6, 9, 12, 15, \ldots, 3n, \ldots\}$, the $3n$ (where n is a natural number) indicates that all the elements of the set are multiples of 3.

Some sets can be placed in a one-to-one correspondence with a proper subset of themselves. Example 1 illustrates this concept for the set of natural numbers.

EXAMPLE 1 ■ Establish a One-to-One Correspondence

Establish a one-to-one correspondence between the set of natural numbers $N = \{1, 2, 3, 4, 5, \ldots, n, \ldots\}$ and the set of even natural numbers $E = \{2, 4, 6, 8, 10, \ldots, 2n, \ldots\}$.

Solution

Write the sets so that one is aligned below the other. Draw arrows to show how you wish to pair the elements of each set. One possible method is shown in the following figure.

$$N = \{1, 2, 3, 4, \ldots, n, \ldots\}$$
$$\updownarrow \updownarrow \updownarrow \updownarrow \qquad \updownarrow$$
$$E = \{2, 4, 6, 8, \ldots, 2n, \ldots\}$$

In the above correspondence, each natural number $n \in N$ is paired with the even number $(2n) \in E$. The *general correspondence* $n \leftrightarrow (2n)$ enables us to determine exactly which element of E will be paired with any given element of N, and vice versa. For instance, under this correspondence, $19 \in N$ is paired with the even number $2 \cdot 19 = 38 \in E$, and $100 \in E$ is paired with the natural number $\frac{1}{2} \cdot 100 = 50 \in N$. The general correspondence $n \leftrightarrow (2n)$ establishes a one-to-one correspondence between the sets.

CHECK YOUR PROGRESS 1   Establish a one-to-one correspondence between the set of natural numbers $N = \{1, 2, 3, 4, 5, \ldots, n, \ldots\}$ and the set of odd natural numbers $D = \{1, 3, 5, 7, 9, \ldots, 2n - 1, \ldots\}$.

Solution   See page S7.

Infinite Sets

Definition of an Infinite Set

A set is an **infinite set** if it can be placed in a one-to-one correspondence with a proper subset of itself.

We know that the set of natural numbers N is an infinite set because in Example 1 we were able to establish a one-to-one correspondence between the elements of N and the elements of one of its proper subsets, E.

QUESTION   *Can the set $\{1, 2, 3\}$ be placed in a one-to-one correspondence with one of its proper subsets?*

ANSWER   *No. The set $\{1, 2, 3\}$ is a finite set with three elements. Every proper subset of $\{1, 2, 3\}$ has two or fewer elements.*

The solution shown in Example 2 is not the only way to establish that S is an infinite set. For instance, $R = \{10, 15, 20, \ldots 5n + 5, \ldots\}$ is also a proper set of S, and the sets S and R can be placed in a one-to-one correspondence as follows.

$S = \{\, 5,\ 10,\ 15,\ 20,\ \ldots,\quad 5n,\quad \ldots\}$

$R = \{10, 15, 20, 25, \ldots, 5n + 5, \ldots\}$

This one-to-one correspondence between S and one of its proper subsets R also establishes that S is an infinite set.

EXAMPLE 2 ■ Verify that a Set is an Infinite Set

Verify that $S = \{5, 10, 15, 20, \ldots, 5n, \ldots\}$ is an infinite set.

Solution

One proper subset of S is $T = \{10, 20, 30, 40, \ldots, 10n, \ldots\}$, which was produced by deleting the odd numbers in S. To establish a one-to-one correspondence between set S and set T, consider the following diagram.

$S = \{\, 5,\ 10, 15, 20, \ldots,\ 5n,\ \ldots\}$

$T = \{10, 20, 30, 40, \ldots, 10n, \ldots\}$

In the above correspondence, each $(5n) \in S$ is paired with $(10n) \in T$. The *general correspondence* $(5n) \leftrightarrow (10n)$ establishes a one-to-one correspondence between S and one of its proper subsets, namely T. Thus S is an infinite set.

CHECK YOUR PROGRESS 2 Verify that $V = \{40, 41, 42, 43, \ldots, 39 + n, \ldots\}$ is an infinite set.

Solution See page S7.

The Cardinality of Infinite Sets

The symbol $\aleph_0$ is used to represent the cardinal number for the set N of natural numbers. ($\aleph$ is the first letter of the Hebrew alphabet and is pronounced *aleph*. $\aleph_0$ is read as "aleph-null.") Using mathematical notation, we write this concept as $n(N) = \aleph_0$. Since $\aleph_0$ represents a cardinality larger than any finite number, it is called a **transfinite number.** Many infinite sets have a cardinality of $\aleph_0$. In Example 3, for instance, we show that the cardinality of the set of integers is $\aleph_0$ by establishing a one-to-one correspondence between the elements of the set of integers and the elements of the set of natural numbers.

EXAMPLE 3 ■ Establish the Cardinality of the Set of Integers

Show that the set of integers $I = \{\ldots, -5, -4, -3, -2, -1, 0, 1, 2, 3, 4, 5, \ldots\}$ has a cardinality of $\aleph_0$.

Solution

First we try to establish a one-to-one correspondence between I and N, with the elements in each set arranged as shown below. No general method of pairing the elements of N with the elements of I seems to emerge from this figure.

$N = \{1, 2, 3, 4, 5, 6, 7, 8, 9, 10, 11, \ldots\}$

?

$I = \{\ldots, -5, -4, -3, -2, -1, 0, 1, 2, 3, 4, 5, \ldots\}$

If we arrange the elements of I as shown in the figure below, then *two* general correspondences, shown by the blue arrows and the red arrows, can be identified.

$$N = \{1, 2, \ 3, \ 4, \ 5, \ 6, \ 7, \ 8, \ 9, \ 10, 11, \ldots, \ 2n - 1, 2n, \ldots\}$$

$$I = \{0, 1, -1, 2, -2, 3, -3, 4, -4, \ 5, -5 \ldots, \ -n + 1, \ n, \ldots\}$$

- Each even natural number $2n$ of N is paired with the integer n of I. This correspondence is shown by the blue arrows.
- Each odd natural number $2n - 1$ of N is paired with the integer $-n + 1$ of I. This correspondence is shown by the red arrows.

Together the two general correspondences $(2n) \leftrightarrow n$ and $(2n - 1) \leftrightarrow (-n + 1)$ establish a one-to-one correspondence between the elements of I and the elements of N. Thus the cardinality of the set of integers must be the same as the cardinality of the set of natural numbers, which is $\aleph_0$.

CHECK YOUR PROGRESS 3   Show that $M = \left\{\frac{1}{2}, \frac{1}{3}, \frac{1}{4}, \frac{1}{5}, \ldots, \frac{1}{n + 1}, \ldots\right\}$ has a cardinality of $\aleph_0$.

Solution   *See page S7.*

Cantor was also able to show that the set of positive rational numbers is equivalent to the set of natural numbers. Recall that a rational number is a number that can be written as a fraction $\frac{p}{q}$ where p and q are integers and $q \neq 0$. Cantor's proof used an array of rational numbers similar to the array shown below.

Theorem   The set $Q+$ of positive rational numbers is equivalent to the set N of natural numbers.

Proof   Consider the following array of positive rational numbers.

✔ **TAKE NOTE**

The rational number $\frac{2}{2}$ is not listed in the second row because $\frac{2}{2} = 1 = \frac{1}{1}$, which is already listed in the first row.

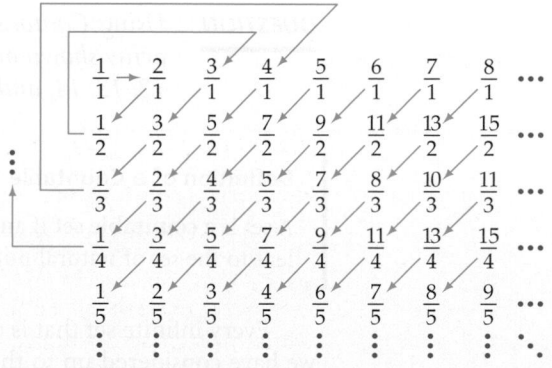

An array of all the positive rational numbers

The first row of the above array contains, in order from smallest to largest, all the positive rational numbers *which when expressed in lowest terms* have a denominator of 1. The second row contains the positive rational numbers *which when expressed in lowest terms* have a denominator of 2. The third row contains the positive rational numbers *which when expressed in lowest terms* have a denominator of 3. This process continues indefinitely.

Cantor reasoned that every positive rational number appears once and only once in this array. Note that $\frac{3}{5}$ appears in the fifth row. In general, if $\frac{p}{q}$ is in lowest terms, then it appears in row q.

At this point Cantor used a numbering procedure that establishes a one-to-one correspondence between the natural numbers and the positive rational numbers in the array. The numbering procedure starts in the upper left corner with $\frac{1}{1}$. Cantor considered this to be the first number in the array, so he assigned the natural number 1 to this rational number. He then moved to the right and assigned the natural number 2 to the rational number $\frac{2}{1}$. From this point on, he followed the diagonal paths shown by the arrows and assigned each number he encountered to the next consecutive natural number. When he reached the bottom of a diagonal, he moved up to the top of the array and continued to number the rational numbers in the next diagonal. The following table shows the first 10 rational numbers Cantor numbered using this scheme.

Rational number in the array	$\frac{1}{1}$	$\frac{2}{1}$	$\frac{1}{2}$	$\frac{3}{1}$	$\frac{3}{2}$	$\frac{1}{3}$	$\frac{4}{1}$	$\frac{5}{2}$	$\frac{2}{3}$	$\frac{1}{4}$
Corresponding natural number	1	2	3	4	5	6	7	8	9	10

This numbering procedure shows that each element of $Q+$ can be paired with exactly one element of N, and each element of N can be paired with exactly one element of $Q+$. Thus $Q+$ and N are equivalent sets. ∎

The negative rational numbers $Q-$ can also be placed in a one-to-one correspondence with the set of natural numbers in a similar manner.

QUESTION *Using Cantor's numbering scheme, which rational numbers in the array shown on page 101 would be assigned the natural numbers 11, 12, 13, 14, and 15?*

Definition of a Countable Set

A set is a **countable set** if and only if it is a finite set or an infinite set that is equivalent to the set of natural numbers.

Every infinite set that is countable has a cardinality of $\aleph_0$. Every infinite set that we have considered up to this point is countable. You might think that all infinite sets are countable; however, Cantor was able to show that this is not the case. Con-

---

ANSWER *The rational numbers in the next diagonal, namely $\frac{5}{1}$, $\frac{7}{2}$, $\frac{4}{3}$, $\frac{3}{4}$, and $\frac{1}{5}$, would be assigned to the natural numbers 11, 12, 13, 14, and 15, respectively.*

sider, for example, $A = \{x \mid x \in R \text{ and } 0 < x < 1\}$. To show that A is *not* a countable set, we use a *proof by contradiction*, where we assume that A is countable and then proceed until we arrive at a contradiction.

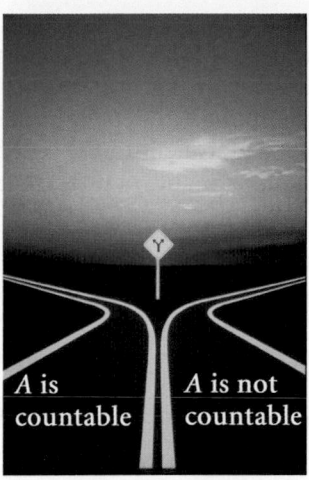

To better understand the concept of a proof by contradiction, consider the situation in which you are at a point where a road splits into two roads. See the figure at the left. Assume you know that only one of the two roads leads to your desired destination. If you can show that one of the roads cannot get you to your destination, then you know, without ever traveling down the other road, that it is the road that leads to your destination. In the following proof, we know that either set A is a countable set or set A is not a countable set. To establish that A is *not* countable, we show that the assumption that A is countable leads to a contradiction. In other words, our assumption that A is countable must be incorrect, and we are forced to conclude that A is not countable.

A is countable   A is not countable

Theorem   The set $A = \{x \mid x \in R \text{ and } 0 < x < 1\}$ is not a countable set.

Proof by contradiction   Either A is countable or A is not countable. Assume A is countable. Then we can place the elements of A, which we will represent by a_1, a_2, a_3, a_4, ..., in a one-to-one correspondence with the elements of the natural numbers as shown below.

$$N = \{1, \quad 2, \quad 3, \quad 4, \quad \ldots, \quad n, \quad \ldots\}$$

$$A = \{a_1, a_2, a_3, a_4, \ldots, a_n, \ldots\}$$

For example, the numbers a_1, a_2, a_3, a_4, ..., a_n, ... could be as shown below.

$$1 \leftrightarrow a_1 = 0 . \boxed{3} 5\ 7\ 3\ 4\ 8\ 5 \ldots$$
$$2 \leftrightarrow a_2 = 0 . 0 \boxed{6} 5\ 2\ 8\ 9\ 1 \ldots$$
$$3 \leftrightarrow a_3 = 0 . 6\ 8 \boxed{2} 3\ 5\ 1\ 4 \ldots$$
$$4 \leftrightarrow a_4 = 0 . 0\ 5\ 0 \boxed{0} 3\ 1\ 0 \ldots$$
$$\vdots$$
$$n \leftrightarrow a_n = 0 . 3\ 1\ 5\ 5\ 7\ 2\ 8 \ldots \boxed{5} \ldots$$
$$\vdots$$

nth decimal digit of a_n

At this point we use a "diagonal technique" to construct a real number d that is greater than 0 and less than 1 and is not in the above list. We construct d by writing a decimal that *differs* from a_1 in the first decimal place, differs from a_2 in the second decimal place, differs from a_3 in the third decimal place, and, in general, differs from a_n in the nth decimal place. For instance, in the above list, a_1 has 3 as its first decimal digit. The first decimal digit of d can be any digit other than 3, say 4. The real number a_2 has 6 as its second decimal digit. The second decimal digit of d can be any digit other than 6, say 7. The real number a_3 has 2 as its third decimal digit. The third decimal digit of d can be any digit other than 2, say 3. Continue in this manner to determine the decimal digits of d. Now $d = 0.473\ldots$ must be in A because $0 < d < 1$. However, d is not in A, because d differs from each of the numbers in A in at least one decimal place.

We have reached a contradiction. Our assumption that the elements of A could be placed in a one-to-one correspondence with the elements of the natural numbers must be false. Thus A is not a countable set.   ■

An infinite set that is not countable is said to be **uncountable.** Because the set $A = \{x \mid x \in R \text{ and } 0 < x < 1\}$ is uncountable, the cardinality of A is not $\aleph_0$. Cantor used the letter c, which is the first letter of the word *continuum,* to represent the cardinality of A. Cantor was also able to show that set A is equivalent to the set of all real numbers R. Thus the cardinality of R is also c. Cantor was able to prove that $c > \aleph_0$.

A Comparison of Transfinite Cardinal Numbers

$c > \aleph_0$

Up to this point, all of the infinite sets we have considered have a cardinality of either $\aleph_0$ or c. The following table lists several infinite sets and the transfinite cardinal number that is associated with each set.

The Cardinality of Some Infinite Sets	
Set	**Cardinal Number**
Natural numbers, N	$\aleph_0$
Integers, I	$\aleph_0$
Rational numbers, Q	$\aleph_0$
Irrational Numbers, $\mathscr{I}$	c
Any set of the form $\{x \mid a \leq x \leq b\}$, where a and b are real numbers and $a \neq b$.	c
Real numbers, R	c

Your intuition may suggest that $\aleph_0$ and c are the only two cardinal numbers associated with infinite sets; however, this is not the case. In fact, Cantor was able to show that no matter how large the cardinal number of a set, we can find a set that has a larger cardinal number. Thus there are infinitely many transfinite numbers. Cantor's proof of this concept is now known as *Cantor's theorem.*

Cantor's Theorem

Let S be any set. The set of all subsets of S has a cardinal number that is larger than the cardinal number of S.

The set of all subsets of S is called the **power set** of S and is denoted by $P(S)$. We can see that Cantor's theorem is true for the finite set $S = \{a, b, c\}$ because the cardinality of S is 3 and S has $2^3 = 8$ subsets. The interesting part of Cantor's theorem is that it also applies to infinite sets.

Some of the following theorems can be established by using the techniques illustrated in the Excursion that follows.

Transfinite Arithmetic Theorems

- For any whole number a, $\aleph_0 + a = \aleph_0$ and $\aleph_0 - a = \aleph_0$

- $\aleph_0 + \aleph_0 = \aleph_0$ and, in general, $\underbrace{\aleph_0 + \aleph_0 + \aleph_0 + \cdots + \aleph_0}_{\text{a finite number of aleph nulls}} = \aleph_0$

- $c + c = c$ and, in general, $\underbrace{c + c + c + \cdots + c}_{\text{a finite number of }c\text{'s}} = c$

- $\aleph_0 + c = c$

- $\aleph_0 c = c$

Math Matters   Criticism and Praise

Georg Cantor's work in the area of infinite sets was not well received by some of his colleagues. For instance, the mathematician Leopold Kronecker tried to stop the publication of some of Cantor's work. He felt many of Cantor's theorems were ridiculous and asked, "How can one infinity be greater than another?" The following quote illustrates that Cantor was aware that his work would attract harsh criticism.

> ...I realize that in this undertaking I place myself in a certain opposition to views widely held concerning the mathematical infinite and to opinions frequently defended on the nature of numbers.[2]

A few mathematicians were willing to show support for Cantor's work. For instance, the famous mathematician David Hilbert stated that Cantor's work was

> ...the finest product of mathematical genius and one of the supreme achievements of purely intellectual human activity.[3]

Excursion

Transfinite Arithmetic

Disjoint sets are often used to explain addition. The sum $4 + 3$, for example, can be deduced by selecting two disjoint sets, one with exactly four elements and one with exactly three elements. See the Venn diagram at the left. Now form the union of the two sets. The union of the two sets has exactly seven elements; thus, $4 + 3 = 7$. In mathematical notation, we write

$$n(A) + n(B) = n(A \cup B)$$
$$4 \quad + \quad 3 \quad = \quad 7$$

(continued)

---

2. *Source:* **http://www-groups.dcs.st-and.ac.uk/%7Ehistory/Mathematicians/Cantor.html**

3. See note 2 above.

Cantor extended this idea to infinite sets. He reasoned that the sum $\aleph_0 + 1$ could be determined by selecting two disjoint sets, one with cardinality of $\aleph_0$ and one with cardinality of 1. In this case the set N of natural numbers and the set $Z = \{0\}$ are appropriate choices. Thus

$$n(N) + n(Z) = n(N \cup Z)$$
$$= n(W)$$
$$\aleph_0 + 1 = \aleph_0$$

and, in general, for any whole number a, $\aleph_0 + a = \aleph_0$.

To find the sum $\aleph_0 + \aleph_0$, use two disjoint sets, each with cardinality of $\aleph_0$. The set E of even natural numbers and the set D of odd natural numbers satisfy the necessary conditions. Since E and D are disjoint sets, we know

$$n(E) + n(D) = n(E \cup D)$$
$$= n(W)$$
$$\aleph_0 + \aleph_0 = \aleph_0$$

Thus $\aleph_0 + \aleph_0 = \aleph_0$ and, in general,

$$\underbrace{\aleph_0 + \aleph_0 + \aleph_0 + \cdots + \aleph_0}_{\text{a finite number of aleph-nulls}} = \aleph_0$$

To determine a difference such as $5 - 3$ using sets, we first select a set A that has exactly five elements. We then find a subset B of this set that has exactly three elements. The difference $5 - 3$ is the cardinal number of the set $A \cap B'$, which is shown in blue in the figure at the left.

To determine $\aleph_0 - 3$, select a set with $\aleph_0$ elements, such as N, and then select a subset of this set that has exactly three elements. One such subset is $C = \{1, 2, 3\}$. The difference $\aleph_0 - 3$ is the cardinal number of the set $N \cap C' = \{4, 5, 6, 7, 8, \ldots\}$. Since $N \cap C'$ is a countably infinite set, we can conclude that $\aleph_0 - 3 = \aleph_0$. This procedure can be generalized to show that for any whole number a, $\aleph_0 - a = \aleph_0$.

Excursion Exercises

1. Use two disjoint sets to show that $\aleph_0 + 2 = \aleph_0$.

2. Use two disjoint sets other than the set of even natural numbers and the set of odd natural numbers to show that $\aleph_0 + \aleph_0 = \aleph_0$.

3. Use sets to show that $\aleph_0 - 6 = \aleph_0$.

4. **a.** Find two sets that can be used to show that $\aleph_0 - \aleph_0 = \aleph_0$. Now find another two sets that can be used to show that $\aleph_0 - \aleph_0 = 1$.

   b. Use the results of Excursion Exercise 4a to explain why subtraction of two transfinite numbers is an undefined operation.

Exercise Set 2.5

1. **a.** Use arrows to establish a one-to-one correspondence between $V = \{a, e, i\}$ and $M = \{3, 6, 9\}$.

    b. How many different one-to-one correspondences between V and M can be established?

2. Establish a one-to-one correspondence between the set of natural numbers $N = \{1, 2, 3, 4, 5, \ldots, n, \ldots\}$ and $F = \{5, 10, 15, 20, \ldots, 5n, \ldots\}$ by stating a general rule that can be used to pair the elements of the sets.

3. Establish a one-to-one correspondence between $D = \{1, 3, 5, \ldots, 2n - 1, \ldots\}$ and $M = \{3, 6, 9, \ldots, 3n, \ldots\}$ by stating a general rule that can be used to pair the elements of the sets.

In Exercises 4–10, state the cardinality of each set.

4. $\{2, 11, 19, 31\}$

5. $\{2, 9, 16, \ldots, 7n - 5, \ldots\}$, where n is a natural number

6. The set Q of rational numbers

7. The set R of real numbers

8. The set $\mathscr{I}$ of irrational numbers

9. $\{x \mid 5 \le x \le 9\}$

10. The set of subsets of $\{1, 5, 9, 11\}$

In Exercises 11–14, determine whether the given sets are equivalent.

11. The set of natural numbers and the set of integers

12. The set of whole numbers and the set of real numbers

13. The set of rational numbers and the set of integers

14. The set of rational numbers and the set of real numbers

In Exercises 15–18, show that the given set is an infinite set by placing it in a one-to-one correspondence with a proper subset of itself.

15. $A = \{5, 10, 15, 20, 25, 30, \ldots, 5n, \ldots\}$

16. $B = \{11, 15, 19, 23, 27, 31, \ldots, 4n + 7, \ldots\}$

17. $C = \left\{ \dfrac{1}{2}, \dfrac{3}{4}, \dfrac{5}{6}, \dfrac{7}{8}, \dfrac{9}{10}, \ldots, \dfrac{2n-1}{2n}, \ldots \right\}$

18. $D = \left\{ \dfrac{1}{2}, \dfrac{1}{3}, \dfrac{1}{4}, \dfrac{1}{5}, \dfrac{1}{6}, \ldots, \dfrac{1}{n+1}, \ldots \right\}$

In Exercises 19–26, show that the given set has a cardinality of $\aleph_0$ by establishing a one-to-one correspondence between the elements of the given set and the elements of N.

19. $\{50, 51, 52, 53, \ldots, n + 49, \ldots\}$

20. $\{10, 5, 0, -5, -10, -15, \ldots, -5n + 15, \ldots\}$

21. $\left\{ 1, \dfrac{1}{3}, \dfrac{1}{9}, \dfrac{1}{27}, \ldots, \dfrac{1}{3^{n-1}}, \ldots \right\}$

22. $\{-12, -18, -24, -30, \ldots, -6n - 6, \ldots\}$

23. $\{10, 100, 1000, \ldots, 10^n, \ldots\}$

24. $\left\{ 1, \dfrac{1}{2}, \dfrac{1}{4}, \dfrac{1}{8}, \ldots, \dfrac{1}{2^{n-1}}, \ldots \right\}$

25. $\{1, 8, 27, 64, \ldots, n^3, \ldots\}$

26. $\{0.1, 0.01, 0.001, 0.0001, \ldots, 10^{-n}, \ldots\}$

Extensions
CRITICAL THINKING

27. **a.** Place the set $M = \{3, 6, 9, 12, 15, \ldots\}$ of positive multiples of 3 in a one-to-one correspondence with the set K of all natural numbers that are not multiples of 3. Write a sentence or two that explains the general rule you used to establish the one-to-one correspondence.

    b. Use your rule to determine what number from K is paired with the number 606 from M.

    c. Use your rule to determine what number from M is paired with the number 899 from K.

In the figure below, every point on line segment AB corresponds to a real number from 0 to 1 and every real number from 0 to 1 corresponds to a point on line segment AB.

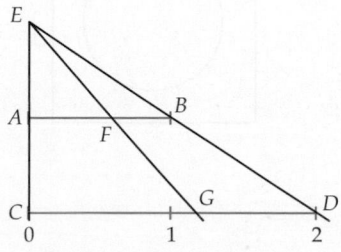

The line segment CD represents the real numbers from 0 to 2. Note that any point F on line segment AB can be paired with a unique point G on line segment CD by drawing a line from E through F. Also, any arbitrary point G on line segment CD can be paired with a unique point F on line segment AB by drawing the line EG. This geometric procedure establishes a one-to-one correspondence between the set $\{x \mid 0 \le x \le 1\}$ and the set $\{x \mid 0 \le x \le 2\}$. Thus $\{x \mid 0 \le x \le 1\} \sim \{x \mid 0 \le x \le 2\}$.

28. Draw a figure that can be used to verify each of the following.

  a. $\{x \mid 0 \le x \le 1\} \sim \{x \mid 0 \le x \le 5\}$

  b. $\{x \mid 2 \le x \le 5\} \sim \{x \mid 1 \le x \le 8\}$

29. Consider the semicircle with arc length 1 and center C and the line L_1 in the following figure. Each point on the semicircle, *other than the endpoints*, represents a unique real number between 0 and 1. Each point on line L_1 represents a unique real number.

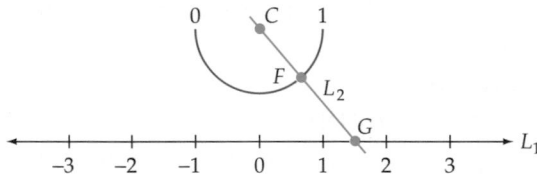

Any line through C that intersects the semicircle at a point other than one of its endpoints will intersect line L_1 at a unique point. Also, any line through C that intersects line L_1 will intersect the semicircle at a unique point that is not an endpoint of the semicircle. What can we conclude from this correspondence?

30. Explain how to use the following figure to verify that the set of all points on the circle is equivalent to the set of all points on the square.

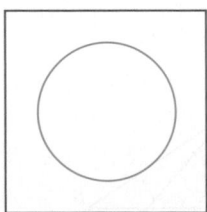

EXPLORATIONS

31. **The Hilbert Hotel** The Hilbert Hotel is an imaginary hotel created by the mathematician David Hilbert (1862–1943). The hotel has an infinite number of rooms. Each room is numbered with a natural number; room 1, room 2, room 3, and so on. Search the Internet for information on Hilbert's Hotel. Write a few paragraphs that explain some of the interesting questions that arise when guests arrive to stay at the hotel.

Mary Pat Campbell has written a song about a hotel with an infinite number of rooms. Her song is titled *Hotel Aleph Null—yeah*. Here are the lyrics for the chorus of her song, which is to be sung to the tune of *Hotel California* by the Eagles. (*Source:* **http://www.marypat.org/mathcamp/doc2001/hellrelays.html#hotel**)[4]

  Hotel Aleph Null—yeah
  Welcome to the Hotel Aleph Null—yeah
  What a lovely place (what a lovely place)
  Got a lot of space
  Packin' em in at the Hotel Aleph Null—yeah
  Any time of year
  You can find space here

32. **The Continuum Hypothesis** Cantor conjectured that no set can have a cardinality larger than $\aleph_0$ but smaller than c. This conjecture has become known as the *Continuum Hypothesis*. Search the Internet for information on the Continuum Hypothesis and write a short report that explains how the Continuum Hypothesis was resolved.

---

4. Reprinted by permission of Mary Pat Campbell.

CHAPTER 2   Summary

Key Terms

aleph-null [p. 100]
cardinal number [p. 56]
complement of a set [p. 64]
countable set [p. 102]
counting number [p. 54]
difference of sets [p. 85]
disjoint sets [p. 75]
element (member) of a set [p. 53]
ellipsis [p. 54]
empty set or null set [p. 56]
equal sets [p. 57]
equivalent sets [p. 57]
finite set [p. 56]
infinite set [p. 99]
integer [p. 54]
intersection of sets [p. 74]
irrational number [p. 54]
natural number [p. 54]
one-to-one correspondence [p. 98]
power set [p. 104]
rational number [p. 54]
real number [p. 54]
roster method [p. 53]
set [p. 53]
set-builder notation [p. 56]
transfinite number [p. 100]
uncountable set [p. 104]
union of sets [p. 75]
universal set [p. 64]
Venn diagram [p. 66]
well-defined set [p. 55]
whole number [p. 54]

Essential Concepts

- **A Subset of a Set**
  Set A is a subset of set B, denoted by $A \subseteq B$, if and only if every element of A is also an element of B.

- **Proper Subset of a Set**
  Set A is a proper subset of set B, denoted by $A \subset B$, if every element of A is an element of B, and $A \neq B$.

- **Subset Relationships**
  $A \subseteq A$, for any set A
  $\varnothing \subseteq A$, for any set A

- **The Number of Subsets of a Set**
  A set with n elements has 2^n subsets.

- **Intersection of Sets**
  The *intersection* of sets A and B, denoted by $A \cap B$, is the set of elements common to both A and B.
  $$A \cap B = \{x \,|\, x \in A \quad \text{and} \quad x \in B\}$$

- **Union of Sets**
  The *union* of sets A and B, denoted by $A \cup B$, is the set that contains all the elements that belong to A or to B or to both.
  $$A \cup B = \{x \,|\, x \in A \quad \text{or} \quad x \in B\}$$

- **De Morgan's Laws**
  $$(A \cap B)' = A' \cup B' \qquad (A \cup B)' = A' \cap B'$$

- **Commutative Properties of Sets**
  $$A \cap B = B \cap A \qquad A \cup B = B \cup A$$

- **Associative Properties of Sets**
  $$(A \cap B) \cap C = A \cap (B \cap C)$$
  $$(A \cup B) \cup C = A \cup (B \cup C)$$

- **Distributive Properties of Sets**
  $$A \cap (B \cup C) = (A \cap B) \cup (A \cap C)$$
  $$A \cup (B \cap C) = (A \cup B) \cap (A \cup C)$$

- **The Inclusion-Exclusion Principle**
  For any finite sets A and B,
  $$n(A \cup B) = n(A) + n(B) - n(A \cap B)$$

- **Cantor's Theorem**
  Let S be any set. The set of all subsets of S has a larger cardinal number than the cardinal number of S.

- **Transfinite Arithmetic Theorems**
  For any whole number a,
  $$\aleph_0 + a = \aleph_0, \quad \aleph_0 - a = \aleph_0, \quad \aleph_0 + \aleph_0 = \aleph_0,$$
  $$\aleph_0 + c = c, \quad \aleph_0 c = c, \quad c + c = c$$

CHAPTER 2   Review Exercises

In Exercises 1–4, use the roster method to write each set.

1. The set of whole numbers less than 8

2. The set of integers that satisfy $x^2 = 64$

3. The set of natural numbers that satisfy $x + 3 \le 7$

4. The set of counting numbers larger than -3 and less than or equal to 6

In Exercises 5–8, use set-builder notation to write each set.

5. The set of integers greater than -6

6. {April, June, September, November}

7. {Kansas, Kentucky}

8. {1, 8, 27, 64, 125}

In Exercises 9–12, determine whether the statement is true or false.

9. $\{3\} \in \{1, 2, 3, 4\}$

10. $-11 \in I$

11. $\{a, b, c\} \sim \{1, 5, 9\}$

12. The set of small numbers is a well-defined set.

In Exercises 13–20, let $U = \{2, 6, 8, 10, 12, 14, 16, 18\}$, $A = \{2, 6, 10\}$, $B = \{6, 10, 16, 18\}$, and $C = \{14, 16\}$. Find each of the following.

13. $A \cap B$

14. $A \cup B$

15. $A' \cap C$

16. $B \cup C'$

17. $A \cup (B \cap C)$

18. $(A \cup C)' \cap B'$

19. $(A \cap B')'$

20. $(A \cup B \cup C)'$

In Exercises 21–24, determine whether the first set is a proper subset of the second set.

21. The set of natural numbers; the set of whole numbers

22. The set of integers; the set of real numbers

23. The set of counting numbers; the set of natural numbers

24. The set of real numbers; the set of rational numbers

In Exercises 25–28, list all the subsets of the given set.

25. {I, II}

26. {s, u, n}

27. {penny, nickel, dime, quarter}

28. {A, B, C, D, E}

In Exercises 29–32, find the number of subsets of the given set.

29. The set of the four musketeers

30. The set of the letters of the English alphabet

31. The set of the letters of "uncopyrightable," which is the longest English word with no repeated letters

32. The set of the seven dwarfs

In Exercises 33–36, draw a Venn diagram to represent the given set.

33. $A \cap B'$

34. $A' \cup B'$

35. $(A \cup B) \cup C'$

36. $A \cap (B' \cup C)$

In Exercises 37–40, draw Venn diagrams to determine whether the expressions are equal for all sets A, B, and C.

37. $A' \cup (B \cup C)$; $(A' \cup B) \cup (A' \cup C)$

38. $(A \cap B) \cap C'$; $(A' \cup B') \cup C$

39. $A \cap (B' \cap C)$; $(A \cup B') \cap (A \cup C)$

40. $A \cap (B \cup C)$; $A' \cap (B \cup C)$

In Exercises 41 and 42, use set notation to describe the shaded region.

41.

42.

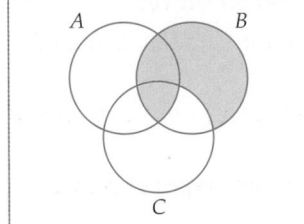

In Exercises 43 and 44, draw a Venn diagram with each of the given elements placed in the correct region.

43. $U = \{e, h, r, d, w, s, t\}$
$A = \{t, r, e\}$
$B = \{w, s, r, e\}$
$C' = \{s, r, d, h\}$

44. $U = \{\alpha, \beta, \Gamma, \gamma, \Delta, \delta, \varepsilon, \theta\}$
$A' = \{\beta, \Delta, \theta, \gamma\}$
$B = \{\delta, \varepsilon\}$
$C = \{\beta, \varepsilon, \Gamma\}$

45. A Survey In a survey at a health club, 208 members indicated that they enjoy aerobic exercises, 145 indicated that they enjoy weight training, 97 indicated that they enjoy both aerobics and weight training, and 135 indicated that they do not enjoy either of these types of exercise. How many members were surveyed?

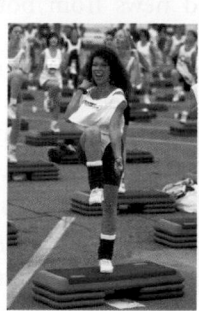

46. A Survey A gourmet coffee bar conducted a survey to determine the preferences of its customers. Of the customers surveyed,

221 like espresso.
127 like cappuccino and chocolate-flavored coffee.
182 like cappuccino.
136 like espresso and chocolate-flavored coffee.
209 like chocolate-flavored coffee.
96 like all three types of coffee.
116 like espresso and cappuccino.
82 like none of these types of coffee.

How many of the customers in the survey:

a. like only chocolate-flavored coffee?

b. like cappuccino and chocolate-flavored coffee but not espresso?

c. like espresso and cappuccino but not chocolate-flavored coffee?

d. like exactly one of the three types of coffee?

In Exercises 47–50, establish a one-to-one correspondence between the sets.

47. $\{1, 3, 6, 10\};$ $\{1, 2, 3, 4\}$

48. $\{x \mid x > 10 \text{ and } x \in N\};$ $\{2, 4, 6, 8, \ldots, 2n, \ldots\}$

49. $\{3, 6, 9, 12, \ldots, 3n, \ldots\};$ $\{10, 100, 1000, \ldots, 10^n, \ldots\}$

50. $\{x \mid 0 \le x \le 1\};$ $\{x \mid 0 \le x \le 4\}$ (*Hint:* Use a drawing.)

In Exercises 51 and 52, show that the given set is an infinite set.

51. $A = \{6, 10, 14, 18, \ldots, 4n + 2, \ldots\}$

52. $B = \left\{ 1, \dfrac{1}{2}, \dfrac{1}{4}, \dfrac{1}{8}, \ldots, \dfrac{1}{2^{n-1}}, \ldots \right\}$

In Exercises 53–60, state the cardinality of each set.

53. $\{5, 6, 7, 8, 6\}$

54. $\{4, 6, 8, 10, 12, \ldots, 22\}$

55. $\{0, \varnothing\}$

56. The set of all states in the U.S. that border the Gulf of Mexico

57. The set of integers less than 1,000,000

58. The set of rational numbers between 0 and 1

59. The set of irrational numbers

60. The set of real numbers between 0 and 1

In Exercises 61–68, find each of the following, where $\aleph_0$ and c are transfinite cardinal numbers.

61. $\aleph_0 - 700$

62. $\aleph_0 + 4100$

63. $\aleph_0 + (\aleph_0 + \aleph_0)$

64. $\aleph_0 + c$

65. $c - 7$

66. $c + (c + c)$

67. $5\aleph_0$

68. $15c$

CHAPTER 2   Test

In Exercises 1–6, let $U = \{1, 2, 3, 4, 5, 6, 7, 8, 9, 10\}$
$A = \{3, 5, 7, 8\}$, $B = \{2, 3, 8, 9, 10\}$, and $C = \{1, 4, 7, 8\}$.
Use the roster method to write each of the following sets.

1. $A \cup B$
2. $A' \cap B$
3. $(A \cap B)'$
4. $(A \cup B')'$
5. $A' \cup (B \cap C')$
6. $A \cap (B' \cup C)$

In Exercises 7 and 8, use set-builder notation to write each of the given sets.

7. $\{0, 1, 2, 3, 4, 5, 6\}$
8. $\{-3, -2, -1, 0, 1, 2\}$

In Exercise 9, state the cardinality of the given set.

9. **a.** The set of whole numbers less than 4
   b. The set of rational numbers between 7 and 8
   c. The set of natural numbers
   d. The set of real numbers

In Exercises 10 and 11, state whether the given sets are equal, equivalent, both, or neither.

10. **a.** the set of natural numbers; the set of integers
    b. the set of whole numbers; the set of positive integers
11. **a.** the set of rational numbers; the set of irrational numbers
    b. the set of real numbers; the set of irrational numbers
12. List all of the subsets of $\{a, b, c, d\}$.
13. Determine the number of subsets of a set with 21 elements.
14. State whether each statement is true or false.
    a. $\{4\} \in \{1, 2, 3, 4, 5, 6, 7\}$
    b. The set of rational numbers is a well-defined set.
    c. $A \subset A$
    d. The set of positive even whole numbers is equivalent to the set of natural numbers.
15. Draw a Venn diagram to represent the given set.
    a. $(A \cup B') \cap C$ **b.** $(A' \cap B) \cup (A \cap C')$
16. Use set notation to describe the shaded region.

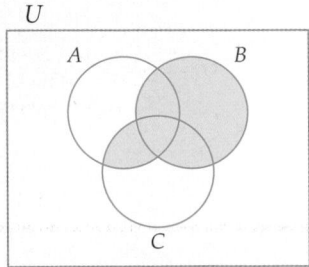

17. **A Survey** In the town of LeMars, 385 families have a CD player, 142 families have a DVD player, 41 families have both a CD player and a DVD player, and 55 families do not have a CD player or a DVD player. How many families live in LeMars?

18. **A Survey** A survey of 1000 households was taken to determine how they obtained news about current events. The survey considered only television, newspapers, and the Internet as sources for news. Of the households surveyed,

    724 obtained news from television.
    545 obtained news from newspapers.
    280 obtained news from the Internet.
    412 obtained news from both television and newspapers.
    185 obtained news from both television and the Internet.
    105 obtained news from television, newspapers, and the Internet.
    64 obtained news from the Internet but not from television or newspapers.

    Of those households that were surveyed,

    a. how many obtained news from television but not from newspapers or the Internet?
    b. how many obtained news from newspapers but not from television or the Internet?
    c. how many obtained news from television or newspapers?
    d. how many did not acquire news from television, newspapers, or the Internet?

19. Show a method that can be used to establish a one-to-one correspondence between the elements of the following sets.

    $$\{5, 10, 15, 20, 25, \ldots, 5n, \ldots\}; \quad W$$

20. Prove that the following set is an infinite set by illustrating a one-to-one correspondence between the elements of the set and the elements of one of the set's proper subsets.

    $$\{3, 6, 9, 12, \ldots, 3n \ldots\}$$

CHAPTER

3 Logic

"I know what you're thinking about," said Tweedledum (to Alice), "but it isn't so, nohow."

"Contrariwise," continued Tweedledee, "if it was so, it might be; and if it were so, it would be: but as it isn't, it ain't. That's logic."

The above excerpt, from Lewis Carroll's *Through the Looking-Glass*, sums up Tweedledee's understanding of logic. In today's complex world, it is not so easy to summarize the topic of logic. For lawyers and business people, logic is the science of correct reasoning. They often use logic to construct valid arguments, analyze legal contracts, and solve complicated problems. The principles of logic can also be used as a production tool. For example, programmers use logic to design computer software, engineers use logic to design the electronic circuits in computers, and mathematicians use logic to solve problems and construct mathematical proofs.

In this chapter, you will encounter several facets of logic. Specifically, you will use logic to

- analyze information and the relationship between statements,

- determine the validity of arguments,

- determine valid conclusions based on given assumptions, and

- analyze electronic circuits.

 For online student resources, visit this textbook's website at **www.cengage.com/math.**

Logic Statements

George Boole
(bōōl) was born in 1815 in Lincoln, England. He was raised in poverty, but he was very industrious and had learned Latin and Greek by the age of 12. Later he mastered German, French, and Italian. His first profession, at the young age of 16, was that of an assistant school teacher. At the age of 20 he started his own school.

In 1849 Boole was appointed the chairperson of mathematics at Queens College in Cork, Ireland. He was known as a dedicated professor who gave detailed lectures. He continued to teach at Queens College until he died of pneumonia in 1864.

Many of Boole's mathematical ideas, such as Boolean algebra, have applications in the areas of computer programming and the design of telephone switching devices. ■

One of the first mathematicians to make a serious study of symbolic logic was Gottfried Wilhelm Leibniz (1646–1716). Leibniz tried to advance the study of logic from a merely philosophical subject to a formal mathematical subject. Leibniz never completely achieved this goal; however, several mathematicians, such as Augustus De Morgan (1806–1871) and George Boole (1815–1864), contributed to the advancement of symbolic logic as a mathematical discipline.

Boole published *The Mathematical Analysis of Logic* in 1848. In 1854 he published the more extensive work *An Investigation of the Laws of Thought*. Concerning this document, the mathematician Bertrand Russell stated, "Pure mathematics was discovered by Boole in a work which is called *The Laws of Thought*." Although some mathematicians feel this is an exaggeration, the following paragraph, extracted from *An Investigation of the Laws of Thought*, gives some insight into the nature and scope of this document.

> The design of the following treatise is to investigate the fundamental laws of those operations of the mind by which reasoning is performed; to give expression to them in the language of a Calculus, and upon this foundation to establish the science of Logic and construct its method; to make the method itself the basis of a general method for the application of the mathematical doctrine of probabilities; and finally, to collect from the various elements of truth brought to view in the course of these inquiries some probable intimations concerning the nature and constitution of the human mind.[1]

Every language contains different types of sentences, such as statements, questions, and commands. For instance,

"Is the test today?" is a question.

"Go get the newspaper" is a command.

"This is a nice car" is an opinion.

"Denver is the capital of Colorado" is a statement of fact.

The symbolic logic that Boole was instrumental in creating applies only to sentences that are *statements* as defined below.

Definition of a Statement

A **statement** is a declarative sentence that is either true or false, but not both true and false.

---

1. Bell, E. T. *Men of Mathematics.* New York: Simon and Schuster, Inc., Touchstone Books, Reissue edition, 1986.

It may not be necessary to determine whether a sentence is true or false to determine whether it is a statement. For instance, the following sentence is either true or false:

Every even number greater than 2 can be written as the sum of two prime numbers.

At this time mathematicians have not determined whether the sentence is true or false, but they do know that it is either true or false and that it is not both true and false. Thus the sentence is a statement.

EXAMPLE 1 ■ **Identify Statements**

Determine whether each sentence is a statement.

a. Florida is a state in the United States.

b. The word *dog* has four letters.

c. How are you?

d. $9^{(9^9)} + 2$ is a prime number.

e. $x + 1 = 5$

Solution

a. Florida is one of the 50 states in the United States, so this sentence is true and it is a statement.

b. The word *dog* consists of exactly three letters, so this sentence is false and it is a statement.

c. The sentence "How are you?" is a question; it is not a declarative sentence. Thus it is not a statement.

d. You may not know whether $9^{(9^9)} + 2$ is a prime number; however, you do know that it is a whole number larger than 1, so it is either a prime number or it is not a prime number. The sentence is either true or it is false, and it is not both true and false, so it is a statement.

e. $x + 1 = 5$ is a statement. It is known as an *open statement*. It is true for $x = 4$, and it is false for any other values of x. For any given value of x, it is true or false but not both.

CHECK YOUR PROGRESS 1   Determine whether each sentence is a statement.

a. Open the door.

b. 7055 is a large number.

c. $4 + 5 = 8$

d. In the year 2009, the president of the United States will be a woman.

e. $x > 3$

Solution   *See page S7.*

Charles Dodgson
(Lewis Carroll)

Math Matters   Charles Dodgson

One of the best-known logicians is Charles Dodgson (1832–1898). Dodgson was educated at Rugby and Oxford, and in 1861 he became a lecturer in mathematics at Oxford. His mathematical works include *A Syllabus of Plane Algebraical Geometry, The Fifth Book of Euclid Treated Algebraically,* and *Symbolic Logic.* Although Dodgson was a distinguished mathematician in his time, he is best known by his pen name Lewis Carroll, which he used when he published *Alice's Adventures in Wonderland* and *Through the Looking-Glass.*

Queen Victoria of the United Kingdom enjoyed *Alice's Adventures in Wonderland* to the extent that she told Dodgson she was looking forward to reading another of his books. He promptly sent her his *Syllabus of Plane Algebraical Geometry,* and it was reported that she was less than enthusiastic about the latter book.

Compound Statements

Connecting statements with words and phrases such as *and, or, not, if … then,* and *if and only if* creates a **compound statement.** For instance, "I will attend the meeting or I will go to school" is a compound statement. It is composed of the two **component statements** "I will attend the meeting" and "I will go to school." The word *or* is a **connective** for the two component statements.

George Boole used symbols such as *p, q, r,* and *s* to represent statements and the symbols $\wedge, \vee, \sim, \rightarrow,$ and $\leftrightarrow$ to represent connectives. See Table 3.1.

Table 3.1 *Logic Symbols*

Original Statement	Connective	Statement in Symbolic Form	Type of Compound Statement
not *p*	not	$\sim p$	negation
p and *q*	and	$p \wedge q$	conjunction
p or *q*	or	$p \vee q$	disjunction
If *p*, then *q*	If … then	$p \rightarrow q$	conditional
p if and only if *q*	if and only if	$p \leftrightarrow q$	biconditional

QUESTION   *What connective is used in a conjunction?*

ANSWER   *The connective and.*

The Truth Table for ~p

p	*~p*
T	F
F	T

Truth Value and Truth Tables

The **truth value** of a statement is true (T) if the statement is true and false (F) if the statement is false. A **truth table** is a table that shows the truth value of a statement for all possible truth values of its components.

The *negation* of the statement "Today is Friday" is the statement "Today is not Friday." In symbolic logic, the tilde symbol ~ is used to denote the negation of a statement. If a statement *p* is true, its negation ~*p* is false, and if a statement *p* is false, its negation ~*p* is true. See the table at the left. The negation of the negation of a statement is the original statement. Thus, ~(~*p*) can be replaced by *p* in any statement.

EXAMPLE 2 ■ Write the Negation of a Statement

Write the negation of each statement.

a. Bill Gates has a yacht.

b. The number 10 is a prime number.

c. The Dolphins lost the game.

Solution

a. Bill Gates does not have a yacht.

b. The number 10 is not a prime number.

c. The Dolphins did not lose the game.

CHECK YOUR PROGRESS 2   Write the negation of each statement.

a. 1001 is divisible by 7.

b. 5 is an even number.

c. The fire engine is not red.

Solution   See page S7.

We will often find it useful to write compound statements in symbolic form.

EXAMPLE 3 ■ Write Compound Statements in Symbolic Form

Consider the following statements.

    p: Today is Friday.

    q: It is raining.

    r: I am going to a movie.

    s: I am not going to the basketball game.

Write the following compound statements in symbolic form.

a. Today is Friday and it is raining.

b. It is not raining and I am going to a movie.

c. I am going to the basketball game or I am going to a movie.

d. If it is raining, then I am not going to the basketball game.

Solution

a. $p \wedge q$ **b.** $\sim q \wedge r$ **c.** $\sim s \vee r$ **d.** $q \rightarrow s$

CHECK YOUR PROGRESS 3   Use p, q, r, and s as defined in Example 3 to write the following compound statements in symbolic form.

a. Today is not Friday and I am going to a movie.

b. I am going to the basketball game and I am not going to a movie.

c. I am going to the movie if and only if it is raining.

d. If today is Friday, then I am not going to a movie.

Solution   *See page S7.*

In the next example, we translate symbolic logic statements into English sentences.

EXAMPLE 4 ■ Translate Symbolic Statements

Consider the following statements.

p: The game will be played in Atlanta.

q: The game will be shown on CBS.

r: The game will not be shown on ESPN.

s: The Dodgers are favored to win.

Write each of the following symbolic statements in words.

a. $q \wedge p$ **b.** $\sim r \wedge s$ **c.** $s \leftrightarrow \sim p$

Solution

a. The game will be shown on CBS and the game will be played in Atlanta.

b. The game will be shown on ESPN and the Dodgers are favored to win.

c. The Dodgers are favored to win if and only if the game will not be played in Atlanta.

CHECK YOUR PROGRESS 4   Consider the following statements.

e: All men are created equal.

t: I am trading places.

a: I get Abe's place.

g: I get George's place.

Use the above information to translate the dialogue in the following speech bubbles.

Solution   *See page S7.*

The Truth Table for $p \wedge q$

p	q	$p \wedge q$
T	T	T
T	F	F
F	T	F
F	F	F

If you order cake *and* ice cream in a restaurant, the waiter will bring *both* cake and ice cream. In general, the **conjunction** $p \wedge q$ is true if both p and q are true, and the conjunction is false if either p or q is false. The truth table at the left shows the four possible cases that arise when we form a conjunction of two statements.

> **Truth Value of a Conjunction**
>
> The conjunction $p \wedge q$ is true if and only if both p and q are true.

Sometimes the word *but* is used in place of the connective *and* to form a conjunction. For instance, "My local phone company is *SBC*, but my long-distance carrier is Sprint" is equivalent to the conjunction "My local phone company is *SBC* and my long-distance carrier is Sprint."

Any **disjunction** $p \vee q$ is true if p is true or q is true or both p and q are true. The truth table at the left shows that the disjunction p or q is false if both p and q are false; however, it is true in all other cases.

The Truth Table for $p \vee q$

p	q	$p \vee q$
T	T	T
T	F	T
F	T	T
F	F	F

> **Truth Value of a Disjunction**
>
> The disjunction $p \vee q$ is true if p is true, if q is true, or if both p and q are true.

EXAMPLE 5 ■ Determine the Truth Value of a Statement

Determine whether each statement is true or false.

a. $7 \geq 5$

b. 5 is a whole number and 5 is an even number.

c. 2 is a prime number and 2 is an even number.

Solution

a. $7 \geq 5$ means $7 > 5$ or $7 = 5$. Because $7 > 5$ is true, the statement $7 \geq 5$ is a true statement.

b. This is a false statement because 5 is not an even number.

c. This is a true statement because each component statement is true.

CHECK YOUR PROGRESS 5   Determine whether each statement is true or false.

a. 21 is a rational number and 21 is a natural number.

b. $4 \leq 9$

c. $-7 \geq -3$

Solution   See page S7.

Truth tables for the conditional and biconditional are given in Section 3.3.

Quantifiers and Negation

In a statement, the word *some* and the phrases *there exists* and *at least one* are called **existential quantifiers**. Existential quantifiers are used as prefixes to assert the existence of something.

In a statement, the words *none*, *no*, *all*, and *every* are called **universal quantifiers**. The universal quantifiers *none* and *no* deny the existence of something, whereas the universal quantifiers *all* and *every* are used to assert that every element of a given set satisfies some condition.

Recall that the negation of a false statement is a true statement and the negation of a true statement is a false statement. It is important to remember this fact when forming the negation of a quantified statement. For instance, what is the negation of the false statement, "All dogs are mean"? You may think that the negation is "No dogs are mean," but this is also a false statement. Thus the statement "No dogs are mean" is not the negation of "All dogs are mean." The negation of "All dogs are mean," which is a false statement, is in fact "Some dogs are not mean," which is a true statement. The statement "Some dogs are not mean" can also be stated as "At least one dog is not mean" or "There exists a dog that is not mean."

What is the negation of the false statement "No doctors write in a legible manner"? Whatever the negation is, we know it must be a true statement. The negation cannot be "All doctors write in a legible manner," because this is also a false statement. The negation is "Some doctors write in a legible manner." This can also be stated as "There exists at least one doctor who writes in a legible manner."

Table 3.2 summarizes the concepts needed to write the negations of statements that contain one of the quantifiers *all*, *none*, or *some*.

Table 3.2 *The Negation of a Statement that Contains a Quantifier*

Original Statement	Negation
All _____ are _____ .	Some _____ are not _____ .
No(ne) _____ .	Some _____ .
Some _____ are not _____ .	All _____ are _____ .
Some _____ .	No(ne) _____ .

EXAMPLE 6 ■ Write the Negation of a Quantified Statement

Write the negation of each of the following statements.

a. Some baseball players are worth a million dollars.
b. All movies are worth the price of admission.
c. No odd numbers are divisible by 2.

Solution
a. No baseball player is worth a million dollars.
b. Some movies are not worth the price of admission.
c. Some odd numbers are divisible by 2.

CHECK YOUR PROGRESS 6 Write the negation of the following statements.

a. All bears are brown.
b. No math class is fun.
c. Some vegetables are not green.

Solution See page S7.

Excursion

Switching Networks

Claude E. Shannon

In 1939, Claude E. Shannon (1916–2001) wrote a thesis on an application of symbolic logic to *switching networks.* A switching network consists of wires and switches that can open or close. Switching networks are used in many electrical appliances, telephone equipment, and computers. Figure 3.1 shows a switching network that consists of a single switch P that connects two terminals. An electric current can flow from one terminal to the other terminal provided the switch P is in the closed position. If P is in the open position, then the current cannot flow from one terminal to the other. If a current can flow between the terminals we say that a network is closed, and if a current cannot flow between the terminals we say that the network is open. We designate this network by the letter P. There exists an analogy between a network P and a statement p in that a network is either open or it is closed, and a statement is either true or it is false.

Figure 3.1

Figure 3.2 *A series network*

Figure 3.3 *A parallel network*

Figure 3.4

Figure 3.2 shows two switches P and Q connected in **series.** This series network is closed if and only if both switches are closed. We will use $P \wedge Q$ to denote this series network because it is analogous to the logic statement $p \wedge q$, which is true if and only if both p and q are true.

Figure 3.3 shows two switches P and Q connected in **parallel.** This parallel network is closed if either P or Q is closed. We will designate this parallel network by $P \vee Q$ because it is analogous to the logic statement $p \vee q$, which is true if p is true or if q is true.

Series and parallel networks can be combined to produce more complicated networks, as shown in Figure 3.4.

The network shown in Figure 3.4 is closed provided P or Q is closed or provided both R and $\sim P$ are closed. Note that the switch $\sim P$ is closed if P is open, and $\sim P$ is open if P is closed. We use the symbolic statement $(P \vee Q) \vee (R \wedge \sim P)$ to represent this network.

If two switches are always open at the same time and always closed at the same time, then we will use the same letter to designate both switches.

(continued)

Excursion Exercises

Write a symbolic statement to represent each of the networks in Excursion Exercises 1–6.

1.

2.

3.

4.

5.

6.

7. Which of the networks in Excursion Exercises 1–6 are closed networks, given that P is closed, Q is open, R is closed, and S is open?

8. Which of the networks in Excursion Exercises 1–6 are closed networks, given that P is open, Q is closed, R is closed, and S is closed?

In Excursion Exercises 9–14, draw a network to represent each statement.

9. $(\sim P \vee Q) \wedge (R \wedge P)$

10. $P \wedge [(Q \wedge \sim R) \vee R]$

11. $[\sim P \wedge Q \wedge R] \vee (P \wedge R)$

12. $(Q \vee R) \vee (S \vee \sim P)$

13. $[(\sim P \wedge R) \vee Q] \vee (\sim R)$

14. $(P \vee Q \vee R) \wedge S \wedge (\sim Q \vee R)$

Warning Circuits The circuits shown in Excursion Exercises 15 and 16 include a switching network, a warning light, and a battery. In each circuit the warning light will turn on only when the switching network is closed.

15. Consider the following circuit.

For each of the following conditions, determine whether the warning light will be on or off.

    a. P is closed and Q is open.   **b.** P is closed and Q is closed.

    c. P is open and Q is closed.   **d.** P is open and Q is open.

(continued)

16. An engineer thinks that the following circuit can be used in place of the circuit shown in Excursion Exercise 15. Do you agree? Explain.

Exercise Set 3.1

In Exercises 1–10, determine whether each sentence is a statement.

1. West Virginia is west of the Mississippi River.
2. 1031 is a prime number.
3. The area code for Storm Lake, Iowa is 512.
4. Some negative numbers are rational numbers.
5. Have a fun trip.
6. Do you like to read?
7. All hexagons have exactly five sides.
8. If x is a negative number, then x^2 is a positive number.
9. Mathematics courses are better than history courses.
10. Every real number is a rational number.

In Exercises 11–18, determine the components of each compound statement.

11. The principal will attend the class on Tuesday or Wednesday.
12. 5 is an odd number and 6 is an even number.
13. A triangle is an acute triangle if and only if it has three acute angles.
14. Some birds can swim and some fish can fly.
15. I ordered a salad and a cola.
16. If this is Saturday, then tomorrow is Sunday.
17. $5 + 2 \geq 6$
18. $9 - 1 \leq 8$

In Exercises 19–22, write the negation of each statement.

19. The Giants lost the game.
20. The lunch was served at noon.
21. The game did not go into overtime.
22. The game was not shown on ABC.

In Exercises 23–32, write each sentence in symbolic form. Represent each component of the sentence with the letter indicated in parentheses. Also state whether the sentence is a conjunction, a disjunction, a negation, a conditional, or a biconditional.

23. If today is Wednesday (w), then tomorrow is Thursday (t).
24. It is not true that Sue took the tickets (t).
25. All squares (s) are rectangles (r).
26. I went to the post office (p) and the bookstore (s).
27. A triangle is an equilateral triangle (l) if and only if it is an equiangular triangle (a).
28. A number is an even number (e) if and only if it has a factor of 2 (t).
29. If it is a dog (d), it has fleas (f).
30. Polynomials that have exactly three terms (p) are called trinomials (t).
31. I will major in mathematics (m) or computer science (c).
32. All pentagons (p) have exactly five sides (s).

In Exercises 33–38, write each symbolic statement in words. Use p, q, r, s, t, and u as defined below.

p: The tour goes to Italy.

q: The tour goes to Spain.

r: We go to Venice.

s: We go to Florence.

t: The hotel fees are included.

u: The meals are not included.

33. $p \wedge \sim q$ **34.** $r \vee s$

35. $r \rightarrow \sim s$ **36.** $p \rightarrow r$

37. $s \leftrightarrow \sim r$ **38.** $\sim t \wedge u$

In Exercises 39–50, use the definitions presented in Table 3.2, page 120, to write the negation of each quantified statement.

39. Some cats do not have claws.

40. Some dogs are not friendly.

41. All classic movies were first produced in black and white.

42. Everybody enjoyed the dinner.

43. None of the numbers were even numbers.

44. At least one student received an A.

45. No irrational number can be written as a terminating decimal.

46. All cameras use film.

47. All cars run on gasoline.

48. None of the students took my advice.

49. Every item is on sale.

50. All of the telephone lines are not busy.

In Exercises 51–64, determine whether each statement is true or false.

51. $7 < 5$ or $3 > 1$.

52. $3 \leq 9$

53. $(-1)^{50} = 1$ and $(-1)^{99} = -1$.

54. $7 \neq 3$ or 9 is a prime number.

55. $-5 \geq -11$

56. $4.5 \leq 5.4$

57. 2 is an odd number or 2 is an even number.

58. 5 is a natural number and 5 is a rational number.

59. There exists an even prime number.

60. The square of any real number is a positive number.

61. Some real numbers are irrational.

62. All irrational numbers are real numbers.

63. Every integer is a rational number.

64. Every rational number is an integer.

Extensions

CRITICAL THINKING

Write Quotations in Symbolic Form In Exercises 65–70, translate each quotation into symbolic form. For each component, indicate what letter you used to represent the component.

65. If you can count your money, you don't have a billion dollars.   *J. Paul Getty*

66. If you aren't fired with enthusiasm, then you will be fired with enthusiasm.   *Vince Lombardi*

67. Those who do not learn from history are condemned to repeat it.   *George Santayana*

68. We don't like their sound, and guitar music is on the way out.   *Decca Recording Company,* rejecting the Beatles in 1962

69. If people concentrated on the really important things in life, there'd be a shortage of fishing poles.   *Doug Larson*

70. If you're killed, you've lost a very important part of your life.   *Brooke Shields*

Write Statements in Symbolic Form In Exercises 71–76, translate each mathematical statement into symbolic form. For each component, indicate what letter you used to represent the component.

71. An angle is a right angle if and only if its measure is 90°.

72. Any angle inscribed in a semicircle is a right angle.

73. If two sides of a triangle are equal in length, the angles opposite those sides are congruent.

74. The sum of the measures of the three angles of any triangle is 180°.

75. All squares are rectangles.

76. If the corresponding sides of two triangles are proportional, then the triangles are similar.

EXPLORATIONS

77. **Raymond Smullyan** is a logician, a philosopher, a professor, and an author of many books on logic and puzzles. Some of his fans rate his puzzle books as the best ever written. Search the Internet to find information on the life of Smullyan and his work in the area of logic. Write a few paragraphs that summarize your findings.

SECTION 3.2 | # Truth Tables, Equivalent Statements, and Tautologies

Truth Tables

In Section 3.1, we defined truth tables for the negation of a statement, the conjunction of two statements, and the disjunction of two statements. Each of these truth tables is shown below for review purposes.

Negation

p	$\sim p$
T	F
F	T

Conjunction

p	q	$p \wedge q$
T	T	T
T	F	F
F	T	F
F	F	F

Disjunction

p	q	$p \vee q$
T	T	T
T	F	T
F	T	T
F	F	F

p	q	Given Statement
T	T	
T	F	
F	T	
F	F	

Standard truth table form for a given statement that involves only the two simple statements p and q

In this section, we consider methods of constructing truth tables for a statement that involves a combination of conjunctions, disjunctions, and/or negations. If the given statement involves only the two simple statements, then start with a table with four rows (see the table at the left), called the **standard truth table form,** and proceed as shown in Example 1.

EXAMPLE 1 ■ Truth Tables

a. Construct a table for $\sim(\sim p \vee q) \vee q$.

b. Use the truth table from part a to determine the truth value of $\sim(\sim p \vee q) \vee q$, given that p is true and q is false.

Solution

a. Start with the standard truth table form and then include a ~*p* column.

p	*q*	~*p*
T	T	F
T	F	F
F	T	T
F	F	T

Now use the truth values from the ~*p* and *q* columns to produce the truth values for ~*p* ∨ *q*, as shown in the following table.

p	*q*	~*p*	~*p* ∨ *q*
T	T	F	T
T	F	F	F
F	T	T	T
F	F	T	T

Negate the truth values in the ~*p* ∨ *q* column to produce the following.

p	*q*	~*p*	~*p* ∨ *q*	~(~*p* ∨ *q*)
T	T	F	T	F
T	F	F	F	T
F	T	T	T	F
F	F	T	T	F

As our last step, we form the disjunction of ~(~*p* ∨ *q*) with *q* and place the results in the rightmost column of the table. See the following table. The shaded column is the truth table for ~(~*p* ∨ *q*) ∨ *q*.

p	*q*	~*p*	~*p* ∨ *q*	~(~*p* ∨ *q*)	~(~*p* ∨ *q*) ∨ *q*	
T	T	F	T	F	T	Row 1
T	F	F	F	T	T	Row 2
F	T	T	T	F	T	Row 3
F	F	T	T	F	F	Row 4

b. In row 2 of the above truth table, we see that when *p* is true, and *q* is false, the statement ~(~*p* ∨ *q*) ∨ *q* in the rightmost column is true.

CHECK YOUR PROGRESS 1

a. Construct a truth table for $(p \wedge \sim q) \vee (\sim p \vee q)$.

b. Use the truth table that you constructed in part a to determine the truth value of $(p \wedge \sim q) \vee (\sim p \vee q)$, given that p is true and q is false.

Solution   See page S8.

Compound statements that involve exactly three simple statements require a standard truth table form with $2^3 = 8$ rows, as shown at the left.

p	q	r	Given Statement
T	T	T	
T	T	F	
T	F	T	
T	F	F	
F	T	T	
F	T	F	
F	F	T	
F	F	F	

Standard truth table form for a statement that involves the three simple statements p, q, and r

EXAMPLE 2 ■ Truth Tables

a. Construct a truth table for $(p \wedge q) \wedge (\sim r \vee q)$.

b. Use the truth table from part a to determine the truth value of $(p \wedge q) \wedge (\sim r \vee q)$, given that p is true, q is true, and r is false.

Solution

a. Using the procedures developed in Example 1, we can produce the following table. The shaded column is the truth table for $(p \wedge q) \wedge (\sim r \vee q)$. The numbers in the squares below the columns denote the order in which the columns were constructed. Each truth value in the column numbered 4 is the conjunction of the truth values to its left in the columns numbered 1 and 3.

p	q	r	$p \wedge q$	$\sim r$	$\sim r \vee q$	$(p \wedge q) \wedge (\sim r \vee q)$	
T	T	T	T	F	T	T	Row 1
T	T	F	T	T	T	T	Row 2
T	F	T	F	F	F	F	Row 3
T	F	F	F	T	T	F	Row 4
F	T	T	F	F	T	F	Row 5
F	T	F	F	T	T	F	Row 6
F	F	T	F	F	F	F	Row 7
F	F	F	F	T	T	F	Row 8
			1	2	3	4	

b. In row 2 of the above truth table we see that $(p \wedge q) \wedge (\sim r \vee q)$ is true when p is true, q is true, and r is false.

CHECK YOUR PROGRESS 2

a. Construct a truth table for $(\sim p \wedge r) \vee (q \wedge \sim r)$.

b. Use the truth table that you constructed in part a to determine the truth value of $(\sim p \wedge r) \vee (q \wedge \sim r)$, given that p is false, q is true, and r is false.

Solution   See page S8.

Thanks to
Cindy Miller
Arvada, CO.
Write to Plugger:
521 SW 11th Ave.
Portland, OR 97205

HEY, WHO IS THIS?

Plugger caller I.D.

Plugger Logic

Alternative Method for the Construction of a Truth Table

In Example 3 we use an *alternative procedure* to construct a truth table. **This alternative procedure generally requires less writing, less time, and less effort than the procedure explained in Examples 1 and 2.**

Alternative Procedure for the Construction of a Truth Table

If the given statement has *n* simple statements, then start with a standard form that has 2^n rows.

1. In each row, enter the truth value for each *simple* statement and their negations.

2. Use the truth values from Step 1 to enter the truth value under each connective within a pair of grouping symbols (parentheses ( ), brackets [ ], braces { }). If some grouping symbols are nested inside other grouping symbols, then work from the inside out.

3. Use the truth values from Step 2 to determine the truth values under the remaining connectives.

EXAMPLE 3 ■ Use the Alternative Procedure to Construct a Truth Table

Construct a truth table for $p \vee [\sim(p \wedge \sim q)]$.

Solution

The given statement $p \vee [\sim(p \wedge \sim q)]$ has the two simple statements p and q. Thus we start with a standard form that has $2^2 = 4$ rows.

Step 1. In each column, enter the truth values for the statements p and $\sim q$, as shown in the columns numbered 1, 2, and 3 of the following table.

p	*q*	*p*	$\vee$	[$\sim$	(*p*	$\wedge$	$\sim q$)]
T	T	T			T		F
T	F	T			T		T
F	T	F			F		F
F	F	F			F		T
		1			2		3

Step 2. Use the truth values in columns 2 and 3 to determine the truth values to enter under the "and" connective. See the column numbered 4. Now negate the truth values in the column numbered 4 to produce the truth values in the column numbered 5.

p	*q*	*p*	$\vee$	[$\sim$	(*p*	$\wedge$	$\sim q$)]
T	T	T		T	T	F	F
T	F	T		F	T	T	T
F	T	F		T	F	F	F
F	F	F		T	F	F	T
		1		5	2	4	3

Step 3. Use the truth values in the columns numbered 1 and 5 to determine the truth values to enter under the "or" connective. See the column numbered 6, which is the truth table for $p \vee [\sim(p \wedge \sim q)]$.

p	q	p	$\vee$	$[\sim$	$(p$	$\wedge$	$\sim q)]$
T	T	T	T	T	T	F	F
T	F	T	T	F	T	T	T
F	T	F	T	T	F	F	F
F	F	F	T	T	F	F	T

| | | 1 | 6 | 5 | 2 | 4 | 3 |

CHECK YOUR PROGRESS 3   Construct a truth table for $\sim p \vee (p \wedge q)$.

Solution   *See page S8.*

MathMatters   A Three-Valued Logic

In traditional logic either a statement is true or it is false. Many mathematicians have tried to extend traditional logic so that sentences that are *partially* true are assigned a truth value other than T or F. Jan Lukasiewicz was one of the first mathematicians to consider a three-valued logic in which a statement is true, false, or "somewhere between true and false." In his three-valued logic, Lukasiewicz classified the truth value of a statement as true (T), false (F), or maybe (M). The following table shows truth values for negation, conjunction, and disjunction in this three-valued logic.

p	q	Negation $\sim p$	Conjunction $p \wedge q$	Disjunction $p \vee q$
T	T	F	T	T
T	M	F	M	T
T	F	F	F	T
M	T	M	M	T
M	M	M	M	M
M	F	M	F	M
F	T	T	F	T
F	M	T	F	M
F	F	T	F	F

historical note

Jan Lukasiewicz (lōō-kä-shä-vēch) (1878–1956) was the Polish Minister of Education in 1919 and served as a professor of mathematics at Warsaw University from 1920–1939. Most of Lukasiewicz's work was in the area of logic. He is well known for developing *polish notation,* which was first used in logic to eliminate the need for parentheses in symbolic statements. Today *reverse polish notation* is used by many computers and calculators to perform computations without the need to enter parentheses. ■

✔ **TAKE NOTE**

In the remaining sections of this chapter, the ≡ symbol will often be used to denote that two statements are equivalent.

Equivalent Statements

Two statements are **equivalent** if they both have the same truth value for all possible truth values of their component statements. Equivalent statements have identical truth values in the final columns of their truth tables. The notation $p \equiv q$ is used to indicate that the statements p and q are equivalent.

EXAMPLE 4 ■ Verify that Two Statements Are Equivalent

Show that $\sim(p \lor \sim q)$ and $\sim p \land q$ are equivalent statements.

Solution

Construct two truth tables and compare the results. The truth tables below show that $\sim(p \lor \sim q)$ and $\sim p \land q$ have the same truth values for all possible truth values of their component statements. Thus the statements are equivalent.

p	q	$\sim(p \lor \sim q)$
T	T	F
T	F	F
F	T	T
F	F	F

p	q	$\sim p \land q$
T	T	F
T	F	F
F	T	T
F	F	F

identical truth values

Thus $\sim(p \lor \sim q) \equiv \sim p \land q$.

CHECK YOUR PROGRESS 4 Show that $p \lor (p \land \sim q)$ and p are equivalent.

Solution See page S9.

The truth tables in Table 3.3 show that $\sim(p \lor q)$ and $\sim p \land \sim q$ are equivalent statements. The truth tables in Table 3.4 show that $\sim(p \land q)$ and $\sim p \lor \sim q$ are equivalent statements.

Table 3.3

p	q	$\sim(p \lor q)$	$\sim p \land \sim q$
T	T	F	F
T	F	F	F
F	T	F	F
F	F	T	T

Table 3.4

p	q	$\sim(p \land q)$	$\sim p \lor \sim q$
T	T	F	F
T	F	T	T
F	T	T	T
F	F	T	T

These equivalences are known as **De Morgan's laws for statements.**

De Morgan's Laws for Statements

For any statements p and q,

$$\sim(p \lor q) \equiv \sim p \land \sim q$$
$$\sim(p \land q) \equiv \sim p \lor \sim q$$

De Morgan's laws can be used to restate certain English sentences in an equivalent form.

EXAMPLE 5 ■ State an Equivalent Form

Use one of De Morgan's laws to restate the following sentence in an equivalent form.

It is not the case that I graduated or I got a job.

Solution

Let p represent the statement "I graduated." Let q represent the statement "I got a job." In symbolic form, the original sentence is $\sim(p \vee q)$. One of De Morgan's laws states that this is equivalent to $\sim p \wedge \sim q$. Thus a sentence that is equivalent to the original sentence is "I did not graduate and I did not get a job."

CHECK YOUR PROGRESS 5 Use one of De Morgan's laws to restate the following sentence in an equivalent form.

It is not true that I am going to the dance and I am going to the game.

Solution See page S9.

Tautologies and Self-Contradictions

A **tautology** is a statement that is always true. A **self-contradiction** is a statement that is always false.

EXAMPLE 6 ■ Verify Tautologies and Self-Contradictions

Show that $p \vee (\sim p \vee q)$ is a tautology.

Solution

Construct a truth table as shown below.

p	q	p	$\vee$	$(\sim p$	$\vee$	$q)$
T	T	T	T	F	T	T
T	F	T	T	F	F	F
F	T	F	T	T	T	T
F	F	F	T	T	T	F
		1	5	2	4	3

The table shows that $p \vee (\sim p \vee q)$ is always true. Thus $p \vee (\sim p \vee q)$ is a tautology.

CHECK YOUR PROGRESS 6 Show that $p \wedge (\sim p \wedge q)$ is a self-contradiction.

Solution See page S9.

QUESTION   *Is the statement $x + 2 = 5$ a tautology or a self-contradiction?*

ANSWER   *Neither. The statement is not true for all values of x, and it is not false for all values of x.*

Excursion

Switching Networks—Part II

The Excursion in Section 3.1 introduced the application of symbolic logic to switching networks. This Excursion makes use of *closure tables* to determine under what conditions a switching network is open or closed. **In a closure table, we use a 1 to designate that a switch or switching network is closed and a 0 to indicate that it is open.**

Figure 3.5 shows a switching network that consists of the single switch *P* and a second network that consists of the single switch ~*P*. The table below shows that the switching network ~*P* is open when *P* is closed and is closed when *P* is open.

Negation Closure Table

P	~P
1	0
0	1

Figure 3.5

Figure 3.6 shows switches *P* and *Q* connected to form a series network. The table below shows that this series network is closed if and only if both *P* and *Q* are closed.

Series Network Closure Table

P	Q	P ∧ Q
1	1	1
1	0	0
0	1	0
0	0	0

Figure 3.6 *A series network*

Figure 3.7 shows switches *P* and *Q* connected to form a parallel network. The table below shows that this parallel network is closed if *P* is closed or if *Q* is closed.

Parallel Network Closure Table

P	Q	P ∨ Q
1	1	1
1	0	1
0	1	1
0	0	0

Figure 3.7 *A parallel network*

(continued)

Now consider the network shown in Figure 3.8. To determine the required conditions under which the network is closed, we first write a symbolic statement that represents the network, and then we construct a closure table.

Figure 3.8

A symbolic statement that represents the network in Figure 3.8 is

$$[(R \vee P) \wedge Q] \wedge (R \vee \sim P)$$

The closure table for this network is shown below.

P	Q	R	[(R	∨	P)	∧	Q]	∧	(R	∨	~P)	
1	1	1	1	1	1	1	1	1	1	1	0	Row 1
1	1	0	0	1	1	1	1	0	0	0	0	Row 2
1	0	1	1	1	1	0	0	0	1	1	0	Row 3
1	0	0	0	1	1	0	0	0	0	0	0	Row 4
0	1	1	1	1	0	1	1	1	1	1	1	Row 5
0	1	0	0	0	0	0	1	0	0	1	1	Row 6
0	0	1	1	1	0	0	0	0	1	1	1	Row 7
0	0	0	0	0	0	0	0	0	0	1	1	Row 8

1   6   2   7   3   9   4   8   5

The rows numbered 1 and 5 of the above table show that the network is closed whenever

- *P* is closed, *Q* is closed, and *R* is closed, or

- *P* is open, *Q* is closed, and *R* is closed.

Thus the switching network in Figure 3.8 is closed provided *Q* is closed and *R* is closed. The switching network is open under all other conditions.

Excursion Exercises

Construct a closure table for each of the following switching networks. Use the closure table to determine the required conditions for the network to be closed.

1.

2.

3.

4.

(continued)

5.

6.

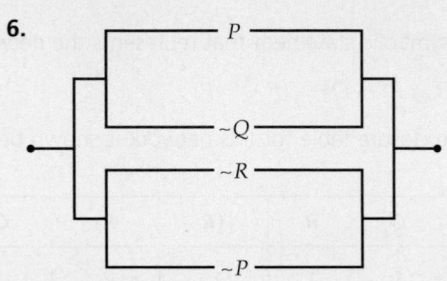

7. *Warning Circuits*

a. The following circuit shows a switching network used in an automobile. The warning buzzer will buzz only when the switching network is closed. Construct a closure table for the switching network.

$$\{P \wedge [(Q \wedge \sim P) \vee (\sim Q \wedge R)]\} \vee [(\sim P \wedge \sim Q) \wedge R]$$

b. An engineer thinks that the following circuit can be used in place of the circuit in part a. Do you agree? *Hint:* Construct a closure table for the switching network and compare your closure table with the closure table in part a.

$$[(P \wedge Q) \wedge \sim R] \vee (\sim Q \wedge R)$$

Exercise Set 3.2

In Exercises 1–10, determine the truth value of the compound statement given that p is a false statement, q is a true statement, and r is a true statement.

1. $p \vee (\sim q \vee r)$

2. $r \wedge \sim (p \vee r)$

3. $(p \wedge q) \vee (\sim p \wedge \sim q)$

4. $(p \wedge q) \vee [(\sim p \wedge \sim q) \vee q]$

5. $[\sim (p \wedge \sim q) \vee r] \wedge (p \wedge \sim r)$

6. $(p \wedge \sim q) \vee [(p \wedge \sim q) \vee r]$

7. $[(p \wedge \sim q) \vee \sim r] \wedge (q \wedge r)$

8. $(\sim p \wedge q) \wedge [(p \wedge \sim q) \vee r]$

9. $[(p \wedge q) \wedge r] \vee [p \vee (q \wedge \sim r)]$

10. $\{[(\sim p \wedge q) \wedge r] \vee [(p \wedge q) \wedge \sim r]\} \vee [p \wedge (q \wedge r)]$

11. **a.** Given that p is a false statement, what can be said about $p \wedge (q \vee r)$?

    b. Explain why it is not necessary to know the truth values of q and r to determine the truth value of $p \wedge (q \vee r)$ in part a above.

12. **a.** Given that q is a true statement, what can be said about $q \vee \sim r$?

    b. Explain why it is not necessary to know the truth value of r to determine the truth value of $q \vee \sim r$ in part a above.

In Exercises 13–28, construct a truth table for each compound statement.

13. $\sim p \vee q$

14. $(q \wedge \sim p) \vee \sim q$

15. $p \wedge \sim q$

16. $p \vee [\sim (p \wedge \sim q)]$

17. $(p \wedge \sim q) \vee [\sim (p \wedge q)]$

18. $(p \vee q) \wedge [\sim (p \vee \sim q)]$

19. $\sim (p \vee q) \wedge (\sim r \vee q)$

20. $[\sim (r \wedge \sim q)] \vee (\sim p \vee q)$

21. $(p \wedge \sim r) \vee [\sim q \vee (p \wedge r)]$

22. $[r \wedge (\sim p \vee q)] \wedge (r \vee \sim q)$

23. $[(p \wedge q) \vee (r \wedge \sim p)] \wedge (r \vee \sim q)$

24. $(p \wedge q) \wedge \{[\sim (\sim p \vee r)] \wedge q\}$

25. $q \vee [\sim r \vee (p \wedge r)]$

26. $\{[\sim (p \vee \sim r)] \wedge \sim q\} \vee r$

27. $(\sim q \wedge r) \vee [p \wedge (q \wedge \sim r)]$

28. $\sim [\sim p \wedge (q \wedge r)]$

In Exercises 29–36, use two truth tables to show that each pair of compound statements are equivalent.

29. $p \vee (p \wedge r);\ p$

30. $q \wedge (q \vee r);\ q$

31. $p \wedge (q \vee r);\ (p \wedge q) \vee (p \wedge r)$

32. $p \vee (q \wedge r);\ (p \vee q) \wedge (p \vee r)$

33. $p \vee (q \wedge \sim p);\ p \vee q$

34. $\sim [p \vee (q \wedge r)];\ \sim p \wedge (\sim q \vee \sim r)$

35. $[(p \wedge q) \wedge r] \vee [p \wedge (q \wedge \sim r)];\ p \wedge q$

36. $[(\sim p \wedge \sim q) \wedge r] \vee [(p \wedge q) \wedge \sim r] \vee [p \wedge (q \wedge r)];$
    $(p \wedge q) \vee [(\sim p \wedge \sim q) \wedge r]$

In Exercises 37–42, make use of one of De Morgan's laws to write the given statement in an equivalent form.

37. It is not the case that it rained or it snowed.

38. I did not pass the test and I did not complete the course.

39. She did not visit France and she did not visit Italy.

40. It is not true that I bought a new car and I moved to Florida.

41. It is not true that she received a promotion or that she received a raise.

42. It is not the case that the students cut classes or took part in the demonstration.

In Exercises 43–48, use a truth table to determine whether the given statement is a tautology.

43. $p \vee \sim p$

44. $q \vee [\sim(q \wedge r) \wedge \sim q]$

45. $(p \vee q) \vee (\sim p \vee q)$

46. $(p \wedge q) \vee (\sim p \vee \sim q)$

47. $(\sim p \vee q) \vee (\sim q \vee r)$

48. $\sim[p \wedge (\sim p \vee q)] \vee q$

In Exercises 49–54, use a truth table to determine whether the given statement is a self-contradiction.

49. $\sim r \wedge r$

50. $\sim(p \vee \sim p)$

51. $p \wedge (\sim p \wedge q)$

52. $\sim[(p \vee q) \vee (\sim p \vee q)]$

53. $[p \wedge (\sim p \vee q)] \vee q$

54. $\sim[p \vee (\sim p \vee q)]$

55. Explain why the statement $7 \leq 8$ is a disjunction.

56. **a.** Why is the statement $5 \leq 7$ true?

b. Why is the statement $7 \leq 7$ true?

Extensions

CRITICAL THINKING

57. How many rows are needed to construct a truth table for the statement $[p \wedge (q \vee \sim r)] \vee (s \wedge \sim t)$?

58. Explain why no truth table can have exactly 100 rows.

COOPERATIVE LEARNING

In Exercises 59 and 60, construct a truth table for the given compound statement. *Hint:* Use a table with 16 rows.

59. $[(p \wedge \sim q) \vee (q \wedge \sim r)] \wedge (r \vee \sim s)$

60. $s \wedge [\sim(\sim r \vee q) \vee \sim p]$

EXPLORATIONS

61. **Disjunctive Normal Form** Read about the *disjunctive normal form* of a statement in a logic text.

a. What is the disjunctive normal form of a statement that has the following truth table?

p	q	r	given statement
T	T	T	T
T	T	F	F
T	F	T	T
T	F	F	F
F	T	T	F
F	T	F	F
F	F	T	T
F	F	F	F

b. Explain why the disjunctive normal form is a valuable concept.

62. **Conjunctive Normal Form** Read about the *conjunctive normal form* of a statement in a logic text. What is the conjunctive normal form of the statement defined by the truth table in Exercise 61a?

SECTION 3.3 | **The Conditional and the Biconditional**

Conditional Statements

> If you don't get in that plane, you'll regret it. Maybe not today, maybe not tomorrow, but soon, and for the rest of your life.

The above quotation is from the movie *Casablanca*. Rick, played by Humphrey Bogart, is trying to convince Ilsa, played by Ingrid Bergman, to get on the plane with Laszlo. The sentence "If you don't get in that plane, you'll regret it" is a *conditional*

Humphrey Bogart and
Ingrid Bergman star in
Casablanca (1942).

statement. **Conditional statements** can be written in *if p, then q* form or in *if p, q* form. For instance, all of the following are conditional statements.

If we order pizza, then we can have it delivered.

If you go to the movie, you will not be able to meet us for dinner.

If *n* is a prime number greater than 2, then *n* is an odd number.

In any conditional statement represented by "If *p*, then *q*" or by "If *p*, *q*", the *p* statement is called the **antecedent** and the *q* statement is called the **consequent.**

EXAMPLE 1 ■ Identify the Antecedent and Consequent of a Conditional

Identify the antecedent and consequent in the following statements.

a. If our school was this nice, I would go there more than once a week.
— *The Basketball Diaries*

b. If you don't stop and look around once in a while, you could miss it.
—Ferris in *Ferris Bueller's Day Off*

c. If you strike me down, I shall become more powerful than you can possibly imagine.—Obi-Wan Kenobi, Star Wars, Episode IV, *A New Hope*

Solution

a. *Antecedent:* our school was this nice
Consequent: I would go there more than once a week

b. *Antecedent:* you don't stop and look around once in a while
Consequent: you could miss it

c. *Antecedent:* you strike me down
Consequent: I shall become more powerful than you can possibly imagine

CHECK YOUR PROGRESS 1   Identify the antecedent and consequent in each of the following conditional statements.

a. If I study for at least 6 hours, then I will get an A on the test.

b. If I get the job, I will buy a new car.

c. If you can dream it, you can do it.

Solution   See page S9.

> **Arrow Notation**
>
> The conditional statement "If *p*, then *q*" can be written using the **arrow notation** *p* → *q*. The arrow notation *p* → *q* is read as "if *p*, then *q*" or as "*p* implies *q*."

The Truth Table for the Conditional *p* → *q*

To determine the truth table for *p* → *q*, consider the advertising slogan for a web authoring software product that states "If you can use a word processor, you can create a webpage." This slogan is a conditional statement. The antecedent is *p*, "you can use a word processor," and the consequent is q, "you can create a webpage." Now consider the truth value of $p \rightarrow q$ for each of the following four possibilities.

Table 3.5

p: you can use a word processor	q: you can create a webpage	$p \rightarrow q$	
T	T	?	Row 1
T	F	?	Row 2
F	T	?	Row 3
F	F	?	Row 4

Row 1: Antecedent T, consequent T   You can use a word processor, and you can create a webpage. In this case the truth value of the advertisement is true. To complete Table 3.5, we place a T in place of the question mark in row 1.

Row 2: Antecedent T, consequent F   You can use a word processor, but you cannot create a webpage. In this case the advertisement is false. We put an F in place of the question mark in row 2 of Table 3.5.

Row 3: Antecedent F, consequent T   You cannot use a word processor, but you can create a webpage. Because the advertisement does not make any statement about what you might or might not be able to do if you cannot use a word processor, we cannot state that the advertisement is false, and we are compelled to place a T in place of the question mark in row 3 of Table 3.5.

Row 4: Antecedent F, consequent F   You cannot use a word processor, and you cannot create a webpage. Once again we must consider the truth value in this case to be true because the advertisement does not make any statement about what you might or might not be able to do if you cannot use a word processor. We place a T in place of the question mark in row 4 of Table 3.5.

The truth table for the conditional $p \rightarrow q$ is given in Table 3.6.

Table 3.6 *The Truth Table for $p \rightarrow q$*

p	q	$p \rightarrow q$
T	T	T
T	F	F
F	T	T
F	F	T

Truth Value of the Conditional $p \rightarrow q$

The conditional $p \rightarrow q$ is false if p is true and q is false. It is true in all other cases.

EXAMPLE 2 ■ Find the Truth Value of a Conditional

Determine the truth value of each of the following.

a. If 2 is an integer, then 2 is a rational number.

b. If 3 is a negative number, then $5 > 7$.

c. If $5 > 3$, then $2 + 7 = 4$.

Solution

a. Because the consequent is true, this is a true statement.

b. Because the antecedent is false, this is a true statement.

c. Because the antecedent is true and the consequent is false, this is a false statement.

CHECK YOUR PROGRESS 2   Determine the truth value of each of the following.

a. If $4 \geq 3$, then $2 + 5 = 6$.

b. If $5 > 9$, then $4 > 9$.

c. If Tuesday follows Monday, then April follows March.

Solution   *See page S9.*

EXAMPLE 3 ■ Construct a Truth Table for a Statement Involving a Conditional

Construct a truth table for $[\,p \wedge (q \vee \sim p)\,] \rightarrow \sim p$.

Solution

Using the generalized procedure for truth table construction, we produce the following table.

p	q	$[\,p$	$\wedge$	$(q$	$\vee$	$\sim p)\,]$	$\rightarrow$	$\sim p$
T	T	T	T	T	T	F	F	F
T	F	T	F	F	F	F	T	F
F	T	F	F	T	T	T	T	T
F	F	F	F	F	T	T	T	T

1		6		2		5		3		7		4

CHECK YOUR PROGRESS 3   Construct a truth table for $[\,p \wedge (p \rightarrow q)\,] \rightarrow q$.

Solution   *See page S9.*

Math Matters   **Use Conditional Statements to Control a Calculator Program**

Computer and calculator programs use conditional statements to control the flow of a program. For instance, the "If…Then" instruction in a TI-83 or TI-84 calculator program directs the calculator to execute a group of commands if a condition is true and to skip to the End statement if the condition is false. See the program steps below.

:If *condition*

:Then (skip to End if *condition* is false)

:*command* if *condition* is true

:*command* if *condition* is true

:End

:*command*

The TI-83/84 program FACTOR shown at the left factors a number N into its prime factors. Note the use of the "If…Then" instructions highlighted in red.

An Equivalent Form of the Conditional

Table 3.7 *The Truth Table for ~p ∨ q*

The truth table for $\sim p \vee q$ is shown in Table 3.7. The truth values in this table are identical to the truth values in Table 3.6. Hence, the conditional $p \rightarrow q$ is equivalent to the disjunction $\sim p \vee q$.

p	q	$\sim p \vee q$
T	T	T
T	F	F
F	T	T
F	F	T

An Equivalent Form of the Conditional $p \rightarrow q$

$p \rightarrow q \equiv \sim p \vee q$

EXAMPLE 4 ■ Write a Conditional in Its Equivalent Disjunctive Form

Write each of the following in its equivalent disjunctive form.

a. If I could play the guitar, I would join the band.

b. If Arnold cannot play, then the Dodgers will lose.

Solution

In each case we write the disjunction of the negation of the antecedent and the consequent.

a. I cannot play the guitar or I would join the band.

b. Arnold can play or the Dodgers will lose.

CHECK YOUR PROGRESS 4   Write each of the following in its equivalent disjunctive form.

a. If I don't move to Georgia, I will live in Houston.

b. If the number is divisible by 2, then the number is even.

Solution   *See page S9.*

The Negation of the Conditional

Because $p \rightarrow q \equiv \sim p \vee q$, an equivalent form of $\sim(p \rightarrow q)$ is given by $\sim(\sim p \vee q)$, which, by one of De Morgan's laws, can be expressed as the conjunction $p \wedge \sim q$.

The Negation of $p \rightarrow q$

$\sim(p \rightarrow q) \equiv p \wedge \sim q$

EXAMPLE 5 ■ Write the Negation of a Conditional Statement

Write the negation of each conditional statement.

a. If they pay me the money, I will sign the contract.

b. If the lines are parallel, then they do not intersect.

Solution

In each case, we write the conjunction of the antecedent and the negation of the consequent.

a. They paid me the money and I did not sign the contract.

b. The lines are parallel and they intersect.

CHECK YOUR PROGRESS 5   Write the negation of each conditional statement.

a. If I finish the report, I will go to the concert.

b. If the square of n is 25, then n is 5 or -5.

Solution   *See page S9.*

The Biconditional

The statement $(p \rightarrow q) \wedge (q \rightarrow p)$ is called a **biconditional** and is denoted by $p \leftrightarrow q$, which is read as "p if and only if q."

Definition of the Biconditional $p \leftrightarrow q$

$p \leftrightarrow q \equiv [(p \rightarrow q) \wedge (q \rightarrow p)]$

Table 3.8 shows that $p \leftrightarrow q$ is true only when the components p and q have the same truth value.

Table 3.8 *The Truth Table for $p \leftrightarrow q$*

p	q	$p \leftrightarrow q$
T	T	T
T	F	F
F	T	F
F	F	T

EXAMPLE 6 ■ Determine the Truth Value of a Biconditional

State whether each biconditional is true or false.

a. $x + 4 = 7$ if and only if $x = 3$.

b. $x^2 = 36$ if and only if $x = 6$.

Solution

a. Both components are true when $x = 3$ and both are false when $x \neq 3$. Both components have the same truth value for any value of x, so this is a true statement.

b. If $x = -6$, the first component is true and the second component is false. Thus this is a false statement.

CHECK YOUR PROGRESS 6   State whether each biconditional is true or false.

a. $x > 7$ if and only if $x > 6$.

b. $x + 5 > 7$ if and only if $x > 2$.

Solution   *See page S9.*

Excursion

Logic Gates

Modern digital computers use *gates* to process information. These gates are designed to receive two types of electronic impulses, which are generally represented as a 1 or a 0. Figure 3.9 shows a *NOT gate*. It is constructed so that a stream of impulses that enter the gate will exit the gate as a stream of impulses in which each 1 is converted to a 0 and each 0 is converted to a 1.

Input stream   Output stream
1100   0011

Figure 3.9 *NOT gate*

Note the similarity between the logical connective *not* and the logic gate NOT. The *not* connective converts the sequence of truth values T F to F T. The NOT gate converts the input stream 1 0 to 0 1. If the 1's are replaced with T's and the 0's with F's, then the NOT logic gate yields the same results as the *not* connective.

Many gates are designed so that two input streams are converted to one output stream. For instance, Figure 3.10 shows an *AND gate*. The AND gate is constructed so that a 1 is the output if and only if both input streams have a 1. In any other situation a 0 is produced as the output.

Input streams   Output stream
1100   1000
1010

Figure 3.10 *AND gate*

Note the similarity between the logical connective *and* and the logic gate AND. The *and* connective combines the sequence of truth values T T F F with the truth values T F T F to produce T F F F. The AND gate combines the input stream 1 1 0 0 with the input stream 1 0 1 0 to produce 1 0 0 0. If the 1's are replaced with T's and the 0's with F's, then the AND logic gate yields the same result as the *and* connective.

The *OR gate* is constructed so that its output is a 0 if and only if both input streams have a 0. All other situations yield a 1 as the output. See Figure 3.11.

Input streams   Output stream
1100   1110
1010

Figure 3.11 *OR gate*

(continued)

Figure 3.12 shows a network that consists of a NOT gate and an AND gate.

Figure 3.12

<u>QUESTION</u>   *What is the output stream for the network in Figure 3.12?*

Excursion Exercises

1. For each of the following, determine the output stream for the given input streams.

a. Input streams   Output stream

b. Input streams   Output stream

c. Input streams   Output stream

2. Construct a network using NOT, AND, and OR gates as needed that accepts the two input streams 1 1 0 0 and 1 0 1 0 and produces the output stream 0 1 1 1.

<u>*ANSWER*</u>   *0 0 1 0*

Exercise Set 3.3

In Exercises 1–6, identify the antecedent and the consequent of each conditional statement.

1. If I had the money, I would buy the painting.

2. If Shelly goes on the trip, she will not be able to take part in the graduation ceremony.

3. If they had a guard dog, then no one would trespass on their property.

4. If I don't get to school before 7:30, I won't be able to find a parking place.

5. If I change my major, I must reapply for admission.

6. If your blood type is type O−, then you are classified as a universal blood donor.

In Exercises 7–14, determine the truth value of the given statement.

7. If x is an even integer, then x^2 is an even integer.

8. If x is a prime number, then $x + 2$ is a prime number.

9. If all frogs can dance, then today is Monday.

10. If all cats are black, then I am a millionaire.

11. If $4 < 3$, then $7 = 8$.

12. If $x < 2$, then $x + 5 < 7$.

13. If $|x| = 6$, then $x = 6$.

14. If $\pi = 3$, then $2\pi = 6$.

In Exercises 15–24, construct a truth table for the given statement.

15. $(p \wedge \sim q) \rightarrow [\sim(p \wedge q)]$

16. $[(p \rightarrow q) \wedge p] \rightarrow p$

17. $[(p \rightarrow q) \wedge p] \rightarrow q$

18. $(\sim p \vee \sim q) \rightarrow \sim(p \wedge q)$

19. $[r \wedge (\sim p \vee q)] \rightarrow (r \vee \sim q)$

20. $[(p \rightarrow \sim r) \wedge q] \rightarrow \sim r$

21. $[(p \rightarrow q) \vee (r \wedge \sim p)] \rightarrow (r \vee \sim q)$

22. $\{p \wedge [(p \rightarrow q) \wedge (q \rightarrow r)]\} \rightarrow r$

23. $[\sim(p \rightarrow \sim r) \wedge \sim q] \rightarrow r$

24. $[p \wedge (r \rightarrow \sim q)] \rightarrow (r \vee q)$

In Exercises 25–30, write each conditional statement in its equivalent disjunctive form.

25. If she could sing, she would be perfect for the part.

26. If he does not get frustrated, he will be able to complete the job.

27. If x is an irrational number, then x is not a terminating decimal.

28. If Mr. Hyde had a brain, he would be dangerous.

29. If the fog does not lift, our flight will be cancelled.

30. If the Yankees win the pennant, Carol will be happy.

In Exercises 31–36, write the negation of each conditional statement in its equivalent conjunctive form.

31. If they offer me the contract, I will accept.

32. If I paint the house, I will get the money.

33. If pigs had wings, pigs could fly.

34. If we had a telescope, we could see that comet.

35. If she travels to Italy, she will visit her relatives.

36. If Paul could play better defense, he could be a professional basketball player.

In Exercises 37–46, state whether the given biconditional is true or false. Assume that x and y are real numbers.

37. $x^2 = 9$ if and only if $x = 3$.

38. x is a positive number if and only if $x > 0$.

39. $|x|$ is a positive number if and only if $x \neq 0$.

40. $|x + y| = x + y$ if and only if $x + y > 0$.

41. A number is a rational number if and only if the number can be written as a terminating decimal.

42. $0.\overline{3}$ is a rational number if and only if $\frac{1}{3}$ is a rational number.

43. $4 = 7$ if and only if $2 = 3$.

44. x is an even number if and only if x is not an odd number.

45. Triangle ABC is an equilateral triangle if and only if triangle ABC is an equiangular triangle.

46. Today is March 1 if and only if yesterday was February 28.

In Exercises 47–52, let v represent "I will take a vacation," let p represent "I get the promotion," and let t represent "I am transferred." Write each of the following statements in symbolic form.

47. If I get the promotion, I will take a vacation.

48. If I am not transferred, I will take a vacation.

49. If I am transferred, then I will not take a vacation.

50. If I will not take a vacation, then I will not be transferred and I get the promotion.

51. If I am not transferred and I get the promotion, then I will take a vacation.

52. If I get the promotion, then I am transferred and I will take a vacation.

In Exercises 53–58, construct a truth table for each statement to determine if the statements are equivalent.

53. $p \rightarrow \sim r; r \vee \sim p$

54. $p \rightarrow q; q \rightarrow p$

55. $\sim p \rightarrow (p \vee r); r$

56. $p \rightarrow q; \sim q \rightarrow \sim p$

57. $p \rightarrow (q \vee r); (p \rightarrow q) \vee (p \rightarrow r)$

58. $\sim q \rightarrow p; p \vee q$

Extensions

CRITICAL THINKING

The statement "All squares are rectangles" can be written as "If a figure is a square, then it is a rectangle." In Exercises 59–64, write each statement given in "All p are q" form in the form "If it is a p, then it is a q."

59. All rational numbers are real numbers.

60. All whole numbers are integers.

61. All repeating decimals are rational numbers.

62. All multiples of 5 end with a 0 or with a 5.

63. All Sauropods are herbivorous.

64. All paintings by Vincent van Gogh are valuable.

EXPLORATIONS

65. A Factor Program If you have access to a TI-83 or a TI-84 calculator, enter the program FACTOR on page 139 into the calculator and demonstrate the program to a classmate.

66. **Calculator Programs** Many calculator programs are available on the Internet. One source for Texas Instruments calculator programs is **ticalc.org.** Search the Internet and write a few paragraphs about the programs you found to be the most interesting.

SECTION 3.4 | The Conditional and Related Statements

Equivalent Forms of the Conditional

Every conditional statement can be stated in many equivalent forms. It is not even necessary to state the antecedent before the consequent. For instance, the conditional "If I live in Boston, then I must live in Massachusetts" can also be stated as

I must live in Massachusetts, if I live in Boston.

Table 3.9 lists some of the various forms that may be used to write a conditional statement.

Table 3.9 *Common Forms of $p \rightarrow q$*

Every conditional statement $p \rightarrow q$ can be written in the following equivalent forms	
If p, then q.	Every p is a q.
If p, q.	q, if p.
p only if q.	q provided p.
p implies q.	q is a necessary condition for p.
Not p or q.	p is a sufficient condition for q.

EXAMPLE 1 ■ Write a Statement in an Equivalent Form

Write each of the following in "If p, then q" form.

a. The number is an even number provided it is divisible by 2.

b. Today is Friday, only if yesterday was Thursday.

Solution

a. The statement "The number is an even number provided it is divisible by 2" is in "q provided p" form. The antecedent is "it is divisible by 2," and the consequent is "the number is an even number." Thus its "If p, then q" form is

   If it is divisible by 2, then the number is an even number.

b. The statement "Today is Friday, only if yesterday was Thursday" is in "p only if q" form. The antecedent is "today is Friday." The consequent is "yesterday was Thursday." Its "If p, then q" form is

   If today is Friday, then yesterday was Thursday.

CHECK YOUR PROGRESS 1 Write each of the following in "If p, then q" form.

a. Every square is a rectangle.

b. Being older than 30 is sufficient to show I am at least 21.

Solution See page S9.

The Converse, the Inverse, and the Contrapositive

Every conditional statement has three related statements. They are called the *converse*, the *inverse*, and the *contrapositive*.

Statements Related to the Conditional Statement

The **converse** of $p \rightarrow q$ is $q \rightarrow p$.

The **inverse** of $p \rightarrow q$ is $\sim p \rightarrow \sim q$.

The **contrapositive** of $p \rightarrow q$ is $\sim q \rightarrow \sim p$.

The above definitions show the following:

■ The converse of $p \rightarrow q$ is formed by interchanging the antecedent p with the consequent q.

■ The inverse of $p \rightarrow q$ is formed by negating the antecedent p and negating the consequent q.

■ The contrapositive of $p \rightarrow q$ is formed by negating both the antecedent p and the consequent q and interchanging these negated statements.

EXAMPLE 2 ■ Write the Converse, Inverse, and Contrapositive of a Conditional

Write the converse, inverse, and contrapositive of

   If I get the job, then I will rent the apartment.

Solution
Converse: If I rent the apartment, then I get the job.
Inverse: If I do not get the job, then I will not rent the apartment.
Contrapositive: If I do not rent the apartment, then I did not get the job.

CHECK YOUR PROGRESS 2   Write the converse, inverse, and contrapositive of

   If we have a quiz today, then we will not have a quiz tomorrow.

Solution   *See page S9.*

Table 3.10 shows that any conditional statement is equivalent to its contrapositive, and that the converse of a conditional statement is equivalent to the inverse of the conditional statement.

Table 3.10 *Truth Tables for the Conditional and Related Statements*

p	q	Conditional $p \rightarrow q$	Converse $q \rightarrow p$	Inverse $\sim p \rightarrow \sim q$	Contrapositive $\sim q \rightarrow \sim p$
T	T	T	T	T	T
T	F	F	T	T	F
F	T	T	F	F	T
F	F	T	T	T	T

$$q \rightarrow p \equiv \sim p \rightarrow \sim q$$
$$p \rightarrow q \equiv \sim q \rightarrow \sim p$$

EXAMPLE 3 ■ Determine Whether Related Statements Are Equivalent

Determine whether the given statements are equivalent.

a. If a number ends with a 5, then the number is divisible by 5.
   If a number is divisible by 5, then the number ends with a 5.

b. If two lines in a plane do not intersect, then the lines are parallel.
   If two lines in a plane are not parallel, then the lines intersect.

Solution
a. The second statement is the converse of the first. The statements are not equivalent.

b. The second statement is the contrapositive of the first. The statements are equivalent.

CHECK YOUR PROGRESS 3 Determine whether the given statements are equivalent.

a. If $a = b$, then $a \cdot c = b \cdot c$.
  If $a \neq b$, then $a \cdot c \neq b \cdot c$.

b. If I live in Nashville, then I live in Tennessee.
  If I do not live in Tennessee, then I do not live in Nashville.

Solution   *See page S9.*

In mathematics, it is often necessary to prove statements that are in "If p, then q" form. If a proof cannot be readily produced, mathematicians often try to prove the contrapositive "If $\sim q$, then $\sim p$." Because a conditional and its contrapositive are equivalent statements, a proof of either statement also establishes the proof of the other statement.

QUESTION   *A mathematician wishes to prove the following statement about the integer x.*

$$\text{If } x^2 \text{ is an odd integer, then } x \text{ is an odd integer.} \quad (I)$$

If the mathematician is able to prove the statement, "If x is an even integer, then x^2 is an even integer," does this also prove statement (I)?

EXAMPLE 4 ■ Use the Contrapositive to Determine a Truth Value

Write the contrapositive of each statement and use the contrapositive to determine whether the original statement is true or false.

a. If $a + b$ is not divisible by 5, then a and b are not both divisible by 5.
b. If x^3 is an odd integer, then x is an odd integer. (Assume x is an integer.)
c. If a geometric figure is not a rectangle, then it is not a square.

Solution
a. If a and b are both divisible by 5, then $a + b$ is divisible by 5. This is a true statement, so the original statement is also true.
b. If x is an even integer, then x^3 is an even integer. This is a true statement, so the original statement is also true.
c. If a geometric figure is a square, then it is a rectangle. This is a true statement, so the original statement is also true.

CHECK YOUR PROGRESS 4   Write the contrapositive of each statement and use the contrapositive to determine whether the original statement is true or false.

a. If $3 + x$ is an odd integer, then x is an even integer. (Assume x is an integer.)
b. If two triangles are not similar triangles, then they are not congruent triangles. *Note:* Similar triangles have the same shape. Congruent triangles have the same size and shape.
c. If today is not Wednesday, then tomorrow is not Thursday.

Solution   *See page S10.*

ANSWER   *Yes, because the second statement is the contrapositive of (I).*

Math Matters   Grace Hopper

Rear Admiral Grace Hopper

Grace Hopper (1906–1992) was a visionary in the field of computer programming. She was a mathematics professor at Vassar from 1931 to 1943, but retired from teaching to start a career in the U.S. Navy at the age of 37.

The Navy assigned Hopper to the Bureau of Ordnance Computation at Harvard University. It was here that she was given the opportunity to program computers. It has often been reported that she was the third person to program the world's first large-scale digital computer. Grace Hopper had a passion for computers and computer programming. She wanted to develop a computer language that would be user-friendly and enable people to use computers in a more productive manner.

Grace Hopper had a long list of accomplishments. She designed some of the first computer compilers, she was one of the first to introduce English commands into computer languages, and she wrote the precursor to the computer language COBOL.

Grace Hopper retired from the Navy (for the first time) in 1966. In 1967 she was recalled to active duty and continued to serve in the Navy until 1986, at which time she was the nation's oldest active duty officer.

In 1951, the UNIVAC I computer that Grace Hopper was programming started to malfunction. The malfunction was caused by a moth that had become lodged in one of the computer's relays. Grace Hopper pasted the moth into the UNIVAC I logbook with a label that read, "computer bug." Since then computer programmers have used the word *bug* to indicate any problem associated with a computer program. Modern computers use logic gates instead of relays to process information, so actual bugs are not a problem; however, bugs such as the "Year 2000 bug" can cause serious problems.

Excursion

Sheffer's Stroke and the NAND Gate

Table 3.11 *Sheffer's stroke*

p	q	$p \mid q$
T	T	F
T	F	T
F	T	T
F	F	T

In 1913, the logician Henry M. Sheffer created a connective that we now refer to as *Sheffer's stroke* (or *NAND*). This connective is often denoted by the symbol |. Table 3.11 shows that $p \mid q$ is equivalent to $\sim(p \wedge q)$. Sheffer's stroke $p \mid q$ is false when both p and q are true and it is true in all other cases.

Any logic statement can be written using only Sheffer's stroke connectives. For instance, Table 3.12 shows that $p \mid p \equiv \sim p$ and $(p \mid p) \mid (q \mid q) \equiv p \vee q$.

Figure 3.13 shows a logic gate called a NAND gate. This gate models the Sheffer's stroke connective in that its output is 0 when both input streams are 1 and its output is 1 in all other cases.

(continued)

Table 3.12

p	q	$p\,|\,p$	$(p\,|\,p)\,|\,(q\,|\,q)$
T	T	F	T
T	F	F	T
F	T	T	T
F	F	T	F

Figure 3.13 *NAND gate*

Excursion Exercises

1. a. Complete a truth table for $p\,|\,(q\,|\,q)$.

   b. Use the results of Excursion Exercise 1a to determine an equivalent statement for $p\,|\,(q\,|\,q)$.

2. a. Complete a truth table for $(p\,|\,q)\,|\,(p\,|\,q)$.

   b. Use the results of Excursion Exercise 2a to determine an equivalent statement for $(p\,|\,q)\,|\,(p\,|\,q)$.

3. a. Determine the output stream for the following network of NAND gates. *Note:* In a network of logic gates, a solid circle • is used to indicate a connection. A symbol such as ⭲ is used to indicate "no connection."

Figure 3.14

   b. What logic gate is modeled by the network in Figure 3.14?

4. NAND gates are functionally complete in that any logic gate can be constructed using only NAND gates. Construct a network of NAND gates that would produce the same output stream as an OR gate.

Exercise Set 3.4

In Exercises 1–10, write each statement in "If p, then q" form.

1. We will be in good shape for the ski trip provided we take the aerobics class.

2. We can get a dog only if we install a fence around the back yard.

3. Every odd prime number is greater than 2.

4. The triangle is a 30°-60°-90° triangle, if the length of the hypotenuse is twice the length of the shorter leg.

5. He can join the band, if he has the talent to play a keyboard.

6. Every theropod is carnivorous.

7. I will be able to prepare for the test only if I have the textbook.

8. I will be able to receive my credential provided Education 147 is offered in the spring semester.

9. Being in excellent shape is a necessary condition for running the Boston marathon.

10. If it is an ankylosaur, it is quadrupedal.

In Exercises 11–24, write the **a.** converse, **b.** inverse, and **c.** contrapositive of the given statement.

11. If I were rich, I would quit this job.

12. If we had a car, then we would be able to take the class.

13. If she does not return soon, we will not be able to attend the party.

14. I will be in the talent show only if I can do the same comedy routine I did for the banquet.

15. Every parallelogram is a quadrilateral.

16. If you get the promotion, you will need to move to Denver.

17. I would be able to get current information about astronomy provided I had access to the Internet.

18. You need four-wheel drive to make the trip to Death Valley.

19. We will not have enough money for dinner, if we take a taxi.

20. If you are the president of the United States, then your age is at least 35.

21. She will visit Kauai only if she can extend her vacation for at least two days.

22. In a right triangle, the acute angles are complementary.

23. Two lines perpendicular to a given line are parallel.

24. If $x + 5 = 12$, then $x = 7$.

In Exercises 25–30, determine whether the given statements are equivalent.

25. If Kevin wins, we will celebrate.
    If we celebrate, then Kevin will win.

26. If I save $1000, I will go on the field trip.
    If I go on the field trip, then I saved $1000.

27. If she attends the meeting, she will make the sale.
    If she does not make the sale, then she did not attend the meeting.

28. If you understand algebra, you can remember algebra.
    If you do not understand algebra, you cannot remember algebra.

29. If $a > b$, then $ac > bc$.
    If $a \leq b$, then $ac \leq bc$.

30. If $a < b$, then $\dfrac{1}{a} > \dfrac{1}{b}$.
    If $\dfrac{1}{a} \leq \dfrac{1}{b}$, then $a \geq b$.
    (Assume $a \neq 0$ and $b \neq 0$.)

In Exercises 31–36, write the contrapositive of the statement and use the contrapositive to determine whether the given statement is true or false.

31. If $3x - 7 = 11$, then $x \neq 7$.

32. If $x \neq 3$, then $5x + 7 \neq 22$.

33. If $a \neq 3$, then $|a| \neq 3$.

34. If $a + b$ is divisible by 3, then a is divisible by 3 and b is divisible by 3.

35. If $\sqrt{a + b} \neq 5$, then $a + b \neq 25$.

36. Assume x is an integer. If x^2 is an even integer, then x is an even integer.

37. What is the converse of the inverse of the contrapositive of $p \rightarrow q$?

38. What is the inverse of the converse of the contrapositive of $p \rightarrow q$?

Extensions

CRITICAL THINKING

39. Give an example of a true conditional statement whose

    a. converse is true.   **b.** converse is false.

40. Give an example of a true conditional statement whose

    a. inverse is true.   **b.** inverse is false.

In Exercises 41–44, determine the original statement if the given statement is related to the original in the manner indicated.

41. *Converse:* If you can do it, you can dream it.

42. *Inverse:* If I did not have a dime, I would not spend it.

43. *Contrapositive:* If I were a singer, I would not be a dancer.

44. *Negation:* Pigs have wings and pigs cannot fly.

45. Explain why it is not possible to find an example of a true conditional statement whose contrapositive is false.

46. If a conditional statement is false, must its converse be true? Explain.

47. **A Puzzle** Lewis Carroll (Charles Dodgson) wrote many puzzles, many of which he recorded in his diaries. Solve the following puzzle, which appears in one of his diaries.

The Dodo says that the Hatter tells lies.
The Hatter says that the March Hare tells lies.
The March Hare says that both the Dodo and the Hatter tell lies.
Who is telling the truth?[2]

Hint: Consider the three different cases in which only one of the characters is telling the truth. In only one of these cases can all three of the statements be true.

EXPLORATIONS

48. **Puzzles** Use a library or the Internet to find puzzles created by Lewis Carroll. For the puzzle that you think is most interesting, write an explanation of the puzzle and give its solution.

SECTION 3.5 | Arguments

historical note

Aristotle
(ăr'ĭ-stŏt'l)
(384–322 B.C.) was an ancient Greek philosopher who studied under Plato. He wrote about many subjects, including logic, biology, politics, astronomy, metaphysics, and ethics. His ideas about logic and the reasoning process have had a major impact on mathematics and philosophy. ∎

Arguments

In this section we consider methods of analyzing arguments to determine whether they are *valid* or *invalid*. For instance, consider the following argument.

> If Aristotle was human, then Aristotle was mortal. Aristotle was human. Therefore, Aristotle was mortal.

To determine whether the above argument is a valid argument, we must first define the terms *argument* and *valid argument*.

Definition of an Argument and a Valid Argument

An **argument** consists of a set of statements called **premises** and another statement called the **conclusion.** An argument is **valid** if the conclusion is true whenever all the premises are assumed to be true. An argument is **invalid** if it is not a valid argument.

In the argument about Aristotle, the two premises and the conclusion are shown below. It is customary to place a horizontal line between the premises and the conclusion.

First Premise:	If Aristotle was human, then Aristotle was mortal.
Second Premise:	Aristotle was human.
Conclusion:	Therefore, Aristotle was mortal.

---

2. The above puzzle is from *Lewis Carroll's Games and Puzzles*, newly compiled and edited by Edward Wakeling. New York: Dover Publications, Inc., copyright 1992, p. 11, puzzle 9, "Who's Telling the Truth?"

Arguments can be written in **symbolic form.** For instance, if we let h represent the statement "Aristotle was human" and m represent the statement "Aristotle was mortal," then the argument can be expressed as

$$h \to m$$
$$\underline{h}$$
$$\therefore m$$

The three dots $\therefore$ are a symbol for "therefore."

EXAMPLE 1 ■ Write an Argument in Symbolic Form

Write the following argument in symbolic form.

The fish is fresh or I will not order it. The fish is fresh. Therefore I will order it.

Solution
Let f represent the statement "The fish is fresh." Let o represent the statement "I will order it." The symbolic form of the argument is

$$f \vee \sim o$$
$$\underline{f}$$
$$\therefore o$$

CHECK YOUR PROGRESS 1 Write the following argument in symbolic form.

If she doesn't get on the plane, she will regret it. She does not regret it. Therefore, she got on the plane.

Solution See page S10.

Arguments and Truth Tables

The following truth table procedure can be used to determine whether an argument is valid or invalid.

> **Truth Table Procedure to Determine the Validity of an Argument**
>
> **1.** Write the argument in symbolic form.
> **2.** Construct a truth table that shows the truth value of each premise and the truth value of the conclusion for all combinations of truth values of the component statements.
> **3.** If the conclusion is true in every row of the truth table in which all the premises are true, the argument is valid. If the conclusion is false in any row in which all of the premises are true, the argument is invalid.

We will now use the above truth table procedure to determine the validity of the argument about Aristotle.

1. Once again we let h represent the statement "Aristotle was human" and m represent the statement "Aristotle was mortal." In symbolic form the argument is

$h \to m$	First premise
$\underline{h}$	Second premise
$\therefore m$	Conclusion

2. Construct a truth table as shown below.

h	m	First premise $h \rightarrow m$	Second premise h	Conclusion m	
T	T	T	T	T	Row 1
T	F	F	T	F	Row 2
F	T	T	F	T	Row 3
F	F	T	F	F	Row 4

3. Row 1 is the only row in which all the premises are true, so it is the only row that we examine. Because the conclusion is true in row 1, the argument is valid.

In Example 2, we use the truth table method to determine the validity of a more complicated argument.

EXAMPLE 2 ■ Determine the Validity of an Argument

Determine whether the following argument is valid or invalid.

> If it rains, then the game will not be played. It is not raining. Therefore, the game will be played.

Solution

If we let *r* represent "it rains" and *g* represent "the game will be played," then the symbolic form is

$$r \rightarrow \sim g$$
$$\underline{\sim r}$$
$$\therefore g$$

The truth table for this argument is as follows:

r	g	First premise $r \rightarrow \sim g$	Second premise $\sim r$	Conclusion g	
T	T	F	F	T	Row 1
T	F	T	F	F	Row 2
F	T	T	T	T	Row 3
F	F	T	T	F	Row 4

QUESTION *Why do we need to examine only rows 3 and 4?*

Because the conclusion in row 4 is false and the premises are both true, we know the argument is invalid.

ANSWER *Rows 3 and 4 are the only rows in which all of the premises are true.*

CHECK YOUR PROGRESS 2 Determine the validity of the following argument.

> If the stock market rises, then the bond market will fall.
>
> The bond market did not fall.
>
> ∴The stock market did not rise.

Solution See page S10.

The argument in Example 3 involves three statements. Thus we use a truth table with $2^3 = 8$ rows to determine the validity of the argument.

EXAMPLE 3 ■ Determine the Validity of an Argument

Determine whether the following argument is valid or invalid.

> If I am going to run the marathon, then I will buy new shoes.
>
> If I buy new shoes, then I will not buy a television.
>
> ∴If I buy a television, I will not run the marathon.

Solution

Label the statements

> *m:* I am going to run the marathon.
>
> *s:* I will buy new shoes.
>
> *t:* I will buy a television.

The symbolic form of the argument is

$$m \rightarrow s$$
$$s \rightarrow \sim t$$
$$\therefore t \rightarrow \sim m$$

The truth table for this argument is as follows:

m	*s*	*t*	First premise $m \rightarrow s$	Second premise $s \rightarrow \sim t$	Conclusion $t \rightarrow \sim m$	
T	T	T	T	F	F	Row 1
T	T	F	T	T	T	Row 2
T	F	T	F	T	F	Row 3
T	F	F	F	T	T	Row 4
F	T	T	T	F	T	Row 5
F	T	F	T	T	T	Row 6
F	F	T	T	T	T	Row 7
F	F	F	T	T	T	Row 8

The only rows in which both premises are true are rows 2, 6, 7, and 8. Because the conclusion is true in each of these rows, the argument is valid.

CHECK YOUR PROGRESS 3 Determine whether the following argument is valid or invalid.

> If I arrive before 8 A.M., then I will make the flight.
> If I make the flight, then I will give the presentation.
> ∴If I arrive before 8 A.M., then I will give the presentation.

Solution *See page S10.*

Standard Forms

Some arguments can be shown to be valid if they have the same symbolic form as an argument that is known to be valid. For instance, we have shown that the argument

$$h \to m$$
$$h$$
$$\therefore m$$

is valid. This symbolic form is known as **modus ponens** or the **law of detachment.** All arguments that have this symbolic form are valid. Table 3.13 shows four symbolic forms and the name used to identify each form. Any argument that has a symbolic form identical to one of these symbolic forms is a valid argument.

✓ **TAKE NOTE**

In logic, the ability to identify standard forms of arguments is an important skill. If an argument has one of the standard forms in Table 3.13, then it is a valid argument. If an argument has one of the standard forms in Table 3.14, then it is an invalid argument. The standard forms can be thought of as laws of logic. Concerning the laws of logic, the logician Gottlob Frege (frā′gə) (1848–1925) stated, "The laws of logic are not like the laws of nature. They…are laws of the laws of nature."

Table 3.13 *Standard Forms of Four Valid Arguments*

Modus ponens	Modus tollens	Law of syllogism	Disjunctive syllogism
$p \to q$	$p \to q$	$p \to q$	$p \lor q$
p	$\sim q$	$q \to r$	$\sim p$
$\therefore q$	$\therefore \sim p$	$\therefore p \to r$	$\therefore q$

The law of syllogism can be extended to include more than two conditional premises. For example, if the premises of an argument are $a \to b$, $b \to c$, $c \to d$, ..., $y \to z$, then a valid conclusion for the argument is $a \to z$. We will refer to any argument of this form with more than two conditional premises as the **extended law of syllogism.**

Table 3.14 shows two symbolic forms associated with invalid arguments. Any argument that has one of these symbolic forms is invalid.

Table 3.14 *Standard Forms of Two Invalid Arguments*

Fallacy of the converse	Fallacy of the inverse
$p \to q$	$p \to q$
q	$\sim p$
$\therefore p$	$\therefore \sim q$

EXAMPLE 4 ■ Use a Standard Form to Determine the Validity of an Argument

Use a standard form to determine whether the following argument is valid or invalid.

> The program is interesting or I will watch the basketball game.
>
> The program is not interesting.
>
> ∴I will watch the basketball game.

Solution

Label the statements

i: The program is interesting.

w: I will watch the basketball game.

In symbolic form the argument is:

$$i \vee w$$
$$\sim i$$
$$\therefore w$$

This symbolic form matches the standard form known as disjunctive syllogism. Thus the argument is valid.

CHECK YOUR PROGRESS 4   Use a standard form to determine whether the following argument is valid or invalid.

> If I go to Florida for spring break, then I will not study.
>
> I did not go to Florida for spring break.
>
> ∴I studied.

Solution   *See page S11.*

Consider an argument with the following symbolic form.

$q \rightarrow r$	Premise 1
$r \rightarrow s$	Premise 2
$\sim t \rightarrow \sim s$	Premise 3
q	Premise 4
$\therefore t$	

To determine whether the argument is valid or invalid using a truth table, we would require a table with $2^4 = 16$ rows. It would be time-consuming to construct such a table and, with the large number of truth values to be determined, we might make an error. Thus we consider a different approach that makes use of a sequence of valid arguments to arrive at a conclusion.

$q \rightarrow r$	Premise 1
$r \rightarrow s$	Premise 2
$\therefore q \rightarrow s$	Law of syllogism

Waterfall by M. C. Escher

M. C. Escher (1898–1972) created many works of art that defy logic. In this lithograph, the water completes a full cycle even though the water is always traveling downward.

$$q \rightarrow s \qquad \text{The previous conclusion}$$

$$\underline{s \rightarrow t} \qquad \text{Premise 3 expressed in an equivalent form}$$

$$\therefore q \rightarrow t \qquad \text{Law of syllogism}$$

$$q \rightarrow t \qquad \text{The previous conclusion}$$

$$\underline{q \qquad\qquad} \text{Premise 4}$$

$$\therefore t \qquad \text{Modus ponens}$$

This sequence of valid arguments shows that *t* is a valid conclusion for the original argument.

EXAMPLE 5 ■ Determine the Validity of an Argument

Determine whether the following argument is valid.

> If the movie was directed by Steven Spielberg (*s*), then I want to see it (*w*). The movie's production costs must exceed 50 million dollars (*c*) or I do not want to see it. The movie's production costs were less than 50 million dollars. Therefore, the movie was not directed by Steven Spielberg.

Solution

In symbolic form the argument is

$$s \rightarrow w \qquad \text{Premise 1}$$

$$c \vee {\sim} w \qquad \text{Premise 2}$$

$$\underline{{\sim} c \qquad\quad} \text{Premise 3}$$

$$\therefore {\sim} s \qquad \text{Conclusion}$$

Premise 2 can be written as ${\sim}w \vee c$, which is equivalent to $w \rightarrow c$. Applying the law of syllogism to Premise 1 and this equivalent form of Premise 2 produces

$$s \rightarrow w \qquad \text{Premise 1}$$

$$\underline{w \rightarrow c} \qquad \text{Equivalent form of Premise 2}$$

$$\therefore s \rightarrow c \qquad \text{Law of syllogism}$$

Combining the above conclusion $s \rightarrow c$ with Premise 3 gives us

$$s \rightarrow c \qquad \text{Conclusion from above}$$

$$\underline{{\sim} c \qquad\quad} \text{Premise 3}$$

$$\therefore {\sim} s \qquad \text{Modus tollens}$$

This sequence of valid arguments has produced the desired conclusion, ${\sim}s$. Thus the original argument is valid.

CHECK YOUR PROGRESS 5   Determine whether the following argument is valid.

> I start to fall asleep if I read a math book. I drink soda whenever I start to fall asleep. If I drink a soda, then I must eat a candy bar. Therefore, I eat a candy bar whenever I read a math book.

Hint: *p* whenever *q* is equivalent to $q \rightarrow p$.

Solution   See page S11.

In the next example, we use standard forms to determine a valid conclusion for an argument.

EXAMPLE 6 ■ Determine a Valid Conclusion for an Argument

Use all of the premises to determine a valid conclusion for the following argument.

We will not go to Japan ($\sim j$) or we will go to Hong Kong (h). If we visit my uncle (u), then we will go to Singapore (s). If we go to Hong Kong, then we will not go to Singapore.

Solution

In symbolic form the argument is

$\sim j \lor h$ Premise 1
$u \rightarrow s$ Premise 2
$\underline{h \rightarrow \sim s}$ Premise 3
$\therefore ?$

The first premise can be written as $j \rightarrow h$. The second premise can be written as $\sim s \rightarrow \sim u$. Therefore, the argument can be written as

$j \rightarrow h$
$\sim s \rightarrow \sim u$
$\underline{h \rightarrow \sim s}$
$\therefore ?$

✔ **TAKE NOTE**

In Example 6 we are rewriting and reordering the statements so that the extended law of syllogism can be applied.

Interchanging the second and third premises yields

$j \rightarrow h$
$h \rightarrow \sim s$
$\underline{\sim s \rightarrow \sim u}$
$\therefore ?$

An application of the extended law of syllogism produces

$j \rightarrow h$
$h \rightarrow \sim s$
$\underline{\sim s \rightarrow \sim u}$
$\therefore j \rightarrow \sim u$

Thus a valid conclusion for the original argument is "If we go to Japan (j), then we will not visit my uncle ($\sim u$)."

CHECK YOUR PROGRESS 6   Use all of the premises to determine a valid conclusion for the following argument.

$\sim m \lor t$
$t \rightarrow \sim d$
$e \lor g$
$\underline{e \rightarrow d}$
$\therefore ?$

Solution   See page S11.

MathMatters   The Paradox of the Unexpected Hanging

The following paradox, known as "the paradox of the unexpected hanging," has proved difficult to analyze.

The man was sentenced on Saturday. "The hanging will take place at noon," said the judge to the prisoner, "on one of the seven days of next week. But you will not know which day it is until you are so informed on the morning of the day of the hanging."

The judge was known to be a man who always kept his word. The prisoner, accompanied by his lawyer, went back to his cell. As soon as the two men were alone the lawyer broke into a grin. "Don't you see?" he exclaimed. "The judge's sentence cannot possibly be carried out."

"I don't see," said the prisoner.

"Let me explain. They obviously can't hang you next Saturday. Saturday is the last day of the week. On Friday afternoon you would still be alive and you would know with absolute certainty that the hanging would be on Saturday. You would know this *before* you were told so on Saturday morning. That would violate the judge's decree."

"True," said the prisoner.

"Saturday, then, is positively ruled out," continued the lawyer. "This leaves Friday as the last day they can hang you. But they can't hang you on Friday because by Thursday afternoon only two days would remain: Friday and Saturday. Since Saturday is not a possible day, the hanging would have to be on Friday. Your knowledge of that fact would violate the judge's decree again. So Friday is out. This leaves Thursday as the last possible day. But Thursday is out because if you're alive Wednesday afternoon, you'll know that Thursday is to be the day."

"I get it," said the prisoner, who was beginning to feel much better. "In exactly the same way I can rule out Wednesday, Tuesday, and Monday. That leaves only tomorrow. But they can't hang me tomorrow because I know it today!"

In brief, the judge's decree seems to be self-refuting. There is nothing logically contradictory in the two statements that make up his decree; nevertheless, it cannot be carried out in practice.

He [the prisoner] is convinced, by what appears to be unimpeachable logic, that he cannot be hanged without contradicting the conditions specified in his sentence. Then, on Thursday morning, to his great surprise, the hangman arrives. Clearly he did not expect him. What is more surprising, the judge's decree is now seen to be perfectly correct. The sentence can be carried out exactly as stated.[3]

---

3. Reprinted with the permission of Simon & Schuster from *The Unexpected Hanging and Other Mathematical Diversions* by Martin Gardner. Copyright © 1969 by Martin Gardner.

Excursion

Fallacies

Any argument that is not valid is called a **fallacy.** Ancient logicians enjoyed the study of fallacies and took pride in their ability to analyze and categorize different types of fallacies. In this Excursion we consider the four fallacies known as *circulus in probando,* the fallacy of experts, the fallacy of equivocation, and the fallacy of accident.

Circulus in Probando

A fallacy of *circulus in probando* is an argument that uses a premise as the conclusion. For instance, consider the following argument.

> The Chicago Bulls are the best basketball team because there is no basketball team that is better than the Chicago Bulls.

The fallacy of *circulus in probando* is also known as *circular reasoning* or *begging the question*.

Fallacy of Experts

A fallacy of experts is an argument that uses an expert (or a celebrity) to lend support to a product or an idea. Often the product or idea is outside the expert's area of expertise. The following endorsements may qualify as fallacy of experts arguments.

> Tiger Woods for Rolex watches
>
> Lindsey Wagner for Ford Motor Company

Fallacy of Equivocation

A fallacy of equivocation is an argument that uses a word with two interpretations in two different ways. The following argument is an example of a fallacy of equivocation.

> The highway sign read $268 fine for littering,
>
> so I decided fine, for $268, I will litter.

Fallacy of Accident

The following argument is an example of a fallacy of accident.

> Everyone should visit Europe.
>
> Therefore, prisoners on death row should be allowed to visit Europe.

Using more formal language, we can state the argument as follows.

> If you are a prisoner on death row (d), then you are a person (p).
>
> If you are a person (p), then you should be allowed to visit Europe (e).
>
> ∴If you are a prisoner on death row, then you should be allowed to visit Europe.

The symbolic form of the argument is

$$d \rightarrow p$$
$$p \rightarrow e$$
$$\therefore d \rightarrow e$$

(continued)

This argument appears to be a valid argument because it has the standard form of the law of syllogism. Common sense tells us the argument is not valid, so where have we gone wrong in our analysis of the argument?

The problem occurs with the interpretation of the word "everyone." Often, when we say "everyone," we really mean "most everyone." A fallacy of accident may occur whenever we use a statement that is often true in place of a statement that is always true.

Excursion Exercises

1. Write an argument that is an example of *circulus in probando*.

2. Give an example of an argument that is a fallacy of experts.

3. Write an argument that is an example of a fallacy of equivocation.

4. Write an argument that is an example of a fallacy of accident.

5. Algebraic arguments often consist of a list of statements. In a valid algebraic argument, each statement (after the premises) can be deduced from the previous statements. The following argument that $1 = 2$ contains exactly one step that is not valid. Identify the step and explain why it is not valid.

Let
$a = b$	• Premise
$a^2 = ab$	• Multiply each side by a.
$a^2 - b^2 = ab - b^2$	• Subtract b^2 from each side.
$(a + b)(a - b) = b(a - b)$	• Factor each side.
$a + b = b$	• Divide each side by $(a - b)$.
$b + b = b$	• Substitute b for a.
$2b = b$	• Collect like terms.
$2 = 1$	• Divide each side by b.

Exercise Set 3.5

In Exercises 1–8, use the indicated letters to write each argument in symbolic form.

1. If you can read this bumper sticker (r), you're too close (c). You can read the bumper sticker. Therefore, you're too close.

2. If Lois Lane marries Clark Kent (m), then Superman will get a new uniform (u). Superman does not get a new uniform. Therefore, Lois Lane did not marry Clark Kent.

3. If the price of gold rises (g), the stock market will fall (s). The price of gold did not rise. Therefore, the stock market did not fall.

4. I am going shopping (s) or I am going to the museum (m). I went to the museum. Therefore, I did not go shopping.

5. If we search the Internet (s), we will find information on logic (i). We searched the Internet. Therefore, we found information on logic.

6. If we check the sports results on the Excite channel (c), we will know who won the match (w). We know who won the match. Therefore, we checked the sports results on the Excite channel.

7. If the power goes off ($\sim p$), then the air conditioner will not work ($\sim a$). The air conditioner is working. Therefore, the power is not off.

8. If it snowed (s), then I did not go to my chemistry class ($\sim c$). I went to my chemistry class. Therefore, it did not snow.

In Exercises 9–24, use a truth table to determine whether the argument is valid or invalid.

9. $p \vee \sim q$
$\underline{\sim q}$
$\therefore p$

10. $\sim p \wedge q$
$\underline{\sim p}$
$\therefore q$

11. $p \rightarrow \sim q$
$\underline{\sim q}$
$\therefore p$

12. $p \rightarrow \sim q$
$\underline{p}$
$\therefore \sim q$

13. $\sim p \to \sim q$
$\underline{\sim p}$
$\therefore \sim q$

14. $\sim p \to q$
$\underline{p}$
$\therefore \sim q$

15. $(p \to q) \land (\sim p \to q)$
$\underline{q}$
$\therefore p$

16. $(p \lor q) \land (p \land q)$
$\underline{p}$
$\therefore q$

17. $(p \land \sim q) \lor (p \to q)$
$\underline{q \lor p}$
$\therefore \sim p \land q$

18. $(p \land \sim q) \to (p \lor q)$
$\underline{q \to \sim p}$
$\therefore p \to q$

19. $(p \land \sim q) \lor (p \lor r)$
$\underline{r}$
$\therefore p \lor q$

20. $(p \to q) \to (r \to \sim q)$
$\underline{p}$
$\therefore \sim r$

21. $p \leftrightarrow q$
$\underline{p \to r}$
$\therefore \sim r \to \sim p$

22. $p \land r$
$\underline{p \to \sim q}$
$\therefore r \to q$

23. $p \land \sim q$
$\underline{p \leftrightarrow r}$
$\therefore q \lor r$

24. $p \to r$
$\underline{r \to q}$
$\therefore \sim p \to \sim q$

In Exercises 25–30, use the indicated letters to write the argument in symbolic form. Then use a truth table to determine whether the argument is valid or invalid.

25. If you finish your homework (h), you may attend the reception (r). You did not finish your homework. Therefore, you cannot go to the reception.

26. The X Games will be held in Oceanside (o) if and only if the city of Oceanside agrees to pay $100,000 in prize money ($a$). If San Diego agrees to pay $200,000 in prize money ($s$), then the city of Oceanside will not agree to pay $100,000 in prize money. Therefore, if the X Games were held in Oceanside, then San Diego did not agree to pay $200,000 in prize money.

27. If I can't buy the house ($\sim b$), then at least I can dream about it (d). I can buy the house or at least I can dream about it. Therefore, I can buy the house.

28. If the winds are from the east (e), then we will not have a big surf ($\sim s$). We do not have a big surf. Therefore, the winds are from the east.

29. If I master college algebra (c), then I will be prepared for trigonometry (t). I am prepared for trigonometry. Therefore, I mastered college algebra.

30. If it is a blot (b), then it is not a clot ($\sim c$). If it is a zlot (z), then it is a clot. It is a blot. Therefore, it is not a zlot.

In Exercises 31–40, determine whether the argument is valid or invalid by comparing its symbolic form with the standard symbolic forms given in Tables 3.13 and 3.14. For each valid argument, state the name of its standard form.

31. If you take Art 151 in the fall, you will be eligible to take Art 152 in the spring. You were not eligible to take Art 152 in the spring. Therefore, you did not take Art 151 in the fall.

32. He will attend Stanford or Yale. He did not attend Yale. Therefore, he attended Stanford.

33. If I had a nickel for every logic problem I have solved, then I would be rich. I have not received a nickel for every logic problem I have solved. Therefore, I am not rich.

34. If it is a dog, then it has fleas. It has fleas. Therefore, it is a dog.

35. If we serve salmon, then Vicky will join us for lunch. If Vicky joins us for lunch, then Marilyn will not join us for lunch. Therefore, if we serve salmon, Marilyn will not join us for lunch.

36. If I go to college, then I will not be able to work for my Dad. I did not go to college. Therefore, I went to work for my Dad.

37. If my cat is left alone in the apartment, then she claws the sofa. Yesterday I left my cat alone in the apartment. Therefore, my cat clawed the sofa.

38. If I wish to use the new software, then I cannot continue to use this computer. I don't wish to use the new software. Therefore, I can continue to use this computer.

39. If Rita buys a new car, then she will not go on the cruise. Rita went on the cruise. Therefore, Rita did not buy a new car.

40. If Hideo Nomo pitches, then I will go to the game. I did not go to the game. Therefore, Hideo Nomo did not pitch.

In Exercises 41–46, use a sequence of valid arguments to show that each argument is valid.

41. $\sim p \to r$
$r \to t$
$\underline{\sim t}$
$\therefore p$

42. $r \to \sim s$
$s \lor \sim t$
$\underline{r}$
$\therefore \sim t$

43. If we sell the boat (s), then we will not go to the river ($\sim r$). If we don't go to the river, then we will go camping (c). If we do not buy a tent ($\sim t$), then we will not go camping. Therefore, if we sell the boat, then we will buy a tent.

44. If it is an ammonite (a), then it is from the Cretaceous period (c). If it is not from the Mesozoic era ($\sim m$), then it is not from the Cretaceous period. If it is from the Mesozoic era, then it is at least 65 million years old (s). Therefore, if it is an ammonite, then it is at least 65 million years old.

45. If the computer is not operating ($\sim o$), then I will not be able to finish my report ($\sim f$). If the office is closed (c), then the computer is not operating. Therefore, if I am able to finish my report, then the office is open.

46. If he reads the manuscript (r), he will like it (l). If he likes it, he will publish it (p). If he publishes it, then you will get royalties (m). You did not get royalties. Therefore, he did not read the manuscript.

Extensions

CRITICAL THINKING

In Exercises 47–50, use all of the premises to determine a valid conclusion for the given argument.

47.
$$\sim(p \land \sim q)$$
$$\underline{\quad p \quad}$$
$$\therefore ?$$

48.
$$\sim s \to q$$
$$\sim t \to \sim q$$
$$\underline{\quad \sim t \quad}$$
$$\therefore ?$$

49. If it is a theropod, then it is not herbivorous. If it is not herbivorous, then it is not a sauropod. It is a sauropod. Therefore, _____ .

50. If you buy the car, you will need a loan. You do not need a loan or you will make monthly payments. You buy the car. Therefore, _____ .

COOPERATIVE LEARNING

51. An Argument by Lewis Carroll The following argument is from *Symbolic Logic* by Lewis Carroll, written in 1896. Determine whether the argument is valid or invalid.

> Babies are illogical.
> Nobody is despised who can manage a crocodile.
> Illogical persons are despised.
> Hence, babies cannot manage crocodiles.

EXPLORATIONS

52. **Fallacies** Consult a logic text or search the Internet for information on fallacies. Write a report that includes examples of at least three of the following fallacies.

Ad hominem
Ad populum
Ad baculum
Ad vercundiam
Non sequitur
Fallacy of false cause
Pluriam interrogationem

SECTION 3.6 | **Euler Diagrams**

Euler Diagrams

Many arguments involve sets whose elements are described using the quantifiers *all, some,* and *none.* The mathematician Leonhard Euler (laônhärt oi′lər) used diagrams to determine whether arguments that involved quantifiers were valid or invalid. The following figures show Euler diagrams that illustrate the four possible relationships that can exist between two sets.

      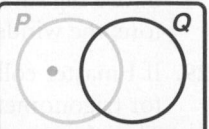

All Ps are Qs.   No Ps are Qs.   Some Ps are Qs.   Some Ps are not Qs.

Euler diagrams

Euler used diagrams to illustrate logic concepts. Some 100 years later, John Venn extended the use of Euler's diagrams to illustrate many types of mathematics. In this section, we will construct diagrams to determine the validity of arguments. We will refer to these diagrams as Euler diagrams.

EXAMPLE 1 ■ Use an Euler Diagram to Determine the Validity of an Argument

Use an Euler diagram to determine whether the following argument is valid or invalid.

> All college courses are fun.
>
> This course is a college course.
>
> ∴This course is fun.

Solution

The first premise indicates that the set of college courses is a subset of the set of fun courses. We illustrate this subset relationship with an Euler diagram, as shown in Figure 3.15. The second premise tells us that "this course" is an element of the set of college courses. If we use c to represent "this course," then c must be placed inside the set of college courses, as shown in Figure 3.16.

Figure 3.15

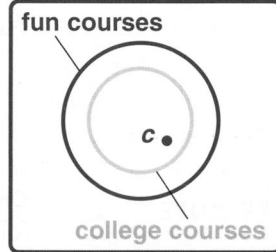

Figure 3.16

Figure 3.16 illustrates that c must also be an element of the set of fun courses. Thus the argument is valid.

CHECK YOUR PROGRESS 1 Use an Euler diagram to determine whether the following argument is valid or invalid.

> All lawyers drive BMW's.
>
> Susan is a lawyer.
>
> ∴Susan drives a BMW.

Solution *See page S11.*

If an Euler diagram can be drawn so that the conclusion does not necessarily follow from the premises, then the argument is invalid. This concept is illustrated in the next example.

This impressionist painting, *Dance at Bougival* by Renoir, is on display at the Museum of Fine Arts, Boston.

EXAMPLE 2 ■ **Use an Euler Diagram to Determine the Validity of an Argument**

Use an Euler diagram to determine whether the following argument is valid or invalid.

> Some impressionists paintings are Renoirs.
> *Dance at Bougival* is an impressionist painting.
> ∴*Dance at Bougival* is a Renoir.

Solution

The Euler diagram in Figure 3.17 illustrates the premise that some impressionist paintings are Renoirs. Let d represent the painting *Dance at Bougival*. Figures 3.18 and 3.19 show that d can be placed in one of two regions.

Figure 3.17

Figure 3.18

Figure 3.19

Although Figure 3.18 supports the argument, Figure 3.19 shows that the conclusion does not necessarily follow from the premises, and thus the argument is invalid.

CHECK YOUR PROGRESS 2 Use an Euler diagram to determine whether the following argument is valid or invalid.

> No prime numbers are negative.
> The number 7 is not negative.
> ∴The number 7 is a prime number.

Solution *See page S12.*

QUESTION *If one particular example can be found for which the conclusion of an argument is true when its premises are true, must the argument be valid?*

Some arguments can be represented by an Euler diagram that involves three sets, as shown in Example 3.

ANSWER *No. To be a valid argument, the conclusion must be true whenever the premises are true. Just because the conclusion is true for one specific example, it does not mean the argument is a valid argument.*

EXAMPLE 3 ■ Use an Euler Diagram to Determine the Validity of an Argument

Use an Euler diagram to determine whether the following argument is valid or invalid.

> No psychologist can juggle.
> All clowns can juggle.
> ∴No psychologist is a clown.

Solution

The Euler diagram in Figure 3.20 shows that the set of psychologists and the set of jugglers are disjoint sets. Figure 3.21 shows that because the set of clowns is a subset of the set of jugglers, no psychologists *p* are elements of the set of clowns. Thus the argument is valid.

Figure 3.20

Figure 3.21

CHECK YOUR PROGRESS 3 Use an Euler diagram to determine whether the following argument is valid or invalid.

> No mathematics professors are good-looking.
> All good-looking people are models.
> ∴No mathematics professor is a model.

Solution *See page S12.*

Math Matters   A Famous Puzzle

Three men decide to rent a room for one night. The regular room rate is $25; however, the desk clerk charges the men $30 because it will be easier for each man to pay one-third of $30 than it would be for each man to pay one-third of $25. Each man pays $10 and the porter shows them to their room.

After a short period of time, the desk clerk starts to feel guilty and gives the porter $5, along with instructions to return the $5 to the three men.

On the way to the room the porter decides to give each man $1 and pocket $2. After all, the men would find it difficult to split $5 evenly.

Thus each man has paid $10 and received a refund of $1. After the refund, the men have paid a total of $27. The porter has $2. The $27 added to the $2 equals $29.

QUESTION *Where is the missing dollar? (See Answer on the following page.)*

Euler Diagrams and the Extended Law of Syllogism

Example 4 uses Euler diagrams to visually illustrate the extended law of syllogism from Section 3.5.

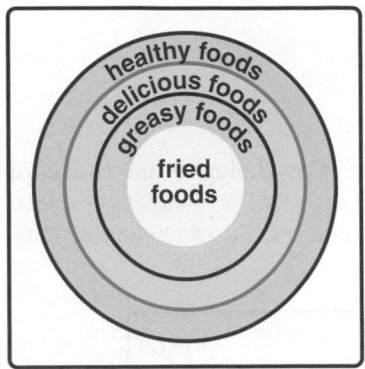

EXAMPLE 4 ■ Use an Euler Diagram to Determine the Validity of an Argument

Use an Euler diagram to determine whether the following argument is valid or invalid.

>   All fried foods are greasy.
>   All greasy foods are delicious.
>   All delicious foods are healthy.
>   ∴ All fried foods are healthy.

Solution
The figure at the left illustrates that every fried food is an element of the set of healthy foods, so the argument is valid.

✔ **TAKE NOTE**

Although the conclusion in Example 4 is false, the argument in Example 4 is valid.

CHECK YOUR PROGRESS 4   Use an Euler diagram to determine whether the following argument is valid or invalid.

>   All squares are rhombi.
>   All rhombi are parallelograms.
>   All parallelograms are quadrilaterals.
>   ∴ All squares are quadrilaterals.

Solution   See page S12.

Using Euler Diagrams to Form Conclusions

In Example 5, we make use of an Euler diagram to determine a valid conclusion for an argument.

ANSWER   *The $2 the porter kept was added to the $27 the men spent to produce a total of $29. The fact that this amount just happens to be close to $30 is a coincidence. All the money can be located if we total the $2 the porter has, the $3 that was returned to the men, and the $25 the desk clerk has, to produce $30.*

EXAMPLE 5 ■ Use an Euler Diagram to Determine the Conclusion for an Argument

Use an Euler diagram and all of the premises in the following argument to determine a valid conclusion for the argument.

All *M*s are *N*s.

No *N*s are *P*s.

∴?

Solution

The first premise indicates that the set of *M*s is a subset of the set of *N*s. The second premise indicates that the set of *N*s and the set of *P*s are disjoint sets. The following Euler diagram illustrates these set relationships. An examination of the Euler diagram allows us to conclude that no *M*s are *P*s.

CHECK YOUR PROGRESS 5   Use an Euler diagram and all of the premises in the following argument to determine a valid conclusion for the argument.

Some rabbits are white.

All white animals like tomatoes.

∴?

Solution   See page S12.

Excursion

Using Logic to Solve Puzzles

Many puzzles can be solved by making an assumption and then checking to see if the assumption is supported by the conditions (premises) associated with the puzzle. For instance, consider the following addition problem in which each letter represents a digit from 0 through 9, and different letters represent different digits.

✔ **TAKE NOTE**

When working with cryptarithms, we assume that the leading digit of each number is a nonzero digit.

```
  T A
+ B T
-----
T E E
```

(continued)

Note that the T in T E E is a carry from the middle column. Because the sum of any two single digits plus a previous carry of at most 1 is 19 or less, the T in T E E must be a 1. Replacing all the T's with 1's produces:

$$
\begin{array}{r}
1\,A \\
+\ B\,1 \\
\hline
1\,E\,E
\end{array}
$$

Now B must be an 8 or a 9, because these are the only digits that would produce a carry into the leftmost column.

Case 1: Assume B is a 9. Then A must be an 8 or smaller, and A + 1 does not produce a carry into the middle column. The sum of the digits in the middle column is 10 thus E is a 0. This presents a dilemma because the units digit of A + 1 must also be a 0, which requires A to be a 9. The assumption that B is a 9 is not supported by the conditions of the problem; thus we reject the assumption that B is a 9.

Case 2: Assume B is an 8. To produce the required carry into the leftmost column, there must be a carry from the column on the right. Thus A must be a 9, and we have the result shown below.

$$
\begin{array}{r}
1\,9 \\
+\ 8\,1 \\
\hline
1\,0\,0
\end{array}
$$

A check shows that this solution satisfies all the conditions of the problem.

Excursion Exercises

Solve the following cryptarithms. Assume that no leading digit is a 0.
(*Source:* **http://www.geocities.com/Athens/Agora/2160/puzzles.html**)[4]

1.
$$
\begin{array}{r}
S\,O \\
+\ S\,O \\
\hline
T\,O\,O
\end{array}
$$

2.
$$
\begin{array}{r}
U\,S \\
+\ A\,S \\
\hline
A\,L\,L
\end{array}
$$

3.
$$
\begin{array}{r}
C\,O\,C\,A \\
+\ C\,O\,L\,A \\
\hline
O\,A\,S\,I\,S
\end{array}
$$

4.
$$
\begin{array}{r}
A\,T \\
E\,A\,S\,T \\
+\ W\,E\,S\,T \\
\hline
S\,O\,U\,T\,H
\end{array}
$$

---

4. Copyright © 1998 by Jorge A C B Soares.

Exercise Set 3.6

In Exercises 1–20, use an Euler diagram to determine whether the argument is valid or invalid.

1. All frogs are poetical.
   Kermit is a frog.

   ∴Kermit is poetical.

2. All Oreo cookies have a filling.
   All Fig Newtons have a filling.

   ∴All Fig Newtons are Oreo cookies.

3. Some plants have flowers.
   All things that have flowers are beautiful.

   ∴Some plants are beautiful.

4. No squares are triangles.
   Some triangles are equilateral.

   ∴No squares are equilateral.

5. No rocker would do the Mariachi.
   All baseball fans do the Mariachi.

   ∴No rocker is a baseball fan.

6. Nuclear energy is not safe.
   Some electric energy is safe.

   ∴No electric energy is nuclear energy.

7. Some birds bite.
   All things that bite are dangerous.

   ∴Some birds are dangerous.

8. All fish can swim.
   That barracuda can swim.

   ∴That barracuda is a fish.

9. All men behave badly.
   Some hockey players behave badly.

   ∴Some hockey players are men.

10. All grass is green.
    That ground cover is not green.

    ∴That ground cover is not grass.

11. Most teenagers drink soda.
    No CEOs drink soda.

    ∴No CEO is a teenager.

12. Some students like history.
    Vern is a student.

    ∴Vern likes history.

13. No mathematics test is fun.
    All fun things are worth your time.

    ∴No mathematics test is worth your time.

14. All prudent people shun sharks.
    No accountant is imprudent.

    ∴No accountant fails to shun sharks.

15. All candidates without a master's degree will not be considered for the position of director.
    All candidates who are not considered for the position of director should apply for the position of assistant.

    ∴All candidates without a master's degree should apply for the position of assistant.

16. Some whales make good pets.
    Some good pets are cute.
    Some cute pets bite.

    ∴Some whales bite.

17. All prime numbers are odd.
    2 is a prime number.

    ∴2 is an odd number.

18. All Lewis Carroll arguments are valid.
    Some valid arguments are syllogisms.

    ∴Some Lewis Carroll arguments are syllogisms.

19. All aerobics classes are fun.
    Jan's class is fun.

    ∴Jan's class is an aerobics class.

20. No sane person takes a math class.
    Some students that take a math class can juggle.

    ∴No sane person can juggle.

In Exercises 21–26, use all of the premises in each argument to determine a valid conclusion for the argument.

21. All Reuben sandwiches are good.
    All good sandwiches have pastrami.
    All sandwiches with pastrami need mustard.

    ∴?

22. All cats are strange.
    Boomer is not strange.

    ∴?

23. All multiples of 11 end with a 5.
    1001 is a multiple of 11.

    ∴?

24. If it isn't broken, then I do not fix it.
    If I do not fix it, then I do not get paid.

    ∴?

25.   Some horses are frisky.
<u>All frisky horses are grey.</u>

∴?

26.   If we like to ski, then we will move to Vail.
If we move to Vail, then we will not buy a house.
<u>If we do not buy a condo, then we will buy a house.</u>

∴?

27.   Examine the following three premises:

1. All people who have an Xbox play video games.

2. All people who play video games enjoy life.

3. Some mathematics professors enjoy life.

Now consider each of the following six conclusions. For each conclusion, determine whether the argument formed by the three premises and the conclusion is valid or invalid.

a. ∴Some mathematics professors have an Xbox.

b. ∴Some mathematics professors play video games.

c. ∴Some people who play video games are mathematics professors.

d. ∴Mathematics professors never play video games.

e. ∴All people who have an Xbox enjoy life.

f. ∴Some people who enjoy life are mathematics professors.

28.   Examine the following three premises:

1. All people who drive pickup trucks like Willie Nelson.

2. All people who like Willie Nelson like country western music.

3. Some people who like heavy metal music like Willie Nelson.

Now consider each of the following five conclusions. For each conclusion, determine whether the argument formed by the three premises and the conclusion is valid or invalid.

a. ∴ Some people who like heavy metal music drive a pickup truck.

b. ∴Some people who like heavy metal music like country western music.

c. ∴Some people who like Willie Nelson like heavy metal music.

d. ∴All people who drive a pickup truck like country western music.

e. ∴People who like heavy metal music never drive a pickup truck.

Extensions

CRITICAL THINKING

29. A Crossnumber Puzzle In the following *crossnumber puzzle,* each square holds a single digit from 0 through 9. Use the clues under the *Across* and *Down* headings to solve the puzzle.

Across

1. One-fourth of 3 across

3. Two more than 1 down with its digits reversed

Down

1. Larger than 20 and less than 30

2. Half of 1 down

EXPLORATIONS

30. **Bilateral Diagrams** Lewis Carroll (Charles Dodgson) devised a *bilateral diagram* (two-part board) to analyze syllogisms. His method has some advantages over Euler diagrams and Venn diagrams. Use a library or the Internet to find information on Carroll's method of analyzing syllogisms. Write a few paragraphs that explain his method and its advantages.

CHAPTER 3   **Summary**

Key Terms

antecedent [p. 137]
argument [p. 152]
arrow notation [p. 137]
biconditional [p. 141]
component statement [p. 116]
compound statement [p. 116]
conclusion [p. 152]
conditional [p. 136]
conjunction [p. 118]
connective [p. 116]
consequent [p. 137]
contrapositive [p. 146]
converse [p. 146]
disjunction [p. 119]
disjunctive form of the conditional [p. 140]
disjunctive syllogism [p. 156]
equivalent statements [p. 129]
Euler diagram [p. 164]
existential quantifier [p. 119]
extended law of syllogism [p. 156]
fallacy of the converse [p. 156]
fallacy of the inverse [p. 156]
invalid argument [p. 152]
inverse [p. 146]
law of syllogism [p. 156]
modus ponens [p. 156]
modus tollens [p. 156]
negation [p. 117]
premise [p. 152]
quantifier [p. 119]
self-contradiction [p. 131]
standard forms of arguments [p. 156]
standard truth table form [p. 125]
statement [p. 114]
symbolic form [p. 116]
tautology [p. 131]
truth table [p. 117]
truth value [p. 117]
universal quantifier [p. 119]
valid argument [p. 152]

Essential Concepts

- **Truth Values**
  $\sim p$ is true if and only if p is false.
  $p \wedge q$ is true if and only if both p and q are true.
  $p \vee q$ is true if and only if p is true, q is true, or both p and q are true.
  The *conditional* $p \rightarrow q$ is false if p is true and q is false. It is true in all other cases.

- **De Morgan's Laws for Statements**
  $\sim(p \wedge q) \equiv \sim p \vee \sim q$ and $\sim(p \vee q) \equiv \sim p \wedge \sim q$

- **Equivalent Forms**
  $p \rightarrow q \equiv \sim p \vee q$
  $\sim(p \rightarrow q) \equiv p \wedge \sim q$
  $p \leftrightarrow q \equiv [(p \rightarrow q) \wedge (q \rightarrow p)]$

- **Statements Related to the Conditional Statement**
  The *converse* of $p \rightarrow q$ is $q \rightarrow p$.
  The *inverse* of $p \rightarrow q$ is $\sim p \rightarrow \sim q$.
  The *contrapositive* of $p \rightarrow q$ is $\sim q \rightarrow \sim p$.

- **Valid Arguments**

Modus ponens	Modus tollens	Law of syllogism	Disjunctive syllogism
$p \rightarrow q$	$p \rightarrow q$	$p \rightarrow q$	$p \vee q$
$\underline{p}$	$\underline{\sim q}$	$\underline{q \rightarrow r}$	$\underline{\sim p}$
$\therefore q$	$\therefore \sim p$	$\therefore p \rightarrow r$	$\therefore q$

- **Invalid Arguments**

Fallacy of the converse	Fallacy of the inverse
$p \rightarrow q$	$p \rightarrow q$
$\underline{q}$	$\underline{\sim p}$
$\therefore p$	$\therefore \sim q$

- **Order of Precedence Agreement**
  If grouping symbols are not used to specify the order in which logical connectives are applied, then we use the following Order of Precedence Agreement.

  First apply the negations from left to right, then apply the conjunctions from left to right, and finally apply the disjunctions from left to right.

In Exercises 1–6, determine whether each sentence is a statement. Assume that a and b are real numbers.

1. How much is a ticket to London?
2. 91 is a prime number.
3. $a > b$
4. $a^2 \geq 0$
5. Lock the car.
6. Clark Kent is Superman.

In Exercises 7–10, write each sentence in symbolic form. Represent each component of the sentence with the letter indicated in parentheses. Also state whether the sentence is a conjunction, a disjunction, a negation, a conditional, or a biconditional.

7. Today is Monday (m) and it is my birthday (b).
8. If x is divisible by 2 (d), then x is an even number (e).
9. I am going to the dance (g) if and only if I have a date (d).
10. All triangles (t) have exactly three sides (s).

In Exercises 11–16, write the negation of each quantified statement.

11. Some dogs bite.
12. Every dessert at the Cove restaurant is good.
13. All winners receive a prize.
14. Some cameras do not use film.
15. None of the students received an A.
16. At least one person enjoyed the story.

In Exercises 17–22, determine whether each statement is true or false.

17. $5 > 2$ or $5 = 2$.
18. $3 \neq 5$ and 7 is a prime number.
19. $4 \leq 7$
20. $-3 < -1$
21. Every repeating decimal is a rational number.
22. There exists a real number that is not positive and not negative.

In Exercises 23–28, determine the truth value of the statement given that p is true, q is false, and r is false.

23. $(p \wedge q) \vee (\sim p \vee q)$
24. $(p \to \sim q) \leftrightarrow \sim(p \vee q)$
25. $(p \wedge \sim q) \wedge (\sim r \vee q)$
26. $(r \wedge \sim p) \vee [(p \vee \sim q) \leftrightarrow (q \to r)]$

27. $[p \wedge (r \to q)] \to (q \vee \sim r)$
28. $(\sim q \vee \sim r) \to [(p \leftrightarrow \sim r) \wedge q]$

In Exercises 29–36, construct a truth table for the given statement.

29. $(\sim p \to q) \vee (\sim q \wedge p)$
30. $\sim p \leftrightarrow (q \vee p)$
31. $\sim(p \vee \sim q) \wedge (q \to p)$
32. $(p \leftrightarrow q) \vee (\sim q \wedge p)$
33. $(r \leftrightarrow \sim q) \vee (p \to q)$
34. $(\sim r \vee \sim q) \wedge (q \to p)$
35. $[p \leftrightarrow (q \to \sim r)] \wedge \sim q$
36. $\sim(p \wedge q) \to (\sim q \vee \sim r)$

In Exercises 37–40, make use of De Morgan's laws to write the given statement in an equivalent form.

37. It is not true that Bob failed the English proficiency test and he registered for a speech course.
38. Ellen did not go to work this morning and she did not take her medication.
39. Wendy will go to the store this afternoon or she will not be able to prepare her fettuccine al pesto recipe.
40. Gina enjoyed the movie, but she did not enjoy the party.

In Exercises 41–44, use a truth table to show that the given pairs of statements are equivalent.

41. $\sim p \to \sim q;\ p \vee \sim q$
42. $\sim p \vee q;\ \sim(p \wedge \sim q)$
43. $p \vee (q \wedge \sim p);\ p \vee q$
44. $p \leftrightarrow q;\ (p \wedge q) \vee (\sim p \wedge \sim q)$

In Exercises 45–48, use a truth table to determine whether the given statement is a tautology or a self-contradiction.

45. $p \wedge (q \wedge \sim p)$
46. $(p \wedge q) \vee (p \to \sim q)$
47. $[\sim(p \to q)] \leftrightarrow (p \wedge \sim q)$
48. $p \vee (p \to q)$

In Exercises 49–52, identify the antecedent and the consequent of each conditional statement.

49. If he has talent, he will succeed.
50. If I had a credential, I could get the job.
51. I will follow the exercise program provided I join the fitness club.
52. I will attend only if it is free.

In Exercises 53–56, write each conditional statement in its equivalent disjunctive form.

53. If she were tall, she would be on the volleyball team.

54. If he can stay awake, he can finish the report.

55. Rob will start provided he is not ill.

56. Sharon will be promoted only if she closes the deal.

In Exercises 57–60, write the negation of each conditional statement in its equivalent conjunctive form.

57. If I get my paycheck, I will purchase a ticket.

58. The tomatoes will get big only if you provide them with plenty of water.

59. If you entered Cleggmore University, then you had a high score on the SAT exam.

60. If Ryan enrolls at a university, then he will enroll at Yale.

In Exercises 61–66, determine whether the given statement is true or false. Assume that x and y are real numbers.

61. $x = y$ if and only if $|x| = |y|$.

62. $x > y$ if and only if $x - y > 0$.

63. If $x + y = 2x$, then $y = x$.

64. If $x > y$, then $\frac{1}{x} > \frac{1}{y}$.

65. If $x^2 > 0$, then $x > 0$.

66. If $x^2 = y^2$, then $x = y$.

In Exercises 67–70, write each statement in "If p, then q" form.

67. Every nonrepeating, nonterminating decimal is an irrational number.

68. Being well known is a necessary condition for a politician.

69. I could buy the house provided I could sell my condominium.

70. Being divisible by 9 is a sufficient condition for being divisible by 3.

In Exercises 71–76, write the **a.** converse, **b.** inverse, and **c.** contrapositive of the given statement.

71. If $x + 4 > 7$, then $x > 3$.

72. All recipes in this book can be prepared in less than 20 minutes.

73. If a and b are both divisible by 3, then $(a + b)$ is divisible by 3.

74. If you build it, they will come.

75. Every trapezoid has exactly two parallel sides.

76. If they like it, they will return.

77. What is the inverse of the contrapositive of $p \rightarrow q$?

78. What is the converse of the contrapositive of the inverse of $p \rightarrow q$?

In Exercises 79–82, determine the original statement if the given statement is related to the original statement in the manner indicated.

79. *Converse:* If $x > 2$, then x is an odd prime number.

80. *Negation:* The senator will attend the meeting and she will not vote on the motion.

81. *Inverse:* If their manager will not contact me, then I will not purchase any of their products.

82. *Contrapositive:* If Ginny can't rollerblade, then I can't rollerblade.

In Exercises 83–86, use a truth table to determine whether the argument is valid or invalid.

83. $(p \wedge \sim q) \wedge (\sim p \rightarrow q)$
$\underline{p\hspace{4.5cm}}$
$\therefore \sim q$

84. $p \rightarrow \sim q$
$\underline{q\hspace{2.5cm}}$
$\therefore \sim p$

85. r
$p \rightarrow \sim r$
$\underline{\sim p \rightarrow q}$
$\therefore p \wedge q$

86. $(p \vee \sim r) \rightarrow (q \wedge r)$
$\underline{r \wedge p\hspace{3cm}}$
$\therefore p \vee q$

In Exercises 87–92, determine whether the argument is valid or invalid by comparing its symbolic form with the symbolic forms in Tables 3.13 and 3.14, page 156.

87. We will serve either fish or chicken for lunch. We did not serve fish for lunch. Therefore, we served chicken for lunch.

88. If Mike is a CEO, then he will be able to afford to make a donation. If Mike can afford to make a donation, then he loves to ski. Therefore, if Mike does not love to ski, he is not a CEO.

89. If we wish to win the lottery, we must buy a lottery ticket. We did not win the lottery. Therefore, we did not buy a lottery ticket.

90. Robert can charge it on his MasterCard or his Visa. Robert does not use his MasterCard. Therefore, Robert charged it to his Visa.

91. If we are going to have a caesar salad, then we need to buy some eggs. We did not buy eggs. Therefore, we are not going to have a caesar salad.

92. If we serve lasagna, then Eva will not come to our dinner party. We did not serve lasagna. Therefore, Eva came to our dinner party.

In Exercises 93–96, use an Euler diagram to determine whether the argument is valid or invalid.

93.   No wizard can yodel.
       All lizards can yodel.
       ∴No wizard is a lizard.

94.   Some dogs have tails.
       Some dogs are big.
       ∴Some big dogs have tails.

95.   All Italian villas are wonderful. It is not wise to invest in expensive villas. Some wonderful villas are expensive. Therefore, it is not wise to invest in Italian villas.

96.   All logicians like to sing "It's a small world after all." Some logicians have been presidential candidates. Therefore, some presidential candidates like to sing "It's a small world after all."

CHAPTER 3   Test

1. Determine whether each sentence is a statement.
   a. Look for the cat.
   b. Clark Kent is afraid of the dark.

2. Write the negation of each statement.
   a. Some trees are not green.
   b. None of the kids had seen the movie.

3. Determine whether each statement is true or false.
   a. $5 \leq 4$
   b. $-2 \geq -2$

4. Determine the truth value of each statement given that p is true, q is false, and r is true.
   a. $(p \vee \sim q) \wedge (\sim r \wedge q)$
   b. $(r \vee \sim p) \vee [(p \vee \sim q) \leftrightarrow (q \to r)]$

In Exercises 5 and 6, construct a truth table for the given statement.

5. $\sim(p \wedge \sim q) \vee (q \to p)$ 6. $(r \leftrightarrow \sim q) \wedge (p \to q)$

7. Use one of De Morgan's laws to write the following in an equivalent form.

   Elle did not eat breakfast and she did not take a lunch break.

8. ✎   What is a tautology?

9. Write $p \to q$ in its equivalent disjunctive form.

10. Determine whether the given statement is true or false. Assume that x, y, and z are real numbers.
    a. $x = y$ if $|x| = |y|$.   b. If $x > y$, then $xz > yz$.

11. Write the a. converse, b. inverse, and c. contrapositive of the following statement.
    $$\text{If } x + 7 > 11, \text{ then } x > 4.$$

12. Write the standard form known as modus ponens.

13. Write the standard form known as the law of syllogism.

In Exercises 14 and 15, use a truth table to determine whether the argument is valid or invalid.

14. $(p \wedge \sim q) \wedge (\sim p \to q)$ 15. r
       $\underline{p\qquad\qquad\qquad\qquad}$ $p \to \sim r$
       $\therefore \sim q$ $\underline{\sim p \to q}$
                                                        $\therefore p \wedge q$

In Exercises 16–20, determine whether the argument is valid or invalid. Explain how you made your decision.

16. If we wish to win the talent contest, we must practice. We did not win the contest. Therefore, we did not practice.

17. Gina will take a job in Atlanta or she will take a job in Kansas City. Gina did not take a job in Atlanta. Therefore, Gina took a job in Kansas City.

18.   No wizard can glow in the dark.
       Some lizards can glow in the dark.
       ∴No wizard is a lizard.

19.   Some novels are worth reading.
       War and Peace is a novel.
       ∴*War and Peace* is worth reading.

20. If I cut my night class, then I will go to the party. I went to the party. Therefore, I cut my night class.

4

Numeration Systems and Number Theory

4.1	**Early Numeration Systems**
4.2	**Place-Value Systems**
4.3	**Different Base Systems**
4.4	**Arithmetic in Different Bases**
4.5	**Prime Numbers**
4.6	**Topics from Number Theory**

We start this chapter with an examination of several numeration systems. A working knowledge of these numeration systems will enable you better to understand and appreciate the advantages of our current Hindu-Arabic numeration system.

The last two sections of this chapter cover prime numbers and topics from the field of number theory. Many of the concepts in number theory are easy to comprehend but difficult, or impossible, to prove. The mathematician Karl Friedrich Gauss (1777–1855) remarked that "it is just this which gives the higher arithmetic (number theory) that magical charm which has made it the favorite science of the greatest mathematicians, not to mention its inexhaustible wealth, wherein it so greatly surpasses other parts of mathematics." Gauss referred to mathematics as "the queen of the sciences," and he considered the field of number theory "the queen of mathematics."

There are many unsolved problems in the field of number theory. One unsolved problem, dating from the year 1742, is *Goldbach's Conjecture,* which states that every even number greater than 2 can be written as the sum of two prime numbers. This conjecture has yet to be proved or disproved, despite the efforts of the world's best mathematicians. A British publishing company has recently offered a $1 million prize to the first person who proves or disproves Goldbach's Conjecture. The company hopes that the prize money will entice young, mathematically talented people to work on the problem. This scenario is similar to the story line in the movie *Good Will Hunting,* in which a mathematics problem posted on a bulletin board attracts the attention of a yet-to-be-discovered math genius, played by Matt Damon.

NUMBER THEORY

THE QUEEN OF MATHEMATICS

For online student resources, visit this textbook's website at **www.cengage.com/math.**

SECTION 4.1 | **Early Numeration Systems**

The Egyptian Numeration System

In mathematics, symbols that are used to represent numbers are called **numerals.** A number can be represented by many different numerals. For instance, the concept of "eightness" is represented by each of the following.

Hindu-Arabic: 8   Tally: 卌 ||| Roman: VIII

Chinese: 八   Egyptian: ||||||||| Babylonian: ᛉᛉᛉᛉᛉᛉᛉᛉ

A **numeration system** consists of a set of numerals and a method of arranging the numerals to represent numbers. The numeration system that most people use today is known as the *Hindu-Arabic numeration system.* It makes use of the 10 numerals 0, 1, 2, 3, 4, 5, 6, 7, 8, and 9. Before we examine the Hindu-Arabic numeration system in detail, it will be helpful to study some of the earliest numeration systems that were developed by the Egyptians, the Romans, and the Chinese.

The Egyptian numeration system uses pictorial symbols called **hieroglyphics** as numerals. The Egyptian hieroglyphic system is an **additive system** because any given number is written by using numerals whose sum equals the number. Table 4.1 gives the Egyptian hieroglyphics for powers of 10 from one to one million.

Table 4.1 *Egyptian Hieroglyphics for Powers of 10*

Hindu-Arabic Numeral	Egyptian Hieroglyphic	Description of Hieroglyphic
1	|	stroke
10	∩	heel bone
100	ϑ	scroll
1000	⚐	lotus flower
10,000	⸍	pointing finger
100,000	⤙	fish
1,000,000	⚲	astonished person

To write the number 300, the Egyptians wrote the scroll hieroglyphic three times: ϑϑϑ. In the Egyptian hieroglyphic system, the order of the hieroglyphics is of no importance. Each of the following Egyptian numerals represents 321.

ϑϑϑ∩∩|, ∩∩ϑ|ϑϑ, ϑ|∩ϑ∩ϑ, |∩ϑ

EXAMPLE 1 ■ Write a Numeral Using Egyptian Hieroglyphics

Write 3452 using Egyptian hieroglyphics.

Solution

3452 = 3000 + 400 + 50 + 2. Thus the Egyptian numeral for 3452 is

𓍦𓍦𓍦𓏢𓏢𓏢𓏢∩∩∩∩∩||

CHECK YOUR PROGRESS 1   Write 201,473 using Egyptian hieroglyphics.

Solution   See page S12.

QUESTION   *Do the Egyptian hieroglyphics* 𓏢𓏢∩| *and* ∩|𓏢𓏢 *represent the same number?*

EXAMPLE 2 ■ Evaluate a Numeral Written Using Egyptian Hieroglyphics

Write ⟗////𓍦𓍦𓍦𓏢𓏢∩||| as a Hindu-Arabic numeral.

Solution

$(2 \times 100{,}000) + (3 \times 10{,}000) + (2 \times 1000) + (4 \times 100) + (1 \times 10) + (3 \times 1) = 232{,}413$

CHECK YOUR PROGRESS 2   Write 𓆼⟗////𓍦𓍦𓍦𓍦𓏢∩∩|||| as a Hindu-Arabic numeral.

Solution   See page S12.

---

historical note

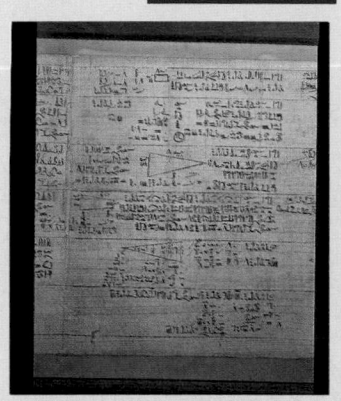

A portion of the Rhind papyrus

The Rhind papyrus is named after Alexander Henry Rhind, who purchased the papyrus in Egypt in A.D. 1858. Today the Rhind papyrus is preserved in the British Museum in London. ■

One of the earliest written documents of mathematics is the Rhind papyrus (see the figure at the left). This tablet was found in Egypt in A.D. 1858, but it is estimated that the writings date back to 1650 B.C. The Rhind papyrus contains 85 mathematical problems. Studying these problems has enabled mathematicians and historians to understand some of the mathematical procedures used in the early Egyptian numeration system.

The operation of addition with Egyptian hieroglyphics is a simple grouping process. In some cases the final sum can be simplified by replacing a group of hieroglyphics by a single hieroglyphic with a larger numeric value. This technique is illustrated in Example 3.

ANSWER   *Yes, they both represent 211.*

EXAMPLE 3 ■ Use Egyptian Hieroglyphics to Find a Sum

Use Egyptian hieroglyphics to find $2452 + 1263$.

Solution

The sum is found by combining the hieroglyphics.

$$
\begin{array}{r}
2452 \\
+\ 1263 \\
\end{array}
$$

Replacing 10 heel bones with one scroll produces

𐦀𐦀𐦀99999999∩|||||| or 3715

The sum is 3715.

CHECK YOUR PROGRESS 3 Use Egyptian hieroglyphics to find $23{,}341 + 10{,}562$.

Solution See page S12.

In the Egyptian numeration system, subtraction is performed by removing some of the hieroglyphics from the larger numeral. In some cases it is necessary to "borrow," as shown in the next example.

EXAMPLE 4 ■ Use Egyptian Hieroglyphics to Find a Difference

Use Egyptian hieroglyphics to find $332{,}246 - 101{,}512$.

Solution

The numerical value of one lotus flower is equivalent to the numerical value of 10 scrolls. Thus

$$
\begin{array}{r}
332{,}246 \\
-\ 101{,}512 \\
\end{array}
$$

The difference is 230,734.

CHECK YOUR PROGRESS 4 Use Egyptian hieroglyphics to find $61{,}432 - 45{,}121$.

Solution See page S12.

✔ **TAKE NOTE**

Five scrolls cannot be removed from two scrolls, so one lotus flower is replaced by ten scrolls, resulting in a total of twelve scrolls. Now five scrolls can be removed from twelve scrolls.

Math Matters   Early Egyptian Fractions

Evidence gained from the Rhind papyrus shows that the Egyptian method of calculating with fractions was much different from the methods we use today. All Egyptian fractions $\left(\text{except for } \frac{2}{3}\right)$ were represented in terms of unit fractions, which are fractions of the form $\frac{1}{n}$, for some natural number $n > 1$. The Egyptians wrote these unit fractions by placing an oval over the numeral that represented the denominator. For example,

$$\overset{\bigcirc}{|||} = \frac{1}{3} \qquad \overset{\bigcirc}{\cap ||||||} = \frac{1}{15}$$

If a fraction was not a unit fraction, then the Egyptians wrote the fraction as the sum of *distinct* unit fractions. For instance,

$$\frac{2}{5} \text{ was written as the sum of } \frac{1}{3} \text{ and } \frac{1}{15}.$$

Of course, $\frac{2}{5} = \frac{1}{5} + \frac{1}{5}$, but (for some mysterious reason) the early Egyptian numeration system didn't allow repetitions. The Rhind papyrus includes a table that shows how to write fractions of the form $\frac{2}{k}$, where k is an odd number from 5 to 101, in terms of unit fractions. Some of these are listed below.

$$\frac{2}{7} = \frac{1}{4} + \frac{1}{28} \qquad \frac{2}{11} = \frac{1}{6} + \frac{1}{66} \qquad \frac{2}{19} = \frac{1}{12} + \frac{1}{76} + \frac{1}{114}$$

Table 4.2 *Roman Numerals*

Hindu-Arabic Numeral	Roman Numeral
1	I
5	V
10	X
50	L
100	C
500	D
1000	M

The Roman Numeration System

The Roman numeration system was used in Europe during the reign of the Roman Empire. Today we still make limited use of Roman numerals on clock faces, on the cornerstones of buildings, and in numbering the volumes of periodicals and books. Table 4.2 shows the numerals used in the Roman numeration system. If the Roman numerals are listed so that each numeral has a larger value than the numeral to its right, then the value of the Roman numeral is found by adding the values of each numeral. For example,

$$\text{CLX} = 100 + 50 + 10 = 160$$

If a Roman numeral is repeated two or three times in succession, we add to determine its numerical value. For instance, $XX = 10 + 10 = 20$ and $CCC = 100 + 100 + 100 = 300$. Each of the numerals I, X, C, and M may be repeated up to three times. The numerals V, L, and D are not repeated.

Although the Roman numeration system is an additive system, it also incorporates a subtraction property. In the Roman numeration system, the value of a numeral is determined by adding the values of the numerals from left to right. However, if the value of a numeral is less than the value of the numeral to its right, the smaller value is subtracted from the next larger value. For instance, $VI = 5 + 1 = 6$; however, $IV = 5 - 1 = 4$. In the Roman numeration system the only numerals whose values can be subtracted from the value of the numeral to

The Roman numeration system evolved over a period of several years, and thus some Roman numerals displayed on ancient structures do not adhere to the basic rules given at the right. For instance, in the Colosseum in Rome (c. A.D. 80), the numeral XXVIIII appears above archway 29 instead of the numeral XXIX. ∎

the right are I, X, and C. Also, the subtraction of these values is allowed only if the value of the numeral to the right is within two rows as shown in Table 4.2. That is, the value of the numeral to be subtracted must be *no less than* one-tenth of the value of the numeral it is to be subtracted from. For instance, XL = 40 and XC = 90, but XD does not represent 490 because the value of X is less than one-tenth the value of D. To write 490 using Roman numerals, we write CDXC.

A Summary of the Basic Rules Employed in the Roman Numeration System

I = 1,   V = 5,   X = 10,   L = 50,   C = 100,   D = 500,   M = 1000

1. If the numerals are listed so that each numeral has a larger value than the numeral to the right, then the value of the Roman numeral is found by adding the values of the numerals.

2. Each of the numerals, I, X, C, and M may be repeated up to three times. The numerals V, L, and D are not repeated. If a numeral is repeated two or three times in succession, we add to determine its numerical value.

3. The only numerals whose values can be subtracted from the value of the numeral to the right are I, X, and C. The value of the numeral to be subtracted must be no less than one-tenth of the value of the numeral to its right.

EXAMPLE 5 ■ Evaluate a Roman Numeral

Write DCIV as a Hindu-Arabic numeral.

Solution
Because the value of D is larger than the value of C, we add their numerical values. The value of I is less than the value of V, so we subtract the smaller value from the larger value. Thus

$$\text{DCIV} = (\text{DC}) + (\text{IV}) = (500 + 100) + (5 - 1) = 600 + 4 = 604$$

CHECK YOUR PROGRESS 5   Write MCDXLV as a Hindu-Arabic numeral.

Solution   *See page S12.*

The spreadsheet program Excel has a function that converts Hindu-Arabic numerals to Roman numerals. In the Edit Formula dialogue box, type

= ROMAN(n),

where n is the number you wish to convert to a Roman numeral.

EXAMPLE 6 ■ Write a Hindu-Arabic Numeral as a Roman Numeral

Write 579 as a Roman numeral.

Solution
$$579 = 500 + 50 + 10 + 10 + 9$$

In Roman numerals 9 is written as IX. Thus 579 = DLXXIX.

CHECK YOUR PROGRESS 6   Write 473 as a Roman numeral.

Solution   *See page S12.*

In the Roman numeration system, a bar over a numeral is used to denote a value 1000 times the value of the numeral. For instance,

$$\overline{\text{V}} = 5 \times 1000 = 5000 \qquad \overline{\text{IV}}\text{LXX} = (4 \times 1000) + 70 = 4070$$

✔ TAKE NOTE

The method of writing a bar over a numeral should be used only to write Roman numerals that cannot be written using the basic rules. For instance, the Roman numeral for 2003 is MMIII, not $\overline{\text{IIIII}}$.

EXAMPLE 7 ■ **Convert Between Roman Numerals and Hindu-Arabic Numerals**

a. Write $\overline{\text{IV}}$DLXXII as a Hindu-Arabic numeral.

b. Write 6125 as a Roman numeral.

Solution

a. $\overline{\text{IV}}$DLXXII = $(\overline{\text{IV}})$ + (DLXXII)
   $= (4 \times 1000) + (572)$
   $= 4572$

b. The Roman numeral 6 is written VI and 125 is written as CXXV. Thus in Roman numerals 6125 is $\overline{\text{VI}}$CXXV.

CHECK YOUR PROGRESS 7

a. Write $\overline{\text{VII}}$CCLIV as a Hindu-Arabic numeral.

b. Write 8070 as a Roman numeral.

Solution   *See page S12.*

Excursion

A Rosetta Tablet for the Traditional Chinese Numeration System

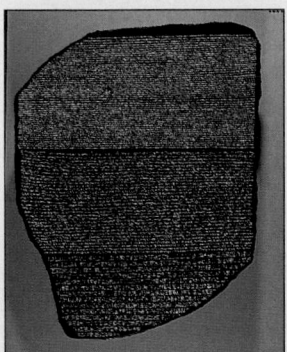

The Rosetta Stone

Most of the knowledge we have gained about early numeration systems has been obtained from inscriptions found on ancient tablets or stones. The information provided by these inscriptions has often been difficult to interpret. For several centuries archeologists had little success in interpreting the Egyptian hieroglyphics they had discovered. Then, in 1799, a group of French military engineers discovered a basalt stone near Rosetta in the Nile delta. This stone, which we now call the Rosetta Stone, has an inscription in three scripts: Greek, Egyptian Demotic, and Egyptian hieroglyphic. It was soon discovered that all three scripts contained the same message. The Greek script was easy to translate, and from its translation, clues were uncovered that enabled scholars to translate many of the documents that up to that time had been unreadable.

Pretend that you are an archeologist. Your team has just discovered an old tablet that displays Roman numerals and traditional Chinese numerals. It also provides hints in the form of a crossword puzzle about the traditional Chinese numeration system. Study the inscriptions on the following tablet and then complete the Excursion Exercises that follow.

(continued)

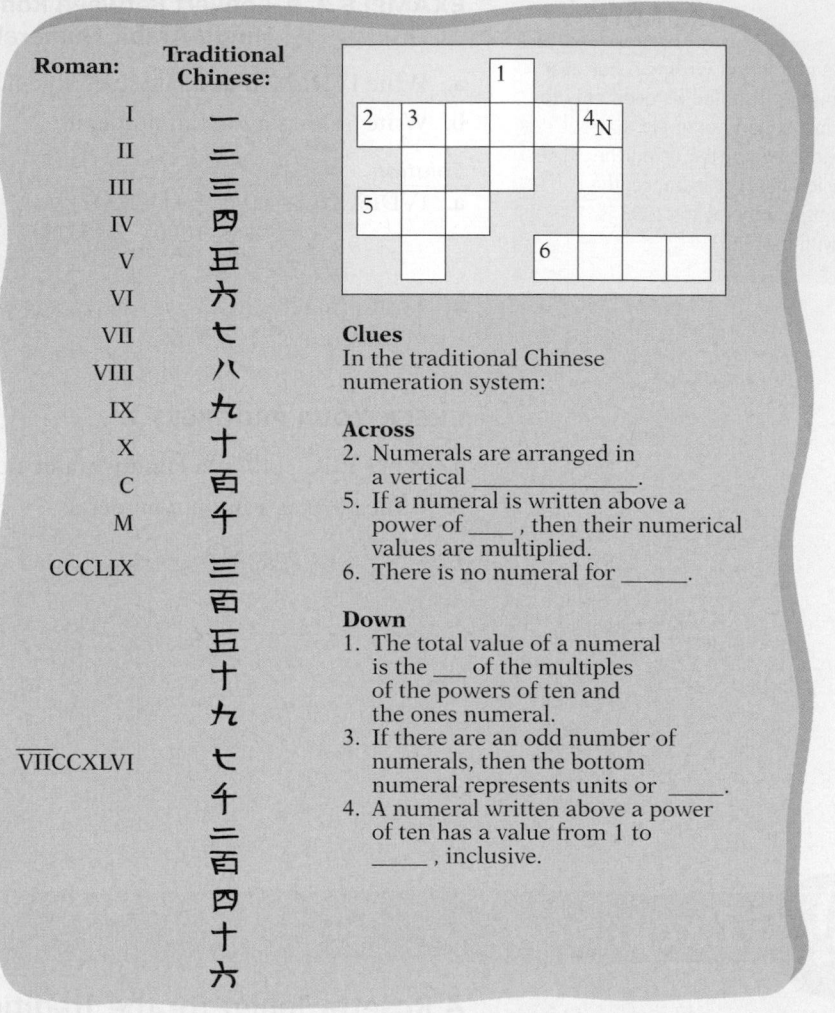

Roman:

I
II
III
IV
V
VI
VII
VIII
IX
X
C
M

CCCLIX

VIICCXLVI

Clues

In the traditional Chinese numeration system:

Across

2. Numerals are arranged in a vertical _____.
5. If a numeral is written above a power of ____ , then their numerical values are multiplied.
6. There is no numeral for _____.

Down

1. The total value of a numeral is the ___ of the multiples of the powers of ten and the ones numeral.
3. If there are an odd number of numerals, then the bottom numeral represents units or _____.
4. A numeral written above a power of ten has a value from 1 to _____ , inclusive.

Excursion Exercises

1. Complete the crossword puzzle shown on the above tablet.

2. Write 26 as a traditional Chinese numeral.

3. Write 357 as a traditional Chinese numeral.

4. Write the Hindu-Arabic numeral given by each of the following traditional Chinese numerals.

a. 八
   百
   九
   十
   六

b. 二
   千
   四
   百
   六
   十
   五

(continued)

5. a. How many Hindu-Arabic numerals are required to write four thousand five hundred twenty-eight?

b. How many traditional Chinese numerals are required to write four thousand five hundred twenty-eight?

6. The traditional Chinese numeration system is no longer in use. Give a reason that may have contributed to its demise.

Exercise Set 4.1

In Exercises 1–12, write each Hindu-Arabic numeral using Egyptian hieroglyphics.

1. 46

2. 82

3. 103

4. 157

5. 2568

6. 3152

7. 23,402

8. 15,303

9. 65,800

10. 43,217

11. 1,405,203

12. 653,271

In Exercises 13–24, write each Egyptian numeral as a Hindu-Arabic numeral.

13. 𓍢𓍢𓏤𓎆𓎆𓏤𓏤𓏤𓏤

14. 𓏤𓍢𓍢𓍢𓎆𓏤𓏤

15. 𓍢𓍢𓍢𓍢𓎆𓎆𓏤𓏤𓏤 𓍢𓍢𓍢𓍢𓎆𓎆𓏤𓏤

16. 𓍢𓎆𓎆𓎆𓎆𓏤𓏤𓏤𓏤𓏤 𓍢𓎆𓎆𓎆𓎆𓏤𓏤𓏤𓏤

17. 𓏤𓍢𓍢𓎆𓎆𓎆𓏤𓏤

18. 𓏤𓏤 𓍢𓍢𓎆𓏤 𓆐𓏤𓏤𓎆𓎆𓍢𓎆𓎆𓏤𓏤

19. 𓆐𓆐𓏤𓏤𓏤𓎆𓎆𓏤

20. 𓏤𓏤𓏤𓏤𓏤𓍢𓍢𓍢𓍢𓍢𓎆𓎆𓎆𓏤𓏤𓏤

21. 𓏤𓏤𓏤𓏤 𓍢𓍢𓍢𓍢𓍢𓍢𓎆𓎆𓎆𓎆𓏤𓏤𓏤𓏤𓏤 𓏤𓏤𓏤𓏤 𓍢𓍢𓍢𓍢𓍢𓎆𓎆𓎆𓎆𓎆𓏤𓏤𓏤𓏤𓏤

22. 𓅆𓆐𓏤𓏤𓏤𓏤𓍢𓍢𓍢𓍢𓍢𓍢𓍢𓎆 𓅆𓆐𓏤 𓍢𓍢𓍢𓍢𓍢𓍢𓎆𓎆𓎆𓏤𓏤𓏤

23. 𓅆𓅆𓅆𓅆𓆏𓏤𓍢𓍢𓏤𓏤𓏤 𓅆𓅆𓅆𓏤𓏤𓏤 𓏤𓍢𓍢𓏤𓏤𓏤

24. 𓅆𓆏𓆏𓏤𓍢𓍢 𓅆𓆏𓆏𓍢𓍢

In Exercises 25–32, use Egyptian hieroglyphics to find each sum or difference.

25. 51 + 43

26. 67 + 58

27. 231 + 435

28. 623 + 124

29. 83 − 51

30. 94 − 23

31. 254 − 198

32. 640 − 278

In Exercises 33–44, write each Roman numeral as a Hindu-Arabic numeral.

33. DCL

34. MCX

35. MCDIX

36. MDCCII

37. MCCXL

38. MMDCIV

39. DCCCXL

40. CDLV

41. $\overline{\text{IX}}$XLIV

42. $\overline{\text{VII}}$DXVII

43. $\overline{\text{XI}}$CDLXI

44. $\overline{\text{IV}}$CCXXI

In Exercises 45–56, write each Hindu-Arabic numeral as a Roman numeral.

45. 157

46. 231

47. 542

48. 783

49. 1197

50. 1039

51. 787

52. 1343

53. 683

54. 959

55. 6898

56. 4357

Egyptian Multiplication The Rhind papyrus contains problems that show a *doubling procedure* used by the Egyptians to find the product of two whole numbers. The following examples illustrate this doubling procedure. In the examples we have used Hindu-Arabic numerals so that you can concentrate on the doubling procedure and not be distracted by the Egyptian hieroglyphics. The first example determines the product 5 × 27 by computing two successive doublings of 27 and then forming the sum of the blue numbers in the rows marked with a check. Note that the rows marked with a check show that one 27 is 27 and four 27's is 108. Thus five 27's is the sum of 27 and 108, or 135.

$$
\begin{array}{cl}
\checkmark\ 1 & 27 \\
\ \ \ 2 & 54 \\
\checkmark\ 4 & \underline{108} \\
\ \ \ 5 & 135
\end{array}
$$

double
double

This sum is the product of 5 and 27.

In the next example, we use the Egyptian doubling procedure to find the product of 35 and 94. Because the sum of 1, 2, and 32 is 35, we add only the blue numbers in the rows marked with a check to find that 35 × 94 = 94 + 188 + 3008 = 3290.

$$
\begin{array}{cl}
\checkmark\ 1 & 94 \\
\checkmark\ 2 & 188 \\
\ \ \ 4 & 376 \\
\ \ \ 8 & 752 \\
\ \ 16 & 1504 \\
\checkmark\ 32 & \underline{3008} \\
\ \ 35 & 3290
\end{array}
$$

double
double
double
double
double

This sum is the product of 35 and 94.

In Exercises 57–64, use the Egyptian doubling procedure to find each product.

57. 8 × 63

58. 4 × 57

59. 7 × 29

60. 9 × 33

61. 17 × 35

62. 26 × 43

63. 23 × 108

64. 72 × 215

Extensions

CRITICAL THINKING

65. a. State a reason why you might prefer to use the Egyptian hieroglyphic numeration system rather than the Roman numeration system.

b. State a reason why you might prefer to use the Roman numeration system rather than the Egyptian hieroglyphic numeration system.

66. What is the largest number that can be written using Roman numerals without using the bar over a numeral or the subtraction property?

EXPLORATIONS

67. **The Ionic Greek Numeration System** The Ionic Greek numeration system assigned numerical values to the letters of the Greek alphabet. Research the Ionic Greek numeration system and write a report that explains this numeration system. Include information about some of the advantages and disadvantages of this system compared with our present Hindu-Arabic numeration system.

68. Some clock faces display the Roman numeral IV as IIII. Research this topic and write a few paragraphs that explain at least three possible reasons for this variation.

69. **The Method of False Position** The Rhind papyrus (see page 179) contained solutions to several mathematical problems. Some of these solutions made use of a procedure called the *method of false position*. Research the method of false position and write a report that explains this method. In your report, include a specific mathematical problem and its solution by the method of false position.

SECTION 4.2 | **Place-Value Systems**

historical note

Abu Ja'far Muhammad ibn Musa al'Khwarizmi
(ca. A.D. 790–850) Al'Khwarizmi (ăl'khwähr'ĭz mee) produced two important texts. One of these texts advocated the use of the Hindu-Arabic numeration system. The twelfth century Latin translation of this book is called *Liber Algoritmi de Numero Indorum,* or *Al-Khwarizmi on the Hindu Art of Reckoning.* In Europe, the people who favored the adoption of the Hindu-Arabic numeration system became known as *algorists* because of Al'Khwarizmi's *Liber Algoritmi de Numero Indorum* text. The Europeans who opposed the Hindu-Arabic system were called *abacists.* They advocated the use of Roman numerals and often performed computations with the aid of an abacus. ∎

Expanded Form

The most common numeration system used by people today is the Hindu-Arabic numeration system. It is called the Hindu-Arabic system because it was first developed in India (around A.D. 800) and then refined by the Arabs. It makes use of the 10 symbols 0, 1, 2, 3, 4, 5, 6, 7, 8, and 9. The reason for the 10 symbols, called *digits,* is related to the fact that we have 10 fingers. The Hindu-Arabic numeration system is also called the *decimal system,* where the word *decimal* is a derivation of the Latin word *decem,* which means "ten."

One important feature of the Hindu-Arabic numeration system is that it is a *place-value* or *positional-value system.* This means that the numerical value of each digit in a Hindu-Arabic numeral depends on its *place* or *position* in the numeral. For instance, the 3 in 31 represents 3 tens, whereas the 3 in 53 represents 3 ones. The Hindu-Arabic numeration system is a **base ten numeration system** because the place values are the powers of 10:

$$\ldots, 10^5, 10^4, 10^3, 10^2, 10^1, 10^0$$

The place value associated with the nth digit of a numeral (counting from right to left) is 10^{n-1}. For instance, in the numeral 7532, the 7 is the fourth digit from the right and is in the $10^{4-1} = 10^3$, or thousands', place. The numeral 2 is the first digit from the right and is in the $10^{1-1} = 10^0$, or ones', place. The *indicated sum* of each digit of a numeral multiplied by its respective place value is called the **expanded form** of the numeral.

EXAMPLE 1 ■ Write a Numeral in its Expanded Form

Write 4672 in expanded form.

Solution

$$4672 = 4000 + 600 + 70 + 2$$
$$= (4 \times 1000) + (6 \times 100) + (7 \times 10) + (2 \times 1)$$

The above expanded form can also be written as

$$(4 \times 10^3) + (6 \times 10^2) + (7 \times 10^1) + (2 \times 10^0)$$

CHECK YOUR PROGRESS 1 Write 17,325 in expanded form.

Solution *See page S13.*

If a number is written in expanded form, it can be simplified to its ordinary decimal form by performing the indicated operations. The *Order of Operations Agreement* states that we should first perform the exponentiations, then perform the multiplications, and finish by performing the additions.

EXAMPLE 2 ■ Simplify a Number Written in Expanded Form

Simplify: $(2 \times 10^3) + (7 \times 10^2) + (6 \times 10^1) + (3 \times 10^0)$

Solution

$$(2 \times 10^3) + (7 \times 10^2) + (6 \times 10^1) + (3 \times 10^0)$$
$$= (2 \times 1000) + (7 \times 100) + (6 \times 10) + (3 \times 1)$$
$$= 2000 + 700 + 60 + 3$$
$$= 2763$$

CHECK YOUR PROGRESS 2 Simplify:

$$(5 \times 10^4) + (9 \times 10^3) + (2 \times 10^2) + (7 \times 10^1) + (4 \times 10^0)$$

Solution See page S13.

In the next few examples, we make use of the expanded form of a numeral to compute sums and differences. An examination of these examples will help you better understand the computational algorithms used in the Hindu-Arabic numeration system.

EXAMPLE 3 ■ Use Expanded Forms to Find a Sum

Use expanded forms of 26 and 31 to find their sum.

Solution

$$\begin{aligned} 26 &= (2 \times 10) + 6 \\ + \ 31 &= (3 \times 10) + 1 \\ \hline &\ (5 \times 10) + 7 = 50 + 7 = 57 \end{aligned}$$

CHECK YOUR PROGRESS 3 Use expanded forms to find the sum of 152 and 234.

Solution See page S13.

If the expanded form of a sum contains one or more powers of 10 that have multipliers larger than 9, then we simplify by rewriting the sum with multipliers that are less than or equal to 9. This process is known as *carrying*.

✔ **TAKE NOTE**

From the expanded forms in Example 4, note that 12 is 1 ten and 2 ones. The 1 ten is added to the 13 tens, resulting in a total of 14 tens. When we add columns of numbers, this is shown as "carry a 1." Because the 1 is placed in the tens column, we are actually adding 10.

$$\begin{array}{r} 1 \\ 85 \\ + \ 57 \\ \hline 142 \end{array}$$

EXAMPLE 4 ■ Use Expanded Forms to Find a Sum

Use expanded forms of 85 and 57 to find their sum.

Solution

$$\begin{aligned} 85 &= (8 \times 10) &+ 5 \\ + \ 57 &= (5 \times 10) &+ 7 \\ \hline &\ (13 \times 10) &+ 12 \\ &\ (10 + 3) \times 10 + 10 + 2 \\ &\ 100 + 30 \quad + 10 + 2 = 100 + 40 + 2 = 142 \end{aligned}$$

CHECK YOUR PROGRESS 4   Use expanded forms to find the sum of 147 and 329.

Solution   *See page S13.*

In the next example, we use the expanded forms of numerals to analyze the concept of "borrowing" in a subtraction problem.

EXAMPLE 5 ■ Use Expanded Forms to Find a Difference

Use the expanded forms of 457 and 283 to find $457 - 283$.

Solution

$$457 = (4 \times 100) + (5 \times 10) + 7$$
$$- \; 283 = (2 \times 100) + (8 \times 10) + 3$$

At this point, this example is similar to Example 4 in Section 4.1. We cannot remove 8 tens from 5 tens, so 1 hundred is replaced by 10 tens.

$$457 = (4 \times 100) + (5 \times 10) + 7$$
$$= (3 \times 100) + (10 \times 10) + (5 \times 10) + 7$$
$$= (3 \times 100) + (15 \times 10) + 7$$

• $4 \times 100 = 3 \times 100 + 100$
  $= 3 \times 100 + 10 \times 10$

We can now remove 8 tens from 15 tens.

$$457 = (3 \times 100) + (15 \times 10) + 7$$
$$- \; 283 = (2 \times 100) + \;\;(8 \times 10) + 3$$
$$= (1 \times 100) + \;\;(7 \times 10) + 4 = 100 + 70 + 4 = 174$$

CHECK YOUR PROGRESS 5   Use expanded forms to find the difference $382 - 157$.

Solution   *See page S13.*

TAKE NOTE

From the expanded forms in Example 5, note that we "borrowed" 1 hundred as 10 tens. This explains how we show borrowing when numbers are subtracted using place value form.

$$\begin{array}{r} 3 \\ \cancel{4}^1 5 7 \\ - \; 2\,83 \\ \hline 1\,74 \end{array}$$

The Babylonian Numeration System

The Babylonian numeration system uses a base of 60. The place values in the Babylonian system are given in the following table.

Table 4.3 *Place Values in the Babylonian Numeration System*

60^3	60^2	60^1	60^0
= 216,000	= 3600	= 60	= 1

The Babylonians recorded their numerals on damp clay using a wedge-shaped stylus. A vertical wedge shape represented one unit and a sideways "vee" shape represented 10 units.

⟙ 1

⟨ 10

To represent a number smaller than 60, the Babylonians used an *additive* feature similar to that used by the Egyptians. For example, the Babylonian numeral for 32 is

For the number 60 and larger numbers, the Babylonians left a small space between groups of symbols to indicate a different place value. This procedure is illustrated in the following example.

EXAMPLE 6 ■ Write a Babylonian Numeral as a Hindu-Arabic Numeral

Write ⟨numeral⟩ as a Hindu-Arabic numeral.

Solution

1 group of 60^2 · · · 31 groups of 60 · · · 25 ones

$$= (1 \times 60^2) + (31 \times 60) + (25 \times 1)$$
$$= 3600 + 1860 + 25$$
$$= 5485$$

CHECK YOUR PROGRESS 6 Write ⟨numeral⟩ as a Hindu-Arabic numeral.

Solution See page S13.

QUESTION   *In the Babylonian numeration system, does* ⟨numeral⟩ = ⟨numeral⟩ ?

In the next example we illustrate a division process that can be used to convert Hindu-Arabic numerals to Babylonian numerals.

EXAMPLE 7 ■ Write a Hindu-Arabic Numeral as a Babylonian Numeral

Write 8503 as a Babylonian numeral.

Solution

The Babylonian numeration system uses place values of

$$60^0, 60^1, 60^2, 60^3, \ldots.$$

Evaluating the powers produces

$$1, 60, 3600, 216{,}000, \ldots$$

The largest of these powers that is contained in 8503 is 3600. One method of finding how many groups of 3600 are in 8503 is to divide 3600 into 8503. Refer to the

---

ANSWER   *No.* ⟨numeral⟩ = 2, *whereas* ⟨numeral⟩ = (1 × 60) + (1 × 1) = 61.

first division shown below. Now divide to determine how many groups of 60 are contained in the remainder 1303.

$$
\begin{array}{r}
2 \\
3600\overline{)8503} \\
7200 \\
\hline
1303
\end{array}
\qquad
\begin{array}{r}
21 \\
60\overline{)1303} \\
120 \\
\hline
103 \\
60 \\
\hline
43
\end{array}
$$

The above computations show that 8503 consists of 2 groups of 3600 and 21 groups of 60, with 43 left over. Thus

$$8503 = (2 \times 60^2) + (21 \times 60) + (43 \times 1)$$

As a Babylonian numeral, 8503 is written

CHECK YOUR PROGRESS 7   Write 12,578 as a Babylonian numeral.

Solution   *See page S13.*

In Example 8 we find the sum of two Babylonian numerals. If a numeral for any power of 60 is larger than 59, then simplify by decreasing that numeral by 60 and increasing the place value to its left by 1.

EXAMPLE 8 ■ Find the Sum of Babylonian Numerals

Find the sum:

Solution

• Combine the symbols for each place value.
• Take away 60 from the ones' place and add 1 to the 60s' place.
• Take away 60 from the 60s' place and add 1 to the 60^2 place.

CHECK YOUR PROGRESS 8   Find the sum:

Solution   *See page S13.*

MathMatters   Zero as a Placeholder and as a Number

When the Babylonian numeration system first began to develop around 1700 B.C., it did not make use of a symbol for zero. The Babylonians merely used an empty space to indicate that a place value was missing. This procedure of "leaving a space" can be confusing. How big is an empty space? Is that one empty space or two empty spaces? Around 300 B.C., the Babylonians started to use the symbol ⚷ to indicate that a particular place value was missing. For instance, 𐎟𐎟 ⚷ ◀𐎟 represented $(2 \times 60^2) + (11 \times 1) = 7211$. In this case the zero placeholder indicates that there are no 60's. There is evidence that although the Babylonians used the zero placeholder, they did not use the number zero.

The Mayan Numeration System

The Mayan civilization existed in the Yucatan area of southern Mexico and in Guatemala, Belize, and parts of El Salvador and Honduras. It started as far back as 9000 B.C. and reached its zenith during the period from A.D. 200 to A.D. 900. Among their many accomplishments, the Maya are best known for their complex hieroglyphic writing system, their sophisticated calendars, and their remarkable numeration system.

The Maya used three calendars—the solar calendar, the ceremonial calendar, and the Venus calendar. The solar calendar consisted of about 365.24 days. Of these, 360 days were divided into 18 months, each with 20 days. The Mayan numeration system was strongly influenced by this solar calendar, as evidenced by the use of the numbers 18 and 20 in determining place values. See Table 4.4.

✔ **TAKE NOTE**

Observe that the place values used in the Mayan numeration system are not all powers of 20.

Table 4.4 *Place Values in the Mayan Numeration System*

	18×20^3	18×20^2	18×20^1	20^1	20^0
...	= 144,000	= 7200	= 360	= 20	= 1

The Mayan numeration system was one of the first systems to use a symbol for zero as a placeholder. The Mayan numeration system used only three symbols. A dot was used to represent 1, a horizontal bar represented 5, and a conch shell represented 0. The following table shows how the Maya used a combination of these three symbols to write the whole numbers from 0 to 19. Note that each numeral contains at most four dots and at most three horizontal bars.

Table 4.5 *Mayan Numerals*

To write numbers larger than 19, the Maya used a vertical arrangement with the largest place value at the top. The following example illustrates the process of converting a Mayan numeral to a Hindu-Arabic numeral.

EXAMPLE 9 ■ Write a Mayan Numeral as a Hindu-Arabic Numeral

Write each of the following as a Hindu-Arabic numeral.

a.   b.

Solution

a.
$$10 \times 360 = 3600$$
$$8 \times 20 = 160$$
$$11 \times 1 = +11$$
$$\overline{3771}$$

b.
$$5 \times 7200 = 36{,}000$$
$$0 \times 360 = 0$$
$$12 \times 20 = 240$$
$$3 \times 1 = + 3$$
$$\overline{36{,}243}$$

CHECK YOUR PROGRESS 9   Write each of the following as a Hindu-Arabic numeral.

a.   b.

Solution   *See page S13.*

In the next example, we illustrate how the concept of place value is used to convert Hindu-Arabic numerals to Mayan numerals.

EXAMPLE 10 ■ Write a Hindu-Arabic Numeral as a Mayan Numeral

Write 7495 as a Mayan numeral.

Solution

The place values used in the Mayan numeration system are

$$20^0, 20^1, 18 \times 20^1, 18 \times 20^2, 18 \times 20^3, \ldots$$

or

$$1, 20, 360, 7200, 144{,}000, \ldots$$

Removing 1 group of 7200 from 7495 leaves 295. No groups of 360 can be obtained from 295, so we divide 295 by the next smaller place value of 20 to find that 295 equals 14 groups of 20 with 15 left over.

$$
\begin{array}{r}
1 \\[-2pt]
7200\overline{)7495} \\
7200 \\ \hline
295
\end{array}
\qquad
\begin{array}{r}
14 \\[-2pt]
20\overline{)295} \\
20 \\ \hline
95 \\
80 \\ \hline
15
\end{array}
$$

Thus

$$7495 = (1 \times 7200) + (0 \times 360) + (14 \times 20) + (15 \times 1)$$

In Mayan numerals, 7495 is written as

CHECK YOUR PROGRESS 10   Write 11,480 as a Mayan numeral.

Solution   *See page S13.*

Excursion

Subtraction via the Nines Complement and the End-Around Carry

In the subtraction $5627 - 2564 = 3063$, the number 5627 is called the *minuend,* 2564 is called the *subtrahend,* and 3063 is called the *difference.* In the Hindu-Arabic base ten system, subtraction can be performed by a process that involves addition and the *nines complement* of the subtrahend. The **nines complement** of a single digit n is the number $9 - n$. For instance, the nines complement of 3 is 6, the nines complement of 1 is 8, and the nines complement of 0 is 9. The nines complement of a number with more than one digit is the number that is formed by taking the nines complement of each digit. The nines complement of 25 is 74 and the nines complement of 867 is 132.

Subtraction by Using the Nines Complement and the End-Around Carry

To subtract by using the nines complement:

1. Add the nines complement of the subtrahend to the minuend.

2. Take away 1 from the leftmost digit and add 1 to the units digit. This is referred to as the end-around carry procedure.

(continued)

The following example illustrates the process of subtracting 2564 from 5627 by using the nines complement.

$$\begin{array}{r} 5627 \\ - \ 2564 \end{array}$$ Minuend
  Subtrahend

$$\begin{array}{r} 5627 \\ + \ 7435 \\ \hline 13062 \end{array}$$ Minuend
  Replace the subtrahend with the nines complement of the subtrahend and add.

$$\begin{array}{r} 13062 \\ + \qquad 1 \\ \hline 3063 \end{array}$$ Take away 1 from the leftmost digit and add 1 to the units digit. This is the end-around carry procedure.

Thus

$$\begin{array}{r} 5627 \\ - \ 2564 \\ \hline 3063 \end{array}$$

If the subtrahend has fewer digits than the minuend, leading zeros should be inserted in the subtrahend so that it has the same number of digits as the minuend. This process is illustrated below for 2547 − 358.

$$\begin{array}{r} 2547 \\ - \ \ \ 358 \end{array}$$ Minuend
  Subtrahend

$$\begin{array}{r} 2547 \\ - \ 0358 \end{array}$$ Insert a leading zero.

$$\begin{array}{r} 2547 \\ + \ 9641 \\ \hline 12188 \end{array}$$ Minuend
  Nines complement of subtrahend

$$\begin{array}{r} 12188 \\ + \qquad 1 \\ \hline 2189 \end{array}$$ Take away 1 from the leftmost digit and add 1 to the units digit.

Verify that 2189 is the correct difference.

Excursion Exercises

For Exercises 1–6, use the nines complement of the subtrahend to find the indicated difference.

1. 724 − 351

2. 2405 − 1608

3. 91,572 − 7824

4. 214,577 − 48,231

5. 3,156,782 − 875,236

6. 54,327,105 − 7,678,235

7. Explain why the nines complement and the end-around carry procedure produce the correct answer to a subtraction problem.

Exercise Set 4.2

In Exercises 1–8, write each numeral in its expanded form.

1. 48   **2.** 93
3. 420   **4.** 501
5. 6803   **6.** 9045
7. 10,208   **8.** 67,482

In Exercises 9–16, simplify each expansion.

9. $(4 \times 10^2) + (5 \times 10^1) + (6 \times 10^0)$
10. $(7 \times 10^2) + (6 \times 10^1) + (3 \times 10^0)$
11. $(5 \times 10^3) + (0 \times 10^2) + (7 \times 10^1) + (6 \times 10^0)$
12. $(3 \times 10^3) + (1 \times 10^2) + (2 \times 10^1) + (8 \times 10^0)$
13. $(3 \times 10^4) + (5 \times 10^3) + (4 \times 10^2) + (0 \times 10^1) + (7 \times 10^0)$
14. $(2 \times 10^5) + (3 \times 10^4) + (0 \times 10^3) + (6 \times 10^2) + (7 \times 10^1) + (5 \times 10^0)$
15. $(6 \times 10^5) + (8 \times 10^4) + (3 \times 10^3) + (0 \times 10^2) + (4 \times 10^1) + (0 \times 10^0)$
16. $(5 \times 10^7) + (3 \times 10^6) + (0 \times 10^5) + (0 \times 10^4) + (7 \times 10^3) + (9 \times 10^2) + (0 \times 10^1) + (2 \times 10^0)$

In Exercises 17–22, use expanded forms to find each sum.

17. 35 + 41   **18.** 42 + 56
19. 257 + 138   **20.** 352 + 461
21. 1023 + 1458   **22.** 3567 + 2651

In Exercises 23–28, use expanded forms to find each difference.

23. 62 − 35   **24.** 193 − 157
25. 4725 − 1362   **26.** 85,381 − 64,156
27. 23,168 − 12,857   **28.** 59,163 − 47,956

In Exercises 29–36, write each Babylonian numeral as a Hindu-Arabic numeral.

29. ⟨⟨▼▼▼

30. ⟨⟨⟨⟨▼▼▼▼▼

31. ▼ ⟨⟨⟨▼▼▼▼▼▼▼

32. ⟨▼▼ ⟨⟨▼▼▼▼▼▼

33. ⟨⟨ ▼▼ ⟨▼▼▼

34. ⟨⟨▼ ⟨▼ ⟨▼▼

35. ⟨ ▼▼▼ ⟨▼ ▼▼▼▼▼▼

36. ⟨⟨▼ ⟨▼ ▼ ⟨⟨⟨▼▼▼▼

In Exercises 37–46, write each Hindu-Arabic numeral as a Babylonian numeral.

37. 42   **38.** 57
39. 128   **40.** 540
41. 5678   **42.** 7821
43. 10,584   **44.** 12,687
45. 21,345   **46.** 24,567

In Exercises 47–52, find the sum of the Babylonian numerals.

47. ⟨⟨⟨⟨▼▼▼▼▼
  + ⟨⟨▼▼▼

48. ⟨⟨⟨⟨▼▼▼▼▼▼▼▼▼
  + ⟨⟨⟨▼▼▼

49. ⟨⟨⟨▼▼▼ ⟨⟨⟨⟨▼▼
  + ⟨⟨⟨▼▼ ⟨⟨▼

50. ⟨⟨⟨⟨▼▼ ⟨⟨⟨⟨⟨▼▼
  + ⟨⟨⟨▼ ⟨⟨⟨▼▼▼

51. ⟨ ⟨⟨⟨▼ ⟨⟨⟨⟨▼▼▼
  + ▼ ⟨⟨▼ ⟨⟨⟨▼▼

52. ⟨⟨ ⟨⟨⟨▼▼▼ ⟨⟨⟨▼▼▼▼▼▼
  + ⟨▼ ⟨⟨⟨▼▼ ⟨⟨⟨⟨▼▼▼▼

In Exercises 53–60, write each Mayan numeral as a Hindu-Arabic numeral.

53.

54.

55.

56.

57.

58.

59.

60.

In Exercises 61–68, write each Hindu-Arabic numeral as a Mayan numeral.

61. 137

62. 253

63. 948

64. 1265

65. 1693

66. 2728

67. 7432

68. 8654

Extensions

CRITICAL THINKING

69. a. State a reason why you might prefer to use the Babylonian numeration system instead of the Mayan numeration system.

b. State a reason why you might prefer to use the Mayan numeration system instead of the Babylonian numeration system.

70. Explain why it might be easy to mistake the number 122 for the number 4 when 122 is written as a Babylonian numeral.

EXPLORATIONS

71. **A Base Three Numeration System** A student has created a *base three* numeration system. The student has named this numeration system ZUT because Z, U, and T are the symbols used in this system: Z represents 0, U represents 1, and T represents 2. The place values in this system are: $\ldots, 3^3 = 27, 3^2 = 9, 3^1 = 3, 3^0 = 1$.

Write each ZUT numeral as a Hindu-Arabic numeral.

a. TU **b.** TZT **c.** UZTT

Write each Hindu-Arabic numeral as a ZUT numeral.

d. 37 **e.** 87 **f.** 144

SECTION 4.3 | **Different Base Systems**

Converting Non-Base-Ten Numerals to Base Ten

Recall that the Hindu-Arabic numeration system is a base ten system because its place values

$$\ldots, 10^5, 10^4, 10^3, 10^2, 10^1, 10^0$$

all have 10 as their base. The Babylonian numeration system is a base sixty system because its place values

$$\ldots, 60^5, 60^4, 60^3, 60^2, 60^1, 60^0$$

all have 60 as their base. In general, a base b (where b is a natural number greater than 1) numeration system has place values of

$$\ldots, b^5, b^4, b^3, b^2, b^1, b^0$$

Many people think that our base ten numeration system was chosen because it is the easiest to use, but this is not the case. In reality most people find it easier to use our base ten system only because they have had a great deal of experience with the base ten system and have not had much experience with non-base-ten systems. In this section, we examine some non-base-ten numeration systems. To reduce the amount of memorization that would be required to learn new symbols for each of these new systems, we will (as far as possible) make use of our familiar Hindu-Arabic symbols. For instance, if we discuss a base four numeration system that requires four basic symbols, then we will use the four Hindu-Arabic symbols 0, 1, 2, and 3 and the place values

$$\ldots, 4^5, 4^4, 4^3, 4^2, 4^1, 4^0$$

The base eight, or **octal,** numeration system uses the Hindu-Arabic symbols 0, 1, 2, 3, 4, 5, 6, and 7 and the place values

$$\ldots, 8^5, 8^4, 8^3, 8^2, 8^1, 8^0$$

To differentiate between bases, we will label each non-base-ten numeral with a subscript that indicates the base. For instance, 23_{four} represents a base four numeral. If a numeral is written without a subscript, then it is understood that the base is ten. Thus 23 written without a subscript is understood to be the base ten numeral 23.

To convert a non-base-ten numeral to base ten, we write the numeral in its expanded form, as shown in the following example.

✓ **TAKE NOTE**

Because 23_{four} is *not* equal to the base ten number 23, it is important *not* to read 23_{four} as "twenty-three." To avoid confusion, read 23_{four} as "two three base four."

EXAMPLE 1 ■ Convert to Base Ten

Convert 2314_{five} to base ten.

Solution

In the base five numeration system, the place values are

$$\ldots, 5^4, 5^3, 5^2, 5^1, 5^0$$

The expanded form of 2314_{five} is

$$
\begin{aligned}
2314_{five} &= (2 \times 5^3) + (3 \times 5^2) + (1 \times 5^1) + (4 \times 5^0) \\
&= (2 \times 125) + (3 \times 25) + (1 \times 5) + (4 \times 1) \\
&= 250 + 75 + 5 + 4 \\
&= 334
\end{aligned}
$$

Thus $2314_{five} = 334$.

CHECK YOUR PROGRESS 1   Convert 3156_{seven} to base ten.

Solution   *See page S13.*

QUESTION   *Does the notation 26_{five} make sense?*

ANSWER   *No. The expression 26_{five} is a meaningless expression because there is no 6 in base five.*

In base two, which is called the **binary numeration system,** the place values are the powers of two.

$$\ldots, 2^7, 2^6, 2^5, 2^4, 2^3, 2^2, 2^1, 2^0$$

The binary numeration system uses only the two digits 0 and 1. These *binary digits* are often called **bits.** To convert a base two numeral to base ten, write the numeral in its expanded form and then evaluate the expanded form.

EXAMPLE 2 ■ Convert to Base Ten

Convert 10110111_{two} to base ten.

Solution

$$
\begin{aligned}
10110111_{two} &= (1 \times 2^7) + (0 \times 2^6) + (1 \times 2^5) + (1 \times 2^4) + (0 \times 2^3) \\
&\quad + (1 \times 2^2) + (1 \times 2^1) + (1 \times 2^0) \\
&= (1 \times 128) + (0 \times 64) + (1 \times 32) + (1 \times 16) + (0 \times 8) \\
&\quad + (1 \times 4) + (1 \times 2) + (1 \times 1) \\
&= 128 + 0 + 32 + 16 + 0 + 4 + 2 + 1 \\
&= 183
\end{aligned}
$$

CHECK YOUR PROGRESS 2   Convert 111000101_{two} to base ten.

Solution   *See page S13.*

TAKE NOTE

The base twelve numeration system is called the **duodecimal system.** A group called the Dozenal Society of America advocates the replacement of our base ten decimal system with the duodecimal system. If you wish to find out more about this organization, you can contact them at: The Dozenal Society of America, Nassau Community College, Garden City, New York. Not surprisingly, the dues are $12 per year and $144 ($12^2 = 144$) for a lifetime membership.

The base twelve numeration system requires 12 distinct symbols. We will use the symbols 0, 1, 2, 3, 4, 5, 6, 7, 8, 9, A, and B as our base twelve numeration system symbols. The symbols 0 through 9 have their usual meaning; however, A is used to represent 10 and B to represent 11.

EXAMPLE 3 ■ Convert to Base Ten

Convert $B37_{twelve}$ to base ten.

Solution

In the base twelve numeration system, the place values are

$$\ldots, 12^4, 12^3, 12^2, 12^1, 12^0$$

Thus

$$
\begin{aligned}
B37_{twelve} &= (11 \times 12^2) + (3 \times 12^1) + (7 \times 12^0) \\
&= 1584 + 36 + 7 \\
&= 1627
\end{aligned}
$$

CHECK YOUR PROGRESS 3   Convert $A5B_{twelve}$ to base ten.

Solution   *See page S14.*

Computer programmers often write programs that use the base sixteen numeration system, which is also called the **hexadecimal system.** This system uses the symbols 0, 1, 2, 3, 4, 5, 6, 7, 8, 9, A, B, C, D, E, and F. Table 4.6 shows that A represents 10, B represents 11, C represents 12, D represents 13, E represents 14, and F represents 15.

Table 4.6 *Decimal and Hexadecimal Equivalents*

Base Ten Decimal	Base Sixteen Hexadecimal
0	0
1	1
2	2
3	3
4	4
5	5
6	6
7	7
8	8
9	9
10	A
11	B
12	C
13	D
14	E
15	F

EXAMPLE 4 ■ Convert to Base Ten

Convert $3E8_{sixteen}$ to base ten.

Solution

In the base sixteen numeration system the place values are

$$\ldots, 16^4, 16^3, 16^2, 16^1, 16^0$$

Thus

$$3E8_{sixteen} = (3 \times 16^2) + (14 \times 16^1) + (8 \times 16^0)$$
$$= 768 + 224 + 8$$
$$= 1000$$

CHECK YOUR PROGRESS 4   Convert $C24F_{sixteen}$ to base ten.

Solution   *See page S14.*

Converting from Base Ten to Another Base

The most efficient method of converting a number written in base ten to another base makes use of a *successive division process*. For example, to convert 219 to base four, divide 219 by 4 and write the quotient 54 and the remainder 3, as shown below. Now divide the quotient 54 by the base to get a new quotient of 13 and a new remainder of 2. Continuing the process, divide the quotient 13 by 4 to get a new quotient of 3 and a remainder of 1. Because our last quotient, 3, is less than the base, 4, we stop the division process. The answer is given by the last quotient, 3, and the remainders, shown in red in the following diagram. That is, $219 = 3123_{four}$.

```
4 | 219
4 |  54    3
4 |  13    2
     3     1
```

You can understand how the successive division process converts a base ten numeral to another base by analyzing the process. The first division shows there are 54 fours in 219, with **3 ones** left over. The second division shows that there are 13 sixteens (two successive divisions by 4 is the same as dividing by 16) in 219, and the remainder 2 indicates that there are **2 fours** left over. The last division shows that there are 3 sixty-fours (three successive divisions by 4 is the same as dividing by 64) in 219, and the remainder 1 indicates that there is **1 sixteen** left over. In mathematical notation these results are written as follows.

$$219 = (3 \times 64) + (1 \times 16) + (2 \times 4) + (3 \times 1)$$
$$= (3 \times 4^3) + (1 \times 4^2) + (2 \times 4^1) + (3 \times 4^0)$$
$$= 3123_{four}$$

EXAMPLE 5 ■ Convert a Base Ten Numeral to Another Base

Convert 5821 to **a.** base three and **b.** base sixteen.

Solution

a.

3	5821	
3	1940	1
3	646	2
3	215	1
3	71	2
3	23	2
3	7	2
	2	1

$5821 = 21222121_{\text{three}}$

b.

16	5821	
16	363	13 $= D_{\text{sixteen}}$
16	22	11 $= B_{\text{sixteen}}$
	1	6

$5821 = 16BD_{\text{sixteen}}$

CHECK YOUR PROGRESS 5 Convert 1952 to **a.** base five and **b.** base twelve.

Solution *See page S14.*

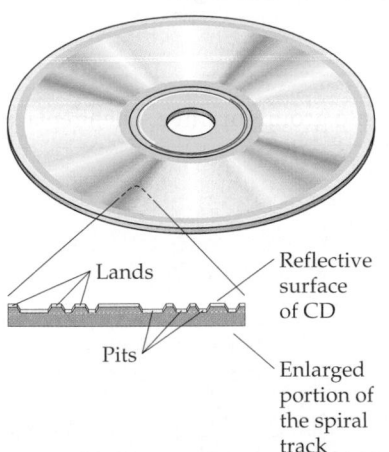

Table 4.7 *Octal and Binary Equivalents*

Octal	Binary
0	000
1	001
2	010
3	011
4	100
5	101
6	110
7	111

Math Matters   **Music by the Numbers**

The binary numeration system is used to encode music on a CD (compact disc). The figure at the left shows the surface of a CD, which consists of flat regions called *lands* and small indentations called *pits*. As a laser beam tracks along a spiral path, the beam is reflected to a sensor when it shines on a land, but it is not reflected to the sensor when it shines on a pit. The sensor interprets a reflection as a 1 and no reflection as a 0. As the CD is playing, the sensor receives a series of 1's and 0's, which the CD player converts to music. On a typical CD, the spiral path that the laser follows loops around the disc over 20,000 times and contains about 650 megabytes of data. A **byte** is eight bits, so this amounts to 5,200,000,000 bits, each of which is represented by a pit or a land.

Lands

Reflective surface of CD

Pits

Enlarged portion of the spiral track

Converting Directly Between Computer Bases

Although computers compute internally by using base two (binary system), humans generally find it easier to compute with a larger base. Fortunately, there are easy conversion techniques that can be used to convert a base two numeral directly to a base eight (octal) numeral or a base sixteen (hexadecimal) numeral. Before we explain the techniques, it will help to become familiar with the information in Table 4.7, which shows the eight octal symbols and their binary equivalents.

To convert from octal to binary, just replace each octal symbol with its three-bit binary equivalent.

EXAMPLE 6 ■ Convert Directly from Base Eight to Base Two

Convert 5724_{eight} directly to binary form.

Solution

$$
\begin{array}{cccc}
5 & 7 & 2 & 4_{\text{eight}} \\
\| & \| & \| & \| \\
101 & 111 & 010 & 100_{\text{two}}
\end{array}
$$

$5724_{\text{eight}} = 101111010100_{\text{two}}$

CHECK YOUR PROGRESS 6   Convert 63210_{eight} directly to binary form.

Solution   *See page S14.*

Because every group of three binary bits is equivalent to an octal symbol, we can convert from binary directly to octal by breaking a binary numeral into groups of three (from right to left) and replacing each group with its octal equivalent.

EXAMPLE 7 ■ Convert Directly from Base Two to Base Eight

Convert 11100101_{two} directly to octal form.

Solution
Starting from the right, break the binary numeral into groups of three. Then replace each group with its octal equivalent.

This zero was inserted to make a group of three.

$$
\begin{array}{ccc}
011 & 100 & 101_{\text{two}} \\
\| & \| & \| \\
3 & 4 & 5_{\text{eight}}
\end{array}
$$

$11100101_{\text{two}} = 345_{\text{eight}}$

CHECK YOUR PROGRESS 7   Convert $111010011100_{\text{two}}$ directly to octal form.

Solution   *See page S14.*

Table 4.8 shows the hexadecimal symbols and their binary equivalents. To convert from hexadecimal to binary, replace each hexadecimal symbol with its four-bit binary equivalent.

EXAMPLE 8 ■ Convert Directly from Base Sixteen to Base Two

Convert $\text{BAD}_{\text{sixteen}}$ directly to binary form.

Solution

$$
\begin{array}{ccc}
B & A & D_{\text{sixteen}} \\
\| & \| & \| \\
1011 & 1010 & 1101_{\text{two}}
\end{array}
$$

$\text{BAD}_{\text{sixteen}} = 101110101101_{\text{two}}$

Table 4.8 *Hexadecimal and Binary Equivalents*

Hexadecimal	Binary
0	0000
1	0001
2	0010
3	0011
4	0100
5	0101
6	0110
7	0111
8	1000
9	1001
A	1010
B	1011
C	1100
D	1101
E	1110
F	1111

CHECK YOUR PROGRESS 8   Convert C5A$_{\text{sixteen}}$ directly to binary form.

Solution   *See page S14.*

Because every group of four binary bits is equivalent to a hexadecimal symbol, we can convert from binary to hexadecimal by breaking the binary numeral into groups of four (from right to left) and replacing each group with its hexadecimal equivalent.

EXAMPLE 9 ■ Convert Directly from Base Two to Base Sixteen

Convert 10110010100011$_{\text{two}}$ directly to hexadecimal form.

Solution
Starting from the right, break the binary numeral into groups of four. Replace each group with its hexadecimal equivalent.

Insert two zeros to make a group of four.

0010	1100	1010	0011$_{\text{two}}$
‖	‖	‖	‖
2	C	A	3

10110010100011$_{\text{two}}$ = 2CA3$_{\text{sixteen}}$

CHECK YOUR PROGRESS 9   Convert 101000111010010$_{\text{two}}$ directly to hexadecimal form.

Solution   *See page S14.*

The Double-Dabble Method

There is a short cut that can be used to convert a base two numeral to base ten. The advantage of this short cut, called the *double-dabble method,* is that you can start at the left of the numeral and work your way to the right without first determining the place value of each bit in the base two numeral.

EXAMPLE 10 ■ Apply the Double-Dabble Method

Use the double-dabble method to convert 1011001$_{\text{two}}$ to base ten.

Solution
Start at the left with the first 1 and move to the right. Every time you pass by a 0, double your current number. Every time you pass by a 1, dabble. Dabbling is accomplished by doubling your current number and adding 1.

$2 \cdot 1$	$2 \cdot 2 + 1$	$2 \cdot 5 + 1$	$2 \cdot 11$	$2 \cdot 22$	$2 \cdot 44 + 1$
double	dabble	dabble	double	double	dabble
2	5	11	22	44	89

1   0   1   1   0   0   1$_{\text{two}}$

As we pass by the final 1 in the units place, we dabble 44 to get 89. Thus 1011001$_{\text{two}}$ = 89.

CHECK YOUR PROGRESS 10   Use the double-dabble method to convert 1110010_{two} to base ten.

Solution   *See page S14.*

Excursion

Information Retrieval via a Binary Search

To complete this Excursion, you must first construct a set of 31 cards that we refer to as a deck of *binary cards*. Templates for constructing the cards are available at our website, **www.cengage.com/math,** under the file name Binary Cards. Use a computer to print the templates onto a medium-weight card stock similar to that used for playing cards. Specific directions are provided with the templates.

We are living in the information age, but information is not useful if it cannot be retrieved when you need it. The binary numeration system is vital to the retrieval of information. To illustrate the connection between retrieval of information and the binary system, examine the card in the following figure. The card is labeled with the base ten numeral 20, and the holes and notches at the top of the card represent 20 in binary notation. A hole is used to indicate a 1 and a notch is used to indicate a 0. In the figure, the card has holes in the third and fifth binary-place-value positions (counting from right to left) and notches cut out of the first, second, and fourth positions.

After you have constructed your deck of binary cards, take a few seconds to shuffle the deck. To find the card labeled with the numeral 20, complete the following process.

1. Use a thin dowel (or the tip of a sharp pencil) to lift out the cards that have a hole in the fifth position. *Keep* these cards and set the other cards off to the side.

2. From the cards that are *kept,* use the dowel to lift out the cards with a hole in the fourth position. Set these cards off to the side.

3. From the cards that are *kept,* use the dowel to lift out the cards that have a hole in the third position. *Keep* these cards and place the others off to the side.

(continued)

4. From the cards that are *kept,* use the dowel to lift out the cards with a hole in the second position. Set these cards off to the side.

5. From the cards that are *kept,* use the dowel to lift out the card that has a hole in the first position. Set this card off to the side.

The card that remains is the card labeled with the numeral 20. You have just completed a binary search.

Excursion Exercises

The binary numeration system can also be used to implement a *sorting* procedure. To illustrate, shuffle your deck of cards. Use the dowel to lift out the cards that have a hole in the rightmost position. Place these cards, *face up,* in the back of the other cards. Now use the dowel to lift out the cards that have a hole in the next position to the left. Place these cards, face up, in back of the other cards. Continue this process of lifting out the cards in the next position to the left and placing them in back of the other cards until you have completed the process for all five positions.

1. Examine the numerals on the cards. What do you notice about the order of the numerals? Explain why they are in this order.

2. If you wanted to sort 1000 cards from smallest to largest value by using the binary sort procedure, how many positions (where each position is either a hole or a notch) would be required at the top of each card? How many positions are needed to sort 10,000 cards?

3. Explain why the above sorting procedure cannot be implemented with base three cards.

Exercise Set 4.3

In Exercises 1–10, convert the given numeral to base ten.

1. 243_{five}

2. 145_{seven}

3. 67_{nine}

4. 573_{eight}

5. 3154_{six}

6. 735_{eight}

7. 13211_{four}

8. 102022_{three}

9. $B5_{\text{sixteen}}$

10. $4A_{\text{twelve}}$

In Exercises 11–20, convert the given base ten numeral to the indicated base.

11. 267 to base five

12. 362 to base eight

13. 1932 to base six

14. 2024 to base four

15. 15,306 to base nine

16. 18,640 to base seven

17. 4060 to base two

18. 5673 to base three

19. 283 to base twelve

20. 394 to base sixteen

In Exercises 21–28, use expanded forms to convert the given base two numeral to base ten.

21. 1101_{two}

22. 10101_{two}

23. 11011_{two}

24. 101101_{two}

25. 1100100_{two}

26. 11110101000_{two}

27. 10001011_{two}

28. 110110101_{two}

In Exercises 29–34, use the double-dabble method to convert the given base two numeral to base ten.

29. 101001_{two}

30. 1110100_{two}

31. 1011010_{two}

32. 10001010_{two}

33. 10100111010_{two}

34. 10000000100_{two}

In Exercises 35–46, convert the given numeral to the indicated base.

35. 34_{six} to base eight

36. 71_{eight} to base five

37. 878_{nine} to base four

38. 546_{seven} to base six

39. 1110_{two} to base five

40. 21200_{three} to base six

41. 3440_{eight} to base nine

42. 1453_{six} to base eight

43. $56_{sixteen}$ to base eight

44. 43_{twelve} to base six

45. $A4_{twelve}$ to base sixteen

46. $C9_{sixteen}$ to base twelve

In Exercises 47–56, convert the given numeral *directly* (without first converting to base ten) to the indicated base.

47. 352_{eight} to base two

48. $A4_{sixteen}$ to base two

49. 11001010_{two} to base eight

50. 111011100101_{two} to base sixteen

51. 101010001_{two} to base sixteen

52. 56721_{eight} to base two

53. $BEF3_{sixteen}$ to base two

54. $6A7B8_{sixteen}$ to base two

55. $BA5CF_{sixteen}$ to base two

56. 47134_{eight} to base two

57. **An Extension** There is a procedure that can be used to convert a base three numeral directly to base ten without using the expanded form of the numeral. Write an explanation of this procedure, which we will call the *triple-whipple-zipple* method. *Hint:* The method is an extension of the double-dabble method.

58. Determine whether the following statements are true or false.

   a. A number written in base two is divisible by 2 if and only if the number ends with a 0.

   b. In base six, the next counting number after 55_{six} is 100_{six}.

   c. In base sixteen, the next counting number after $3BF_{sixteen}$ is $3C0_{sixteen}$.

Extensions

CRITICAL THINKING

The D'ni Numeration System In the computer game *Riven*, a D'ni numeration system is used. Although the D'ni numeration system is a base twenty-five numeration system with 25 distinct numerals, you really need to memorize only the first five numerals, which are shown below.

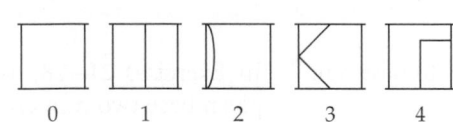

The basic D'ni numerals

If two D'ni numerals are placed side-by-side, then the numeral on the left is in the twenty-fives' place and the numeral on the right is in the ones' place. Thus

is the D'ni numeral for $(3 \times 25) + (2 \times 1) = 77$.

59. Convert the following D'ni numeral to base ten.

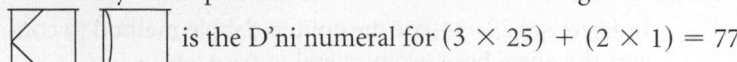

60. Convert the following D'ni numeral to base ten.

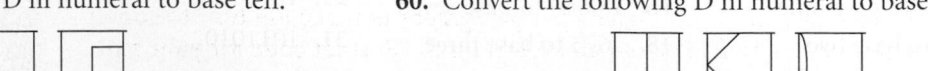

Rotating any of the D'ni numerals for 1, 2, 3, and 4 by a 90° counterclockwise rotation produces a numeral with a value five times its original value. For instance, rotating the numeral for 1 produces ⊟ , which is the D'ni numeral for 5, and

rotating the numeral for 2 produces ⊡ , which is the D'ni numeral for 10.

61. Write the D'ni numeral for 15.   **62.** Write the D'ni numeral for 20.

In the D'ni numeration system, explained above, many numerals are obtained by rotating a basic numeral and then overlaying it on one of the basic numerals. For instance, if you rotate the D'ni numeral for 1, you get the numeral for 5. If you then overlay the numeral for 5 on the numeral for 1, you get the numeral for $5 + 1 = 6$.

5 overlayed on 1 produces 6.

63. Write the D'ni numeral for 8.   **64.** Write the D'ni numeral for 22.

65. Convert the following D'ni numeral to base ten.   **66.** Convert the following D'ni numeral to base ten.

67. a. State one advantage of the hexadecimal numeration system over the decimal numeration system.

   b. State one advantage of the decimal numeration system over the hexadecimal numeration system.

68. a. State one advantage of the D'ni numeration system over the decimal numeration system.

   b. State one advantage of the decimal numeration system over the D'ni numeration system.

EXPLORATIONS

69. **The ASCII Code** ASCII, pronounced *ask-key,* is an acronym for the American Standard Code for Information Interchange. In this code, each of the characters that can be typed on a computer keyboard is represented by a number. For instance, the letter A is assigned the number 65, which when written as an 8-bit binary numeral is 01000001. Research the topic of ASCII. Write a report about ASCII and its applications.

70. **The Postnet Code** The U.S. Postal Service uses a *Postnet code* to write zip codes + 4 on envelopes. The Postnet code is a bar code that is based on the binary numeration system. Postnet code is very useful because it can be read by a machine. Write a few paragraphs that explain how to convert a zip code + 4 to its Postnet code. What is the Postnet code for your zip code + 4?

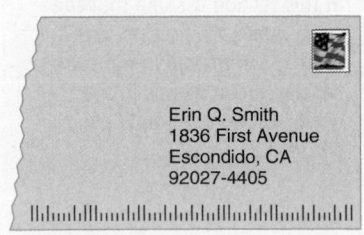

Erin Q. Smith
1836 First Avenue
Escondido, CA
92027-4405

Addition in Different Bases

Most computers and calculators make use of the base two (binary) numeration system to perform arithmetic computations. For instance, if you use a calculator to find the sum of 9 and 5, the calculator first converts the 9 to 1001_{two} and the 5 to 101_{two}. The calculator uses electronic circuitry called *binary adders* to find the sum of 1001_{two} and 101_{two} as 1110_{two}. The calculator then converts 1110_{two} to base ten and displays the sum 14. All of the conversions and the base two addition are done internally in a fraction of a second, which gives the user the impression that the calculator performed the addition in base ten.

The following examples illustrate how to perform arithmetic in different bases. We first consider the operation of addition in the binary numeration system. Table 4.9 is an addition table for base two. It is similar to the base ten addition table that you memorized in elementary school, except that it is much smaller because base two involves only the bits 0 and 1. The numerals shown in red in Table 4.9 illustrate that $1_{\text{two}} + 1_{\text{two}} = 10_{\text{two}}$.

Table 4.9 *A Binary Addition Table*

Second addend

+	0	1
0	0	1
1	1	10

First addend

Sums

EXAMPLE 1 ■ Add Base Two Numerals

Find the sum of 11110_{two} and 1011_{two}.

Solution
Arrange the numerals vertically, keeping the bits of the same place value in the same column.

$$
\begin{array}{r}
1\;1\;1\;1\;0_{\text{two}} \\
+\quad 1\;0\;1\;1_{\text{two}} \\
\hline
1_{\text{two}}
\end{array}
$$

Start by adding the bits in the ones' column: $0_{\text{two}} + 1_{\text{two}} = 1_{\text{two}}$. Then move left and add the bits in the twos' column. When the sum of the bits in a column exceeds 1, the addition will involve carrying, as shown below.

$$
\begin{array}{r}
^{1}\\
1\;1\;1\;1\;0_{\text{two}} \\
+\quad 1\;0\;1\;1_{\text{two}} \\
\hline
0\;1_{\text{two}}
\end{array}
$$

Add the bits in the twos' column.
$1_{\text{two}} + 1_{\text{two}} = 10_{\text{two}}$
Write the 0 in the twos' column and carry the 1 to the fours' column.

TAKE NOTE

In this section assume that the small numerals, used to indicate a carry, are written in the same base as the numerals in the given addition (multiplication) problem.

$$\begin{array}{r} \overset{1}{}\,\overset{1}{}\\ 1\;1\;1\;1\;0_{\text{two}} \\ +\quad 1\;0\;1\;1_{\text{two}} \\ \hline 0\;0\;1_{\text{two}} \end{array}$$

Add the bits in the fours' column.
$(1_{\text{two}} + 1_{\text{two}}) + 0_{\text{two}} = 10_{\text{two}} + 0_{\text{two}} = 10_{\text{two}}$
Write the 0 in the fours' column and carry the 1 to the eights' column.

$$\begin{array}{r} \overset{1}{}\,\overset{1}{}\\ 1\;1\;1\;1\;0_{\text{two}} \\ +\quad 1\;0\;1\;1_{\text{two}} \\ \hline 1\;0\;1\;0\;0\;1_{\text{two}} \end{array}$$

Add the bits in the eights' column.
$(1_{\text{two}} + 1_{\text{two}}) + 1_{\text{two}} = 10_{\text{two}} + 1_{\text{two}} = 11_{\text{two}}$
Write a 1 in the eights' column and carry a 1 to the sixteens' column. Continue to add the bits in each column to the left of the eights' column.

The sum of 11110_{two} and 1011_{two} is 101001_{two}.

CHECK YOUR PROGRESS 1   Find the sum of 11001_{two} and 1101_{two}.

Solution   *See page S14.*

Table 4.10 *A Base Four Addition Table*

+	0	1	2	3
0	0	1	2	3
1	1	2	3	10
2	2	3	10	11
3	3	10	11	12

There are four symbols in base four, namely 0, 1, 2, and 3. Table 4.10 shows a base four addition table that lists all the sums that can be produced by adding two base four digits. The numerals shown in red in Table 4.10 illustrate that $2_{\text{four}} + 3_{\text{four}} = 11_{\text{four}}$.

In the next example we compute the sum of two numbers written in base four.

EXAMPLE 2 ■ Add Base Four Numerals

Find the sum of 23_{four} and 13_{four}.

Solution
Arrange the numerals vertically, keeping the digits of the same place value in the same column.

$$\begin{array}{r} \text{\tiny SIXTEENS} \quad \text{\tiny FOURS} \quad \text{\tiny ONES} \\ \overset{1}{}\\ 2\;3_{\text{four}} \\ +\quad 1\;3_{\text{four}} \\ \hline 2_{\text{four}} \end{array}$$

Add the digits in the ones' column.
Table 4.10 shows that $3_{\text{four}} + 3_{\text{four}} = 12_{\text{four}}$.
Write the 2 in the ones' column and carry the 1 to the fours' column.

$$\begin{array}{r} \overset{1}{}\,\overset{1}{}\\ 2\;3_{\text{four}} \\ +\quad 1\;3_{\text{four}} \\ \hline 1\;0\;2_{\text{four}} \end{array}$$

Add the digits in the fours' column:
$(1_{\text{four}} + 2_{\text{four}}) + 1_{\text{four}} = 3_{\text{four}} + 1_{\text{four}} = 10_{\text{four}}$.
Write the 0 in the fours' column and carry the 1 to the sixteens' column. Bring down the 1 that was carried to the sixteens' column to form the sum 102_{four}.

The sum of 23_{four} and 13_{four} is 102_{four}.

CHECK YOUR PROGRESS 2   Find $32_{four} + 12_{four}$.

Solution   *See page S14.*

In the previous examples we used a table to determine the necessary sums. However, it is generally quicker to find a sum by computing the base ten sum of the digits in each column and then converting each base ten sum back to its equivalent in the given base. The next two examples illustrate this summation technique.

EXAMPLE 3 ■ Add Base Six Numerals

Find $25_{six} + 32_{six} + 42_{six}$.

Solution

Arrange the numerals vertically, keeping the digits of the same place value in the same column.

$$
\begin{array}{r}
\overset{1}{2}\;|\;5_{six} \\
3\;|\;2_{six} \\
+\quad 4\;|\;2_{six} \\
\hline
3_{six}
\end{array}
$$

Add the digits in the ones' column:
$5_{six} + 2_{six} + 2_{six} = 5 + 2 + 2 = 9$.
Convert 9 to base six. ($9 = 13_{six}$)
Write the 3 in the ones' column and carry the 1 to the sixes' column.

$$
\begin{array}{r}
\overset{1}{}\;\overset{1}{2}\;|\;5_{six} \\
3\;|\;2_{six} \\
+\quad 4\;|\;2_{six} \\
\hline
1\;|\;4\;|\;3_{six}
\end{array}
$$

Add the digits in the sixes' column and convert the sum to base six.
$1_{six} + 2_{six} + 3_{six} + 4_{six} = 1 + 2 + 3 + 4 = 10 = 14_{six}$
Write the 4 in the sixes' column and carry the 1 to the thirty-sixes' column. Bring down the 1 that was carried to the thirty-sixes' column to form the sum 143_{six}.

$25_{six} + 32_{six} + 42_{six} = 143_{six}$

CHECK YOUR PROGRESS 3   Find $35_{seven} + 46_{seven} + 24_{seven}$.

Solution   *See page S14.*

In the next example, we solve an addition problem that involves a base greater than ten.

EXAMPLE 4 ■ Add Base Twelve Numerals

Find $A97_{twelve} + 8BA_{twelve}$.

Solution

$$\begin{array}{r} \overset{1}{A\ \ 9\ }\ 7_{twelve} \\ +\ \ 8\ \ B\ \ A_{twelve} \\ \hline 5_{twelve} \end{array}$$

Add the digits in the ones' column.
$7_{twelve} + A_{twelve} = 7 + 10 = 17$
Convert 17 to base twelve. ($17 = 15_{twelve}$)
Write the 5 in the ones' column and carry the 1 to the twelves' column.

$$\begin{array}{r} \overset{1}{A}\ \overset{1}{9}\ 7_{twelve} \\ +\ \ 8\ \ B\ \ A_{twelve} \\ \hline 9\ \ 5_{twelve} \end{array}$$

Add the digits in the twelves' column.
$1_{twelve} + 9_{twelve} + B_{twelve} = 1 + 9 + 11 = 21 = 19_{twelve}$
Write the 9 in the twelves' column and carry the 1 to the one hundred forty-fours' column.

$$\begin{array}{r} \overset{1}{\ }\ \overset{1}{A}\ \overset{1}{9}\ 7_{twelve} \\ +\ \ \ 8\ \ B\ \ A_{twelve} \\ \hline 1\ \ 7\ \ 9\ \ 5_{twelve} \end{array}$$

Add the digits in the one hundred forty-fours' column.
$1_{twelve} + A_{twelve} + 8_{twelve} = 1 + 10 + 8 = 19 = 17_{twelve}$
Write the 7 in the one hundred forty-fours' column and carry the 1 to the one thousand seven hundred twenty-eights' column. Bring down the 1 that was carried to the one thousand seven hundred twenty-eights' column to form the sum 1795_{twelve}.

$A97_{twelve} + 8BA_{twelve} = 1795_{twelve}$

CHECK YOUR PROGRESS 4   Find $AC4_{sixteen} + 6E8_{sixteen}$.

Solution   *See page S14.*

Subtraction in Different Bases

To subtract two numbers written in the same base, begin by arranging the numbers vertically, keeping digits that have the same place value in the same column. It will be necessary to borrow whenever a digit in the subtrahend is greater than its corresponding digit in the minuend. Every number that is borrowed will be a power of the base.

EXAMPLE 5 ■ Subtract Base Seven Numerals

Find $463_{seven} - 124_{seven}$.

Solution
Arrange the numerals vertically, keeping the digits of the same place value in the same column.

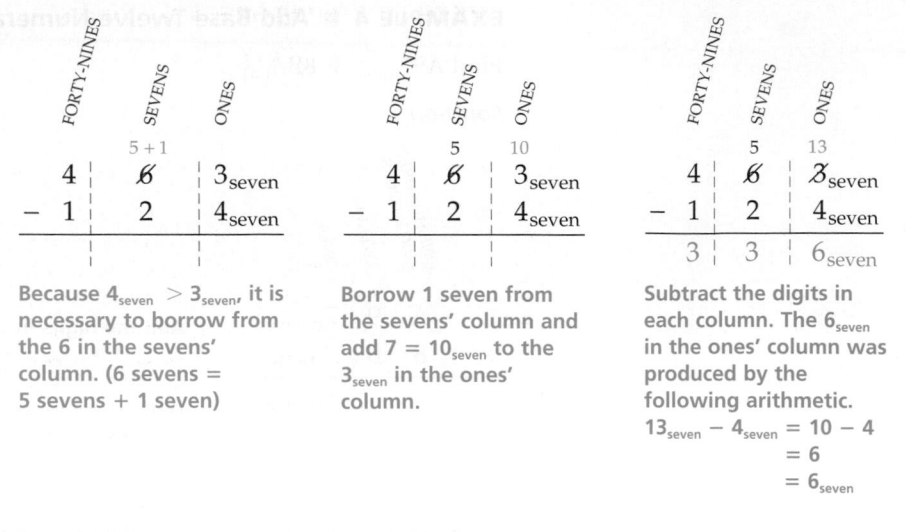

Because $4_{seven} > 3_{seven}$, it is necessary to borrow from the 6 in the sevens' column. (6 sevens = 5 sevens + 1 seven)

Borrow 1 seven from the sevens' column and add $7 = 10_{seven}$ to the 3_{seven} in the ones' column.

Subtract the digits in each column. The 6_{seven} in the ones' column was produced by the following arithmetic.
$$13_{seven} - 4_{seven} = 10 - 4$$
$$= 6$$
$$= 6_{seven}$$

$$463_{seven} - 124_{seven} = 336_{seven}$$

CHECK YOUR PROGRESS 5   Find $365_{nine} - 183_{nine}$.

Solution   *See page S14.*

Table 4.11 *Decimal and Hexadecimal Equivalents*

Base Ten Decimal	Base Sixteen Hexadecimal
0	0
1	1
2	2
3	3
4	4
5	5
6	6
7	7
8	8
9	9
10	A
11	B
12	C
13	D
14	E
15	F

EXAMPLE 6 ■ **Subtract Base Sixteen Numerals**

Find $7AB_{sixteen} - 3E4_{sixteen}$.

Solution

Table 4.11 shows the hexadecimal digits and their decimal equivalents. Because $B_{sixteen}$ is greater than $4_{sixteen}$, there is no need to borrow to find the difference in the ones' column. However, $A_{sixteen}$ is less than $E_{sixteen}$, so it is necessary to borrow to find the difference in the sixteens' column.

$B_{sixteen} - 4_{sixteen} = 11 - 4$
$= 7$
$= 7_{sixteen}$

Borrow 1 two hundred fifty-six from the two hundred fifty-sixes' column and write 10 in the sixteens' column.

$10_{sixteen} + A_{sixteen} = 1A_{sixteen}$
The C in the sixteens' column was produced by the following arithmetic.
$1A_{sixteen} - E_{sixteen} = 26 - 14$
$= 12$
$= C_{sixteen}$

$$7AB_{sixteen} - 3E4_{sixteen} = 3C7_{sixteen}$$

CHECK YOUR PROGRESS 6   Find $83A_{\text{twelve}} - 467_{\text{twelve}}$.

Solution   See page S14.

Multiplication in Different Bases

Table 4.12 *A Base Four Multiplication Table*

×	0	1	2	3
0	0	0	0	0
1	0	1	2	3
2	0	2	10	12
3	0	3	12	21

To perform multiplication in bases other than base ten, it is often helpful to first write a multiplication table for the given base. Table 4.12 shows a multiplication table for base four. The numbers shown in red in the table illustrate that $2_{\text{four}} \times 3_{\text{four}} = 12_{\text{four}}$. You can verify this result by converting the numbers to base ten, multiplying in base ten, and then converting back to base four. Here is the actual arithmetic.

$$2_{\text{four}} \times 3_{\text{four}} = 2 \times 3 = 6 = 12_{\text{four}}$$

QUESTION   *What is $5_{\text{six}} \times 4_{\text{six}}$?*

EXAMPLE 7 ■ Multiply Base Four Numerals

Use the base four multiplication table to find $3_{\text{four}} \times 123_{\text{four}}$.

Solution
Arrange the numerals vertically, keeping the digits of the same place value in the same column. Use Table 4.12 to multiply 3_{four} times each digit in 123_{four}. If any of these multiplications produces a two-digit product, then write down the digit on the right and carry the digit on the left.

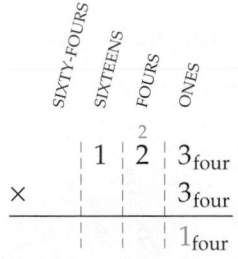

$3_{\text{four}} \times 3_{\text{four}} = 21_{\text{four}}$
Write the 1 in the ones' column and carry the 2.

$3_{\text{four}} \times 2_{\text{four}} = 12_{\text{four}}$
$12_{\text{four}} + 2_{\text{four}}$(the carry) $= 20_{\text{four}}$
Write the 0 in the fours' column and carry the 2.

$3_{\text{four}} \times 1_{\text{four}} = 3_{\text{four}}$
$3_{\text{four}} + 2_{\text{four}}$(the carry) $= 11_{\text{four}}$
Write a 1 in the sixteens' column and carry a 1 to the sixty-fours' column. Bring down the 1 that was carried to the sixty-fours' column to form the product 1101_{four}.

$$3_{\text{four}} \times 123_{\text{four}} = 1101_{\text{four}}$$

CHECK YOUR PROGRESS 7   Find $2_{\text{four}} \times 213_{\text{four}}$.

Solution   See page S14.

ANSWER $5_{\text{six}} \times 4_{\text{six}} = 20 = 32_{\text{six}}$

Writing all of the entries in a multiplication table for a large base such as base twelve can be time-consuming. In such cases you may prefer to multiply in base ten and then convert each product back to the given base. The next example illustrates this multiplication method.

EXAMPLE 8 ■ Multiply Base Twelve Numerals

Find $53_{\text{twelve}} \times 27_{\text{twelve}}$.

Solution

Arrange the numerals vertically, keeping the digits of the same place value in the same column. Start by multiplying each digit of the multiplicand (53_{twelve}) by the ones' digit of the multiplier (27_{twelve}).

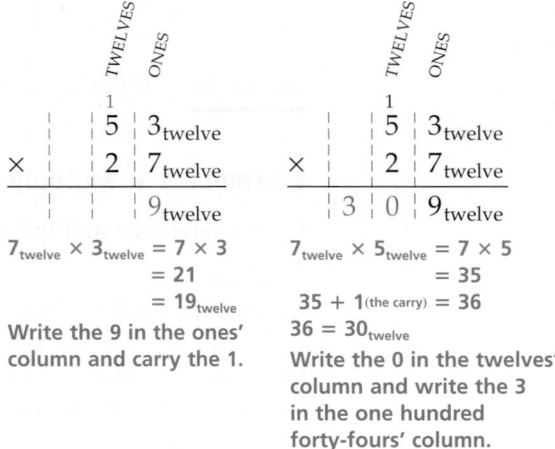

$7_{\text{twelve}} \times 3_{\text{twelve}} = 7 \times 3$
$\qquad\qquad\quad = 21$
$\qquad\qquad\quad = 19_{\text{twelve}}$

Write the 9 in the ones' column and carry the 1.

$7_{\text{twelve}} \times 5_{\text{twelve}} = 7 \times 5$
$\qquad\qquad\quad = 35$
$35 + 1_{\text{(the carry)}} = 36$
$36 = 30_{\text{twelve}}$

Write the 0 in the twelves' column and write the 3 in the one hundred forty-fours' column.

Now multiply each digit of the multiplicand by the twelves' digit of the multiplier.

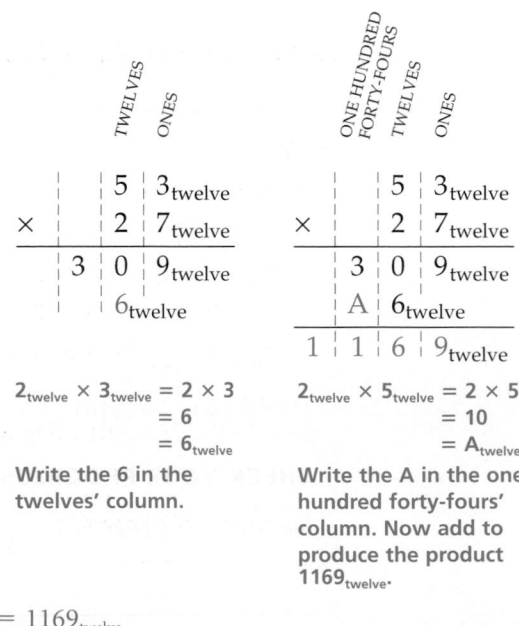

$2_{\text{twelve}} \times 3_{\text{twelve}} = 2 \times 3$
$\qquad\qquad\quad = 6$
$\qquad\qquad\quad = 6_{\text{twelve}}$

Write the 6 in the twelves' column.

$2_{\text{twelve}} \times 5_{\text{twelve}} = 2 \times 5$
$\qquad\qquad\quad = 10$
$\qquad\qquad\quad = A_{\text{twelve}}$

Write the A in the one hundred forty-fours' column. Now add to produce the product 1169_{twelve}.

$53_{\text{twelve}} \times 27_{\text{twelve}} = 1169_{\text{twelve}}$

CHECK YOUR PROGRESS 8   Find $25_{eight} \times 34_{eight}$.

Solution   *See page S15.*

The Fields Medal

Math Matters   **The Fields Medal**

A Nobel Prize is awarded each year in the categories of chemistry, physics, physiology, medicine, literature, and peace. However, no award is given in mathematics. Why Alfred Nobel chose not to provide an award in the category of mathematics is unclear. There has been some speculation that Nobel had a personal conflict with the mathematician Gosta Mittag-Leffler.

The Canadian mathematician John Charles Fields (1863–1932) felt that a prestigious award should be given in the area of mathematics. Fields helped establish the Fields Medal, which was first given to Lars Valerian Ahlfors and Jesse Douglas in 1936. The International Congress of Mathematicians had planned to give two Fields Medals every four years after 1936, but because of World War II, the next Fields Medals were not given until 1950.

It was Fields's wish that the Fields Medal recognize both existing work and the promise of future achievement. Because of this concern for future achievement, the International Congress of Mathematicians decided to restrict those eligible for the Fields Medal to mathematicians under the age of 40.

Division in Different Bases

To perform a division in a base other than base ten, it is helpful to first make a list of a few multiples of the divisor. This procedure is illustrated in the following example.

EXAMPLE 9 ■ Divide Base Seven Numerals

Find $253_{seven} \div 3_{seven}$.

Solution
First list a few multiples of the divisor 3_{seven}.

$$3_{seven} \times 0_{seven} = 3 \times 0 = 0 = 0_{seven} \qquad 3_{seven} \times 4_{seven} = 3 \times 4 = 12 = 15_{seven}$$
$$3_{seven} \times 1_{seven} = 3 \times 1 = 3 = 3_{seven} \qquad 3_{seven} \times 5_{seven} = 3 \times 5 = 15 = 21_{seven}$$
$$3_{seven} \times 2_{seven} = 3 \times 2 = 6 = 6_{seven} \qquad 3_{seven} \times 6_{seven} = 3 \times 6 = 18 = 24_{seven}$$
$$3_{seven} \times 3_{seven} = 3 \times 3 = 9 = 12_{seven}$$

Because $3_{seven} \times 6_{seven} = 24_{seven}$ is slightly less than 25_{seven}, we pick 6 as our first numeral in the quotient when dividing 25_{seven} by 3_{seven}.

$$
\begin{array}{r}
6 \\
3_{seven} \overline{)2\ 5\ 3}_{seven} \\
\underline{2\ 4} \\
1
\end{array}
$$

$3_{seven} \times 6_{seven} = 24_{seven}$

Subtract 24_{seven} from 25_{seven}.

$$\begin{array}{r} 6\ 3_{\text{seven}} \\ 3_{\text{seven}})\overline{2\ 5\ 3_{\text{seven}}} \\ \underline{2\ 4} \end{array}$$

quotient

$$\begin{array}{r} 1\ 3 \\ \underline{1\ 2} \\ 1 \end{array}$$

Bring down the 3.

$3_{\text{seven}} \times 3_{\text{seven}} = 12_{\text{seven}}$

Subtract 12_{seven} from 13_{seven}.

remainder

Thus $253_{\text{seven}} \div 3_{\text{seven}} = 63_{\text{seven}}$ with a remainder of 1_{seven}.

CHECK YOUR PROGRESS 9   Find $324_{\text{five}} \div 3_{\text{five}}$.

Solution   *See page S15.*

In a base two division problem, the only multiples of the divisor that are used are zero times the divisor and one times the divisor.

EXAMPLE 10 ■ Divide Base Two Numerals

Find $101011_{\text{two}} \div 11_{\text{two}}$.

Solution

The divisor is 11_{two}. The multiples of the divisor that may be needed are $11_{\text{two}} \times 0_{\text{two}} = 0_{\text{two}}$ and $11_{\text{two}} \times 1_{\text{two}} = 11_{\text{two}}$. Also note that because $10_{\text{two}} - 1_{\text{two}} = 2 - 1 = 1 = 1_{\text{two}}$, we know that

$$\begin{array}{r} 10_{\text{two}} \\ - \underline{1_{\text{two}}} \\ 1_{\text{two}} \end{array}$$

$$\begin{array}{r} 1\ 1\ 1\ 0_{\text{two}} \\ 11_{\text{two}})\overline{1\ 0\ 1\ 0\ 1\ 1_{\text{two}}} \\ \underline{1\ 1} \\ 1\ 0\ 0 \\ \underline{1\ 1} \\ 1\ 1 \\ \underline{1\ 1} \\ 0\ 1 \\ \underline{0} \\ 1 \end{array}$$

Therefore, $101011_{\text{two}} \div 11_{\text{two}} = 1110_{\text{two}}$ with a remainder of 1_{two}.

CHECK YOUR PROGRESS 10   Find $1110011_{\text{two}} \div 10_{\text{two}}$.

Solution   *See page S15.*

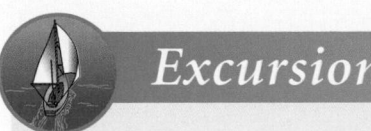

Excursion

Subtraction in Base Two via the Ones Complement and the End-Around Carry

Computers and calculators are often designed so that the number of required circuits is minimized. Instead of using separate circuits to perform addition and subtraction, engineers make use of an *end-around carry procedure* that uses addition to perform subtraction. The end-around carry procedure also makes use of the ones complement of a number. In base two, the ones complement of 0 is 1 and the ones complement of 1 is 0. Thus the ones complement of any base two number can be found by changing each 1 to a 0 and each 0 to a 1.

Subtraction Using the Ones Complement and the End-Around Carry

To subtract a base two number from a larger base two number:

1. Add the ones complement of the subtrahend to the minuend.

2. Take away 1 from the leftmost bit and add 1 to the units bit.

The following example illustrates the process of subtracting 1001_{two} from 1101_{two} using the ones complement and the end-around carry procedure.

$$
\begin{array}{r}
1101_{two} \\
-\ 1001_{two}
\end{array}
$$
Minuend
Subtrahend

$$
\begin{array}{r}
1101_{two} \\
+\ 0110_{two} \\
\hline
10011_{two}
\end{array}
$$
Replace the subtrahend with the ones complement of the subtrahend and add.

$$
\begin{array}{r}
10011_{two} \\
+\ 1_{two} \\
\hline
100_{two}
\end{array}
$$
Take away 1 from the leftmost bit and add 1 to the ones bit. This is the end-around carry procedure.

$1101_{two} - 1001_{two} = 100_{two}$

If the subtrahend has fewer bits than the minuend, leading zeros should be inserted in the subtrahend so that it has the same number of bits as the minuend. This process is illustrated below for the subtraction $1010110_{two} - 11001_{two}$.

$$
\begin{array}{r}
1010110_{two} \\
-\ 11001_{two}
\end{array}
$$
Minuend
Subtrahend

$$
\begin{array}{r}
1010110_{two} \\
-\ 0011001_{two}
\end{array}
$$
Insert two leading zeros.

$$
\begin{array}{r}
1010110_{two} \\
+\ 1100110_{two} \\
\hline
10111100_{two}
\end{array}
$$
Ones complement of subtrahend

(continued)

$$\begin{array}{r} 10111100_{\text{two}} \\ + \quad\quad 1_{\text{two}} \\ \hline 111101_{\text{two}} \end{array}$$

Take away 1 from the leftmost bit
and add 1 to the ones bit.

$$1010110_{\text{two}} - 11001_{\text{two}} = 111101_{\text{two}}$$

Excursion Exercises

Use the ones complement of the subtrahend and the end-around carry method to find each difference.

1. $1110_{\text{two}} - 1001_{\text{two}}$

2. $101011_{\text{two}} - 100010_{\text{two}}$

3. $101001010_{\text{two}} - 1011101_{\text{two}}$

4. $111011100110_{\text{two}} - 101010100_{\text{two}}$

5. $1111101011_{\text{two}} - 1001111_{\text{two}}$

6. $1110010101100_{\text{two}} - 100011110_{\text{two}}$

Exercise Set 4.4

In Exercises 1–12, find each sum in the same base as the addends.

1. $204_{\text{five}} + 123_{\text{five}}$

2. $323_{\text{four}} + 212_{\text{four}}$

3. $5625_{\text{seven}} + 634_{\text{seven}}$

4. $1011_{\text{two}} + 101_{\text{two}}$

5. $110101_{\text{two}} + 10011_{\text{two}}$

6. $11001010_{\text{two}} + 1100111_{\text{two}}$

7. $8B5_{\text{twelve}} + 578_{\text{twelve}}$

8. $379_{\text{sixteen}} + 856_{\text{sixteen}}$

9. $C489_{\text{sixteen}} + BAD_{\text{sixteen}}$

10. $221_{\text{three}} + 122_{\text{three}}$

11. $435_{\text{six}} + 245_{\text{six}}$

12. $5374_{\text{eight}} + 615_{\text{eight}}$

In Exercises 13–24, find each difference.

13. $434_{\text{five}} - 143_{\text{five}}$

14. $534_{\text{six}} - 241_{\text{six}}$

15. $7325_{\text{eight}} - 563_{\text{eight}}$

16. $6148_{\text{nine}} - 782_{\text{nine}}$

17. $11010_{\text{two}} - 1011_{\text{two}}$

18. $111001_{\text{two}} - 10101_{\text{two}}$

19. $11010100_{\text{two}} - 1011011_{\text{two}}$

20. $9C5_{\text{sixteen}} - 687_{\text{sixteen}}$

21. $43A7_{\text{twelve}} - 289_{\text{twelve}}$

22. $BAB2_{\text{twelve}} - 475_{\text{twelve}}$

23. $762_{\text{nine}} - 367_{\text{nine}}$

24. $3223_{\text{four}} - 133_{\text{four}}$

In Exercises 25–38, find each product.

25. $3_{\text{six}} \times 145_{\text{six}}$

26. $5_{\text{seven}} \times 542_{\text{seven}}$

27. $2_{\text{three}} \times 212_{\text{three}}$

28. $4_{\text{five}} \times 4132_{\text{five}}$

29. $5_{\text{eight}} \times 7354_{\text{eight}}$

30. $11_{\text{two}} \times 11011_{\text{two}}$

31. $10_{\text{two}} \times 101010_{\text{two}}$

32. $101_{\text{two}} \times 110100_{\text{two}}$

33. $25_{\text{eight}} \times 453_{\text{eight}}$

34. $43_{\text{six}} \times 1254_{\text{six}}$

35. $132_{\text{four}} \times 1323_{\text{four}}$

36. $43_{\text{twelve}} \times 895_{\text{twelve}}$

37. $5_{\text{sixteen}} \times BAD_{\text{sixteen}}$

38. $23_{\text{sixteen}} \times 798_{\text{sixteen}}$

In Exercises 39–49, find each quotient and remainder.

39. $132_{\text{four}} \div 2_{\text{four}}$

40. $124_{\text{five}} \div 2_{\text{five}}$

41. $231_{\text{four}} \div 3_{\text{four}}$

42. $672_{\text{eight}} \div 5_{\text{eight}}$

43. $5341_{\text{six}} \div 4_{\text{six}}$

44. $11011_{\text{two}} \div 10_{\text{two}}$

45. $101010_{\text{two}} \div 11_{\text{two}}$

46. $1011011_{\text{two}} \div 100_{\text{two}}$

47. $457_{\text{twelve}} \div 5_{\text{twelve}}$

48. $832_{\text{sixteen}} \div 7_{\text{sixteen}}$

49. $234_{\text{five}} \div 12_{\text{five}}$

50. If $232_x = 92$, find the base x.

51. If $143_x = 10200_{three}$, find the base x.

52. If $46_x = 101010_{two}$, find the base x.

53. Consider the addition $384 + 245$.

    a. Use base ten addition to find the sum.

    b. Convert 384 and 245 to base two.

    c. Find the base two sum of the base two numbers you found in part b.

    d. Convert the base two sum from part c to base ten.

    e. How does the answer to part a compare with the answer to part d?

54. Consider the subtraction $457 - 318$.

    a. Use base ten subtraction to find the difference.

    b. Convert 457 and 318 to base two.

    c. Find the base two difference of the base two numbers you found in part b.

    d. Convert the base two difference from part c to base ten.

    e. How does the answer to part a compare with the answer to part d?

55. Consider the multiplication 247×26.

    a. Use base ten multiplication to find the product.

    b. Convert 247 and 26 to base two.

    c. Find the base two product of the base two numbers you found in part b.

    d. Convert the base two product from part c to base ten.

    e. How does the answer to part a compare with the answer to part d?

Extensions

CRITICAL THINKING

56. Explain the error in the following base eight subtraction.

$$\begin{array}{r} 751_{eight} \\ -\ 126_{eight} \\ \hline 625_{eight} \end{array}$$

57. Determine the base used in the following multiplication.

$$314_{base\ x} \times 24_{base\ x} = 11202_{base\ x}$$

58. The base ten number 12 is an even number. In base seven, 12 is written as 15_{seven}. Is 12 an odd number in base seven?

59. Explain why there is no numeration system with a base of 1.

60. **A Cryptarithm** In the following base four addition problem, each letter represents one of the numerals 0, 1, 2, or 3. No two different letters represent the same numeral. Determine which digit is represented by each letter.

$$\begin{array}{r} \mathbf{N\ O}_{four} \\ +\ \mathbf{A\ T}_{four} \\ \hline \mathbf{N\ O\ T}_{four} \end{array}$$

61. **A Cryptarithm** In the following base six addition problem, each letter represents one of the numerals 0, 1, 2, 3, 4, or 5. No two different letters represent the same numeral. Determine which digit is represented by each letter.

$$\begin{array}{r} \mathbf{M\ A}_{six} \\ +\ \mathbf{A\ S}_{six} \\ \hline \mathbf{M\ O\ M}_{six} \end{array}$$

EXPLORATIONS

62. **Negative Base Numerals** It is possible to use a negative number as the base of a numeration system. For instance, the negative base four numeral $32_{negative\ four}$ represents the number $3 \times (-4)^1 + 2 \times (-4)^0 = -12 + 2 = -10$.

    a. Convert each of the following negative base numerals to base 10:

      $143_{negative\ five}$

      $74_{negative\ nine}$

      $10110_{negative\ two}$

    b. Write -27 as a negative base five numeral.

    c. Write 64 as a negative base three numeral.

    d. Write 112 as a negative base ten numeral.

| # Prime Numbers

Prime Numbers

Number theory is a mathematical discipline that is primarily concerned with the properties that are exhibited by the natural numbers. The mathematician Carl Friedrich Gauss established many theorems in number theory. As we noted in the chapter opener, Gauss called mathematics the queen of the sciences and number theory the queen of mathematics. Many topics in number theory involve the concept of a *divisor* or *factor*.

Definition of Divisor

The natural number a is a **divisor** or **factor** of the natural number b provided there exists a natural number j such that $aj = b$.

In less formal terms, a natural number a is a divisor of the natural number b provided $b \div a$ has a remainder of 0. For instance, 10 has divisors of 1, 2, 5, and 10 because each of these numbers divides into 10 with a remainder of 0.

EXAMPLE 1 ■ Find Divisors

Determine all of the natural number divisors of each number.

a. 6   **b.** 42   **c.** 17

Solution

a. Divide 6 by 1, 2, 3, 4, 5, and 6. The division of 6 by 1, 2, 3, and 6 each produces a natural number quotient and a remainder of 0. Thus 1, 2, 3, and 6 are divisors of 6. Dividing 6 by 4 and 6 by 5 does not produce a remainder of 0. Therefore 4 and 5 are not divisors of 6.

b. The only natural numbers from 1 to 42 that divide into 42 with a remainder of 0 are 1, 2, 3, 6, 7, 14, 21, and 42. Thus the divisors of 42 are 1, 2, 3, 6, 7, 14, 21, and 42.

c. The only divisors of 17 are 1 and 17.

CHECK YOUR PROGRESS 1   Determine all of the natural number divisors of each number.

a. 9   **b.** 11   **c.** 24

Solution   *See page S15.*

It is worth noting that every natural number greater than 1 has itself as a factor and 1 as a factor. If a natural number greater than 1 has only 1 and itself as factors, then it is a very special number known as a *prime number*.

> **Definition of a Prime Number and a Composite Number**
>
> A **prime number** is a natural number greater than 1 that has exactly two factors (divisors): itself and 1.
> A **composite number** is a natural number greater than 1 that is not a prime number.

✔ **TAKE NOTE**

The natural number 1 is neither a prime number nor a composite number.

The ten smallest prime numbers are 2, 3, 5, 7, 11, 13, 17, 19, 23, and 29. Each of these numbers has only itself and 1 as factors. The ten smallest composite numbers are 4, 6, 8, 9, 10, 12, 14, 15, 16, and 18.

EXAMPLE 2 ■ **Classify a Number as a Prime Number or a Composite Number**

Determine whether each number is a prime number or a composite number.

a. 41   **b.** 51   **c.** 119

Solution
a. The only divisors of 41 and 1 are 41. Thus 41 is a prime number.
b. The divisors of 51 are 1, 3, 17, and 51. Thus 51 is a composite number.
c. The divisors of 119 are 1, 7, 17, and 119. Thus 119 is a composite number.

CHECK YOUR PROGRESS 2   Determine whether each number is a prime number or a composite number.

a. 47   **b.** 171   **c.** 91

Solution   *See page S15.*

QUESTION   *Are all prime numbers odd numbers?*

Divisibility Tests

To determine whether one number is divisible by a smaller number, we often apply a **divisibility test,** which is a procedure that enables one to determine whether the smaller number is a divisor of the larger number without actually dividing the smaller number into the larger number. Table 4.13 provides divisibility tests for the numbers 2, 3, 4, 5, 6, 8, 9, 10, and 11.

ANSWER   *No. The even number 2 is a prime number.*

Table 4.13 *Base Ten Divisibility Tests*

A number is divisible by the following divisor if:	Divisibility Test	Example
2	The number is an even number.	846 is divisible by 2 because 846 is an even number.
3	The sum of the digits of the number is divisible by 3.	531 is divisible by 3 because $5 + 3 + 1 = 9$ is divisible by 3.
4	The last two digits of the number form a number that is divisible by 4.	1924 is divisible by 4 because the last two digits form the number 24, which is divisible by 4.
5	The number ends with a 0 or a 5.	8785 is divisible by 5 because it ends with 5.
6	The number is divisible by 2 and by 3.	972 is divisible by 6 because it is divisible by 2 and also by 3.
8	The last three digits of the number form a number that is divisible by 8.	19,168 is divisible by 8 because the last three digits form the number 168, which is divisible by 8.
9	The sum of the digits of the number is divisible by 9.	621,513 is divisible by 9 because the sum of the digits is 18, which is divisible by 9.
10	The last digit is 0.	970 is divisible by 10 because it ends with 0.
11	Start at one end of the number and compute the sum of every other digit. Next compute the sum of the remaining digits. If the difference of these sums is divisible by 11, then the original number is divisible by 11.	4807 is divisible by 11 because the difference of the sum of the digits shown in blue $(8 + 7 = 15)$ and the sum of the remaining digits shown in red $(4 + 0 = 4)$ is $15 - 4 = 11$, which is divisible by 11.

EXAMPLE 3 ■ Apply Divisibility Tests

Use divisibility tests to determine whether 16,278 is divisible by the following numbers.

a. 2   **b.** 3   **c.** 5   **d.** 8   **e.** 11

Solution

a. Because 16,278 is an even number, it is divisible by 2.

b. The sum of the digits of 16,278 is 24, which is divisible by 3. Therefore, 16,278 is divisible by 3.

c. The number 16,278 does not end with a 0 or a 5. Therefore, 16,278 is not divisible by 5.

d. The last three digits of 16,278 form the number 278, which is not divisible by 8. Thus 16,278 is not divisible by 8.

e. The sum of the digits with even place-value powers is $1 + 2 + 8 = 11$. The sum of the digits with odd place-value powers is $6 + 7 = 13$. The difference of these sums is $13 - 11 = 2$. This difference is not divisible by 11, so 16,278 is not divisible by 11.

CHECK YOUR PROGRESS 3   Use divisibility tests to determine whether 341,565 is divisible by each of the following numbers.

a. 3   **b.** 4   **c.** 10   **d.** 11

Solution   *See page S15.*

Prime Factorization

The **prime factorization** of a composite number is a factorization that contains only prime numbers. Many proofs in number theory make use of the following important theorem.

> ### The Fundamental Theorem of Arithmetic
>
> Every composite number can be written as a unique product of prime numbers (disregarding the order of the factors).

To find the prime factorization of a composite number, rewrite the number as a product of two smaller natural numbers. If these smaller numbers are both prime numbers, then you are finished. If either of the smaller numbers is not a prime number, then rewrite it as a product of smaller natural numbers. Continue this procedure until all factors are primes. In Example 4 we make use of a *tree diagram* to organize the factorization process.

EXAMPLE 4 ■ Find the Prime Factorization of a Number

Determine the prime factorization of the following numbers.

a. 84   **b.** 495   **c.** 4004

Solution

a. The following tree diagrams show two different ways of finding the prime factorization of 84, which is $2 \cdot 2 \cdot 3 \cdot 7 = 2^2 \cdot 3 \cdot 7$. Each number in the tree is equal to the product of the two smaller numbers below it. The numbers (in red) at the extreme ends of the branches are the prime factors.

$$84 = 2^2 \cdot 3 \cdot 7$$

b.

$$495 = 3^2 \cdot 5 \cdot 11$$

The following compact division procedure can also be used to determine the prime factorization of a number.

2	4004
2	2002
7	1001
11	143
	13

In this procedure we use only prime number divisors, and we continue until the last quotient is a prime number. The prime factorization is the product of all the prime numbers, which are shown in red.

c.
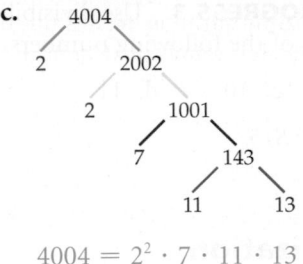

$$4004 = 2^2 \cdot 7 \cdot 11 \cdot 13$$

CHECK YOUR PROGRESS 4   Determine the prime factorization of the following.

a. 315   **b.** 273   **c.** 1309

Solution   See page S15.

Math Matters   Srinivasa Ramanujan

On January 16, 1913, the young 26-year-old Srinivasa Ramanujan (Rä-mä′noo-jûn) sent a letter from Madras, India, to the illustrious English mathematician G. H. Hardy. The letter requested that Hardy give his opinion about several mathematical ideas that Ramanujan had developed. In the letter Ramanujan explained, "I have not trodden through the conventional regular course which is followed in a University course, but I am striking out a new path for myself." Much of the mathematics was written using unconventional terms and notation; however, Hardy recognized (after many detailed readings and with the help of other mathematicians at Cambridge University) that Ramanujan was "a mathematician of the highest quality, a man of altogether exceptional originality and power."

On March 17, 1914, Ramanujan set sail for England, where he joined Hardy in a most unusual collaboration that lasted until Ramanujan returned to India in 1919. The following famous story is often told to illustrate the remarkable mathematical genius of Ramanujan.

Srinivasa Ramanujan
(1887–1920)

After Hardy had taken a taxicab to visit Ramanujan, he made the remark that the license plate number for the taxi was "1729, a rather dull number." Ramanujan immediately responded by saying that 1729 was a most interesting number, because it is the smallest natural number that can be expressed in two different ways as the sum of two cubes.

$$1^3 + 12^3 = 1729 \quad \text{and} \quad 9^3 + 10^3 = 1729$$

An interesting biography of the life of Srinivasa Ramanujan is given in *The Man Who Knew Infinity: A Life of the Genius Ramanujan* by Robert Kanigel.[1]

---

1. Kanigel, Robert. *The Man Who Knew Infinity: A Life of the Genius Ramanujan.* New York: Simon & Schuster, 1991.

To determine whether a natural number is a prime number, it is necessary to consider only divisors from 2 up to the square root of the number, because every composite number n has at least one divisor less than or equal to $\sqrt{n}$. The proof of this statement is outlined in Exercise 77 of this section.

▼ **point of interest**

In article 329 of *Disquisitiones Arithmeticae*, Gauss wrote:

"The problem of distinguishing prime numbers from composite numbers and of resolving the latter into their prime factors is known to be one of the most important and useful in arithmetic... The dignity of the science itself seems to require that every possible means be explored for the solution of a problem so elegant and so celebrated." (*Source: The Little Book of Big Primes* by Paulo Ribenboim. New York: Springer-Verlag, 1991.)

It is possible to determine whether a natural number n is a prime number by checking each natural number from 2 up to the largest integer not greater than $\sqrt{n}$ to see whether each is a divisor of n. If none of these numbers is a divisor of n, then n is a prime number. For large values of n, this division method is generally time-consuming and tedious. The Greek astronomer and mathematician Eratosthenes (about 276–192 B.C.) recognized that multiplication is generally easier than division, and he devised a method that makes use of multiples to determine every prime number in a list of natural numbers. Today we call this method the *Sieve of Eratosthenes.*

To sift prime numbers, first make a list of consecutive natural numbers. In Table 4.14 we have listed the consecutive counting numbers from 2 to 100.

- Cross out every multiple of 2 larger than 2. The next smallest remaining number in the list is 3. Cross out every multiple of 3 larger than 3.

- Call the next smallest remaining number in the list k. Cross out every multiple of k larger than k. Repeat this step for all $k < \sqrt{100}$.

Table 4.14 *The Sieve Method of Finding Primes*

	2	3	4	5	6	7	8	9	10
11	12	13	14	15	16	17	18	19	20
21	22	23	24	25	26	27	28	29	30
31	32	33	34	35	36	37	38	39	40
41	42	43	44	45	46	47	48	49	50
51	52	53	54	55	56	57	58	59	60
61	62	63	64	65	66	67	68	69	70
71	72	73	74	75	76	77	78	79	80
81	82	83	84	85	86	87	88	89	90
91	92	93	94	95	96	97	98	99	100

The numbers in blue that are not crossed out are prime numbers. Table 4.14 shows that there are 25 prime numbers less than 100.

Over 2000 years ago, Euclid proved that the set of prime numbers is an infinite set. Euclid's proof is an *indirect proof* or a *proof by contradiction*. Essentially his proof shows that for any finite list of prime numbers, we can create a number T, as described below, such that any prime factor of T can be shown to be a prime number that is not in the list. Thus there must be an infinite number of primes because it is not possible for all of the primes to be in any finite list.

Euclid's Proof Assume *all* of the prime numbers are contained in the list p_1, p_2, p_3, ..., p_r. Let $T = (p_1 \cdot p_2 \cdot p_3 \cdots p_r) + 1$. Either T is a prime number or T has a prime divisor. If T is a prime then it is a prime that is not in our list and we have reached a contradiction. If T is not prime, then one of the primes p_1, p_2, p_3, ..., p_r must be a divisor of T. However, the number T is not divisible by any of the primes p_1, p_2, p_3, ..., p_r because each p_i divides $p_1 \cdot p_2 \cdot p_3 \cdots p_r$ but does not divide 1. Hence any prime divisor of T, say p, is a prime number that is not in the list p_1, p_2, p_3, ..., p_r. So p is yet another prime number, and p_1, p_2, p_3, ..., p_r is not a complete list of all the prime numbers.

We conclude this section with two quotations about prime numbers. The first is by the illustrious mathematician Paul Erdös (1913–1996); the second by the mathematics professor Don B. Zagier of the Max-Planck Institute, Bonn, Germany.

> It will be millions of years before we'll have any understanding, and even then it won't be a complete understanding, because we're up against the infinite.— P. Erdös, about prime numbers in *Atlantic Monthly*, November 1987, p. 74. *Source:* **http://www.mlahanas.de/Greeks/Primes.htm**.

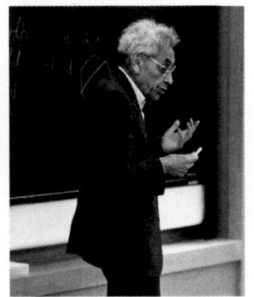

Paul Erdös

In a 1975 lecture, D. Zagier commented,

> There are two facts about the distribution of prime numbers of which I hope to convince you so overwhelmingly that they will be permanently engraved in your hearts. The first is that, despite their simple definition and role as the building blocks of the natural numbers, the prime numbers grow like weeds among the natural numbers, seeming to obey no other law than that of chance, and nobody can predict where the next one will sprout. The second fact is even more astonishing, for it states just the opposite: that the prime numbers exhibit stunning regularity, that there are laws governing their behavior, and that they obey these laws with almost military precision.—(Havil 2003, p. 171). *Source:* **http://mathworld. wolfram.com/PrimeNumber.html**.

Don B. Zagier

Excursion

The Distribution of the Primes

Many mathematicians have searched without success for a mathematical formula that can be used to generate the sequence of prime numbers. We know that the prime numbers form an infinite sequence. However, the distribution of the prime numbers within the sequence of natural numbers is very complicated. The ratio of prime numbers to composite numbers appears to become smaller and smaller as larger and larger numbers are considered. In general, the number of consecutive composite numbers that come

(continued)

between two prime numbers tends to increase as the size of the numbers becomes larger; however, this increase is erratic and appears to be unpredictable.

In this Excursion we refer to a list of two or more consecutive composite numbers as a **prime desert.** For instance, 8, 9, 10 is a prime desert because it consists of three consecutive composite numbers. The longest prime desert shown in Table 4.14 is the seven consecutive composite numbers 90, 91, 92, 93, 94, 95, and 96. A formula that involves *factorials* can be used to form prime deserts of any finite length.

> **Definition of *n* factorial**
>
> If n is a natural number, then $n!$, which is read "n factorial," is defined as
>
> $$n! = n \cdot (n - 1) \cdot \cdots \cdot 3 \cdot 2 \cdot 1$$

As an example of a factorial, consider $4! = 4 \cdot 3 \cdot 2 \cdot 1 = 24$.

The sequence

$$4! + 2, 4! + 3, 4! + 4$$

is a prime desert of the three composite numbers 26, 27, and 28. Figure 4.1 below shows a prime desert of 10 consecutive composite numbers. Figure 4.2 shows a procedure that can be used to produce a prime desert of n composite numbers, where n is any natural number greater than 2.

$$
\left.
\begin{aligned}
&11! + 2\\
&11! + 3\\
&11! + 4\\
&11! + 5\\
&11! + 6\\
&\quad\vdots\\
&11! + 10\\
&11! + 11
\end{aligned}
\right\}
\begin{aligned}
&\text{A prime desert of}\\
&\text{10 consecutive}\\
&\text{composite}\\
&\text{numbers}
\end{aligned}
\qquad
\left.
\begin{aligned}
&(n + 1)! + 2\\
&(n + 1)! + 3\\
&(n + 1)! + 4\\
&(n + 1)! + 5\\
&(n + 1)! + 6\\
&\quad\vdots\\
&(n + 1)! + n\\
&(n + 1)! + (n + 1)
\end{aligned}
\right\}
\begin{aligned}
&\text{A prime desert of}\\
&n \text{ consecutive}\\
&\text{composite}\\
&\text{numbers}
\end{aligned}
$$

Figure 4.1   **Figure 4.2**

A prime desert of length one million is shown by the sequence

$$1,000,001! + 2;\ 1,000,001! + 3;\ 1,000,001! + 4;\ \ldots;\ 1,000,001! + 1,000,001$$

It appears that the distribution of prime numbers is similar to the situation wherein a mathematical gardener plants an infinite number of grass seeds on a windy day. Many of the grass seeds fall close to the gardener, but some are blown down the street and into the next neighborhood. There are gaps where no grass seeds are within 1 mile of each other. Farther down the road there are gaps where no grass seeds are within 10 miles of each other. No matter how far the gardener travels and how long it has been since the last grass seed was spotted, the gardener knows that more grass seeds will appear.

Excursion Exercises

1.   Explain how you know that each of the numbers

$$1,000,001! + 2;\ 1,000,001! + 3;\ 1,000,001! + 4;\ \ldots;\ 1,000,001! + 1,000,001$$

is a composite number.

(continued)

2. Use factorials to generate the numbers in a prime desert of 12 consecutive composite numbers. Now use a calculator to evaluate each number in this prime desert.

3. Use factorials and "..." notation to represent a prime desert of
   a. 20 consecutive composite numbers.
   b. 500,000 consecutive composite numbers.
   c. 7 billion consecutive composite numbers.

Exercise Set 4.5

In Exercises 1–10, determine all natural number divisors of the given number.

1. 20
2. 32
3. 65
4. 75
5. 41
6. 79
7. 110
8. 150
9. 385
10. 455

In Exercises 11–20, determine whether each number is a prime number or a composite number.

11. 21
12. 31
13. 37
14. 39
15. 101
16. 81
17. 79
18. 161
19. 203
20. 211

In Exercises 21–28, use the divisibility tests in Table 4.13 to determine whether the given number is divisible by each of the following: 2, 3, 4, 5, 6, 8, 9, and 10.

21. 210
22. 314
23. 51
24. 168
25. 2568
26. 3525
27. 4190
28. 6123

In Exercises 29–40, write the prime factorization of the number.

29. 18
30. 48
31. 120
32. 380
33. 425
34. 625
35. 1024
36. 1410
37. 6312
38. 3155
39. 18,234
40. 19,345

41. Use the Sieve of Eratosthenes procedure to find all prime numbers from 2 to 200. *Hint:* Because $\sqrt{200} \approx 14.1$, you need to continue the sieve procedure up to $k = 13$. Note: You do not need to consider $k = 14$ because 14 is not a prime number.

42. Use your list of prime numbers from Exercise 41 to find the number of prime numbers from:
    a. 2 to 50
    b. 51 to 100
    c. 101 to 150
    d. 151 to 200

43. **Twin Primes** If the natural numbers n and $n + 2$ are both prime numbers, then they are said to be **twin primes.** For example, 11 and 13 are twin primes. It is not known whether the set of twin primes is an infinite set or a finite set. Use the list of primes from Exercise 41 to write all twin primes less than 200.

44. **Twin Primes** Find a pair of twin primes between 200 and 300. See Exercise 43.

45. **Twin Primes** Find a pair of twin primes between 300 and 400. See Exercise 43.

46. **A Prime Triplet** If the natural numbers n, $n + 2$, and $n + 4$ are all prime numbers, then they are said to be **prime triplets.** Write a few sentences that explain why the prime triplets 3, 5, and 7 are the only prime triplets.

47. Goldbach's Conjecture In 1742, Christian Goldbach conjectured that every even number greater than 2 can be written as the sum of two prime numbers. Many mathematicians have tried to prove or disprove this conjecture without succeeding. Show that *Goldbach's conjecture* is true for each of the following even numbers.

a. 24   b. 50

c. 86   d. 144

e. 210   f. 264

48. ✎ **Perfect Squares** The square of a natural number is called a **perfect square**. Pick six perfect squares. For each perfect square, determine the number of distinct natural-number factors of the perfect square. Make a conjecture about the number of distinct natural-number factors of any perfect square.

Every prime number has a divisibility test. Many of these divisibility tests are slight variations of the following divisibility test for 7.

A divisibility test for 7 To determine whether a given base ten number is divisible by 7, double the ones digit of the given number. Find the difference between this number and the number formed by omitting the ones digit from the given number. If necessary, repeat this procedure until you obtain a small final difference.

If the final difference is divisible by 7, then the given number is also divisible by 7.

If the final difference is not divisible by 7, then the given number is not divisible by 7.

Example Use the above divisibility test to determine whether 301 is divisible by 7.

Solution The double of the ones digit is 2. Subtracting 2 from 30, which is the number formed by omitting the ones digit from the original number, yields 28. Because 28 is divisible by 7, the original number 301 is divisible by 7.

In Exercises 49–56, use the above divisibility test for 7 to determine whether each number is divisible by 7.

49. 182   50. 203

51. 1001   52. 2403

53. 11,561   54. 13,842

55. 204,316   56. 789,327

A divisibility test for 13 To determine whether a given base ten number is divisible by 13, multiply the ones digit of the given number by 4. Find the sum of this multiple of 4 and the number formed by omitting the ones digit from the given number. If necessary, repeat this procedure until you obtain a small final sum.

If the final sum is divisible by 13, then the given number is divisible by 13.

If the final sum is not divisible by 13, then the given number is not divisible by 13.

Example Use the above divisibility test to determine whether 1079 is divisible by 13.

Solution Four times the ones digit is 36. The number formed by omitting the ones digit is 107. The sum of 36 and 107 is 143. Now repeat the procedure on 143. Four times the ones digit is 12. The sum of 12 and 14, which is the number formed by omitting the ones digit, is 26. Because 26 is divisible by 13, the original number 1079 is divisible by 13.

In Exercises 57–64, use the above divisibility test for 13 to determine whether each number is divisible by 13.

57. 91   58. 273

59. 1885   60. 8931

61. 14,507   62. 22,184

63. 13,351   64. 85,657

Extensions
CRITICAL THINKING

65. Factorial Primes A prime number of the form $n! \pm 1$ is called a **factorial prime**. Recall that the notation $n!$ is called n factorial and represents the product of all natural numbers from 1 to n. For example, $4! = 4 \cdot 3 \cdot 2 \cdot 1 = 24$. Factorial primes are of interest to mathematicians because they often signal the end or the beginning of a lengthy string of consecutive composite numbers. See the Excursion on page 226.

a. Find the smallest value of n such that $n! + 1$ and $n! - 1$ are twin primes.

b. Find the smallest value of n for which $n! + 1$ is a composite number and $n! - 1$ is a prime number.

66. **Primorial Primes** The notation $p\#$ represents the product of all the prime numbers less than or equal to the prime number p. For instance,

$$3\# = 2 \cdot 3 = 6$$

$$5\# = 2 \cdot 3 \cdot 5 = 30$$

$$11\# = 2 \cdot 3 \cdot 5 \cdot 7 \cdot 11 = 2310$$

A **primorial prime** is a prime number of the form $p\# \pm 1$. For instance, $3\# + 1 = 2 \cdot 3 + 1 = 7$ and $3\# - 1 = 2 \cdot 3 - 1 = 5$ are both primorial primes. Large primorial primes are often examined in the search for a pair of large twin primes.

a. Find the smallest prime number p, where $p \geq 7$, such that $p\# + 1$ and $p\# - 1$ are twin primes.

b. Find the smallest prime number p, such that $p\# + 1$ is a prime number but $p\# - 1$ is a composite number.

67. **A Divisibility Test for 17** Determine a divisibility test for 17. *Hint*: One divisibility test for 17 is similar to the divisibility test for 7 on the previous page in that it involves the last digit of the given number and the operation of subtraction.

68. **A Divisibility Test for 19** Determine a divisibility test for 19. *Hint*: One divisibility test for 19 is similar to the divisibility test for 13 on the previous page in that it involves the last digit of the given number and the operation of addition.

Number of Divisors of a Composite Number The following method can be used to determine the number of divisors of a composite number. First find the prime factorization (in exponential form) of the composite number. Add 1 to each exponent in the prime factorization and then compute the product of these exponents. This product is equal to the number of divisors of the composite number. To illustrate that this procedure yields the correct result, consider the composite number 12, which has the six divisors 1, 2, 3, 4, 6, and 12. The prime factorization

of 12 is $2^2 \cdot 3^1$. Adding 1 to each of the exponents produces the numbers 3 and 2. The product of 3 and 2 is 6, which agrees with the result obtained by listing all of the divisors.

In Exercises 69–74, determine the number of divisors of each composite number.

69. 60	**70.** 84
71. 297	**72.** 288
73. 360	**74.** 875

EXPLORATIONS

75. **Kummer's Proof** In the 1870s, the mathematician Eduard Kummer used a proof similar to the following to show that there exist an infinite number of prime numbers. Supply the missing reasons in parts a and b.

a. *Proof* Assume there exist only a finite number of prime numbers, say p_1, p_2, $p_3, \ldots, p_r$. Let $N = p_1 p_2 p_3 \cdots p_r > 2$. The natural number $N - 1$ has at least one common prime factor with N. Why?

b. Call the common prime factor from part a p_i. Now p_i divides N and p_i divides $N - 1$. Thus p_i divides their difference: $N - (N - 1) = 1$. Why?

This leads to a contradiction, because no prime number is a divisor of 1. Hence Kummer concluded that the original assumption was incorrect, and there must exist an infinite number of prime numbers.

76. *Theorem* If a number of the form $111 \ldots 1$ is a prime number, then the number of 1's in the number is a prime number. For instance,

$$11 \text{ and } 1{,}111{,}111{,}111{,}111{,}111{,}111$$

are prime numbers, and the number of 1's in each number (two in the first number and 19 in the second number) is a prime number.

a. What is the converse of the above theorem? Is the converse of a theorem always true?

b. The number $111 = 3 \cdot 37$, so 111 is not a prime number. Explain why this does not contradict the above theorem.

77. State the missing reasons in parts a, b, and c of the following proof.

Theorem Every composite number n has at least one divisor less than or equal to $\sqrt{n}$.

a. *Proof* Assume a is a divisor of n. Then there exists a natural number j such that $aj = n$. Why?

b. Now a and j cannot both be greater than $\sqrt{n}$, because this would imply that $aj > \sqrt{n}\sqrt{n}$. However, $\sqrt{n}\sqrt{n}$ simplifies to n, which equals aj. What contradiction does this lead to?

c. Thus either a or j must be less than or equal to $\sqrt{n}$. Because j is also a divisor of n, the proof is complete. How do we know that j is a divisor of n?

78. **The RSA Algorithm** In 1977, Ron Rivest, Adi Shamir, and Leonard Adleman invented a method for encrypting information. Their method is known as the RSA algorithm. Today the RSA algorithm is used by both the Microsoft Internet Explorer and Netscape Navigator Web browsers, as well as by VISA and MasterCard to ensure secure electronic credit card transactions. The RSA algorithm involves large prime numbers. Research the RSA algorithm and write a report about some of the reasons why this algorithm has become one of the most popular of all the encryption algorithms.

79. **Theorems and Conjectures** Use the Internet or a text on prime numbers to determine whether each of the following statements is an established theorem or a conjecture. (*Note:* n represents a natural number).

a. There are infinitely many twin primes.

b. There are infinitely many primes of the form $n^2 + 1$.

c. There is always a prime number between n and $2n$ for $n \geq 2$.

d. There is always a prime number between n^2 and $(n + 1)^2$.

e. Every odd number greater than 5 can be written as the sum of three primes.

f. Every positive even number can be written as the difference of two primes.

SECTION 4.6 | # Topics from Number Theory

Perfect, Deficient, and Abundant Numbers

The ancient Greek mathematicians personified the natural numbers. For instance, they considered the odd natural numbers as male and the even natural numbers as female. They also used the concept of a *proper factor* to classify a natural number as *perfect*, *deficient*, or *abundant*. The **proper factors** of a natural number n include all natural number factors of n except for the number n itself. For instance, the proper factors of 10 are 1, 2, and 5. The proper factors of 16 are 1, 2, 4, and 8.

Perfect, Deficient, and Abundant Numbers

A natural number is

■ **perfect** if it is equal to the sum of its proper factors.

■ **deficient** if it is greater than the sum of its proper factors.

■ **abundant** if it is less than the sum of its proper factors.

EXAMPLE 1 ■ **Classify a Number as Perfect, Deficient, or Abundant**

Determine whether the following numbers are perfect, deficient, or abundant.

a. 6   **b.** 20   **c.** 25

Solution

a. The proper factors of 6 are 1, 2, and 3. The sum of these proper factors is $1 + 2 + 3 = 6$. Because 6 is equal to the sum of its proper divisors, 6 is a perfect number.

b. The proper factors of 20 are 1, 2, 4, 5, and 10. The sum of these proper factors is $1 + 2 + 4 + 5 + 10 = 22$. Because 20 is less than the sum of its proper factors, 20 is an abundant number.

c. The proper factors of 25 are 1 and 5. The sum of these proper factors is $1 + 5 = 6$. Because 25 is greater than the sum of its proper factors, 25 is a deficient number.

CHECK YOUR PROGRESS 1   Determine whether the following numbers are perfect, deficient, or abundant.

a. 24   **b.** 28   **c.** 35

Solution   See page S15.

Mersenne Numbers and Perfect Numbers

As a French monk in the religious order known as the Minims, Marin Mersenne (mər-sĕn′) devoted himself to prayer and his studies, which included topics from number theory. Mersenne took it upon himself to collect and disseminate mathematical information to scientists and mathematicians through Europe. Mersenne was particularly interested in prime numbers of the form $2^n - 1$, where n is a prime number. Today numbers of the form $2^n - 1$, where n is a prime number, are known as **Mersenne numbers.**

Some Mersenne numbers are prime and some are composite. For instance, the Mersenne numbers $2^2 - 1$ and $2^3 - 1$ are prime numbers, but the Mersenne number $2^{11} - 1 = 2047$ is not prime because $2047 = 23 \cdot 89$.

Marin Mersenne
(1588–1648)

EXAMPLE 2 ■ **Determine Whether a Mersenne Number is a Prime Number**

Determine whether the Mersenne number $2^5 - 1$ is a prime number.

Solution

$2^5 - 1 = 31$ and 31 is a prime number. Thus $2^5 - 1$ is a Mersenne prime.

CHECK YOUR PROGRESS 2   Determine whether the Mersenne number $2^7 - 1$ is a prime number.

Solution   See page S16.

The ancient Greeks knew that the first four perfect numbers were 6, 28, 496, and 8128. In fact, proposition 36 from Volume IX of Euclid's *Elements* states a procedure that uses Mersenne primes to produce a perfect number.

> **Euclid's Procedure for Generating a Perfect Number**
>
> If n and $2^n - 1$ are both prime numbers, then $2^{n-1}(2^n - 1)$ is a perfect number.

Euclid's procedure shows how every Mersenne prime can be used to produce a perfect number. For instance,

If $n = 2$, then $2^{2-1}(2^2 - 1) = 2(3) = 6$.

If $n = 3$, then $2^{3-1}(2^3 - 1) = 4(7) = 28$.

If $n = 5$, then $2^{5-1}(2^5 - 1) = 16(31) = 496$.

If $n = 7$, then $2^{7-1}(2^7 - 1) = 64(127) = 8128$.

The fifth perfect number was not discovered until the year 1461. It is $2^{12}(2^{13} - 1) = 33{,}550{,}336$. The sixth and seventh perfect numbers were discovered in 1588 by P. A. Cataldi. In exponential form, they are $2^{16}(2^{17} - 1)$ and $2^{18}(2^{19} - 1)$. It is interesting to observe that the ones' digits of the first five perfect numbers alternate: 6, 8, 6, 8, 6. Evaluate $2^{16}(2^{17} - 1)$ and $2^{18}(2^{19} - 1)$ to determine if this alternating pattern continues for the first seven perfect numbers.

EXAMPLE 3 ■ Use a Given Mersenne Prime Number to Write a Perfect Number

In 1750, Leonhard Euler proved that $2^{31} - 1$ is a Mersenne prime. Use Euclid's theorem to write the perfect number associated with this prime.

Solution

Euler's theorem states that if n and $2^n - 1$ are both prime numbers, then $2^{n-1}(2^n - 1)$ is a perfect number. In this example $n = 31$, which is a prime number. We are given that $2^{31} - 1$ is a prime number, so the perfect number we seek is $2^{30}(2^{31} - 1)$.

CHECK YOUR PROGRESS 3   In 1883, I. M. Pervushin proved that $2^{61} - 1$ is a Mersenne prime. Use Euclid's theorem to write the perfect number associated with this prime.

Solution   *See page S16.*

QUESTION   *Must a perfect number produced by Euclid's perfect-number-generating procedure be an even number?*

The search for Mersenne primes and their associated perfect numbers still continues. As of July 2005, only 42 Mersenne primes (and 42 perfect numbers) had been discovered. The largest of these 42 Mersenne primes is $(2^{25{,}964{,}951} - 1)$. See Table 4.15 on page 234. This gigantic Mersenne prime number is also the largest known prime number as of July 2005. It has 7,816,230 digits and it was discovered on February 18, 2005 by Dr. Martin Nowak, who used his 2.4-gigahertz Pentium 4 personal computer and a program that is available on the Internet. (*Source:* **http://www.mersenne.org**) More information about this program is given in the *Math Matters* on page 235.

ANSWER   *Yes. The 2^{n-1} factor of $2^{n-1}(2^n - 1)$ ensures that this product will be an even number.*

Table 4.15 *Some Mersenne Primes and Their Associated Perfect Numbers*

	Mersenne Prime	Perfect Number	Date	Discoverer
1	$2^2 - 1$	$2^1(2^2 - 1) = 6$	B.C.	
2	$2^3 - 1$	$2^2(2^3 - 1) = 28$	B.C.	
3	$2^5 - 1$	$2^4(2^5 - 1) = 496$	B.C.	
4	$2^7 - 1$	$2^6(2^7 - 1) = 8128$	B.C.	
5	$2^{13} - 1$	$2^{12}(2^{13} - 1) = 33{,}550{,}336$	1461	Unknown
6	$2^{17} - 1$	$2^{16}(2^{17} - 1) = 8{,}589{,}869{,}056$	1588	Cataldi
7	$2^{19} - 1$	$2^{18}(2^{19} - 1) = 137{,}438{,}691{,}328$	1588	Cataldi
	$\vdots$	$\vdots$	$\vdots$	$\vdots$
32	$2^{756839} - 1$	$2^{756838}(2^{756839} - 1)$	1992	Slowinski and Gage
33	$2^{859433} - 1$	$2^{859432}(2^{859433} - 1)$	1994	Slowinski and Gage
34	$2^{1257787} - 1$	$2^{1257786}(2^{1257787} - 1)$	1996	Slowinski and Gage
35	$2^{1398269} - 1$	$2^{1398268}(2^{1398269} - 1)$	1996	Armengaud and Woltman, et al. (GIMPS)
36	$2^{2976221} - 1$	$2^{2976220}(2^{2976221} - 1)$	1997	Spence and Woltman, et al. (GIMPS)
37	$2^{3021377} - 1$	$2^{3021376}(2^{3021377} - 1)$	1998	Clarkson, Woltman, and Kurowski, et al. (GIMPS, PrimeNet)
38	$2^{6972593} - 1$	$2^{6972592}(2^{6972593} - 1)$	1999	Hajratwala, Woltman, and Kurowski, et al. (GIMPS, PrimeNet)
?	$2^{13466917} - 1$	$2^{13466916}(2^{13466917} - 1)$	2001	Cameron, Woltman, and Kurowski, et al. (GIMPS, PrimeNet)
?	$2^{20996011} - 1$	$2^{20996010}(2^{20996011} - 1)$	2003	Shafer, Woltman, Kurowski, et al. (GIMPS, PrimeNet)
?	$2^{24036583} - 1$	$2^{24036582}(2^{24036583} - 1)$	2004	Findley, Woltman, Kurowski, et al. (GIMPS, PrimeNet)
?	$2^{25964951} - 1$	$2^{25964950}(2^{25964951} - 1)$	2005	Nowak, Woltman, Kurowski, et al. (GIMPS, PrimeNet)

Source: The Little Book of Big Primes and the GIMPS homepage (**http://www.mersenne.org**)
Note: A complete listing of Mersenne primes is given at **http://www.utm.edu/research/primes/mersenne/**

The numbers to the right of the question marks in the bottom four rows of Table 4.15 are the 39th through the 42nd Mersenne primes that have been discovered. They may not be the 39th, 40th, 41st, and 42nd Mersenne primes because there are many smaller numbers that have yet to be tested.

WANTED!
$100,000 REWARD
TO THE PERSON OR GROUP
THAT FIRST DISCOVERS
A TEN-MILLION-DIGIT
PRIME NUMBER

Math Matters   The Great Internet Mersenne Prime Search

From 1952 to 1996, large-scale computers were used to find Mersenne primes. However, during the past few years, small personal computers working in parallel have joined in the search. This search using personal computers has been organized by a fast-growing Internet organization known as the Great Internet Mersenne Prime Search (GIMPS). Members of this group use the Internet to download a Mersenne prime program that runs on their personal computers. Each member is assigned a range of numbers to check for Mersenne primes. A search over a specified range of numbers can take several weeks, but because the program is designed to run in the background, you can still use your computer to perform its regular duties. As of July 2005, eight Mersenne primes had been discovered by the members of GIMPS (see the bottom eight rows of Table 4.15). One of the current goals of GIMPS is to find a prime number that has more than 10 million digits. In fact, the Electronic Frontier Foundation is offering a $100,000 reward to the person or group to discover a 10-million-digit prime number. If you are using your computer just to run a screen saver, why not join in the search? You can get the needed program and additional information at

> **http://www.mersenne.org**

Who knows, maybe you will discover a new Mersenne prime and share in the reward money. Of course, we know that you really just want to have your name added to Table 4.15.

The Number of Digits in b^x

To determine the number of digits in a Mersenne number, mathematicians make use of the following formula, which involves finding the *greatest integer* of a number. **The greatest integer** of a number k is the greatest integer less than or equal to k. For instance, the greatest integer of 5 is 5 and the greatest integer of 7.8 is 7.

> **The Number of Digits in b^x**
>
> The number of digits in the number b^x, where b is a natural number less than 10 and x is a natural number, is the greatest integer of $(x \log b) + 1$.

✔ **TAKE NOTE**

If 2^{19} were a power of 10, such as 100,000, then $2^{19} - 1$ would equal 99,999 and it would have one less digit than 2^{19}. However, we know 2^{19} is not a power of 10 and thus $2^{19} - 1$ has the same number of digits as 2^{19}.

CALCULATOR NOTE

To evaluate 19 log 2 on a TI-83/84 calculator press

19 `LOG` 2 `)` `ENTER`

On a scientific calculator press

19 `×` 2 `LOG` `=`

EXAMPLE 4 ■ Determine the Number of Digits in a Mersenne Number

Find the number of digits in the Mersenne prime number $2^{19} - 1$.

Solution
First consider just 2^{19}. The base b is 2. The exponent x is 19.

$$(x \log b) + 1 = (19 \log 2) + 1$$
$$\approx 5.72 + 1$$
$$= 6.72$$

The greatest integer of 6.72 is 6. Thus 2^{19} has **six digits**. The Mersenne prime number $2^{19} - 1$ also has six digits. See the Take Note in the margin.

CHECK YOUR PROGRESS 4   Find the number of digits in the Mersenne prime number $2^{2976221} - 1$.

Solution   See page S16.

Euclid's perfect-number-generating formula produces only *even* perfect numbers. Do odd perfect numbers exist? As of July 2005, no odd perfect number had been discovered and no one had been able to prove either that odd perfect numbers exist or that they do not exist. The question of the existence of an odd perfect number is one of the major unanswered questions of number theory.

Fermat's Last Theorem

In 1637, the French mathematician Pierre de Fermat wrote in the margin of a book:

> It is impossible to divide a cube into two cubes, or a fourth power into two fourth powers, or in general any power greater than the second into two like powers, and I have a truly marvelous demonstration of it. But this margin will not contain it.

This problem, which became known as **Fermat's Last Theorem,** can also be stated in the following manner.

Fermat's Last Theorem

There are no natural numbers x, y, z, and n that satisfy $x^n + y^n = z^n$, where n is greater than 2.

Fermat's Last Theorem has attracted a great deal of attention over the last three centuries. The theorem has become so well known that it is simply called "FLT." Here are some of the reasons for its popularity:

- Very little mathematical knowledge is required to understand the statement of FLT.
- FLT is an extension of the well-known Pythagorean theorem $x^2 + y^2 = z^2$, which has several natural number solutions. Two such solutions are $3^2 + 4^2 = 5^2$ and $5^2 + 12^2 = 13^2$.
- It seems so simple. After all, while reading the text *Arithmetica* by Diophantus, Fermat wrote that he had discovered a *truly marvelous proof* of FLT. The only reason that Fermat gave for not providing his proof was that the margin of *Arithmetica* was too narrow to contain it.

Many famous mathematicians have worked on FLT. Some of these mathematicians tried to disprove FLT by searching for natural numbers x, y, z, and n that satisfied $x^n + y^n = z^n$, $n > 2$.

EXAMPLE 5 ■ **Check a Possible Solution to Fermat's Last Theorem**

Determine whether $x = 6$, $y = 8$, and $n = 3$ satisfies the equation $x^n + y^n = z^n$, where z is a natural number.

Solution

Substituting 6 for x, 8 for y, and 3 for n in $x^n + y^n = z^n$ yields

$$6^3 + 8^3 = z^3$$
$$216 + 512 = z^3$$
$$728 = z^3$$

The real solution of $z^3 = 728$ is $\sqrt[3]{728} \approx 8.99588289$, which is not a natural number. Thus $x = 6$, $y = 8$, and $n = 3$ does not satisfy the equation $x^n + y^n = z^n$, where z is a natural number.

CHECK YOUR PROGRESS 5 Determine whether $x = 9$, $y = 11$, and $n = 4$ satisfies the equation $x^n + y^n = z^n$, where z is a natural number.

Solution *See page S16.*

▼ **point of interest**

Andrew Wiles

Fermat's Last Theorem had been labeled by some mathematicians as the world's hardest mathematical problem. After solving Fermat's Last Theorem, Andrew Wiles made the following remarks: "Having solved this problem there's certainly a sense of loss, but at the same time there is this tremendous sense of freedom. I was so obsessed by this problem that for eight years I was thinking about it all the time—when I woke up in the morning to when I went to sleep at night. That's a long time to think about one thing. That particular odyssey is now over. My mind is at rest."

In the eighteenth century, the great mathematician Leonhard Euler was able to make some progress on a proof of FLT. He adapted a technique that he found in Fermat's notes about another problem. In this problem, Fermat gave an outline of how to prove that the special case $x^4 + y^4 = z^4$ has no natural number solutions. Using a similar procedure, Euler was able to show that $x^3 + y^3 = z^3$ also has no natural number solutions. Thus all that was left was to show that $x^n + y^n = z^n$ has no solutions with n greater than 4.

In the nineteenth century, additional work on FLT was done by Sophie Germain, Augustin Louis Cauchy, and Gabriel Lame. Each of these mathematicians produced some interesting results, but FLT still remained unsolved.

In 1983, the German mathematician Gerd Faltings used concepts from differential geometry to prove that the number of solutions to FLT must be finite. Then, in 1988, the Japanese mathematician Yoichi Miyaoka claimed he could show that the number of solutions to FLT was not only finite, but that the number of solutions was zero, and thus he had proved FLT. At first Miyaoka's work appeared to be a valid proof, but after a few weeks of examination a flaw was discovered. Several mathematicians looked for a way to repair the flaw, but eventually they came to the conclusion that although Miyaoka had developed some interesting mathematics, he had failed to establish the validity of FLT.

In 1993, Andrew Wiles of Princeton University made a major advance toward a proof of FLT. Wiles first became familiar with FLT when he was only 10 years old. At his local public library, Wiles first learned about FLT in the book *The Last Problem* by Eric Temple Bell. In reflecting on his first thoughts about FLT, Wiles recalled

> It looked so simple, and yet all the great mathematicians in history couldn't solve it. Here was a problem that I, a ten-year-old, could understand and I knew from that moment that I would never let it go. I had to solve it.[2]

2. Singh, Simon. *Fermat's Enigma: The Quest to Solve the World's Greatest Mathematical Problem.* New York: Walker Publishing Company, Inc., 1997, p. 6.

Wiles took a most unusual approach to solving FLT. Whereas most contemporary mathematicians share their ideas and coordinate their efforts, Wiles decided to work alone. After 7 years of working in the attic of his home, Wiles was ready to present his work. In June of 1993 Wiles gave a series of three lectures at the Isaac Newton Institute in Cambridge, England. After showing that FLT was a corollary of his major theorem, Wiles's concluding remark was "I think I'll stop here." Many mathematicians in the audience felt that Wiles had produced a valid proof of FLT, but a formal verification by several mathematical referees was required before Wiles's work could be classified as an official proof. The verification process was lengthy and complex. Wiles's written work was about 200 pages in length, it covered several different areas of mathematics, and it used hundreds of sophisticated logical arguments and a great many mathematical calculations. Any mistake could result in an invalid proof. Thus it was not too surprising when a flaw was discovered in late 1993. The flaw did not necessarily imply that Wiles's proof could not be repaired, but it did indicate that it was not a valid proof in its present form.

It appeared that once again the proof of FLT had eluded a great effort by a well-known mathematician. Several months passed and Wiles was still unable to fix the flaw. It was a most depressing period for Wiles. He felt that he was close to solving one of the world's hardest mathematical problems, yet all of his creative efforts failed to turn the flawed proof into a valid proof. Several mathematicians felt that it was not possible to repair the flaw, but Wiles did not give up. Finally, in late 1994, Wiles had an insight that eventually led to a valid proof. The insight required Wiles to seek additional help from Richard Taylor, who had been a student of Wiles. On October 15, 1994, Wiles and Taylor presented to the world a proof that has now been judged to be a valid proof of FLT. Their proof is certainly not the "truly marvelous proof" that Fermat said he had discovered. But it has been deemed a wonderful proof that makes use of several new mathematical procedures and concepts.

Excursion

A Sum of the Divisors Formula

Consider the numbers 10, 12, and 28 and the sums of the proper factors of these numbers.

$$10: 1 + 2 + 5 = 8 \qquad 12: 1 + 2 + 3 + 4 + 6 = 16$$
$$28: 1 + 2 + 4 + 7 + 14 = 28$$

From the above sums we see that 10 is a deficient number, 12 is an abundant number, and 28 is a perfect number. The goal of this Excursion is to find a method that will enable us to determine whether a number is deficient, abundant, or perfect without having to first find all of its proper factors and then compute their sum.

(continued)

In the following example, we use the number 108 and its prime factorization $2^2 \cdot 3^3$ to illustrate that every factor of 108 can be written as a product of powers of its prime factors. Table 4.16 includes all the proper factors of 108 (the numbers in blue) plus the factor $2^2 \cdot 3^3$, which is 108 itself. The sum of each column is shown at the bottom (the numbers in red).

Table 4.16 *Every Factor of 108 Expressed as a Product of Powers of its Prime Factors*

	1	$1 \cdot 3$	$1 \cdot 3^2$	$1 \cdot 3^3$
	2	$2 \cdot 3$	$2 \cdot 3^2$	$2 \cdot 3^3$
	2^2	$2^2 \cdot 3$	$2^2 \cdot 3^2$	$2^2 \cdot 3^3$
Sum	7	$7 \cdot 3$	$7 \cdot 3^2$	$7 \cdot 3^3$

The sum of *all* the factors of 108 is the sum of the numbers in the bottom row.

$$\text{Sum of all factors of } 108 = 7 + 7 \cdot 3 + 7 \cdot 3^2 + 7 \cdot 3^3$$
$$= 7(1 + 3 + 3^2 + 3^3) = 7(40) = 280$$

To find the sum of just the *proper* factors, we must subtract 108 from 280, which gives us 172. Thus 108 is an abundant number.

We now look for a pattern for the sum of all the factors. Note that

This result suggests that the sum of the factors of a number can be found by finding the sum of all the prime power factors of each prime factor and then computing the product of those sums. Because we are interested only in the sum of the proper factors, we subtract the original number. Although we have not proved this result, it is a true statement and can save much time and effort. For instance, the sum of the proper factors of 3240 can be found as follows:

$$3240 = 2^3 \cdot 3^4 \cdot 5$$

Compute the sum of *all* the prime power factors of each prime factor.

$$1 + 2 + 2^2 + 2^3 = 15 \qquad 1 + 3 + 3^2 + 3^3 + 3^4 = 121 \qquad 1 + 5 = 6$$

The sum of the proper factors of 3240 is $(15)(121)(6) - 3240 = 7650$. Thus 3240 is an abundant number.

Excursion Exercises

Use the above technique to find the sum of the proper factors of each number and then state whether the number is deficient, abundant, or perfect.

1. 200   **2.** 262   **3.** 325   **4.** 496

5. Use deductive reasoning to prove that every prime number is deficient.

6. Use inductive reasoning to decide whether every multiple of 6 greater than 6 is abundant.

Exercise Set 4.6

In Exercises 1–16, determine whether each number is perfect, deficient, or abundant.

1. 18   **2.** 32

3. 91   **4.** 51

5. 19   **6.** 144

7. 204   **8.** 128

9. 610   **10.** 508

11. 291   **12.** 1001

13. 176   **14.** 122

15. 260   **16.** 258

In Exercises 17–20, determine whether each Mersenne number is a prime number.

17. $2^3 - 1$ **18.** $2^5 - 1$

19. $2^7 - 1$ **20.** $2^{13} - 1$

21. In 1876, E. Lucas proved, without the aid of a computer, that $2^{127} - 1$ is a Mersenne prime. Use Euclid's theorem to write the perfect number associated with this prime.

22. In 1952, R. M. Robinson proved, with the aid of a computer, that $2^{521} - 1$ is a Mersenne prime. Use Euclid's theorem to write the perfect number associated with this prime.

In Exercises 23–28, determine the number of digits in the given Mersenne prime.

23. $2^{17} - 1$ **24.** $2^{132049} - 1$

25. $2^{1398269} - 1$ **26.** $2^{3021377} - 1$

27. $2^{6972593} - 1$ **28.** $2^{20996011} - 1$

29. Verify that $x = 9$, $y = 15$, and $n = 5$ do not yield a solution to the equation $x^n + y^n = z^n$ where z is a natural number.

30. Verify that $x = 7$, $y = 19$, and $n = 6$ do not yield a solution to the equation $x^n + y^n = z^n$ where z is a natural number.

31. Determine whether each of the following statements is a true statement, a false statement, or a conjecture.

  a. If n is a prime number, then $2^n - 1$ is also a prime number.

  b. Fermat's Last Theorem is called his last theorem because we believe that it was the last theorem he proved.

  c. All perfect numbers of the form $2^{n-1}(2^n - 1)$ are even numbers.

  d. Every perfect number is an even number.

32. Prove that $4078^n + 3433^n = 12{,}046^n$ cannot be a solution to the equation $x^n + y^n = z^n$ where n is a natural number. *Hint:* Examine the ones' digits of the powers.

33. **Fermat's Little Theorem** A theorem known as *Fermat's Little Theorem* states, "If n is a prime number and a is any natural number, then $a^n - a$ is divisible by n." Verify Fermat's Little Theorem for

  a. $n = 7$ and $a = 12$.

  b. $n = 11$ and $a = 8$.

34. **Amicable Numbers** The Greeks considered the pair of numbers 220 and 284 to be *amicable* or *friendly* numbers because the sum of the proper divisors of one of the numbers is the other number.

  The sum of the proper factors of 220 is

$$1 + 2 + 4 + 5 + 10 + 11 + 20 + 22 +$$
$$44 + 55 + 110 = 284$$

  The sum of the proper factors of 284 is

$$1 + 2 + 4 + 71 + 142 = 220$$

Determine whether

  a. 60 and 84 are amicable numbers.

  b. 1184 and 1210 are amicable numbers.

35. **A Sum of Cubes Property** The perfect number 28 can be written as $1^3 + 3^3$. The perfect number 496 can be written as $1^3 + 3^3 + 5^3 + 7^3$. Verify that the next perfect number, 8128, can also be written as the sum of the cubes of consecutive odd natural numbers, starting with 1^3.

36. **A Sum of the Digits Theorem** If you sum the digits of any even perfect number (except 6), then sum the digits of the resulting number, and repeat this process until you get a single digit, that digit will be 1.

  As an example, consider the perfect number 28. The sum of its digits is 10. The sum of the digits of 10 is 1.

Verify the previous theorem for each of the following perfect numbers.

a. 496   b. 8128

c. 33,550,336   d. 8,589,869,056

37. A Sum of Reciprocals Theorem The sum of the reciprocals of all the positive divisors of a perfect number is always 2.

Verify the above theorem for each of the following perfect numbers.

a. 6   b. 28

Extensions

CRITICAL THINKING

38. The Smallest Odd Abundant Number Determine the smallest odd abundant number. *Hint:* It is greater than 900 but less than 1000.

39. Fermat Numbers Numbers of the form $2^{2^m} + 1$, where m is a whole number, are called *Fermat numbers*. Fermat believed that all Fermat numbers were prime. Prove that Fermat was wrong.

EXPLORATIONS

40. Semiperfect Numbers Any number that is the sum of *some or all* of its proper divisors is called a **semiperfect number.** For instance, 12 is a semiperfect number because it has 1, 2, 3, 4, and 6 as proper factors, and $12 = 1 + 2 + 3 + 6$.

The first twenty-five semiperfect numbers are 6, 12, 18, 20, 24, 28, 30, 36, 40, 42, 48, 54, 56, 60, 66, 72, 78, 80, 84, 88, 90, 96, 100, 102, and 104. It has been established that every natural number multiple of a semiperfect number is semiperfect and that a semiperfect number cannot be a deficient number.

a. Use the definition of a semiperfect number to verify that 20 is a semiperfect number.

b. Explain how to verify that 200 is a semiperfect number without examining its proper factors.

41. Weird Numbers Any number that is an abundant number but not a semiperfect number (see Exercise 40) is called a **weird number.** Find the only weird number less than 100. *Hint:* The abundant numbers less than 100 are 12, 18, 20, 24, 30, 36, 40, 42, 48, 54, 56, 60, 66, 70, 72, 78, 80, 84, 88, 90, and 96.

42. A False Prediction In 1811 Peter Barlow wrote, in his text *Theory of Numbers,* that the eighth perfect number, $2^{30}(2^{31} - 1) = 2,305,843,008,139,952,128$, which was discovered by Leonhard Euler in 1772, "is the greatest [perfect number] that will be discovered; for as they are merely curious, without being useful, it is not likely that any person will attempt to find one beyond it." (*Source:* **http://www.utm-edu/research/primes/mersenne/index.html**)

The current search for larger and larger perfect numbers shows that Barlow's prediction did not come true. Search the Internet for answers to the question "Why do people continue the search for large perfect numbers (or large prime numbers)?" Write a brief summary of your findings.

CHAPTER 4   Summary

Key Terms

additive system [p. 178]
amicable numbers [p. 240]
Babylonian numeration system [p. 189]
base ten [p. 187]
binary adders [p. 208]
binary numeration system [p. 199]
bit [p. 199]
decimal system [p. 187]
digits [p. 187]
divisibility test [p. 221]
double-dabble method [p. 203]
duodecimal system [p. 199]
Egyptian multiplication procedure [p. 186]
expanded form [p. 187]
factorial prime [p. 230]
Fermat numbers [p. 241]
Fermat's Little Theorem [p. 240]
Goldbach's conjecture [p. 228]
hexadecimal system [p. 199]
hieroglyphics [p. 178]
Hindu-Arabic numeration system [p. 178]
indirect proof [p. 226]
Mayan numeration system [p. 192]
Mersenne number [p. 232]
Mersenne prime [p. 232]
number theory [p. 220]
numeral [p. 178]
numeration system [p. 178]
octal numeration system [p. 201]
perfect square [p. 229]
place-value or positional-value system [p. 187]
prime factorization [p. 223]
prime triplets [p. 228]
primorial prime [p. 230]

proof by contradiction [p. 226]
proper factor [p. 231]
Roman numeration system [p. 181]
Sieve of Eratosthenes [p. 225]
successive division process [p. 200]
twin primes [p. 228]
zero as a place holder [p. 192]

Essential Concepts

- A *base b numeration system* (where b is a natural number greater than 1) has place values of $\ldots, b^5, b^4, b^3, b^2, b^1, b^0$.

- The natural number a is a *divisor*, or *factor*, of the natural number b provided there exists a natural number j such that $aj = b$.

- A *prime number* is a natural number greater than 1 that has exactly two factors (divisors), itself and 1. A *composite number* is a natural number greater than 1 that is not a prime number.

- **The Fundamental Theorem of Arithmetic**
  Every composite number can be written as a unique product of prime numbers (disregarding the order of the factors).

- A natural number is *perfect* if it is equal to the sum of its proper factors. It is *deficient* if it is greater than the sum of its proper factors. It is *abundant* if it is less than the sum of its proper factors.

- **Euclid's Perfect-Number-Generating Procedure**
  If n and $2^n - 1$ are both prime numbers, then $2^{n-1}(2^n - 1)$ is a perfect number.

- **Fermat's Last Theorem**
  There are no natural numbers x, y, z, and n that satisfy $x^n + y^n = z^n$ with n greater than 2.

CHAPTER 4   Review Exercises

1. Write 4,506,325 using Egyptian hieroglyphics.
2. Write 3,124,043 using Egyptian hieroglyphics.
3. Write the Egyptian hieroglyphic

   as a Hindu-Arabic numeral.

4. Write the Egyptian hieroglyphic

   as a Hindu-Arabic numeral.

In Exercises 5–8, write each Roman numeral as a Hindu-Arabic numeral.

5. CCCXLIX   **6.** DCCLXXIV
7. $\overline{\text{IX}}$DCXL   **8.** $\overline{\text{XCII}}$CDXLIV

In Exercises 9–12, write each Hindu-Arabic numeral as a Roman numeral.

9. 567   **10.** 823
11. 2489   **12.** 1335

In Exercises 13 and 14, write each Hindu-Arabic numeral in expanded form.

13. 432   **14.** 456,327

In Exercises 15 and 16, simplify each expanded form.

15. $(5 \times 10^6) + (3 \times 10^4) + (8 \times 10^3) + (2 \times 10^2) + (4 \times 10^0)$

16. $(3 \times 10^5) + (8 \times 10^4) + (7 \times 10^3) + (9 \times 10^2) + (6 \times 10^1)$

In Exercises 17–20, write each Babylonian numeral as a Hindu-Arabic numeral.

17. ⟨▼▼▼   ⟨⟨▼

18. ⟨⟨▼▼▼▼▼▼   ⟨⟨⟨⟨▼▼▼

19. ⟨⟨▼   ⟨▼▼▼▼   ▼

20. ⟨⟨▼▼▼▼   ⟨▼▼▼▼▼▼   ⟨⟨⟨▼▼▼

In Exercises 21–24, write each Hindu-Arabic numeral as a Babylonian numeral.

21. 721   **22.** 1080
23. 12,543   **24.** 19,281

In Exercises 25–28, write each Mayan numeral as a Hindu-Arabic numeral.

25. ⋯⋯ / ⋯⋯

26. ⋯ / ═══ / ⋅

27. ⋅ / 👁

28. ═══ / ⋯⋯ / 👁

In Exercises 29–32, write each Hindu-Arabic numeral as a Mayan numeral.

29. 522   **30.** 346
31. 1862   **32.** 1987

In Exercises 33–36, convert each numeral to base ten.

33. 45_{six} **34.** 172_{nine}
35. $\text{E3}_{\text{sixteen}}$ **36.** $\text{1BA}_{\text{twelve}}$

In Exercises 37–40, convert each numeral to the indicated base.

37. 346_{nine} to base six   **38.** 1532_{six} to base eight
39. 275_{twelve} to base nine   **40.** $\text{67A}_{\text{sixteen}}$ to base twelve

In Exercises 41–48, convert each numeral directly (without first converting to base ten) to the indicated base.

41. 11100_{two} to base eight
42. 1010100_{two} to base eight
43. 1110001101_{two} to base sixteen
44. 11101010100_{two} to base sixteen
45. 25_{eight} to base two
46. 1472_{eight} to base two
47. $\text{4A}_{\text{sixteen}}$ to base two
48. $\text{C72}_{\text{sixteen}}$ to base two

In Exercises 49–56, perform the indicated operation.

49. $235_{\text{six}} + 144_{\text{six}}$ **50.** $673_{\text{eight}} + 345_{\text{eight}}$
51. $672_{\text{nine}} - 135_{\text{nine}}$ **52.** $1332_{\text{four}} - 213_{\text{four}}$
53. $25_{\text{eight}} \times 542_{\text{eight}}$ **54.** $43_{\text{five}} \times 3421_{\text{five}}$
55. $1010101_{\text{two}} \div 11_{\text{two}}$ **56.** $321_{\text{four}} \div 12_{\text{four}}$

In Exercises 57–60, determine the prime factorization of the given number.

57. 45   **58.** 54
59. 153   **60.** 285

In Exercises 61–64, determine whether the given number is a prime number or a composite number.

61. 501   **62.** 781
63. 689   **64.** 1003

In Exercises 65–68, determine whether the given number is perfect, deficient, or abundant.

65. 28   **66.** 81
67. 144   **68.** 200

In Exercises 69 and 70, use Euclid's perfect-number-generating procedure to write the perfect number associated with the given Mersenne prime.

69. $2^{61} - 1$ **70.** $2^{1279} - 1$

In Exercises 71–74, use the Egyptian doubling procedure to find the given product.

71. 8×46 **72.** 9×57
73. 14×83 **74.** 21×143

In Exercises 75–78, use the double-dabble method to convert each base two numeral to base ten.

75. 110011010_{two} **76.** 100010101_{two}
77. 10000010001_{two} **78.** 11001010000_{two}

79. State the (base ten) divisibility test for 3.
80. State the (base ten) divisibility test for 6.
81. State the Fundamental Theorem of Arithmetic.
82. How many odd perfect numbers had been discovered as of July 2005?
83. Find the number of digits in the Mersenne number $2^{132049} - 1$.
84. Find the number of digits in the Mersenne number $2^{2976221} - 1$.

CHAPTER 4   **Test**

---

1. Write 3124 using Egyptian hieroglyphics.
2. Write the Egyptian hieroglyphic

as a Hindu-Arabic numeral.
3. Write the Roman numeral MCDXLVII as a Hindu-Arabic numeral.
4. Write 2609 as a Roman numeral.
5. Write 67,485 in expanded form.
6. Simplify:

$$(5 \times 10^5) + (3 \times 10^4) + (2 \times 10^2)$$
$$+ (8 \times 10^1) + (4 \times 10^0)$$

7. Write the Babylonian numeral

as a Hindu-Arabic numeral.
8. Write 9675 as a Babylonian numeral.
9. Write the Mayan numeral

· · ·
—·—
═══
———

as a Hindu-Arabic numeral.

10. Write 502 as a Mayan numeral.
11. Convert 3542_{six} to base ten.
12. Convert 2148 to **a.** base eight and **b.** base twelve.
13. Convert 4567_{eight} to binary form.
14. Convert 101010110111_{two} to hexadecimal form.

In Exercises 15–18, perform the indicated operation.

15. $34_{five} + 23_{five}$
16. $462_{eight} - 147_{eight}$
17. $101_{two} \times 101110_{two}$
18. $431_{seven} \div 5_{seven}$

19. Determine the prime factorization of 230.
20. Determine whether 1001 is a prime number or a composite number.
21. Use divisibility tests to determine whether 1,737,285,147 is divisible by **a.** 2, **b.** 3, or **c.** 5.
22. Use divisibility tests to determine whether 19,531,333,276 is divisible by **a.** 4, **b.** 6, or **c.** 11.
23. Determine whether 96 is perfect, deficient, or abundant.
24. Use Euclid's perfect-number-generating procedure to write the perfect number associated with the Mersenne prime $2^{17} - 1$.

5

Applications of Equations

5.1 First-Degree Equations and Formulas

5.2 Rate, Ratio, and Proportion

5.3 Percent

5.4 Second-Degree Equations

In your study of mathematics, you have probably noticed that the problems became less concrete and more abstract. Problems that are concrete provide information pertaining to a specific instance. Abstract problems are theoretical; they are stated without reference to a specific instance. Here's an example of a concrete problem:

If one candy bar costs 25 cents, how many candy bars can be purchased with 2 dollars?

To solve this problem, you need to calculate the number of cents in 2 dollars (multiply 2 by 100), and divide the result by the cost per candy bar (25 cents).

$$\frac{100 \cdot 2}{25} = \frac{200}{25} = 8$$

If one candy bar costs 25 cents, 8 candy bars can be purchased with 2 dollars.

Here is a related abstract problem:

If one candy bar costs c cents, how many candy bars can be purchased with d dollars?

Use the same procedure to solve the related abstract problem. Calculate the number of cents in d dollars (multiply d by 100), and divide the result by the cost per candy bar (c cents).

$$\frac{100 \cdot d}{c} = \frac{100d}{c}$$

If one candy bar costs c cents, $\frac{100d}{c}$ candy bars can be purchased with d dollars.

It is the variables in the problem above that makes it abstract. At the heart of the study of algebra is the use of variables. Variables enable us to generalize situations and state relationships among quantities. These relationships are often stated in the form of equations. In this chapter, we will be using equations to solve applications.

For online student resources, visit this textbook's website at **www.cengage.com/math.**

| SECTION 5.1 | **First-Degree Equations and Formulas** |

Solving First-Degree Equations

The fuel economy, in miles per gallon, of a particular car traveling at a speed of v miles per hour can be calculated using the variable expression $-0.02v^2 + 1.6v + 3$, where $10 \leq v \leq 75$. For example, suppose the speed of a car is 30 miles per hour. We can calculate the fuel economy by substituting 30 for v in the variable expression and then using the Order of Operations Agreement to evaluate the resulting numerical expression.

$$-0.02v^2 + 1.6v + 3$$
$$-0.02(30)^2 + 1.6(30) + 3 = -0.02(900) + 1.6(30) + 3$$
$$= -18 + 48 + 3$$
$$= 33$$

The fuel economy is 33 miles per gallon.

The **terms** of a variable expression are the addends of the expression. The expression $-0.02v^2 + 1.6v + 3$ has three terms. The terms $-0.02v^2$ and $1.6v$ are **variable terms** because each contains a variable. The term 3 is a **constant term;** it does not contain a variable.

Each variable term is composed of a **numerical coefficient** and a **variable part** (the variable or variables and their exponents). For the variable term $-0.02v^2$, -0.02 is the coefficient and v^2 is the variable part.

Like terms of a variable expression are terms with the same variable part. Constant terms are also like terms. Examples of like terms are

$4x$ and $7x$

$9y$ and y

$5x^2y$ and $6x^2y$

8 and -3

An **equation** expresses the equality of two mathematical expressions. Each of the following is an equation.

$8 + 5 = 13$

$4y - 6 = 10$

$x^2 - 2x + 1 = 0$

$b = 7$

Each of the equations below is a **first-degree equation in one variable.** *First degree* means that the variable has an exponent of 1.

$x + 11 = 14$

$3z + 5 = 8z$

$2(6y - 1) = 34$

TAKE NOTE

Recall that the Order of Operations Agreement states that when simplifying a numerical expression you should perform the operations in the following order:

1. Perform operations inside parentheses.

2. Simplify exponential expressions.

3. Do multiplication and division from left to right.

4. Do addition and subtraction from left to right.

▼ point of interest

One of the most famous equations is $E = mc^2$. This equation, stated by Albert Einstein (īn′stīn), shows that there is a relationship between mass m and energy E. In this equation, c is the speed of light.

✓ TAKE NOTE

It is important to note the difference between an expression and an equation. An equation contains an equals sign; an expression doesn't.

historical note

———

Finding solutions of equations has been a principal aim of mathematics for thousands of years. However, the equals sign did not occur in any text until 1557, when Robert Recorde (c. 1510–1558) used the symbol in *The Whetstone of Witte*. ∎

QUESTION   *Which of the following are first-degree equations in one variable?*

a. $5y + 4 = 9 - 3(2y + 1)$ **b.** $\sqrt{x} + 9 = 16$

c. $p = -14$ **d.** $2x - 5 = x^2 - 9$

e. $3y + 7 = 4z - 10$

A **solution** of an equation is a number that, when substituted for the variable, results in a true equation.

3 is a solution of the equation $x + 4 = 7$ because $3 + 4 = 7$.

9 is not a solution of the equation $x + 4 = 7$ because $9 + 4 \neq 7$.

To **solve an equation** means to find all solutions of the equation. The following properties of equations are often used to solve equations.

Properties of Equations

Addition Property

The same number can be added to each side of an equation without changing the solution of the equation.

If $a = b$, then $a + c = b + c$.

Subtraction Property

The same number can be subtracted from each side of an equation without changing the solution of the equation.

If $a = b$, then $a - c = b - c$.

Multiplication Property

Each side of an equation can be multiplied by the same *nonzero* number without changing the solution of the equation.

If $a = b$ and $c \neq 0$, then $ac = bc$.

Division Property

Each side of an equation can be divided by the same *nonzero* number without changing the solution of the equation.

If $a = b$ and $c \neq 0$, then $\dfrac{a}{c} = \dfrac{b}{c}$.

✔ **TAKE NOTE**

In the Multiplication Property, it is necessary to state $c \neq 0$ so that the solutions of the equation are not changed. For example, if $\frac{1}{2}x = 4$, then $x = 8$. But if we multiply each side of the equation by 0, we have

$$0 \cdot \frac{1}{2}x = 0 \cdot 4$$

$$0 = 0$$

The solution $x = 8$ is lost.

In solving a first-degree equation in one variable, the goal is to rewrite the equation with the variable alone on one side of the equation and a constant term on the other side of the equation. The constant term is the solution of the equation.

———

ANSWER   *The equations in **a** and **c** are first-degree equations in one variable. The equation in **b** is not a first-degree equation in one variable because it contains the square root of a variable. The equation in **d** contains a variable with an exponent other than 1. The equation in **e** contains two variables.*

For example, to solve the equation $t + 9 = -4$, use the Subtraction Property to subtract the constant term (9) from each side of the equation.

$$t + 9 = -4$$
$$t + 9 - 9 = -4 - 9$$
$$t = -13$$

Now the variable (t) is alone on one side of the equation and a constant term (-13) is on the other side. The solution is -13.

To solve the equation $-5q = 120$, use the Division Property. Divide each side of the equation by the coefficient -5.

$$-5q = 120$$
$$\frac{-5q}{-5} = \frac{120}{-5}$$
$$q = -24$$

Now the variable (q) is alone on one side of the equation and a constant (-24) is on the other side. The solution is -24.

EXAMPLE 1 ■ **Solve a First-Degree Equation Using One of the Properties of Equations**

Solve.

a. $y - 8 = 17$ **b.** $4x = -2$ **c.** $-5 = 9 + b$ **d.** $-a = -36$

Solution

a. Because 8 is subtracted from y, use the Addition Property to add 8 to each side of the equation.

$$y - 8 = 17$$
$$y - 8 + 8 = 17 + 8$$
$$y = 25 \qquad \text{• A check will show that 25 is a solution.}$$

The solution is 25.

b. Because x is multiplied by 4, use the Division Property to divide each side of the equation by 4.

$$4x = -2$$
$$\frac{4x}{4} = \frac{-2}{4}$$
$$x = -\frac{1}{2} \qquad \text{• A check will show that } -\frac{1}{2} \text{ is a solution.}$$

The solution is $-\frac{1}{2}$.

c. Because 9 is added to b, use the Subtraction Property to subtract 9 from each side of the equation.

$$-5 = 9 + b$$
$$-5 - 9 = 9 - 9 + b$$
$$-14 = b$$

The solution is -14.

✔ **TAKE NOTE**

When the coefficient of a variable is 1 or negative 1, the 1 is usually not written; $1a$ is written as a, and $-1a$ is written as $-a$.

d. The coefficient of the variable is -1. Use the Multiplication Property to multiply each side of the equation by -1.

$$-a = -36$$
$$-1(-1a) = -1(-36)$$
$$a = 36$$

The solution is 36.

CHECK YOUR PROGRESS 1   Solve.

a. $c - 6 = -13$ **b.** $4 = -8z$ **c.** $22 + m = -9$ **d.** $5x = 0$

Solution   *See page S16.*

When solving more complicated first-degree equations in one variable, use the following sequence of steps.

Steps for Solving a First-Degree Equation in One Variable

1. If the equation contains fractions, multiply each side of the equation by the least common multiple (LCM) of the denominators to clear the equation of fractions.

2. Use the Distributive Property to remove parentheses.

3. Combine any like terms on the right side of the equation and any like terms on the left side of the equation.

4. Use the Addition or Subtraction Property to rewrite the equation with only one variable term and only one constant term.

5. Use the Multiplication or Division Property to rewrite the equation with the variable alone on one side of the equation and a constant term on the other side of the equation.

If one of the above steps is not needed to solve a given equation, proceed to the next step. Remember that the goal is to rewrite the equation with the variable alone on one side of the equation and a constant term on the other side of the equation.

EXAMPLE 2 ■ Solve a First-Degree Equation Using the Properties of Equations

Solve.

a. $5x + 9 = 23 - 2x$ **b.** $8x - 3(4x - 5) = -2x + 6$

c. $\dfrac{3x}{4} - 6 = \dfrac{x}{3} - 1$

Solution

a. There are no fractions (Step 1) or parentheses (Step 2). There are no like terms on either side of the equation (Step 3). Use the Addition Property to rewrite the equation with only one variable term (Step 4). Add $2x$ to each side of the equation.

$$5x + 9 = 23 - 2x$$
$$5x + 2x + 9 = 23 - 2x + 2x$$
$$7x + 9 = 23$$

Use the Subtraction Property to rewrite the equation with only one constant term (Step 4). Subtract 9 from each side of the equation.

$$7x + 9 - 9 = 23 - 9$$
$$7x = 14$$

Use the Division Property to rewrite the equation with the x alone on one side of the equation (Step 5). Divide each side of the equation by 7.

$$\frac{7x}{7} = \frac{14}{7}$$
$$x = 2$$

The solution is 2.

b. There are no fractions (Step 1). Use the Distributive Property to remove parentheses (Step 2).

$$8x - 3(4x - 5) = -2x + 6$$
$$8x - 12x + 15 = -2x + 6$$

Combine like terms on the left side of the equation (Step 3). Then rewrite the equation with the variable alone on one side and a constant on the other.

$$-4x + 15 = -2x + 6 \qquad \text{• Combine like terms.}$$
$$-4x + 2x + 15 = -2x + 2x + 6 \qquad \text{• The Addition Property}$$
$$-2x + 15 = 6$$
$$-2x + 15 - 15 = 6 - 15 \qquad \text{• The Subtraction Property}$$
$$-2x = -9$$
$$\frac{-2x}{-2} = \frac{-9}{-2} \qquad \text{• The Division Property}$$
$$x = \frac{9}{2}$$

The solution is $\dfrac{9}{2}$.

historical note

The letter x is used universally as the standard letter for a single unknown, which is why x-rays were so named. The scientists who discovered them did not know what they were, and so labeled them the "unknown rays," or x-rays. ■

c. The equation contains fractions (Step 1); multiply each side of the equation by the LCM of the denominators. Then rewrite the equation with the variable alone on one side and a constant on the other.

$$\frac{3x}{4} - 6 = \frac{x}{3} - 1$$

$$12\left(\frac{3x}{4} - 6\right) = 12\left(\frac{x}{3} - 1\right) \qquad \bullet \text{ The Multiplication Property}$$

$$12 \cdot \frac{3x}{4} - 12 \cdot 6 = 12 \cdot \frac{x}{3} - 12 \cdot 1 \qquad \bullet \text{ The Distributive Property}$$

$$9x - 72 = 4x - 12$$

$$9x - 4x - 72 = 4x - 4x - 12 \qquad \bullet \text{ The Subtraction Property}$$

$$5x - 72 = -12$$

$$5x - 72 + 72 = -12 + 72 \qquad \bullet \text{ The Addition Property}$$

$$5x = 60$$

$$\frac{5x}{5} = \frac{60}{5} \qquad \bullet \text{ The Division Property}$$

$$x = 12$$

The solution is 12.

CHECK YOUR PROGRESS 2 Solve.

a. $4x + 3 = 7x + 9$ **b.** $7 - (5x - 8) = 4x + 3$ **c.** $\frac{3x - 1}{4} + \frac{1}{3} = \frac{7}{3}$

Solution See page S16.

Math Matters **The Hubble Space Telescope**

The Hubble Space Telescope missed the stars it was targeted to photograph during the second week of May, 1990, because it was pointing in the wrong direction. The telescope was off by about one-half of one degree as a result of an arithmetic error—an addition instead of a subtraction.

Applications

In some applications of equations, we are given an equation that can be used to solve the application. This is illustrated in Example 3.

Humerus

EXAMPLE 3 ■ Solve an Application

Forensic scientists have determined that the equation $H = 2.9L + 78.1$ can be used to approximate the height H, in centimeters, of an adult on the basis of the length L, in centimeters, of the adult's humerus (the bone extending from the shoulder to the elbow).

a. Use this equation to approximate the height of an adult whose humerus measures 36 centimeters.

b. According to this equation, what is the length of the humerus of an adult whose height is 168 centimeters?

Solution

a. Substitute 36 for L in the given equation. Solve the resulting equation for H.

$$H = 2.9L + 78.1$$
$$H = 2.9(36) + 78.1$$
$$H = 104.4 + 78.1$$
$$H = 182.5$$

The adult's height is approximately 182.5 centimeters.

b. Substitute 168 for H in the given equation. Solve the resulting equation for L.

$$H = 2.9L + 78.1$$
$$168 = 2.9L + 78.1$$
$$168 - 78.1 = 29L + 78.1 - 78.1$$
$$89.9 = 2.9L$$
$$\frac{89.9}{2.9} = \frac{2.9L}{2.9}$$
$$31 = L$$

The length of the adult's humerus is approximately 31 centimeters.

CHECK YOUR PROGRESS 3   The amount of garbage generated by each person living in the United States has been increasing and is approximated by the equation $P = 0.05Y - 95$, where P is the number of pounds of garbage generated per person per day and Y is the year.

a. Find the amount of garbage generated per person per day in 1990.

b. According to the equation, in what year will 5.6 pounds of garbage be generated per person per day?

Solution   See page S17.

In many applied problems, we are not given an equation that can be used to solve the problem. Instead, we must use the given information to write an equation whose solution answers the question stated in the problem. This is illustrated in Examples 4 and 5.

EXAMPLE 4 ■ Solve an Application of First-Degree Equations

The cost of electricity in a certain city is $.08 for each of the first 300 kWh (kilowatt-hours) and $.13 for each kilowatt-hour over 300 kWh. Find the number of kilowatt-hours used by a family that receives a $51.95 electric bill.

Solution

Let $k =$ the number of kilowatt-hours used by the family. Write an equation and then solve the equation for k.

$.08 for each of the first 300 kWh + $.13 for each kilowatt-hour over 300	=	$51.95

$$0.08(300) + 0.13(k - 300) = 51.95$$
$$24 + 0.13k - 39 = 51.95$$
$$0.13k - 15 = 51.95$$
$$0.13k - 15 + 15 = 51.95 + 15$$
$$0.13k = 66.95$$
$$\frac{0.13k}{0.13} = \frac{66.95}{0.13}$$
$$k = 515$$

The family used 515 kWh of electricity.

✔ **TAKE NOTE**

If the family uses 500 kilowatt-hours of electricity, they are billed $.13 per kilowatt-hour for 200 kilowatt-hours (500 − 300). If they use 650 kilowatt-hours, they are billed $.13 per kilowatt-hour for 350 kilowatt-hours (650 − 300). If they use k kilowatt-hours, $k > 300$, they are billed $.13 per kilowatt-hour for $(k - 300)$ kilowatt-hours.

CHECK YOUR PROGRESS 4   For a classified ad, a newspaper charges $11.50 for the first three lines and $1.50 for each additional line for an ad that runs for three days, or $17.50 for the first three lines and $2.50 for each additional line for an ad that runs for seven days. You want your ad to run for seven days. Determine the number of lines you can place in the ad for $30.

Solution   See page S17.

EXAMPLE 5 ■ Solve an Application of First-Degree Equations

In January, 1990, the population of New Mexico was 1,515,100 and the population of West Virginia was 1,793,500. During the 1990s, New Mexico's population increased at an average rate of 21,235 people per year while West Virginia's population decreased at an average rate of 15,600 people per year. If these rate changes remained stable, in what year would the populations of New Mexico and West Virginia have been the same? Round to the nearest year.

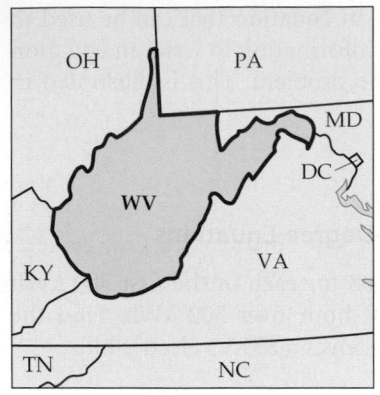

point of interest

Is the population of your state increasing or decreasing? You can find out by checking a reference such as the *Information Please Almanac,* which was the source for the data in Example 5 and Check Your Progress 5.

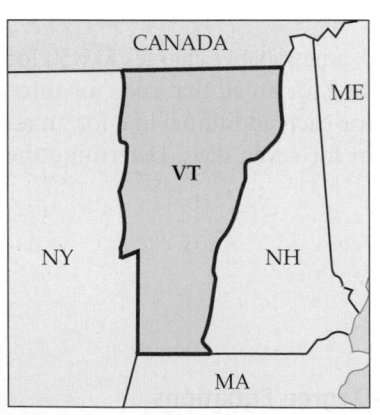

Solution

Let $n =$ the number of years until the populations are the same. Write an equation and then solve the equation for n.

| The 1990 population of New Mexico plus the annual increase times n | $=$ | the 1990 population of West Virginia minus the annual decrease times n |

$$1{,}515{,}100 + 21{,}235n = 1{,}793{,}500 - 15{,}600n$$
$$1{,}515{,}100 + 21{,}235n + 15{,}600n = 1{,}793{,}500 - 15{,}600n + 15{,}600n$$
$$1{,}515{,}100 + 36{,}835n = 1{,}793{,}500$$
$$1{,}515{,}100 - 1{,}515{,}100 + 36{,}835n = 1{,}793{,}500 - 1{,}515{,}100$$
$$36{,}835n = 278{,}400$$
$$\frac{36{,}835n}{36{,}835} = \frac{278{,}400}{36{,}835}$$
$$n \approx 8$$

The variable n represents the number of years after 1990. Add 8 to the year 1990.

$$1990 + 8 = 1998$$

To the nearest year, the populations would have been the same in 1998.

CHECK YOUR PROGRESS 5 In January, 1990, the population of North Dakota was 638,800 and the population of Vermont was 562,576. During the 1990s, North Dakota's population decreased at an average rate of 1370 people per year while Vermont's population increased at an average rate of 5116 people per year. If these rate changes remained stable, in what year would the populations of North Dakota and Vermont be the same? Round to the nearest year.

Solution   See page S17.

Literal Equations

A **literal equation** is an equation that contains more than one variable. Examples of literal equations are:

$$2x + 3y = 6$$
$$4a - 2b + c = 0$$

A **formula** is a literal equation that states a relationship between two or more quantities in an application problem. Examples of formulas are shown below. These formulas are taken from physics, mathematics, and business.

$$\frac{1}{R_1} + \frac{1}{R_2} = \frac{1}{R}$$
$$s = a + (n - 1)d$$
$$A = P + Prt$$

QUESTION *Which of the following are literal equations?*

   a. $5a - 3b = 7$ ***b.*** $a^2 + b^2 = c^2$

   c. $a_1 + (n - 1)d$ ***d.*** $3x - 7 = 5 + 4x$

The addition, subtraction, multiplication, and division properties of equations can be used to solve some literal equations for one of the variables. In solving a literal equation for one of the variables, the goal is to rewrite the equation so that the letter being solved for is alone on one side of the equation and all numbers and other variables are on the other side. This is illustrated in Example 6.

EXAMPLE 6 ■ Solve a Literal Equation

a. Solve $A = P(1 + i)$ for i.

b. Solve $I = \dfrac{E}{R + r}$ for R.

Solution

a. The goal is to rewrite the equation so that i is alone on one side of the equation and all other numbers and letters are on the other side. We will begin by using the Distributive Property on the right side of the equation.

$$A = P(1 + i)$$
$$A = P + Pi$$

Subtract P from each side of the equation.

$$A - P = P - P + Pi$$
$$A - P = Pi$$

Divide each side of the equation by P.

$$\frac{A - P}{P} = \frac{Pi}{P}$$

$$\frac{A - P}{P} = i$$

b. The goal is to rewrite the equation so that R is alone on one side of the equation and all other variables are on the other side of the equation. Because the equation contains a fraction, we will first multiply both sides of the equation by the denominator $R + r$ to clear the equation of fractions.

$$I = \frac{E}{R + r}$$

$$(R + r)I = (R + r)\frac{E}{R + r}$$

$$RI + rI = E$$

ANSWER   *a and b are literal equations. c is not an equation. d does not have more than one variable.*

Subtract from the left side of the equation the term that does not contain a capital R.

$$RI + rI - rI = E - rI$$
$$RI = E - rI$$

Divide each side of the equation by I.

$$\frac{RI}{I} = \frac{E - rI}{I}$$
$$R = \frac{E - rI}{I}$$

CHECK YOUR PROGRESS 6

a. Solve $s = \dfrac{A + L}{2}$ for L.

b. Solve $L = a(1 + ct)$ for c.

Solution   *See page S17.*

Excursion

Body Mass Index

Body mass index, or **BMI,** expresses the relationship between a person's height and weight. It is a measurement for gauging a person's weight-related level of risk for high blood pressure, heart disease, and diabetes. A BMI value of 25 or less indicates a very low to low risk; a BMI value of 25 to 30 indicates a low to moderate risk; a BMI of 30 or more indicates a moderate to very high risk.

The formula for body mass index is

$$B = \frac{705W}{H^2}$$

where B is the BMI, W is weight in pounds, and H is height in inches.

To determine how much a woman who is 5'4" should weigh in order to have a BMI of 24, first convert 5'4" to inches.

$$5'4'' = 5(12)'' + 4'' = 60'' + 4'' = 64''$$

(continued)

Substitute 24 for B and 64 for H in the body mass index formula. Then solve the resulting equation for W.

$$B = \frac{705W}{H^2}$$

$$24 = \frac{705W}{64^2}$$ • $B = 24, H = 64$

$$24 = \frac{705W}{4096}$$

$$4096(24) = 4096\left(\frac{705W}{4096}\right)$$ • **Multiply each side of the equation by 4096.**

$$98,304 = 705W$$

$$\frac{98,304}{705} = \frac{705W}{705}$$ • **Divide each side of the equation by 705.**

$$139 \approx W$$

A woman who is 5′4″ should weigh about 139 pounds in order to have a BMI of 24.

Excursion Exercises

1. Amy is 140 pounds and 5′8″ tall. Calculate Amy's BMI. Round to the nearest tenth. Rank Amy as a low, moderate, or high risk for weight-related disease.

2. Carlos is 6′1″ and weighs 225 pounds. Calculate Carlos's BMI. Round to the nearest tenth. Would you rank Carlos as a low, moderate, or high risk for weight-related disease?

3. Roger is 5′11″. How much should he weigh in order to have a BMI of 25? Round to the nearest pound.

4. Brenda is 5′3″. How much should she weigh in order to have a BMI of 24? Round to the nearest pound.

5. Bohdan weighs 185 pounds and is 5′9″. How many pounds must Bohdan lose in order to reach a BMI of 23? Round to the nearest pound.

6. Pat is 6′3″ and weighs 245 pounds. Calculate the number of pounds Pat must lose in order to reach a BMI of 22. Round to the nearest pound.

7. Zack weighs 205 pounds and is 6′0″. He would like to lower his BMI to 20.

    a. By how many points must Zack lower his BMI? Round to the nearest tenth.

    b. How many pounds must Zack lose in order to reach a BMI of 20? Round to the nearest pound.

8. Felicia weighs 160 pounds and is 5′7″. She would like to lower her BMI to 20.

    a. By how many points must Felicia lower her BMI? Round to the nearest tenth.

    b. How many pounds must Felicia lose in order to reach a BMI of 20? Round to the nearest pound.

Exercise Set 5.1

1. What is the difference between an expression and an equation? Provide an example of each.

2. What is the solution of the equation $x = 8$? Use your answer to explain why the goal in solving

an equation is to get the variable alone on one side of the equation.

3. Explain how to check the solution of an equation.

In Exercises 4–41, solve the equation.

4. $x + 7 = -5$

5. $9 + b = 21$

6. $-9 = z - 8$

7. $b - 11 = 11$

8. $-3x = 150$

9. $-48 = 6z$

10. $-9a = -108$

11. $-\dfrac{3}{4}x = 15$

12. $\dfrac{5}{2}x = -10$

13. $-\dfrac{x}{4} = -2$

14. $\dfrac{2x}{5} = -8$

15. $4 - 2b = 2 - 4b$

16. $4y - 10 = 6 + 2y$

17. $5x - 3 = 9x - 7$

18. $10z + 6 = 4 + 5z$

19. $3m + 5 = 2 - 6m$

20. $6a - 1 = 2 + 2a$

21. $5x + 7 = 8x + 5$

22. $2 - 6y = 5 - 7y$

23. $4b + 15 = 3 - 2b$

24. $2(x + 1) + 5x = 23$

25. $9n - 15 = 3(2n - 1)$

26. $7a - (3a - 4) = 12$

27. $5(3 - 2y) = 3 - 4y$

28. $9 - 7x = 4(1 - 3x)$

29. $2(3b + 5) - 1 = 10b + 1$

30. $2z - 2 = 5 - (9 - 6z)$

31. $4a + 3 = 7 - (5 - 8a)$

32. $5(6 - 2x) = 2(5 - 3x)$

33. $4(3y + 1) = 2(y - 8)$

34. $2(3b - 5) = 4(6b - 2)$

35. $3(x - 4) = 1 - (2x - 7)$

36. $\dfrac{2y}{3} - 4 = \dfrac{y}{6} - 1$

37. $\dfrac{x}{8} + 2 = \dfrac{3x}{4} - 3$

38. $\dfrac{2x - 3}{3} + \dfrac{1}{2} = \dfrac{5}{6}$

39. $\dfrac{2}{3} + \dfrac{3x + 1}{4} = \dfrac{5}{3}$

40. $\dfrac{1}{2}(x + 4) = \dfrac{1}{3}(3x - 6)$

41. $\dfrac{3}{4}(x - 8) = \dfrac{1}{2}(2x + 4)$

Car Payments The monthly car payment on a 60-month car loan at a 9 percent rate is calculated by using the formula $P = 0.02076L$, where P is the monthly car payment and L is the loan amount. Use this formula for Exercises 42 and 43.

42. If you can afford a maximum monthly car payment of \$300, what is the maximum loan amount you can afford? Round to the nearest cent.

43. If the maximum monthly car payment you can afford is $350, what is the maximum loan amount you can afford? Round to the nearest cent.

Cassette Tape The music you hear when listening to a magnetic cassette tape is the result of the magnetic tape passing over magnetic heads, which read the magnetic information on the tape. The length of time a tape will play depends on the length of the tape and the operating speed of the tape player. The formula is $T = \frac{L}{S}$, where T is the time in seconds, L is the length of the tape in inches, and S is the operating speed in inches per second. Use this formula for Exercises 44–46.

44. How long a tape does a marine biologist need to record 16 seconds of whale songs at an operating speed of $1\frac{7}{8}$ inches per second?

45. How long a tape does a police officer need to record a 3-minute confession at an operating speed of $7\frac{1}{2}$ inches per second?

46. A U2 cassette tape takes 50 minutes to play on a system with an operating speed of $3\frac{3}{4}$ inches per second. Find the length of the tape.

Deep-Sea Diving The pressure on a diver can be calculated using the formula $P = 15 + \frac{1}{2}D$, where P is the pressure in pounds per square inch and D is the depth in feet. Use this formula for Exercises 47 and 48.

47. Find the depth of a diver when the pressure on the diver is 45 pounds per square inch.

48. Find the depth of a diver when the pressure on the diver is 55 pounds per square inch.

Foot Races The world-record time for a 1-mile race can be approximated by $t = 17.08 - 0.0067y$, where y is the year of the race, $1950 \leq y \leq 2006$, and t is the time, in minutes, of the race. Use this formula for Exercises 49 and 50.

49. Approximate the year in which the first "4-minute mile" was run. The actual year was 1954.

50. In 1985, the world-record time for a 1-mile race was 3.77 minutes. For what year does the equation predict this record time?

Black Ice Black ice is an ice covering on roads that is especially difficult to see and therefore extremely dangerous for motorists. The distance a car traveling at 30 miles per hour will slide after its brakes are applied is related to the outside temperature by the formula $C = \frac{1}{4}D - 45$, where C is the Celsius temperature and D is the distance, in feet, that the car will slide. Use this formula for Exercises 51 and 52.

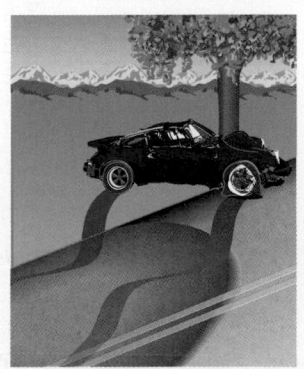

51. Determine the distance a car will slide on black ice when the outside air temperature is $-3°C$.

52. How far will a car slide on black ice when the outside air temperature is $-11°C$?

Crickets The formula $N = 7C - 30$ approximates N, the number of times per minute a cricket chirps when the air temperature is C degrees Celsius. Use this formula for Exercises 53 and 54.

53. What is the approximate air temperature when a cricket chirps 100 times per minute? Round to the nearest tenth.

54. Determine the approximate air temperature when a cricket chirps 140 times per minute. Round to the nearest tenth.

Bowling In order to equalize all the bowlers' chances of winning, some players in a bowling league are given a handicap, or a bonus of extra points. Some leagues use the formula $H = 0.8(200 - A)$, where H is the handicap and A is the bowler's average score in past games. Use this formula for Exercises 55 and 56.

55. A bowler has a handicap of 20. What is the bowler's average score?

56. Find the average score of a bowler who has a handicap of 25.

In Exercises 57–69, write an equation as part of solving the problem.

57. Depreciation As a result of depreciation, the value of a car is now $13,200. This is three-fifths of its original value. Find the original value of the car.

58. Computers The operating speed of a personal computer is 100 gigahertz. This is one-third the speed of a newer model. Find the speed of the newer personal computer.

59. **College Tuition** The graph below shows average tuition and fees at private four-year colleges for selected years.

a. For the 1988–89 school year, the average tuition and fees at private four-year colleges were $171 more than five times the average tuition and fees at public four-year colleges. Determine the average tuition and fees at public four-year colleges for the school year 1988–89.

b. For the 2003–04 school year, the average tuition and fees at private four-year colleges were $934 more than four times the average tuition and fees at public four-year colleges. Find the average tuition and fees at public four-year colleges for the school year 2003–04.

Tuition and Fees at Private Four-Year Colleges

Source: The College Board

60. **Adoption** In a recent year, Americans adopted 21,616 children from foreign countries. In the graph on the next page are the top three countries where the children were born.

a. The number of children adopted from China was 1489 more than three times the number adopted from South Korea. Determine the number of children adopted from South Korea that year.

b. The number of children adopted from Russia was 259 more than six times the number adopted from Kazakhstan. Determine the number of children from Kazakhstan that Americans adopted that year.

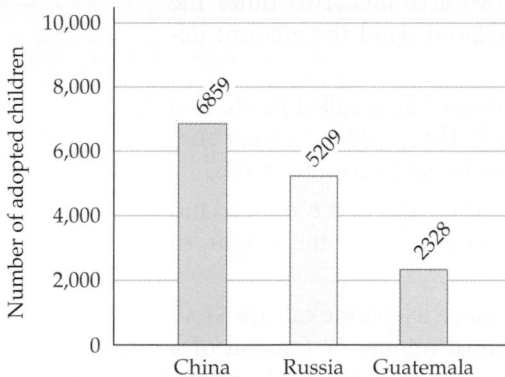

Birth Countries of Adopted American Children

Source: U.S. State Department

61. Installment Purchases The purchase price of a big-screen TV, including finance charges, was $3276. A down payment of $450 was made, and the remainder was paid in 24 equal monthly installments. Find the monthly payment.

62. Auto Repair The cost to replace a water pump in a sports car was $600. This included $375 for the water pump and $45 per hour for labor. How many hours of labor were required to replace the water pump?

63. Space Vehicles The table below provides statistics on the space shuttle *Discovery*, on which John Glenn was a crew member in 1998. His previous space flight was on the Friendship 7 in 1962. (*Source: Time* magazine, August 17, 1998)

a. The lift-off thrust of the Discovery was 85,000 kilograms less than 20 times the lift-off thrust of the Friendship 7. Find the lift-off thrust of the Friendship 7.

b. The weight of the Discovery was 290 kilograms greater than 36 times the weight of the Friendship 7. Find the weight of the Friendship 7.

The Space Shuttle *Discovery*	
Crew size	7
Crew work area	66 cubic meters
Windows	5
Computers	5
Toggle switches	856
Lift-off thrust	3,175,000 kilograms
Weight	69,770 kilograms

64. **College Staffing** A university employs a total of 600 teaching assistants and research assistants. There are three times as many teaching assistants as research assistants. Find the number of research assistants employed by the university.

65. **Wages** A service station attendant is paid time-and-a-half for working over 40 hours per week. Last week the attendant worked 47 hours and earned $631.25. Find the attendant's regular hourly wage.

66. **Investments** An investor deposited $5000 in two accounts. Two times the smaller deposit is $1000 more than the larger deposit. Find the amount deposited in each account.

67. **Computers** A computer screen consists of tiny dots of light called *pixels*. In a certain graphics mode, there are 1040 vertical pixels. This is 400 more than one-half the number of horizontal pixels. Find the number of horizontal pixels.

68. **Shipping** An overnight mail service charges $5.60 for the first 6 ounces and $.85 for each additional ounce or fraction of an ounce. Find the weight, in ounces, of a package that cost $10.70 to deliver.

69. **Telecommunications** The charges for a long-distance telephone call are $1.42 for the first 3 minutes and $.65 for each additional minute or fraction of a minute. If charges for a call were $10.52, for how many minutes did the phone call last?

In Exercises 70–87, solve the formula for the indicated variable.

70. $A = \dfrac{1}{2} bh$; h (Geometry)

71. $P = a + b + c$; b (Geometry)

72. $d = rt$; t (Physics)

73. $E = IR$; R (Physics)

74. $PV = nRT$; R (Chemistry)

75. $I = Prt$; r (Business)

76. $P = 2L + 2W$; W (Geometry)

77. $F = \dfrac{9}{5} C + 32$; C (Temperature conversion)

78. $P = R - C$; C (Business)

79. $A = P + Prt$; t (Business)

80. $S = V_0 t - 16t^2$; V_0 (Physics)

81. $T = fm - gm$; f (Engineering)

82. $P = \dfrac{R - C}{n}$; R (Business)

83. $R = \dfrac{C - S}{t}$; S (Business)

84. $V = \dfrac{1}{3} \pi r^2 h$; h (Geometry)

85. $A = \dfrac{1}{2} h(b_1 + b_2)$; b_2 (Geometry)

86. $a_n = a_1 + (n - 1)d$; d (Mathematics)

87. $S = 2\pi r^2 + 2\pi rh$; h (Geometry)

In Exercises 88 and 89, solve the equation for y.

88. $2x - y = 4$ 89. $4x + 3y = 6$

In Exercises 90 and 91, solve the equation for x.

90. $ax + by + c = 0$ 91. $y - y_1 = m(x - x_1)$

Extensions

CRITICAL THINKING

In Exercises 92–95, solve the equation.

92. $3(4x + 2) = 7 - 4(1 - 3x)$

93. $9 - (6 - 4x) = 3(1 - 2x)$

94. $4(x + 5) = 30 - (10 - 4x)$

95. $7(x - 20) - 5(x - 22) = 2x - 30$

96. Use the numbers 5, 10, and 15 to make equations by filling in the boxes: $x + \square = \square - \square$. Each equation must use all three numbers.

   a. What is the largest possible solution of these equations?

   b. What is the smallest possible solution of these equations?

97. Solve the equation $ax + b = cx + d$ for x. Is your solution valid for all numbers a, b, c, and d? Explain.

COOPERATIVE LEARNING

98. Some equations have no solution. For instance, $x = x + 1$ has no solution. If we subtract x from each side of the equation, the result is $0 = 1$, which is not a true statement. One possible interpretation of the equation $x = x + 1$ is "A number is equal to one more than itself." Because there is no number that is equal to one more than itself, the equation has no solution.

Now consider the equation $ax + b = cx + d$. Determine what conditions on a, b, c, and d will result in an equation with no solution.

EXPLORATIONS

99. Recall that formulas state relationships among quantities. When we know there is an explicit relationship between two quantities, often we can write a formula to express the relationship.

For example, the Hooksett tollbooth on Interstate 93 in New Hampshire collects a toll of $.75 from each car that passes through the toll. We can write a formula that describes the amount of money collected from passenger cars on any given day.

Let A be the total amount of money collected, and let c be the number of cars that pass through the tollbooth on a given day. Then

$$A = \$.75c$$

is a formula that expresses the total amount of money collected from passenger cars on any given day.

a. How much money is collected from passenger cars on a day on which 5500 passenger cars pass through the toll?

b. How many passenger cars passed through the toll on a day on which $3243.75 was collected in tolls from passenger cars?

Write formulas for each of the following situations. Include as part of your answer a list of variables that were used, and state what each variable represents.

c. Write a formula to represent the total cost to rent a copier from a company that charges $325 per month plus $.04 per copy made.

d. Suppose you buy a used car with 30,000 miles on it. You expect to drive the car about 750 miles per month. Write a formula to represent the total number of miles the car has been driven after you have owned it for m months.

e. A parking garage charges $2.50 for the first hour and $1.75 for each additional hour. Write a formula to represent the parking charge for parking in this garage for h hours.

f. Write a formula to represent the total cost to rent a car from a company that rents cars for $19.95 per day plus 25¢ for every mile driven over 100 miles.

g. Think of a mathematical relationship that can be modeled by a formula. Identify the variables in the relationship and write a formula that models the relationship.

| **Rate, Ratio, and Proportion**

Rates

The word *rate* is used frequently in our everyday lives. It is used in such contexts as unemployment rate, tax rate, interest rate, hourly rate, infant mortality rate, school dropout rate, inflation rate, and postage rate.

A **rate** is a comparison of two quantities. A rate can be written as a fraction.

A car travels 135 miles on 6 gallons of gas. The miles-to-gallons rate is written

$$\frac{135 \text{ miles}}{6 \text{ gallons}}$$

Note that the units (miles and gallons) are written as part of the rate.

▼ **point of interest**

Unit rates are used in a wide variety of situations. One unit rate you may not be familiar with is used in the airline industry: cubic feet of air per minute per person. Typical rates are: economy class, 7 cubic feet/minute/person; first class, 50 cubic feet/minute/person; cockpit, 150 cubic feet/minute/person.

A **unit rate** is a rate in which the number in the denominator is 1. To find a unit rate, divide the number in the numerator of the rate by the number in the denominator of the rate. For the example above,

$$135 \div 6 = 22.5$$

The unit rate is $\dfrac{22.5 \text{ miles}}{1 \text{ gallon}}$.

This rate can be written 22.5 miles/gallon or 22.5 miles per gallon, where the word *per* has the meaning "for every."

Unit rates make comparisons easier. For example, if you travel 37 miles per hour and I travel 43 miles per hour, we know that I am traveling faster than you are. It is more difficult to compare speeds if we are told that you are traveling $\dfrac{111 \text{ miles}}{3 \text{ hours}}$ and I am traveling $\dfrac{172 \text{ miles}}{4 \text{ hours}}$.

EXAMPLE 1 ■ **Calculate a Unit Rate**

A dental hygienist earns $780 for working a 40-hour week. What is the hygienist's hourly rate of pay?

Solution
The hygienist's rate of pay is $\dfrac{\$780}{40 \text{ hours}}$.
To find the hourly rate of pay, divide 780 by 40.

$$780 \div 40 = 19.5$$

$$\frac{\$780}{40 \text{ hours}} = \frac{\$19.50}{1 \text{ hour}} = \$19.50/\text{hour}$$

The hygienist's hourly rate of pay is $19.50 per hour.

CHECK YOUR PROGRESS 1   You pay $4.92 for 1.5 pounds of hamburger. What is the cost per pound?

Solution   See page S18.

EXAMPLE 2 ■ **Solve an Application of Unit Rates**

A teacher earns a salary of $34,200 per year. Currently the school year is 180 days. If the school year were extended to 220 days, as is proposed in some states, what annual salary should the teacher be paid if the salary is based on the number of days worked per year?

Solution
Find the current salary per day.

$$\frac{\$34,200}{180 \text{ days}} = \frac{\$190}{1 \text{ day}} = \$190/\text{day}$$

Multiply the salary per day by the number of days in the proposed school year.

$$\frac{\$190}{1 \text{ day}} \cdot 220 \text{ days} = \$190(220) = \$41,800$$

The teacher's annual salary should be $41,800.

CHECK YOUR PROGRESS 2   In July 2004, the federal minimum wage was $5.15 per hour, and the minimum wage in California was $6.75. How much greater is an employee's pay for working 35 hours and earning the California minimum wage rather than the federal minimum wage?

Solution   *See page S18.*

Grocery stores are required to provide customers with unit price information. The **unit price** of a product is its cost per unit of measure. Unit pricing is an application of unit rate.

The price of a 2-pound box of spaghetti is $1.89. The unit price of the spaghetti is the cost per pound. To find the unit price, write the rate as a unit rate.

The numerator is the price and the denominator is the quantity. Divide the number in the numerator by the number in the denominator.

$$\frac{\$1.89}{2 \text{ pounds}} = \frac{\$.945}{1 \text{ pound}}$$

The unit price of the spaghetti is $.945 per pound.

Unit pricing is used by consumers to answer the question "Which is the better buy?" The answer is that the product with the lower unit price is the more economical purchase.

EXAMPLE 3 ■ Determine the More Economical Purchase

Which is the more economical purchase, an 18-ounce jar of peanut butter priced at $3.49 or a 12-ounce jar of peanut butter priced at $2.59?

Solution
Find the unit price for each item.

$$\frac{\$3.49}{18 \text{ ounces}} \approx \frac{\$.194}{1 \text{ ounce}} \qquad \frac{\$2.59}{12 \text{ ounces}} \approx \frac{\$.216}{1 \text{ ounce}}$$

Compare the two prices per ounce.

$$\$.194 < \$.216$$

The item with the lower unit price is the more economical purchase.
The more economical purchase is the 18-ounce jar priced at $3.49.

CHECK YOUR PROGRESS 3   Which is the more economical purchase, 32 ounces of detergent for $2.99 or 48 ounces of detergent for $3.99?

Solution   *See page S18.*

point of interest

According to the Centers for Disease Control, in a recent year the teen birth rate in the United States fell to 45.8 births per 1000 females age 15 to 19.

Rates such as crime statistics or data on fatalities are often written as rates per hundred, per thousand, per hundred thousand, or per million. For example, the table below shows bicycle deaths per million people in a recent year in the states with the highest and the lowest rates. (*Source:* Environmental Working Group)

Rates of Bicycle Fatalities (Deaths per Million People)			
Highest		**Lowest**	
Florida	8.8	North Dakota	1.7
Arizona	7.0	Oklahoma	1.6
Louisiana	5.9	New Hampshire	1.4
South Carolina	5.4	West Virginia	1.2
North Carolina	4.5	Rhode Island	1.1

The rates in this table are easier to read than they would be if they were unit rates. As a comparison, consider that the bicycle fatalities in North Carolina would be written as 0.0000045 as a unit rate. Also, it is easier to understand that 7 out of every million people living in Arizona die in bicycle accidents than to consider that 0.000007 out of every person in Arizona dies in a bicycle accident.

QUESTION   *What does the rate given for Oklahoma mean?*

Another application of rates is in the area of international trade. Suppose a company in France purchases a shipment of sneakers from an American company. The French company must exchange euros, which is France's currency, for U.S. dollars in order to pay for the order. The number of euros that are equivalent to one U.S. dollar is called the *exchange rate*. The table below shows the exchange rates per U.S. dollar for three foreign countries and the European Union on July 2, 2004. Use this table for Example 4 and Check Your Progress 4.

Exchange Rates per U.S. Dollar	
British Pound	0.5458
Canadian Dollar	1.3240
Japanese Yen	108.2600
Euro	0.8110

EXAMPLE 4 ■ Solve an Application Using Exchange Rates

a. How many Japanese yen are needed to pay for an order costing $10,000?

b. Find the number of British pounds that would be exchanged for $5000.

Solution

a. Multiply the number of yen per $1 by 10,000.

$$10,000(108.2600) = 1,082,600$$

1,082,600 yen are needed to pay for an order costing $10,000.

ANSWER   *Oklahoma's rate of 1.6 means that 1.6 out of every million people living in Oklahoma die in bicycle accidents.*

b. Multiply the number of pounds per $1 by 5000.

$$5000(0.5458) = 2729$$

2729 British pounds would be exchanged for $5000.

CHECK YOUR PROGRESS 4

a. How many Canadian dollars would be needed to pay for an order costing $20,000?

b. Find the number of euros that would be exchanged for $25,000.

Solution   *See page S18.*

Solution   *See page S18.*

▼ point of interest

It is believed that billiards was invented in France during the reign of Louis XI (1423–1483). In the United States, the standard billiard table is 4 feet 6 inches by 9 feet. This is a ratio of 1:2. The same ratio holds for carom and snooker tables, which are 5 feet by 10 feet.

Ratios

A **ratio** is the comparison of two quantities that have the same units. A ratio can be written in three different ways:

1. As a fraction $\dfrac{2}{3}$

2. As two numbers separated by a colon (:)   2:3

3. As two numbers separated by the word *to*   2 to 3

Although units, such as hours, miles, or dollars, are written as part of a rate, units are not written as part of a ratio.

According to the most recent census, there are 50 million married women in the United States, and 30 million of these women work in the labor force. The ratio of the number of married women who are employed in the labor force to the total number of married women in the country is calculated below. Note that the ratio is written in simplest form.

$$\frac{30,000,000}{50,000,000} = \frac{3}{5} \quad \text{or} \quad 3:5 \quad \text{or} \quad 3 \text{ to } 5$$

The ratio 3 to 5 tells us that 3 out of every 5 married women in the United States are part of the labor force.

Given that 30 million of the 50 million married women in the country work in the labor force, we can calculate the number of married women who do not work in the labor force.

$$50 \text{ million} - 30 \text{ million} = 20 \text{ million}$$

The ratio of the number of married women who are not in the labor force to the number of married women who are is:

$$\frac{20,000,000}{30,000,000} = \frac{2}{3} \quad \text{or} \quad 2:3 \quad \text{or} \quad 2 \text{ to } 3$$

The ratio 2 to 3 tells us that for every 2 married women who are not in the labor force, there are 3 married women who are in the labor force.

EXAMPLE 5 ■ Determine a Ratio in Simplest Form

A survey revealed that, on average, eighth-graders watch approximately 21 hours of television each week. Find the ratio, as a fraction in simplest form, of the number of hours spent watching television to the total number of hours in a week.

Solution

A ratio is the comparison of two quantities with the same units. In this problem we are given both hours and weeks. We must first convert one week to hours.

$$\frac{24 \text{ hours}}{1 \text{ day}} \cdot 7 \text{ days} = (24 \text{ hours})(7) = 168 \text{ hours}$$

Write in simplest form the ratio of the number of hours spent watching television to the number of hours in one week.

$$\frac{21 \text{ hours}}{1 \text{ week}} = \frac{21 \text{ hours}}{168 \text{ hours}} = \frac{21}{168} = \frac{1}{8}$$

The ratio is $\frac{1}{8}$.

CHECK YOUR PROGRESS 5

a. According to the National Low Income Housing Coalition, a minimum-wage worker ($5.15 per hour) living in New Jersey would have to work 120 hours per week to afford the rent on an average two-bedroom apartment and be within the federal standard of 30% of income for housing. Find the ratio, as a fraction in simplest form, of the number of hours a minimum-wage worker would spend working per week to the total number of hours in a week.

b. Although a minimum-wage worker in New Jersey would have to work 120 hours per week to afford a two-bedroom rental, the national average is 60 hours of work per week. For this "average" worker, find the ratio, written using the word *to*, of the number of hours per week spent working to the number of hours not spent working.

Solution   *See page S18.*

A **unit ratio** is a ratio in which the number in the denominator is 1. One situation in which a unit ratio is used is student–faculty ratios. The table below shows the number of full-time men and women undergraduates, as well as the number of full-time faculty at two universities in the Pacific 10. Use this table for Example 6 and Check Your Progress 6. (*Source: Barron's Profile of American Colleges*, 26th edition, c. 2005)

University	Men	Women	Faculty
Oregon State University	7509	6478	1352
University of Oregon	6742	7710	798

EXAMPLE 6 ■ Determine a Unit Ratio

 Calculate the student–faculty ratio at Oregon State University. Round to the nearest whole number. Write the ratio using the word *to*.

Solution

Add the number of male undergraduates and the number of female undergraduates to determine the total number of students.

$$7509 + 6478 = 13,987$$

Write the ratio of the total number of students to the number of faculty. Divide the numerator and denominator by the denominator. Then round the numerator to the nearest whole number.

$$\frac{13{,}987}{1352} \approx \frac{10.3454}{1} \approx \frac{10}{1}$$

The ratio is approximately 10 to 1.

CHECK YOUR PROGRESS 6

 Calculate the student–faculty ratio at the University of Oregon. Round to the nearest whole number. Write the ratio using the word *to*.

Solution   *See page S18.*

Math Matters   Scale Model Buildings

George E. Slye of Tuftonboro, New Hampshire, has built scale models of more than 100 of the best-known buildings in America and Canada. From photographs, floor plans, roof plans, and architectural drawings, Slye has constructed a replica of each building using a scale of 1 inch per 200 feet.

The buildings and landmarks are grouped together on an 8-foot-by-8-foot base as if they were all erected in a single city. Slye's city includes such well-known landmarks as New York's Empire State Building, Chicago's Sears Tower, Boston's John Hancock Tower, Seattle's Space Needle, and San Francisco's Golden Gate Bridge.

Proportions

Thus far in this section we have discussed rates and ratios. Now that you have an understanding of rates and ratios, you are ready to work with proportions. A **proportion** is an equation that states the equality of two rates or ratios. The following are examples of proportions.

$$\frac{250 \text{ miles}}{5 \text{ hours}} = \frac{50 \text{ miles}}{1 \text{ hour}} \qquad \frac{3}{6} = \frac{1}{2}$$

The first example above is the equality of two rates. Note that the units in the numerators (miles) are the same and the units in the denominators (hours) are the same. The second example is the equality of two ratios. Remember that units are not written as part of a ratio.

The definition of a proportion can be stated as follows: If $\frac{a}{b}$ and $\frac{c}{d}$ are equal ratios or rates, then $\frac{a}{b} = \frac{c}{d}$ is a proportion.

Each of the four members in a proportion is called a **term**. Each term is numbered as shown below.

The second and third terms of the proportion are called the **means** and the first and fourth terms are called the **extremes**.

If we multiply both sides of the proportion by the product of the denominators, we obtain the following result.

$$\frac{a}{b} = \frac{c}{d}$$

$$bd\left(\frac{a}{b}\right) = bd\left(\frac{c}{d}\right)$$

$$ad = bc$$

Note that ad is the product of the extremes and bc is the product of the means. In any proportion, the product of the means equals the product of the extremes. This is sometimes phrased, "the cross products are equal."

In the proportion $\frac{3}{4} = \frac{9}{12}$, the cross products are equal.

$$\frac{3}{4} \quad \frac{9}{12} \qquad 4 \cdot 9 = 36 \longleftarrow \text{ Product of the means}$$
$$\qquad\qquad\qquad 3 \cdot 12 = 36 \longleftarrow \text{ Product of the extremes}$$

QUESTION   *For the proportion $\frac{5}{8} = \frac{10}{16}$, **a.** name the first and third terms, **b.** write the product of the means, and **c.** write the product of the extremes.*

ANSWER   *a. The first term is 5. The third term is 10. **b.** The product of the means is $8(10) = 80$. **c.** The product of the extremes is $5(16) = 80$.*

Sometimes one of the terms in a proportion is unknown. In this case, it is necessary to solve the proportion for the unknown number. The **cross-products method,** which is based on the fact that the product of the means equals the product of the extremes, can be used to solve the proportion. Remember that the cross-products method is just a short cut for multiplying each side of the equation by the least common multiple of the denominators.

Cross-Products Method of Solving a Proportion

If $\dfrac{a}{b} = \dfrac{c}{d}$, then $ad = bc$.

EXAMPLE 7 ■ Solve a Proportion

Solve: $\dfrac{8}{5} = \dfrac{n}{6}$

Solution

Use the cross-products method of solving a proportion: the product of the means equals the product of the extremes. Then solve the resulting equation for n.

$$\frac{8}{5} = \frac{n}{6}$$

$$8 \cdot 6 = 5 \cdot n$$

$$48 = 5n$$

$$\frac{48}{5} = \frac{5n}{5}$$

$$9.6 = n$$

The solution is 9.6.

✔ TAKE NOTE

Be sure to check the solution.

$$\frac{8}{5} = \frac{9.6}{6}$$

$$8 \cdot 6 = 5 \cdot 9.6$$

$$48 = 48$$

The solution checks.

CHECK YOUR PROGRESS 7   Solve: $\dfrac{42}{x} = \dfrac{5}{8}$

Solution   *See page S18.*

Proportions are useful for solving a wide variety of application problems. Remember that when we use the given information to write a proportion involving two rates, the units in the numerators of the rates need to be the same and the units in the denominators of the rates need to be the same. It is helpful to keep in mind that when we write a proportion, we are stating that two rates or ratios are equal.

✔ **TAKE NOTE**

We have written a proportion with the unit "miles" in the numerators and the unit "gallons" in the denominators. It would also be correct to have "gallons" in the numerators and "miles" in the denominators.

EXAMPLE 8 ■ **Solve an Application Using a Proportion**

If you travel 290 miles in your car on 15 gallons of gasoline, how far can you travel in your car on 12 gallons of gasoline under similar driving conditions?

Solution
Let $x =$ the unknown number of miles.
Write a proportion and then solve the proportion for x.

$$\frac{290 \text{ miles}}{15 \text{ gallons}} = \frac{x \text{ miles}}{12 \text{ gallons}}$$

$$\frac{290}{15} = \frac{x}{12}$$

$$290 \cdot 12 = 15 \cdot x$$

$$3480 = 15x$$

$$232 = x$$

You can travel 232 miles on 12 gallons of gasoline.

CHECK YOUR PROGRESS 8 On a map, a distance of 2 centimeters represents 15 kilometers. What is the distance between two cities that are 7 centimeters apart on the map?

Solution See page S18.

EXAMPLE 9 ■ **Solve an Application Using a Proportion**

The table below shows three of the universities in the Big Ten Conference and their student–faculty ratios. (*Source: Barron's Profile of American Colleges*, 26th edition, c. 2005) There are approximately 31,100 full-time undergraduate students at Michigan State University. Approximate the number of faculty at Michigan State University.

University	Student–Faculty Ratio
Michigan State University	13 to 1
University of Illinois	15 to 1
University of Iowa	11 to 1

Solution

Let $F =$ the number of faculty members.

Write a proportion and then solve the proportion for F.

$$\frac{13 \text{ students}}{1 \text{ faculty}} = \frac{31,100 \text{ students}}{F \text{ faculty}}$$

$$13 \cdot F = 1(31,100)$$

$$13F = 31,100$$

$$\frac{13F}{13} = \frac{31,100}{13}$$

$$F \approx 2392$$

There are approximately 2392 faculty members at Michigan State University.

CHECK YOUR PROGRESS 9   The profits of a firm are shared by its two partners in the ratio 7:5. If the partner receiving the larger amount of this year's profits receives $28,000, what amount does the other partner receive?

Solution   *See page S18.*

EXAMPLE 10 ■ Solve an Application Using a Proportion

In the United States, the average annual number of deaths per million people aged 5 to 34 from asthma is 3.5. Approximately how many people aged 5 to 34 die from asthma each year in this country? Use a figure of 150,000,000 for the number of U.S. residents who are 5 to 34 years old. (*Source:* National Center for Health Statistics)

Solution

Let $d =$ the number of people aged 5 to 34 who die each year from asthma in the United States. Write and solve a proportion. One rate is 3.5 deaths per million people.

$$\frac{3.5 \text{ deaths}}{1,000,000 \text{ people}} = \frac{d \text{ deaths}}{150,000,000 \text{ people}}$$

$$3.5(150,000,000) = 1,000,000 \cdot d$$

$$525,000,000 = 1,000,000d$$

$$\frac{525,000,000}{1,000,000} = \frac{1,000,000d}{1,000,000}$$

$$525 = d$$

In the United States, approximately 525 people aged 5 to 34 die each year from asthma.

CHECK YOUR PROGRESS 10

New York City has the highest death rate from asthma in the United States. The average annual number of deaths per million people aged 5 to 34 from asthma in New York City is 10.1. Approximately how many people aged 5 to 34 die from asthma each year in New York City? Use a figure of 4,000,000 for the number of residents 5 to 34 years old in New York City. Round to the nearest whole number. (*Source:* National Center for Health Statistics)

Solution   See page S18.

MathMatters   **Scale Models for Special Effects**

Special-effects artists use scale models to create dinosaurs, exploding spaceships, and aliens. A scale model is produced by using ratios and proportions to determine the size of the scale model.

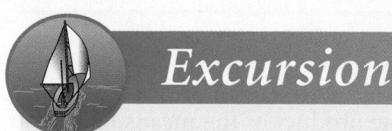

Excursion

Earned Run Average

Earned Run Average Leaders		
Year	Player, club	ERA
	National League	
1990	Danny Darwin, Houston	2.21
1991	Dennis Martinez, Montreal	2.39
1992	Bill Swift, San Francisco	2.08
1993	Greg Maddux, Atlanta	2.36
1994	Greg Maddux, Atlanta	1.56
1995	Greg Maddux, Atlanta	1.63
1996	Kevin Brown, Florida	1.89
1997	Pedro Martinez, Montreal	1.90
1998	Greg Maddux, Atlanta	2.22
1999	Randy Johnson, Arizona	2.48
2000	Kevin Brown, Los Angeles	2.58
2001	Randy Johnson, Arizona	2.49
2002	Randy Johnson, Arizona	2.32
2003	Jason Schmidt, San Francisco	2.34
2004	Jake Peavy, San Diego	2.27
	American League	
1990	Roger Clemens, Boston	1.93
1991	Roger Clemens, Boston	2.62
1992	Roger Clemens, Boston	2.41
1993	Kevin Appier, Kansas City	2.56
1994	Steve Ontiveros, Oakland	2.65
1995	Randy Johnson, Seattle	2.48
1996	Juan Guzman, Toronto	2.93
1997	Roger Clemens, Toronto	2.05
1998	Roger Clemens, Toronto	2.65
1999	Pedro Martinez, Boston	2.07
2000	Pedro Martinez, Boston	1.74
2001	Freddy Garcia, Seattle	3.05
2002	Pedro Martinez, Boston	2.26
2003	Pedro Martinez, Boston	2.22
2004	Johan Santana, Minnesota	2.61

One measure of a pitcher's success is earned run average. **Earned run average (ERA)** is the number of earned runs a pitcher gives up for every nine innings pitched. The definition of an earned run is somewhat complicated, but basically an earned run is a run that is scored as a result of hits and base running that involves no errors on the part of the pitcher's team. If the opposing team scores a run on an error (for example, a fly ball that should have been caught in the outfield was fumbled), then that run is not an earned run.

A proportion is used to calculate a pitcher's ERA. Remember that the statistic involves the number of earned runs per *nine innings*. The answer is always rounded to the nearest hundredth. Here is an example.

During the 2004 baseball season, Johan Santana gave up 66 earned runs and pitched 228 innings for the Minnesota Twins. To calculate Johan Santana's ERA, let $x = $ the number of earned runs for every nine innings pitched. Write a proportion and then solve it for x.

$$\frac{66 \text{ earned runs}}{228 \text{ innings}} = \frac{x}{9 \text{ innings}}$$

$$66 \cdot 9 = 228 \cdot x$$

$$594 = 228x$$

$$\frac{594}{228} = \frac{228x}{228}$$

$$2.61 \approx x$$

Johan Santana's ERA for the 2004 season was 2.61.

Excursion Exercises

1. In 1979, his rookie year, Jeff Reardon pitched 21 innings for the New York Mets and gave up four earned runs. Calculate Reardon's ERA for 1979.

2. Roger Clemens's first year with the Boston Red Sox was 1984. During that season, he pitched 133.1 innings and gave up 64 earned runs. Calculate Clemens's ERA for 1984.

3. During the 2003 baseball season, Ben Sheets of the Milwaukee Brewers pitched 220.2 innings and gave up 109 earned runs. During the 2004 season, he gave up 71 earned runs and pitched 237.0 innings. During which season was his ERA lower? How much lower?

4. In 1987, Nolan Ryan had the lowest ERA of any pitcher in the major leagues. He gave up 65 earned runs and pitched 211.2 innings for the Houston Astros. Calculate Ryan's ERA for 1987.

5. Find the necessary statistics for a pitcher on your "home team," and calculate that pitcher's ERA.

Exercise Set 5.2

1. Provide two examples of situations in which unit rates are used.

2. Explain why unit rates are used to describe situations involving units such as miles per gallon.

3. What is the purpose of exchange rates in international trade?

4. Provide two examples of situations in which ratios are used.

5. Explain why ratios are used to describe situations involving information such as student-teacher ratios.

6. What does the phrase "the cross products are equal" mean?

7. Explain why the product of the means in a proportion equals the product of the extremes.

In Exercises 8–13, write the expression as a unit rate.

8. 582 miles in 12 hours

9. 138 miles on 6 gallons of gasoline

10. 544 words typed in 8 minutes

11. 100 meters in 8 seconds

12. $9100 for 350 shares of stock

13. 1000 square feet of wall covered with 2.5 gallons of paint

Solve Exercises 14–19.

14. **Wages** A machinist earns $490 for working a 35-hour week. What is the machinist's hourly rate of pay?

15. **Space Vehicles** Each of the Space Shuttle's solid rocket motors burns 680,400 kilograms of propellant in 2.5 minutes. How much propellant does each motor burn in 1 minute?

16. **Photography** During filming, an IMAX camera uses 65-mm film at a rate of 5.6 feet per second.

    a. At what rate per minute does the camera go through film?

    b. How quickly does the camera use a 500-foot roll of 65-mm film? Round to the nearest second.

17. **Consumerism** Which is the more economical purchase, a 32-ounce jar of mayonnaise for $2.79 or a 24-ounce jar of mayonnaise for $2.09?

18. **Consumerism** Which is the more economical purchase, an 18-ounce box of corn flakes for $2.89 or a 24-ounce box of corn flakes for $3.89?

19. **Wages** You have a choice of receiving a wage of $34,000 per year, $2840 per month, $650 per week, or $16.50 per hour. Which pay choice would you take? Assume a 40-hour work week and 52 weeks of work per year.

20. **Baseball** Baseball statisticians calculate a hitter's at-bats per home run by dividing the number of times the player has been at bat by the number of home runs the player has hit.

    a. Calculate the at-bats per home run for each player in the table on the following page. Round to the nearest tenth.

    b. Which player has the lowest rate of at-bats per home run? Which player has the second lowest rate?

    c. Why is this rate used for comparison rather than the number of home runs a player has hit?

Babe Ruth

Year	Baseball Player	Number of Times at Bat	Number of Home Runs Hit	Number of At-Bats per Home Run
1921	Babe Ruth	540	59	_____
1927	Babe Ruth	540	60	_____
1930	Hack Wilson	585	56	_____
1932	Jimmie Foxx	585	58	_____
1938	Hank Greenberg	556	58	_____
1961	Roger Maris	590	61	_____
1961	Mickey Mantle	514	54	_____
1964	Willie Mays	558	52	_____
1977	George Foster	615	52	_____
1998	Mark McGwire	509	70	_____
1998	Sammy Sosa	643	66	_____
2001	Barry Bonds	476	73	_____
2002	Alex Rodriguez	624	57	_____

21. **Population Density** The table below shows the population and area of three countries. The population density of a country is the number of people per square mile.

   a. Which country has the lowest population density?

   b. How many more people per square mile are there in India than in the United States? Round to the nearest whole number.

Country	Population	Area (in square miles)
Australia	19,626,000	2,938,000
India	1,067,018,000	1,146,000
United States	287,998,000	3,535,000

22. **E-mail** Forrester Research, Inc., compiled the following estimates on consumer use of e-mail in the United States.

   a. Complete the last column of the table on the following page by calculating the estimated number of messages per day that each user receives. Round to the nearest tenth.

   b. The predicted number of messages per person per day in 2005 is how many times the estimated number in 1993?

Year	Number of Users (in millions)	Messages per Day (in millions)	Messages per Person per Day
1993	8	17	_____
1997	55	150	_____
2001	135	500	_____
2005	170	5000	_____

Exchange Rates The table below shows the exchange rates per U.S. dollar for four foreign countries on July 2, 2004. Use this table for Exercises 23 to 26.

Exchange Rates per U.S. Dollar	
Australian Dollar	1.4021
Danish Krone	6.0374
Indian Rupee	45.650
Mexican Peso	11.443

23. How many Danish krona are equivalent to $10,000?

24. Find the number of Indian rupees that would be exchanged for $45,000.

25. Find the cost, in Mexican pesos, of an order of American computer hardware costing $38,000.

26. Calculate the cost, in Australian dollars, of an American car costing $29,000.

Health Researchers at the Centers for Disease Control and Prevention estimate that 5 million young people living today will die of tobacco-related diseases. Almost one-third of children who become regular smokers will die of a smoking-related illness such as heart disease or lung cancer. The table below shows, for eight states in our nation, the number of children under 18 who are expected to become smokers and the number who are projected to die of smoking-related illness. Use the table for Exercises 27 and 28.

State	Projected Number of Smokers	Projected Number of Deaths
Alabama	260,639	83,404
Alaska	56,246	17,999
Arizona	307,864	98,516
Arkansas	155,690	49,821
California	1,446,550	462,896
Colorado	271,694	86,942
Connecticut	175,501	56,160
Delaware	51,806	16,578

27. Find the ratio of the projected number of smokers in each state listed to the projected number of deaths. Round to the nearest thousandth. Write the ratio using the word *to*.

28. **a.** Did the researchers calculate different probabilities of death from smoking-related illnesses for each state?

    b. If the projected number of smokers in Florida is 928,464, what would you expect the researchers to project as the number of deaths from smoking-related illnesses in Florida?

Student–Faculty Ratios The table below shows the number of full-time men and women undergraduates and the number of full-time faculty at universities in the Big East. Use this table for Exercises 29 to 32. Round ratios to the nearest whole number. (*Source: Barron's Profile of American Colleges*, 26th edition, c. 2005)

University	Men	Women	Faculty
Boston College	6292	9756	1283
Georgetown University	2940	3386	655
Syracuse University	4722	6024	815
University of Connecticut	6762	7489	842
West Virginia University	8878	7665	1289

29. Calculate the student–faculty ratio at Syracuse University. Write the ratio using a colon and using the word *to*. What does this ratio mean?

30. Which school listed has the lowest student–faculty ratio?

31. Which school listed has the highest student–faculty ratio?

32. Which schools listed have the same student–faculty ratio?

33. **Debt–Equity Ratio** A bank uses the ratio of a borrower's total monthly debt to total monthly income to determine eligibility for a loan. This ratio is called the debt–equity ratio. First National Bank requires that a borrower have a debt–equity ratio that is less than $\frac{2}{5}$. Would the homeowner whose monthly income and debt are given below qualify for a loan using these standards?

Monthly Income (in dollars)		Monthly Debt (in dollars)	
Salary	3400	Mortgage	1800
Interest	83	Property tax	104
Rent	640	Insurance	27
Dividends	34	Credit cards	354
		Car loan	199

Solve Exercises 34–49. Round to the nearest hundredth.

34. $\dfrac{3}{8} = \dfrac{x}{12}$

35. $\dfrac{3}{y} = \dfrac{7}{40}$

36. $\dfrac{7}{12} = \dfrac{25}{d}$

37. $\dfrac{16}{d} = \dfrac{25}{40}$

38. $\dfrac{15}{45} = \dfrac{72}{c}$

39. $\dfrac{120}{c} = \dfrac{144}{25}$

40. $\dfrac{65}{20} = \dfrac{14}{a}$

41. $\dfrac{4}{a} = \dfrac{9}{5}$

42. $\dfrac{0.5}{2.3} = \dfrac{b}{20}$

43. $\dfrac{1.2}{2.8} = \dfrac{b}{32}$

44. $\dfrac{0.7}{1.2} = \dfrac{6.4}{x}$

45. $\dfrac{2.5}{0.6} = \dfrac{165}{x}$

46. $\dfrac{y}{6.25} = \dfrac{16}{87}$

47. $\dfrac{y}{2.54} = \dfrac{132}{640}$

48. $\dfrac{1.2}{0.44} = \dfrac{m}{14.2}$

49. $\dfrac{12.5}{m} = \dfrac{102}{55}$

Solve Exercises 50–61.

50. Gravity The ratio of weight on the moon to weight on Earth is $1:6$. How much would a 174-pound person weigh on the moon?

51. Management A management consulting firm recommends that the ratio of middle-management salaries to management trainee salaries be $5:4$. Using this recommendation, what is the annual middle-management salary if the annual management trainee salary is $36,000?

52. Gardening A gardening crew uses 2 pounds of fertilizer for every 100 square feet of lawn. At this rate, how many pounds of fertilizer does the crew use on a lawn that measures 2500 square feet?

53. Medication The dosage of a cold medication is 2 milligrams for every 80 pounds of body weight. How many milligrams of this medication are required for a person who weighs 220 pounds?

54. Fuel Consumption If your car can travel 70.5 miles on 3 gallons of gasoline, how far can the car travel on 14 gallons of gasoline?

55. Scale Drawings The scale on the architectural plans for a new house is 1 inch equals 3 feet. Find the length and width of a room that measures 5 inches by 8 inches on the drawing.

56. Scale Drawings The scale on a map is 1.25 inches equals 10 miles. Find the distance between Carlsbad and Del Mar, which are 2 inches apart on the map.

57. Elections A pre-election survey showed that two out of every three eligible voters would cast ballots in the county election. There are 240,000 eligible voters in the county. How many people are expected to vote in the election?

58. Interior Decorating A paint manufacturer suggests using 1 gallon of paint for every 400 square feet of wall. At this rate, how many gallons of paint would be required to paint a room that has 1400 square feet of wall?

59. Mileage Amanda Chicopee bought a new car and drove 7000 miles in the first four months. At the same rate, how many miles will Amanda drive in 3 years?

60. Lotteries Three people put their money together to buy lottery tickets. The first person put in $25, the second person put in $30, and the third person put in $35. One of their tickets was a winning ticket. If they won $4.5 million, what was the first person's share of the winnings?

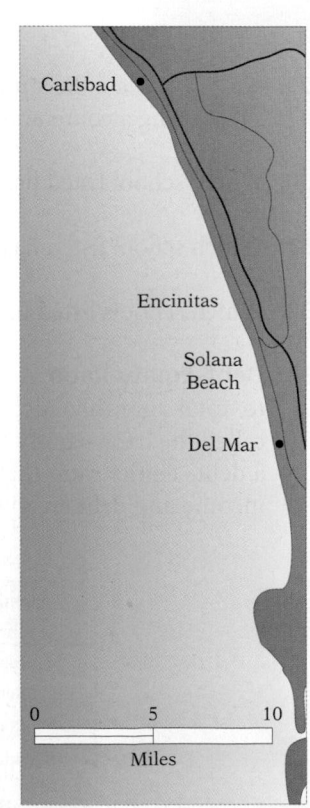

Carlsbad

Encinitas

Solana Beach

Del Mar

0   5   10

Miles

61. **Nutrition** A pancake 4 inches in diameter contains 5 grams of fat. How many grams of fat are in a pancake 6 inches in diameter? Explain how you arrived at your answer.

Extensions
CRITICAL THINKING

62. **Homicide Rates** For U.S. cities with populations over 100,000, those with the highest homicide rates in a recent year are listed below, along with the number of murders in each city and the homicide rate per 100,000 people. (*Source:* FBI Uniform Crime Reports)

a. Explain what the statistics for Atlanta mean.

b. What information not provided here was needed to calculate the homicide rates given for each city?

City	Total Number of Murders	Homicide Rate per 100,000 People
Washington	397	73
New Orleans	351	72
Richmond, VA	112	55
Atlanta	196	47
Baltimore	328	46

In Exercises 63 and 64, assume each denominator is a non-zero real number.

63. Determine whether the statement is true or false.

a. The quotient $a \div b$ is a ratio.   **b.** If $\dfrac{a}{b} = \dfrac{c}{d}$, then $\dfrac{b}{a} = \dfrac{d}{c}$.

c. If $\dfrac{a}{b} = \dfrac{c}{d}$, then $\dfrac{a}{c} = \dfrac{b}{d}$.   **d.** If $\dfrac{a}{b} = \dfrac{c}{d}$, then $\dfrac{a}{d} = \dfrac{c}{b}$.

64. If $\dfrac{a}{b} = \dfrac{c}{d}$, show that $\dfrac{a+b}{b} = \dfrac{c+d}{d}$.

COOPERATIVE LEARNING

65. **Advertising** Advertising rates for most daytime programs are lower than for shows aired during prime time. Advertising rates for widely popular sporting events are higher than for contests fewer people are interested in. In 2004, the cost of a 30-second advertisement during the Super Bowl was approximately $2.25 million! The rates vary because they are based on a cost per thousand viewers.

a. Explain why different time slots and different shows demand different advertising rates.

b. Why are advertisers concerned about the gender and age of the audience watching a particular program?

c. How do Nielsen ratings help determine what advertising rates can be charged for an ad airing during a particular program?

66. 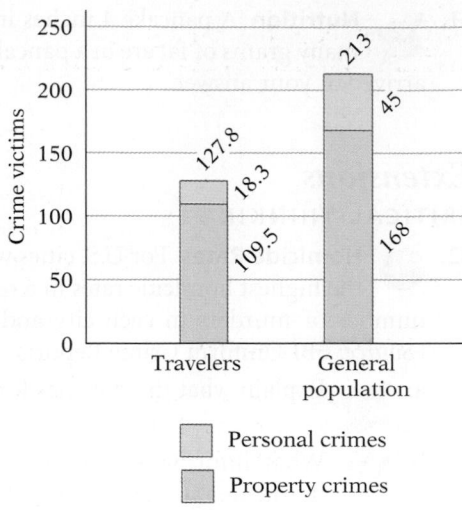 **Crime Rates** According to a recent study, the crime rate against travelers in the United States is lower than that against the general population. The article reporting this study included a bar graph similar to the one at the right.

a. Why are the figures reported based on crime victims per 1000 adults per year?

b. Use the given figures to write the proportion

$$\frac{\text{personal crimes against travelers}}{\text{property crimes against travelers}} = $$

$$\frac{\text{personal crimes against general population}}{\text{property crimes against general population}}$$

Is the proportion true?

c. Why might the crime rate against travelers be lower than that against the general population?

Crime Victims per 1000 Adults per Year

Source: Travel Industry Association of America

EXPLORATIONS

67. **The House of Representatives** The 50 states in the United States are listed below by their USPS two-letter abbreviations. The number following each state is the figure provided by the U.S. Bureau of the Census for the population of that state in 2000. Figures are in millions and are rounded to the nearest hundred thousand.

Populations of the 50 States in the United States, 2000 Census (in millions)				
AL 4.4	HI 1.2	MA 6.3	NM 1.8	SD 0.8
AK 0.6	ID 1.3	MI 9.9	NY 19.0	TN 5.7
AZ 5.1	IL 12.4	MN 4.9	NC 8.0	TX 20.9
AR 2.7	IN 6.1	MS 2.8	ND 0.6	UT 2.2
CA 33.9	IA 2.9	MO 5.6	OH 11.4	VT 0.6
CO 4.3	KS 2.7	MT 0.9	OK 3.5	VA 7.1
CT 3.4	KY 4.0	NE 1.7	OR 3.4	WA 5.9
DE 0.8	LA 4.5	NV 2.0	PA 12.3	WV 1.8
FL 16.0	ME 1.3	NH 1.2	RI 1.0	WI 5.4
GA 8.2	MD 5.3	NJ 8.4	SC 4.0	WY 0.5

The House of Representatives has a total of 435 members. These members represent the 50 states in proportion to each state's population. As stated in Article XIV, Section 2, of the Constitution of the United States, "Representatives shall be apportioned among the several states according to their respective numbers, counting the whole number of persons in each state." Based on the populations for the states given above, determine how many representatives each state should elect to Congress.

Compare your list against the actual number of representatives each state has. These numbers can be found in most almanacs.

Percents

An understanding of percent is vital to comprehending the events that take place in our world today. We are constantly confronted with phrases such as "unemployment of 5%," "annual inflation of 7%," "6% increase in fuel prices," "25% of the daily minimum requirement," and "increase in tuition and fees of 10%."

Percent means "for every 100." Therefore, unemployment of 5% means that 5 out of every 100 people are unemployed. An increase in tuition of 10% means that tuition has gone up $10 for every $100 it cost previously.

QUESTION   *When adults were asked to name their favorite cookie, 52% said chocolate chip. What does this statistic mean? (Source:* WEAREVER*)*

A percent is a ratio of a number to 100. Thus $\frac{1}{100} = 1\%$, $\frac{50}{100} = 50\%$, and $\frac{99}{100} = 99\%$. Because $1\% = \frac{1}{100}$ and $\frac{1}{100} = 0.01$, we can also write 1% as 0.01.

$$1\% = \frac{1}{100} = \mathbf{0.01}$$

The equivalence $1\% = 0.01$ is used to write a percent as a decimal or to write a decimal as a percent.

To write 17% as a decimal:

$$17\% = 17(1\%) = 17(0.01) = 0.17$$

Note that this is the same as removing the percent sign and moving the decimal point two places to the left.

To write 0.17 as a percent:

$$0.17 = 17(0.01) = 17(1\%) = 17\%$$

Note that this is the same as moving the decimal point two places to the right and writing a percent sign at the right of the number.

ANSWER   *52 out of every 100 people surveyed responded that their favorite cookie was chocolate chip. (In the same survey, the following responses were also given: oatmeal raisin, 10%; peanut butter, 9%; oatmeal, 7%; sugar, 4%; molasses, 4%; chocolate chip oatmeal, 3%.)*

EXAMPLE 1 ■ Write a Percent as a Decimal

Write the percent as a decimal.

a. 24%   **b.** 183%   **c.** 6.5%   **d.** 0.9%

Solution

To write a percent as a decimal, remove the percent sign and move the decimal point two places to the left.

a. 24% $=$ 0.24

b. 183% $=$ 1.83

c. 6.5% $=$ 0.065

d. 0.9% $=$ 0.009

CHECK YOUR PROGRESS 1   Write the percent as a decimal.

a. 74%   **b.** 152%   **c.** 8.3%   **d.** 0.6%

Solution   See page S19.

point of interest

According to a Pathfinder Research Group survey, more than 94% of adults have heard of the Three Stooges. The choices of a favorite, among those who have one, were:

Curly: 52%
Moe: 31%
Larry: 12%
Curly Joe: 3%
Shemp: 2%

EXAMPLE 2 ■ Write a Decimal as a Percent

Write the decimal as a percent.

a. 0.62   **b.** 1.5   **c.** 0.059   **d.** 0.008

Solution

To write a decimal as a percent, move the decimal point two places to the right and write a percent sign.

a. 0.62 $=$ 62%

b. 1.5 $=$ 150%

c. 0.059 $=$ 5.9%

d. 0.008 $=$ 0.8%

CHECK YOUR PROGRESS 2   Write the decimal as a percent.

a. 0.3   **b.** 1.65   **c.** 0.072   **d.** 0.004

Solution   See page S19.

The equivalence 1% $= \frac{1}{100}$ is used to write a percent as a fraction. To write 16% as a fraction:

$$16\% = 16(1\%) = 16\left(\frac{1}{100}\right) = \frac{16}{100} = \frac{4}{25}$$

Note that this is the same as removing the percent sign and multiplying by $\frac{1}{100}$. The fraction is written in simplest form.

EXAMPLE 3 ■ Write a Percent as a Fraction

Write the percent as a fraction.

a. 25%   **b.** 120%   **c.** 7.5%   **d.** $33\frac{1}{3}\%$

Solution
To write a percent as a fraction, remove the percent sign and multiply by $\frac{1}{100}$. Then write the fraction in simplest form.

a. $25\% = 25\left(\frac{1}{100}\right) = \frac{25}{100} = \frac{1}{4}$

b. $120\% = 120\left(\frac{1}{100}\right) = \frac{120}{100} = 1\frac{20}{100} = 1\frac{1}{5}$

c. $7.5\% = 7.5\left(\frac{1}{100}\right) = \frac{7.5}{100} = \frac{75}{1000} = \frac{3}{40}$

d. $33\frac{1}{3}\% = \frac{100}{3}\% = \frac{100}{3}\left(\frac{1}{100}\right) = \frac{1}{3}$

CHECK YOUR PROGRESS 3   Write the percent as a fraction.

a. 8%   **b.** 180%   **c.** 2.5%   **d.** $66\frac{2}{3}\%$

Solution   *See page S19.*

To write a fraction as a percent, first write the fraction as a decimal. Then write the decimal as a percent.

EXAMPLE 4 ■ Write a Fraction as a Percent

Write the fraction as a percent.

a. $\frac{3}{4}$ **b.** $\frac{5}{8}$ **c.** $\frac{1}{6}$ **d.** $1\frac{1}{2}$

Solution
To write a fraction as a percent, write the fraction as a decimal. Then write the decimal as a percent.

a. $\frac{3}{4} = 0.75 = 75\%$

b. $\frac{5}{8} = 0.625 = 62.5\%$

c. $\frac{1}{6} = 0.16\overline{6} = 16.\overline{6}\%$

d. $1\frac{1}{2} = 1.5 = 150\%$

✓ TAKE NOTE

To write a fraction as a decimal, divide the number in the numerator by the number in the denominator. For example,

$$\frac{4}{5} = 4 \div 5 = 0.8.$$

CHECK YOUR PROGRESS 4   Write the fraction as a percent.

a. $\dfrac{1}{4}$ **b.** $\dfrac{3}{8}$ **c.** $\dfrac{5}{6}$ **d.** $1\dfrac{2}{3}$

Solution   *See page S19.*

Math Matters   College Graduates' Job Expectations

The table below shows the expectations of a recent class of college graduates. (*Source:* Yankelovich Partners for Phoenix Home Life Mutual Insurance)

	Men	Women
Expect a job by graduation	31%	23%
Expect a job within 6 months	32%	23%
Expect a starting pay of $30,000 or more	55%	43%
Expect to be richer than their parents	64%	59%

Percent Problems: The Proportion Method

Finding the solution of an application problem involving percent generally requires writing and solving an equation. Two methods of writing the equation will be developed in this section—the *proportion method* and the *basic percent equation*. We will present the proportion method first.

The proportion method of solving a percent problem is based on writing two ratios. One ratio is the percent ratio, written $\dfrac{\text{percent}}{100}$. The second ratio is the amount-to-base ratio, written $\dfrac{\text{amount}}{\text{base}}$. These two ratios form the proportion used to solve percent problems.

The Proportion Used to Solve Percent Problems

$$\frac{\text{Percent}}{100} = \frac{\text{amount}}{\text{base}}$$

Diagram of the Proportion Method
of Solving Percent Problems

The proportion method can be illustrated by a diagram. The rectangle at the left is divided into two parts. On the left, the whole rectangle is represented by 100 and the part by percent. On the right, the whole rectangle is represented by the *base* and the part by the *amount*. The ratio of percent to 100 is equal to the ratio of the amount to the base.

When solving a percent problem, first identify the percent, the base, and the amount. It is helpful to know that the base usually follows the phrase "percent of."

QUESTION   In the statement "15% of 40 is 6," which number is the percent? Which number is the base? Which number is the amount?

EXAMPLE 5 ■ Solve a Percent Problem for the Base Using the Proportion Method

The average size of a house in 2003 was 2137 square feet. This is approximately 130% of the average size of a house in 1979. What was the average size of a house in 1979? Round to the nearest whole number.

Solution

We want to answer the question "130% of what number is 2137?" Write and solve a proportion. The percent is 130%. The amount is 2137. The base is the average size of a house in 1979.

$$\frac{\text{Percent}}{100} = \frac{\text{amount}}{\text{base}}$$

$$\frac{130}{100} = \frac{2137}{B}$$

$$130 \cdot B = 100(2137)$$

$$130B = 213,700$$

$$\frac{130B}{130} = \frac{213,700}{130}$$

$$B \approx 1644$$

The average size of a house in 1979 was 1644 square feet.

CHECK YOUR PROGRESS 5   A used Chevrolet Blazer was purchased for $22,400. This was 70% of the cost of the Blazer when new. What was the cost of the Blazer when it was new?

Solution   *See page S19.*

▼ **point of interest**

According to the U.S. Department of Agriculture, of the 356 billion pounds of food produced annually in the United States, about 96 billion pounds are wasted. This is approximately 27% of all the food produced in the United States.

EXAMPLE 6 ■ Solve a Percent Problem for the Percent Using the Proportion Method

During 1996, Texas suffered through one of its longest droughts in history. Of the $5 billion in losses caused by the drought, $1.1 billion was direct losses to ranchers. What percent of the total losses was direct losses to ranchers?

ANSWER   *The percent is 15. The base is 40. (It follows the phrase "percent of.") The amount is 6.*

Solution

We want to answer the question "What percent of $5 billion is $1.1 billion?" Write and solve a proportion. The base is $5 billion. The amount is $1.1 billion. The percent is unknown.

$$\frac{\text{Percent}}{100} = \frac{\text{amount}}{\text{base}}$$

$$\frac{p}{100} = \frac{1.1}{5}$$

$$p \cdot 5 = 100(1.1)$$

$$5p = 110$$

$$\frac{5p}{5} = \frac{110}{5}$$

$$p = 22$$

Direct losses to ranchers represent 22% of the total losses.

CHECK YOUR PROGRESS 6

Of the approximately 1,300,000 enlisted women and men in the U.S. military, 416,000 are over the age of 30. What percent of the enlisted people are over the age of 30?

Solution   *See page S19.*

EXAMPLE 7 ■ Solve a Percent Problem for the Amount Using the Proportion Method

In a certain year, Blockbuster Video customers rented 24% of the approximately 3.7 billion videos rented that year. How many million videos did Blockbuster Video rent that year?

Solution

We want to answer the question "24% of 3.7 billion is what number?" Write and solve a proportion. The percent is 24%. The base is 3.7 billion. The amount is the number of videos Blockbuster Video rented during the year.

$$\frac{\text{Percent}}{100} = \frac{\text{amount}}{\text{base}}$$

$$\frac{24}{100} = \frac{A}{3.7}$$

$$24(3.7) = 100(A)$$

$$88.8 = 100A$$

$$\frac{88.8}{100} = \frac{100A}{100}$$

$$0.888 = A$$

The number 0.888 is in billions. We need to convert it to millions.

0.888 billion = 888 million

Blockbuster Video rented approximately 888 million videos that year.

CHECK YOUR PROGRESS 7   A General Motors buyers' incentive program offered a 3.5% rebate on the selling price of a new car. What rebate would a customer receive who purchased a $32,500 car under this program?

Solution   *See page S19.*

Percent Problems: The Basic Percent Equation

A second method of solving a percent problem is to use the basic percent equation.

> **The Basic Percent Equation**
>
> $PB = A$, where P is the percent, B is the base, and A is the amount.

When solving a percent problem using the proportion method, we have to first identify the percent, the base, and the amount. The same is true when solving percent problems using the basic percent equation. Remember that the base usually follows the phrase "percent of."

When using the basic percent equation, the percent must be written as a decimal or a fraction. This is illustrated in Example 8.

EXAMPLE 8 ■ **Solve a Percent Problem for the Amount Using the Basic Percent Equation**

A real estate broker receives a commission of 3% of the selling price of a house. Find the amount the broker receives on the sale of a $275,000 home.

Solution
We want to answer the question "3% of $275,000 is what number?" Use the basic percent equation. The percent is 3% = 0.03. The base is 275,000. The amount is the amount the broker receives on the sale of the home.

$$PB = A$$
$$0.03(275,000) = A$$
$$8250 = A$$

The real estate broker receives a commission of $8250 on the sale.

CHECK YOUR PROGRESS 8   New Hampshire public school teachers contribute 5% of their wages to the New Hampshire Retirement System. What amount is contributed during one year by a teacher whose annual salary is $32,685?

Solution   *See page S19.*

EXAMPLE 9 ▪ Solve a Percent Problem for the Base Using the Basic Percent Equation

An investor received a payment of $480, which was 12% of the value of the investment. Find the value of the investment.

Solution
We want to answer the question "12% of what number is 480?" Use the basic percent equation. The percent is 12% = 0.12. The amount is 480. The base is the value of the investment.

$$PB = A$$
$$0.12B = 480$$
$$\frac{0.12B}{0.12} = \frac{480}{0.12}$$
$$B = 4000$$

The value of the investment is $4000.

CHECK YOUR PROGRESS 9   A real estate broker receives a commission of 3% of the selling price of a house. Find the selling price of a home on whose sale the broker received a commission of $14,370.

Solution   See page S19.

EXAMPLE 10 ▪ Solve a Percent Problem for the Percent Using the Basic Percent Equation

If you answer 96 questions correctly on a 120-question exam, what percent of the questions did you answer correctly?

Solution
We want to answer the question "What percent of 120 questions is 96 questions?" Use the basic percent equation. The base is 120. The amount is 96. The percent is unknown.

$$PB = A$$
$$P \cdot 120 = 96$$
$$\frac{P \cdot 120}{120} = \frac{96}{120}$$
$$P = 0.8$$
$$P = 80\%$$

You answered 80% of the questions correctly.

CHECK YOUR PROGRESS 10   If you answer 63 questions correctly on a 90-question exam, what percent of the questions did you answer correctly?

Solution   See page S19.

The table below shows the average cost in the United States for five of the most popular home remodeling projects and the average percent of that cost recouped when the home is sold. Use this table for Example 11 and Check Your Progress 11. (*Source:* National Association of Home Builders)

Home Remodeling Project	Average Cost	Percent Recouped
Addition to the master suite	$36,472	84%
Attic bedroom	$22,840	84%
Major kitchen remodeling	$21,262	90%
Bathroom addition	$11,645	91%
Minor kitchen remodeling	$8,507	94%

point of interest

According to Campus Concepts, two-thirds of college students say they have a job. Their average earnings per month:
  Less than $100: 4%
  $100–199: 10%
  $200–299: 13%
  $300–399: 12%
  $400–499: 11%
  $500 or more: 17%

EXAMPLE 11 ■ Solve an Application Using the Basic Percent Equation

 Find the difference between the cost of adding an attic bedroom to your home and the amount by which the addition increases the sale price of your home.

Solution

The cost of building the attic bedroom is $22,840, and the sale price increases by 84% of that amount. We need to find the difference between $22,840 and 84% of $22,840.

Use the basic percent equation to find 84% of $22,840. The percent is 84% = 0.84. The base is 22,840. The amount is unknown.

$$PB = A$$
$$0.84(22,840) = A$$
$$19,185.60 = A$$

Subtract 19,185.60 (the amount of the cost that is recouped when the home is sold) from 22,840 (the cost of building the attic bedroom).

$$22,840 - 19,185.60 = 3654.40$$

The difference between the cost of the addition and the increase in value of your home is $3654.40.

CHECK YOUR PROGRESS 11

Find the difference between the cost of a major kitchen remodeling in your home and the amount by which the remodeling increases the sale price of your home.

Solution   *See page S20.*

Percent Increase

When a family moves from one part of the country to another, they are concerned about the difference in the cost of living. Will food, housing, and gasoline cost more in that part of the country? Will they need a larger salary in order to make ends meet?

We can use one number to represent the increased cost of living from one city to another so that no matter what salary you make, you can determine how much you will need to earn in order to maintain the same standard of living. That one number is a percent.

For example, look at the information in the table below. (*Source:* **www .homefair.com/homefair/cmr/salcalc.html**)

If you live in	and are moving to	you will need to make this percent of your current salary
Cincinnati, Ohio	San Francisco, California	236%
St. Louis, Missouri	Boston, Massachusetts	213%
Denver, Colorado	New York, New York	239%

A family in Cincinnati living on $60,000 per year would need 236% of their current income to maintain the same standard of living in San Francisco. Likewise, a family living on $150,000 per year would need 236% of their current income.

$$60,000(2.36) = 141,600 \qquad 150,000(2.36) = 354,000$$

The family from Cincinnati living on $60,000 would need an annual income of $141,600 in San Francisco to maintain their standard of living. The family living on $150,000 would need an annual income of $354,000 in San Francisco to maintain their standard of living.

We have used one number, 236%, to represent the increase in the cost of living from Cincinnati to San Francisco. No matter what a family's present income, they can use 236% to determine their necessary comparable income.

QUESTION *How much would a family in Denver, Colorado living on $55,000 per year need in New York City to maintain a comparable lifestyle? Use the table above.*

The percent used to determine the increase in the cost of living is a *percent increase*. **Percent increase** is used to show how much a quantity has increased over its original value. Statements that illustrate the use of percent increase include "sales volume increased by 11% over last year's sales volume" and "employees received an 8% pay increase."

The **federal debt** is the amount the government owes after borrowing the money it needs to pay for its expenses. It is considered a good measure of how much of the government's spending is financed by debt as opposed to taxation. The graph below shows the federal debt, according to the U.S. Department of the Treasury, at the end of the fiscal years 1980, 1985, 1990, 1995, and 2000. A fiscal year is the 12-month period that the annual budget spans, from October 1 to September 30. Use the graph for Example 12 and Check Your Progress 12.

Amount of increase

Original value

New value

ANSWER *In New York City, the family would need $55,000(2.39) = $131,450 per year to maintain a comparable lifestyle.*

historical note

The largest percent increase, for a single day, in the Dow Jones Industrial Average occurred on October 6, 1931. The Dow gained approximately 15% of its value. ∎

EXAMPLE 12 ■ Solve an Application Involving Percent Increase

 Find the percent increase in the federal debt from 1980 to 1995. Round to the nearest tenth of a percent.

Solution

Calculate the amount of increase in the federal debt from 1980 to 1995.

$$4.97 - 0.91 = 4.06$$

We will use the basic percent equation. (The proportion method could also be used.) The base is the debt in 1980. The amount is the amount of increase in the debt. The percent is unknown.

$$PB = A$$

$$P \cdot 0.91 = 4.06$$

$$\frac{P \cdot 0.91}{0.91} = \frac{4.06}{0.91}$$

$$P \approx 4.462$$

The percent increase in the federal debt from 1980 to 1995 was 446.2%.

CHECK YOUR PROGRESS 12

 Find the percent increase in the federal debt from 1985 to 2000. Round to the nearest tenth of a percent.

Solution   *See page S20.*

Notice in Example 12 that the percent increase is a measure of the *amount of increase* over an *original value*. Therefore, in the basic percent equation, the amount A is the *amount of increase* and the base B is the *original value*, in this case the debt in 1980.

Percent Decrease

The federal debt is not the same as the federal deficit. The **federal deficit** is the amount by which government spending exceeds the federal budget. The table below shows projected federal deficits. (*Source:* U.S. Government Office of Management and Budget) Note that the deficit listed for 2006 is less than the deficit listed for 2005.

Year	Federal Deficit
2005	$363.570 billion
2006	$267.632 billion
2007	$241.272 billion
2008	$238.969 billion
2009	$237.076 billion

The decrease in the federal deficit can be expressed as a percent. First find the amount of decrease in the deficit from 2005 to 2006.

$$363.570 - 267.632 = 95.938$$

We will use the basic percent equation to find the percent. The base is the deficit in 2005. The amount is the amount of decrease.

$$PB = A$$

$$P \cdot 363.57 = 95.938$$

$$\frac{P \cdot 363.57}{363.57} = \frac{95.938}{363.57}$$

$$P \approx 0.264$$

The federal deficit is projected to decrease by 26.4% from 2005 to 2006.

The percent used to measure the decrease in the federal deficit is a *percent decrease*. **Percent decrease** is used to show how much a quantity has decreased from its original value. Statements that illustrate the use of percent decrease include "the president's approval rating has decreased 9% over last month" and "there has been a 15% decrease in the number of industrial accidents."

Note in the deficit example above that the percent decrease is a measure of the *amount of decrease* over an *original value*. Therefore, in the basic percent equation, the amount A is the *amount of decrease* and the base B is the *original value*, in this case the deficit in 2005.

EXAMPLE 13 ■ Solve an Application Involving Percent Decrease

In 1994, the average price per mile of flight on a commercial airplane was $.16. From 1994 to 2002, that price decreased 25%. (*Source:* U.S. Transportation Department; Air Transport Association) Find the average price per mile of flight in 2002.

Solution

We will write and solve a proportion. (The basic percent equation could also be used.) The percent is 25%. The base is $.16. The amount is unknown.

$$\frac{\text{Percent}}{100} = \frac{\text{amount}}{\text{base}}$$

$$\frac{25}{100} = \frac{A}{0.16}$$

$$25(0.16) = 100 \cdot A$$

$$4 = 100A$$

$$\frac{4}{100} = \frac{100A}{100}$$

$$0.04 = A$$

Subtract the decrease in price from the average price per mile in 1994.

$$0.16 - 0.04 = 0.12$$

The average price per mile of flight in 2002 was $.12.

CHECK YOUR PROGRESS 13

 The number of passenger car fatalities in the United States in 2002 was 20,416. This number decreased 3.81% in 2003. (*Source: Time*, May 10, 2004) Find the number of passenger car fatalities in the United States in 2003.

Solution   *See page S20.*

Excursion

Federal Income Tax

Income taxes are the chief source of revenue for the federal government. If you are employed, your employer probably withholds some money from each of your paychecks for federal income tax. At the end of each year, your employer sends you a **Wage and Tax Statement Form (W-2 form)**, which states the amount of money you earned that year and how much was withheld for taxes.

Every employee is required by law to prepare an income tax return by April 15 of each year and send it to the Internal Revenue Service (IRS). On the income tax return, you must report your total income, or **gross income.** Then you subtract from the gross income any adjustments (such as deductions for charitable contributions or exemptions for people who are dependent on your income) to determine your **adjusted gross income.** You use your adjusted gross income and either a tax table or a tax rate schedule to determine your **tax liability,** or the amount of income you owe to the federal government.

After calculating your tax liability, compare it with the amount withheld for federal income tax, as shown on your W-2 form. If the tax liability is less than the amount withheld, you are entitled to a tax refund. If the tax liability is greater than the amount withheld, you owe the IRS money; you have a **balance due.**

The 2004 Tax Rate Schedules table is shown on page 296. To use this table for the exercises that follow, first classify the taxpayer as single, married filing jointly, or married filing separately. Then determine into which range the adjusted gross income falls. Then perform the calculations shown to the right of that range to determine the tax liability.

For example, consider a taxpayer who is single and has an adjusted gross income of $48,720. To find this taxpayer's tax liability, use the portion of the table headed "Schedule X" for taxpayers whose filing status is single.

An income of $48,720 falls in the range $29,050 to $70,350. The tax is $4000.00 + 25% of the amount over $29,050. Find the amount over $29,050.

$$\$48{,}720 - \$29{,}050 = \$19{,}670$$

(continued)

Calculate the tax liability:

$$\$4000.00 + 25\%(\$19{,}670) = \$4000.00 + 0.25(\$19{,}670)$$
$$= \$4000.00 + \$4917.50$$
$$= \$8917.50$$

The taxpayer's liability is $8917.50.

2004 Tax Rate Schedules

Single—Schedule X

If line 5 is: Over—	But not over—	The tax is:	of the amount over—
$0	$7,150	... 10%	$0
7,150	29,050	$715.00 + 15%	7,150
29,050	70,350	4,000.00 + 25%	29,050
70,350	146,750	14,325.00 + 28%	70,350
146,750	319,100	35,717.00 + 33%	146,750
319,100	...	92,592.50 + 35%	319,100

Married filing jointly or Qualifying widow(er)—Schedule Y-1

If line 5 is: Over—	But not over—	The tax is:	of the amount over—
$0	$14,300	... 10%	$0
14,300	58,100	$1,430.00 + 15%	14,300
58,100	117,250	8,000.00 + 25%	58,100
117,250	178,650	22,787.50 + 28%	117,250
178,650	319,100	39,979.50 + 33%	178,650
319,100	...	86,328.00 + 35%	319,100

Married filing separately—Schedule Y-2

If line 5 is: Over—	But not over—	The tax is:	of the amount over—
$0	$7,150	... 10%	$0
7,150	29,050	$715.00 + 15%	7,150
29,050	58,625	4,000.00 + 25%	29,050
58,625	89,325	11,393.75 + 28%	58,625
89,325	159,550	19,989.75 + 33%	89,325
159,550	...	43,164.00 + 35%	159,550

(continued)

Excursion Exercises

Use the 2004 Tax Rate Schedules to solve Exercises 1–8.

1. Joseph Abruzzio is married and filing separately. He has an adjusted gross income of $63,850. Find Joseph's tax liability.

2. Angela Lopez is single and has an adjusted gross income of $31,680. Find Angela's tax liability.

3. Dee Pinckney is married and filing jointly. She has an adjusted gross income of $58,120. The W-2 form shows the amount withheld as $7124. Find Dee's tax liability and determine her tax refund or balance due.

4. Jeremy Littlefield is single and has an adjusted gross income of $72,800. His W-2 form lists the amount withheld as $18,420. Find Jeremy's tax liability and determine his tax refund or balance due.

5. Does a taxpayer in the 33% tax bracket pay 33% of his or her earnings in income tax? Explain your answer.

6. A single taxpayer has an adjusted gross income of $154,000. On what amount of the $154,000 does the taxpayer pay 33% to the Internal Revenue Service?

7. In the table for single taxpayers, how were the figures $715.00 and $4000.00 arrived at?

8. In the table for married persons filing jointly, how were the figures $1430.00 and $8000.00 arrived at?

Exercise Set 5.3

1. Name three situations in which percent is used.

2. Explain why multiplying a number by 100% does not change the value of the number.

3. Multiplying a number by 300% is the same as multiplying it by what whole number?

4. Describe each ratio in the proportion used to solve a percent problem.

5. Employee A had an annual salary of $32,000, Employee B had an annual salary of $38,000, and Employee C had an annual salary of $36,000 before each employee was given a 5% raise. Which of the three employees' annual salaries is now the highest? Explain how you arrived at your answer.

6. Each of three employees earned an annual salary of $35,000 before Employee A was given a 3% raise, Employee B was given a 6% raise, and Employee C was given a 4.5% raise. Which of the three employees' annual salaries is now the highest? Explain how you arrived at your answer.

Complete the table of equivalent fractions, decimals, and percents.

	Fraction	Decimal	Percent
7.	$\frac{1}{2}$		
8.		0.75	
9.			40%
10.	$\frac{3}{8}$		
11.		0.7	
12.			56.25%
13.	$\frac{11}{20}$		
14.		0.52	
15.			15.625%
16.	$\frac{9}{50}$		

17. **Baseball** In 1997, for the first time in major league baseball's history, interleague baseball games were played during the regular season. According to a Harris Poll, 73% of fans approved and 20% of fans disapproved of the change.

   a. How many fans, out of every 100 surveyed, approved of interleague games?

   b. Did more fans approve or disapprove of the change?

   c. Fans surveyed gave one of three responses: approve, disapprove, or don't know. What percent of the fans surveyed responded that they didn't know? Explain how you calculated the percent.

Solve Exercises 18–34.

18. **Income Tax** In 2004, 34.2 million accountants e-filed income tax returns. This was 114% of the number who e-filed in 2003. (*Source:* Internal Revenue Service) Find the number of accountants who e-filed income tax returns in 2003.

19. **Charitable Contributions** During a recent year, charitable contributions in the United States totaled $190 billion. The graph at the right shows to whom this money was donated. Determine how much money was donated to educational organizations. (*Source:* Giving USA 2000/AAFRC Trust for Philanthropy)

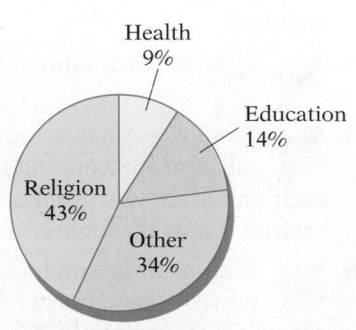

Health
9%

Education
14%

Religion
43%

Other
34%

Recipients of Charitable Contributions in the United States

20. **Health Insurance** Of the 44 million people in the United States who do not have health insurance, 13.2 million are between the ages of 18 and 24. What percent of the people in the United States who do not have health insurance are between the ages of 18 and 24? (*Source:* U.S. Census Bureau)

21. **Motorists** A survey of 1236 adults nationwide asked, "What irks you most about the actions of other motorists?" The response "tailgaters" was given by 293 people. What percent of those surveyed were most irked by tailgaters? Round to the nearest tenth of a percent. (*Source:* Reuters/Zogby)

22. **Television** A survey by the *Boston Globe* questioned elementary and middle-school students about television. Sixty-eight students, or 42.5% of those surveyed, said that they had a television in their bedrooms at home. How many students were included in the survey?

23. a. **Vacations** Women who are planning a 7-day vacation budget an average of $290 for meals. This is 21.0% of the total amount budgeted for the trip. What is the total amount women budget for a week's vacation? Round to the nearest dollar.

b. Men who are planning a 7-day vacation budget an average of $438 for lodging. This is 26.9% of the total amount budgeted for the trip. What is the total amount men budget for a week's vacation? Round to the nearest dollar. (*Source:* American Express Travel Index)

24. **Pets** The average costs associated with owning a dog over its average 11-year life span are shown in the graph at the right. These costs do not include the price of the puppy when purchased. The category labeled "Other" includes such expenses as fencing and repairing furniture damaged by the pet.

a. Calculate the total of all the expenses.

b. What percent of the total is each category? Round to the nearest tenth of a percent.

c. If the price of the puppy were included in these data, how would it affect the percents you calculated in part b?

d. What does it mean to say that these are average costs?

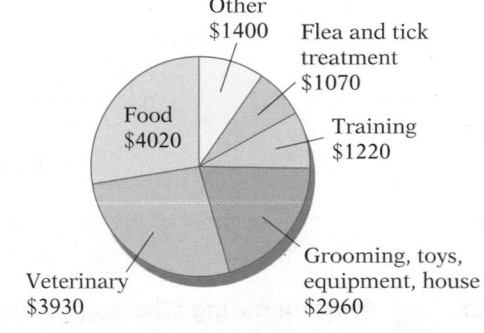

Cost of Owning a Dog

Source: American Kennel Club, *USA Today* research

25. **Time Management** The two circle graphs show how surveyed employees actually spend their time and how they would prefer to spend their time. Assume that employees have 112 hours a week that are not spent sleeping. Round answers to the nearest tenth of an hour. (*Source: Wall Street Journal* Supplement from *Families and Work Institute*)

a. What is the actual number of hours per week that employees spend with family and friends?

b. What is the number of hours that employees would prefer to spend on their jobs or careers?

c. What is the difference between the number of hours an employee would prefer to spend on him- or herself and the actual amount of time the employee spends on him- or herself?

26. **Prison Inmates** The graph below shows the number of prison inmates in the United States for the years 1990, 1995, and 2000.

  a. What percent of the number of state inmates is the number of federal inmates in 1990? in 2000? Round to the nearest tenth of a percent.

  b. If the ratio of federal inmates to state inmates in 1990 had remained constant, how many state inmates would there have been in 2000, when there were 145,416 federal inmates? Is this more or less than the actual number of state inmates in 2000? Does this mean that the number of federal inmates is growing at a more rapid rate or that the number of state inmates is growing at a more rapid rate?

  c. Explain how parts a and b are two methods of measuring the same change.

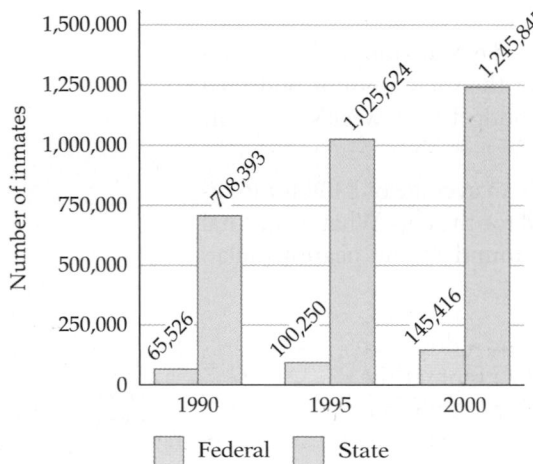

Number of Inmates in the United States

Source: Bureau of Justice Statistics

27. **Telecommuting** The graph below shows the projected growth in the number of telecommuters.

  a. During which 2-year period is the percent increase in the number of telecommuters the greatest?

  b. During which 2-year period is the percent increase in the number of telecommuters the lowest?

  c. Does the growth in telecommuting increase more slowly or more rapidly as we move from 1998 to 2006?

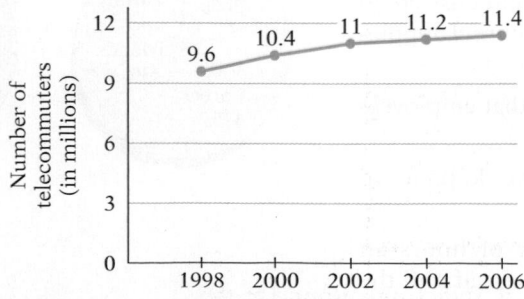

Projected Growth in Telecommuting

28. ⬤ **Highway Fatalities** In a recent year, the states listed below had the highest rates of truck-crash fatalities. (*Source:* Citizens for Reliable and Safe Highways)

State	Number of Truck-Crash Fatalities	Number of Truck-Crash Fatalities per 100,000 People
Alabama	160	3.76
Arkansas	102	4.11
Idaho	38	3.27
Iowa	86	3.10
Mississippi	123	4.56
Montana	30	3.45
West Virginia	53	2.90
Wyoming	17	3.54

a. What state has the highest rate of truck-crash deaths?

For each of the following states, find the population to the nearest thousand people. Calculate the percent of the population of each state that died in truck accidents. Round to the nearest hundred thousandth of a percent.

b. Mississippi

c. West Virginia

d. Montana

e. Compare the percents in parts b, c, and d to the numbers of truck-crash fatalities per 100,000 people listed in the table. Based on your observations, what percent of the population of Idaho do you think was killed in truck accidents?

f. ✎ Explain the relationship between the rates in the table and the percents you calculated.

29. ⬤ **High-Tech Employees** The table below lists the states with the highest rates of high-tech employees per 1000 workers. High-tech employees are those employed in the computer and electronics industries. Also provided is the civilian labor force for each of these states. (*Source:* American Electronics Association; U.S. Bureau of Labor Statistics)

State	High-Tech Employees per 1000 Workers	Labor Force
Arizona	53	2,229,300
California	62	10,081,300
Colorado	75	2,200,500
Maryland	51	2,798,400
Massachusetts	75	3,291,100
Minnesota	55	4,173,500
New Hampshire	78	663,000
New Jersey	55	4,173,500
Vermont	52	332,200
Virginia	52	3,575,000

a. Find the number of high-tech employees in each state listed. Round to the nearest whole number.

b. Which state has the highest rate of high-tech employment? Which state has the largest number of high-tech employees?

c. The computer and electronics industries employ approximately 4 million workers. Do more or less than half of the high-tech employees work in the 10 states listed in the table?

d. What percent of the state's labor force is employed in the computer and electronics industries in Massachusetts? in New Jersey? in Virginia? Round to the nearest tenth of a percent.

e. Compare your answers to part d with the numbers of high-tech employees per 1000 workers listed in the table. Based on your observations, what percent of the labor force in Arizona is employed in the high-tech industries?

f. Explain the relationship between the rates in the table and the percents you calculated.

30. Consumption of Eggs During the last 40 years, the consumption of eggs in the United States has decreased by 35%. Forty years ago, the average consumption was 400 eggs per person per year. What is the average consumption of eggs today?

31. Millionaire Households The table at the right shows the estimated number of millionaire households in the United States for selected years.

Year	Number of Households Containing Millionaires
1975	350,000
1997	3,500,000
2005	5,600,000

a. What is the percent increase in the estimated number of millionaire households from 1975 to 1997?

b. Find the percent increase in the estimated number of millionaire households from 1997 to 2005.

c. Find the percent increase in the estimated number of millionaire households from 1975 to 2005.

d. Provide an explanation for the dramatic increase in the estimated number of millionaire households from 1975 to 2005.

32. Demographics The graph at the right shows the projected growth of the number of Americans aged 85 and older.

a. What is the percent increase in the population of this age group from 1995 to 2030?

b. What is the percent increase in the population of this age group from 2030 to 2050?

c. What is the percent increase in the population of this age group from 1995 to 2050?

d. How many times larger is the population in 2050 than in 1995? How could you determine this number from the answer to part c?

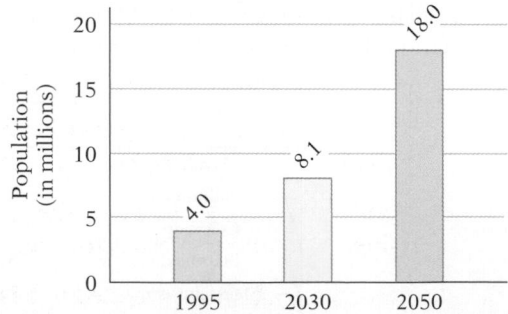

Projected Growth (in millions) of the Population of Americans Aged 85 and Older

Source: U.S. Census Bureau

33. Occupations The Bureau of Labor Statistics provides information on the fastest-growing occupations in this country. These are listed in the table on the following page, along with the predicted percent increase in employment from 2000 to 2010.

Occupation	Employment in 2000	Percent Increase 2000–2010
Software engineers (applications)	380,000	100%
Computer support specialists	506,000	97%
Software engineers (systems)	317,000	90%
Network and computer systems administrators	229,000	82%
Network and data communications analysts	119,000	77%
Desktop publishers	38,000	67%
Database administrators	106,000	66%
Personal and home care aides	414,000	62%
Computer systems analysts	431,000	60%
Medical assistants	329,000	57%
Social and human service assistants	271,000	54%
Physician assistants	58,000	53%
Medical records/health information technicians	136,000	49%
Computer and information systems managers	313,000	48%
Home health aides	615,000	47%
Physical therapist aides	36,000	46%
Occupational therapist aides	9,000	45%
Physical therapist assistants	44,000	45%
Audiologists	13,000	45%
Fitness trainers and aerobics instructors	158,000	40%
Computer and information scientists (research)	28,000	40%
Occupational therapist assistants	17,000	40%
Veterinary and laboratory animal assistants	55,000	40%
Speech–language pathologists	88,000	39%
Mental health/substance abuse social workers	83,000	39%
Dental assistants	247,000	37%
Dental hygienists	147,000	37%
Teachers	234,000	37%
Pharmacy technicians	190,000	36%

a. Which occupation employed the largest number of people in 2000?

b. Which occupation is expected to have the largest percent increase in employment between 2000 and 2010?

c. What increase is expected in the number of people employed as fitness trainers and aerobics instructors between 2000 to 2010?

d. How many people are expected to be employed as teachers in 2010?

e. Is it expected that more people will be employed as home health aides or as computer support specialists in 2010?

f. Why can't the answer to part e be determined by simply comparing the percent increases for the two occupations?

g. From the list, choose an occupation that interests you. Calculate the projected number of people who will be employed in that occupation in 2010.

34. 🥧 **Elections** According to the Committee for the Study of the American Electorate, the voter turnout in the 2004 presidential election was higher in all but four states than it was in the 2000 election. The four states with lower voter turnout are listed below.

a. How many Maine voters turned out to vote in the 2004 presidential election?

b. How many people in Arizona voted in the 2004 election?

c. How many more people voted in the 2000 election than in the 2004 election in the state of Alaska?

State	2000 Voter Turnout	Percent Decrease in Voter Turnout in 2004 Election
Alaska	280,000	12.4%
Arizona	1,632,000	2.3%
Maine	664,000	0.9%
Montana	433,000	0.1%

Extensions
CRITICAL THINKING

35. **Salaries** Your employer agrees to give you a 5% raise after one year on the job, a 6% raise the next year, and a 7% raise the following year. Is your salary after the third year greater than, less than, or the same as it would be if you had received a 6% raise each year?

36. 🥧 **Work Habits** Approximately 73% of Americans who work in large offices work on weekends, either at home or in the office. The table below shows the average number of hours these workers report they work on a weekend. Approximately what percent of Americans who work in large offices work 11 or more hours on weekends?

Numbers of Hours Worked on Weekends	Percent
0 – 1	3%
2 – 5	32%
6 – 10	42%
11 or more	23%

37. **Car Purchases** In a survey of consumers, approximately 43% said they would be willing to pay $1500 more for a new car if the car had an EPA rating of 80 miles per gallon. If your car currently gets 28 miles per gallon and you drive approximately 10,000 miles per year, in how many months would your savings on gasoline pay for the increased cost of such a car? Assume that the average cost of gasoline is $2.00 per gallon. Round to the nearest whole number.

COOPERATIVE LEARNING

38. **Demography** The statistical study of human populations is referred to as **demography.** Many groups are interested in the sizes of certain segments of the population and projections of population growth. For example, public school administrators want estimates of the number of school-age children who will be living in their districts 10 years from now.

The U.S. government provides estimates of the future U.S. population. You can find these projections at the Census Bureau website at **www.census.gov.** Three different projections are provided: a lowest series, a middle series, and a highest series. These series reflect different theories on how fast the population of this country will grow.

The table below contains data from the Census Bureau website. The figures are from the middle series of projections.

	Age	Under 5	5 – 17	18 – 24	25 – 34	35 – 44	45 – 54	55 – 64	65 – 74	75 & older
2010	Male	9,712	26,544	13,338	18,535	22,181	18,092	11,433	8,180	6,165
	Female	9,274	25,251	12,920	18,699	22,478	18,938	12,529	9,956	10,408
2050	Male	13,877	35,381	18,462	24,533	23,352	21,150	20,403	16,699	19,378
	Female	13,299	33,630	17,871	24,832	24,041	22,344	21,965	18,032	24,751

For the following exercises, round all percents to the nearest tenth of a percent.

a. Which of the age groups listed are of interest to public school officials?

b. Which age groups are of interest to nursing home administrators?

c. Which age groups are of concern to accountants determining benefits to be paid out by the Social Security Administration during the next decade?

d. Which age group is of interest to manufacturers of disposable diapers?

e. Which age group is of primary concern to college and university admissions officers?

f. In which age groups do the males outnumber the females? In which do the females outnumber the males?

g. What percent of the projected population aged 75 and older in the year 2010 is female? Does this percent decrease in 2050? If so, by how much?

h. Find the difference between the percent of the population that will be 65 or over in 2010 and the percent that will be 65 or older in 2050.

i. Assume that the work force consists of people aged 25 to 64. What percent increase is expected in this population from 2010 to 2050?

j. What percent of the population is the work force expected to be in 2010? What percent of the population is the work force expected to be in 2050?

k. Why are the answers to parts h, i, and j of concern to the Social Security Administration?

l. Describe any patterns you see in the table.

m. Calculate a statistic based on the data in the table and explain why it would be of interest to an institution (such as a school system) or a manufacturer of consumer goods (such as disposable diapers).

39. **Nielsen Ratings** Nielsen Media Research surveys television viewers to determine the numbers of people watching particular shows. There are an estimated
105.5 million U.S. households with televisions. Each **rating point** represents 1%
of that number, or 1,055,000 households. Therefore, for instance, if *60 Minutes*
received a rating of 5.8, then 5.8% of all U.S. households with televisions, or
$(0.058)(105,500,000) = 6,119,000$ households, were tuned to that program.

   A rating point does not mean that 1,055,000 people are watching a program.
A rating point refers to the number of households with television sets tuned to
that program; there may be more than one person watching a television set in the
household.

   Nielsen Media Research also describes a program's share of the market. **Share**
is the percent of households with television sets in use that are tuned to a program. Suppose that the same week that *60 Minutes* received 5.8 rating points, the
show received a share of 11%. This would mean that 11% of all households with
a television *turned on* were turned to *60 Minutes*, whereas 5.8% of all households
with a television were turned to the program.

   a. If *CSI* received a Nielsen rating of 10.1 and a share of 17, how many TV households watched the program that week? How many TV households were watching television during that hour? Round to the nearest hundred thousand.

   b. Suppose *Dateline Friday* received a rating of 5.6 and a share of 11. How many
   TV households watched the program that week? How many TV households
   were watching television during that hour? Round to the nearest hundred
   thousand.

   c. Suppose *Everybody Loves Raymond* received a rating of 7.5 during a week in
   which 19,781,000 people were watching the show. Find the average number of
   people per TV household who watched the program. Round to the nearest
   tenth.

   Nielsen Media Research has a website on the Internet. You can locate the
   site by using a search engine. The site does not list rating points or market
   share, but these statistics can be found on other websites by using a search engine.

   d. Find the top two primetime broadcast television shows for last week. Calculate the numbers of TV households that watched these programs. Compare
   the figures with the top two cable TV programs for last week.

| **Second-Degree Equations**

Second-Degree Equations in Standard Form

In Section 5.1, we introduced first-degree equations in one variable. The topic of
this section is second-degree equations in one variable. A **second-degree equation
in one variable** is an equation that can be written in the form $ax^2 + bx + c = 0$,
where a and b are coefficients, c is a constant, and $a \neq 0$. An equation of this form
is also called a **quadratic equation.** Here are three examples of second-degree equations in one variable.

▼ **point of interest**

The word *quadratic* comes from
the Latin word *quadratus*, which
means "to make square." Note
that the highest term in a
quadratic equation contains the
variable squared.

$$4x^2 - 7x + 1 = 0 \qquad a = 4, b = -7, c = 1$$
$$3z^2 - 6 = 0 \qquad a = 3, b = 0, c = -6$$
$$t^2 + 10t = 0 \qquad a = 1, b = 10, c = 0$$

Note that although the value of a cannot be 0, the value of b or c can be 0.

A second-degree equation is in **standard form** when the expression $ax^2 + bx + c$ is in **descending order** (the exponents on the variables decrease from left to right) and set equal to zero. For instance, $2x^2 + 8x - 3 = 0$ is written in standard form; $x^2 = 4x - 8$ is not in standard form.

QUESTION   *Which of the following are second-degree equations written in standard form?*

a. $3y^2 + 5y - 2 = 0$ *b.* $8p - 4p^2 + 7 = 0$

c. $z^3 - 6z + 9 = 0$ *d.* $4r^2 + r - 1 = 6$

e. $v^2 - 16 = 0$

EXAMPLE 1 ■ Write a Quadratic Equation in Standard Form

Write the equation $x^2 = 3x - 8$ in standard form.

Solution

Subtract $3x$ from each side of the equation.

$$x^2 = 3x - 8$$
$$x^2 - 3x = 3x - 3x - 8$$
$$x^2 - 3x = -8$$

Then add 8 to each side of the equation.

$$x^2 - 3x + 8 = -8 + 8$$
$$x^2 - 3x + 8 = 0$$

CHECK YOUR PROGRESS 1   Write $2s^2 = 6 - 4s$ in standard form.

Solution   See page S20.

Solving Second-Degree Equations by Factoring

Recall that the Multiplication Property of Zero states that the product of a number and zero is zero.

If a is a real number, then $a \cdot 0 = 0$.

Consider the equation $a \cdot b = 0$. If this is a true equation, then either $a = 0$ or $b = 0$. This is summarized in the Principle of Zero Products.

ANSWER   *The equations in **a** and **e** are second-degree equations in standard form. The equation in **b** is not in standard form because $8p - 4p^2 + 7$ is not written in descending order. The equation in **c** is not a second-degree equation because there is an exponent of 3 on the variable. The equation in **d** is not in standard form because the expression on the left side is not set equal to 0.*

Principle of Zero Products

If the product of two factors is zero, then at least one of the factors must be zero.

If $ab = 0$, then $a = 0$ or $b = 0$.

The Principle of Zero Products is often used to solve equations. This is illustrated in Example 2.

EXAMPLE 2 ■ Solve an Equation Using the Principle of Zero Products

Solve: $(x - 4)(x + 6) = 0$

Solution

In the expression $(x - 4)(x + 6)$, we are multiplying two numbers. Because their product is 0, one of the numbers must be equal to zero. The number $x - 4 = 0$ or the number $x + 6 = 0$. Solve each of these equations for x.

$$(x - 4)(x + 6) = 0$$

$$x - 4 = 0 \qquad x + 6 = 0$$
$$x = 4 \qquad x = -6$$

$$\text{Check:} \quad \begin{array}{c|c} (x - 4)(x + 6) = 0 \\ \hline (4 - 4)(4 + 6) & 0 \\ (0)(10) & 0 \\ 0 = 0 \end{array} \qquad \begin{array}{c|c} (x - 4)(x + 6) = 0 \\ \hline (-6 - 4)(-6 + 6) & 0 \\ (-10)(0) & 0 \\ 0 = 0 \end{array}$$

The solutions are 4 and -6.

✔ **TAKE NOTE**

Note that both 4 and -6 check as solutions. The equation $(x - 4)(x + 6) = 0$ has two solutions.

CHECK YOUR PROGRESS 2   Solve: $(n + 5)(2n - 3) = 0$

Solution   See page S20.

historical note

Chu Shih-chieh, a Chinese mathematician who lived around 1300, wrote the book *Ssu-yuan yu-chien*, which dealt with equations of degree as high as 14. ■

A second-degree equation can be solved by using the Principle of Zero Products when the expression $ax^2 + bx + c$ is factorable. This is illustrated in Example 3.

EXAMPLE 3 ■ Solve a Quadratic Equation by Factoring

Solve: $2x^2 + x = 6$

Solution

In order to use the Principle of Zero Products to solve a second-degree equation, the equation must be in standard form. Subtract 6 from each side of the given equation.

$$2x^2 + x = 6$$
$$2x^2 + x - 6 = 6 - 6$$
$$2x^2 + x - 6 = 0$$

Factor $2x^2 + x - 6$.

$$(2x - 3)(x + 2) = 0$$

These solutions can be checked on a scientific calculator. Many calculators require the following keystrokes.

2 [X] [(] 1.5 [INV] [X²] [)]

[+] 1.5 [=]

and

2 [X] [(] 2 [+/-] [INV] [X²] [)]

[+] 2 [+/-] [=]

On a graphing calculator, enter

2 [X] 1.5 [x²] [+] 1.5

[ENTER]

and

2 [X] [(] [(-)] 2 [)] [x²] [+]

[(-)] 2 [ENTER]

In each case, the display is 6.

Use the Principle of Zero Products. Set each factor equal to zero. Then solve each equation for x.

$$2x - 3 = 0 \qquad\qquad x + 2 = 0$$
$$2x = 3 \qquad\qquad\quad x = -2$$
$$x = \frac{3}{2}$$

Check:

$2x^2 + x = 6$		$2x^2 + x = 6$	
$2\left(\dfrac{3}{2}\right)^2 + \dfrac{3}{2}$	6	$2(-2)^2 + (-2)$	6
$2\left(\dfrac{9}{4}\right) + \dfrac{3}{2}$	6	$2(4) + (-2)$	6
$\dfrac{9}{2} + \dfrac{3}{2}$	6	$8 + (-2)$	6
$6 = 6$		$6 = 6$	

The solutions are $\dfrac{3}{2}$ and -2.

CHECK YOUR PROGRESS 3   Solve: $2x^2 = x + 1$

Solution   *See page S20.*

Note from Example 3 the steps involved in solving a second-degree equation by factoring. These are outlined below.

Solving a Second-Degree Equation by Factoring

1. Write the equation in standard form.

2. Factor the expression $ax^2 + bx + c$.

3. Use the Principle of Zero Products to set each factor of the polynomial equal to zero.

4. Solve each of the resulting equations for the variable.

Solving Second-Degree Equations by Using the Quadratic Formula

When using only integers, not all second-degree equations can be solved by factoring. Any equation that cannot be solved easily by factoring can be solved by using the *quadratic formula*, which is given on the following page.

The Quadratic Formula

The solutions of the equation $ax^2 + bx + c = 0$, $a \neq 0$, are

$$x = \frac{-b + \sqrt{b^2 - 4ac}}{2a} \quad \text{and} \quad x = \frac{-b - \sqrt{b^2 - 4ac}}{2a}$$

The quadratic formula is frequently written in the form

$$x = \frac{-b \pm \sqrt{b^2 - 4ac}}{2a}$$

To use the quadratic formula, first write the second-degree equation in standard form. Determine the values of a, b, and c. Substitute the values of a, b, and c into the quadratic formula. Then evaluate the resulting expression.

✔ TAKE NOTE

If you need to review material on simplifying radical expressions, see Lesson 9.2A on the CD that you received with this book.

EXAMPLE 4 ■ Solve a Quadratic Equation by Using the Quadratic Formula

Solve the equation $2x^2 = 4x - 1$ by using the quadratic formula. Give exact solutions and approximate solutions to the nearest thousandth.

Solution

Write the equation in standard form by subtracting $4x$ from each side of the equation and adding 1 to each side of the equation. Then determine the values of a, b, and c.

$$2x^2 = 4x - 1$$
$$2x^2 - 4x + 1 = 0$$
$$a = 2, b = -4, c = 1$$

Substitute the values of a, b, and c into the quadratic formula. Then evaluate the resulting expression.

$$x = \frac{-b \pm \sqrt{b^2 - 4ac}}{2a}$$

$$x = \frac{-(-4) \pm \sqrt{(-4)^2 - 4(2)(1)}}{2(2)} = \frac{4 \pm \sqrt{16 - 8}}{4}$$

$$= \frac{4 \pm \sqrt{8}}{4} = \frac{4 \pm 2\sqrt{2}}{4} = \frac{2(2 \pm \sqrt{2})}{2(2)} = \frac{2 \pm \sqrt{2}}{2}$$

CALCULATOR NOTE

To find the decimal approximation of $\frac{2 + \sqrt{2}}{2}$ on a scientific calculator, use the following keystrokes.

Note that parentheses are used to ensure that the entire numerator is divided by the denominator.

On a graphing calculator, enter

[( ] [2] [+] [2nd] [√] [2] [ )] [ )]
[÷] [2] [ENTER]

The exact solutions are $\dfrac{2 + \sqrt{2}}{2}$ and $\dfrac{2 - \sqrt{2}}{2}$.

$$\frac{2 + \sqrt{2}}{2} \approx 1.707 \qquad \frac{2 - \sqrt{2}}{2} \approx 0.293$$

To the nearest thousandth, the solutions are 1.707 and 0.293.

CHECK YOUR PROGRESS 4 Solve the equation $2x^2 = 8x - 5$ by using the quadratic formula. Give exact solutions and approximate solutions to the nearest thousandth.

Solution   See page S20.

The exact solutions to Example 4 are irrational numbers. It is also possible for a quadratic equation to have no real number solutions. This is illustrated in Example 5.

EXAMPLE 5 ■ Solve a Quadratic Equation by Using the Quadratic Formula

Solve by using the quadratic formula: $t^2 + 7 = 3t$

Solution

Write the equation in standard form by subtracting $3t$ from each side of the equation. Then determine the values of a, b, and c.

$$t^2 + 7 = 3t$$
$$t^2 - 3t + 7 = 0$$
$$a = 1, b = -3, c = 7$$

Substitute the values of a, b, and c into the quadratic formula. Then evaluate the resulting expression.

$$t = \frac{-b \pm \sqrt{b^2 - 4ac}}{2a}$$

$$t = \frac{-(-3) \pm \sqrt{(-3)^2 - 4(1)(7)}}{2(1)}$$

$$= \frac{3 \pm \sqrt{9 - 28}}{2} = \frac{3 \pm \sqrt{-19}}{2}$$

$\sqrt{-19}$ is not a real number.

The equation has no real number solutions.

CHECK YOUR PROGRESS 5   Solve by using the quadratic formula: $z^2 = -6 - 2z$

Solution   *See page S21.*

✔ **TAKE NOTE**

The square root of a negative number is not a real number because there is no real number that, when squared, equals a negative number. Therefore, $\sqrt{-19}$ is not a real number.

Math Matters   The Discriminant

In Example 5, the second-degree equation has no real number solutions. In the quadratic formula, the quantity $b^2 - 4ac$ under the radical sign is called the **discriminant**. When a, b, and c are real numbers, the discriminant determines whether or not a quadratic equation has real number solutions.

> **The Effect of the Discriminant on the Solutions of a Second-Degree Equation**
>
> **1.** If $b^2 - 4ac \geq 0$, the equation has real number solutions.
>
> **2.** If $b^2 - 4ac < 0$, the equation has no real number solutions.

For example, for the equation $x^2 - 4x - 5 = 0$, $a = 1$, $b = -4$, and $c = -5$.

$$b^2 - 4ac = (-4)^2 - 4(1)(-5) = 16 + 20 = 36$$
$$36 > 0$$

The discriminant is greater than 0. The equation has real number solutions.

Applications of Second-Degree Equations

Second-degree equations have many applications to the real world. Examples 6 and 7 illustrate two such applications.

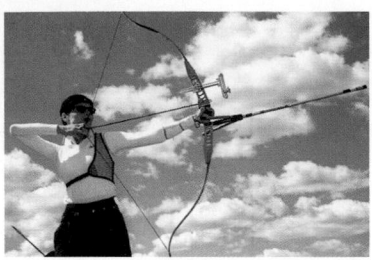

EXAMPLE 6 ■ Solve an Application of Quadratic Equations by Factoring

An arrow is projected into the air with an initial velocity of 48 feet per second. At what times will the arrow be 32 feet above the ground? Use the equation $h = 48t - 16t^2$, where h is the height, in feet, above the ground after t seconds.

Solution

We are asked to find the times when the arrow will be 32 feet above the ground, so we are given a value for h. Substitute 32 for h in the given equation and solve for t.

$$h = 48t - 16t^2$$
$$32 = 48t - 16t^2$$

This is a second-degree equation. Write the equation in standard form by adding $16t^2$ to each side of the equation and subtracting $48t$ from each side of the equation.

$$16t^2 - 48t + 32 = 0$$
$$16(t^2 - 3t + 2) = 0$$
$$t^2 - 3t + 2 = 0 \qquad \text{• Divide each side of the equation by 16.}$$
$$(t - 1)(t - 2) = 0$$
$$t - 1 = 0 \qquad t - 2 = 0$$
$$t = 1 \qquad\qquad t = 2$$

The arrow will be 32 feet above the ground 1 second after its release and 2 seconds after its release.

✔ **TAKE NOTE**

It would also be correct to subtract 32 from each side of the equation. However, many people prefer to have the coefficient of the squared term positive.

CHECK YOUR PROGRESS 6 An object is projected into the air with an initial velocity of 64 feet per second. At what times will the object be on the ground? Use the equation $h = 64t - 16t^2$, where h is the height, in feet, above the ground after t seconds.

Solution See page S21.

EXAMPLE 7 ■ Solve an Application of Quadratic Equations by Using the Quadratic Formula

A baseball player hits a ball. The height of the ball above the ground after t seconds can be approximated by the equation $h = -16t^2 + 75t + 5$. When will the ball hit the ground? Round to the nearest hundredth of a second.

Solution

We are asked to determine the number of seconds from the time the ball is hit until it is on the ground. When the ball is on the ground, its height above the ground is 0 feet. Substitute 0 for *h* and solve for *t*.

$$h = -16t^2 + 75t + 5$$
$$0 = -16t^2 + 75t + 5$$
$$16t^2 - 75t - 5 = 0$$

This is a second-degree equation. It is not easily factored. Use the quadratic formula to solve for *t*.

$$a = 16, \ b = -75, \ c = -5$$
$$t = \frac{-b \pm \sqrt{b^2 - 4ac}}{2a}$$
$$t = \frac{-(-75) \pm \sqrt{(-75)^2 - 4(16)(-5)}}{2(16)} = \frac{75 \pm \sqrt{5945}}{32}$$
$$t = \frac{75 + \sqrt{5945}}{32} \approx 4.75 \qquad t = \frac{75 - \sqrt{5945}}{32} \approx -0.07$$

The ball strikes the ground 4.75 seconds after the baseball player hits it.

CHECK YOUR PROGRESS 7   A basketball player shoots at a basket that is 25 feet away. The height *h*, in feet, of the ball above the ground after *t* seconds is given by $h = -16t^2 + 32t + 6.5$. How many seconds after the ball is released does it hit the basket? Note: The basket is 10 feet off the ground. Round to the nearest hundredth.

Solution   *See page S21.*

> ✔ **TAKE NOTE**
>
> The time until the ball hits the ground cannot be a negative number. Therefore, −0.07 second is not a solution of this application.

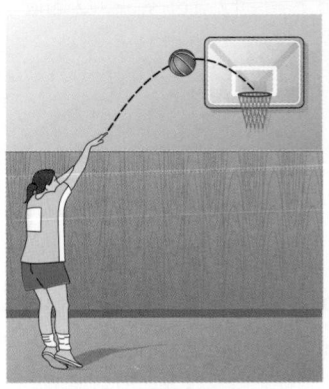

Excursion

The Sum and Product of the Solutions of a Quadratic Equation

The solutions of the equation $x^2 + 3x - 10 = 0$ are -5 and 2.

$$x^2 + 3x - 10 = 0$$
$$(x + 5)(x - 2) = 0$$
$$x + 5 = 0 \qquad x - 2 = 0$$
$$x = -5 \qquad x = 2$$

Note that the sum of the solutions is equal to $-b$, the opposite of the coefficient of *x*.

$$-5 + 2 = -3$$

The product of the solutions is equal to *c*, the constant term.

$$-5(2) = -10$$

> ✔ **TAKE NOTE**
>
> Look closely at the example at the right, in which -5 and 2 are solutions of the quadratic equation $(x + 5)(x - 2) = 0$. Using variables, we can state that if s_1 and s_2 are solutions of a quadratic equation, then the quadratic equation can be written in the form $(x - s_1)(x - s_2) = 0$.

(continued)

This illustrates the following theorem regarding the solutions of a quadratic equation.

The Sum and Product of the Solutions of a Quadratic Equation

If s_1 and s_2 are the solutions of a quadratic equation of the form $ax^2 + bx + c = 0$, $a \neq 0$, then

the sum of the solutions $s_1 + s_2 = -\dfrac{b}{a}$, and

the product of the solutions $s_1 s_2 = \dfrac{c}{a}$

TAKE NOTE

The result is the same if we let $s_1 = 6$ and $s_2 = -2$.

In this section, the method we used to check the solutions of a quadratic equation was to substitute the solutions back into the original equation. An alternative method is to use the sum and product of the solutions.

For example, let's check that -2 and 6 are the solutions of the equation $x^2 - 4x - 12 = 0$. For this equation, $a = 1$, $b = -4$, and $c = -12$. Let $s_1 = -2$ and $s_2 = 6$.

$$s_1 + s_2 = -\dfrac{b}{a} \qquad\qquad s_1 s_2 = \dfrac{c}{a}$$

$$
\begin{array}{c|c}
-2 + 6 & -\dfrac{-4}{1} \\[2mm]
\hline
4 = 4
\end{array}
\qquad
\begin{array}{c|c}
-2(6) & \dfrac{-12}{1} \\[2mm]
\hline
-12 = -12
\end{array}
$$

The solutions check.

In Example 4, we found that the exact solutions of the equation $2x^2 = 4x - 1$ are $\dfrac{2 + \sqrt{2}}{2}$ and $\dfrac{2 - \sqrt{2}}{2}$. Use the sum and product of the solutions to check these solutions.

Write the equation in standard form. Then determine the values of a, b, and c.

$$2x^2 = 4x - 1$$

$$2x^2 - 4x + 1 = 0$$

$$a = 2,\ b = -4,\ c = 1$$

Let $s_1 = \dfrac{2 + \sqrt{2}}{2}$ and $s_2 = \dfrac{2 - \sqrt{2}}{2}$

TAKE NOTE

If you need to review material on adding and multiplying radical expressions, see Lessons 9.2B and 9.2C on the CD that you received with this book.

$$s_1 + s_2 = -\dfrac{b}{a} \qquad\qquad\qquad s_1 s_2 = \dfrac{c}{a}$$

$$
\begin{array}{c|c}
\dfrac{2 + \sqrt{2}}{2} + \dfrac{2 - \sqrt{2}}{2} & -\dfrac{-4}{2} \\[3mm]
\hline
\dfrac{2 + \sqrt{2} + 2 - \sqrt{2}}{2} & 2 \\[3mm]
\dfrac{4}{2} & 2 \\[3mm]
2 = 2
\end{array}
\qquad
\begin{array}{c|c}
\left(\dfrac{2 + \sqrt{2}}{2}\right)\left(\dfrac{2 - \sqrt{2}}{2}\right) & \dfrac{1}{2} \\[3mm]
\hline
\dfrac{4 - 2}{4} & \dfrac{1}{2} \\[3mm]
\dfrac{2}{4} & \dfrac{1}{2} \\[3mm]
\dfrac{1}{2} = \dfrac{1}{2}
\end{array}
$$

The solutions check.

(continued)

If we divide both sides of the equation $ax^2 + bx + c = 0$, $a \neq 0$, by a, the result is the equation

$$x^2 + \frac{b}{a}x + \frac{c}{a} = 0$$

Using this model and the sum and products of the solutions of a quadratic equation, we can find a quadratic equation given its solutions. The method is given below.

A Quadratic Equation with Solutions s_1 and s_2

A quadratic equation with solutions s_1 and s_2 is

$$x^2 - (s_1 + s_2)x + s_1 s_2 = 0$$

To write a quadratic equation that has solutions $\frac{2}{3}$ and 1, let $s_1 = \frac{2}{3}$ and $s_2 = 1$. Substitute these values into the equation $x^2 - (s_1 + s_2)x + s_1 s_2 = 0$ and simplify.

$$x^2 - (s_1 + s_2)x + s_1 s_2 = 0$$

$$x^2 - \left(\frac{2}{3} + 1\right)x + \left(\frac{2}{3} \cdot 1\right) = 0$$

$$x^2 - \frac{5}{3}x + \frac{2}{3} = 0$$

Assuming we want a, b, and c to be integers, then we can multiply each side of the equation by 3 to clear fractions.

$$3\left(x^2 - \frac{5}{3}x + \frac{2}{3}\right) = 3(0)$$

$$3x^2 - 5x + 2 = 0$$

A quadratic equation with solutions $\frac{2}{3}$ and 1 is $3x^2 - 5x + 2 = 0$.

Excursion Exercises

In Exercises 1–8, solve the equation and then check the solutions using the sum and product of the solutions.

1. $x^2 - 10 = 3x$ **2.** $x^2 + 16 = 8x$

3. $3x^2 + 5x = 12$ **4.** $3x^2 + 8x = 3$

5. $x^2 = 6x + 3$ **6.** $x^2 = 2x + 5$

7. $4x + 1 = 4x^2$ **8.** $x + 1 = x^2$

In Exercises 9–16, write a quadratic equation that has integer coefficients and has the given pair of solutions.

9. -1 and 6 **10.** -5 and -4

11. 3 and $\frac{1}{2}$ **12.** $-\frac{3}{4}$ and 2

13. $\frac{1}{4}$ and $-\frac{3}{2}$ **14.** $\frac{2}{3}$ and $-\frac{2}{3}$

15. $2 + \sqrt{2}$ and $2 - \sqrt{2}$ **16.** $1 + \sqrt{3}$ and $1 - \sqrt{3}$

Exercise Set 5.4

1. ✎ Explain the importance of writing a second-degree equation in standard form as the first step in solving the equation. Include in your explanation how the Principle of Zero Products is used to solve the equation.

2. ✎ Explain why the restriction $a \neq 0$ is given in the definition of a quadratic equation.

3. Write a second-degree equation that you can solve by factoring.

4. Write a second-degree equation that you can solve by using the quadratic formula but not by factoring.

Solve Exercises 5–28. First try to solve the equation by factoring. If you are unable to solve the equation by factoring, solve the equation by using the quadratic formula. For equations with solutions that are irrational numbers, give exact solutions and approximate solutions to the nearest thousandth.

5. $r^2 - 3r = 10$
6. $p^2 + 5p = 6$
7. $t^2 = t + 1$
8. $u^2 = u + 3$

9. $y^2 - 6y = 4$
10. $w^2 + 4w = 2$
11. $9z^2 - 18z = 0$
12. $4y^2 + 20y = 0$

13. $z^2 = z + 4$
14. $r^2 = r - 1$
15. $2s^2 = 4s + 5$
16. $3u^2 = 6u + 1$

17. $r^2 = 4r + 7$
18. $s^2 + 6s = 1$
19. $2x^2 = 9x + 18$
20. $3y^2 = 4y + 4$

21. $6x - 11 = x^2$
22. $-8y - 17 = y^2$
23. $4 - 15u = 4u^2$
24. $3 - 2y = 8y^2$

25. $6y^2 - 4 = 5y$
26. $6v^2 - 3 = 7v$
27. $y - 2 = y^2 - y - 6$
28. $8s - 11 = s^2 - 6s + 8$

Solve Exercises 29–43. Round answers to nearest hundredth.

29. **Golf** The height h, in feet, of a golf ball t seconds after it has been hit is given by the equation $h = -16t^2 + 60t$. How many seconds after the ball is hit will the height of the ball be 36 feet?

30. **Geometry** The area A, in square meters, of a rectangle with a perimeter of 100 meters is given by the equation $A = 50w - w^2$, where w is the width of the rectangle in meters. What is the width of a rectangle if its area is 400 square meters?

31. **Mathematics** In the diagram below, the total number of circles T when there are n rows is given by $T = 0.5n^2 + 0.5n$. Verify the formula for the four figures shown. Determine the number of rows when the total number of circles is 55.

32. **Astronautics** If an astronaut on the moon throws a ball upward with an initial velocity of 6 meters per second, its approximate height h, in meters, after t seconds is given by the equation $h = -0.8t^2 + 6t$. How long after it is released will the ball be 8 meters above the surface of the moon?

33. **Stopping Distance** When a driver decides to stop a car, it takes time first for the driver to react and put a foot on the brake, and then it takes additional time for the car to slow down. The total distance traveled during this period of time is called the *stopping distance* of the car. For some cars, the stopping distance d, in feet, is given by the equation $d = 0.05r^2 + r$, where r is the speed of the car in miles per hour.

   a. Find the distance needed to stop a car traveling at 60 miles per hour.

   b. If skid marks at an accident site are 75 feet long, how fast was the car traveling?

34. **Cliff Divers** At La Quebrada in Acapulco, Mexico, cliff divers dive from a rock cliff that is 27 meters above the water. The equation $h = -x^2 + 2x + 27$ describes the height h, in meters, of the diver above the water when the diver is x feet away from the cliff.

   a. When the diver enters the water, how far is the diver from the cliff?

   b. Does the diver ever reach a height of 28 meters above the water? If so, how far is the diver from the cliff at that time?

   c. Does the diver ever reach a height of 30 meters above the water? If so, how far is the diver from the cliff at that time?

35. **Football** The hang time of a football that is kicked on the opening kickoff is given by $s = -16t^2 + 88t + 1$, where s is the height in feet of the football t seconds after leaving the kicker's foot. What is the hang time of a kickoff that hits the ground without being caught?

36. **Softball** In a slow pitch softball game, the height of a ball thrown by a pitcher can be approximated by the equation $h = -16t^2 + 24t + 4$, where h is the height, in feet, of the ball and t is the time, in seconds, since it was released by the pitcher. If a batter hits the ball when it is 2 feet off the ground, for how many seconds has the ball been in the air?

37. **Fire Science** The path of water from a hose on a fire tugboat can be approximated by the equation $y = -0.005x^2 + 1.2x + 10$, where y is the height, in feet, of the water above the ocean when the water is x feet from the tugboat. When the water from the hose is 5 feet above the ocean, at what distance from the tugboat is it?

38. **Springboard Diving** An event in the Summer Olympics is 10-meter springboard diving. In this event, the height h, in meters, of a diver above the water t seconds after jumping is given by the equation $h = -4.9t^2 + 7.8t + 10$. What is the height above the water of a diver after 2 seconds?

39. **Soccer** A penalty kick in soccer is made from a penalty mark that is 36 feet from a goal that is 8 feet high. A possible equation for the flight of a penalty kick is $h = -0.002x^2 + 0.36x$, where h is the height, in feet, of the ball x feet from the goal. Assuming that the flight of the kick is toward the goal and that it is not touched by the goalie, will the ball land in the net?

40. **Stopping Distance** In Germany there are no speed limits on some portions of the autobahn (the highway). Other portions have a speed limit of 180 kilometers per hour (approximately 112 miles per hour). The distance d, in meters, required to stop a car traveling v kilometers per hour is $d = 0.0056v^2 + 0.14v$. Approximate the maximum speed a driver can be going and still be able to stop within 150 meters.

German Autobahn System

41. **Model Rockets** A model rocket is launched with an initial velocity of 200 feet per second. The height h, in feet, of the rocket t seconds after the launch is given by $h = -16t^2 + 200t$. How many seconds after the launch will the rocket be 300 feet above the ground? Round to the nearest hundredth of a second.

42. **Fountains** The Water Arc is a fountain that shoots water across the Chicago River from a water cannon. The path of the water can be approximated by the equation $h = -0.006x^2 + 1.2x + 10$, where x is the horizontal distance, in feet, from the cannon and h is the height, in feet, of the water above the river. On one particular day, some people were walking along the opposite side of the river from the Water Arc when a pulse of water was shot in their direction. If the distance from the Water Arc to the people was 220 feet, did they get wet from the cannon's water?

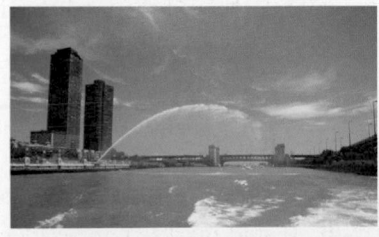

43. **First-Class Postage** The graph below shows the cost for a first-class postage stamp from the 1950s to 2005. A second-degree equation that approximately models these data is $y = 0.0099x^2 - 0.8084x + 16.8750$, where $x \geq 50$ and $x = 50$ for the year 1950, and y is the cost in cents of a first-class stamp. Using the model equation, determine what the model predicts the cost of a first-class stamp will be in the year 2025. Round to the nearest cent.

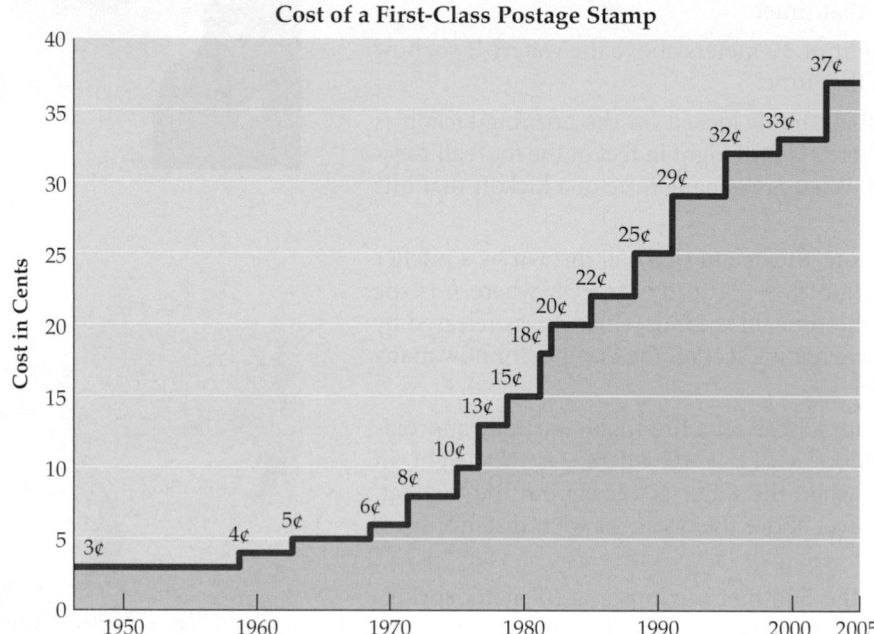

Cost of a First-Class Postage Stamp

Extensions

CRITICAL THINKING

44. Show that the solutions of the equation $ax^2 + bx = 0$, $a \neq 0$, are 0 and $-\dfrac{b}{a}$.

45. In a second-degree equation in standard form, why is the expression $ax^2 + bx + c$ factorable over the integers only when the discriminant is a perfect square? (See Math Matters, page 311.)

46. A wire 8 feet long is cut into two pieces. A circle is formed from one piece and a square is formed from the other. The total area of both figures is given by $A = \dfrac{1}{16}(8 - x)^2 + \dfrac{x^2}{4\pi}$. What is the length of each piece of wire if the total area is 4.5 square feet? Round to the nearest thousandth.

In Exercises 47–52, solve the equation for x.

47. $x^2 + 16ax + 48a^2 = 0$

48. $x^2 - 8bx + 15b^2 = 0$

49. $2x^2 + 3bx + b^2 = 0$

50. $3x^2 - 4cx + c^2 = 0$

51. $2x^2 - xy - 3y^2 = 0$

52. $x^2 - 4xy + 4y^2 = 0$

COOPERATIVE LEARNING

53. Show that the equation $x^2 + bx - 1 = 0$ always has real number solutions, regardless of the value of b.

54. Show that the equation $2x^2 + bx - 2 = 0$ always has real number solutions, regardless of the value of b.

CHAPTER 5 **Summary**

Key Terms

constant term [p. 246]
descending order [p. 307]
equation [p. 246]
extremes of a proportion [p. 270]
first-degree equation in one variable [p. 246]
formula [p. 254]
like terms [p. 246]
literal equation [p. 254]
means of a proportion [p. 270]
numerical coefficient [p. 246]
percent [p. 283]
percent decrease [p. 294]
percent increase [p. 292]
proportion [p. 270]
quadratic equation [p. 306]
rate [p. 263]
ratio [p. 267]
second-degree equation in one variable [p. 306]
solution of an equation [p. 247]
solve an equation [p. 247]
standard form [p. 307]
term of a proportion [p. 270]
terms of a variable expression [p. 246]
unit price [p. 265]
unit rate [p. 264]
unit ratio [p. 268]
variable part [p. 246]
variable term [p. 246]

Essential Concepts

- **Properties of Equations**

  Addition Property
  The same number can be added to each side of an equation without changing the solution of the equation.
  If $a = b$, then $a + c = b + c$.

  Subtraction Property
  The same number can be subtracted from each side of an equation without changing the solution of the equation.
  If $a = b$, then $a - c = b - c$.

  Multiplication Property
  Each side of an equation can be multiplied by the same nonzero number without changing the solution of the equation.
  If $a = b$ and $c \neq 0$, then $ac = bc$.

  Division Property
  Each side of an equation can be divided by the same nonzero number without changing the solution of the equation.
  If $a = b$ and $c \neq 0$, then $\frac{a}{c} = \frac{b}{c}$.

- **Steps for Solving a First-Degree Equation in One Variable**

  1. If the equation contains fractions, multiply each side of the equation by the least common multiple (LCM) of the denominators to clear the equation of fractions.

  2. Use the Distributive Property to remove parentheses.

  3. Combine any like terms on the right side of the equation and any like terms on the left side of the equation.

  4. Use the Addition or Subtraction Property to rewrite the equation with only one variable term and only one constant term.

  5. Use the Multiplication or Division Property to rewrite the equation with the variable alone on one side of the equation and a constant on the other side of the equation.

- **Solve a Literal Equation for One of the Variables**
  The goal is to rewrite the equation so that the letter being solved for is alone on one side of the equation and all numbers and other variables are on the other side.

- **Calculate a Unit Rate**
  Divide the number in the numerator of the rate by the number in the denominator of the rate.

- **Write a Ratio**
  A ratio can be written in three different ways: as a fraction, as two numbers separated by a colon (:), or as two numbers separated by the word *to*. Although units, such as hours, miles, or dollars, are written as part of a rate, units are not written as part of a ratio.

- **Cross-Products Method of Solving a Proportion**
  If $\frac{a}{b} = \frac{c}{d}$, then $ad = bc$.

- **Write a Percent as a Decimal**
  Remove the percent sign and move the decimal point two places to the left.

■ **Write a Decimal as a Percent**
Move the decimal point two places to the right and write a percent sign.

■ **Write a Percent as a Fraction**
Remove the percent sign and multiply by $\frac{1}{100}$.

■ **Write a Fraction as a Percent**
First write the fraction as a decimal. Then write the decimal as a percent.

■ **Proportion Used to Solve Percent Problems**
$\frac{\text{Percent}}{100} = \frac{\text{amount}}{\text{base}}$

■ **Basic Percent Equation**
$PB = A$, where P is the percent, B is the base, and A is the amount.

■ **Principle of Zero Products**
If the product of two factors is zero, then at least one of the factors must be zero.
If $ab = 0$, then $a = 0$ or $b = 0$.

■ **Solving a Second-Degree Equation by Factoring**

1. Write the equation in standard form.
2. Factor the polynomial $ax^2 + bx + c$.
3. Use the Principle of Zero Products to set each factor of the polynomial equal to zero.
4. Solve each of the resulting equations for the variable.

■ **The Quadratic Formula**
The solutions of the equation $ax^2 + bx + c = 0$, $a \neq 0$, are $x = \dfrac{-b \pm \sqrt{b^2 - 4ac}}{2a}$.

CHAPTER 5   **Review Exercises**

In Exercises 1–8, solve the equation.

1. $5x + 3 = 10x - 17$

2. $3x + \dfrac{1}{8} = \dfrac{1}{2}$

3. $6x + 3(2x - 1) = -27$

4. $\dfrac{5}{12} = \dfrac{n}{8}$

5. $4y^2 + 9 = 0$

6. $x^2 - x = 30$

7. $x^2 = 4x - 1$

8. $x + 3 = x^2$

In Exercises 9 and 10, solve the formula for the given variable.

9. $4x + 3y = 12$; y

10. $f = v + at$; t

11. Meteorology In June, the temperature at various elevations of the Grand Canyon can be approximated by the equation $T = -0.005x + 113.25$, where T is the temperature in degrees Fahrenheit and x is the elevation (distance above sea level) in feet. Use this equation to find the elevation at Inner Gorge, the bottom of the canyon, where the temperature is 101°F.

12. Falling Objects Find the time it takes for the velocity of a falling object to increase from 4 feet per second to 100 feet per second. Use the equation $v = v_0 + 32t$, where v is the final velocity of the falling object, v_0 is the initial velocity, and t is the time it takes for the object to fall.

13. **Chemistry** A chemist mixes 100 grams of water at 80°C with 50 grams of water at 20°C. Use the formula $m_1(T_1 - T) = m_2(T - T_2)$ to find the final temperature of the water after mixing. In this equation, m_1 is the quantity of water at the hotter temperature, T_1 is the temperature of the hotter water, m_2 is the quantity of water at the cooler temperature, T_2 is the temperature of the cooler water, and T is the final temperature of water after mixing.

14. **Computer Bulletin Board Service** A computer bulletin board service charges $4.25 per month plus $.08 for each minute over 30 minutes that the service is used. For how many minutes did a subscriber use this service during a month in which the monthly charge was $4.97?

15. **Fuel Consumption** An automobile was driven 326.6 miles on 11.5 gallons of gasoline. Find the number of miles driven per gallon of gas.

16. **Real Estate** A house with an original value of $280,000 increased in value to $350,000 in 5 years. Write, as a fraction in simplest form, the ratio of the increase in value to the original value of the house.

17. **Farming Cropland** The graph below shows the average value per acre of farm cropland in the United States. The average value per acre of farm cropland in 2003 was $800 less than twice the average value in 1997. Find the average value per acre of U.S. farm cropland in 1997.

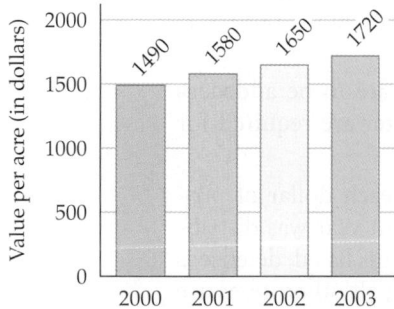

Average Value Per Acre of U.S. Farm Cropland

Source: National Agricultural Statistics Service

18. **City Populations** The table below shows the population and area of the five most populous cities in the United States.

   a. The cities are listed in the table according to population, from largest to smallest. Rank the cities according to population density, from largest to smallest.

   b. How many more people per square mile are there in New York than in Houston? Round to the nearest whole number.

City	Population	Area (in square miles)
New York	8,008,000	321.8
Los Angeles	3,695,000	467.4
Chicago	2,896,000	228.469
Houston	1,954,000	594.03
Philadelphia	1,519,000	136

19. **Student–Faculty Ratios** The table below shows the number of full-time men and women undergraduates, as well as the number of full-time faculty, at the six colleges in Arizona. In parts a, b, and c, round ratios to the nearest whole number. (*Source: Barron's Profile of American Colleges*, 26th edition, c. 2005)

University	Men	Women	Faculty
Arizona State University	14,875	16,054	1,722
Embry-Riddle Aeronautical University	1,181	244	87
Grand Canyon University	450	880	96
Northern Arizona University	4,468	6,566	711
Prescott College	305	435	49
University of Arizona	11,283	12,822	1,495

  a. Calculate the student–faculty ratio at Prescott College. Write the ratio using a colon and using the word *to*. What does this ratio mean?

  b. Which school listed has the lowest student–faculty ratio? the highest?

  c. Which schools listed have the same student–faculty ratio?

20. **Advertising** The Randolph Company spent $350,000 for advertising last year. Department A and Department B share the cost of advertising in the ratio 3:7. Find the amount allocated to each department.

21. **Gardening** Three tablespoons of a liquid plant fertilizer are to be added to every 4 gallons of water. How many tablespoons of fertilizer are required for 10 gallons of water?

22. **Federal Expenditures** The table below shows how each dollar of projected spending by the federal government for a recent year was distributed. (*Source:* Office of Management and Budget) Of the items listed, defense is the only discretionary spending by the federal government; all other items are fixed expenditures. The government predicted total expenses of $2,230 billion for the year.

  a. Is at least one-fifth of federal spending discretionary spending?

  b. Find the ratio of the fixed expenditures to the discretionary spending.

  c. Find the amount of the budget to be spent on fixed expenditures.

  d. Find the amount of the budget to be spent on Social Security.

How Your Federal Tax Dollar Is Spent	
Health care	23 cents
Social Security	22 cents
Defense	18 cents
Other social aid	15 cents
Remaining government agencies and programs	14 cents
Interest on national debt	8 cents

23. **Demographics** According to the U.S. Bureau of the Census, the population of males and females in the United States in 2025 and 2050 is projected to be as shown in the table on the following page.

Year	Males	Females
2025	164,119,000	170,931,000
2050	193,234,000	200,696,000

a. What percent of the projected population in 2025 is female? Round to the nearest tenth of a percent.

b. Does the percent of the projected population that is female in 2050 differ by more or less than 1 percent from the percent that is female in 2025?

24. **Populations** According to the Scarborough Report, San Francisco is the city that has the highest percentage of people with a current U.S. passport: 38.6% of the population, or approximately 283,700 people, have a U.S. passport. Estimate the population of San Francisco. Round to the nearest hundred.

25. **Organ Transplants** The graph at the right shows the number of people, in thousands, that are listed on the national patient waiting list for organ transplants. What percent of those listed are waiting for a kidney transplant? Round to the nearest tenth of a percent.

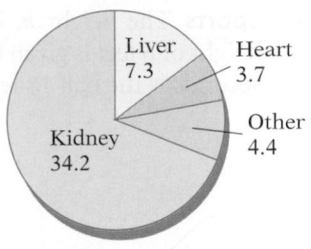

Number of People on the National Waiting List for Organ Transplants (in thousands)

Source: United Network for Organ Sharing

26. **Nutrition** The table at the right shows the fat, saturated fat, cholesterol, and calorie content of a 90-gram ground-beef burger and a 90-gram soy burger.

a. Compared to the beef burger, by what percent is the fat content decreased in the soy burger?

b. What is the percent decrease in cholesterol in the soy burger compared to the beef burger?

c. Calculate the percent decrease in calories in the soy burger compared to the beef burger.

	Beef Burger	Soy Burger
Fat	24 g	4 g
Saturated fat	10 g	1.5 g
Cholesterol	75 mg	0 mg
Calories	280	140

27. **Music Sales** According to Nielsen SoundScan, album sales fell from 785.1 million in 2000 to 656.3 million in 2003. What percent decrease does this represent? Round to the nearest tenth of a percent.

28. **Soccer** The chart below shows, by age group, the number of girls playing youth soccer. Also shown is the percent of total youth soccer players who are girls. (*Source:* American Youth Soccer Organization)

Age group	5 – 6	7 – 8	9 – 10	11 – 12	13 – 14	15 – 16	17 – 18
Number of girls playing	23,805	45,181	46,758	39,939	26,157	11,518	4,430
Percent of all players	33%	33%	36%	40%	41%	42%	38%

a. Which age group has the greatest number of girls playing youth soccer?

b. Which age group has the largest percent of girls participating in youth soccer?

c. What percent of the girls playing youth soccer are ages 7 to 10? Round to the nearest tenth of a percent. Is this more or less than half of all the girls playing?

d. How many boys ages 17 to 18 play youth soccer? Round to the nearest ten.

e. The girls playing youth soccer represent 36% of all youth soccer players. How many young people play youth soccer? Round to the nearest hundred.

29. **Model Rockets** A small rocket is shot from the edge of a cliff. The height h, in meters, of the rocket above the cliff is given by $h = 30t - 5t^2$, where t is the time in seconds after the rocket is shot. Find the times at which the rocket is 25 meters above the cliff.

30. **Sports** The height h, in feet, of a ball t seconds after being thrown from a height of 6 feet is given by the equation $h = -16t^2 + 32t + 6$. After how many seconds is the ball 18 feet above the ground? Round to the nearest tenth.

CHAPTER 5	**Test**

In Exercises 1–5, solve the equation.

1. $\dfrac{x}{4} - 3 = \dfrac{1}{2}$

2. $x + 5(3x - 20) = 10(x - 4)$

3. $\dfrac{7}{16} = \dfrac{x}{12}$

4. $x^2 = 12x - 27$

5. $3x^2 - 4x = 1$

In Exercises 6 and 7, solve the formula for the given variable.

6. $x - 2y = 15$; y

7. $C = \dfrac{5}{9}(F - 32)$; F

8. **Geysers** Old Faithful is a geyser in Yellowstone National Park. It is so named because of its regular eruptions for the past 100 years. An equation that can predict the approximate time until the next eruption is $T = 12.4L + 32$, where T is the time, in minutes, until the next eruption and L is the duration, in minutes, of the last eruption. Use this equation to determine the duration of the last eruption when the time between two eruptions is 63 minutes.

9. **Fines** A library charges a fine for each overdue book. The fine is 15¢ for the first day plus 7¢ a day for each additional day the book is overdue. If the fine for a book is 78¢, how many days overdue is the book?

10. **Rate of Speed** You drive 246.6 miles in 4.5 hours. Find your average rate in miles per hour.

11. **Parks** The table below lists the largest city parks in the United States. The land acreage of Griffith Park in Los Angeles is 3 acres more than five times the acreage of New York's Central Park. What is the acreage of Central Park?

City Park	Land Acreage
Cullen Park (Houston)	10,534
Fairmont Park (Philadelphia)	8,700
Griffith Park (Los Angeles)	4,218
Eagle Creek Park (Indianapolis)	3,800
Pelham Bay Park (Bronx, NY)	2,764
Mission Bay Park (San Diego)	2,300

12. **Baseball** The table below shows six Major League lifetime record holders for batting. (*Source: Information Please Almanac*)

   a. Calculate the number of at-bats per home run for each player in the table. Round to the nearest thousandth.

   b. The players are listed in the table alphabetically. Rank the players according to the number of at-bats per home run, starting with the best rate.

Baseball Player	Number of Times at Bat	Number of Home Runs Hit	Number of At-Bats per Home Run
Ty Cobb	11,429	4,191	_____
Billy Hamilton	6,284	2,163	_____
Rogers Hornsby	8,137	2,930	_____
Joe Jackson	4,981	1,774	_____
Tris Speaker	10,195	3,514	_____
Ted Williams	7,706	2,654	_____

13. **Golf** In a recent year, the gross revenue from television rights, merchandise, corporate hospitality and tickets for the four major men's golf tournaments was as shown in the table at the right. What is the ratio, as a fraction in simplest form, of the gross revenue from the British Open to the gross revenue from the U.S. Open?

Golf Championship	Gross Revenue (in millions)
U. S. Open	$35
PGA Championship	$30.5
The Masters	$22
British Open	$20

14. **Partnerships** The two partners in a partnership share the profits of their business in the ratio 5 : 3. Last year the profits were $180,000. Find the amount received by each partner.

15. **Gardening** The directions on a bag of plant food recommend one-half pound for every 50 square feet of lawn. How many pounds of plant food should be used on a lawn that measures 275 square feet?

16. **Crime Rates** The table below lists the U.S. cities with populations over 100,000 that had the highest number of violent crimes per 1000 residents per year. The violent crimes include murder, rape, aggravated assault, and robbery. (*Source:* FBI Uniform Crime Reports)

City	Violent Crimes per 1000 People
Baltimore	13.4
Baton Rouge	13.9
Gainesville, Florida	14.2
Lawton, Oklahoma	13.3
Los Angeles - Long Beach	14.2
Miami - Dade	18.9
New Orleans	13.3
New York	13.9

a. Which city has the highest rate of violent crimes?

b. The population of Baltimore is approximately 703,000. Estimate the number of violent crimes committed in that city. Round to the nearest whole number.

17. **Pets** During a recent year, nearly 1.2 million dogs or litters were registered with the American Kennel Club. The most popular breed was the Labrador retriever, with 172,841 registered. What percent of the registrations were Labrador retrievers? Round to the nearest tenth of a percent. (*Source:* American Kennel Club)

18. **Digital Camera Sales** The graph at the right shows the projected worldwide sales of digital cameras for 2004 to 2007.

a. What percent of the total number of digital cameras expected to be sold during the four years is the number of the digital cameras sold in 2004? Round to the nearest tenth of a percent.

b. Between which two consecutive years shown in the graph is the percent increase the greatest?

c. What is the percent increase in the projected number of digital cameras sold from 2004 to 2007? Round to the nearest tenth of a percent.

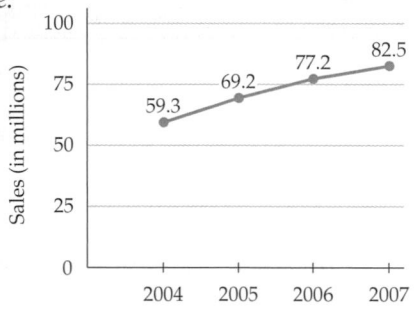

Projected Worldwide Sales of Digital Cameras

Source: IDC

19. **Working Farms** The number of working farms in the United States in 1977 was 2.5 million. In 1987, there were 2.2 million working farms, and in 1997, there were 2.0 million working farms. (*Source:* CNN)

a. Find the percent decrease in the number of working farms from 1977 to 1997.

b. If the percent decrease in the number of working farms from 1997 to 2017 is the same as it was from 1977 to 1997, how many working farms will there be in the United States in 2017?

c. Provide an explanation for the decrease in the number of working farms in the United States.

20. **Shot Put** The equation $h = -16t^2 + 28t + 6$, where $0 \leq t \leq 1.943$, can be used to find the height h, in feet, of a shot t seconds after a shot putter has released it. After how many seconds is the shot 10 feet above the ground? Round to the nearest tenth of a second.

CHAPTER

6

Applications of Functions

6.1	Rectangular Coordinates and Functions
6.2	Properties of Linear Functions
6.3	Finding Linear Models
6.4	Quadratic Functions
6.5	Exponential Functions
6.6	Logarithmic Functions

The Clarence Buckingham Memorial Fountain, better known as Buckingham Fountain, is one of the largest fountains in the world. A major landmark of Chicago, it is located at Columbus Drive in Grant Park and is made of Georgia pink marble.

Kate Buckingham, who dedicated the fountain to the people of Chicago in memory of her brother Clarence, funded the project. Edward H. Bennett designed the fountain to represent Lake Michigan, with four sea horses, built by sculptor Marcel Loyau, to symbolize the four states that touch the lake: Wisconsin, Illinois, Indiana, and Michigan. Buckingham Fountain opened on May 26, 1927.

The fountain operates from April 1 to November 1 each year and runs from 10:00 A.M. to 11:00 P.M. each day. Every hour on the hour for 20 minutes, the fountain produces a major water display. Beginning at dusk, the water display is accompanied by lights and music. The fountain has 133 nozzles that spray 14,000 gallons of water per minute. The water that shoots upward from the center nozzle of the fountain can reach heights of 135 feet in the air. A quadratic function, one of the topics of this chapter, can be used to approximate the height of a given volume of water t seconds after it shoots upward from the center nozzle. For more information on this application, see Exercise 43, page 373.

For online student resources, visit this textbook's website at
www.cengage.com/math.

327

Introduction to Rectangular Coordinate Systems

When archeologists excavate a site, a *coordinate grid* is laid over the site so that records can be kept not only of what was found but also of *where* it was found. The grid below is from an archeological dig at Poggio Colla, a site in the Mugello about 20 miles northeast of Florence, Italy.

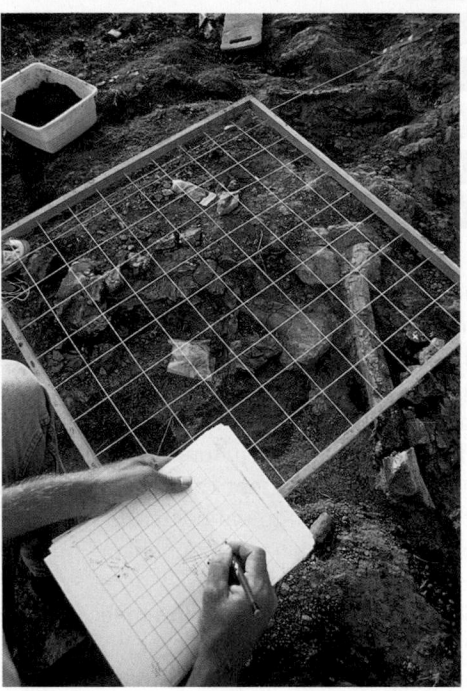

historical note

The concept of a coordinate system developed over time, culminating in 1637 with the publication of *Discourse on the Method for Rightly Directing One's Reason and Searching for Truth in the Sciences* by René Descartes (1596–1650) and *Introduction to Plane and Solid Loci* by Pierre de Fermat (1601–1665). Of the two mathematicians, Descartes is usually given more credit for developing the concept of a coordinate system. In fact, he became so famous in Le Haye, the town in which he was born, that the town was renamed Le Haye–Descartes. ∎

In mathematics we encounter a similar problem, that of locating a point in a plane. One way to solve the problem is to use a *rectangular coordinate system*.

A **rectangular coordinate system** is formed by two number lines, one horizontal and one vertical, that intersect at the zero point of each line. The point of intersection is called the **origin.** The two number lines are called the **coordinate axes,** or simply the **axes.** Frequently, the horizontal axis is labeled the *x*-axis and the vertical axis is labeled the *y*-axis. In this case, the axes form what is called the ***xy*-plane.**

The two axes divide the plane into four regions called **quadrants,** which are numbered counterclockwise, using Roman numerals, from I to IV, starting at the upper right.

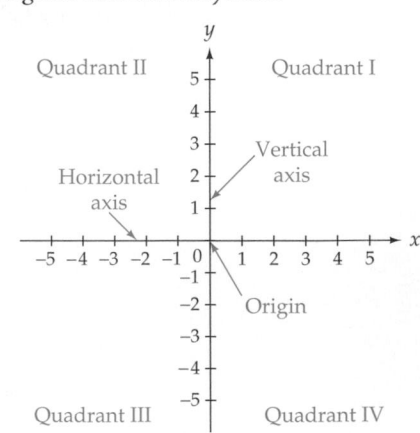

Each point in the plane can be identified by a pair of numbers called an **ordered pair.** The first number of the ordered pair measures a horizontal change from the *y*-axis and is called the **abscissa,** or **x-coordinate.** The second number of the ordered pair measures a vertical change from the *x*-axis and is called the **ordinate,** or **y-coordinate.** The ordered pair (x, y) associated with a point is also called the **coordinates** of the point.

To **graph,** or **plot,** a point means to place a dot at the coordinates of the point. For example, to graph the ordered pair $(4, 3)$, start at the origin. Move 4 units to the right and then 3 units up. Draw a dot. To graph $(-3, -4)$, start at the origin. Move 3 units left and then 4 units down. Draw a dot.

The **graph of an ordered pair** is the dot drawn at the coordinates of the point in the plane. The graphs of the ordered pairs $(4, 3)$ and $(-3, -4)$ are shown above.

The graphs of the points whose coordinates are $(2, 3)$ and $(3, 2)$ are shown at the right. Note that they are different points. The order in which the numbers in an ordered pair are listed is important.

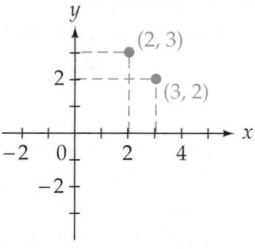

If the axes are labeled with letters other than *x* or *y*, then we refer to the ordered pair using the given labels. For instance, if the horizontal axis is labeled *t* and the vertical axis is labeled *d*, then the ordered pairs are written as (t, d). We sometimes refer to the first number in an ordered pair as the **first coordinate** of the ordered pair and to the second number as the **second coordinate** of the ordered pair.

One purpose of a coordinate system is to draw a picture of the solutions of an **equation in two variables.** Examples of equations in two variables are shown at the right.

$$y = 3x - 2$$
$$x^2 + y^2 = 25$$
$$s = t^2 - 4t + 1$$

A **solution of an equation in two variables** is an ordered pair that makes the equation a true statement. For instance, as shown below, $(2, 4)$ is a solution of $y = 3x - 2$ but $(3, -1)$ is not a solution of the equation.

$y = 3x - 2$		
4	$3(2) - 2$	• $x = 2, y = 4$
4	$6 - 2$	
$4 = 4$		• Checks.

$y = 3x - 2$		
-1	$3(3) - 2$	• $x = 3, y = -1$
-1	$9 - 2$	
$-1 \neq 7$		• Does not check.

QUESTION   Is $(-2, 1)$ a solution of $y = 3x + 7$?

ANSWER   *Yes, because $1 = 3(-2) + 7$.*

The **graph of an equation in two variables** is a drawing of all the ordered-pair solutions of the equation. To create a graph of an equation, find some ordered-pair solutions of the equation, plot the corresponding points, and then connect the points with a smooth curve.

EXAMPLE 1 ■ Graph an Equation in Two Variables

Graph $y = 3x - 2$.

Solution

To find ordered-pair solutions, select various values of x and calculate the corresponding values of y. Plot the ordered pairs. After the ordered pairs have been graphed, draw a smooth curve through the points. It is convenient to keep track of the solutions in a table.

When choosing values of x, we often choose integer values because the resulting ordered pairs are easier to graph.

x	$3x - 2 = y$	(x, y)
-2	$3(-2) - 2 = -8$	$(-2, -8)$
-1	$3(-1) - 2 = -5$	$(-1, -5)$
0	$3(0) - 2 = -2$	$(0, -2)$
1	$3(1) - 2 = 1$	$(1, 1)$
2	$3(2) - 2 = 4$	$(2, 4)$
3	$3(3) - 2 = 7$	$(3, 7)$

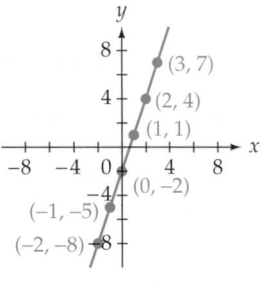

CHECK YOUR PROGRESS 1 Graph $y = -2x + 3$.

Solution See page S21.

The graph of $y = 3x - 2$ is shown again at the left. Note that the ordered pair $\left(\frac{4}{3}, 2\right)$ is a solution of the equation and is a point on the graph. The ordered pair $(4, 8)$ is *not* a solution of the equation and is *not* a point on the graph. Every ordered-pair solution of the equation is a point on the graph, and every point on the graph is an ordered-pair solution of the equation.

EXAMPLE 2 ■ Graph an Equation in Two Variables

Graph $y = x^2 + 4x$.

Solution

Select various values of x and calculate the corresponding values of y. Plot the ordered pairs. After the ordered pairs have been graphed, draw a smooth curve through the points. Here is a table showing some possible ordered pairs.

x	$x^2 + 4x = y$	(x, y)
-5	$(-5)^2 + 4(-5) = 5$	$(-5, 5)$
-4	$(-4)^2 + 4(-4) = 0$	$(-4, 0)$
-3	$(-3)^2 + 4(-3) = -3$	$(-3, -3)$
-2	$(-2)^2 + 4(-2) = -4$	$(-2, -4)$
-1	$(-1)^2 + 4(-1) = -3$	$(-1, -3)$
0	$(0)^2 + 4(0) = 0$	$(0, 0)$
1	$(1)^2 + 4(1) = 5$	$(1, 5)$

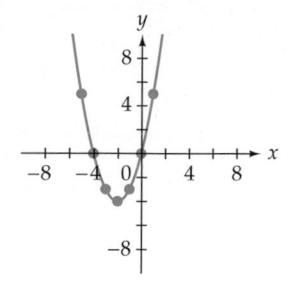

TAKE NOTE

As this example shows, it may be necessary to graph quite a number of points before a reasonably accurate graph can be drawn.

CHECK YOUR PROGRESS 2   Graph $y = -x^2 + 1$.

Solution   See page S21.

Math Matters   Computer Software Program Coordinate Systems

Some computer software programs use a coordinate system that is different from the xy-coordinate system we have discussed. For instance, in one particular software program, the origin $(0, 0)$ represents the top left point of a computer screen, as shown at the left. The points $(150, 100)$, $(300, 300)$, $(400, 200)$, and $(650, 400)$ are shown on the graph.

Introduction to Functions

An important part of mathematics is the study of the relationship between known quantities. Exploring relationships between known quantities frequently results in equations in two variables. For instance, as a car is driven, the fuel in the gas tank is burned. There is a correspondence between the number of gallons of fuel used and the number of miles traveled. If a car gets 25 miles per gallon, then the car consumes 0.04 gallon of fuel for each mile driven. For the sake of simplicity, we will assume that the car always consumes 0.04 gallon of gasoline for each mile driven. The equation $g = 0.04d$ defines how the number of gallons used, g, depends on the number of miles driven, d.

TAKE NOTE

A car that uses 1 gallon of gas to travel 25 miles uses $\frac{1}{25} = 0.04$ gallon to travel 1 mile.

Distance traveled (in miles), d	25	50	100	250	300
Fuel used (in gallons), g	1	2	4	10	12

The ordered pairs in this table are only some of the possible ordered pairs. Other possibilities are $(90, 3.6)$, $(125, 5)$, and $(235, 9.4)$. If all of the ordered pairs of the equation were drawn, the graph would appear as a portion of a line. The graph of the equation and the ordered pairs we have calculated are shown on the following page. Note that the graphs of all the ordered pairs are on the same line.

$$g = 0.04d, d \geq 0$$

QUESTION   *What is the meaning of the ordered pair (125, 5)?*

The ordered pairs, the graph, and the equation are all different ways of expressing the correspondence, or relationship, between the two variables. This correspondence, which pairs the number of miles driven with the number of gallons of fuel used, is called a *function*.

Here are some additional examples of functions, along with a specific example of each correspondence.

✔ TAKE NOTE

Because the square of any real number is a positive number or zero ($0^2 = 0$), the range of the function that pairs a number with its square contains the positive numbers and zero. Therefore, the range is the nonnegative real numbers. The difference between *nonnegative* numbers and *positive* numbers is that nonnegative numbers include zero; positive numbers do not include zero.

To each real number 5	there corresponds ⟶	its square 25
To each score on an exam 87	there corresponds ⟶	a grade B
To each student Alexander Sterling	there corresponds ⟶	a student identification number S18723519

An important fact about each of these correspondences is that each result is *unique*. For instance, for the real number 5, there is *exactly one* square, 25. With this in mind, we now state the definition of a function.

Definition of a Function

A **function** is a correspondence, or relationship, between two sets called the **domain** and **range** such that for each element of the domain there corresponds *exactly one* element of the range.

As an example of domain and range, consider the function that pairs a test score with a letter grade. The domain is the real numbers from 0 to 100. The range is the letters A, B, C, D, and F.

Test score	Grade
90–100	A
80–89	B
70–79	C
60–69	D
0–59	F

ANSWER   *A car that gets 25 miles per gallon can travel 125 miles on 5 gallons of fuel.*

As shown above, a function can be described in terms of ordered pairs or by a graph. Functions can also be defined by equations in two variables. For instance, when gravity is the only force acting on a falling body, a function that describes the distance s, in feet, an object will fall in t seconds is given by $s = 16t^2$.

Given a value of t (time), the value of s (the distance the object falls) can be found. For instance, given $t = 3$,

$$s = 16t^2$$
$$s = 16(3)^2 \quad \text{• Replace } t \text{ by } \mathbf{3}.$$
$$s = 16(9) \quad \text{• Simplify.}$$
$$s = 144$$

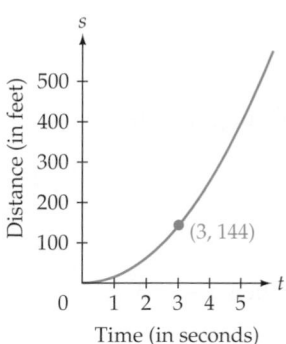

The object falls 144 feet in 3 seconds.

Because the distance the object falls *depends on* how long it has been falling, s is called the **dependent variable** and t is called the **independent variable.** Some of the ordered pairs of this function are $(3, 144)$, $(1, 16)$, $(0, 0)$, and $\left(\frac{1}{4}, 1\right)$. The ordered pairs can be written as (t, s), where $s = 16t^2$. By substituting $16t^2$ for s, we can also write the ordered pairs as $(t, 16t^2)$. For the equation $s = 16t^2$, we say that "distance is a function of time." A graph of the function is shown at the left.

Not all equations in two variables define a function. For instance,

$$y^2 = x^2 + 9$$

is not an equation that defines a function because

$$5^2 = 4^2 + 9 \qquad \text{and} \qquad (-5)^2 = 4^2 + 9$$

The ordered pairs $(4, 5)$ and $(4, -5)$ both belong to the equation. Consequently, there are two ordered pairs with the same first coordinate, 4, but *different* second coordinates, 5 and -5. By definition, the equation does not define a function. The phrase "y is a function of x," or a similar phrase with different variables, is used to describe those equations in two variables that define functions.

Functional notation is frequently used for equations that define functions. Just as the letter x is commonly used as a variable, the letter f is commonly used to name a function.

To describe the relationship between a number and its square using functional notation, we can write $f(x) = x^2$. The symbol $f(x)$ is read "the value of f at x" or "f of x." The symbol $f(x)$ is the **value of the function** and represents the value of the dependent variable for a given value of the independent variable. We will often write $y = f(x)$ to emphasize the relationship between the independent variable, x, and the dependent variable, y. Remember: y and $f(x)$ are different symbols for the same number. Also, the *name* of the function is f; the *value* of the function at x is $f(x)$.

The letters used to represent a function are somewhat arbitrary. All of the following equations represent the same function.

$$\left.\begin{array}{l} f(x) = x^2 \\ g(t) = t^2 \\ P(v) = v^2 \end{array}\right\} \quad \text{Each of these equations represents the square function.}$$

The process of finding $f(x)$ for a given value of x is called **evaluating the function.** For instance, to evaluate $f(x) = x^2$ when $x = 4$, replace x by 4 and simplify.

$$f(x) = x^2$$
$$f(4) = 4^2 = 16 \quad \text{• Replace } x \text{ by } \mathbf{4}. \text{ Then simplify.}$$

TAKE NOTE

The notation $f(x)$ does *not* mean "f times x." The letter f stands for the name of the function, and $f(x)$ is the value of the function at x.

The *value* of the function is 16 when $x = 4$. This means that an ordered pair of the function is $(4, 16)$.

EXAMPLE 3 ■ Evaluate a Function

Evaluate $s(t) = 2t^2 - 3t + 1$ when $t = -2$.

Solution
$$s(t) = 2t^2 - 3t + 1$$
$$s(-2) = 2(-2)^2 - 3(-2) + 1 \quad \text{• Replace } t \text{ by } -2. \text{ Then simplify.}$$
$$= 15$$

The value of the function is 15 when $t = -2$.

CHECK YOUR PROGRESS 3   Evaluate $f(z) = z^2 - z$ when $z = -3$.

Solution   See page S22.

Any letter or combination of letters can be used to name a function. In the next example, the letters *SA* are used to name a *Surface Area* function.

EXAMPLE 4 ■ Application of Evaluating a Function

The surface area of a cube (the sum of the areas of each of the six faces) is given by $SA(s) = 6s^2$, where $SA(s)$ is the surface area of the cube and s is the length of one side of the cube. Find the surface area of a cube that has a side of length 10 centimeters.

Solution
$$SA(s) = 6s^2$$
$$SA(10) = 6(10)^2 \quad \text{• Replace } s \text{ by } 10.$$
$$= 6(100) \quad \text{• Simplify.}$$
$$= 600$$

The surface area of the cube is 600 square centimeters.

Diagonal

CHECK YOUR PROGRESS 4   A **diagonal** of a polygon is a line segment from one vertex to a nonadjacent vertex, as shown at the left. The total number of diagonals of a polygon is given by $N(s) = \dfrac{s^2 - 3s}{2}$, where $N(s)$ is the total number of diagonals and s is the number of sides of the polygon. Find the total number of diagonals of a polygon with 12 sides.

Solution   See page S22.

Math Matters   The Special Theory of Relativity

In 1905, Albert Einstein published a paper that set the framework for relativity theory. This theory, now called the Special Theory of Relativity, explains, among other things, how mass changes for a body in motion. Essentially, the theory states that the mass of a body is a function of its velocity. That is, the mass of a body changes as its speed increases.

The function can be given by $M(v) = \dfrac{m_0}{\sqrt{1 - \dfrac{v^2}{c^2}}}$, where m_0 is the mass of the body at rest (its mass when its speed is zero) and c is the velocity of light, which Einstein showed was the same for all observers. The table below shows how a 5-kilogram mass increases as its speed becomes closer and closer to the speed of light.

Speed	Mass (kilograms)
30 meters/second—speed of a car on an expressway	5
240 meters/second—speed of a commercial jet	5
3.0×10^7 meters/second—10% of the speed of light	5.025
1.5×10^8 meters/second—50% of the speed of light	5.774
2.7×10^8 meters/second—90% of the speed of light	11.471

Note that for speeds of everyday objects, such as a car or plane, the increase in mass is negligible. Physicists have verified these increases using particle accelerators that can accelerate a particle such as an electron to more than 99.9% of the speed of light.

Graphs of Functions

Often the graph of a function can be drawn by finding ordered pairs of the function, plotting the points corresponding to the ordered pairs, and then connecting the points with a smooth curve.

For example, to graph $f(x) = x^3 + 1$, select several values of x and evaluate the function at each value. Recall that $f(x)$ and y are different symbols for the same quantity.

x	$f(x) = x^3 + 1$	(x, y)
-2	$f(-2) = (-2)^3 + 1 = -7$	$(-2, -7)$
-1	$f(-1) = (-1)^3 + 1 = 0$	$(-1, 0)$
0	$f(0) = (0)^3 + 1 = 1$	$(0, 1)$
1	$f(1) = (1)^3 + 1 = 2$	$(1, 2)$
2	$f(2) = (2)^3 + 1 = 9$	$(2, 9)$

Plot the ordered pairs and draw a smooth curve through the points.

EXAMPLE 5 ■ **Graph a Function**

Graph $h(x) = x^2 - 3$.

Solution

x	$h(x) = x^2 - 3$	(x, y)
−3	$h(-3) = (-3)^2 - 3 = 6$	(−3, 6)
−2	$h(-2) = (-2)^2 - 3 = 1$	(−2, 1)
−1	$h(-1) = (-1)^2 - 3 = -2$	(−1, −2)
0	$h(0) = (0)^2 - 3 = -3$	(0, −3)
1	$h(1) = (1)^2 - 3 = -2$	(1, −2)
2	$h(2) = (2)^2 - 3 = 1$	(2, 1)
3	$h(3) = (3)^2 - 3 = 6$	(3, 6)

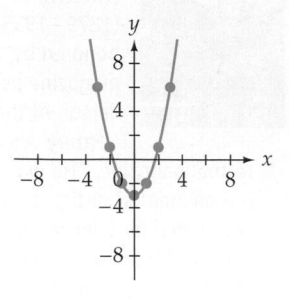

Plot the ordered pairs and draw a smooth curve through the points.

CHECK YOUR PROGRESS 5   Graph $f(x) = 2 - \dfrac{3}{4}x$.

Solution   *See page S22.*

Excursion

Dilations of a Geometric Figure

A **dilation** of a geometric figure changes the size of the figure by either enlarging it or reducing it. This is accomplished by multiplying the coordinates of the figure by a positive number called the **dilation constant.** Examples of enlarging (multiplying the coordinates by a number greater than 1) and reducing (multiplying the coordinates by a number between 0 and 1) a geometric figure are shown at the top of the following page.

(continued)

▼ point of interest

Photocopy machines have reduction and enlargement features that function essentially as constants of dilation. The numbers are usually expressed as a percent. A copier selection of 50% reduces the size of the object being copied by 50%. A copier selection of 125% increases the size of the object being copied by 25%.

ABCD was enlarged by multiplying its coordinates by 2. The result is A'B'C'D'.

ABCD was reduced by multiplying its coordinates by $\frac{1}{3}$. The result is A'B'C'D'.

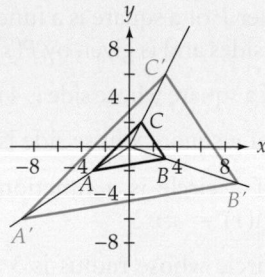

When each of the coordinates of a figure is multiplied by the same number in order to produce a dilation, the **center of dilation** will be the origin of the coordinate system. For triangle ABC at the left, a constant of dilation of 3 was used to produce triangle A'B'C'. Note that lines through the corresponding vertices of the two triangles intersect at the origin, the center of dilation. The center of dilation, however, can be any point in the plane.

Excursion Exercises

1. A dilation is performed on the figure with vertices $A(-2, 0)$, $B(2, 0)$, $C(4, -2)$, $D(2, -4)$, and $E(-2, -4)$.

   a. Draw the original figure and a new figure using 2 as the dilation constant.

   b. Draw the original figure and a new figure using $\frac{1}{2}$ as the dilation constant.

2. Because each of the coordinates of a geometric figure is multiplied by a number, the lengths of the sides of the figure will change. It is possible to show that the lengths change by a factor equal to the constant of dilation. In this exercise, you will examine the effect of a dilation on the angles of a geometric figure. Draw some figures and then draw a dilation of each figure using the origin as the center of dilation. Using a protractor, determine whether the measures of the angles of the dilated figure are different from the measures of the corresponding angles of the original figure.

3. Graphic artists use centers of dilation to create three-dimensional effects. Consider the block letter A shown at the left. Draw another block letter A by changing the center of dilation to see how it affects the 3-D look of the letter. Programs such as PowerPoint use these methods to create various shading options for design elements in a presentation.

Center of dilation

P

4. Draw an enlargement and a reduction of the figure at the left for the given center of dilation P.

5. On a blank piece of paper, draw a rectangle 4 inches by 6 inches with the center of the rectangle in the center of the paper. Make various photocopies of the rectangle using the reduction and enlargement settings on a copy machine. Where is the center of dilation for the copy machine?

Exercise Set 6.1

1. Graph the ordered pairs $(0, -1)$, $(2, 0)$, $(3, 2)$, and $(-1, 4)$.

2. Graph the ordered pairs $(-1, -3)$, $(0, -4)$, $(0, 4)$, and $(3, -2)$.

3. Draw a line through all points with an x-coordinate of 2.

4. Draw a line through all points with an x-coordinate of -3.

5. Draw a line through all points with a y-coordinate of -3.

6. Draw a line through all points with a y-coordinate of 4.

7. Graph the ordered-pair solutions of $y = x^2$ when $x = -2, -1, 0, 1$, and 2.

8. Graph the ordered-pair solutions of $y = -x^2 + 1$ when $x = -2, -1, 0, 1$, and 2.

9. Graph the ordered-pair solutions of $y = |x + 1|$ when $x = -5, -3, 0, 3$, and 5.

10. Graph the ordered-pair solutions of $y = -2|x|$ when $x = -3, -1, 0, 1$, and 3.

11. Graph the ordered-pair solutions of $y = -x^2 + 2$ when $x = -2, -1, 0$, and 1.

12. Graph the ordered-pair solutions of $y = -x^2 + 4$ when $x = -3, -1, 0, 1$, and 3.

13. Graph the ordered-pair solutions of $y = x^3 - 2$ when $x = -1, 0$, and 1.

14. Graph the ordered-pair solutions of $y = -x^3 + 1$ when $x = -1, 0, 1$, and 2.

In Exercises 15–24, graph each equation.

15. $y = 2x - 1$

16. $y = -3x + 2$

17. $y = \dfrac{2}{3}x + 1$

18. $y = -\dfrac{x}{2} - 3$

19. $y = \dfrac{1}{2}x^2$

20. $y = \dfrac{1}{3}x^2$

21. $y = 2x^2 - 1$

22. $y = -3x^2 + 2$

23. $y = |x - 1|$

24. $y = |x - 3|$

In Exercises 25–32, evaluate the function for the given value.

25. $f(x) = 2x + 7; x = -2$

26. $y(x) = 1 - 3x; x = -4$

27. $f(t) = t^2 - t - 3; t = 3$

28. $P(n) = n^2 - 4n - 7; n = -3$

29. $v(s) = s^3 + 3s^2 - 4s - 2; s = -2$

30. $f(x) = 3x^3 - 4x^2 + 7; x = 2$

31. $T(p) = \dfrac{p^2}{p - 2}; p = 0$

32. $s(t) = \dfrac{4t}{t^2 + 2}; t = 2$

33. **Geometry** The perimeter P of a square is a function of the length s of one of its sides and is given by $P(s) = 4s$.

   a. Find the perimeter of a square whose side is 4 meters.

   b. Find the perimeter of a square whose side is 5 feet.

34. **Geometry** The area of a circle is a function of its radius and is given by $A(r) = \pi r^2$.

   a. Find the area of a circle whose radius is 3 inches. Round to the nearest tenth of a square inch.

   b. Find the area of a circle whose radius is 12 centimeters. Round to the nearest tenth of a square centimeter.

35. **Sports** The height h, in feet, of a ball that is released 4 feet above the ground with an initial velocity of 80 feet per second is a function of the time t, in seconds, the ball is in the air and is given by
$$h(t) = -16t^2 + 80t + 4, \quad 0 \le t \le 5.04$$

   a. Find the height of the ball above the ground 2 seconds after it is released.

   b. Find the height of the ball above the ground 4 seconds after it is released.

36. **Forestry** The distance d, in miles, a forest fire ranger can see from an observation tower is a function of the height h, in feet, of the tower above level ground and is given by $d(h) = 1.5\sqrt{h}$.

   a. Find the distance a ranger can see whose eye level is 20 feet above level ground. Round to the nearest tenth of a mile.

   b. Find the distance a ranger can see whose eye level is 35 feet above level ground. Round to the nearest tenth of a mile.

37. Sound The speed s, in feet per second, of sound in air depends on the temperature t of the air in degrees Celsius and is given by $s(t) = \dfrac{1087\sqrt{t + 273}}{16.52}$.

    a. What is the speed of sound in air when the temperature is 0°C (the temperature at which water freezes)? Round to the nearest foot per second.

    b. What is the speed of sound in air when the temperature is 25°C? Round to the nearest foot per second.

38. Softball In a softball league in which each team plays every other team three times, the number of games N that must be scheduled depends on the number of teams n in the league and is given by $N(n) = \dfrac{3}{2}n^2 - \dfrac{3}{2}n$.

    a. How many games must be scheduled for a league that has five teams?

    b. How many games must be scheduled for a league that has six teams?

39. Mixtures The percent concentration P of salt in a particular salt water solution depends on the number of grams x of salt that are added to the solution and is given by $P(x) = \dfrac{100x + 100}{x + 10}$.

    a. What is the original percent concentration of salt?

    b. What is the percent concentration of salt after 5 more grams of salt are added?

40. Pendulums The time T, in seconds, it takes a pendulum to make one swing depends on the length of the pendulum and is given by $T(L) = 2\pi\sqrt{\dfrac{L}{32}}$, where L is the length of the pendulum in feet.

    a. Find the time it takes the pendulum to make one swing if the length of the pendulum is 3 feet. Round to the nearest hundredth of a second.

    b. Find the time it takes the pendulum to make one swing if the length of the pendulum is 9 inches. Round to the nearest tenth of a second.

In Exercises 41–56, graph the function.

41. $f(x) = 2x - 5$

42. $f(x) = -2x + 4$

43. $f(x) = -x + 4$

44. $f(x) = 3x - 1$

45. $g(x) = \dfrac{2}{3}x + 2$

46. $h(x) = \dfrac{5}{2}x - 1$

47. $F(x) = -\dfrac{1}{2}x + 3$

48. $F(x) = -\dfrac{3}{4}x - 1$

49. $f(x) = x^2 - 1$

50. $f(x) = x^2 + 2$

51. $f(x) = -x^2 + 4$

52. $f(x) = -2x^2 + 5$

53. $g(x) = x^2 - 4x$

54. $h(x) = x^2 + 4x$

55. $P(x) = x^2 - x - 6$

56. $P(x) = x^2 - 2x - 3$

Extensions

CRITICAL THINKING

57. Geometry Find the area of the rectangle.

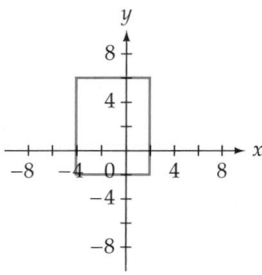

58. Geometry Find the area of the triangle.

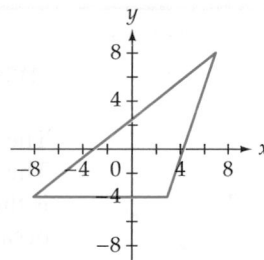

59. Suppose f is a function. Is it possible to have $f(2) = 4$ and $f(2) = 7$? Explain your answer.

60. Suppose f is a function and $f(a) = 4$ and $f(b) = 4$. Does this mean that $a = b$?

61. If $f(x) = 2x + 5$ and $f(a) = 9$, find a.

62. If $f(x) = x^2$ and $f(a) = 9$, find a.

63. Let $f(a, b) =$ the sum of a and b.
    Let $g(a, b) =$ the product of a and b.
    Find $f(2, 5) + g(2, 5)$.

64. Let $f(a, b) =$ the greatest common factor of a and b and let $g(a, b) =$ the least common multiple of a and b. Find $f(14, 35) + g(14, 35)$.

65. Given $f(x) = x^2 + 3$, for what value of x is $f(x)$ least?

66. Given $f(x) = -x^2 + 4x$, for what value of x is $f(x)$ greatest?

EXAMPLE 1 ■ Find the *x*- and *y*-intercepts of a Graph

Find the *x*- and *y*-intercepts of the graph of $g(x) = -3x + 2$.

Solution

When a graph crosses the *x*-axis, the *y*-coordinate of the point is 0. Therefore, to find the *x*-intercept, replace $g(x)$ by 0 and solve the equation for *x*. [Recall that $g(x)$ is another name for *y*.]

$$g(x) = -3x + 2$$
$$0 = -3x + 2 \quad \text{• Replace } g(x) \text{ by 0.}$$
$$-2 = -3x$$
$$\frac{2}{3} = x$$

The *x*-intercept is $\left(\frac{2}{3}, 0\right)$.

When a graph crosses the *y*-axis, the *x*-coordinate of the point is 0. Therefore, to find the *y*-intercept, evaluate the function when *x* is 0.

$$g(x) = -3x + 2$$
$$g(0) = -3(0) + 2 \quad \text{• Evaluate } g(x) \text{ when } x = 0. \text{ Then simplify.}$$
$$= 2$$

The *y*-intercept is $(0, 2)$.

CHECK YOUR PROGRESS 1   Find the *x*- and *y*-intercepts of the graph of $f(x) = \frac{1}{2}x + 3$.

Solution   See page S22.

In Example 1, note that the *y*-coordinate of the *y*-intercept of $g(x) = -3x + 2$ has the same value as *b* in the equation $f(x) = mx + b$. This is always true.

> **y-intercept**
>
> The *y*-intercept of the graph of $f(x) = mx + b$ is $(0, b)$.

If we evaluate the linear function that models pressure on a diver, $P(d) = 64d + 2100$, at 0, we have

$$P(d) = 64d + 2100$$
$$P(0) = 64(0) + 2100 = 2100$$

In this case, the *P*-intercept (the intercept on the vertical axis) is $(0, 2100)$. In the context of the application, this means that the pressure on a diver 0 feet below the ocean's surface is 2100 pounds per square foot. Another way of saying "zero feet below the ocean's surface" is "at sea level." Thus the pressure on the diver, or anyone else for that matter, at sea level is 2100 pounds per square foot.

Both the *x*- and *y*-intercept can have meaning in an application problem. This is demonstrated in the next example.

✔ **TAKE NOTE**

To find the *y*-intercept of $y = mx + b$ [we have replaced $f(x)$ by *y*], let $x = 0$. Then

$$y = mx + b$$
$$y = m(0) + b$$
$$= b$$

The *y*-intercept is $(0, b)$. This result is shown at the right.

✔ **TAKE NOTE**

We are working with the function $P(d) = 64d + 2100$. Therefore, the intercepts on the horizontal axis of a graph of the function are *d*-intercepts rather than *x*-intercepts, and the intercept on the vertical axis is a *P*-intercept rather than a *y*-intercept.

EXAMPLE 2 ■ Application of the Intercepts of a Linear Function

After a parachute is deployed, a function that models the height of the parachutist above the ground is $f(t) = -10t + 2800$, where $f(t)$ is the height, in feet, of the parachutist t seconds after the parachute is deployed. Find the intercepts on the vertical and horizontal axes and explain what they mean in the context of the problem.

Solution
To find the intercept on the vertical axis, evaluate the function when t is 0.

$$f(t) = -10t + 2800$$
$$f(0) = -10(0) + 2800 = 2800$$

The intercept on the vertical axis is $(0, 2800)$. This means that the parachutist is 2800 feet above the ground when the parachute is deployed.

To find the intercept on the horizontal axis, set $f(t) = 0$ and solve for t.

$$f(t) = -10t + 2800$$
$$0 = -10t + 2800$$
$$-2800 = -10t$$
$$280 = t$$

The intercept on the horizontal axis is $(280, 0)$. This means that the parachutist reaches the ground 280 seconds after the parachute is deployed. Note that the parachutist reaches the ground when $f(t) = 0$.

CHECK YOUR PROGRESS 2   A function that models the descent of a certain small airplane is given by $g(t) = -20t + 8000$, where $g(t)$ is the height, in feet, of the airplane t seconds after it begins its descent. Find the intercepts on the vertical and horizontal axes, and explain what they mean in the context of the problem.

Solution   *See page S22.*

Slope of a Line

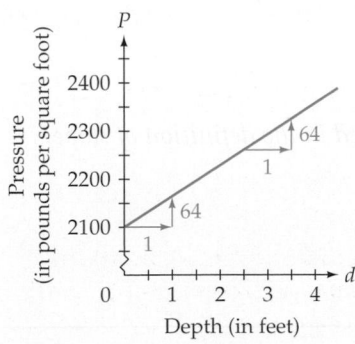

Pressure (in pounds per square foot)
Depth (in feet)

Consider again the linear function $P(d) = 64d + 2100$, which models the pressure on a diver as the diver descends below the ocean's surface. From the graph at the left, you can see that when the depth of the diver increases by 1 foot, the pressure on the diver increases by 64 pounds per square foot. This can be verified algebraically.

$P(0) = 64(0) + 2100 = 2100$ • Pressure at sea level
$P(1) = 64(1) + 2100 = 2164$ • Pressure after descending **1** foot
$2164 - 2100 = 64$ • Change in pressure

If we choose two other depths that differ by 1 foot, such as 2.5 feet and 3.5 feet (see the graph at the left), the change in pressure is the same.

$P(2.5) = 64(2.5) + 2100 = 2260$ • Pressure at **2.5** feet below the surface
$P(3.5) = 64(3.5) + 2100 = 2324$ • Pressure at **3.5** feet below the surface
$2324 - 2260 = 64$ • Change in pressure

The **slope** of a line is the change in the vertical direction caused by one unit of change in the horizontal direction. For $P(d) = 64d + 2100$, the slope is 64. In the context of the problem, the slope means that the pressure on a diver increases by 64 pounds per square foot for each additional foot the diver descends. Note that the slope (64) has the same value as the coefficient of d in $P(d) = 64d + 2100$. This connection between the slope and the coefficient of the variable in a linear function always holds.

Slope

For a linear function given by $f(x) = mx + b$, the slope of the graph of the function is m, the coefficient of the variable.

QUESTION   *What is the slope of each of the following?*

       a. $y = -2x + 3$ **b.** $f(x) = x + 4$ **c.** $g(x) = 3 - 4x$

       d. $y = \dfrac{1}{2}x - 5$

The slope of a line can be calculated by using the coordinates of any two distinct points on the line and the following formula.

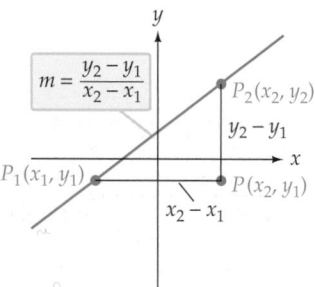

Slope of a Line

Let (x_1, y_1) and (x_2, y_2) be two points on a nonvertical line. Then the **slope** of the line through the two points is the ratio of the change in the y-coordinates to the change in the x-coordinates.

$$m = \frac{\text{change in } y}{\text{change in } x} = \frac{y_2 - y_1}{x_2 - x_1}, x_1 \neq x_2$$

QUESTION   *Why is the restriction $x_1 \neq x_2$ required in the definition of slope?*

ANSWER   **a.** -2 **b.** 1 **c.** -4 **d.** $\dfrac{1}{2}$

ANSWER   *If $x_1 = x_2$, then the difference $x_2 - x_1 = 0$. This would make the denominator 0, and division by 0 is not defined.*

EXAMPLE 3 ■ **Find the Slope of a Line Between Two Points**

Find the slope of the line between the two points.

a. $(-4, -3)$ and $(-1, 1)$ **b.** $(-2, 3)$ and $(1, -3)$

c. $(-1, -3)$ and $(4, -3)$ **d.** $(4, 3)$ and $(4, -1)$

Solution

a. $(x_1, y_1) = (-4, -3)$, $(x_2, y_2) = (-1, 1)$

$$m = \frac{y_2 - y_1}{x_2 - x_1} = \frac{1 - (-3)}{-1 - (-4)} = \frac{4}{3}$$

The slope is $\frac{4}{3}$. A *positive* slope indicates that the line slopes *upward* to the right. For this particular line, the value of *y increases* by $\frac{4}{3}$ when *x* increases by 1.

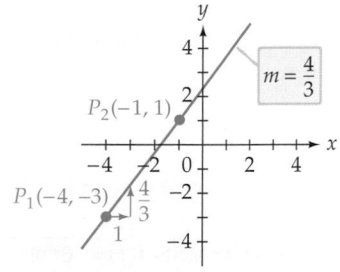

b. $(x_1, y_1) = (-2, 3)$, $(x_2, y_2) = (1, -3)$

$$m = \frac{y_2 - y_1}{x_2 - x_1} = \frac{-3 - 3}{1 - (-2)} = \frac{-6}{3} = -2$$

The slope is -2. A *negative* slope indicates that the line slopes *downward* to the right. For this particular line, the value of *y decreases* by 2 when *x* increases by 1.

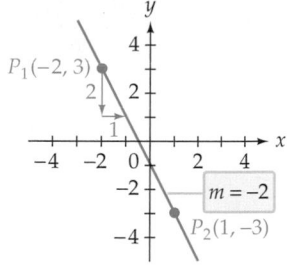

c. $(x_1, y_1) = (-1, -3)$, $(x_2, y_2) = (4, -3)$

$$m = \frac{y_2 - y_1}{x_2 - x_1} = \frac{-3 - (-3)}{4 - (-1)} = \frac{0}{5} = 0$$

The slope is 0. A *zero* slope indicates that the line is *horizontal*. For this particular line, the value of *y stays the same* when *x* increases by any amount.

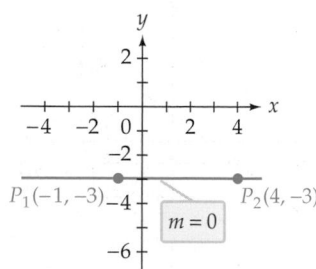

d. $(x_1, y_1) = (4, 3)$, $(x_2, y_2) = (4, -1)$

$$m = \frac{y_2 - y_1}{x_2 - x_1} = \frac{-1 - 3}{4 - 4} = \frac{-4}{0} \quad \begin{array}{l}\text{Division by 0}\\ \text{is undefined.}\end{array}$$

If the denominator of the slope formula is zero, the line has *no slope*. Sometimes we say that the slope of a vertical line is *undefined*.

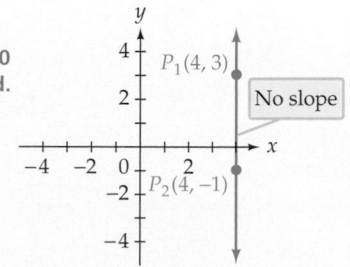

CHECK YOUR PROGRESS 3 Find the slope of the line between the two points.

a. $(-6, 5)$ and $(4, -5)$ **b.** $(-5, 0)$ and $(-5, 7)$

c. $(-7, -2)$ and $(8, 8)$ **d.** $(-6, 7)$ and $(1, 7)$

Solution *See page S22.*

Suppose a jogger is running at a constant velocity of 6 miles per hour. Then the linear function $d = 6t$ relates the time t, in hours, spent running to the distance traveled d, in miles. A table of values is shown below.

Time, t, in hours	0	0.5	1	1.5	2	2.5
Distance, d, in miles	0	3	6	9	12	15

Whether we write $f(t) = 6t$ or $d = 6t$, the equation represents a linear function. $f(t)$ and d are different symbols for the same quantity.

Because the equation $d = 6t$ represents a linear function, the slope of the graph of the equation is 6. This can be confirmed by choosing any two points on the graph shown below and finding the slope of the line between the two points. The points $(0.5, 3)$ and $(2, 12)$ are used here.

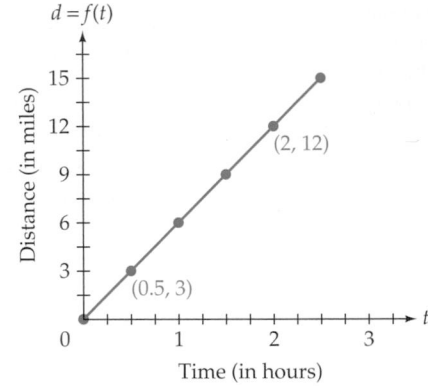

$$m = \frac{\text{change in } d}{\text{change in } t} = \frac{12 \text{ miles} - 3 \text{ miles}}{2 \text{ hours} - 0.5 \text{ hours}} = \frac{9 \text{ miles}}{1.5 \text{ hours}} = 6 \text{ miles per hour}$$

This example demonstrates that the slope of the graph of an object in uniform motion is the same as the velocity of the object. In a more general way, any time we discuss the velocity of an object, we are discussing the slope of the graph that describes the relationship between the distance the object travels and the time it travels.

EXAMPLE 4 ■ Application of the Slope of a Linear Function

The function $T(x) = -6.5x + 20$ approximates the temperature $T(x)$, in degrees Celsius, at x kilometers above sea level. What is the slope of this function? Write a sentence that explains the meaning of the slope in the context of this application.

Solution

For the linear function $T(x) = -6.5x + 20$, the slope is the coefficient of x. Therefore, the slope is -6.5. The slope means that the temperature is decreasing (because the slope is negative) 6.5°C for each 1-kilometer increase in height above sea level.

CHECK YOUR PROGRESS 4   The distance that a homing pigeon can fly can be approximated by $d(t) = 50t$, where $d(t)$ is the distance, in miles, flown by the pigeon in t hours. Find the slope of this function. What is the meaning of the slope in the context of the problem?

Solution   *See page S23.*

Math Matters

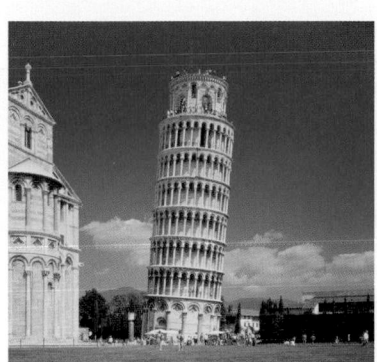

Galileo Galilei (găl-ĭ'lā-ē) (1564–1642) was one of the most influential scientists of his time. In addition to inventing the telescope, with which he discovered the moons of Jupiter, Galileo successfully argued that Aristotle's assertion that heavy objects drop at a greater velocity than lighter ones was incorrect. According to legend, Galileo went to the top of the Leaning Tower of Pisa and dropped two balls at the same time, one weighing twice the other. His assistant, standing on the ground, observed that both balls reached the ground at the same time.

There is no historical evidence that Galileo actually performed this experiment, but he did do something similar. Galileo correctly reasoned that if Aristotle's assertion were true, then balls of different weights should roll down a ramp at different speeds. Galileo did carry out this experiment and was able to show that, in fact, balls of different weights reached the end of the ramp at the same time. Galileo was not able to determine why this happened, and it took Issac Newton, born the same year that Galileo died, to formulate the first theory of gravity.

Slope–Intercept Form of a Straight Line

The value of the slope of a line gives the change in y for a *1-unit* change in x. For instance, a slope of -3 means that y changes by -3 as x changes by 1; a slope of $\frac{4}{3}$ means that y changes by $\frac{4}{3}$ as x changes by 1. Because it is difficult to graph a change of $\frac{4}{3}$, it is easier to think of a fractional slope in terms of integer changes in x and y. As shown at the right, for a slope of $\frac{4}{3}$ we have

$$m = \frac{\text{change in } y}{\text{change in } x} = \frac{4}{3}$$

That is, for a slope of $\frac{4}{3}$, y changes by 4 as x changes by 3.

EXAMPLE 5 ■ **Graph a Line Given a Point on the Line and the Slope**

Draw the line that passes through $(-2, 4)$ and has slope $-\frac{3}{4}$.

Solution
Place a dot at $(-2, 4)$ and then rewrite $-\frac{3}{4}$ as $\frac{-3}{4}$. Starting from $(-2, 4)$, move 3 units down (the change in y) and then 4 units to the right (the change in x). Place a dot at that location and then draw a line through the two points.

CHECK YOUR PROGRESS 5   Draw the line that passes through $(2, 4)$ and has slope -1.

Solution   *See page S23.*

Because the slope and y-intercept can be determined directly from the equation $f(x) = mx + b$, this equation is called the *slope–intercept form* of a straight line.

> **Slope–Intercept Form of the Equation of a Line**
>
> The graph of $f(x) = mx + b$ is a straight line with slope m and y-intercept $(0, b)$.

When a function is written in this form, it is possible to create a quick graph of the function.

EXAMPLE 6 ■ **Graph a Linear Function Using the Slope and y-intercept**

Graph $f(x) = -\frac{2}{3}x + 4$ by using the slope and y-intercept.

Solution
From the equation, the slope is $-\frac{2}{3}$ and the y-intercept is $(0, 4)$. Place a dot at the y-intercept. We can write the slope as $m = -\frac{2}{3} = \frac{-2}{3}$. Starting from the y-intercept, move 2 units down and 3 units to the right and place another dot. Now draw a line through the two points.

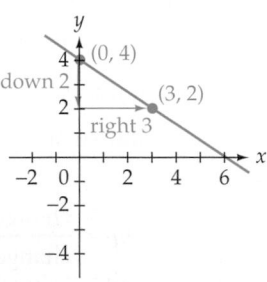

CHECK YOUR PROGRESS 6   Graph $y = \frac{3}{4}x - 5$ by using the slope and y-intercept.

Solution   *See page S23.*

Excursion

Negative Velocity

We can expand the concept of velocity to include negative velocity. Suppose a car travels in a straight line starting at a given point. If the car is moving to the right, then we say that its velocity is positive. If the car is moving to the left, then we say that its velocity is negative. For instance, a velocity of −45 miles per hour means the car is moving to the left at 45 miles per hour.

If we were to graph the motion of an object on a distance–time graph, a positive velocity would be indicated by a positive slope; a negative velocity would be indicated by a negative slope.

The graph at the left represents a car traveling on a straight road. Answer the following questions on the basis of this graph.

1. Between what two times is the car moving to the right?
2. Between what two times does the car have a positive velocity?
3. Between what two times is the car moving to the left?
4. Between what two times does the car have a negative velocity?
5. After 2 hours, how far is the car from its starting position?
6. How long after the car leaves its starting position does it return to its starting position?
7. What is the velocity of the car during its first 2 hours of travel?
8. What is the velocity of the car during its last 4 hours of travel?

The graph below represents another car traveling on a straight road, but this car's motion is a little more complicated. Use this graph for the questions below.

9. What is the slope of the line between hours 3 and 4?
10. What is the velocity of the car between hours 3 and 4? Is the car moving?
11. During which of the following intervals of time is the absolute value of the velocity greatest: 0 to 2 hours, 2 to 3 hours, 3 to 4 hours, or 4 to 8 hours? (Recall that the absolute value of a real number *a* is the distance between *a* and 0 on the number line.)

Exercise Set 6.2

In Exercises 1–14, find the x- and y-intercepts of the graph of the equation.

1. $f(x) = 3x - 6$

2. $f(x) = 2x + 8$

3. $y = \dfrac{2}{3}x - 4$

4. $y = -\dfrac{3}{4}x + 6$

5. $y = -x - 4$

6. $y = -\dfrac{x}{2} + 1$

7. $3x + 4y = 12$

8. $5x - 2y = 10$

9. $2x - 3y = 9$

10. $4x + 3y = 8$

11. $\dfrac{x}{2} + \dfrac{y}{3} = 1$

12. $\dfrac{x}{3} - \dfrac{y}{2} = 1$

13. $x - \dfrac{y}{2} = 1$

14. $-\dfrac{x}{4} + \dfrac{y}{3} = 1$

15. **Crickets** There is a relationship between the number of times a cricket chirps per minute and the air temperature. A linear model of this relationship is given by
$$f(x) = 7x - 30$$
where x is the temperature in degrees Celsius and $f(x)$ is the number of chirps per minute. Find and discuss the meaning of the x-intercept in the context of this application.

16. **Travel** An approximate linear model that gives the remaining distance, in miles, a plane must travel from Los Angeles to Paris is given by
$$s(t) = 6000 - 500t$$
where $s(t)$ is the remaining distance t hours after the flight begins. Find and discuss the meaning, in the context of this application, of the intercepts on the vertical and horizontal axes.

17. **Refrigeration** The temperature of an object taken from a freezer gradually rises and can be modeled by
$$T(x) = 3x - 15$$
where $T(x)$ is the Fahrenheit temperature of the object x minutes after being removed from the freezer. Find and discuss the meaning, in the context of this application, of the intercepts on the vertical and horizontal axes.

18. **Retirement Account** A retired biologist begins withdrawing money from a retirement account according to the linear model
$$A(t) = 100{,}000 - 2500t$$
where $A(t)$ is the amount, in dollars, remaining in the account t months after withdrawals begin. Find and discuss the meaning, in the context of this application, of the intercepts on the vertical and horizontal axes.

In Exercises 19–36, find the slope of the line containing the two points.

19. $(1, 3), (3, 1)$

20. $(2, 3), (5, 1)$

21. $(-1, 4), (2, 5)$

22. $(3, -2), (1, 4)$

23. $(-1, 3), (-4, 5)$

24. $(-1, -2), (-3, 2)$

25. $(0, 3), (4, 0)$

26. $(-2, 0), (0, 3)$

27. $(2, 4), (2, -2)$

28. $(4, 1), (4, -3)$

29. $(2, 5), (-3, -2)$

30. $(4, 1), (-1, -2)$

31. $(2, 3), (-1, 3)$

32. $(3, 4), (0, 4)$

33. $(0, 4), (-2, 5)$

34. $(-2, 3), (-2, 5)$

35. $(-3, -1), (-3, 4)$

36. $(-2, -5), (-4, -1)$

37. **Travel** The graph below shows the relationship between the distance traveled by a motorist and the time of travel. Find the slope of the line between the two points shown on the graph. Write a sentence that states the meaning of the slope in the context of this application.

38. **Depreciation** The graph below shows the relationship between the value of a building and the depreciation allowed for income tax purposes. Find the slope of the line between the two points shown on the graph. Write a sentence that states the meaning of the slope in the context of this application.

39. **Income tax** The graph below shows the relationship between the amount of tax and the amount of taxable income between \$29,050 and \$70,350. Find the slope of the line between the two points shown on the graph. Write a sentence that states the meaning of the slope in the context of this application.

(graph with points (70,350, 14,325) and (29,050, 4000); y-axis Tax (in dollars) with values 14,325 and 4000; x-axis Taxable income (in dollars) with values 29,050 and 70,350)

40. **Mortgages** The graph below shows the relationship between the monthly payment on a mortgage and the amount of the mortgage. Find the slope of the line between the two points shown on the graph. Write a sentence that states the meaning of the slope in the context of this application.

(graph with points (250,000, 1750) and (100,000, 700); y-axis Monthly payment (in dollars) with values 1750 and 700; x-axis Mortgage (in dollars) with values 100,000 and 250,000)

41. **Foot Races** The graph below shows the relationship between distance and time for the 5000-meter run for the world record by Deena Drossin in 2002. (Assume Drossin ran the race at a constant rate.) Find the slope of the line between the two points shown on the graph. Round to the nearest tenth. Write a sentence that states the meaning of the slope in the context of this application.

(graph with points (14.54, 5000) and (0, 0); y-axis Distance (in meters) with values 5000 and 2500; x-axis Time (in minutes) with value 14.54)

42. **Foot Races** The graph below shows the relationship between distance and time for the 10,000-meter run for the world record by Sammy Kipketer in 2002. (Assume Kipketer ran the race at a constant rate.) Find the slope of the line between the two points shown on the graph. Round to the nearest tenth. Write a sentence that states the meaning of the slope in the context of this application.

(graph with points (27.11, 10,000) and (0, 0); y-axis Distance (in meters) with values 10,000 and 5000; x-axis Time (in minutes) with value 27.11)

43. Graph the line that passes through the point $(-1, -3)$ and has slope $\frac{4}{3}$.

44. Graph the line that passes through the point $(-2, -3)$ and has slope $\frac{5}{4}$.

45. Graph the line that passes through the point $(-3, 0)$ and has slope -3.

46. Graph the line that passes through the point $(2, 0)$ and has slope -1.

In Exercises 47–52, graph using the slope and y-intercept.

47. $f(x) = \dfrac{1}{2}x + 2$ **48.** $f(x) = \dfrac{2}{3}x - 3$

49. $f(x) = -\dfrac{3}{2}x$ **50.** $f(x) = \dfrac{3}{4}x$

51. $f(x) = \dfrac{1}{3}x - 1$ **52.** $f(x) = -\dfrac{3}{2}x + 6$

Extensions
CRITICAL THINKING

53. Jogging Lois and Tanya start from the same place on a straight jogging course, at the same time, and jog in the same direction. Lois is jogging at 9 kilometers per hour, and Tanya is jogging at 6 kilometers per hour. The graphs on the following page show the distance each jogger has traveled in x hours and the distance between the joggers in x hours. Which graph represents the distance Lois has traveled in x hours? Which graph represents the distance Tanya has traveled in x

hours? Which graph represents the distance between Lois and Tanya in x hours?

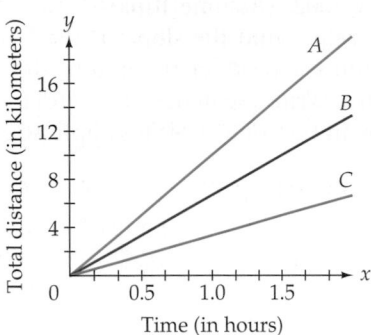

54. Chemistry A chemist is filling two cans from a faucet that releases water at a constant rate. Can 1 has a diameter of 20 millimeters and can 2 has a diameter of 30 millimeters.

   a. In the following graph, which line represents the depth of the water in can 1 after x seconds?

   b. Use the graph to estimate the difference in the depths of the water in the two cans after 15 seconds.

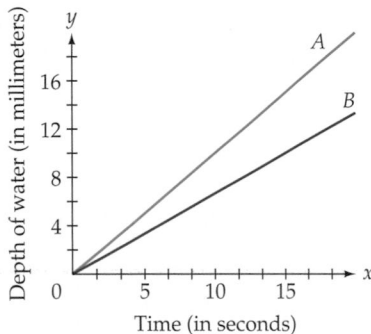

55. ANSI The American National Standards Institute (ANSI) states that the slope of a wheelchair ramp must not exceed $\frac{1}{12}$.

Does the ramp pictured above meet the requirements of ANSI?

56. ANSI A ramp for a wheelchair must be 14 inches high. What is the minimum length of this ramp so that it meets the ANSI requirements stated in Exercise 55?

57. If $(2, 3)$ are the coordinates of a point on a line that has slope 2, what is the y-coordinate of the point on the line at which $x = 4$?

58. If $(-1, 2)$ are the coordinates of a point on a line that has slope -3, what is the y-coordinate of the point on the line at which $x = 1$?

59. If $(1, 4)$ are the coordinates of a point on a line that has slope $\frac{2}{3}$, what is the y-coordinate of the point on the line at which $x = -2$?

60. If $(-2, -1)$ are the coordinates of a point on a line that has slope $\frac{3}{2}$, what is the y-coordinate of the point on the line at which $x = -6$?

61. What effect does increasing the coefficient of x have on the graph of $y = mx + b$?

62. What effect does decreasing the coefficient of x have on the graph of $y = mx + b$?

63. What effect does increasing the constant term have on the graph of $y = mx + b$?

64. What effect does decreasing the constant term have on the graph of $y = mx + b$?

65. Do the graphs of all straight lines have a y-intercept? If not, give an example of one that does not.

66. If two lines have the same slope and the same y-intercept, must the graphs of the lines be the same? If not, give an example.

EXPLORATIONS

67. Construction When you climb a staircase, the flat part of a stair that you step on is called the *tread* of the stair. The *riser* is the vertical part of the stair. The slope of a staircase is the ratio of the length of the riser to the length of the tread. Because the design of a staircase may affect safety, most cities have building codes that give rules for the design of a staircase.

   a. The traditional design of a staircase calls for a 9-inch tread and an 8.25-inch riser. What is the slope of this staircase?

b. A newer design for a staircase uses an 11-inch tread and a 7-inch riser. What is the slope of this staircase?

c. An architect is designing a house with a staircase that is 8 feet high and 12 feet long. Is the architect using the traditional design in part a or the newer design in part b? Explain your answer.

d. Staircases that have a slope between 0.5 and 0.7 are usually considered safer than those with a slope greater than 0.7. Design a safe staircase that goes from the first floor of a house to the second floor, which is 9 feet above the first floor.

e. Measure the tread and riser for three staircases you encounter. Do these staircases match the traditional design in part a or the newer design in part b?

68. Geometry In the diagram at the right, lines l_1 and l_2 are perpendicular with slopes m_1 and m_2, respectively, and $m_1 > 0$ and $m_2 < 0$. Line segment $\overline{AC}$ has length 1.

a. Show that the length of $\overline{BC}$ is m_1.

b. Show that the length of $\overline{CD}$ is $-m_2$. Note that because m_2 is a negative number, $-m_2$ is a positive number.

c. Show that right triangles ACB and DCA are similar triangles. **Similar triangles** have the same shape; the corresponding angles are equal, and corresponding sides are in proportion. (*Suggestion:* Show that the measure of angle ADC equals the measure of angle BAC.)

d. Show that $\dfrac{m_1}{1} = \dfrac{1}{-m_2}$. Use the fact that the ratios of corresponding sides of similar triangles are equal.

e. Use the equation in part d to show that $m_1 m_2 = -1$.

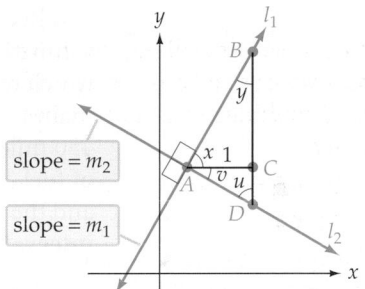

Finding Linear Models

Finding Linear Models

Suppose that a car uses 0.04 gallon of gas per mile driven and that the fuel tank, which holds 18 gallons of gas, is full. Using this information, we can determine a linear model for the amount of fuel remaining in the gas tank after driving x miles.

Recall that a linear function is one that can be written in the form $f(x) = mx + b$, where m is the slope of the line and b is the y-intercept. The slope is the rate at which the car is using fuel, 0.04 gallon per mile. Because the car is consuming the fuel, the amount of fuel in the tank is decreasing. Therefore, the slope is negative and we have $m = -0.04$.

The amount of fuel in the tank depends on the number of miles, x, the car has been driven. Before the car starts (that is, when $x = 0$), there are 18 gallons of gas in the tank. The y-intercept is $(0, 18)$.

Using this information, we can create the linear function.

$$f(x) = mx + b$$
$$f(x) = -0.04x + 18 \quad \text{• Replace } m \text{ by } -0.04 \text{ and } b \text{ by } 18.$$

The linear function that models the amount of fuel remaining in the tank is given by $f(x) = -0.04x + 18$, where $f(x)$ is the amount of fuel, in gallons, remaining after driving x miles. The graph of the function is shown at the left.

The x-intercept of a graph is the point at which $f(x) = 0$. For this application, $f(x) = 0$ when there are 0 gallons of fuel remaining in the tank. Thus, replacing $f(x)$ by 0 in $f(x) = -0.04x + 18$ and solving for x will give the number of miles the car can be driven before running out of gas.

$$f(x) = -0.04x + 18$$
$$0 = -0.04x + 18 \qquad \text{• Replace } f(x) \text{ by } \mathbf{0}.$$
$$-18 = -0.04x$$
$$450 = x$$

The car can travel 450 miles before running out of gas.

Recall that the domain of a function is all possible values of x, and the range of a function is all possible values of $f(x)$. For the function $f(x) = -0.04x + 18$, which was used above to model the fuel remaining in the gas tank of the car, the domain is $\{x \mid 0 \le x \le 450\}$ because the fuel tank is empty when the car has traveled 450 miles. The range is $\{y \mid 0 \le y \le 18\}$ because the tank can hold up to 18 gallons of fuel. Sometimes it is convenient to write the domain $\{x \mid 0 \le x \le 450\}$ as $[0, 450]$ and the range $\{y \mid 0 \le y \le 18\}$ as $[0, 18]$. The notation $[0, 450]$ and $[0, 18]$ is called **interval notation.** Using interval notation, a domain of $\{x \mid a \le x \le b\}$ is written $[a, b]$ and a range of $\{y \mid c \le y \le d\}$ is written $[c, d]$.

QUESTION   *Why does it not make sense for the domain of $f(x) = -0.04x + 18$ to exceed 450?*

EXAMPLE 1 ■ **Application of Finding a Linear Model Given the Slope and *y*-intercept**

Suppose a 20-gallon gas tank contains 2 gallons when a motorist decides to fill up the tank. If the gas pump fills the tank at a rate of 0.1 gallon per second, find a linear function that models the amount of fuel in the tank t seconds after fueling begins.

Solution
When fueling begins, at $t = 0$, there are 2 gallons of gas in the tank. Therefore, the y-intercept is $(0, 2)$. The slope is the rate at which fuel is being added to the tank. Because the amount of fuel in the tank is increasing, the slope is positive and we have $m = 0.1$. To find the linear function, replace m and b by their respective values.

$$f(t) = mt + b$$
$$f(t) = 0.1t + 2 \qquad \text{• Replace } m \text{ by } \mathbf{0.1} \text{ and } b \text{ by } \mathbf{2}.$$

The linear function is $f(t) = 0.1t + 2$, where $f(t)$ is the number of gallons of fuel in the tank t seconds after fueling begins.

ANSWER   *If $x > 450$, then $f(x) < 0$. This would mean that the tank has negative gallons of gas. For instance, $f(500) = -2$.*

CHECK YOUR PROGRESS 1   The boiling point of water at sea level is 100°C. The boiling point decreases 3.5°C per 1 kilometer increase in altitude. Find a linear function that gives the boiling point of water as a function of altitude.

Solution   *See page S23.*

For each of the previous examples, the known point on the graph of the linear function was the *y*-intercept. This information enabled us to determine *b* for the linear function $f(x) = mx + b$. In some cases, a point other than the *y*-intercept is given. In such a case, the *point–slope formula* is used to find the equation of the line.

✔ **TAKE NOTE**

Using parentheses may help when substituting into the point–slope formula.

$$y - y_1 = m(x - x_1)$$
$$y - (\ ) = (\ )[x - (\ )]$$

Point–Slope Formula of a Straight Line

Let (x_1, y_1) be a point on a line and let *m* be the slope of the line. Then the equation of the line can be found using the point–slope formula

$$y - y_1 = m(x - x_1)$$

EXAMPLE 2 ■ **Find the Equation of a Line Given the Slope and a Point on the Line**

Find the equation of the line that passes through $(1, -3)$ and has slope -2.

Solution

$$y - y_1 = m(x - x_1)$$ • Use the point–slope formula.
$$y - (-3) = -2(x - 1)$$ • $m = -2$, $(x_1, y_1) = (1, -3)$
$$y + 3 = -2x + 2$$
$$y = -2x - 1$$

✔ **TAKE NOTE**

Recall that $f(x)$ and *y* are different symbols for the same quantity, the value of the function at *x*.

Note that we wrote the equation of the line as $y = -2x - 1$. We could also write the equation in functional notation as $f(x) = -2x - 1$.

CHECK YOUR PROGRESS 2   Find the equation of the line that passes through $(-2, 2)$ and has slope $-\frac{1}{2}$.

Solution   *See page S23.*

EXAMPLE 3 ■ **Application of Finding a Linear Model Given a Point and the Slope**

Based on data from the *Kelley Blue Book*, the value of a certain car decreases approximately $250 per month. If the value of the car 2 years after it was purchased was $14,000, find a linear function that models the value of the car after *x* months of ownership. Use this function to find the value of the car after 3 years of ownership.

Solution

Let V represent the value of the car after x months. Then $V = 14,000$ when $x = 24$ (2 years is 24 months). A solution of the equation is $(24, 14,000)$. The car is decreasing in value at a rate of \$250 per month. Therefore, the slope is -250. Now use the point–slope formula to find the linear equation that models the function.

$$V - V_1 = m(x - x_1)$$
$$V - 14,000 = -250(x - 24) \qquad \bullet\ x_1 = \mathbf{24},\ V_1 = \mathbf{14,000},\ m = \mathbf{-250}$$
$$V - 14,000 = -250x + 6000$$
$$V = -250x + 20,000$$

A linear function that models the value of the car after x months of ownership is $V(x) = -250x + 20,000$.

To find the value of the car after 3 years (36 months), evaluate the function when $x = 36$.

$$V(x) = -250x + 20,000$$
$$V(36) = -250(36) + 20,000 = 11,000$$

The value of the car is \$11,000 after 3 years of ownership.

CHECK YOUR PROGRESS 3   During a brisk walk, a person burns about 3.8 calories per minute. If a person has burned 191 calories in 50 minutes, determine a linear function that models the number of calories burned after t minutes.

Solution   *See page S23.*

The next example shows how to find the equation of a line given two points on the line.

✔ **TAKE NOTE**

There are many ways to find the equation of a line. However, in every case, there must be enough information to determine a point on the line and to find the slope of the line. When you are doing problems of this type, look for different ways that information may be presented. For instance, in Example 4, even though the slope of the line is not given, knowing two points enables us to find the slope.

EXAMPLE 4 ■ **Find the Equation of a Line Given Two Points on the Line**

Find the equation of the line that passes through $P_1(6, -4)$ and $P_2(3, 2)$.

Solution

Find the slope of the line between the two points.

$$m = \frac{y_2 - y_1}{x_2 - x_1} = \frac{2 - (-4)}{3 - 6} = \frac{6}{-3} = -2$$

Use the point–slope formula to find the equation of the line.

$$y - y_1 = m(x - x_1)$$
$$y - (-4) = -2(x - 6) \qquad \bullet\ m = \mathbf{-2},\ x_1 = \mathbf{6},\ y_1 = \mathbf{-4}$$
$$y + 4 = -2x + 12$$
$$y = -2x + 8$$

CHECK YOUR PROGRESS 4   Find the equation of the line that passes through $P_1(-2, 3)$ and $P_2(4, 1)$.

Solution   *See page S23.*

Math Matters   Perspective: Using Straight Lines in Art

Many paintings we see today have a three-dimensional quality to them, even though they are painted on a flat surface. This was not always the case. It wasn't until the Renaissance that artists started to paint "in perspective." Using lines is one way to create this perspective. Here is a simple example.

Draw a dot, called the *vanishing point,* and a rectangle on a piece of paper. Draw windows as shown. To keep the perspective accurate, the lines through opposite corners of the windows should be parallel. A table in proper perspective is created in the same way.

This method of creating perspective was employed by Leonardo da Vinci. Use the Internet to find and print a copy of his painting *The Last Supper.* Using a ruler, see whether you can find the vanishing point by drawing two lines along the top edges of the windows on the sides of the painting.

Regression Lines

There are many situations in which a linear function can be used to approximate collected data. For instance, the table below shows the maximum exercise heart rates for specific individuals of various ages who exercise regularly.

Age, x, in years	20	25	30	32	43	55	28	42	50	55	62
Heart rate, y, in maximum beats per minute	160	150	148	145	140	130	155	140	132	125	125

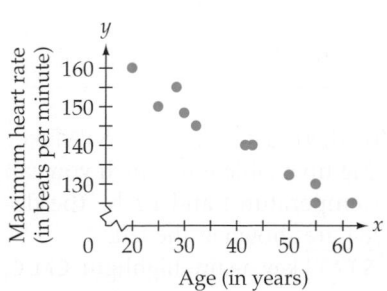

The graph of $y = -\frac{5}{6}x + \frac{530}{3}$

The graph at the left, called a **scatter diagram,** is a graph of the ordered pairs of the table. These ordered pairs suggest that the maximum exercise heart rate for an individual decreases as the person's age increases.

Although these points do not lie on one line, it is possible to find a line that *approximately fits* the data. One way to do this is to select two data points and then find the equation of the line that passes through the two points. To do this, we first find the slope of the line between the two points and then use the point–slope formula to find the equation of the line. Suppose we choose $(20, 160)$ as P_1 and $(62, 125)$ as P_2. Then the slope of the line between P_1 and P_2 is

$$m = \frac{y_2 - y_1}{x_2 - x_1} = \frac{125 - 160}{62 - 20} = -\frac{35}{42} = -\frac{5}{6}$$

Now use the point–slope formula.

$$y - y_1 = m(x - x_1)$$

$$y - 160 = -\frac{5}{6}(x - 20) \qquad \bullet\ m = -\frac{5}{6},\ x_1 = 20,\ y_1 = 160$$

$$y - 160 = -\frac{5}{6}x + \frac{50}{3} \qquad \bullet\ \text{Multiply by } -\frac{5}{6}.$$

$$y = -\frac{5}{6}x + \frac{530}{3} \qquad \bullet\ \text{Add 160 to each side of the equation.}$$

The graph of $y = -\frac{5}{6}x + \frac{530}{3}$ is shown at the left. This line *approximates* the data.

Maximum heart rate (in beats per minute) vs Age (in years), with Regression line labeled.

The equation of the line we found by choosing two data points gives an approximate linear model for the data. If we had chosen different points, the result would have been a different equation. Among all the lines that can be chosen, statisticians generally pick the *least-squares line*, which is also called the *regression line*. The **regression line** is the line for which the sum of the squares of the vertical distances between the data points and the line is a minimum.

A graphing calculator can be used to find the equation of the regression line for a given set of data. For instance, the equation of the regression line for the maximum heart rate data is given by $y = -0.827x + 174$. The graph of this line is shown at the left. Using this model, an exercise physiologist can determine the recommended maximum exercise heart rate for an individual of any particular age.

For example, suppose an individual is 28 years old. The physiologist would replace x by 28 and determine the value of y.

$$y = -0.827x + 174$$
$$y = -0.827(28) + 174 \quad \bullet \text{ Replace } x \text{ by } \mathbf{28}.$$
$$= 150.844$$

The maximum exercise heart rate recommended for a 28-year-old person is approximately 151 beats per minute.

The calculation of the equation of the regression line can be accomplished with a graphing calculator by using the STAT key.

The table below shows the data collected by a chemistry student who is trying to determine a relationship between the temperature, in degrees Celsius, and volume, in liters, of 1 gram of oxygen at a constant pressure. Chemists refer to this relationship as Charles's Law.

Temperature, T, in degrees Celsius	−100	−75	−50	−25	0	25	50
Volume, V, in liters	0.43	0.5	0.57	0.62	0.7	0.75	0.81

To find the equation of the regression line for these data, press the STAT key and then select EDIT from the menu. This will bring up a table into which you can enter data. Let L1 be the independent variable (temperature) and L2 be the dependent variable (volume). Screens from a TI-83/84 are shown at the left.

Once the data have been entered, select the STAT key again, highlight CALC, and arrow down to LinReg(ax+b) to see the linear regression equation. Selecting this option will paste LinReg(ax+b) onto the home screen. Now you can just press ENTER and the values for a and b will appear on the screen. Entering LinReg(ax+b)L1,L2,Y1 not only shows the results on the home screen, but pastes the regression equation into Y1 in the Y= editor. This will enable you to easily graph or evaluate the regression equation.

For this set of data, the regression equation, with the coefficient and constant rounded to the nearest ten-millionth, is $V = 0.0025286T + 0.6889286$. To determine the volume of 1 gram of oxygen when the temperature is −30°C, replace T by −30 and evaluate the expression. This can be done using your calculator. Use the Y-VARS menu to place Y1 on the screen (VARS ▷ ENTER ENTER). Then enter the value −30, within parentheses, as shown at the left. After hitting ENTER, the volume will be displayed as approximately 0.61 liter.

CALCULATOR NOTE

If r and r^2 do not appear on the screen of your TI-83/84, press [2nd] CATALOG D (above the 0 key) and then scroll down to DiagnosticsOn. Press [ENTER] twice. Now repeat the procedure, described on the previous page, for finding the linear regression equation. This time the r and r^2 values will also be displayed.

You may have noticed some additional results on the screen when the regression equation was calculated. The variable r is called the **correlation coefficient,** and r^2 is called the **coefficient of determination.** Statisticians use these numbers to determine how well the regression equation approximates the data. If $r = 1$, the data exactly fit a line of positive slope. If $r = -1$, the data exactly fit a line of negative slope. In general, the closer r^2 is to 1, the closer the data fit a linear model. For our purposes, we will assume that the given data are approximated by a linear function.

EXAMPLE 5 ■ Find a Linear Regression Equation

Sodium thiosulfate is used by photographers to develop some types of film. The amount of this chemical that will dissolve in water depends on the temperature of the water. The table below gives the number of grams of sodium thiosulfate that will dissolve in 100 milliliters of water at various temperatures.

Temperature, x, in degrees Celsius	20	35	50	60	75	90	100
Sodium thiosulfate dissolved, y, in grams	50	80	120	145	175	205	230

a. Find the linear regression equation for these data.

b. How many grams of sodium thiosulfate does the model predict will dissolve in 100 milliliters of water when the temperature is 70°C? Round to the nearest tenth of a gram.

Solution

a. Using a calculator, the regression equation is $y = 2.2517731x + 5.2482270$.

b. Evaluate the regression equation when $x = 70$.

$$y = 2.2517731x + 5.2482270$$
$$= 2.2517731(70) + 5.2482270 \qquad \text{• Replace } x \text{ by 70.}$$
$$= 162.872344$$

Approximately 162.9 grams of sodium thiosulfate will dissolve when the temperature is 70°C.

CHECK YOUR PROGRESS 5   The heights and weights of women swimmers on a college swim team are given in the table below.

Height, x, in inches	68	64	65	67	62	67	65
Weight, y, in pounds	132	108	108	125	102	130	105

a. Find the linear regression equation for these data.

b. Use your regression equation to estimate the weight of a woman swimmer who is 63 inches tall. Round to the nearest pound.

Solution   See page S23.

Excursion

A Linear Business Model

Two people decide to open a business reconditioning toner cartridges for copy machines. They rent a building for $7000 per year and estimate that building maintenance, taxes, and insurance will cost $6500 per year. Each person wants to make $12 per hour in the first year and will work 10 hours per day for 260 days of the year. Assume that it costs $28 to restore a cartridge and that the restored cartridge can be sold for $45.

1. Write a linear function for the total cost C to operate the business and restore n cartridges during the first year, not including the hourly wage the owners wish to earn.

2. Write a linear function for the total revenue R the business will earn during the first year by selling n cartridges.

3. How many cartridges must the business restore and sell annually to break even, not including the hourly wage the owners wish to earn?

4. How many cartridges must the business restore and sell annually for the owners to pay all expenses and earn the hourly wage they desire?

5. Suppose the entrepreneurs are successful in their business and are restoring and selling 25 cartridges each day of the 260 days they are open. What will be their hourly wage for the year if all the profit is shared equally?

6. As the company becomes successful and is selling and restoring 25 cartridges each day of the 260 days it is open, the entrepreneurs decide to hire a part-time employee 4 hours per day and to pay the employee $8 per hour. How many additional cartridges must be restored and sold each year just to cover the cost of the new employee? You can neglect employee costs such as social security, worker's compensation, and other benefits.

7. Suppose the company decides that it could increase its business by advertising. Answer Exercises 1, 2, 3, and 5 if the owners decide to spend $400 per month on advertising.

Exercise Set 6.3

In Exercises 1–8, find the equation of the line that passes through the given point and has the given slope.

1. $(0, 5)$, $m = 2$

2. $(2, 3)$, $m = \dfrac{1}{2}$

3. $(-1, 7)$, $m = -3$

4. $(0, 0)$, $m = \dfrac{1}{2}$

5. $(3, 5)$, $m = -\dfrac{2}{3}$

6. $(0, -3)$, $m = -1$

7. $(-2, -3)$, $m = 0$

8. $(4, -5)$, $m = -2$

In Exercises 9–16, find the equation of the line that passes through the given points.

9. $(0, 2)$, $(3, 5)$

10. $(0, -3)$, $(-4, 5)$

11. $(0, 3)$, $(2, 0)$

12. $(-2, -3)$, $(-1, -2)$

13. $(2, 0)$, $(0, -1)$

14. $(3, -4)$, $(-2, -4)$

15. $(-2, 5)$, $(2, -5)$

16. $(2, 1)$, $(-2, -3)$

17. **Hotel Industry** The operator of a hotel estimates that 500 rooms per night will be rented if the room rate per night is $75. For each $10 increase in the price of a room, six fewer rooms per night will be rented. Determine a linear function that will predict the number of rooms that will be rented per night for a given price per room. Use this model to predict the number of rooms that will be rented if the room rate is $100 per night.

18. **Construction** A general building contractor estimates that the cost to build a new home is $30,000 plus $85 for each square foot of floor space in the house. Determine a linear function that gives the cost of building a house that contains x square feet of floor space. Use this model to determine the cost to build a house that contains 1800 square feet of floor space.

19. **Travel** A plane travels 830 miles in 2 hours. Determine a linear model that will predict the number of miles the plane can travel in a given interval of time. Use this model to predict the distance the plane will travel in $4\frac{1}{2}$ hours.

20. **Compensation** An account executive receives a base salary plus a commission. On $20,000 in monthly sales, an account executive would receive compensation of $1800. On $50,000 in monthly sales, an account executive would receive compensation of $3000. Determine a linear function that yields the compensation of a sales executive for x dollars in monthly sales. Use this model to determine the compensation of an account executive who has $85,000 in monthly sales.

21. **Car Sales** A manufacturer of economy cars has determined that 50,000 cars per month can be sold at a price of $9000 per car. At a price of $8750, the number of cars sold per month would increase to 55,000. Determine a linear function that predicts the number of cars that will be sold at a price of x dollars. Use this model to predict the number of cars that will be sold at a price of $8500.

22. **Calculator Sales** A manufacturer of graphing calculators has determined that 10,000 calculators per week will be sold at a price of $95 per calculator. At a price of $90, it is estimated that 12,000 calculators will be sold. Determine a linear function that predicts the number of calculators that will be sold per week at a price of x dollars. Use this model to predict the number of calculators that will be sold at a price of $75.

23. **Stress** A research hospital did a study on the relationship between stress and diastolic blood pressure. The results from eight patients in the study are given in the table below. The units for blood pressure values are measured in milliliters of mercury.

Stress test score, x	55	62	58	78	92	88	75	80
Blood pressure, y	70	85	72	85	96	90	82	85

a. Find the linear regression equation for these data. Round to the nearest hundredth.

b. Use the regression equation to estimate the diastolic blood pressure of a person whose stress test score was 85. Round to the nearest whole number.

24. **Hourly wages** The average hourly earnings, in dollars, of nonfarm workers in the United States for the years 1996 to 2003 are given in the table below. (*Source:* Bureau of Labor Statistics)

Year, x	1996	1997	1998	1999	2000	2001	2002	2003
Hourly wage, y	12.03	12.49	13.00	13.47	14.00	14.53	14.95	15.35

a. Using $x = 0$ to correspond to 1990, find the linear regression equation for these data. Round to the nearest hundredth.

b. Use the regression equation to estimate the expected average hourly wage, to the nearest cent, in 2015.

25. **High School Graduates** The table below shows the numbers of students, in thousands, who have graduated from or are projected to graduate from high school for the years 1996 to 2005. (*Source:* U.S. Bureau of Labor Statistics)

Year, x	1996	1997	1998	1999	2000	2001	2002	2003	2004	2005
Number of students (in thousands), y	2540	2633	2740	2786	2820	2837	2886	2929	2935	2944

a. Using $x = 0$ to correspond to 1996, find the linear regression equation for these data. Round to the nearest hundredth.

b. Use the regression equation to estimate the expected number of high school graduates in 2010. Round to the nearest thousand students.

26. **Fuel Efficiency** An automotive engineer studied the relationship between the speed of a car and the number of miles traveled per gallon of fuel consumed at that speed. The results of the study are shown in the table below.

Speed (in miles per hour), x	40	25	30	50	60	80	55	35	45
Consumption (in miles per gallon), y	26	27	28	24	22	21	23	27	25

a. Find the linear regression equation for these data. Round to the nearest hundredth.

b. Use the regression equation to estimate the expected number of miles traveled per gallon of fuel consumed for a car traveling at 65 miles per hour. Round to the nearest mile per hour.

27. **Meteorology** A meteorologist studied the maximum temperatures at various latitudes for January of a certain year. The results of the study are shown in the table below.

Latitude (in °N), x	22	30	36	42	56	51	48
Maximum temperature (in °F), y	80	65	47	54	21	44	52

a. Find the linear regression equation for these data. Round to the nearest hundredth.

b. Use the regression equation to estimate the expected maximum temperature in January at a latitude of 45°N. Round to the nearest degree.

28. **Zoology** A zoologist studied the running speeds of animals in terms of the animals' body lengths. The results of the study are shown in the table below.

Body length (in centimeters), x	1	9	15	16	24	25	60
Running speed (in meters per second), y	1	2.5	7.5	5	7.4	7.6	20

a. Find the linear regression equation for these data. Round to the nearest hundredth.

b. Use the regression equation to estimate the expected running speed of a deer mouse, whose body length is 10 centimeters. Round to the nearest tenth of a centimeter.

Extensions

CRITICAL THINKING

29. A line contains the points $(4, -1)$ and $(2, 1)$. Find the coordinates of three other points on the line.

30. If f is a linear function for which $f(1) = 3$ and $f(-1) = 5$, find $f(4)$.

31. The ordered pairs $(0, 1)$, $(4, 9)$ and $(3, n)$ are solutions of the same linear equation. Find n.

32. The ordered pairs $(2, 2)$, $(-1, 5)$ and $(3, n)$ are solutions of the same linear equation. Find n.

33. Is there a linear function that contains the ordered pairs $(2, 4)$, $(-1, -5)$, and $(0, 2)$? If so, find the function and explain why there is such a function. If not, explain why there is no such function.

34. Is there a linear function that contains the ordered pairs $(5, 1)$, $(4, 2)$, and $(0, 6)$? If so, find the function and explain why there is such a function. If not, explain why there is no such function.

35. Travel Assume that the maximum speed your car will travel varies linearly with the steepness of the hill it is climbing or descending. If the hill is 5° up, your car can travel 77 kilometers per hour. If the hill is 2° down $(-2°)$, your car can travel 154 kilometers per hour. When your car's top speed is 99 kilometers per hour, how steep is the hill? State your answer in degrees, and note whether the car is climbing or descending.

EXPLORATIONS

36. Boating A person who can row at a rate of 3 miles per hour in calm water is trying to cross a river in which a current of 4 miles per hour runs perpendicular to the direction of rowing. See the figure at the right.

Because of the current, the boat is being pushed downstream at the same time that it is moving across the river. Because the boat is traveling at 3 miles per hour in the x direction, its horizontal position after t hours is given by $x = 3t$. The current is pushing the boat in the negative y direction at 4 miles per hour. Therefore, the boat's vertical position after t hours is given by $y = -4t$, where -4 indicates that the boat is moving downstream. The set of equations $x = 3t$ and $y = -4t$ are called **parametric equations,** and t is called the **parameter.**

a. What is the location of the boat after 15 minutes (0.25 hour)?

b. If the river is 1 mile wide, how far down the river will the boat be when it reaches the other shore? *Hint:* Find the time it takes the boat to cross the river by solving $x = 3t$ for t when $x = 1$. Then replace t by this value in $y = -4t$ and simplify.

c. For the parametric equations $x = 3t$ and $y = -4t$, write y in terms of x by solving $x = 3t$ for t and then substituting this expression into $y = -4t$.

37. **Aviation** In the diagram below, a plane flying at 5000 feet above sea level begins a gradual ascent.

   a. Determine parametric equations for the path of the plane. *Hint:* See Exercise 36.

   b. What is the altitude of the plane 5 minutes after it begins its ascent?

   c. What is the altitude of the plane after it has traveled 12,000 feet in the positive x direction?

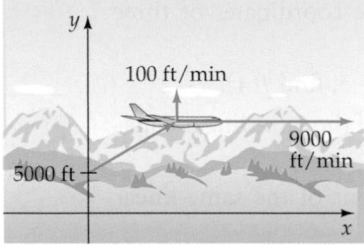

SECTION 6.4 | **Quadratic Functions**

Properties of Quadratic Functions

▼ **point of interest**

The suspension cables of some bridges, such as the Golden Gate Bridge, have the shape of a parabola.

The photo above shows the roadway of the bridge being assembled in sections and attached to suspender ropes. The bridge was opened to vehicles on May 28, 1937.

Recall that a linear function is a function of the form $f(x) = mx + b$. The graph of a linear function has certain characteristics. It is a straight line with slope m and y-intercept $(0, b)$.

A **quadratic function** in a single variable x is a function of the form $f(x) = ax^2 + bx + c$, $a \neq 0$. Examples of quadratic functions are given below.

$$f(x) = x^2 - 3x + 1 \quad \bullet \; a = 1, b = -3, c = 1$$
$$g(t) = -2t^2 - 4 \quad \bullet \; a = -2, b = 0, c = -4$$
$$h(p) = 4 - 2p - p^2 \quad \bullet \; a = -1, b = -2, c = 4$$
$$f(x) = 2x^2 + 6x \quad \bullet \; a = 2, b = 6, c = 0$$

The graph of a quadratic function in a single variable x is a **parabola.** The graphs of two of these quadratic functions are shown below.

For the figure on the left above, $f(x) = 2x^2 - 4x - 3$. The value of a is *positive* $(a = 2)$ and the graph opens up. For the figure on the right above,

$f(x) = -x^2 + 4x + 3$. The value of a is *negative* $(a = -1)$ and the graph opens down. The point at which the graph of a parabola has a minimum or a maximum is called the *vertex* of the parabola. The **vertex** of a parabola is the point with the smallest y-coordinate when $a > 0$ and the point with largest y-coordinate when $a < 0$.

The **axis of symmetry** of the graph of a quadratic function is a vertical line that passes through the vertex of the parabola. To understand the concept of the axis of symmetry of a graph, think of folding the graph along that line. The two portions of the graph will match up.

TAKE NOTE

The axis of symmetry is a vertical line. The vertex of the parabola lies on the axis of symmetry.

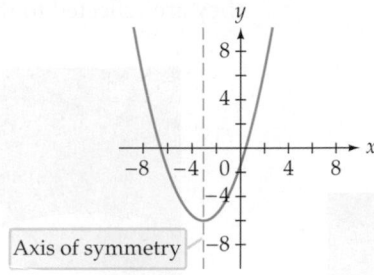

The following formula enables us to determine the vertex of a parabola.

Vertex of a Parabola

Let $f(x) = ax^2 + bx + c$ be the equation of a parabola. The coordinates of the vertex are

$$\left(-\frac{b}{2a}, f\left(-\frac{b}{2a} \right) \right).$$

EXAMPLE 1 ■ Find the Vertex of a Parabola

Find the vertex of the parabola whose equation is $y = -3x^2 + 6x + 1$.

Solution

$$x = -\frac{b}{2a} = -\frac{6}{2(-3)} = 1 \qquad \bullet \text{ Find the } x\text{-coordinate of the vertex.}$$
$$a = -3, b = 6$$

$$y = -3x^2 + 6x + 1 \qquad \bullet \text{ Find the } y\text{-coordinate of the vertex by}$$
$$\text{replacing } x \text{ by } 1 \text{ and solving for } y.$$

$$y = -3(1)^2 + 6(1) + 1$$
$$y = 4$$

The vertex is $(1, 4)$.

CHECK YOUR PROGRESS 1 Find the vertex of the parabola whose equation is $y = x^2 - 2$.

Solution See page S23.

Math Matters   Paraboloids

The movie *Contact* was based on a novel by astronomer Carl Sagan. In the movie, Jodie Foster plays an astronomer who is searching for extraterrestrial intelligence. One scene from the movie takes place at the Very Large Array (VLA) in New Mexico. The VLA consists of 27 large radio telescopes whose dishes are paraboloids, the three-dimensional version of a parabola. A parabolic shape is used because of the following reflective property: When the parallel rays of light, or radio waves, strike the surface of a parabolic mirror whose axis of symmetry is parallel to these rays, they are reflected to the same point.

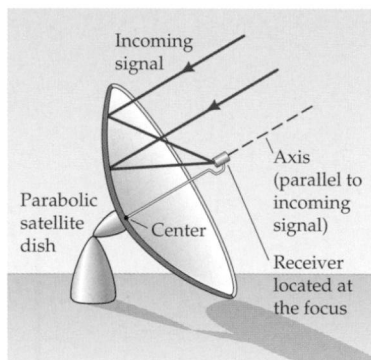

The photos above show the layout of the radio telescopes of the VLA and a more detailed picture of one of the telescopes. The figure at the far right shows the reflective property of a parabola. Note that all the incoming rays are reflected to the focus.

The reflective property of a parabola is also used in optical telescopes and headlights on a car. In the case of headlights, the bulb is placed at the focus and the light is reflected along parallel rays from the reflective surface of the headlight, thereby making a more concentrated beam of light.

x-Intercepts of Parabolas

Recall that a point at which a graph crosses the *x*- or *y*-axis is called an *intercept* of the graph. The *x*-intercepts of the graph of an equation can be found by setting $y = 0$.

The graph of $y = x^2 + 3x - 4$ is shown at the left. The points whose coordinates are $(-4, 0)$ and $(1, 0)$ are *x*-intercepts of the graph. We can algebraically determine the *x*-intercepts by solving an equation.

EXAMPLE 2 ■ Find the *x*-intercepts of a Parabola

Find the *x*-intercepts of the graph of the parabola given by the equation.

a. $y = 4x^2 + 4x + 1$ **b.** $y = x^2 + 2x - 2$

✔ TAKE NOTE

When a quadratic equation has a double root, as in part a, the graph of the quadratic equation just touches the x-axis and is said to be *tangent* to the x-axis. See the graph at the right. Some graphs of parabolas do not have any x-intercepts.

✔ TAKE NOTE

Try to solve the quadratic equation by factoring (as we did in part a). If that cannot be done easily, then use the quadratic formula, as we did in part b.

Solution

a. $y = 4x^2 + 4x + 1$
$0 = 4x^2 + 4x + 1$ • Let $y = 0$.
$0 = (2x + 1)(2x + 1)$ • Solve for x by factoring.

$2x + 1 = 0 \qquad\qquad 2x + 1 = 0$

$x = -\dfrac{1}{2} \qquad\qquad x = -\dfrac{1}{2}$

The x-intercept is $\left(-\dfrac{1}{2}, 0\right)$.

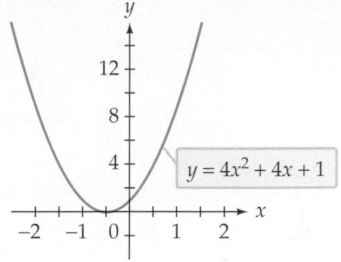

b. $y = x^2 + 2x - 2$
$0 = x^2 + 2x - 2$ • Let $y = 0$. The trinomial $x^2 + 2x - 2$ is nonfactorable over the integers.

$x = \dfrac{-b \pm \sqrt{b^2 - 4ac}}{2a}$ • Use the quadratic formula to solve for x. $a = 1$, $b = 2$, $c = -2$

$ = \dfrac{-(2) \pm \sqrt{(2)^2 - 4(1)(-2)}}{2(1)} = \dfrac{-2 \pm \sqrt{4 + 8}}{2}$

$ = \dfrac{-2 \pm \sqrt{12}}{2} = \dfrac{-2 \pm 2\sqrt{3}}{2} = -1 \pm \sqrt{3}$

The x-intercepts are $\left(-1 + \sqrt{3}, 0\right)$ and $\left(-1 - \sqrt{3}, 0\right)$.

CHECK YOUR PROGRESS 2   Find the x-intercepts of the graph of the parabola given by the equation.

a. $y = 2x^2 - 5x + 2$ **b.** $y = x^2 + 4x + 4$

Solution   *See page S23.*

▼ point of interest

Calculus is a branch of mathematics that demonstrates, among other things, how to find the maximum or minimum of functions other than quadratic functions. These are very important problems in applied mathematics. For instance, an automotive engineer wants to design a car whose shape will *minimize* the effect of air flow. Another engineer tries to *maximize* the efficiency of a car's engine. Similarly, an economist may try to determine what business practices will *minimize* cost and *maximize* profit.

Minimum and Maximum of a Quadratic Function

Note that for the graphs below, when $a > 0$, the vertex is the point with the minimum y-coordinate. When $a < 0$, the vertex is the point with the maximum y-coordinate.

Finding the minimum or maximum value of a quadratic function is a matter of finding the vertex of the graph of the function.

EXAMPLE 3 ■ Find the Minimum or Maximum Value of a Quadratic Function

Find the maximum value of $f(x) = -2x^2 + 4x + 3$.

Solution

$$x = -\frac{b}{2a} = -\frac{4}{2(-2)} = 1$$ • Find the *x*-coordinate of the vertex. $a = -2, b = 4$

$$f(x) = -2x^2 + 4x + 3$$ • Find the *y*-coordinate of the vertex by replacing *x* by **1** and solving for *y*.

$$f(1) = -2(1)^2 + 4(1) + 3$$
$$f(1) = 5$$

The vertex is $(1, 5)$.

The maximum value of the function is 5, the *y*-coordinate of the vertex.

CHECK YOUR PROGRESS 3   Find the minimum value of $f(x) = 2x^2 - 3x + 1$.

Solution   *See page S24.*

QUESTION   *The vertex of a parabola that opens up is $(-4, 7)$. What is the minimum value of the function?*

Applications of Quadratic Functions

EXAMPLE 4 ■ Application of Finding the Minimum of a Quadratic Function

A mining company has determined that the cost c, in dollars per ton, of mining a mineral is given by $c(x) = 0.2x^2 - 2x + 12$, where x is the number of tons of the mineral that are mined. Find the number of tons of the mineral that should be mined to minimize the cost. What is the minimum cost?

Solution
To find the number of tons of the mineral that should be mined to minimize the cost and to find the minimum cost, find the *x*- and *y*-coordinates of the vertex of the graph of $c(x) = 0.2x^2 - 2x + 12$.

$$x = -\frac{b}{2a} = -\frac{-2}{2(0.2)} = 5$$ • Find the *x*-coordinate of the vertex. $a = 0.2, b = -2$

ANSWER   *The minimum value of the function is 7, the y-coordinate of the vertex.*

To minimize the cost, 5 tons of the mineral should be mined.

$$c(x) = 0.2x^2 - 2x + 12$$ • Find the *y*-coordinate of the vertex by replacing *x* by **5** and solving for *y*.

$$c(5) = 0.2(5)^2 - 2(5) + 12$$
$$c(5) = 7$$

The minimum cost per ton is $7.

CHECK YOUR PROGRESS 4   The height *s*, in feet, of a ball thrown straight up is given by $s(t) = -16t^2 + 64t + 4$, where *t* is the time in seconds after the ball is released. Find the time it takes the ball to reach its maximum height. What is the maximum height?

Solution   *See page S24.*

EXAMPLE 5 ■ Application of Finding the Maximum of a Quadratic Function

A lifeguard has 600 feet of rope with buoys attached to lay out a rectangular swimming area on a lake. If the beach forms one side of the rectangle, find the dimensions of the rectangle that will enclose the greatest swimming area.

Beach

Solution
Let *l* represent the length of the rectangle, let *w* represent the width of the rectangle, and let *A* (which is unknown) represent the area of the rectangle. See the figure at the left. Use these variables to write expressions for the perimeter and area of the rectangle.

Perimeter: $w + l + w = 600$ • There are **600** feet of rope.
$$2w + l = 600$$

Area: $A = lw$

The goal is to maximize *A*. To do this, first write *A* in terms of a single variable. This can be accomplished by solving $2w + l = 600$ for *l* and then substituting into $A = lw$.

$$2w + l = 600$$ • Solve for *l*.
$$l = -2w + 600$$

$$A = lw$$
$$= (-2w + 600)w$$ • Substitute $-2w + 600$ for *l*.
$$A = -2w^2 + 600w$$ • Multiply. This is now a quadratic equation.
$$a = -2, b = 600$$

Find the *w*-coordinate of the vertex.

$$w = -\frac{b}{2a} = -\frac{600}{2(-2)} = 150$$ • Find the *w*-coordinate of the vertex. $a = -2, b = 600$

The width is 150 feet. To find *l*, replace *w* by 150 in $l = -2w + 600$ and solve for *l*.

$$l = -2w + 600$$
$$l = -2(150) + 600 = -300 + 600 = 300$$

The length is 300 feet. The dimensions of the rectangle with maximum area are 150 feet by 300 feet.

CHECK YOUR PROGRESS 5 A mason is forming a rectangular floor for a storage shed. The perimeter of the rectangle is 44 feet. What dimensions will give the floor a maximum area?

Solution *See page S24.*

Excursion

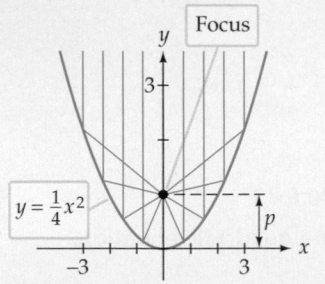

Reflective Properties of a Parabola

The fact that the graph of $y = ax^2 + bx + c$ is a parabola is based on the following geometric definition of a parabola.

> **Definition of a Parabola**
>
> A parabola is the set of points in the plane that are equidistant from a fixed line (the **directrix**) and a fixed point (the **focus**) not on the line.

This geometric definition of a parabola is illustrated in the figure at the left. Basically, for a point to be on a parabola, the distance from the point to the focus must equal the distance from the point to the directrix. Note also that the vertex is halfway between the focus and the directrix. This distance is traditionally labeled p.

The general form of the equation of a parabola that opens up with vertex at the origin can be written in terms of the distance p between the vertex and focus as $y = \frac{1}{4p}x^2$. For this equation, the coordinates of the focus are $(0, p)$. For instance, to find the coordinates of the focus for $y = \frac{1}{4}x^2$, let $\frac{1}{4p} = \frac{1}{4}$ and solve for p.

$$\frac{1}{4p} = \frac{1}{4}$$

$$1 = \frac{4p}{4} \qquad \bullet \text{ Multiply each side of the equation by } 4p.$$

$$1 = p \qquad \bullet \text{ Simplify the right side of the equation.}$$

The coordinates of the focus are $(0, 1)$.

1. Find the coordinates of the focus for the parabola whose equation is $y = 0.4x^2$.

Optical telescopes work on the same principle as radio telescopes (see Math Matters, p. 366) except that light hits a mirror that has been shaped into a paraboloid. The light is reflected to the focus, where another mirror reflects it through a lens to the observer. See the diagram at the top of the following page.

(continued)

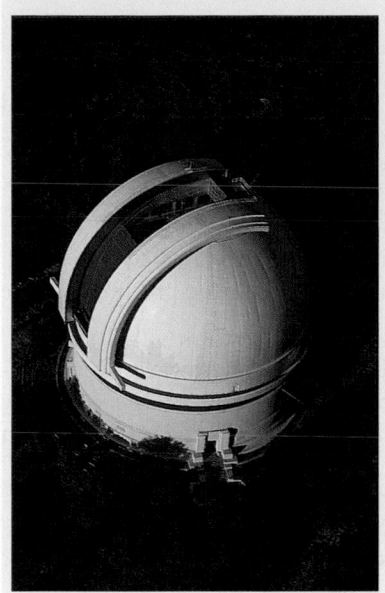

Palomar Observatory with the shutters open.

Eyepiece

Parabolic mirror

2. The telescope at the Palomar Observatory in California has a parabolic mirror. The circle at the top of the parabolic mirror has a 200-inch diameter. An equation that approximates the parabolic cross-section of the surface of the mirror is $y = \frac{1}{2639}x^2$, where x and y are measured in inches. How far is the focus from the vertex of the mirror?

If a point on a parabola whose vertex is at the origin is known, then the equation of the parabola can be found. For instance, if $(4, 1)$ is a point on a parabola with vertex at the origin, then we can find the equation as follows:

$y = \frac{1}{4p}x^2$ • **Begin with the general form of the equation of a parabola.**

$1 = \frac{1}{4p}(4)^2$ • **The known point is $(4, 1)$. Replace x by 4 and y by 1.**

$1 = \frac{4}{p}$ • **Solve for p.**

$p = 4$ • **$p = 4$ in the equation $y = \frac{1}{4p}x^2$.**

The equation of the parabola is $y = \frac{1}{16}x^2$.

Find a flashlight and measure the diameter of its lens cover and the depth of the reflecting parabolic surface. See the diagram below.

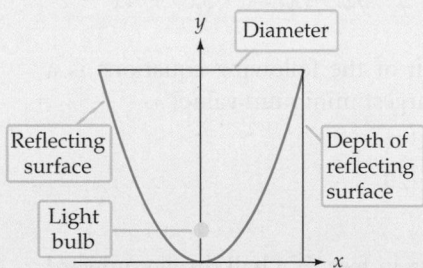

y Diameter

Reflecting surface

Depth of reflecting surface

Light bulb

x

3. If coordinate axes are set up as shown, find the equation of the parabola.

4. Find the location of the focus. Explain why the light bulb should be placed at this point.

Exercise Set 6.4

In Exercises 1–12, find the vertex of the graph of the equation.

1. $y = x^2 - 2$ **2.** $y = x^2 + 2$

3. $y = -x^2 - 1$ **4.** $y = -x^2 + 3$

5. $y = -\frac{1}{2}x^2 + 2$ **6.** $y = \frac{1}{2}x^2$

7. $y = 2x^2 - 1$ **8.** $y = x^2 - 2x$

9. $y = x^2 - x - 2$ **10.** $y = x^2 - 3x + 2$

11. $y = 2x^2 - x - 5$ **12.** $y = 2x^2 - x - 3$

In Exercises 13–24, find the *x*-intercepts of the parabola given by the equation.

13. $y = 2x^2 - 4x$ **14.** $y = 3x^2 + 6x$

15. $y = 4x^2 + 11x + 6$ **16.** $y = x^2 - 9$

17. $y = x^2 + 2x - 1$ **18.** $y = x^2 + 4x - 3$

19. $y = -x^2 - 4x - 5$ **20.** $y = -x^2 - 2x + 1$

21. $y = -x^2 + 4x + 1$ **22.** $y = x^2 + 6x + 10$

23. $y = 2x^2 - 5x - 3$ **24.** $y = x^2 - 2$

In Exercises 25–32, find the minimum or maximum value of the quadratic function. State whether the value is a minimum or a maximum.

25. $f(x) = x^2 - 2x + 3$ **26.** $f(x) = 2x^2 + 4x$

27. $f(x) = -2x^2 + 4x - 5$ **28.** $f(x) = 3x^2 + 3x - 2$

29. $f(x) = x^2 - 5x + 3$ **30.** $f(x) = 2x^2 - 3x$

31. $f(x) = -x^2 - x + 2$ **32.** $f(x) = -3x^2 + 4x - 2$

33. The graph of which of the following equations is a parabola with the largest minimum value?

a. $y = x^2 - 2x - 3$

b. $y = x^2 - 10x + 20$

c. $y = 3x^2 - 1$

34. Sports The height *s*, in feet, of a ball thrown upward at an initial speed of 64 feet per second from a cliff 50 feet above an ocean beach is given by the function

$$s(t) = -16t^2 + 64t + 50$$

where *t* is the time in seconds after the ball is released. Find the maximum height above the beach that the ball will attain.

35. Sports The height *s*, in feet, of a ball thrown upward at an initial speed of 80 feet per second from a platform 50 feet high is given by

$$s(t) = -16t^2 + 80t + 50$$

where *t* is the time in seconds after the ball is released. Find the maximum height above the ground that the ball will attain.

36. Revenue A manufacturer of microwave ovens estimates that the revenue *R*, in dollars, the company receives is related to the price *p*, in dollars, of an oven by the function

$$R(p) = 125p - 0.25p^2$$

What price per oven will give the maximum revenue?

37. Manufacturing A manufacturer of camera lenses estimates that the average monthly cost *C* of producing camera lenses is given by the function

$$C(x) = 0.1x^2 - 20x + 2000$$

where *x* is the number of lenses produced each month. Find the number of lenses the company should produce to minimize the average cost.

38. Water Treatment A pool is treated with a chemical to reduce the number of algae. The number of algae in the pool *t* days after the treatment can be approximated by the function

$$A(t) = 40t^2 - 400t + 500$$

How many days after treatment will the pool have the least number of algae?

39. Civil Engineering The suspension cable that supports a footbridge hangs in the shape of a parabola. The height *h*, in feet, of the cable above the bridge is given by the function

$$h(x) = 0.25x^2 - 0.8x + 25, \, 0 < x < 3.2$$

where *x* is the distance in feet measured from the left tower toward the right tower. What is the minimum height of the cable above the bridge?

40. Annual Income The net annual income *I*, in dollars, of a family physician can be modeled by the equation

$$I(x) = -290(x - 48)^2 + 148{,}000$$

where *x* is the age of the physician and $27 \leq x \leq 70$. Find (a) the age at which the physician's income will be a maximum and (b) the maximum income.

41. Pitching Karen is throwing an orange to her brother Saul, who is standing on the balcony of their home. The height h, in feet, of the orange above the ground t seconds after it is thrown is given by

$$h(t) = -16t^2 + 32t + 4, 0 \le t \le 2.118$$

If Saul's outstretched arms are 18 feet above the ground, will the orange ever be high enough so that he can catch it?

42. Football Some football fields are built in a parabolic-mound shape so that water will drain off the field. A model for the shape of such a field is given by

$$h(x) = -0.00023475x^2 + 0.0375x$$

where h is the height of the field in feet at a distance of x feet from the sideline and $0 \le x \le 159.744$. What is the maximum height of the field? Round to the nearest tenth of a foot.

43. Fountains The Buckingham Memorial Fountain in Chicago shoots water from a nozzle within the fountain. The height h, in feet, of the water above the ground t seconds after it leaves the nozzle is given by

$$h(t) = -16t^2 + 90t + 15, h \ge 15$$

What is the maximum height of the water spout? Round to the nearest tenth of a foot.

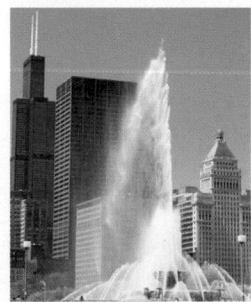

44. Stopping Distance On wet concrete, the stopping distance s, in feet, of a car traveling v miles per hour is given by

$$s(v) = 0.055v^2 + 1.1v, s \ge 0$$

At what maximum speed could a car be traveling on wet concrete and still stop at a stop sign 44 feet away?

45. Fuel Efficiency The fuel efficiency of an average car is given by the equation

$$E(v) = -0.018v^2 + 1.476v + 3.4, E \ge 0$$

where E is the fuel efficiency in miles per gallon and v is the speed of the car in miles per hour.

a. What speed will yield the maximum fuel efficiency?

b. What is the maximum fuel efficiency?

46. Ranching A rancher has 200 feet of fencing to build a rectangular corral alongside an existing fence. Determine the dimensions of the corral that will maximize the enclosed area.

Extensions

CRITICAL THINKING

In Exercises 47 and 48, find the value of k such that the graph of the function contains the given point.

47. $f(x) = x^2 - 3x + k; (2, 5)$

48. $f(x) = 2x^2 + kx - 3; (4, -3)$

49. For $f(x) = 2x^2 - 5x + k$, we have $f\left(-\frac{3}{2}\right) = 0$. Find another value of x for which $f(x) = 0$.

50. For what values of k does the graph of $f(x) = 2x^2 - kx + 8$ just touch the x-axis without crossing it?

EXPLORATIONS

A real number x is called a **zero of a function** if the function evaluated at x is 0. That is, if $f(x) = 0$, then x is called a zero of the function. For instance, evaluating $f(x) = x^2 + x - 6$ when $x = -3$, we have

$$f(x) = x^2 + x - 6$$
$$f(-3) = (-3)^2 + (-3) - 6 \qquad \text{• Replace } x \text{ by } -3.$$
$$f(-3) = 9 - 3 - 6 = 0$$

For this function, $f(-3) = 0$, so -3 is a zero of the function.

51. Verify that 2 is a zero of $f(x) = x^2 + x - 6$ by showing that $f(2) = 0$.

The graph of $f(x) = x^2 + x - 6$ is shown below. Note that the graph crosses the x-axis at -3 and 2, the two zeros of the function. The points $(-3, 0)$ and $(2, 0)$ are x-intercepts of the graph.

Consider the equation $0 = x^2 + x - 6$, which is $f(x) = x^2 + x - 6$ with $f(x)$ replaced by 0. By solving $0 = x^2 + x - 6$, we get

$$0 = x^2 + x - 6$$
$$0 = (x + 3)(x - 2) \qquad \text{• Solve by factoring.}$$
$$x + 3 = 0 \qquad x - 2 = 0$$
$$x = -3 \qquad x = 2$$

Observe that the solutions of the equation are the zeros of the function. This important connection among the real zeros of a function, the x-intercepts of the graph, and the real solutions of an equation is the basis of using a graphing calculator to solve an equation. The method discussed below of solving a quadratic equation using a graphing calculator is based on a TI-83/84 calculator. Other calculators will necessitate a slightly different approach.

Approximate the solutions of $x^2 + 4x = 6$ by using a graphing calculator.

i. Write the equation in standard form.

$$x^2 + 4x = 6$$
$$x^2 + 4x - 6 = 0$$

Press $\boxed{\text{Y=}}$ and enter $x^2 + 4x - 6$ for Y1.

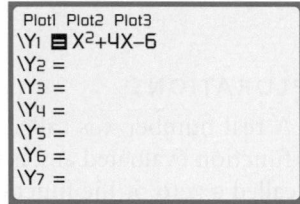

ii. Press $\boxed{\text{GRAPH}}$. If the graph does not appear on the screen, press $\boxed{\text{ZOOM}}$ 6.

iii. Press $\boxed{\text{2nd}}$ CALC 2. Note that the second menu item is zero. This will begin the calculation of the zeros of the function, which are the solutions of the equation.

iv. At the bottom of the screen you will see `LeftBound?` This is asking you to move the blinking cursor so that it is to the *left* of the first *x*-intercept. Use the left arrow key to move the cursor to the left of the first *x*-intercept. The values of *x* and *y* that appear on your calculator may be different from the ones shown here. Just be sure you are to the left of the *x*-intercept. When you are done, press ENTER .

v. At the bottom of the screen you will see `RightBound?` This is asking you to move the blinking cursor so that it is to the *right* of the *x*-intercept. Use the right arrow key to move the cursor to the right of the *x*-intercept. The values of *x* and *y* that appear on your calculator may be different from the ones shown here. Just be sure you are to the right of the *x*-intercept. When you are done, press ENTER .

vi. At the bottom of the screen you will see `Guess?` This is asking you to move the blinking cursor so that it is close to the *x*-intercept. Use the arrow keys to move the cursor to the approximate *x*-intercept. The values of *x* and *y* that appear on your calculator may be different from the ones shown here. When you are done, press ENTER .

vii. The zero of the function is approximately -5.162278. Thus one approximate solution of $x^2 + 4x = 6$ is -5.162278. Note that the value of y is given as $Y1 = {}^-1E^-12$. This is how the calculator writes a number in scientific notation. We would normally write $Y1 = -1.0 \times 10^{-12}$. This number is very close to zero.

To find the other solution, repeat steps **iii** through **vi**. The screens are shown below.

A second zero of the function is approximately 1.1622777. Thus the two solutions of $x^2 + 4x = 6$ are approximately -5.162278 and 1.1622777.

In Exercises 52–57, find the solutions of the equation. Round to the nearest hundredth.

52. $x^2 + 3x - 4 = 0$

53. $x^2 - 4x - 5 = 0$

54. $x^2 + 3.4x = 4.15$

55. $2x^2 - \dfrac{5}{9}x = \dfrac{3}{8}$

56. $\pi x^2 - \sqrt{17}x - 2 = 0$

57. $\sqrt{2}x^2 + x - \sqrt{7} = 0$

In Exercises 58–60, find the real solutions of the equation.

58. $x^3 - 2x^2 - 5x + 6 = 0$

59. $x^3 + 2x^2 - 11x - 12 = 0$

60. $x^4 + 2x^3 - 13x^2 - 14x + 24 = 0$

This method of finding solutions can be extended to find the real zeros, and therefore the real solutions, of any equation that can be graphed.

| **Exponential Functions**

Introduction to Exponential Functions

In 1965, Gordon Moore, one of the cofounders of Intel Corporation, observed that the maximum number of transistors that could be placed on a microprocessor seemed to be doubling every 18 to 24 months. The table below shows how the maximum number of transistors on various Intel processors has changed over time. (*Source:* **www.intel.com/technology/mooreslaw/index.htm**)

Year, x	1971	1978	1982	1985	1989	1993	1997	1999	2000	2002	2003
Number of transistors per microprocessor (in thousands), y	2.3	29	120	275	1180	3100	7500	24,000	42,000	220,000	410,000

The curve in Figure 6.1 that approximately passes through the points associated with the data for the years 1971 to 2003 is the graph of a mathematical model of the data. The model is an *exponential function.* Because y is increasing (growing), it is an *exponential growth function.*

When light enters water, the intensity of the light decreases with the depth of the water. The graph in Figure 6.2 shows a model, for Lake Michigan, of the decrease in the percent of light available as the depth of the water increases. This model is also an exponential function. In this case y is decreasing (decaying), and the model is an *exponential decay function.*

Figure 6.1

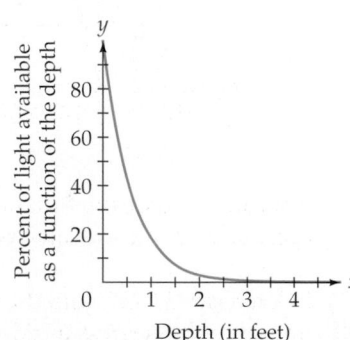

Figure 6.2

The **exponential function** is defined by $f(x) = b^x$, where b is called the base, $b > 0$, $b \neq 1$, and x is any real number.

The base b of $f(x) = b^x$ must be positive. If the base were a negative number, the value of the function would not be a real number for some values of x. For instance, if $b = -4$ and $x = \frac{1}{2}$, then $f(\frac{1}{2}) = (-4)^{1/2} = \sqrt{-4}$, which is not a real number. Also, $b \neq 1$ because when $b = 1$, $b^x = 1^x = 1$, a constant function.

At the right we evaluate $f(x) = 2^x$ for $x = 3$ and $x = -2$.

$$f(x) = 2^x$$
$$f(3) = 2^3 = 8$$
$$f(-2) = 2^{-2} = \frac{1}{2^2} = \frac{1}{4}$$

To evaluate the exponential function $f(x) = 2^x$ for an irrational number such as $x = \sqrt{2}$, we use a rational approximation of $\sqrt{2}$ (for instance, 1.4142) and a calculator to obtain an approximation of the function.

$$f(\sqrt{2}) = 2^{\sqrt{2}} \approx 2^{1.4142} \approx 2.6651$$

EXAMPLE 1 ■ Evaluate an Exponential Function

Evaluate $f(x) = 3^x$ at $x = 2$, $x = -4$, and $x = \pi$. Round approximate results to the nearest hundred thousandth.

Solution
$$f(2) = 3^2 = 9$$
$$f(-4) = 3^{-4} = \frac{1}{3^4} = \frac{1}{81}$$
$$f(\pi) = 3^\pi \approx 3^{3.1415927} \approx 31.54428$$

CHECK YOUR PROGRESS 1 Evaluate $g(x) = \left(\frac{1}{2}\right)^x$ when $x = 3$, $x = -1$, and $x = \sqrt{3}$. Round approximate results to the nearest thousandth.

Solution See page S24.

Graphs of Exponential Functions

The graph of $f(x) = 2^x$ is shown below. The coordinates of some of the points on the graph are given in the table.

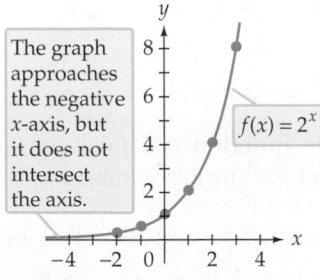

The graph approaches the negative x-axis, but it does not intersect the axis.

$f(x) = 2^x$

Figure 6.3

x	$f(x) = 2^x$	(x, y)
-2	$f(-2) = 2^{-2} = \frac{1}{4}$	$\left(-2, \frac{1}{4}\right)$
-1	$f(-1) = 2^{-1} = \frac{1}{2}$	$\left(-1, \frac{1}{2}\right)$
0	$f(0) = 2^0 = 1$	$(0, 1)$
1	$f(1) = 2^1 = 2$	$(1, 2)$
2	$f(2) = 2^2 = 4$	$(2, 4)$
3	$f(3) = 2^3 = 8$	$(3, 8)$

Observe that the values of *y increase* as *x* increases. This is an exponential growth function. This is typical of the graph of all exponential functions for which the base is *greater than* 1. For the function $f(x) = 2^x$, $b = 2$, which is greater than 1.

Now consider the graph of an exponential function for which the base is between 0 and 1. The graph of $f(x) = \left(\frac{1}{2}\right)^x$ is shown below. The coordinates of some of the points on the graph are given in the table.

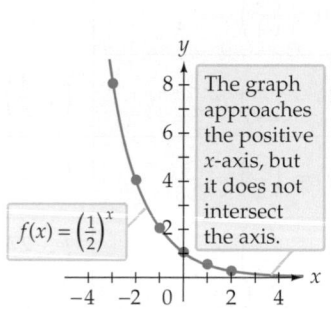

Figure 6.4

x	$f(x) = \left(\dfrac{1}{2}\right)^x$	(x, y)
-3	$f(-3) = \left(\dfrac{1}{2}\right)^{-3} = 8$	$(-3, 8)$
-2	$f(-2) = \left(\dfrac{1}{2}\right)^{-2} = 4$	$(-2, 4)$
-1	$f(-1) = \left(\dfrac{1}{2}\right)^{-1} = 2$	$(-1, 2)$
0	$f(0) = \left(\dfrac{1}{2}\right)^{0} = 1$	$(0, 1)$
1	$f(1) = \left(\dfrac{1}{2}\right)^{1} = \dfrac{1}{2}$	$\left(1, \dfrac{1}{2}\right)$
2	$f(2) = \left(\dfrac{1}{2}\right)^{2} = \dfrac{1}{4}$	$\left(2, \dfrac{1}{4}\right)$

Observe that the values of *y decrease* as *x* increases. This is an exponential decay function. This is typical of the graph of all exponential functions for which the positive base is *less than* 1. For the function $f(x) = \left(\frac{1}{2}\right)^x$, $b = \frac{1}{2}$, which is less than 1.

QUESTION   *Is $f(x) = 0.25^x$ an exponential growth or exponential decay function?*

EXAMPLE 2 ■ Graph an Exponential Function

State whether $g(x) = \left(\frac{3}{4}\right)^x$ is an exponential growth function or an exponential decay function. Then graph the function.

Solution

Because the base $\frac{3}{4}$ is less than 1, *g* is an exponential decay function. Because it is an exponential decay function, the *y*-values will decrease as *x* increases. The *y*-intercept of the graph is the point $(0, 1)$, and the graph also passes through $\left(1, \frac{3}{4}\right)$. Plot a few additional points. (See the table on the following page.) Then draw a smooth curve through the points, as shown on the following page.

ANSWER   *The base is 0.25, which is less than 1. It is an exponential decay function.*

x	$g(x) = \left(\dfrac{3}{4}\right)^x$	(x, y)
−3	$g(-3) = \left(\dfrac{3}{4}\right)^{-3} = \dfrac{64}{27}$	$\left(-3, \dfrac{64}{27}\right)$
−2	$g(-2) = \left(\dfrac{3}{4}\right)^{-2} = \dfrac{16}{9}$	$\left(-2, \dfrac{16}{9}\right)$
−1	$g(-1) = \left(\dfrac{3}{4}\right)^{-1} = \dfrac{4}{3}$	$\left(-1, \dfrac{4}{3}\right)$
0	$g(0) = \left(\dfrac{3}{4}\right)^{0} = 1$	(0, 1)
1	$g(1) = \left(\dfrac{3}{4}\right)^{1} = \dfrac{3}{4}$	$\left(1, \dfrac{3}{4}\right)$
2	$g(2) = \left(\dfrac{3}{4}\right)^{2} = \dfrac{9}{16}$	$\left(2, \dfrac{9}{16}\right)$
3	$g(3) = \left(\dfrac{3}{4}\right)^{3} = \dfrac{27}{64}$	$\left(3, \dfrac{27}{64}\right)$

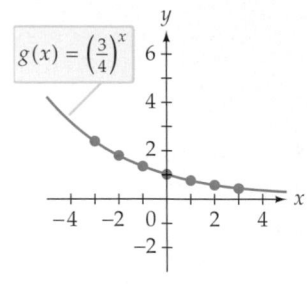

CHECK YOUR PROGRESS 2   State whether $f(x) = \left(\frac{3}{2}\right)^x$ is an exponential growth function or an exponential decay function. Then graph the function.

Solution   See page S24.

The Natural Exponential Function

The irrational number π is often used in applications that involve circles. Another irrational number, denoted by the letter e, is useful in applications that involve growth or decay.

n	$\left(1 + \dfrac{1}{n}\right)^n$
10	2.59374246
100	2.70481383
1000	2.71692393
10,000	2.71814593
100,000	2.71826824
1,000,000	2.71828047

Definition of e

The number e is defined as the number that

$$\left(1 + \frac{1}{n}\right)^n$$

approaches as n increases without bound.

The letter e was chosen in honor of the Swiss mathematician Leonhard Euler. He was able to compute the value of e to several decimal places by evaluating $\left(1 + \frac{1}{n}\right)^n$ for large values of n, as shown at the left. The value of e accurate to eight decimal places is 2.71828183.

The Natural Exponential Function

For all real numbers x, the function defined by $f(x) = e^x$ is called the **natural exponential function.**

A calculator with an e^x key can be used to evaluate e^x for specific values of x. For instance,

$$e^2 \approx 7.389056, \qquad e^{3.5} \approx 33.115452, \qquad \text{and} \qquad e^{-1.4} \approx 0.246597$$

The graph of the natural exponential function can be constructed by plotting a few points or by using a graphing utility.

EXAMPLE 3 ■ Graph a Natural Exponential Function

 Graph $f(x) = e^x$.

Solution

Use a calculator to find range values for a few domain values. The range values in the table below have been rounded to the nearest tenth.

x	-2	-1	0	1	2
$f(x) = e^x$	0.1	0.4	1.0	2.7	7.4

Plot the points given in the table and then connect the points with a smooth curve. Because $e > 1$, as x increases, e^x increases. Thus the values of y increase as x increases. As x decreases, e^x becomes closer to zero. For instance, when $x = -5$, $e^{-5} \approx 0.0067$. Thus as x decreases, the graph gets closer and closer to the x-axis. The y-intercept is $(0, 1)$.

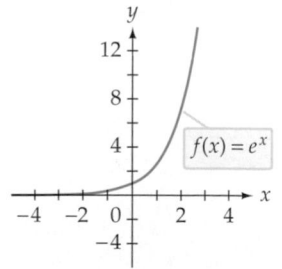

In the figure at the right, compare the graph of $f(x) = e^x$ with the graphs of $g(x) = 2^x$ and $h(x) = 3^x$. Because $2 < e < 3$, the graph of $f(x) = e^x$ is between the graphs of g and h.

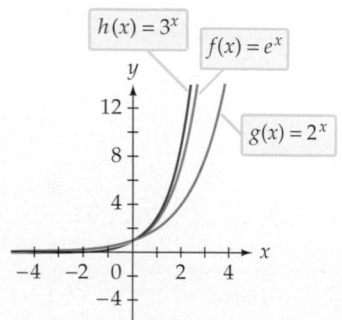

CHECK YOUR PROGRESS 3 Graph $f(x) = e^{-x} + 2$.

Solution See page S24.

Applications of Exponential Functions

Many applications can be effectively modeled by an exponential function. For instance, when money is deposited into a compound interest account, the value of the money can be represented by an exponential growth function. When physicians use a test that involves a radioactive element, the amount of radioactivity remaining in the patient's body can be modeled by an exponential decay function.

TAKE NOTE

Here is an application of exponential functions. Assume that you have a long strip of paper that is $\frac{1}{16}$ inch thick and can be folded in half infinitely many times. After how many folds would the paper be as high as the Empire State Building (1250 feet)?

EXAMPLE 4 ■ Application of an Exponential Function

 When an amount of money P is placed in an account that earns compound interest, the value A of the money after t years is given by the compound interest formula

$$A = P\left(1 + \frac{r}{n}\right)^{nt}$$

where r is the annual interest rate as a decimal and n is the number of compounding periods per year. Suppose \$500 is placed in an account that earns 8% interest compounded daily. Find the value of the investment after 5 years.

Solution
Use the compound interest formula. Because interest is compounded daily, $n = 365$.

$$A = P\left(1 + \frac{r}{n}\right)^{nt}$$
$$= 500\left(1 + \frac{0.08}{365}\right)^{365(5)} \qquad • \ P = 500,\ r = 0.08,\ n = 365,\ t = 5$$
$$\approx 500(1.491759) \approx 745.88$$

After 5 years, there is \$745.88 in the account.

CHECK YOUR PROGRESS 4 The radioactive isotope iodine-131 is used to monitor thyroid activity. The number of grams N of iodine-131 in the body t hours after an injection is given by $N(t) = 1.5\left(\frac{1}{2}\right)^{t/193.7}$. Find the number of grams of the isotope in the body 24 hours after an injection. Round to the nearest ten-thousandth.

Solution *See page S25.*

The next example is based on Newton's Law of Cooling. This exponential function can be used to model the temperature of something that is being cooled.

EXAMPLE 5 ■ Application of an Exponential Function

A cup of coffee is heated to 160°F and placed in a room that maintains a temperature of 70°F. The temperature of the coffee after t minutes is given by $T(t) = 70 + 90e^{-0.0485t}$. Find the temperature of the coffee 20 minutes after it is placed in the room. Round to the nearest degree.

Solution

Evaluate the function $T(t) = 70 + 90e^{-0.0485t}$ for $t = 20$.

$$T(t) = 70 + 90e^{-0.0485t}$$
$$T(20) = 70 + 90e^{-0.0485(20)} \quad \bullet \text{ Substitute 20 for } t.$$
$$\approx 70 + 34.1$$
$$\approx 104.1$$

After 20 minutes the temperature of the coffee is about 104°F.

CHECK YOUR PROGRESS 5 The function $A(t) = 200e^{-0.014t}$ gives the amount of aspirin, in milligrams, in a patient's bloodstream t minutes after the aspirin has been administered. Find the amount of aspirin in the patient's bloodstream after 45 minutes. Round to the nearest milligram.

Solution *See page S25.*

Math Matters   Marie Curie

In 1903, Marie Sklodowska-Curie (1867–1934) became the first woman to receive a Nobel prize in physics. She was awarded the prize along with her husband, Pierre Curie, and Henri Becquerel for their discovery of radioactivity. In fact, Marie Curie coined the word *radioactivity.*

In 1911, Marie Curie became the first person to win a second Nobel prize, this time alone and in chemistry, for the isolation of radium. She also discovered the element polonium, which she named after Poland, her birthplace. The radioactive phenomena that she studied are modeled by exponential decay functions.

The stamp at the left was printed in 1938 to commemorate Pierre and Marie Curie. When the stamp was issued, there was a surcharge added to the regular price of the stamp. The additional revenue was donated to cancer research. Marie Curie died in 1934 from leukemia, which was caused by her constant exposure to radiation from the radioactive elements she studied.

In 1935, one of Marie Curie's daughters, Irene Joloit-Curie, won a Nobel prize in chemistry.

Exponential Regression

Earlier in this chapter we examined linear regression models. In some cases, an exponential function may more closely model a set of data.

EXAMPLE 6 ■ Find an Exponential Regression Equation

A diamond merchant has determined the values of several white diamonds that have different weights, measured in carats, but are similar in quality. See the table below.

4.00 ct	3.00 ct	2.00 ct	1.75 ct	1.50 ct	1.25 ct	1.00 ct	0.75 ct	0.50 ct
$14,500	$10,700	$7900	$7300	$6700	$6200	$5800	$5000	$4600

Find an exponential growth function that models the values of the diamonds as a function of their weights and use the model to predict the value of a 3.5-carat diamond of similar quality.

Solution

Use a graphing calculator to find the regression equation. The calculator display below shows that the exponential regression equation is $y \approx 4067.6(1.3816)^x$, where x is the carat weight of the diamond and y is the value of the diamond.

```
ExpReg
  y = a*b^x
  a = 4067.641145
  b = 1.381644186
  r² = .994881215
  r = .9974373238
```

To use the regression equation to predict the value of a 3.5-carat diamond of similar quality, substitute 3.5 for x and evaluate.

$$y \approx 4067.6(1.3816)^x$$
$$y \approx 4067.6(1.3816)^{3.5}$$
$$y \approx 12,609$$

According to the modeling function, the value of a 3.5-carat diamond of similar quality is $12,609.

Notice on the calculator screen above that r^2, the coefficient of determination, is about 0.9949, which is very close to 1. This indicates that the equation $y \approx 4067.6(1.3816)^x$ provides a good fit for the data.

CHECK YOUR PROGRESS 6   The following table shows Earth's atmospheric pressure P at an altitude of a kilometers. Find an exponential function that models the atmospheric pressure as a function of altitude. Use the function to estimate, to the nearest tenth, the atmospheric pressure at an altitude of 24 kilometers.

Altitude, a, above sea level, in kilometers	Atmospheric pressure, P, in newtons per square centimeter
0	10.3
2	8.0
4	6.4
6	5.1
8	4.0
10	3.2
12	2.5
14	2.0
16	1.6
18	1.3

Solution   *See page S25.*

Excursion

Chess and Exponential Functions

According to legend, when Sissa Ben Dahir of India invented the game of chess, King Shirham was so impressed with the game that he summoned the game's inventor and offered him the reward of his choosing. The inventor pointed to the chessboard and requested, for his reward, one grain of wheat on the first square, two grains of wheat on the second square, four grains on the third square, eight grains on the fourth square, and so on for all 64 squares on the chessboard. The king considered this a very modest reward and said he would grant the inventor's wish.

1. This portion of this Excursion will enable you to find a formula for the total amount of wheat on the first n squares of the chessboard. You may want to use the chart below as you answer the questions. It may help you to see a pattern.

Square number, n	1	2	3	4	5	6	7
Number of grains of wheat on square n	1	2	4				
Total number of grains of wheat on squares 1 through n	1	$1 + 2 =$	$3 + 4 =$				

a. How many grains of wheat are on each of the first seven squares?

(continued)

What is the total number (the sum) of grains of wheat on the first

b. two squares?

c. three squares?

d. four squares?

e. five squares?

f. six squares?

g. seven squares?

2. Use inductive reasoning to find a function that gives the total number (the sum) of grains of wheat on the first n squares of the chessboard. Test your function to ensure that it works for parts b through g.

3. If all 64 squares of the chessboard are piled with wheat as requested by Sissa Ben Dahir, how many grains of wheat are on the board?

4. A grain of wheat weighs approximately 0.000008 kilogram. Find the total weight of the wheat requested by Sissa Ben Dahir.

5. In a recent year, a total of 6.5×10^8 metric tons of wheat were produced in the world. At this level, how many years of wheat production would be required to fill the request of Sissa Ben Dahir? *Hint:* One metric ton equals 1000 kilograms.

Exercise Set 6.5

1. Given $f(x) = 3^x$, evaluate:
   a. $f(2)$ **b.** $f(0)$ **c.** $f(-2)$

2. Given $H(x) = 2^x$, evaluate:
   a. $H(-3)$ **b.** $H(0)$ **c.** $H(2)$

3. Given $g(x) = 2^{x+1}$, evaluate:
   a. $g(3)$ **b.** $g(1)$ **c.** $g(-3)$

4. Given $F(x) = 3^{x-2}$, evaluate:
   a. $F(-4)$ **b.** $F(-1)$ **c.** $F(0)$

5. Given $G(r) = \left(\frac{1}{2}\right)^{2r}$, evaluate:
   a. $G(0)$ **b.** $G\left(\frac{3}{2}\right)$ **c.** $G(-2)$

6. Given $R(t) = \left(\frac{1}{3}\right)^{3t}$, evaluate:
   a. $R\left(-\frac{1}{3}\right)$ **b.** $R(1)$ **c.** $R(-2)$

7. Given $h(x) = e^{x/2}$, evaluate the following. Round to the nearest ten-thousandth.
   a. $h(4)$ **b.** $h(-2)$ **c.** $h\left(\frac{1}{2}\right)$

8. Given $f(x) = e^{2x}$, evaluate the following. Round to the nearest ten-thousandth.

   a. $f(-2)$ **b.** $f\left(-\frac{2}{3}\right)$ **c.** $f(2)$

9. Given $H(x) = e^{-x+3}$, evaluate the following. Round to the nearest ten-thousandth.
   a. $H(-1)$ **b.** $H(3)$ **c.** $H(5)$

10. Given $g(x) = e^{-x/2}$, evaluate the following. Round to the nearest ten-thousandth.
    a. $g(-3)$ **b.** $g(4)$ **c.** $g\left(\frac{1}{2}\right)$

11. Given $F(x) = 2^{x^2}$, evaluate the following. Round to the nearest ten-thousandth.
    a. $F(2)$ **b.** $F(-2)$ **c.** $F\left(\frac{3}{4}\right)$

12. Given $Q(x) = 2^{-x^2}$, evaluate:
    a. $Q(3)$ **b.** $Q(-1)$ **c.** $Q(-2)$

13. Given $f(x) = e^{-x^2/2}$, evaluate the following. Round to the nearest ten-thousandth.
    a. $f(-2)$ **b.** $f(2)$ **c.** $f(-3)$

14. Given $h(x) = e^{-2x} + 1$, evaluate the following. Round to the nearest ten-thousandth.
    a. $h(-1)$ **b.** $h(3)$ **c.** $h(-2)$

In Exercises 15–24, graph the function.

15. $f(x) = 2^x + 1$

16. $f(x) = 3^x - 2$

17. $g(x) = 3^{x/2}$

18. $h(x) = 2^{-x/2}$

19. $f(x) = 2^{x+3}$

20. $g(x) = 4^{-x} + 1$

21. $H(x) = 2^{2x}$

22. $F(x) = 2^{-x}$

23. $f(x) = e^{-x}$

24. $y(x) = e^{2x}$

Investments In Exercises 25 and 26, use the compound interest formula $A = P\left(1 + \dfrac{r}{n}\right)^{nt}$, where P is the amount deposited, A is the value of the money after t years, r is the annual interest rate as a decimal, and n is the number of compounding periods per year.

25. A computer network specialist deposits $2500 into a retirement account that earns 7.5% annual interest, compounded daily. What is the value of the investment after 20 years?

26. A $10,000 certificate of deposit (CD) earns 5% annual interest, compounded daily. What is the value of the investment after 20 years?

27. Investments Some banks now use continuous compounding of an amount invested. In this case, the equation that models the value of an initial investment of P dollars in t years at an annual interest rate of r is given by $A = Pe^{rt}$. Using this equation, find the value in 5 years of an investment of $2500 that earns 5% annual interest.

28. Isotopes An isotope of technetium is used to prepare images of internal body organs. This isotope has a half-life (time required for half the material to erode) of approximately 6 hours. If a patient is injected with 30 milligrams of this isotope, what will be the technetium level in the patient after 3 hours? Use the function $A(t) = 30\left(\frac{1}{2}\right)^{t/6}$, where A is the technetium level, in milligrams, in the patient after t hours. Round to the nearest tenth.

29. Isotopes Iodine-131 is an isotope that is used to study the functioning of the thyroid gland. This isotope has a half-life (time required for half the material to erode) of approximately 8 days. If a patient is given an injection that contains 8 micrograms of iodine-131, what will be the iodine level in the patient after 5 days? Use the function $A(t) = 8\left(\frac{1}{2}\right)^{t/8}$, where A is the amount of the isotope, in micrograms, in the patient after t days. Round to the nearest tenth.

30. Welding The percent of correct welds that a student can make will increase with practice and can be approximated by the function $P(t) = 100[1 - (0.75)^t]$, where P is the percent of correct welds and t is the number of weeks of practice. Find the percent of correct welds that a student will make after 4 weeks of practice. Round to the nearest percent.

31. Music The "concert A" note on a piano is the first A below middle C. When that key is struck, the string associated with the key vibrates 440 times per second. The next A above concert A vibrates twice as fast. An exponential function with a base of two is used to determine the frequency of the 11 notes between the two A's. Find this function. *Hint:* The function is of the form $f(x) = k \cdot 2^{(cx)}$, where k and c are constants. Also $f(0) = 440$ and $f(12) = 880$.

32. Atmospheric Pressure Atmospheric pressure changes as you rise above Earth's surface. At an altitude of h kilometers, where $0 < h < 80$, the pressure P in newtons per square centimeter is approximately modeled by the function

$$P(h) = 10.13e^{-0.116h}.$$

a. What is the approximate pressure at 40 kilometers above Earth?

b. What is the approximate pressure on Earth's surface?

c. Does atmospheric pressure increase or decrease as you rise above Earth's surface?

33. Automobiles The number of automobiles in the United States in 1900 was around 8000. In the year 2000, the number of automobiles in the United States reached 200 million. Find an exponential model for the data and use the model to predict the number of automobiles in the United States in 2010. Use $t = 0$ to represent the year 1900. Round to the nearest hundred thousand automobiles.

34. Panda Population One estimate gives the world panda population as 3200 in 1980 and 590 in 2000. Find an exponential model for the data and use the model to predict the panda population in 2040. Use $t = 0$ to represent the year 1980. Round to the nearest whole number.

35. Polonium An initial amount of 100 micrograms of polonium decays to 75 micrograms in approximately 34.5 days. Find an exponential model for the amount of polonium in the sample after t days. Round to the nearest hundredth of a microgram.

36. **The Film Industry** The table below shows the number of multidisc DVDs, with three or more discs, released each year. (*Source: DVD Release Report*)

Year, x	1999	2000	2001	2002	2003
Titles released, y	11	57	87	154	283

a. Find an exponential regression equation for this data using $x = 0$ to represent 1995. Round to the nearest hundredth.

b. Use the equation to predict the number of multidisc DVDs released in 2008.

37. **Meteorology** The table below shows the saturation of water in air at various air temperatures.

Temperature (in °C)	0	5	10	20	25	30
Saturation (in millimeters of water per cubic meter of air)	4.8	6.8	9.4	17.3	23.1	30.4

a. Find an exponential regression equation for these data. Round to the nearest thousandth.

b. Use the equation to predict the number of milliliters of water per cubic meter of air at a temperature of 15°C. Round to the nearest tenth.

38. **Snow Making** Artificial snow is made at a ski resort by combining air and water in a ratio that depends on the outside air temperature. The table below shows the rate of air flow needed for various temperatures.

Temperature (in °F)	0	5	10	15	20
Air flow (in cubic feet per minute)	3.0	3.6	4.7	6.1	9.9

a. Find an exponential regression equation for these data. Round to the nearest hundredth.

b. Use the equation to predict the air flow needed when the temperature is 25°F. Round to the nearest tenth of a cubic foot per minute.

Extensions

CRITICAL THINKING

An exponential model for population growth or decay can be accurate over a short period of time. However, this model begins to fail because it does not account for the natural resources necessary to support growth, nor does it account for death within the population. Another model, called the *logistic model,* can account for some of these effects. The logistic model is given by

$$P(t) = \frac{mP_0}{P_0 + (m - P_0)e^{-kt}},$$ where $P(t)$ is the population at time t, m is the maximum population that can be supported, P_0 is the population when $t = 0$, and k is a positive constant that is related to the growth of the population.

39. Earth's Population One model of Earth's population is given by

$$P(t) = \frac{280}{4 + 66e^{-0.021t}}.$$ In this equation, $P(t)$ is the population in billions and t is the number of years after 1980. Round answers to the nearest hundred million people.

a. According to this model, what was Earth's population in the year 2000?

b. According to this model, what will be Earth's population in the year 2010?

c. If t is very large, say greater than 500, then $e^{-0.021t} \approx 0$. What does this suggest about the maximum population that Earth can support?

40. Wolf Population Game wardens have determined that the maximum wolf population in a certain preserve is 1000 wolves. Suppose the population of wolves in the preserve in the year 2000 was 500, and that k is estimated to be 0.025.

a. Find a logistic function for the number of wolves in the preserve in year t, where t is the number of years after 2000.

b. Find the estimated wolf population in 2015.

EXPLORATIONS

41. Car Payments The formula used to calculate a monthly lease payment or a monthly car payment (for a purchase rather than a lease) is given by $P = \dfrac{Ar(1 + r)^n - Vr}{(1 + r)^n - 1}$, where P is the monthly payment, A is the amount of the loan, r is the *monthly* interest rate as a decimal, n is the number of months of the loan or lease, and V is the residual value of the car at the end of the lease. For a car purchase, $V = 0$.

a. If the annual interest rate for a loan is 9%, what is the monthly interest rate as a decimal?

b. Write the formula for a monthly car payment when the car is purchased rather than leased.

c. Suppose you lease a car for 5 years. Find the monthly lease payment if the lease amount is $10,000, the residual value is $6000, and the annual interest rate is 6%.

d. Suppose you purchase a car and secure a 5-year loan for $10,000 at an annual interest rate of 6%. Find the monthly payment.

e. Why are the answers to parts c and d different?

The total amount C that has been repaid on a loan or lease is given by $C = \dfrac{(P - Ar)[(1 + r)^n - 1]}{r}$.

f. Using the lease payment in part c, find the total amount that will be repaid in 5 years. How much remains to be paid?

g. Using the monthly payment in part d, find the total amount that will be repaid in 5 years. How much remains to be paid?

h. Explain why the answers to parts f and g make sense.

SECTION 6.6 | Logarithmic Functions

Introduction to Logarithmic Functions

Time (in hours)	Number of Bacteria
0	1000
1	2000
2	4000
3	8000

Suppose a bacteria colony that originally contained 1000 bacteria doubled in size every hour. Then the table at the left would show the number of bacteria in that colony after 1, 2, and 3 hours.

The exponential function $A = 1000(2^t)$, where A is the number of bacteria in the colony at time t, is a model of the growth of the colony. For instance, when $t = 3$ hours, we have

$A = 1000(2^t)$
$A = 1000(2^3)$ • Replace t by **3**.
$A = 1000(8) = 8000$

After 3 hours there are 8000 bacteria in the colony.

Now we ask, "How long will it take for there to be 32,000 bacteria in the colony?" To answer the question, we must solve the *exponential equation* $32,000 = 1000(2^t)$. By trial and error, we find that when $t = 5$,

$A = 1000(2^t)$
$A = 1000(2^5)$ • Replace t by **5**.
$A = 1000(32) = 32,000$

After 5 hours there will be 32,000 bacteria in the colony.

Now suppose we want to know how long it will be before the colony reaches 50,000 bacteria. To answer that question, we must find t such that $50,000 = 1000(2^t)$. Using trial and error again, we find that

$1000(2^5) = 32,000$ and $1000(2^6) = 64,000$

Because 50,000 is between 32,000 and 64,000, we conclude that t is between 5 and 6 hours. If we try $t = 5.5$ (halfway between 5 and 6), we get

$A = 1000(2^t)$
$A = 1000(2^{5.5})$ • Replace t by **5.5**.
$A \approx 1000(45.25) = 45,250$

TAKE NOTE

Note that on page 389 when we tried $t = 5.5$, we stated that the actual value of t must be greater than 5.5 and that 5.644 is a little greater than 5.5.

 TAKE NOTE

Read $\log_b x$ as "the logarithm of x, base b" or "log base b of x."

 TAKE NOTE

The idea of a function that performs the opposite of a given function occurs frequently. For instance, the opposite of a "doubling" function, one that doubles a given number, is a "halving" function, one that takes one-half of a given number. We could write $f(x) = 2x$ for the doubling function and $g(x) = \frac{1}{2}x$ for the halving function. We call these functions *inverse functions* of one another. In a similar manner, exponential and logarithmic functions are inverses of one another.

In 5.5 hours, there are approximately 45,250 bacteria in the colony. Because this is less than 50,000, the value of t must be a little greater than 5.5.

We could continue to use trial and error to find the correct value of t, but it would be more efficient if we could just solve the exponential equation $50,000 = 1000(2^t)$ for t. If we follow the procedures for solving equations that were discussed earlier in the text, we have

$$50,000 = 1000(2^t)$$
$$50 = 2^t \qquad \text{• Divide each side of the equation by 1000.}$$

To proceed to the next step, it would be helpful to have a function that would find the power of 2 that produces 50.

Around the mid-sixteenth century, mathematicians created such a function, which we now call a *logarithmic function*. We write the solution of $50 = 2^t$ as $t = \log_2 50$. This is read "t equals the logarithm base 2 of 50." and it means "t equals the power of 2 that produces 50." When logarithms were first introduced, tables were used to find a numerical value of t. Today, a calculator is used. Using a calculator, we can approximate the value of t as 5.644. This means that $2^{5.644} \approx 50$.

The equivalence of the expressions $50 = 2^t$ and $t = \log_2 50$ are described in the following definition of logarithm.

Definition of Logarithm

For $b > 0$, $b \neq 1$, $y = \log_b x$ is equivalent to $x = b^y$.

For every exponential equation there is a corresponding logarithmic equation, and for every logarithmic equation there is a corresponding exponential equation. Here are some examples.

Exponential Equation	Logarithmic Equation
$2^5 = 32$	$\log_2 32 = 5$
$3^2 = 9$	$\log_3 9 = 2$
$5^{-2} = \dfrac{1}{25}$	$\log_5 \dfrac{1}{25} = -2$
$7^0 = 1$	$\log_7 1 = 0$

QUESTION   *Which of the following is the logarithmic form of $4^3 = 64$?*

     a. $\log_4 3 = 64$ ***b.*** $\log_3 4 = 64$ ***c.*** $\log_4 64 = 3$

The equation $y = \log_b x$ is the logarithmic form of $b^y = x$, and the equation $b^y = x$ is the *exponential form* of $y = \log_b x$. These two forms state exactly the same relationship between x and y.

ANSWER   **c.** $\log_4 64 = 3$ is equivalent to $4^3 = 64$.

historical note

Logarithms were developed independently by Jobst Burgi (1552–1632) and John Napier (1550–1617) as a means of simplifying the calculations of astronomers. The idea was to devise a method by which two numbers could be multiplied by performing additions. Napier is usually given credit for logarithms because he published his results first.

In Napier's original work, the logarithm of 10,000,000 was 0. After this work was published, Napier, in discussions with Henry Briggs (1561–1631), decided that tables of logarithms would be easier to use if the logarithm of 1 were 0. Napier died before new tables could be prepared, and Briggs took on the task. His table consisted of logarithms accurate to 30 decimal places, all accomplished without a calculator! ■

EXAMPLE 1 ■ Write a Logarithmic Equation in Exponential Form and an Exponential Equation in Logarithmic Form

a. Write $2 = \log_{10}(x + 5)$ in exponential form.

b. Write $2^{3x} = 64$ in logarithmic form.

Solution

Use the definition of logarithm: $y = \log_b x$ if and only if $b^y = x$.

a. $2 = \log_{10}(x + 5)$ if and only if $10^2 = x + 5$.

b. $2^{3x} = 64$ if and only if $\log_2 64 = 3x$.

CHECK YOUR PROGRESS 1

a. Write $\log_2(4x) = 10$ in exponential form.

b. Write $10^3 = 2x$ in logarithmic form.

Solution　*See page S25.*

The relationship between the exponential and logarithmic forms can be used to evaluate some logarithms. The solutions to these types of problems are based on the Equality of Exponents Property.

Equality of Exponents Property

If $b > 0$ and $b^x = b^y$, then $x = y$.

EXAMPLE 2 ■ Evaluate Logarithmic Expressions

Evaluate the logarithms.

a. $\log_8 64$　　**b.** $\log_2\left(\dfrac{1}{8}\right)$

Solution

a. $\log_8 64 = x$ 　　• Write an equation.

$\quad\quad 8^x = 64$ 　　• Write the equation in its equivalent exponential form.

$\quad\quad 8^x = 8^2$ 　　• Write 64 in exponential form using 8 as the base.

$\quad\quad\quad x = 2$ 　　• Solve for x using the Equality of Exponents Property.

$\log_8 64 = 2$

b. $\log_2\left(\dfrac{1}{8}\right) = x$ 　　• Write an equation.

$\quad\quad 2^x = \dfrac{1}{8}$ 　　• Write the equation in its equivalent exponential form.

$\quad\quad 2^x = 2^{-3}$ 　　• Write $\dfrac{1}{8}$ in exponential form using 2 as the base.

$\quad\quad\quad x = -3$ 　　• Solve for x using the Equality of Exponents Property.

$\log_2\left(\dfrac{1}{8}\right) = -3$

✔ **TAKE NOTE**

If you need to review material on negative exponents, see Lesson 6.1B on the CD that you received with this book.

CHECK YOUR PROGRESS 2   Evaluate the logarithms.

a. $\log_{10} 0.001$ **b.** $\log_5 125$

Solution   *See page S25.*

EXAMPLE 3 ■ Solve a Logarithmic Equation

Solve: $\log_3 x = 2$

Solution

$\log_3 x = 2$

$3^2 = x$ • Write the equation in its equivalent exponential form.

$9 = x$ • Simplify the exponential expression.

CHECK YOUR PROGRESS 3   Solve: $\log_2 x = 6$

Solution   *See page S25.*

Not all logarithms can be evaluated by rewriting the logarithm in its equivalent exponential form and using the Equality of Exponents Property. For instance, if we tried to evaluate $\log_{10} 18$, it would be necessary to solve the equivalent exponential equation $10^x = 18$. The difficulty here is trying to rewrite 18 in exponential form with 10 as a base.

Common and Natural Logarithms

Two of the most frequently used logarithmic functions are *common logarithms,* which have base 10, and *natural logarithms,* which have base e (the base of the natural exponential function).

> **Common and Natural Logarithms**
>
> The function defined by $f(x) = \log_{10} x$ is called the **common logarithmic function.** It is customarily written without the base as $f(x) = \log x$.
>
> The function defined by $f(x) = \log_e x$ is called the **natural logarithmic function.** It is customarily written as $f(x) = \ln x$.

Most scientific or graphing calculators have a $\boxed{\log}$ key for evaluating common logarithms and a $\boxed{\ln}$ key to evaluate natural logarithms. For instance,

$\log 24 \approx 1.3802112$ and $\ln 81 \approx 4.3944492$

EXAMPLE 4 ■ Solve Common and Natural Logarithmic Equations

Solve each of the following equations. Round to the nearest thousandth.

a. $\log x = -1.5$ **b.** $\ln x = 3$

Solution

a. $\log x = -1.5$

$10^{-1.5} = x$ • Write the equation in its equivalent exponential form.

$0.032 \approx x$ • Simplify the exponential expression.

b. $\ln x = 3$

$e^3 = x$ • Write the equation in its equivalent exponential form.

$20.086 \approx x$ • Simplify the exponential expression.

CHECK YOUR PROGRESS 4   Solve each of the following equations. Round to the nearest thousandth.

a. $\log x = -2.1$ **b.** $\ln x = 2$

Solution   *See page S25.*

Math Matters   Zipf's Law

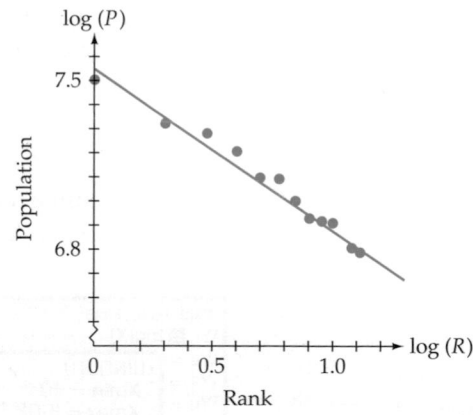

George Zipf (1902–1950) was a lecturer in German and philology (the study of the change in a language over time) at Harvard University. Zipf's Law, as originally formulated, referred to the frequency of occurrence of words in a book, magazine article, or other written material, and its rank. The word used most frequently had rank 1, the next most frequent word had rank 2, and so on. Zipf hypothesized that if the x-axis were the logarithm of a word's rank and the y-axis were the logarithm of the frequency of the word, then the graph of rank versus frequency would lie on approximately a straight line.

Zipf's Law has been extended to demographics. For instance, let the population of a U.S. state be *P* and its rank in population be *R*. The graph of the points $(\log R, \log P)$ lie on approximately a straight line. The graph above shows Zipf's Law as applied to the populations and ranks of the 12 most populated states according to the 2000 census.

Recently, Zipf's Law has been applied to web site traffic, where web sites are ranked according to the number of hits they receive. Assumptions about web traffic are used by engineers and programmers who study ways to make the web more efficient.

Graphs of Logarithmic Functions

The graph of a logarithmic function can be drawn by first rewriting the function in its exponential form. This procedure is illustrated in Example 5.

EXAMPLE 5 ■ Graph a Logarithmic Function

Graph $f(x) = \log_3 x$.

Solution

To graph $f(x) = \log_3 x$, first write the equation in the form $y = \log_3 x$. Then write the equivalent exponential equation $x = 3^y$. Because this equation is solved for x, choose values of y and calculate the corresponding values of x, as shown in the table below.

$x = 3^y$	$\dfrac{1}{9}$	$\dfrac{1}{3}$	1	3	9
y	-2	-1	0	1	2

Plot the ordered pairs and connect the points with a smooth curve, as shown at the left.

CHECK YOUR PROGRESS 5   Graph $f(x) = \log_5 x$.

Solution   *See page S25.*

The graphs of $y = \log x$ and $y = \ln x$ can be drawn on a graphing calculator by using the $\boxed{\texttt{log}}$ and $\boxed{\texttt{ln}}$ keys. The graphs are shown below for a TI-83/84 calculator.

Applications of Logarithmic Functions

Many applications can be modeled by logarithmic functions.

EXAMPLE 6 ■ Application of a Logarithmic Function

During the 1980s and 1990s, the average time T of a major league baseball game tended to increase each year. If the year 1981 is represented by $x = 1$, then the function

$$T(x) = 149.57 + 7.63 \ln x$$

approximates the average time T, in minutes, of a major league baseball game for the years $x = 1$ to $x = 19$.

a. Use the function to determine the average time of a major league baseball game during the 1981 season and during the 1999 season. Round to the nearest hundredth of a minute.

b. By how much did the average time of a major league baseball game increase from 1981 to 1999?

Solution

a. The year 1981 is represented by $x = 1$ and the year 1999 by $x = 19$.

$$T(1) = 149.57 + 7.63 \ln(1) = 149.57$$

In 1981 the average time of a major league baseball game was about 149.57 minutes.

$$T(19) = 149.57 + 7.63 \ln(19) \approx 172.04$$

In 1999 the average time of a major league baseball game was about 172.04 minutes.

b. $T(19) - T(1) \approx 172.04 - 149.57 \approx 22.47$

From 1981 to 1999, the average time of a major league baseball game increased by about 22.47 minutes.

The following figure shows the graph of T with axes labeled "Average time of a baseball game (in minutes)" on the vertical axis T (with values 150, 160, 170, 180) and "Year ($x = 1$ represents 1981)" on the horizontal axis x (with values 0, 5, 10, 15, 20). The curve is labeled $T(x) = 149.57 + 7.63 \ln(x)$.

CHECK YOUR PROGRESS 6   The following function models the average typing speed S, in words per minute, of a student who has been typing for t months.

$$S(t) = 5 + 29 \ln(t + 1), \quad 0 \le t \le 9$$

a. Use the function to determine the student's average typing speed when the student first started to type and the student's average typing speed after 3 months. Round to the nearest whole word per minute.

b. By how much did the typing speed increase during the 3 months?

Solution   See page S25.

historical note

The Richter scale was created by the seismologist Charles Francis Richter (rĭk′tər) (1900–1985) in 1935.

Richter was born in Ohio. At the age of 16, he and his mother moved to Los Angeles, where he enrolled at the University of Southern California. He went on to study physics at Stanford University. Richter was a professor of seismology at the Seismological Laboratory at California Institute of Technology (Caltech) from 1936 until he retired in 1970. ■

Logarithmic functions are often used to convert very large or very small numbers into numbers that are easier to comprehend. For instance, the *Richter scale*, which measures the magnitude of an earthquake, uses a logarithmic function to scale the intensity of an earthquake's shock waves I into a number M, which for most earthquakes is in the range of 0 to 10. The intensity I of an earthquake is often given in terms of the constant I_0, where I_0 is the intensity of the smallest earthquake (called a **zero-level earthquake**) that can be measured on a seismograph near the earthquake's epicenter. The following formula is used to compute the Richter scale magnitude of an earthquake.

The Richter Scale Magnitude of an Earthquake

An earthquake with an intensity of I has a Richter scale magnitude of

$$M = \log\left(\frac{I}{I_0}\right)$$

where I_0 is the measure of the intensity of a zero-level earthquake.

✔ **TAKE NOTE**

Notice in Example 7 that we did not need to know the value of I_0 to determine the Richter scale magnitude of the quake.

EXAMPLE 7 ■ Find the Magnitude of an Earthquake

Find the Richter scale magnitude of the 2003 Amazonas, Brazil, earthquake, which had an intensity of $I = 12{,}589{,}254 I_0$. Round to the nearest tenth.

Solution

$$M = \log\left(\frac{I}{I_0}\right) = \log\left(\frac{12{,}589{,}254 I_0}{I_0}\right) = \log(12{,}589{,}254) \approx 7.1$$

The 2003 Amazonas, Brazil, earthquake had a Richter scale magnitude of 7.1.

CHECK YOUR PROGRESS 7   What is the Richter scale magnitude of an earthquake whose intensity is twice that of the Amazonas, Brazil, earthquake in Example 7?

Solution   See page S25.

If you know the Richter scale magnitude of an earthquake, then you can determine the intensity of the earthquake.

EXAMPLE 8 ■ Find the Intensity of an Earthquake

Find the intensity of the 2003 Colina, Mexico, earthquake, which measured 7.6 on the Richter scale. Round to the nearest thousand.

Solution

$$\log\left(\frac{I}{I_0}\right) = 7.6$$

$$\frac{I}{I_0} = 10^{7.6} \qquad \text{• Write in exponential form.}$$

$$I = 10^{7.6} I_0 \qquad \text{• Solve for } I.$$

$$I \approx 39{,}810{,}717 I_0$$

The 2003 Colina, Mexico, earthquake had an intensity that was approximately 39,811,000 times the intensity of a zero-level earthquake.

CHECK YOUR PROGRESS 8   On April 29, 2003, an earthquake measuring 4.6 on the Richter scale struck Fort Payne, Alabama. Find the intensity of the quake. Round to the nearest thousand.

Solution   See page S25.

▼ **point of interest**

The pH scale was created by the Danish biochemist Søren Sørensen (sû′rn-sn) in 1909 to measure the acidity of water used in the brewing of beer. pH is an abbreviation for *pondus hydrogenii,* which translates as "potential hydrogen."

Logarithmic scales are also used in chemistry. Chemists use logarithms to determine the pH of a liquid, which is a measure of the liquid's **acidity** or **alkalinity.** (You may have tested the pH of a swimming pool or an aquarium.) Pure water, which is considered neutral, has a pH of 7.0. The pH scale ranges from 0 to 14, with 0 corresponding to the most acidic solutions and 14 to the most alkaline. Lemon juice has a pH of about 2, whereas household ammonia measures about 11.

Specifically, the acidity of a solution is a function of the hydronium-ion concentration of the solution. Because the hydronium-ion concentration of a solution can be very small (with values as low as 0.00000001), pH measures the acidity or alkalinity of a solution using a logarithmic scale.

✔ **TAKE NOTE**

One mole is equivalent to 6.022×10^{23} ions.

The pH of a Solution

The pH of a solution with a hydronium-ion concentration of H^+ moles per liter is given by

$$pH = -\log[H^+]$$

EXAMPLE 9 ■ Calculate the pH of a Liquid

Find the pH of each liquid. Round to the nearest tenth.

a. Orange juice containing an H^+ concentration of 2.8×10^{-4} mole per liter

b. Milk containing an H^+ concentration of 3.97×10^{-7} mole per liter

c. A baking soda solution containing an H^+ concentration of 3.98×10^{-9} mole per liter

Solution

a. $pH = -\log[H^+]$

   $pH = -\log(2.8 \times 10^{-4}) \approx 3.6$

   The orange juice has a pH of about 3.6.

b. $pH = -\log[H^+]$

   $pH = -\log(3.97 \times 10^{-7}) \approx 6.4$

   The milk has a pH of about 6.4.

c. $pH = -\log[H^+]$

   $pH = -\log(3.98 \times 10^{-9}) \approx 8.4$

   The baking soda solution has a pH of about 8.4.

CHECK YOUR PROGRESS 9   Find the pH of each liquid. Round to the nearest tenth.

a. A cleaning solution containing an H^+ concentration of 2.41×10^{-13} mole per liter

b. A cola soft drink containing an H^+ concentration of 5.07×10^{-4} mole per liter

c. Rainwater containing an H^+ concentration of 6.31×10^{-5} mole per liter

Solution   *See pages S25–S26.*

In Example 9, the hydronium-ion concentrations of orange juice and milk were given as 2.8×10^{-4} and 3.97×10^{-7}, respectively.

The following figure illustrates the pH scale, along with the corresponding hydronium-ion concentrations. A solution with a pH less than 7 is an **acid,** and a solution with a pH greater than 7 is an **alkaline solution,** or a **base.** Because the scale is logarithmic, a solution with a pH of 5 is 10 times more acidic than a solution with a pH of 6. From Example 9 we see that the orange juice and milk are acids, whereas the baking soda solution is a base.

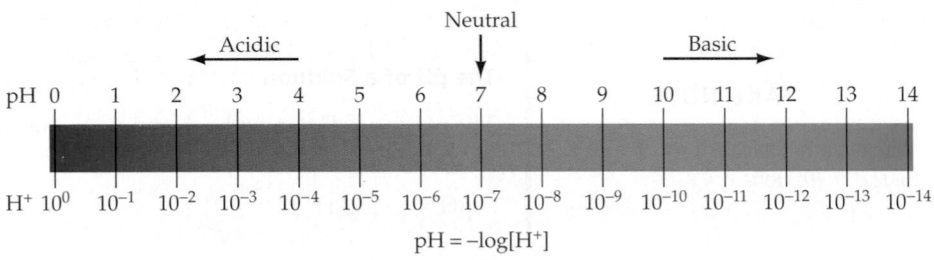

The figure above shows how the pH function scales small numbers on the H^+ axis into larger and more convenient numbers on the pH axis.

EXAMPLE 10 ■ Find the Hydronium-Ion Concentration of a Liquid

A sample of blood has a pH of 7.3. Find the hydronium-ion concentration of the blood.

Solution

$$\text{pH} = -\log[H^+]$$

$$7.3 = -\log[H^+] \qquad \text{• Substitute \textbf{7.3} for pH.}$$

$$-7.3 = \log[H^+] \qquad \text{• Multiply both sides by } -1.$$

$$10^{-7.3} = H^+ \qquad \text{• Change to exponential form.}$$

$$5.0 \times 10^{-8} \approx H^+ \qquad \text{• Evaluate } 10^{-7.3} \text{ and write the answer in scientific notation.}$$

The hydronium-ion concentration of the blood is about 5.0×10^{-8} mole per liter.

CHECK YOUR PROGRESS 10   The water in the Great Salt Lake in Utah has a pH of 10.0. Find the hydronium-ion concentration of the water.

Solution   See page S26.

Excursion

point of interest

Benford's Law has been used to identify fraudulent accountants. In most cases these accountants are unaware of Benford's Law and have replaced valid numbers with numbers selected at random. Their numbers do not conform to Benford's Law. Hence, an audit is warranted.

Benford's Law

The authors of this text know some interesting details about your finances. For instance, of the last 100 checks you have written, about 30% are for amounts that start with a 1. Also, you have written about three times as many checks for amounts that start with a 2 as you have for amounts that start with a 7.

We are sure of these results because of a mathematical formula known as *Benford's Law*. This law was first discovered by the mathematician Simon Newcomb in 1881 and was then rediscovered by the physicist Frank Benford in 1938. Benford's Law states that the probability P that the first digit of a number selected from a wide range of numbers d is given by

$$P(d) = \log\left(1 + \frac{1}{d}\right)$$

1. Use Benford's Law to complete the table and bar graph shown below.

d	$P(d) = \log(1 + 1/d)$
1	0.301
2	0.176
3	0.125
4	_____
5	_____
6	_____
7	_____
8	_____
9	_____

Benford's Law applies to most data with a wide range. For instance, it applies to

- the populations of the cities in the United States
- the numbers of dollars in the savings accounts at your local bank
- the numbers of miles driven during a month by each person in a state

2. Use Benford's Law to find the probability that in a U.S. city selected at random, the number of telephones in that city will be a number starting with a 6.

3. Use Benford's Law to find how many times as many purchases you have made for dollar amounts that start with a 1 than for dollar amounts that start with a 9.

4. Explain why Benford's Law would not apply to the set of telephone numbers in a small city such as Le Mars, Iowa.

5. Explain why Benford's Law would not apply to the set of all the ages, in years, of the students at a local high school.

Exercise Set 6.6

In Exercises 1–8, write the exponential equation in logarithmic form.

1. $7^2 = 49$

2. $10^3 = 1000$

3. $5^4 = 625$

4. $2^{-3} = \dfrac{1}{8}$

5. $10^{-4} = 0.0001$

6. $3^5 = 729$

7. $10^y = x$

8. $e^y = x$

In Exercises 9–16, write the logarithmic equation in exponential form.

9. $\log_3 81 = 4$

10. $\log_2 16 = 4$

11. $\log_5 125 = 3$

12. $\log_4 64 = 3$

13. $\log_4 \dfrac{1}{16} = -2$

14. $\log_2 \dfrac{1}{16} = -4$

15. $\ln x = y$

16. $\log x = y$

In Exercises 17–24, evaluate the logarithm.

17. $\log_3 81$

18. $\log_7 49$

19. $\log 100$

20. $\log 0.001$

21. $\log_3 \dfrac{1}{9}$

22. $\log_7 \dfrac{1}{7}$

23. $\log_2 64$

24. $\log 0.01$

In Exercises 25–32, solve the equation for x.

25. $\log_3 x = 2$

26. $\log_5 x = 1$

27. $\log_7 x = -1$

28. $\log_8 x = -2$

29. $\log_3 x = -2$

30. $\log_5 x = 3$

31. $\log_4 x = 0$

32. $\log_4 x = -1$

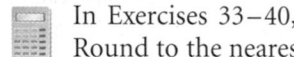 In Exercises 33–40, use a calculator to solve for x. Round to the nearest hundredth.

33. $\log x = 2.5$

34. $\log x = 3.2$

35. $\ln x = 2$

36. $\ln x = 4$

37. $\log x = 0.35$

38. $\log x = 0.127$

39. $\ln x = \dfrac{8}{3}$

40. $\ln x = \dfrac{1}{2}$

In Exercises 41–46, graph the function.

41. $g(x) = \log_2 x$

42. $g(x) = \log_4 x$

43. $f(x) = \log_3(2x - 1)$

44. $f(x) = -\log_2 x$

45. $f(x) = \log_2(x - 1)$

46. $f(x) = \log_3(x - 2)$

Light The percent of light that will pass through a material is given by the formula $\log P = -kd$, where P is the percent of light passing through the material, k is a constant that depends on the material, and d is the thickness of the material in centimeters. Use this formula for Exercises 47 and 48.

47. The constant k for a piece of opaque glass that is 0.5 centimeters thick is 0.2. Find the percent of light that will pass through the glass. Round to the nearest percent.

48. The constant k for a piece of tinted glass is 0.5. How thick is a piece of this glass that allows 60% of the light incident to the glass to pass through it? Round to the nearest hundredth of a centimeter.

Sound The number of decibels, D, of a sound can be given by the equation $D = 10(\log I + 16)$, where I is the power of the sound measured in watts. Use this formula for Exercises 49 and 50. Round to the nearest decibel.

49. Find the number of decibels of normal conversation. The power of the sound of normal conversation is approximately 3.2×10^{-10} watts.

50. The loudest sound made by an animal is made by the blue whale and can be heard over 500 miles away. The power of the sound is 630 watts. Find the number of decibels of the sound emitted by the blue whale.

pH of a Solution For Exercises 51 and 52, use the equation

$$\text{pH} = -\log(\text{H}^+),$$

where H^+ is the hydronium-ion concentration of a solution. Round to the nearest hundredth.

51. Find the pH of the digestive solution of the stomach, for which the hydronium-ion concentration is 0.045 mole per liter.

52. Find the pH of a morphine solution used to relieve pain, for which the hydronium-ion concentration is 3.2×10^{-10} mole per liter.

Earthquakes For Exercises 53–57, use the Richter scale equation $M = \log \dfrac{I}{I_0}$, where M is the magnitude of an earthquake, I is the intensity of the shock waves, and I_0 is the measure of the intensity of a zero-level earthquake.

53. On May 21, 2003, an earthquake struck Northern Algeria. The earthquake had an intensity of $I = 6{,}309{,}573 I_0$. Find the Richter scale magnitude of the earthquake. Round to the nearest tenth.

54. The earthquake on November 17, 2003, in the Aleutian Islands of Moska had an intensity of $I = 63{,}095{,}734 I_0$. Find the Richter scale magnitude of the earthquake. Round to the nearest tenth.

55. An earthquake in Japan on March 2, 1933 measured 8.9 on the Richter scale. Find the intensity of the earthquake in terms of I_0. Round to the nearest whole number.

56. An earthquake that occurred in China in 1978 measured 8.2 on the Richter scale. Find the intensity of the earthquake in terms of I_0. Round to the nearest whole number.

57. How many times as strong is an earthquake whose magnitude is 8 than one whose magnitude is 6?

Astronomy Astronomers use the distance modulus function $M(r) = 5 \log r - 5$, where M is the distance modulus and r is the distance of a star from Earth in parsecs. (One parsec is approximately 1.92×10^{13} miles, or approximately 20 trillion miles.) Use this function for Exercises 58 and 59. Round to the nearest tenth.

58. The distance modulus of the star Betelgeuse is 5.89. How many parsecs from Earth is this star?

59. The distance modulus of Alpha Centauri is -1.11. How many parsecs from Earth is this star?

World's Oil Supply One model for the time it will take for the world's oil supply to be depleted is given by the function $T(r) = 14.29 \ln(0.00411r + 1)$, where r is the estimated oil reserves in billions of barrels and T is the time in years before that amount of oil is depleted. Use this function for Exercises 60 and 61. Round to the nearest tenth of a year.

60. How many barrels of oil are necessary to last 20 years?

61. How many barrels of oil are necessary to last 50 years?

Extensions

CRITICAL THINKING

62. As mentioned in this section, the main motivation for the development of logarithms was to aid astronomers and other scientists with arithmetic calculations. The idea was to allow scientists to multiply large numbers by adding the logarithms of the numbers. Dividing large numbers was accomplished by subtracting the logarithms of the numbers. Follow through the exercises below to see how this was accomplished. For simplicity, we will use small numbers (2 and 3) to illustrate the procedure.

   a. Write each of the equations $\log 2 = 0.30103$ and $\log 3 = 0.47712$ in exponential form.

   b. Replace 2 and 3 in $x = 2 \cdot 3$ with the exponential expressions from part a. (In this exercise, we know that x is 6. However, if the two numbers were very large, the value of x would not be obvious.)

   c. Simplify the exponential expression. Recall that to multiply two exponential expressions with the same base, *add* the exponents.

   d. If you completed part c correctly, you should have
   $$x = 10^{0.77815}$$
   Write this expression in logarithmic form.

   e. Using a calculator, verify that the solution of the equation you created in part d is 6. *Note:* When tables of logarithms were used, a scientist would have looked through the table to find 0.77815 and observed that it was the logarithm of 6.

63. Replace the denominator 2 and the numerator 3 in $x = \dfrac{3}{2}$ by the exponential expressions from part a of Exercise 62. Simplify the expression by *subtracting* the exponents. Write the answer in logarithmic form and verify that $x = 1.5$.

64. Write a few sentences explaining how adding the logarithms of two numbers can be used to find the product of the two numbers.

65. Write a few sentences explaining how subtracting the logarithms of two numbers can be used to find the quotient of the two numbers.

EXPLORATIONS

Earthquakes Seismologists generally determine the Richter scale magnitude of an earthquake by examining a *seismogram*, an example of which is shown below.

The magnitude of an earthquake cannot be determined just by examining the amplitude of a seismogram, because this amplitude decreases as the distance between the epicenter of the earthquake and the observation station increases. To account for the distance between the epicenter and the observation station, a seismologist examines a seismogram for both small waves, called *p-waves,* and larger waves, called *s-waves.* The Richter scale magnitude *M* of the earthquake is a function of both the amplitude *A* of the s-waves and the time *t* between the occurrence of the s-waves and the occurrence of the p-waves. In the 1950's, Charles Richter developed the formula on the right to determine the magnitude *M* of an earthquake from the data in a seismogram.

66. Find the Richter scale magnitude of the earthquake that produced the seismogram shown on page 401. Round to the nearest tenth.

67. Find the Richter scale magnitude of the earthquake that produced the seismograph shown on the right. Round to the nearest tenth.

The Amplitude-Time-Difference Formula

The Richter scale magnitude of an earthquake is given by

$$M = \log A + 3 \log 8t - 2.92$$

where *A* is the amplitude, in millimeters, of the s-waves on a seismogram and *t* is the time, in seconds, between the s-waves and the p-waves.

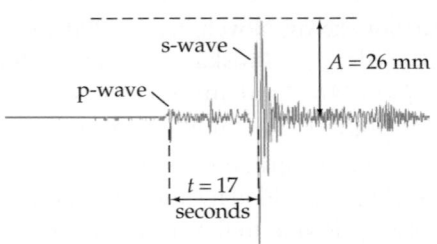

CHAPTER 6	# Summary

Key Terms

Essential Concepts

- **Functional Notation**
  The symbol $f(x)$ is the value of the function and represents the value of the dependent variable for a given value of the independent variable.

- **Linear Function**
  A linear function is one that can be written in the form $f(x) = mx + b$, where m is the coefficient of x and b is a constant. The slope of the graph of the function is m, the coefficient of x.

- **y-Intercept of a Linear Function**
  The y-intercept of the graph of $f(x) = mx + b$ is $(0, b)$.

- **Slope of a Line**
  Let (x_1, y_1) and (x_2, y_2) be two points on a line. Then the slope of the line through the two points is the ratio of the change in the y-coordinates to the change in the x-coordinates.
  $$m = \frac{\text{change in } y}{\text{change in } x} = \frac{y_2 - y_1}{x_2 - x_1}, x_1 \neq x_2$$

- **Slope–Intercept Form of the Equation of a Line**
  The graph of $f(x) = mx + b$ is a straight line with slope m and y-intercept $(0, b)$.

- **Point–Slope Formula of a Straight Line**
  Let (x_1, y_1) be a point on a line and let m be the slope of the line. Then the equation of the line can be found using the point–slope formula
  $$y - y_1 = m(x - x_1).$$

- **Vertex of a Parabola**
  Let $f(x) = ax^2 + bx + c, a \neq 0$, be the equation of a parabola. Then the coordinates of the vertex are
  $$\left(-\frac{b}{2a}, f\left(-\frac{b}{2a}\right)\right).$$

- **Definition of Logarithm**
  For $b > 0$, $b \neq 1$, $y = \log_b x$ is equivalent to $x = b^y$.

- **Equality of Exponents Property**
  If $b > 0$ and $b^x = b^y$, then $x = y$.

- **Richter Scale**
  An earthquake with an intensity of I has a Richter scale magnitude of $M = \log\left(\frac{I}{I_0}\right)$, where I_0 is the measure of the intensity of a zero-level earthquake.

- **The pH of a Solution**
  The pH of a solution with a hydronium-ion concentration of H^+ moles per liter is given by pH $= -\log[H^+]$.

CHAPTER 6 Review Exercises

1. Draw a line through all points with an x-coordinate of 4.

2. Draw a line through all points with a y-coordinate of 3.

3. Graph the ordered-pair solutions of $y = 2x^2$ when $x = -2, -1, 0, 1$, and 2.

4. Graph the ordered-pair solutions of $y = 2x^2 - 5$ when $x = -2, -1, 0, 1$, and 2.

5. Graph the ordered-pair solutions of $y = -2x + 1$ when $x = -2, -1, 0, 1$, and 2.

6. Graph the ordered-pair solutions of $y = |x + 1|$ when $x = -5, -3, 0, 3$, and 5.

In Exercises 7–16, graph the equation.

7. $y = -2x + 1$

8. $y = 3x + 2$

9. $f(x) = x^2 + 2$

10. $f(x) = x^2 - 3x + 1$

11. $y = |x + 4|$

12. $f(x) = 2|x| - 1$

13. $f(x) = 2^x - 3$

14. $f(x) = 3^{-x+2}$

15. $f(x) = e^{0.5x}$

16. $f(x) = \log_2(x - 2)$

In Exercises 17–23, evaluate the function for the given value.

17. $f(x) = 4x - 5; x = -2$

18. $g(x) = 2x^2 - x - 2; x = 3$

19. $s(t) = \frac{4}{3t - 5}; t = -1$

20. $R(s) = s^3 - 2s^2 + s - 3; s = -2$

21. $f(x) = 2^{x-3}; x = 5$

22. $g(x) = \left(\frac{2}{3}\right)^x; x = 2$

23. $T(r) = 2e^r + 1; r = 2$. Round to the nearest hundredth.

24. **Geometry** The volume of a sphere is a function of its radius and is given by $V(r) = \dfrac{4\pi r^3}{3}$, where r is the radius of the sphere.

    a. Find the volume of a sphere whose radius is 3 inches. Round to the nearest tenth of a cubic inch.

    b. Find the volume of a sphere whose radius is 12 centimeters. Round to the nearest tenth of a cubic centimeter.

25. **Sports** The height h of a ball that is released 5 feet above the ground with an initial velocity of 96 feet per second is a function of the time t, in seconds, the ball is in the air and is given by $h(t) = -16t^2 + 96t + 5$.

    a. Find the height of the ball above the ground 2 seconds after it is released.

    b. Find the height of the ball above the ground 4 seconds after it is released.

26. **Mixtures** The percent concentration P of sugar in a water solution depends on the amount of sugar that is added to the solution and is given by $P(x) = \dfrac{100x + 100}{x + 20}$, where x is the number of grams of sugar that are added.

    a. What is the original percent concentration of sugar?

    b. What is the percent concentration of sugar after 10 more grams of sugar are added? Round to the nearest tenth of a percent.

In Exercises 27–30, find the x- and y-intercepts of the graph of the function.

27. $f(x) = 2x + 10$

28. $f(x) = \dfrac{3}{4}x - 9$

29. $3x - 5y = 15$

30. $4x + 3y = 24$

31. **Depreciation** The accountant for a small business uses the model $V(t) = 25,000 - 5000t$ to approximate the value, $V(t)$, of a small truck t years after its purchase. Find and discuss the meaning of the intercepts, on the vertical and horizontal axes, in the context of this application.

In Exercises 32–35, find the slope of the line containing the given points.

32. $(3, 2), (2, -3)$

33. $(-1, 4), (-3, -1)$

34. $(2, -5), (-4, -5)$

35. $(5, 2), (5, 7)$

36. **The Film Industry** The following graph shows annual projections for revenue from home video rentals. Find the slope of the line and write a sentence that explains the meaning of

the slope in the context of this application. (*Source:* Forrester Research)

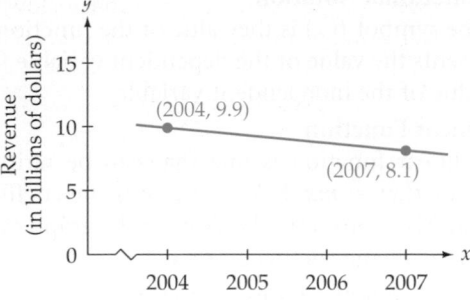

37. Graph the line that passes through the point $(3, -2)$ and has slope -2.

38. Graph the line that passes through the point $(-1, -3)$ and has slope $\dfrac{3}{4}$.

In Exercises 39–42, find the equation of the line that contains the given point and has the given slope.

39. $(-2, 3), m = 2$

40. $(1, -4), m = 1$

41. $(-3, 1), m = \dfrac{2}{3}$

42. $(4, 1), m = \dfrac{1}{4}$

43. Graph $f(x) = \dfrac{3}{2}x - 1$ using the slope and y-intercept.

44. **Interior Decorating** A dentist's office is being recarpeted. The cost to install the new carpet is $100 plus $25 per square yard of carpeting.

    a. Determine a linear function for the cost to carpet the office.

    b. Use this function to determine the cost to carpet 32 square yards of floor space.

45. **Gasoline Sales** The manager of Valley Gas Mart has determined that 10,000 gallons of regular unleaded gasoline can be sold each week if the price is the same as that of Western QuickMart, a gas station across the street. If the manager increases the price $.02 above Western QuickMart's price, the manager will sell 500 less gallons per week. If the manager decreases the price $.02 below that of Western QuickMart, 500 more gallons of gasoline per week will be sold.

    a. Determine a linear function that will predict the number of gallons of gas per week that Valley Gas Mart can sell as a function of the price relative to that of Western QuickMart.

    b. Use the model to predict the number of gallons of gasoline Valley Gas Mart will sell if its price is $.03 below that of Western QuickMart.

46. 🖩 🥧 **BMI** The body mass index (BMI) of a person is a measure of the person's ideal body weight. The data in the table below show the BMI for different weights for a person 5'6" tall.

BMI Data for Person 5'6" Tall			
Weight (in pounds)	BMI	Weight (in pounds)	BMI
110	18	160	26
120	19	170	27
125	20	180	29
135	22	190	31
140	23	200	32
145	23	205	33
150	24	215	35

Source: Centers for Disease Control and Prevention

a. Find the linear regression equation for this data. Round to the nearest hundred thousandth.

b. Use the regression equation to estimate the BMI for a person 5'6" tall whose weight is 158 pounds. Round to the nearest whole number.

In Exercises 47–50, find the vertex of the graph of the function.

47. $y = x^2 + 2x + 4$ **48.** $y = -2x^2 - 6x + 1$

49. $f(x) = -3x^2 + 6x - 1$ **50.** $f(x) = x^2 + 5x - 1$

In Exercises 51–54, find the x-intercepts of the parabola given by the equation.

51. $y = x^2 + x - 20$ **52.** $y = x^2 + 2x - 1$

53. $f(x) = 2x^2 + 9x + 4$ **54.** $f(x) = x^2 + 4x + 6$

In Exercises 55–58, find the minimum or maximum value of the quadratic function. State whether the value is a maximum or a minimum.

55. $y = -x^2 + 4x + 1$ **56.** $y = 2x^2 + 6x - 3$

57. $f(x) = x^2 - 4x - 1$ **58.** $f(x) = -2x^2 + 3x - 1$

59. Physics The height s, in feet, of a rock thrown upward at an initial speed of 80 feet per second from a cliff 25 feet above an ocean beach is given by the function $s(t) = -16t^2 + 80t + 25$, where t is the time in seconds after the rock is released. Find the maximum height above the beach that the rock will attain.

60. Manufacturing A manufacturer of rewritable CDs (CD-RW) estimates that the average daily cost C of producing a single CD-RW is given by $C(x) = 0.01x^2 - 40x + 50,000$, where x is the number of CD-RWs produced each day. Find the number of CD-RWs the company should produce in order to minimize the average daily cost.

61. Investments A \$5000 certificate of deposit (CD) earns 6% annual interest compounded daily. What is the value of the investment after 15 years? Use the compound interest formula $A = P\left(1 + \frac{r}{n}\right)^{nt}$, where P is the amount deposited, A is the value of the money after t years, r is the annual interest rate as a decimal, and n is the number of compounding periods per year.

62. Isotopes An isotope of technetium has a half-life of approximately 6 hours. If a patient is injected with 10 milligrams of this isotope, what will be the technetium level in the patient after 2 hours? Use the function $A(t) = 10\left(\frac{1}{2}\right)^{t/6}$, where A is the technetium level, in milligrams, in the patient after t hours. Round to the nearest hundredth of a milligram.

63. Isotopes Iodine-131 has a half-life of approximately 8 days. If a patient is given an injection that contains 8 micrograms of iodine-131, what will be the iodine level in the patient after 10 days? Use the function $A(t) = 8\left(\frac{1}{2}\right)^{t/8}$, where A is the amount of iodine-131, in micrograms, in the patient after t days. Round to the nearest hundredth of a milligram.

64. Golf A golf ball is dropped from a height of 6 feet. On each successive bounce, the ball rebounds to a height that is $\frac{2}{3}$ of the previous height.

a. Find an exponential model for the height of the ball after the nth bounce.

b. What is the height of the ball after the fifth bounce? Round to the nearest hundredth of a foot.

65. 🖩 **The Film Industry** When a new movie is released, there is initially a surge in the number of people who go to see the movie. After 2 weeks, attendance generally begins to drop off. The data in the following table show the number of people attending a certain movie; $t = 0$ represents the number of patrons 2 weeks after the movie's initial release.

Number of weeks two weeks after release, t	0	1	2	3	4
Number of people (in thousands), N	250	162	110	65	46

a. Find an exponential regression equation for these data. Round to the nearest ten-thousandth.

b. Use the equation to predict the number of people who will attend the movie 8 weeks after it has been released.

In Exercises 66–69, evaluate the logarithm.

66. $\log_3 243$

67. $\log_2 \dfrac{1}{16}$

68. $\log_4 \dfrac{1}{4}$

69. $\log_2 64$

In Exercises 70–73, solve for x. Round to the nearest ten-thousandth.

70. $\log_4 x = 3$

71. $\log_3 x = \dfrac{1}{3}$

72. $\ln x = 2.5$

73. $\log x = 2.4$

74. Astronomy Use the distance modulus function $M(r) = 5 \log r - 5$, where M is the distance modulus and r is the distance of a star from Earth in parsecs, to find the distance in parsecs to a star whose distance modulus is 3.2. Round to the nearest tenth of a parsec.

75. Sound The number of decibels, D, of a sound can be given by the function $D(I) = 10(\log I + 16)$, where I is the power of the sound measured in watts. The pain threshold for a sound for most humans is approximately 0.01 watt. Find the number of decibels of this sound.

CHAPTER 6   **Test**

In Exercises 1 and 2, evaluate the function for the given value of the independent variable.

1. $s(t) = -3t^2 + 4t - 1$; $t = -2$

2. $f(x) = 3^{x-4}$; $x = 2$

3. Evaluate: $\log_5 125$

4. Solve for x: $\log_6 x = 2$

In Exercises 5–8, graph the function.

5. $f(x) = 2x - 3$

6. $f(x) = x^2 + 2x - 3$

7. $f(x) = 2^x - 5$

8. $f(x) = \log_3(x - 1)$

9. Find the slope of the line that passes through $(3, -1)$ and $(-2, -4)$.

10. Find the equation of the line that passes through $(3, 5)$ and has slope $\dfrac{2}{3}$.

11. Find the vertex of the graph of $f(x) = x^2 + 6x - 1$.

12. Find the x-intercepts of the parabola given by the equation $y = x^2 + 2x - 8$.

13. Find the minimum or maximum value of the quadratic function $y = -x^2 - 3x + 10$ and state whether the value is a minimum or a maximum.

14. Travel The distance d, in miles, a small plane is from its final destination is given by $d(t) = 250 - 100t$, where t is the time, in hours, remaining for the flight. Find and discuss the meaning of the intercepts of the graph of the function.

15. Sports The height h, in feet, of a ball that is thrown straight up and released 4 feet above the ground is given by $h(t) = -16t^2 + 96t + 4$, where t is the time in seconds. Find the maximum height the ball attains.

16. Isotopes A radioactive isotope has a half-life of 5 hours. If a chemist has a 10-gram sample of this isotope, what amount will remain after 8 hours? Use the function $A(t) = 10\left(\frac{1}{2}\right)^{t/5}$, where A is the amount of the isotope, in grams, remaining after t hours. Round to the nearest hundredth of a gram.

17. Earthquakes Two earthquakes struck Papua, Indonesia, in February 2004. One had a magnitude of 7.0 on the Richter scale, and the second one had a magnitude of 7.3 on the Richter scale. How many times as great was the intensity of the second earthquake than that of the first? Round to the nearest tenth.

18. Farming The manager of an orange grove has determined that when there are 320 trees per acre, the average yield per tree is 260 pounds of oranges. If the number of trees is increased to 330 trees per acre, the average yield per tree decreases to 245 pounds. Find a linear model for the average yield per tree as a function of the number of trees per acre.

19. Farming Giant pumpkin contests are popular at many state fairs. Suppose the data below show the weights, in pounds, of the winning pumpkins at recent fairs, where $x = 0$ represents 2000.

Year, x	0	1	2	3	4
Weight (in pounds), y	650	715	735	780	820

a. Find a linear regression equation for these data.

b. Use the regression equation to predict the winning weight in 2008. Round to the nearest pound.

20. Light The equation $\log P = -kd$ gives the relationship between the percent P, as a decimal, of light passing through a substance of thickness d. The value of k for a swimming pool is approximately 0.05. At what depth, in meters, will the percent of light be 75% of the light at the surface of the pool? Round to the nearest tenth.

CHAPTER

7

Mathematical Systems

7.1	Modular Arithmetic
7.2	Applications of Modular Arithmetic
7.3	Introduction to Group Theory

The Iran-Contra scandal surfaced in 1986, and in 1987 Oliver North testified before Congress regarding his involvement. One of the situations that came to light involved the transfer of $10 million to a Swiss bank account for the Contras. North had given the account number 368.430.22.1 to Secretary of State Elliott Abrams on a card typed by North's secretary, Fawn Hall. The number was reportedly incorrect, and the money was mistakenly transferred to the account of a Swiss businessman. The second and third digits of the correct account number, 386.430.22.1, had been transposed.

The transposing of two adjacent digits is one of the most common human errors made when copying a number or entering a number into a computer. Every day, millions of numbers are transmitted electronically. Credit card numbers travel across the Internet, money is transferred from one bank account to another, and goods are ordered by product number. To help prevent incorrect numbers from being transmitted, many numbers have an added digit called a *check digit*. Mathematical systems, such as *modular arithmetic*, have been used to design methods that detect errors using the check digit. Computers then usually can catch the error and alert the user before forwarding an incorrect number. Modular arithmetic and some of its applications—detecting errors in credit card numbers, product numbers, such as the Universal Product Code (UPC), and money order numbers—are discussed in Sections 7.1 and 7.2.

 For online student resources, visit this textbook's website at **www.cengage.com/math.**

CHAPTER

SECTION 7.1 | Modular Arithmetic

▼ point of interest

The abbreviation A.M. comes from the Latin *ante* (before) *meridiem* (midday). The abbreviation P.M. comes from the Latin *post* (after) *meridiem* (midday).

Figure 7.1a

Figure 7.1b

Figure 7.2

Introduction to Modular Arithmetic

Many clocks have the familiar 12-hour design. We designate whether the time is before noon or after noon by using the abbreviations A.M. and P.M. A reference to 7:00 A.M. means 7 hours after 12:00 midnight; a reference to 7:00 P.M. means 7 hours after 12:00 noon. In both cases, once 12 is reached on the clock, we begin again with 1.

If we want to determine a time in the future or in the past, it is necessary to consider whether we have passed 12 o'clock. To determine the time 8 hours after 3 o'clock, we add 3 and 8. Because we did not pass 12 o'clock, the time is 11 o'clock (Figure 7.1a). However, to determine the time 8 hours after 9 o'clock, we must take into consideration that once we have passed 12 o'clock, we begin again with 1. Therefore, 8 hours after 9 o'clock is 5 o'clock, as shown in Figure 7.1b.

We will use the symbol $\oplus$ to denote addition on a 12-hour clock. Using this notation,

$$3 \oplus 8 = 11 \quad \text{and} \quad 9 \oplus 8 = 5$$

on a 12-hour clock.

We can also perform subtraction on a 12-hour clock. If the time now is 10 o'clock, then 7 hours ago the time was 3 o'clock, which is the difference between 10 and 7 ($10 - 7 = 3$). However, if the time now is 3 o'clock, then, using Figure 7.2, we see that 7 hours ago it was 8 o'clock. If we use the symbol $\ominus$ to denote subtraction on a 12-hour clock, we can write

$$10 \ominus 7 = 3 \quad \text{and} \quad 3 \ominus 7 = 8$$

EXAMPLE 1 ■ Perform Clock Arithmetic

Evaluate each of the following, where $\oplus$ and $\ominus$ indicate addition and subtraction, respectively, on a 12-hour clock.

a. $8 \oplus 7$ **b.** $7 \oplus 12$ **c.** $8 \ominus 11$ **d.** $2 \ominus 8$

Solution
Calculate using a 12-hour clock.

a. $8 \oplus 7 = 3$ **b.** $7 \oplus 12 = 7$ **c.** $8 \ominus 11 = 9$ **d.** $2 \ominus 8 = 6$

CHECK YOUR PROGRESS 1   Evaluate each of the following using a 12-hour clock.

a. $6 \oplus 10$ **b.** $5 \oplus 9$ **c.** $7 \ominus 11$ **d.** $5 \ominus 10$

Solution   *See page S26.*

Monday = 1   Friday = 5
Tuesday = 2   Saturday = 6
Wednesday = 3   Sunday = 7
Thursday = 4

A similar example involves day-of-the-week arithmetic. If we associate each day of the week with a number, as shown at the left, then 6 days after Friday is Thursday; 16 days after Monday is Wednesday. Symbolically, we write

$$5 \boxplus 6 = 4 \quad \text{and} \quad 1 \boxplus 16 = 3$$

Note: We are using the $\boxplus$ symbol for days-of-the-week arithmetic to distinguish from the $\oplus$ symbol for clock arithmetic.

Another way to determine the day of the week is to note that when the sum $5 + 6 = 11$ is divided by 7, the number of days in a week, the remainder is 4, the number associated with Thursday. When $1 + 16 = 17$ is divided by 7, the remainder is 3, the number associated with Wednesday. This works because the days of the week repeat every 7 days.

The same method can be applied to 12-hour-clock arithmetic. From Example 1a, when $8 + 7 = 15$ is divided by 12, the number of hours on a 12-hour clock, the remainder is 3, the time 7 hours after 8 o'clock.

Situations such as these that repeat in cycles are represented mathematically by using **modular arithmetic,** or **arithmetic modulo** n.

historical note

The congruent symbol consisting of three horizontal bars was introduced in print in 1801 by Carl Friedrich Gauss (1777–1855). ∎

Modulo n

Two integers a and b are said to be **congruent modulo** n, where n is a natural number called the **modulus,** if the remainder when a is divided by n equals the remainder when b is divided by n. In this case, we write $a \equiv b \bmod n$. The statement $a \equiv b \bmod n$ is called a **congruence.**

For instance,

$29 \equiv 11 \bmod 3$ because $29 \div 3 = 9$ remainder 2 and $11 \div 3 = 3$ remainder 2. Both 29 and 11 have the same remainder when divided by 3.

$5 \not\equiv 37 \bmod 6$ because $5 \div 6 = 0$ remainder 5 and $37 \div 6 = 6$ remainder 1. The numbers 5 and 37 have different remainders when divided by 6.

QUESTION   *Is $33 \equiv 49 \bmod 4$?*

For a given number n, there are infinitely many numbers that are congruent modulo n. For example, 2, 5, 8, 11, 14, ... are all congruent to 2 modulo 3. Each number in the list has the same remainder, 2, when divided by 3.

The fact that there are infinitely many numbers congruent to a given modulus n is used in personal digital assistants (PDAs), computers, calendar programs, and other electronic devices so that the day of the week at any future or past date can be calculated. For instance, if today is Tuesday, then 7 days from now, 14 days from now, 21 days from now, and so on with multiples of 7, will all be Tuesdays. Note that 7, 14, 21, ... are all congruent to 0 modulo 7.

Now suppose today is Friday. To determine the day of the week 16 days from now, we observe that 14 days from now the day will be Friday, so 16 days from now the day will be Sunday. Note that the remainder when 16 is divided by 7 is 2, or, using modular notation, $16 \equiv 2 \bmod 7$. The 2 signifies 2 days after Friday, which is Sunday.

EXAMPLE 2 ■ Calculate a Day of the Week

July 4, 2010 is a Sunday. What day of the week is July 4, 2015?

Solution

There are 5 years between the two dates. Each year has 365 days except 2012, which has one extra day because it is a leap year. So the total number of days between

---

ANSWER   *Yes. $33 \div 4 = 8$ remainder 1, and $49 \div 4 = 12$ remainder 1. Both 33 and 49 have the same remainder when divided by 4.*

historical note

historical note

The Julian calendar, introduced by Julius Caesar in 46 B.C. and named after him, contained 12 months and 365 days. Every fourth year, an additional day was added to the year to compensate for the difference between an ordinary year and a solar year. However, a solar year actually consists of 365.2422 days, not 365.25 days as assumed by Caesar. The difference between these numbers is 0.0078 days.

Although this is a small number, after a few centuries had passed, the ordinary year and the solar year no longer matched. If something were not done to rectify the situation, after a period of time the summer season in the northern hemisphere would be in December and the winter season would be in July.

To bring the seasons back in phase, Pope Gregory removed 10 days from October in 1582. The new calendar was called the Gregorian calendar and is the one we use today. This calendar did not win general acceptance until 1752. ■

✔ TAKE NOTE

Recall that the natural numbers are the usual counting numbers: 1, 2, 3, 4, . . . The set of whole numbers consists of the natural numbers and zero.

✔ TAKE NOTE

Remember that m mod n means the remainder when m is divided by n. For Example 3, we must find the remainder of the sum of $23 + 38$ when divided by 12.

the two dates is $5 \cdot 365 + 1 = 1826$. Because $1826 \div 7 = 260$ remainder 6, $1826 \equiv 6 \bmod 7$. Any multiple of 7 days past a given day will be the same day of the week. So the day of the week 1826 days after July 4, 2010 will be the same as the day 6 days after July 4, 2010. Thus July 4, 2015 will be a Saturday.

CHECK YOUR PROGRESS 2 In 2008, Abraham Lincoln's birthday falls on Tuesday, February 12. On what day of the week does Lincoln's birthday fall in 2017?

Solution *See page S26.*

Math Matters   A Leap-Year Formula

The calculation in Example 2 required that we consider whether the intervening years contained a leap year. There is a formula, based on modular arithmetic, that can be used to determine which years are leap years.

The calendar we use today is called the Gregorian calendar. This calendar differs from the Julian calendar (see the margin note at the left) in that leap years do not always occur every fourth year. Here is the rule: Let Y be the year. If $Y \equiv 0 \bmod 4$, then Y is a leap year unless $Y \equiv 0 \bmod 100$. In that case, Y is not a leap year unless $Y \equiv 0 \bmod 400$. Then Y is a leap year.

Using this rule, 2008 is a leap year because $2008 \equiv 0 \bmod 4$ and 2013 is not a leap year because $2013 \not\equiv 0 \bmod 4$. The year 1900 was *not* a leap year because $1900 \equiv 0 \bmod 100$ but $1900 \not\equiv 0 \bmod 400$. The year 2000 was a leap year because $2000 \equiv 0 \bmod 100$ and $2000 \equiv 0 \bmod 400$.

Arithmetic Operations Modulo *n*

Arithmetic modulo n, where n is a natural number, uses a variation of the standard rules of arithmetic we have used before. Perform the arithmetic operation and then divide by the modulus. The answer is the remainder. Thus the result of an arithmetic operation mod n is always a whole number less than n.

EXAMPLE 3 ■ Addition Modulo *n*

Evaluate: $(23 + 38) \bmod 12$

Solution

Add $23 + 38$ to produce 61. Then divide by the modulus, 12. The answer is the remainder.

$$12\overline{)61} \qquad 23 + 38 = 61$$
$$\underline{60}$$
$$1$$

$(23 + 38) \bmod 12 \equiv 1$

The answer is 1.

CHECK YOUR PROGRESS 3 Evaluate: $(51 + 72) \bmod 3$

Solution *See page S26.*

In modular arithmetic, adding the modulus to a number does not change the value of the number. For instance,

$13 \equiv 6 \bmod 7$		$10 \equiv 1 \bmod 3$	
$20 \equiv 6 \bmod 7$	• Add 7 to 13.	$13 \equiv 1 \bmod 3$	• Add 3 to 10.
$27 \equiv 6 \bmod 7$	• Add 7 to 20.	$16 \equiv 1 \bmod 3$	• Add 3 to 13.

To understand why the value does not change, consider $7 \equiv 0 \bmod 7$ and $3 \equiv 0 \bmod 3$. That is, in mod 7 arithmetic, 7 is equivalent to 0; in mod 3 arithmetic, 3 is equivalent to 0. Just as adding 0 to a number does not change the value of the number in regular arithmetic, in modular arithmetic adding the modulus to a number does not change the value of the number. This property of modular arithmetic is sometimes used in subtraction.

When subtracting two numbers modulo n, if the difference is positive, divide the difference by the modulus. The answer is the remainder. If the difference is negative, repeatedly add the modulus to the difference until you first reach a whole number. The whole number is the answer.

EXAMPLE 4 ■ Subtraction Modulo n

Evaluate each of the following.

a. $(33 - 16) \bmod 6$ b. $(14 - 27) \bmod 5$

Solution

a. Subtract $33 - 16 = 17$. The result is positive. Divide the difference by the modulus, 6. The answer is the remainder.

$$\begin{array}{r} 2 \\ 6\overline{)17} \\ \underline{12} \\ 5 \end{array}$$

$(33 - 16) \bmod 6 \equiv 5$

b. Subtract $14 - 27 = -13$. The result is negative. Repeatedly add the modulus, 5, to -13 until a whole number is reached.

$-13 + 5 = -8$

$-8 + 5 = -3$

$-3 + 5 = 2$

$(14 - 27) \bmod 5 \equiv 2$

CHECK YOUR PROGRESS 4 Evaluate: $(21 - 43) \bmod 7$

Solution *See page S26.*

The methods of adding and subtracting in modular arithmetic can be used for clock arithmetic and days-of-the-week arithmetic.

EXAMPLE 5 ■ Calculating Times

Disregarding A.M. or P.M., if it is 5 o'clock now, what time was it 57 hours ago?

Solution

The time can be determined by calculating $(5 - 57) \bmod 12$. Because $5 - 57 = -52$, a negative number, repeatedly add the modulus, 12, to the difference until the first whole number is reached. By doing this, we get $(5 - 57) \bmod 12 \equiv 8$. Therefore, if it is 5 o'clock now, 57 hours ago it was 8 o'clock.

CHECK YOUR PROGRESS 5   If today is Tuesday, what day of the week will it be 93 days from now?

Solution   *See page S26.*

✔ **TAKE NOTE**

In Example 5, repeatedly adding the modulus to the difference results in the following.

$$-52 + 12 = -40$$
$$-40 + 12 = -28$$
$$-28 + 12 = -16$$
$$-16 + 12 = -4$$
$$-4 + 12 = 8$$

Problems involving multiplication can also be performed modulo n.

EXAMPLE 6 ■ Multiplication Modulo n

Evaluate: $(15 \cdot 23) \bmod 11$

Solution

Find the product $15 \cdot 23$ and then divide by the modulus, 11. The answer is the remainder.

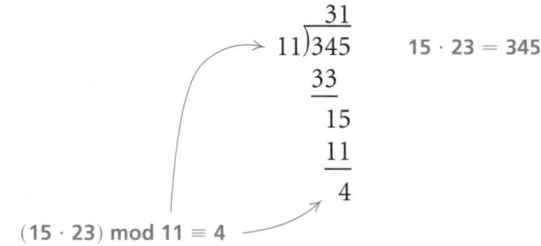

$$15 \cdot 23 = 345$$

$(15 \cdot 23) \bmod 11 \equiv 4$

The answer is 4.

CHECK YOUR PROGRESS 6   Evaluate: $(33 \cdot 41) \bmod 17$

Solution   *See page S26.*

Solving Congruence Equations

Solving a congruence equation means finding all whole number values of the variable for which the congruence is true.

For example, to solve $3x + 5 \equiv 3 \bmod 4$, we search for whole number values of x for which the congruence is true.

$3(0) + 5 \not\equiv 3 \bmod 4$

$3(1) + 5 \not\equiv 3 \bmod 4$

$3(2) + 5 \equiv 3 \bmod 4$ **2 is a solution.**

$3(3) + 5 \not\equiv 3 \bmod 4$

$3(4) + 5 \not\equiv 3 \bmod 4$

$3(5) + 5 \not\equiv 3 \bmod 4$

$3(6) + 5 \equiv 3 \bmod 4$ **6 is a solution.**

If we continued trying values, we would find that 10 and 14 are also solutions. Note that the solutions 6, 10, and 14 are all congruent to 2 modulo 4. In general, once a solution is determined, additional solutions can be found by repeatedly adding the modulus to the original solution. Thus the solutions of $3x + 5 \equiv 3 \bmod 4$ are 2, 6, 10, 14, 18, ...

When solving a congruence equation, it is necessary to check only the whole numbers less than the modulus. For the congruence equation $3x + 5 \equiv 3 \bmod 4$, we needed to check only 0, 1, 2, and 3. Each time a solution is found, additional solutions can be found by repeatedly adding the modulus to it.

A congruence equation can have more than one solution among the whole numbers less than the modulus. The next example illustrates that you must check *all* whole numbers less than the modulus.

EXAMPLE 7 ■ Solve a Congruence Equation

Solve: $2x + 1 \equiv 3 \bmod 10$

Solution
Beginning with 0, substitute each whole number less than 10 into the congruence equation.

$x = 0$	$2(0) + 1 \not\equiv 3 \bmod 10$	Not a solution
$x = 1$	$2(1) + 1 \equiv 3 \bmod 10$	A solution
$x = 2$	$2(2) + 1 \not\equiv 3 \bmod 10$	Not a solution
$x = 3$	$2(3) + 1 \not\equiv 3 \bmod 10$	Not a solution
$x = 4$	$2(4) + 1 \not\equiv 3 \bmod 10$	Not a solution
$x = 5$	$2(5) + 1 \not\equiv 3 \bmod 10$	Not a solution
$x = 6$	$2(6) + 1 \equiv 3 \bmod 10$	A solution
$x = 7$	$2(7) + 1 \not\equiv 3 \bmod 10$	Not a solution
$x = 8$	$2(8) + 1 \not\equiv 3 \bmod 10$	Not a solution
$x = 9$	$2(9) + 1 \not\equiv 3 \bmod 10$	Not a solution

The solutions between 0 and 9 are 1 and 6; the remaining solutions are determined by repeatedly adding the modulus, 10, to these solutions. The solutions are 1, 6, 11, 16, 21, 26, ...

CHECK YOUR PROGRESS 7 Solve: $4x + 1 \equiv 5 \bmod 12$

Solution *See page S26.*

Not all congruence equations have a solution. For instance, $5x + 1 \equiv 3 \bmod 5$ has no solution, as shown below.

$x = 0$	$5(0) + 1 \not\equiv 3 \bmod 5$	Not a solution
$x = 1$	$5(1) + 1 \not\equiv 3 \bmod 5$	Not a solution
$x = 2$	$5(2) + 1 \not\equiv 3 \bmod 5$	Not a solution
$x = 3$	$5(3) + 1 \not\equiv 3 \bmod 5$	Not a solution
$x = 4$	$5(4) + 1 \not\equiv 3 \bmod 5$	Not a solution

Because no whole number value of x less than the modulus is a solution, there is no solution.

Additive and Multiplicative Inverses in Modular Arithmetic

Recall that if the sum of two numbers is 0, then the numbers are *additive inverses* of each other. For instance, $8 + (-8) = 0$, so 8 is the additive inverse of -8, and -8 is the additive inverse of 8.

The same concept applies in modular arithmetic. For example, $(3 + 5) \equiv 0 \bmod 8$. Thus, in mod 8 arithmetic, 3 is the additive inverse of 5 and 5 is the additive inverse of 3. **Here we consider only those whole numbers smaller than the modulus.** Note that $3 + 5 = 8$; that is, the sum of a number and its additive inverse equals the modulus. Using this fact, we can easily find the additive inverse of a number for any modulus. For instance, in mod 11 arithmetic, the additive inverse of 5 is 6 because $5 + 6 = 11$.

EXAMPLE 8 ■ Find the Additive Inverse

Find the additive inverse of 7 in mod 16 arithmetic.

Solution
In mod 16 arithmetic, $7 + 9 = 16$, so the additive inverse of 7 is 9.

CHECK YOUR PROGRESS 8 Find the additive inverse of 6 in mod 12 arithmetic.

Solution *See page S26.*

If the product of two numbers is 1, then the numbers are **multiplicative inverses** of each other. For instance, $2 \cdot \frac{1}{2} = 1$, so 2 is the multiplicative inverse of $\frac{1}{2}$, and $\frac{1}{2}$ is the multiplicative inverse of 2. The same concept applies to modular arithmetic (although the multiplicative inverses will always be natural numbers). For example, in mod 7 arithmetic, 5 is the multiplicative inverse of 3 (and 3 is the multiplicative inverse of 5) because $5 \cdot 3 \equiv 1 \bmod 7$. (Here we will concern ourselves only with natural numbers less than the modulus.) To find the multiplicative inverse of $a \bmod m$, solve the modular equation $ax \equiv 1 \bmod m$ for x.

EXAMPLE 9 ■ Find a Multiplicative Inverse

In mod 7 arithmetic, find the multiplicative inverse of 2.

Solution

To find the multiplicative inverse of 2, solve the equation $2x \equiv 1 \bmod 7$ by trying different natural number values of x less than the modulus.

$$2x \equiv 1 \bmod 7$$

$2(1) \not\equiv 1 \bmod 7$ • Try $x = 1$.
$2(2) \not\equiv 1 \bmod 7$ • Try $x = 2$.
$2(3) \not\equiv 1 \bmod 7$ • Try $x = 3$.
$2(4) \equiv 1 \bmod 7$ • Try $x = 4$.

In mod 7 arithmetic, the multiplicative inverse of 2 is 4.

CHECK YOUR PROGRESS 9   Find the multiplicative inverse of 5 in mod 11 arithmetic.

Solution   *See page S26.*

> ### ✔ TAKE NOTE
>
> In mod m arithmetic, every number has an additive inverse but not necessarily a multiplicative inverse. For instance, in mod 12 arithmetic, 3 does not have a multiplicative inverse. You should verify this by trying to solve the equation $3x \equiv 1 \bmod 12$ for x.
>
> A similar situation occurs in standard arithmetic. The number 0 does not have a multiplicative inverse because there is no solution of the equation $0x = 1$.

Excursion

Computing the Day of the Week

A function that is related to the modulo function is called the *floor function*. In the modulo function, we determine the remainder when one number is divided by another. In the floor function, we determine the quotient (and ignore the remainder) when one number is divided by another. The symbol for the floor function is $\lfloor \ \ \rfloor$. Here are some examples.

$$\left\lfloor \frac{2}{3} \right\rfloor = 0, \quad \left\lfloor \frac{10}{2} \right\rfloor = 5, \quad \left\lfloor \frac{17}{2} \right\rfloor = 8, \quad \text{and} \quad \left\lfloor \frac{2}{\sqrt{2}} \right\rfloor = 1$$

Using the floor function, we can write a formula that gives the day of the week for any date on the Gregorian calendar. The formula, known as Zeller's Congruence, is given by

$$x \equiv \left(\left\lfloor \frac{13m - 1}{5} \right\rfloor + \left\lfloor \frac{y}{4} \right\rfloor + \left\lfloor \frac{c}{4} \right\rfloor + d + y - 2c \right) \bmod 7$$

where

d is the day of the month

m is the month using 1 for March, 2 for April, . . . , 10 for December; January and February are assigned the values 11 and 12, respectively

y is the last two digits of the year if the month is March through December; if the month is January or February, y is the last two digits of the year *minus 1*

c is the first two digits of the year

x is the day of the week (using 0 for Sunday, 1 for Monday, . . . , 6 for Saturday)

(continued)

For example, to determine the day of the week on July 4, 1776, we have $c = 17$, $y = 76$, $d = 4$, and $m = 5$. Using these values, we can calculate x.

$$x \equiv \left(\left\lfloor \frac{13(5) - 1}{5} \right\rfloor + \left\lfloor \frac{76}{4} \right\rfloor + \left\lfloor \frac{17}{4} \right\rfloor + 4 + 76 - 2(17) \right) \bmod 7$$

$$\equiv (12 + 19 + 4 + 4 + 76 - 34) \bmod 7$$

$$\equiv 81 \bmod 7$$

Solving $x \equiv 81 \bmod 7$ for x, we get $x = 4$. Therefore, July 4, 1776 was a Thursday.

Excursion Exercises

1. Determine the day of the week on which you were born.

2. Determine the day of the week on which Abraham Lincoln's birthday (February 12) will fall in 2155.

3. Determine the day of the week on which January 1, 2020 will fall.

4. Determine the day of the week on which Valentine's Day (February 14), 1950, fell.

Exercise Set 7.1

In Exercises 1–16, evaluate each expression, where ⊕ and ⊖ indicate addition and subtraction, respectively, using a 12-hour clock.

1. $3 \oplus 5$
2. $6 \oplus 7$
3. $8 \oplus 4$
4. $5 \oplus 10$
5. $11 \oplus 3$
6. $8 \oplus 8$
7. $7 \oplus 9$
8. $11 \oplus 10$
9. $10 \ominus 6$
10. $2 \ominus 6$
11. $3 \ominus 8$
12. $5 \ominus 7$
13. $10 \ominus 11$
14. $5 \ominus 5$
15. $4 \ominus 9$
16. $1 \ominus 4$

Military Time In Exercises 17–24, evaluate each expression, where △̟ and △̠ indicate addition and subtraction, respectively, using military time. (Military time uses a 24-hour clock, where 2:00 A.M. is equivalent to 0200 hours and 10 P.M. is equivalent to 2200 hours.)

17. $1800 \; \triangle \!\!\!\!+ \; 0900$
18. $1600 \; \triangle \!\!\!\!+ \; 1200$
19. $0800 \; \triangle \!\!\!\!+ \; 2000$
20. $1300 \; \triangle \!\!\!\!+ \; 1300$
21. $1000 \; \triangle \; 1400$
22. $1800 \; \triangle \; 1900$
23. $0200 \; \triangle \; 0500$
24. $0600 \; \triangle \; 2200$

In Exercises 25–28, evaluate each expression, where ⊞ and ⊟ indicate addition and subtraction, respectively, using days-of-the-week arithmetic.

25. $6 \boxplus 4$
26. $3 \boxplus 5$
27. $2 \boxminus 3$
28. $3 \boxminus 6$

In Exercises 29–38, determine whether the congruence is true or false.

29. $5 \equiv 8 \bmod 3$
30. $11 \equiv 15 \bmod 4$
31. $5 \equiv 20 \bmod 4$
32. $7 \equiv 21 \bmod 3$

33. $21 \equiv 45 \bmod 6$ 34. $18 \equiv 60 \bmod 7$
35. $88 \equiv 5 \bmod 9$ 36. $72 \equiv 30 \bmod 5$
37. $100 \equiv 20 \bmod 8$ 38. $25 \equiv 85 \bmod 12$

39. List five different natural numbers that are congruent to 8 modulo 6.
40. List five different natural numbers that are congruent to 10 modulo 4.

In Exercises 41–62, perform the modular arithmetic.

41. $(9 + 15) \bmod 7$ 42. $(12 + 8) \bmod 5$
43. $(5 + 22) \bmod 8$ 44. $(50 + 1) \bmod 15$
45. $(42 + 35) \bmod 3$ 46. $(28 + 31) \bmod 4$
47. $(37 + 45) \bmod 12$ 48. $(62 + 21) \bmod 2$
49. $(19 - 6) \bmod 5$ 50. $(25 - 10) \bmod 4$
51. $(48 - 21) \bmod 6$ 52. $(60 - 32) \bmod 9$
53. $(8 - 15) \bmod 12$ 54. $(3 - 12) \bmod 4$
55. $(15 - 32) \bmod 7$ 56. $(24 - 41) \bmod 8$
57. $(6 \cdot 8) \bmod 9$ 58. $(5 \cdot 12) \bmod 4$
59. $(9 \cdot 15) \bmod 8$ 60. $(4 \cdot 22) \bmod 3$
61. $(14 \cdot 18) \bmod 5$ 62. $(26 \cdot 11) \bmod 15$

Clocks and Calendars In Exercises 63–70, use modular arithmetic to determine each of the following.

63. Disregarding A.M. or P.M., if it is now 7 o'clock,
    a. what time will it be 59 hours from now?
    b. what time was it 62 hours ago?
64. Disregarding A.M. or P.M., if it is now 2 o'clock,
    a. what time will it be 40 hours from now?
    b. what time was it 34 hours ago?
65. If today is Friday,
    a. what day of the week will it be 25 days from now?
    b. what day of the week was it 32 days ago?
66. If today is Wednesday,
    a. what day of the week will it be 115 days from now?
    b. what day of the week was it 81 days ago?
67. In 2005, Halloween (October 31) fell on a Monday. On what day of the week will Halloween fall in the year 2015?
68. In 2002, April Fool's Day (April 1) fell on a Monday. On what day of the week will April Fool's Day fall in 2013?

69. Valentine's Day (February 14) fell on a Tuesday in 2006. On what day of the week will Valentine's Day fall in 2020?
70. Cinco de Mayo (May 5) fell on a Sunday in 2002. On what day of the week will Cinco de Mayo fall in 2018?

In Exercises 71–82, find all whole number solutions of the congruence equation.

71. $x \equiv 10 \bmod 3$
72. $x \equiv 12 \bmod 5$
73. $2x \equiv 12 \bmod 5$
74. $3x \equiv 8 \bmod 11$
75. $(2x + 1) \equiv 5 \bmod 4$
76. $(3x + 1) \equiv 4 \bmod 9$
77. $(2x + 3) \equiv 8 \bmod 12$
78. $(3x + 12) \equiv 7 \bmod 10$
79. $(2x + 2) \equiv 6 \bmod 4$
80. $(5x + 4) \equiv 2 \bmod 8$
81. $(4x + 6) \equiv 5 \bmod 8$
82. $(4x + 3) \equiv 3 \bmod 4$

In Exercises 83–88, find the additive inverse and the multiplicative inverse, if it exists, of the given number.

83. 4 in modulo 9 arithmetic
84. 4 in modulo 5 arithmetic
85. 7 in modulo 10 arithmetic
86. 11 in modulo 16 arithmetic
87. 3 in modulo 8 arithmetic
88. 6 in modulo 15 arithmetic

Modular division can be performed by considering the related multiplication problem. For instance, if $5 \div 7 = x$, then $x \cdot 7 = 5$. Similarly, the quotient $(5 \div 7) \bmod 8$ is the solution to the congruence equation $x \cdot 7 \equiv 5 \bmod 8$, which is 3. In Exercises 89–94, find the given quotient.

89. $(2 \div 7) \bmod 8$

90. $(4 \div 5) \bmod 8$

91. $(6 \div 4) \bmod 9$

92. $(2 \div 3) \bmod 5$

93. $(5 \div 6) \bmod 7$

94. $(3 \div 4) \bmod 7$

Extensions

CRITICAL THINKING

95. Verify that the division $5 \div 8$ has no solution in modulo 8 arithmetic.

96. Verify that the division $4 \div 4$ has more than one solution in modulo 10 arithmetic.

97. Disregarding A.M. or P.M., if it is now 3:00, what time of day will it be in 3500 hours?

98. Using military time, if it is currently 1100 hours, determine what time of day it will be in 4250 hours.

99. There is only one whole number solution between 0 and 11 of the congruence equation

$$(x^2 + 3x + 7) \equiv 2 \bmod 11$$

Find the solution.

100. There are only two whole number solutions between 0 and 27 of the congruence equation

$$(x^2 + 5x + 4) \equiv 1 \bmod 27$$

Find the solutions.

EXPLORATIONS

101. Random Numbers Computers often need to generate lists of random numbers to simulate real world situations or even to run video games. However, this is not as simple as it sounds, so sometimes *pseudorandom numbers* are used instead. Pseudorandom numbers are not truly random, because they are determined by several initially chosen values, but they are still useful. One method of generating a list of

pseudorandom numbers is called the *linear congruential method*. This method was developed by D. H. Lehmer in 1949. Start by choosing the first random natural number, x_0, also called the *seed*. Next choose natural number values for m, the modulus, a multiplier a, and an increment c. Each successive random number is determined from the preceding number by using the congruence equation

$$x_{n+1} \equiv (ax_n + c) \bmod m$$

For instance, if $m = 9$, $a = 5$, $c = 6$, and we chose $x_0 = 2$ as the seed, then

$$x_1 \equiv (5x_0 + 6) \bmod 9 \equiv (5 \cdot 2 + 6) \bmod 9$$
$$\equiv 16 \bmod 9 \equiv 7$$

and

$$x_2 \equiv (5x_1 + 6) \bmod 9 \equiv (5 \cdot 7 + 6) \bmod 9$$
$$\equiv 41 \bmod 9 \equiv 5$$

Each number generated will be a whole number between 0 and $m - 1$, inclusive.

A Table of Random Numbers

35	86	76	52	01	10	09	73	25	33
42	96	64	89	47	37	54	20	48	05
93	03	19	64	50	08	42	26	89	53
07	15	09	37	67	99	01	90	25	29
61	47	80	15	73	12	80	79	99	70
68	50	34	07	27	66	06	57	47	17
24	06	45	57	18	31	06	01	08	05
56	92	02	05	16	85	26	97	76	02
70	48	05	32	54	63	57	33	21	35
47	78	03	52	96	73	79	64	57	53
86	07	14	90	56	98	52	01	77	67
77	32	39	80	82	11	80	50	54	31
80	83	06	28	89	83	45	29	96	34
84	01	86	50	75	88	68	54	02	00
49	69	87	51	76	99	59	46	73	48
09	50	17	46	85	65	48	11	76	74
80	15	17	72	70	80	12	43	56	35
72	14	77	40	27	74	35	09	98	17
91	48	66	25	22	69	91	62	68	03
85	14	14	22	56	09	89	32	05	05
76	86	68	47	92	91	49	91	45	23
68	58	26	94	03	80	33	69	45	98

a. To generate pseudorandom numbers from 0 to 10, we need to choose $m = 11$. For $a = 3$, $c = 4$, and $x_0 = 5$, determine the first five pseudorandom numbers that are generated.

b. Determine the next five pseudorandom numbers in part a. Can you observe a shortcoming of the linear congruential method? Explain.

c. There is a more complicated version of the linear congruential method that does not depend on knowing the previously generated number in the list:

$$x_n \equiv \left(a^n x_0 + c \cdot \frac{a^n - 1}{a - 1} \right) \bmod m$$

Use this formula to find x_3 and x_5 using the same initial values given in part a, and verify that you get the same pseudorandom numbers x_3 and x_5 as you did in part a.

d. Use the formula given in part c to compute the first eight pseudorandom numbers that are generated using the initial values $a = 13$, $c = 21$, $m = 80$, and $x_0 = 59$.

102. Many people consider the 13th of the month an unlucky day when it falls on a Friday.

a. Does every year have a Friday the 13th? Explain why or why not.

b. What is the greatest number of Friday the 13ths that can occur in one year? Can you find a recent year in which this number occurred? *Hint:* A non-leap year can have two consecutive months where the 13th is a Friday.

ISBN, UPC, and Credit Card Numbers

Every book that is cataloged in the Library of Congress must have an ISBN (International Standard Book Number). The ISBN for the third edition of the *American Heritage Dictionary* is 0-395-44895-6. The first number, 0, indicates that the book is written in English. The next three numbers, 395, indicate the publisher (Houghton Mifflin Company). The five numbers 44895 identify the book (*American Heritage Dictionary*), and the last digit is called a *check digit*. This digit is chosen so as to satisfy the following congruence.

$$0(10) + 3(9) + 9(8) + 5(7) + 4(6) + 4(5) + 8(4) + 9(3) + 5(2) + x \equiv 0 \bmod 11$$
$$0 + 27 + 72 + 35 + 24 + 20 + 32 + 27 + 10 + x \equiv 0 \bmod 11$$
$$247 + x \equiv 0 \bmod 11$$

The digit 6 is selected as the check digit of the ISBN because $247 + 6 = 253$ and $253 \div 11 = 23$ remainder 0. Because the ISBN congruence equation has a modulus of 11, the value of x could be any number from 0 to 10. A check digit of 10 is coded as an X.

One purpose of the ISBN method of coding books is to ensure that orders placed for books are filled accurately. For instance, suppose a clerk sends an order for the *American Heritage Dictionary* and inadvertently enters the number 0-395-44985-6 (the 8 and the adjacent 9 have been transposed). Now

$$0(10) + 3(9) + 9(8) + 5(7) + 4(6) + 4(5) + 9(4) + 8(3) + 5(2) + 6 = 254$$

If we divide 254 by 11, the remainder is not zero. Thus $254 \not\equiv 0 \bmod 11$. Because the congruence is not true, we know there is an error in the order.

EXAMPLE 1 ■ Determine a Check Digit for an ISBN

Determine the ISBN check digit for the book *A Brief History of Time* by Stephen Hawking. The first nine digits of the ISBN are 0-553-05340-_?_ .

Solution
Use the ISBN congruence equation.

$$0(10) + 5(9) + 5(8) + 3(7) + 0(6) + 5(5) + 3(4) + 4(3) + 0(2) + x \equiv 0 \bmod 11$$
$$155 + x \equiv 0 \bmod 11$$

To solve the congruence equation, try whole number values of x that are less than the modulus. Because $155 + 10 = 165 \equiv 0 \bmod 11$, the check digit is 10. Recall that a check digit of 10 is recorded as an X. Therefore, the ISBN is 0-553-05340-X.

CHECK YOUR PROGRESS 1   A purchase order for the book *Mathematica: A System for Doing Mathematics by Computer* includes the ISBN 0-201-15502-4. Determine whether this is a valid ISBN.

Solution   *See page S27.*

QUESTION   *Could 1-805-53X97-X be a valid ISBN?*

Another coding scheme that is closely related to the ISBN is the UPC (Universal Product Code). This number is placed on many items and is particularly useful in grocery stores. A check-out clerk passes the product by a scanner, which reads the number from a bar code and records the price on the cash register. If the price of an item changes for a promotional sale, the price is updated in the computer, thereby relieving a clerk of having to reprice each item. In addition to pricing items, the UPC gives the store manager accurate information about inventory and the buying habits of the store's customers.

ANSWER   *No. X can appear only as the check digit.*

The UPC is a 12-digit number that satisfies a congruence equation. The last digit is the check digit. Here is the UPC for the DVD release of the film *The Matrix*, along with the UPC congruence equation.

$$0\text{-}85391\text{-}77372\text{-}6$$

$$0(3) + 8(1) + 5(3) + 3(1) + 9(3) + 1(1) + 7(3) + 7(1) + 3(3) + 7(1) + 2(3) + x \equiv 0 \bmod 10$$

$$104 + x \equiv 0 \bmod 10$$

The digit 6 is selected as the last digit (the check digit) of the UPC because $104 + 6 = 110$ and $110 \div 10 = 11$ remainder 0. Because the UPC congruence equation has a modulus of 10, the value of x, the check digit, can be any whole number from 0 to 9.

The UPC method is not quite as accurate as the ISBN method when it comes to detecting transpositions of digits. Recall that in the ISBN method, when two digits are transposed, the congruence equation is no longer true. This does not always happen with the UPC method. For instance, suppose the 2 and the 7 preceding it in the UPC above are transposed. The new UPC is 0-85391-77327-6. Using this number and the UPC congruence equation, we have

$$0\text{-}85391\text{-}77327\text{-}6$$

$$0(3) + 8(1) + 5(3) + 3(1) + 9(3) + 1(1) + 7(3) + 7(1) +$$
$$3(3) + 2(1) + 7(3) + 6 = 120 \equiv 0 \bmod 10$$

Notice that the congruence is still true modulo 10 even though the UPC is not correct. This is the result of an unfortunate coincidence; if any other two digits had been transposed, the result would have been a false congruence. It can be shown that undetected transposition errors of adjacent digits a and b occur only when $|a - b| = 5$. In this case, the two transposed digits are 2 and 7, and $|2 - 7| = |-5| = 5$.

EXAMPLE 2 ■ Determine the Check Digit for a UPC

A new product a company has developed has been assigned the UPC 0-21443-32912- ? . Determine the check digit for the UPC.

Solution
Use the UPC congruence equation.

$$0(3) + 2(1) + 1(3) + 4(1) + 4(3) + 3(1) + 3(3) +$$
$$2(1) + 9(3) + 1(1) + 2(3) + x \equiv 0 \bmod 10$$
$$69 + x \equiv 0 \bmod 10$$

To solve the congruence equation, try whole number values of x that are less than the modulus. Because $69 + 1 \equiv 0 \bmod 10$, the check digit is 1.

CHECK YOUR PROGRESS 2   Is 1-32342-65933-9 a valid UPC?

Solution   *See page S27.*

Companies that issue credit cards also use modular arithmetic to determine whether a credit card number is valid. This is especially important in e-commerce, where credit card information is frequently sent over the Internet. The primary coding method is based on the *Luhn algorithm,* which uses mod 10 arithmetic.

Credit card numbers are normally 13 to 16 digits long. The first one to four digits are used to identify the card issuer. The table below shows the identification prefixes used by four popular card issuers.

▼ **point of interest**

Hans Peter Luhn was born in Germany and later joined IBM in the U.S. as a senior research engineer. He was awarded a patent in 1960 for the algorithm that bears his name. Credit card companies began using the algorithm shortly after its creation. The algorithm is in the public domain and is still widely used to identify valid card numbers.

Card Issuer	Prefix	Number of digits
MasterCard	51 to 55	16
Visa	4	13 or 16
American Express	34 or 37	15
Discover	6011	16

The Luhn algorithm, used to determine whether a credit card number is valid, is calculated as follows: Beginning with the next-to-last digit (the last digit is the check digit) and reading from right to left, double every other digit. If a digit becomes a two-digit number after being doubled, treat the number as two individual digits. Now find the sum of the new list of digits; the final sum must equal 0 mod 10. The Luhn algorithm is demonstrated in the next example.

EXAMPLE 3 ■ **Determine a Valid Credit Card Number**

Determine whether 5234 8213 3410 1298 is a valid credit card number.

Solution
Highlight every other digit, beginning with the next-to-last digit and reading from right to left.

 5 2 3 4 8 2 1 3 3 4 1 0 1 2 9 8

Next double each of the highlighted digits.

 10 2 6 4 16 2 2 3 6 4 2 0 2 2 18 8

Finally, add all digits, treating two-digit numbers as two single digits.

$$(1 + 0) + 2 + 6 + 4 + (1 + 6) + 2 + 2 + 3 + 6 + 4 + 2 + 0 +$$
$$2 + 2 + (1 + 8) + 8 = 60$$

Because $60 \equiv 0$ mod 10, this is a valid credit card number.

CHECK YOUR PROGRESS 3   Is 6011 0123 9145 2317 a valid credit card number?

Solution   *See page S27.*

Cryptology

Related to codes on books and grocery items are secret codes. These codes are used to send messages between people, companies, or nations. It is hoped that by devising a code that is difficult to break, the sender can prevent the communication from being read if it is intercepted by an unauthorized person. **Cryptology** is the study of making and breaking secret codes.

Before we discuss how messages are coded, we need to define a few terms. **Plaintext** is a message before it is coded. The line

SHE WALKS IN BEAUTY LIKE THE NIGHT

from Lord Byron's poem "She Walks in Beauty" is in plaintext. **Ciphertext** is the message after it has been written in code. The line

ODA SWHGO EJ XAWQPU HEGA PDA JECDP

is the same line of the poem in ciphertext.

The method of changing from plaintext to ciphertext is called **encryption.** The line from the poem was encrypted by substituting each letter in plaintext with the letter that is 22 letters after that letter in the alphabet. (Continue from the beginning when the end of the alphabet is reached.) This is called a *cyclical coding scheme* because each letter of the alphabet is shifted the same number of positions. The original alphabet and the substitute alphabet are shown below.

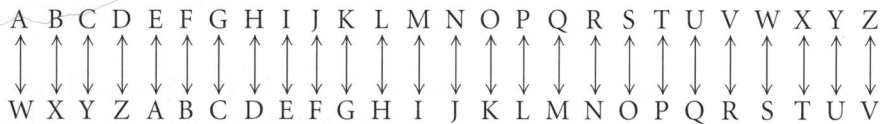

To **decrypt** a message means to take the ciphertext message and write it in plaintext. If a cryptologist thinks a message has been encrypted using a cyclical substitution code like the one shown above, the key to the code can be found by taking a word from the message (usually one of the longer words) and continuing the alphabet for each letter of the word. When a recognizable word appears, the key can be determined. This method is shown below using the ciphertext word XAWQPU.

X	A	W	Q	P	U
Y	B	X	R	Q	V
Z	C	Y	S	R	W
A	D	Z	T	S	X
B	E	A	U	T	Y

Shift four positions

Once a recognizable word has been found (BEAUTY), count the number of positions that the letters have been shifted (four, in this case). To decode the message, substitute the letter of the normal alphabet that comes four positions after the letter in the ciphertext.

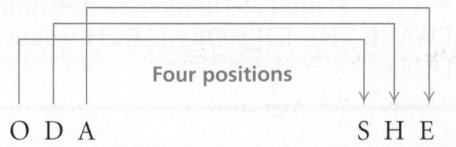

Cyclical encrypting using the alphabet is related to modular arithmetic. We begin with the normal alphabet and associate each letter with a number as shown in Table 7.1.

Table 7.1 *Numerical Equivalents for the Letters of the Alphabet*

A	B	C	D	E	F	G	H	I	J	K	L	M	N	O	P	Q	R	S	T	U	V	W	X	Y	Z
1	2	3	4	5	6	7	8	9	10	11	12	13	14	15	16	17	18	19	20	21	22	23	24	25	0

If the encrypting code is to shift each letter of the plaintext message m positions, then the corresponding letter in the ciphertext message is given by $c \equiv (p + m) \bmod 26$, where p is the numerical equivalent of the plaintext letter and c is the numerical equivalent of the ciphertext letter. The letter Z is coded as 0 because $26 \equiv 0 \bmod 26$.

Each letter in Lord Byron's poem was shifted 22 positions ($m = 22$) to the right. To code the plaintext letter S in the word SHE, we use the congruence $c \equiv (p + m) \bmod 26$.

$$c \equiv (p + m) \bmod 26$$
$$c \equiv (19 + 22) \bmod 26$$
$$c \equiv 41 \bmod 26$$
$$c = 15$$

• $p = 19$ (S is the 19th letter.)
$m = 22$, the number of positions the letter is shifted

The 15th letter is O. Thus S is coded as O.

Once plaintext has been converted to ciphertext, there must be a method by which the person receiving the message can return the message to plaintext. For the cyclical code, the congruence is $p \equiv (c + n) \bmod 26$, where p and c are defined as before and $n = 26 - m$. The letter O in ciphertext is decoded below using the congruence $p \equiv (c + n) \bmod 26$.

$$p \equiv (c + n) \bmod 26$$
$$p \equiv (15 + 4) \bmod 26$$
$$p \equiv 19 \bmod 26$$
$$p = 19$$

• $c = 15$ (O is the 15th letter.)
$n = 26 - m = 26 - 22 = 4$

The 19th letter is S. Thus O is decoded as S.

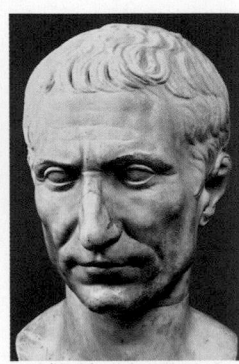

Julius Caesar

MathMatters   **A Cipher of Caesar**

Julius Caesar supposedly used a cyclical alphabetic encrypting code to communicate with his generals. The messages were encrypted using the congruence $c \equiv (p + 3) \bmod 26$ (in modern notation). Using this coding scheme, the message BEWARE THE IDES OF MARCH would be coded as EHZDUH WKH LGHV RI PDUFK.

EXAMPLE 4 ■ Write Messages Using Cyclical Coding

Use the cyclical alphabetic encrypting code that shifts each letter 11 positions to

a. code CATHERINE THE GREAT   **b.** decode TGLY ESP EPCCTMWP.

Solution

a. The encrypting congruence is $c \equiv (p + 11) \bmod 26$. Replace p by the numerical equivalent of each letter of plaintext and determine c. The results for CATHERINE are shown below.

C	$c \equiv (3 + 11) \bmod 26 \equiv 14 \bmod 26 \equiv 14$	Code C as N.
A	$c \equiv (1 + 11) \bmod 26 \equiv 12 \bmod 26 \equiv 12$	Code A as L.
T	$c \equiv (20 + 11) \bmod 26 \equiv 31 \bmod 26 \equiv 5$	Code T as E.
H	$c \equiv (8 + 11) \bmod 26 \equiv 19 \bmod 26 \equiv 19$	Code H as S.
E	$c \equiv (5 + 11) \bmod 26 \equiv 16 \bmod 26 \equiv 16$	Code E as P.
R	$c \equiv (18 + 11) \bmod 26 \equiv 29 \bmod 26 \equiv 3$	Code R as C.
I	$c \equiv (9 + 11) \bmod 26 \equiv 20 \bmod 26 \equiv 20$	Code I as T.
N	$c \equiv (14 + 11) \bmod 26 \equiv 25 \bmod 26 \equiv 25$	Code N as Y.
E	$c \equiv (5 + 11) \bmod 26 \equiv 16 \bmod 26 \equiv 16$	Code E as P.

Continuing, the plaintext would be coded as NLESPCTYP ESP RCPLE.

b. Because $m = 11$, $n = 26 - 11 = 15$. The ciphertext is decoded by using the congruence $p \equiv (c + 15) \bmod 26$. The results for TGLY are shown below.

T	$c \equiv (20 + 15) \bmod 26 \equiv 35 \bmod 26 \equiv 9$	Decode T as I.
G	$c \equiv (7 + 15) \bmod 26 \equiv 22 \bmod 26 \equiv 22$	Decode G as V.
L	$c \equiv (12 + 15) \bmod 26 \equiv 27 \bmod 26 \equiv 1$	Decode L as A.
Y	$c \equiv (25 + 15) \bmod 26 \equiv 40 \bmod 26 \equiv 14$	Decode Y as N.

Continuing, the ciphertext would be decoded as IVAN THE TERRIBLE.

CHECK YOUR PROGRESS 4   Use the cyclical alphabetic encrypting code that shifts each letter 17 positions to

a. encode ALPINE SKIING   **b.** decode TIFJJ TFLEKIP JBZZEX.

Solution   *See page S27.*

The practicality of a cyclical alphabetic coding scheme is limited because it is relatively easy for a cryptologist to determine the coding scheme. (Recall the method used for the line from Lord Byron's poem.) A coding scheme that is a little more difficult to break is based on the congruence $c \equiv (ap + m) \bmod 26$, where a and 26 do not have a common factor. (For instance, a cannot be 14 because 14 and 26 have a common factor of 2.) The reason why a and 26 cannot have a common factor is related to the procedure for determining the decoding congruence. However, we will leave that discussion to other math courses.

EXAMPLE 5 ■ Encode a Message

Use the congruence $c \equiv (5p + 2) \bmod 26$ to encode the message LASER PRINTER.

Money Orders Some money orders have serial numbers that consist of a 10-digit number followed by a check digit. The check digit is chosen to be the sum of the first 10 digits mod 9. In Exercises 23–26, determine the check digit for the given money order serial number.

23. 0316615498-? **24.** 5492877463-?

25. 1331497533-? **26.** 3414793288-?

Air Travel Many printed airline tickets contain a 10-digit document number followed by a check digit. The check digit is chosen to be the sum of the first 10 digits mod 7. In Exercises 27–30, determine whether the given number is a valid document number.

27. 1182649758 2 **28.** 1260429984 4

29. 2026178914 5 **30.** 2373453867 6

Credit Card Numbers In Exercises 31–38, determine whether the given credit card number is a valid number.

31. 4417-5486-1785-6411 **32.** 5164-8295-1229-3674

33. 5591-4912-7644-1105 **34.** 6011-4988-1002-6487

35. 6011-0408-4977-3158 **36.** 4896-4198-8760-1970

37. 3715-548731-84466 **38.** 3401-714339-12041

Encryption In Exercises 39–44, encode the message by using a cyclical alphabetic encrypting code that shifts the message the stated number of positions.

39. 8 positions: THREE MUSKETEERS

40. 6 positions: FLY TONIGHT

41. 12 positions: IT'S A GIRL

42. 9 positions: MEET AT NOON

43. 3 positions: STICKS AND STONES

44. 15 positions: A STITCH IN TIME

Decoding In Exercises 45–48, use a cyclical alphabetic encrypting code that shifts the letters the stated number of positions to decode the encrypted message.

45. 18 positions: SYW GX WFDAYZLWFEWFL

46. 20 positions: CGUACHUNCIH LOFYM NBY QILFX

47. 15 positions: UGXTCS XC CTTS

48. 8 positions: VWJWLG QA XMZNMKB

Decoding In Exercises 49–52, use a cyclical alphabetic encrypting code to decode the encrypted message.

49. YVIBZM RDGG MJWDINJI

50. YBZAM HK YEBZAM

51. UDGIJCT RDDZXT

52. AOB HVS HCFDSRCSG

53. Encryption Julius Caesar supposedly used an encrypting code equivalent to the congruence $c \equiv (p + 3) \mod 26$. Use the congruence to encrypt the message "men willingly believe what they wish."

54. Decoding Julius Caesar supposedly used an encrypting code equivalent to the congruence $c \equiv (p + 3) \mod 26$. Use the congruence to decrypt the message WKHUH DUH QR DFFLGHQWV.

55. Encryption Use the encrypting congruence $c \equiv (3p + 2) \mod 26$ to code the message TOWER OF LONDON.

56. Encryption Use the encrypting congruence $c \equiv (5p + 3) \mod 26$ to code the message DAYLIGHT SAVINGS TIME.

57. Encryption Use the encrypting congruence $c \equiv (7p + 8) \mod 26$ to code the message PARALLEL LINES.

58. Encryption Use the encrypting congruence $c \equiv (3p + 11) \mod 26$ to code the message NONE SHALL PASS.

59. Decoding Decode the message LOFT JGMK LBS MNWMK that was encrypted using the congruence $c \equiv (3p + 4) \mod 26$.

60. Decoding Decode the message BTYW SCRBKN UCYN that was encrypted using the congruence $c \equiv (5p + 6) \mod 26$.

61. Decoding Decode the message SNUUHQ FM VFALHDZ that was encrypted using the congruence $c \equiv (5p + 9) \mod 26$.

62. Decoding Decode the message GBBZ OJQBWJ TBR GJHI that was encrypted using the congruence $c \equiv (7p + 1) \mod 26$.

Extensions

CRITICAL THINKING

63. **Money Orders** Explain why the method used to determine the check digit of the money order serial numbers in Exercises 23–26 will not detect a transposition of digits among the first 10 digits.

64.  **UPC Codes** Explain why the transposition of adjacent digits a and b in a UPC will go undetected only when $|a - b| = 5$.

Springfield Public Library

2 8888 00000 0001

EXPLORATIONS

65. Banking When banks process an Electronic Funds Transfer (EFT), they assign a nine-digit routing number, where the ninth digit is a check digit. The check digit is chosen such that when the nine digits are multiplied in turn by the numbers 3, 7, 1, 3, 7, 1, 3, 7, and 1, the sum of the resulting products is 0 mod 10. For instance, 123456780 is a valid routing number because

$$1(3) + 2(7) + 3(1) + 4(3) + 5(7) + 6(1)$$
$$+ 7(3) + 8(7) + 0(1) = 150$$

and $150 \equiv 0 \bmod 10$.

a. Compute the check digit for the routing number 72859372-?

b. Verify that 584926105 is a valid routing number.

c. If a bank clerk inadvertantly types the routing number in part b as 584962105, will the computer be able to detect the error?

d.  A bank employee accidentally transposed the 6 and the 1 in the routing number from part b and entered the number 584921605 into the computer system, but the computer did not detect an error. Explain why.

66. Bar Codes The Codabar system is a bar code method developed in 1972 that is commonly used in libraries.

Each bar code contains a 14-digit number, where the 14th digit is a check digit. The various check digit schemes discussed in this section are designed to detect errors, but they cannot catch every possible error. The Codabar method is more thorough and will detect any single mistyped digit as well as any adjacent digits that have been transposed, with the exception of 9–0 and 0–9. To determine the check digit, label the first 13 digits a_1 through a_{13}. The check digit is given by

$$(-2a_1 - a_2 - 2a_3 - a_4 - 2a_5 - a_6 - 2a_7 - a_8$$
$$- 2a_9 - a_{10} - 2a_{11} - a_{12} - 2a_{13} - r) \bmod 10$$

where r is the number of digits from the digits a_1, a_3, a_5, a_7, a_9, a_{11}, and a_{13} that are greater than or equal to 5. For example, the bar code with the number 3194870254381-? has digits a_3, a_5, and a_9 that are greater than or equal to 5. Thus $r = 3$ and

$$-2(3) - 1 - 2(9) - 4 - 2(8) - 7 - 2(0)$$
$$- 2 - 2(5) - 4 - 2(3) - 8 - 2(1) - 3 = -87$$
$$\equiv 3 \bmod 10$$

The check digit is 3.

a. Find the check digit for the bar code number 1982273895263-?.

b. Find the check digit for the bar code number 6328293856384-?.

| # Introduction to Group Theory

Introduction to Groups

An **algebraic system** is a set of elements along with one or more operations for combining the elements. The real numbers with the operations of addition and multiplication are an example of an algebraic system. Mathematicians call this particular algebraic system a *field*.

In the previous two sections of this chapter we discussed operations modulo n. Consider the set $\{0, 1, 2, 3, 4, 5\}$ and addition modulo 6. The set of elements is $\{0, 1, 2, 3, 4, 5\}$ and the operation is addition modulo 6. In this case there is only one operation. This is an example of an algebraic system called a *group*.

In addition to fields and groups, there are other types of algebraic systems. It is the properties of an algebraic system that distinguish it from another algebraic system. In this section, we will focus on groups.

Definition of a Group

A **group** is a set of elements, with one operation, that satisfies the following four properties.

1. The set is closed with respect to the operation.
2. The operation satisfies the associative property.
3. There is an identity element.
4. Each element has an inverse.

Note from the above definition that a group is an algebraic system with *one* operation and that the operation must have certain characteristics. The first of these characteristics is that the set is *closed* with respect to the operation. **Closure** means that if any two elements are combined using the operation, the result must be an element of the set.

For example, the set $\{0, 1, 2, 3, 4, 5\}$ with addition modulo 6 as the operation is closed. If we add two numbers of this set, modulo 6, the result is always a number of the set. For instance, $(3 + 5) \bmod 6 \equiv 2$ and $(1 + 3) \bmod 6 \equiv 4$.

As another example, consider the whole numbers $\{0, 1, 2, 3, 4, \ldots\}$ with multiplication as the operation. If we multiply two whole numbers, the result is a whole number. For instance, $5 \cdot 9 = 45$ and $12 \cdot 15 = 180$. Thus the set of whole numbers is closed using multiplication as the operation. However, the set of whole numbers is not closed with division as the operation. For example, even though $36 \div 9 = 4$ (a whole number), $6 \div 4 = 1.5$, which is not a whole number. Therefore, the set of whole numbers is not closed with respect to division.

QUESTION   *a. Is the set of whole numbers closed with respect to addition?*

b. Is the set of whole numbers closed with respect to subtraction?

The second requirement of a group is that the operation must satisfy the associative property. Recall that the Associative Property of Addition states that $a + (b + c) = (a + b) + c$. Addition modulo 6 is an associative operation. For instance, if we use the symbol $\triangledown$ to represent addition modulo 6, then

$$2 \triangledown (5 \triangledown 3) = 2 \triangledown (8 \bmod 6) = 2 \triangledown 2 = 4$$

and

$$(2 \triangledown 5) \triangledown 3 = (7 \bmod 6) \triangledown 3 = 1 \triangledown 3 = 4$$

Thus $2 \triangledown (5 \triangledown 3) = (2 \triangledown 5) \triangledown 3$.

Although there are some operations that do not satisfy the associative property, we will assume that an operation used in this section is associative.

The third requirement of a group is that the set must contain an *identity element*. An **identity element** is an element that, when combined with a second element using the group's operation, always returns the second element. As an illustration, if zero is added to a number, there is no change: $6 + 0 = 6$ and $0 + 1.5 = 1.5$. The number 0 is called an *additive identity*. Similarly, if we multiply any number by 1, there is no change: $\frac{1}{2} \cdot 1 = \frac{1}{2}$ and $1 \cdot 5 = 5$. The number 1 is called a *multiplicative identity*. For the set $\{0, 1, 2, 3, 4, 5\}$ with addition modulo 6 as the operation, the identity element is 0. As we will soon see, an identity element does not always have to be zero or one.

ANSWER   *a. Yes. The sum of any two whole numbers is a whole number.   b. No. The difference between any two whole numbers is not always a whole number. For instance, $5 - 8 = -3$, but -3 is not a whole number.*

The numbers 3 and -3 are called *additive inverses*. Adding these two numbers results in the additive identity: $3 + (-3) = 0$. The numbers $\frac{2}{3}$ and $\frac{3}{2}$ are called *reciprocals* or *multiplicative inverses*. Multiplying these two numbers results in the multiplicative identity: $\frac{2}{3} \cdot \frac{3}{2} = 1$. The last requirement of a group is that each element must have an *inverse*. This is a little more difficult to see for the set $\{0, 1, 2, 3, 4, 5\}$ with addition modulo 6 as the operation. However, using addition modulo 6, we have

$$(0 + 0) \bmod 6 \equiv 0 \qquad (2 + 4) \bmod 6 \equiv 0$$
$$(1 + 5) \bmod 6 \equiv 0 \qquad (3 + 3) \bmod 6 \equiv 0$$

The above equations show that 0 is its own inverse, 1 and 5 are inverses, 2 and 4 are inverses, and 3 is its own inverse. Therefore, every element of this set has an inverse.

We have shown that the set $\{0, 1, 2, 3, 4, 5\}$ with addition modulo 6 as the operation is a group because it satisfies the four conditions stated in the definition of a group (see page 432).

historical note

Niels Henrik Abel (1802–1829) was born near Stavenger, Norway. His mathematical prowess was recognized quite early in his schooling and he was encouraged to pursue a career in mathematics.

Abel became interested in trying to find a formula similar to the quadratic formula that could be used to solve all fifth-degree equations. In the process, he discovered that it was impossible to find such a formula. Part of Abel's proof investigated whether the equation $s_1 s_2 x = s_2 s_1 x$ was true; in other words, his conclusion depended on whether or not the commutative property held true. ∎

EXAMPLE 1 ■ Verify the Properties of a Group

Show that the integers with addition as the operation form a group.

Solution

We must show that the four properties of a group are satisfied.

1. The sum of two integers is always an integer. For instance,

$$-12 + 5 = -7 \qquad \text{and} \qquad -14 + (-21) = -35$$

Therefore, the integers are closed with respect to addition.

2. The associative property of addition holds true for the integers.

3. The identity element is 0, which is an integer. Therefore, the integers have an identity element for addition.

4. Each element has an inverse. If a is an integer, then $-a$ is the inverse of a.

Because each of the four conditions of a group is satisfied, the integers with addition as the operation form a group.

CHECK YOUR PROGRESS 1   Do the integers with multiplication as the operation form a group?

Solution *See page S28.*

Recall that the **commutative property** for an operation states that the order in which two elements are combined does not affect the result. For each of the groups discussed thus far, the operation has satisfied the commutative property. For example, the group $\{0, 1, 2, 3, 4, 5\}$ with addition modulo 6 satisfies the commutative property, since for instance $2 + 5 = 5 + 2$. Groups in which the operation satisfies the commutative property are called **commutative groups** or **abelian groups,** after Niels Abel (see the note at the left). The type of group we will look at next is an example of a *nonabelian group*. A **nonabelian group** is a group whose operation does not satisfy the commutative property.

Symmetry Groups

The concept of a group is very general. The elements that make up a group do not have to be numbers and the operation does not have to be addition or multiplication. Also, a group does not have to satisfy the commutative property. We will now look at another group, called a *symmetry group*, an extension of which plays an important role in the study of atomic reactions. Symmetry groups are based on *regular polygons*. A **regular polygon** is a polygon all of whose sides have the same length and all of whose angles have the same measure.

Consider two equilateral triangles, one placed inside the other, with their vertices numbered clockwise from 1 to 3. The larger triangle is the *reference triangle*. If we pick up the smaller triangle, there are several different ways in which we can set it back in its place. Each possible positioning of the inner triangle will be an element of a group. For instance, we can pick up the triangle and replace it exactly as we found it. We will call this position I; it will represent no change in position.

Now pick up the smaller triangle, rotate it 120° clockwise, and set it down again on top of the reference triangle. The result is shown below.

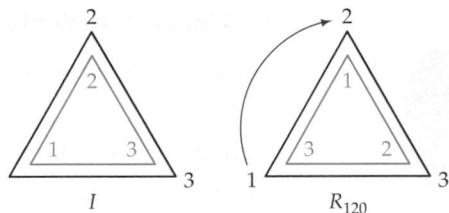

Notice that the vertex originally at vertex 1 of the reference triangle is now at vertex 2, 2 is now at 3, and 3 is now at 1. We call the rotation of the triangle 120° clockwise R_{120}.

Now return the smaller triangle to its original position, where the numbers on the vertices of the triangles coincide. Consider a 240° rotation of the smaller triangle. The result of this rotation is shown below.

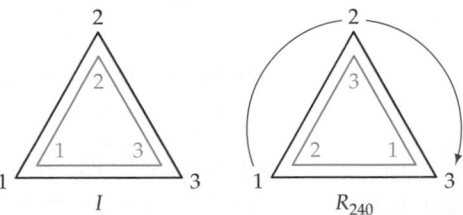

Notice that the vertex originally at vertex 1 of the reference triangle is now at vertex 3, 2 is now at 1, and 3 is now at 2. We call the rotation of the triangle 240° clockwise R_{240}.

If the original triangle were rotated 360°, there would be no apparent change. The vertex at 1 would return to 1, the vertex at 2 would return to 2, and the vertex at 3 would return to 3. Because this rotation does not produce a new arrangement of the vertices, we consider it the same as the element we named I.

If we rotate the inner triangle *counterclockwise* 120°, the effect is the same as rotating it 240° clockwise. This rotation does not produce a different arrangement of the vertices. Similarly, a counterclockwise rotation of 240° is the same as a clockwise rotation of 120°.

In addition to rotating the triangle clockwise 120° and 240° as we did above, we could rotate the triangle about a line of symmetry that goes through a vertex before setting the triangle back down. Because there are three vertices, there are three possible results. These are shown below.

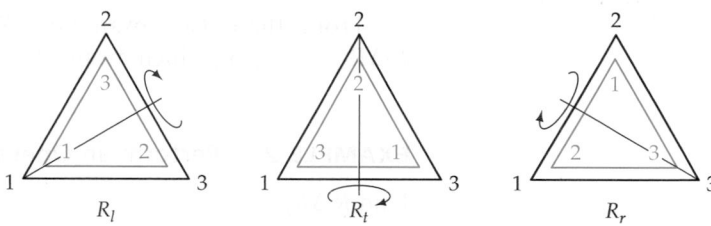

For rotation R_l, the bottom *left* vertex does not change, but vertices 2 and 3 are interchanged. If we rotate the triangle about the line of symmetry through the *top* vertex, rotation R_t, vertex 2 does not change but vertices 1 and 3 are interchanged. For rotation R_r, the bottom *right* vertex does not change but vertices 1 and 2 are interchanged.

The six positions of the vertices we have seen thus far are the only possibilities: I (the triangle without any rotation), R_{120}, R_{240}, R_l, R_t, and R_r. These positions are shown below (without the reference triangle).

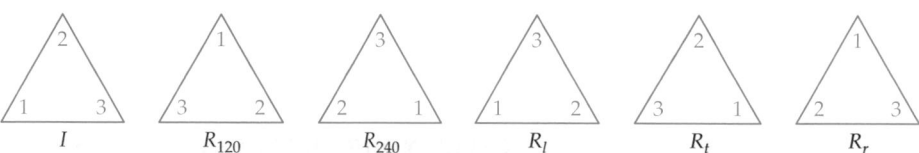

As we will see, these rotations are elements that form a group.

A group must have an operation, a method by which two elements of the group can be combined to form a third element that must also be a member of the group. (Recall that a group operation must be closed.) The operation we will use is called "followed by" and is symbolized by Δ. Next we show an example of how this operation works.

Consider $R_l \Delta R_{240}$. This means we rotate the original triangle, labeled as I, about the line of symmetry through vertex 1 "followed by" (without returning to the original position) a clockwise rotation of 240°. The result is one of the elements of the group, R_t. This operation is shown below.

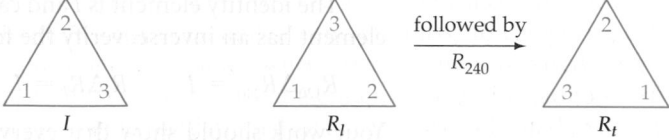

Now try reversing the operation and consider $R_{240} \Delta R_l$. This means we rotate the original triangle, I, clockwise 240° "followed by" (without returning to the

Permutation Groups

The triangular symmetry group discussed previously is an example of a special kind of group called a *permutation group*. A **permutation** is a rearrangement of objects. For instance, if we start with the arrangement of objects [♦ ♥ ♣], then one permutation of these objects is the rearrangement [♥ ♣ ♦]. If we consider each permutation of these objects as an element of a set, then the set of all possible permutations forms a group. The elements of the group are not numbers or the objects themselves, but rather the different permutations of the objects that are possible.

If we start with the numbers 1 2 3, we can represent permutations of the numbers using the same symbolic method that we used for the triangular symmetry group. For example, the permutation that rearranges 1 2 3 to 2 3 1 can be written

$\begin{pmatrix} 1 & 2 & 3 \\ 2 & 3 & 1 \end{pmatrix}$, which means that 1 is replaced by 2, 2 is replaced by 3, and 3 is replaced by 1.

There are only six distinct permutations of the numbers 1 2 3. We list and label them below. The identity element is named *I*.

$$I = \begin{pmatrix} 1 & 2 & 3 \\ 1 & 2 & 3 \end{pmatrix}, A = \begin{pmatrix} 1 & 2 & 3 \\ 2 & 3 & 1 \end{pmatrix}, B = \begin{pmatrix} 1 & 2 & 3 \\ 3 & 1 & 2 \end{pmatrix}$$

$$C = \begin{pmatrix} 1 & 2 & 3 \\ 1 & 3 & 2 \end{pmatrix}, D = \begin{pmatrix} 1 & 2 & 3 \\ 3 & 2 & 1 \end{pmatrix}, E = \begin{pmatrix} 1 & 2 & 3 \\ 2 & 1 & 3 \end{pmatrix}$$

The operation for the group is "followed by," which we will again denote by the symbol Δ. One can verify that the six elements along with this operation do indeed form a group.

▼ point of interest

You may have played with a "15 puzzle" like the one pictured above. There is one empty slot that allows the numbered tiles to move around the board. The goal is to arrange the tiles in numerical order. The puzzle can be analyzed in the context of group theory, where each element of a group is a permutation of the tiles. If one were to remove two adjacent tiles and replace them with their positions switched, group theory can be used to prove that the puzzle becomes impossible to solve.

EXAMPLE 4 ■ Perform an Operation in a Permutation Group

Find *B*Δ*C*, where *B* and *C* are elements of the permutation group defined above.

Solution

$B\Delta C = \begin{pmatrix} 1 & 2 & 3 \\ 3 & 1 & 2 \end{pmatrix} \Delta \begin{pmatrix} 1 & 2 & 3 \\ 1 & 3 & 2 \end{pmatrix}$. In the first permutation, 1 is replaced by 3. In the second permutation, 3 is replaced by 2. When we combine these two actions, 1 is ultimately replaced by 2. Similarly, in the first permutation 2 is replaced by 1, which remains as 1 in the second permutation. 3 is replaced by 2, which is in turn replaced by 3. When these actions are combined, 3 remains as 3. The result of the operation is $\begin{pmatrix} 1 & 2 & 3 \\ 2 & 1 & 3 \end{pmatrix}$. Thus we see that $B\Delta C = E$.

CHECK YOUR PROGRESS 4 Compute *E*Δ*B*, where *E* and *B* are elements of the permutation group defined previously.

Solution See page S28.

EXAMPLE 5 ■ Inverse Element of a Permutation Group

One of the requirements of a group is that each element must have an inverse. Find the inverse of the element B of the permutation group defined previously.

Solution

Because $B = \begin{pmatrix} 1 & 2 & 3 \\ 3 & 1 & 2 \end{pmatrix}$ replaces 1 with 3, 2 with 1, and 3 with 2, its inverse must reverse these replacements. Thus we need to replace 3 with 1, 1 with 2, and 2 with 3.

The inverse is the element $\begin{pmatrix} 1 & 2 & 3 \\ 2 & 3 & 1 \end{pmatrix} = A$. To verify,

$$B \Delta A = \begin{pmatrix} 1 & 2 & 3 \\ 3 & 1 & 2 \end{pmatrix} \Delta \begin{pmatrix} 1 & 2 & 3 \\ 2 & 3 & 1 \end{pmatrix} = \begin{pmatrix} 1 & 2 & 3 \\ 1 & 2 & 3 \end{pmatrix} \text{ and}$$

$$A \Delta B = \begin{pmatrix} 1 & 2 & 3 \\ 2 & 3 & 1 \end{pmatrix} \Delta \begin{pmatrix} 1 & 2 & 3 \\ 3 & 1 & 2 \end{pmatrix} = \begin{pmatrix} 1 & 2 & 3 \\ 1 & 2 & 3 \end{pmatrix}.$$

CHECK YOUR PROGRESS 5   Find the inverse of the element D of the permutation group defined previously.

Solution   See page S28.

> ### TAKE NOTE
>
> In a nonabelian group, the order in which the two elements are combined with the group operation can affect the result. For an element to be the inverse of another element, combining the elements must give the identity element regardless of the order used.

If we consider a group with more than three numbers or objects, the number of different permutations increases dramatically. The permutation group of the five numbers 1 2 3 4 5 has 120 elements, and there are over 40,000 permutations of the numbers 1 2 3 4 5 6 7 8. In Exercise Set 7.3, you are asked to examine the permutations of 1 2 3 4.

Excursion

Wallpaper Groups

The symmetry group we studied based on an equilateral triangle involved rotations of the triangle that retained the position of the triangle within a reference triangle. We will now look at symmetries of an infinitely large object.

Imagine that the pattern shown in Figure 7.3 on the following page continues forever in every direction. You can think of it as an infinitely large sheet of wallpaper. Overlaying this sheet is a transparent sheet with the same pattern.

Visualize shifting the transparent sheet of wallpaper upward until the printed cats realign in what appears to be the same position. This is called a **translation.** Any such translation, in which we can shift the paper in one direction until the pattern aligns with its original appearance, is an element of a group. There are several directions in which we can shift the wallpaper (up, down, and diagonally), and an infinite number of distances we can shift the wallpaper. So the group has an infinite number of elements. Several elements are shown in Figure 7.4. Not shifting the paper at all is also considered an element; we will call it *I*, because it is the identity element for the group. As with the symmetry groups, the operation is "followed by," denoted by **Δ.**

(continued)

        c. Find two different center points about which a 120° rotation is an element of the group.

        d. Identify three distinct lines that could serve as axes of reflection for elements of the group.

Figure 7.6

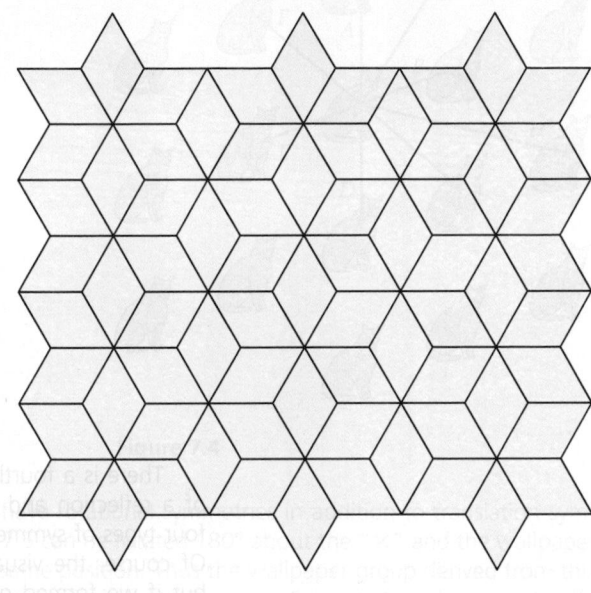

Figure 7.7

Exercise Set 7.3

1. Is the set $\{-1, 1\}$ closed with respect to the operation
  a. multiplication?
  b. addition?

2. Is the set of all even integers closed with respect to
  a. multiplication?
  b. addition?

3. Is the set of all odd integers closed with respect to
  a. multiplication?
  b. addition?

4. Is the set of all negative real numbers closed with respect to
  a. addition?   **b.** subtraction?
  c. multiplication?   **d.** division?

In Exercises 5–18, determine whether the set forms a group with respect to the given operation. (You may assume the operation is associative.) If the set does not form a group, determine which properties fail.

5. The even integers; addition

6. The even integers; multiplication

7. The real numbers; addition

8. The real numbers; division

9. The real numbers; multiplication

10. The real numbers *except* 0; multiplication

11. The rational numbers; addition
(Recall that a rational number is any number that can be expressed as a fraction.)

12. The positive rational numbers; multiplication

13. {0, 1, 2, 3}; addition modulo 4

14. {0, 1, 2, 3, 4}; addition modulo 6

15. {0, 1, 2, 3}; multiplication modulo 4

16. {1, 2, 3, 4}; multiplication modulo 5

17. {−1, 1}; multiplication

18. {−1, 1}; division

Exercises 19−24 refer to the triangular symmetry group discussed in this section.

19. Find $R_t \Delta R_{120}$.

20. Find $R_{240} \Delta R_r$.

21. Find $R_r \Delta R_t$.

22. Find $R_t \Delta R_l$.

23. Which element is the inverse of R_{240}?

24. Which element is the inverse of R_t?

We can form another symmetry group by using rotations of a square rather than a triangle. Start with a square with corners labeled 1 through 4, placed in a reference square.

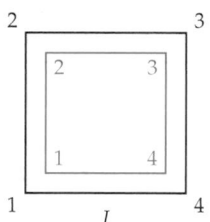

I

The current position of the inner square is labeled I. We can rotate the inner square clockwise 90° to give an element of the group, R_{90}. Similarly, we can rotate the square 180° or 270° to obtain the elements R_{180} and R_{270}. In addition, we can rotate the square about any of the lines of symmetry shown below.

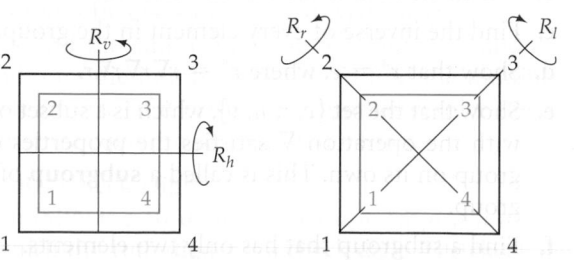

As before, the operation is "followed by," denoted by Δ. Exercises 25−34 refer to this symmetry group of the square.

25. Find $R_{90} \Delta R_v$.

26. Find $R_r \Delta R_{180}$.

27. Find $R_h \Delta R_{270}$.

28. Find $R_l \Delta R_h$.

29. List each of the eight elements of the group in symbolic notation. For instance, $I = \begin{pmatrix} 1 & 2 & 3 & 4 \\ 1 & 2 & 3 & 4 \end{pmatrix}$.

30. Use symbolic notation to find $R_v \Delta R_l$.

31. Use symbolic notation to find $R_h \Delta R_{90}$.

32. Use symbolic notation to find $R_{180} \Delta R_r$.

33. Find the inverse of the element R_{270}.

34. Find the inverse of the element R_v.

Exercises 35−42 refer to the group of permutations of the numbers 1 2 3 discussed in this section.

35. Find $A \Delta B$.

36. Find $B \Delta A$.

37. Find $B \Delta E$.

38. Find $D \Delta C$.

39. Find $C \Delta A$.

40. Find $B \Delta B$.

41. Find the inverse of the element A.

42. Find the inverse of the element E.

We can form a new permutation group by considering all permutations of the numbers 1 2 3 4. Exercises 43−50 refer to this group.

43. List all 24 elements of the group. Use symbolic notation, such as $I = \begin{pmatrix} 1 & 2 & 3 & 4 \\ 1 & 2 & 3 & 4 \end{pmatrix}$.

44. Find $\begin{pmatrix} 1 & 2 & 3 & 4 \\ 4 & 2 & 1 & 3 \end{pmatrix} \Delta \begin{pmatrix} 1 & 2 & 3 & 4 \\ 2 & 1 & 4 & 3 \end{pmatrix}$.

45. Find $\begin{pmatrix} 1 & 2 & 3 & 4 \\ 1 & 4 & 2 & 3 \end{pmatrix} \Delta \begin{pmatrix} 1 & 2 & 3 & 4 \\ 2 & 3 & 4 & 1 \end{pmatrix}$.

46. Find $\begin{pmatrix} 1 & 2 & 3 & 4 \\ 3 & 2 & 1 & 4 \end{pmatrix} \Delta \begin{pmatrix} 1 & 2 & 3 & 4 \\ 3 & 4 & 2 & 1 \end{pmatrix}$.

47. Find the inverse of $\begin{pmatrix} 1 & 2 & 3 & 4 \\ 2 & 4 & 1 & 3 \end{pmatrix}$.

48. Find the inverse of $\begin{pmatrix} 1 & 2 & 3 & 4 \\ 3 & 4 & 1 & 2 \end{pmatrix}$.

■ **Symmetry Group of an Equilateral Triangle**

The group has six elements, which consist of the different possible rotations that return the triangle to its reference triangle:

     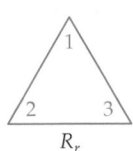

The group operation is "followed by," denoted by Δ. The operation is noncommutative.

■ **Symbolic Notation for the Symmetry Group of an Equilateral Triangle**

The six elements of the group are

$$I = \begin{pmatrix} 1 & 2 & 3 \\ 1 & 2 & 3 \end{pmatrix} \qquad R_{120} = \begin{pmatrix} 1 & 2 & 3 \\ 2 & 3 & 1 \end{pmatrix}$$

$$R_{240} = \begin{pmatrix} 1 & 2 & 3 \\ 3 & 1 & 2 \end{pmatrix} \qquad R_l = \begin{pmatrix} 1 & 2 & 3 \\ 1 & 3 & 2 \end{pmatrix}$$

$$R_t = \begin{pmatrix} 1 & 2 & 3 \\ 3 & 2 & 1 \end{pmatrix} \qquad R_r = \begin{pmatrix} 1 & 2 & 3 \\ 2 & 1 & 3 \end{pmatrix}$$

where, for instance, $\begin{pmatrix} 1 & 2 & 3 \\ 2 & 3 & 1 \end{pmatrix}$ signifies that the vertex of the equilateral triangle originally at vertex 1 of the reference triangle moves to vertex 2, the vertex at 2 moves to 3, and the vertex at 3 moves to 1.

■ **Permutation Group of the Numbers 1, 2, 3**

The group consists of the six permutations of the numbers 1, 2, 3:

$$I = \begin{pmatrix} 1 & 2 & 3 \\ 1 & 2 & 3 \end{pmatrix} \qquad A = \begin{pmatrix} 1 & 2 & 3 \\ 2 & 3 & 1 \end{pmatrix}$$

$$B = \begin{pmatrix} 1 & 2 & 3 \\ 3 & 1 & 2 \end{pmatrix} \qquad C = \begin{pmatrix} 1 & 2 & 3 \\ 1 & 3 & 2 \end{pmatrix}$$

$$D = \begin{pmatrix} 1 & 2 & 3 \\ 3 & 2 & 1 \end{pmatrix} \qquad E = \begin{pmatrix} 1 & 2 & 3 \\ 2 & 1 & 3 \end{pmatrix}$$

The group operation is "followed by," denoted by Δ.

CHAPTER 7 Review Exercises

In Exercises 1–8, evaluate each expression, where ⊕ and ⊖ indicate addition and subtraction, respectively, using a 12-hour clock.

1. 9 ⊕ 5

2. 8 ⊕ 6

3. 10 ⊕ 7

4. 7 ⊕ 11

5. 6 ⊖ 9

6. 2 ⊖ 10

7. 3 ⊖ 4

8. 7 ⊖ 12

In Exercises 9 and 10, evaluate each expression, where ⊞ and ⊟ indicate addition and subtraction, respectively, using days-of-the-week arithmetic.

9. 5 ⊞ 5

10. 2 ⊟ 5

In Exercises 11–14, determine whether the congruence is true or false.

11. $17 \equiv 2 \bmod 5$

12. $14 \equiv 24 \bmod 4$

13. $35 \equiv 53 \bmod 10$

14. $12 \equiv 36 \bmod 8$

In Exercises 15–22, perform the modular arithmetic.

15. $(8 + 12) \bmod 3$

16. $(15 + 7) \bmod 6$

17. $(42 - 10) \bmod 8$

18. $(19 - 8) \bmod 4$

19. $(7 \cdot 5) \bmod 9$

20. $(12 \cdot 9) \bmod 5$

21. $(15 \cdot 10) \bmod 11$

22. $(41 \cdot 13) \bmod 8$

Clocks and Calendars In Exercises 23 and 24, use modular arithmetic to determine each of the following.

23. Disregarding A.M. or P.M., if it is now 5 o'clock,

 a. what time will it be 45 hours from now?

 b. what time was it 71 hours ago?

24. In 2005, April 15 (the day taxes are due in the U.S.) fell on a Friday. On what day of the week will April 15 fall in 2013?

In Exercises 25–28, find all whole number solutions of the congruence equation.

25. $x \equiv 7 \bmod 4$

26. $2x \equiv 5 \bmod 9$

27. $(2x + 1) \equiv 6 \bmod 5$

28. $(3x + 4) \equiv 5 \bmod 11$

In Exercises 29 and 30, find the additive inverse and the multiplicative inverse, if it exists, of the given number.

29. 5 in mod 7 arithmetic

30. 7 in mod 12 arithmetic

In Exercises 31 and 32, perform the modular division by solving a related multiplication problem.

31. $(2 \div 5) \bmod 7$

32. $(3 \div 4) \bmod 5$

ISBN Numbers In Exercises 33 and 34, determine the correct check digit for each ISBN.

33. *Oliver Twist* by Charles Dickens, 0-812-58003-?

34. *Interview with the Vampire* by Anne Rice, 0-394-49821-?

UPC Codes In Exercises 35 and 36, determine the correct check digit for the UPC.

35. 0-29000-07004-? (Planters Almonds)

36. 0-85391-89512-? (*Best in Show* DVD)

Credit Card Numbers In Exercises 37–40, determine whether the given credit card number is a valid number.

37. 5126-6993-4231-2956

38. 5383-0118-3416-5931

39. 3412-408439-82594

40. 6011-5185-8295-8328

Encryption In Exercises 41 and 42, encode the message using a cyclical alphabetic encrypting code that shifts the message the stated number of positions.

41. 7 positions: MAY THE FORCE BE WITH YOU

42. 11 positions: CANCEL ALL PLANS

Encryption In Exercises 43 and 44, use a cyclical alphabetic encrypting code to decode the encrypted message.

43. PXXM UDLT CXVXAAXF

44. HVS ROM VOG OFFWJSR

45. Encryption Use the encrypting congruence $c \equiv (3p + 6) \bmod 26$ to encrypt the message END OF THE LINE.

46. Encryption Decode the message WEU LKGGMF NHM NMGN that was encrypted using the congruence $c \equiv (7p + 4) \bmod 26$.

In Exercises 47–50, determine whether the set is a group with respect to the given operation. (You may assume the operation is associative.) If the set is not a group, determine which properties fail.

47. All rational numbers *except* 0; multiplication

48. All multiples of 3; addition

49. All negative integers; multiplication

50. $\{1, 2, 3, 4, 5, 6, 7, 8, 9, 10\}$; multiplication modulo 11

Exercises 51 and 52 refer to the triangular symmetry group discussed in Section 7.3.

51. Find $R_t \Delta R_r$.

52. Find $R_{240} \Delta R_t$.

Exercises 53–56 refer to the square symmetry group discussed in Exercises 25–34 of Section 7.3.

53. Find $R_h \Delta R_{90}$.

54. Find $R_l \Delta R_v$.

55. Find the inverse of the element R_{180}.

56. Find the inverse of the element R_r.

In Exercises 57–61, a rectangle with corners labeled 1 through 4 is placed in a reference rectangle as shown below.

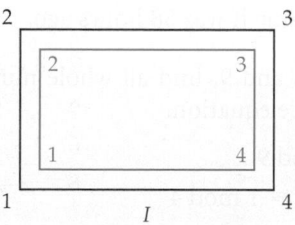

We can form a group in which each element is a rotation of the inner rectangle that allows us to reposition the inner rectangle within the reference rectangle, similar to the symmetry groups discussed in Section 7.3. We again use the "followed by" operation, Δ. (This group is called the *Klein 4-group*.)

57. Explain why this group has only four elements.

58. List each element in symbolic notation.

59. Is this group commutative?

60. Show that each element is its own inverse.

61. Of the three non-identity elements, show that the combination of any two by the operation Δ is always the third element.

Exercises 62 and 63 refer to the group of permutations of the numbers 1 2 3 discussed in Section 7.3.

62. Find $C\Delta E$.

63. Find $E\Delta D$.

In Exercises 64 and 65, consider the group of permutations of the numbers 1 2 3 4 5 with the operation Δ.

64. Find $\begin{pmatrix} 1 & 2 & 3 & 4 & 5 \\ 4 & 3 & 5 & 1 & 2 \end{pmatrix}\Delta\begin{pmatrix} 1 & 2 & 3 & 4 & 5 \\ 5 & 2 & 4 & 3 & 1 \end{pmatrix}$.

65. Find the inverse of $\begin{pmatrix} 1 & 2 & 3 & 4 & 5 \\ 3 & 5 & 1 & 4 & 2 \end{pmatrix}$.

CHAPTER 7   **Test**

---

1. Evaluate each expression, where $\oplus$ and $\ominus$ indicate addition and subtraction, respectively, using a 12-hour clock.

   a. $8 \oplus 7$ **b.** $2 \ominus 9$

2. Military Time Evaluate each expression, where $\triangle\!\!\!+$ and $\triangle\!\!\!-$ indicate addition and subtraction, respectively, using military time.

   a. $1500 \,\triangle\!\!\!+\, 1100$ **b.** $0400 \,\triangle\!\!\!-\, 1500$

3. Determine whether the congruence is true or false.

   a. $8 \equiv 20 \bmod 3$ **b.** $61 \equiv 38 \bmod 7$

In Exercises 4–6, perform the modular arithmetic.

4. $(25 + 9) \bmod 6$

5. $(31 - 11) \bmod 7$

6. $(5 \cdot 16) \bmod 12$

7. Scheduling Disregarding A.M. or P.M., if it is now 3 o'clock, use modular arithmetic to determine

   a. what time it will be 27 hours from now.

   b. what time it was 58 hours ago.

In Exercises 8 and 9, find all whole number solutions of the congruence equation.

8. $x \equiv 5 \bmod 9$

9. $(2x + 3) \equiv 1 \bmod 4$

10. Find the additive inverse and the multiplicative inverse, if it exists, of 5 in modulo 9 arithmetic.

11. ISBN Number Determine the correct check digit for the ISBN 0-441-56959-? (*Neuromancer* by William Gibson).

12. UPC Codes Determine the correct check digit for the UPC 0-72878-27533-? (Herdez Salsa Verde).

13. Credit Card Numbers Determine whether the credit card number 4232-8180-5736-4876 is a valid number.

14. Encryption Encrypt the plaintext message REPORT BACK using the cyclical alphabetic encrypting code that shifts letters 10 positions.

15. Encryption Decode the message UTSTG DPFM that was encrypted using the congruence $c \equiv (3p + 5) \bmod 26$.

16. a. Is the set of all odd positive integers closed with respect to multiplication? Explain.

   b. Is the set of all odd positive integers closed with respect to addition? Explain.

17. Determine whether the set of all odd integers with multiplication as the operation is a group. (You may assume the operation is associative.) If the set is not a group, explain which properties fail.

18. In the symmetry group of an equilateral triangle, determine the result of the operation.

   a. $R_{120}\Delta R_l$ **b.** $R_t\Delta R_{240}$

19. In the permutation group of the numbers 1, 2, 3, determine the result of the operation.

$$\begin{pmatrix} 1 & 2 & 3 \\ 3 & 1 & 2 \end{pmatrix}\Delta\begin{pmatrix} 1 & 2 & 3 \\ 3 & 2 & 1 \end{pmatrix}$$

20. In the permutation group of the numbers 1, 2, 3, 4 with the operation Δ, find the inverse element of

$$\begin{pmatrix} 1 & 2 & 3 & 4 \\ 3 & 1 & 4 & 2 \end{pmatrix}.$$

CHAPTER 8

Geometry

8.1 Basic Concepts of Euclidean Geometry

8.2 Perimeter and Area of Plane Figures

8.3 Properties of Triangles

8.4 Volume and Surface Area

8.5 Introduction to Trigonometry

8.6 Non-Euclidean Geometry

8.7 Fractals

Look closely at each of the four rectangles shown below. Which rectangle seems to be the most pleasant to look at?

Rectangle A

Rectangle B

Rectangle C

Rectangle D

The length of rectangle A is three times its width; the ratio of the length to the width is 3:1. Rectangle B is a square, so its length is equal to its width; the ratio of the length to the width is 1:1. The ratio of the length of rectangle C to its width is 1.2:1. The shape of rectangle D is referred to as a *golden rectangle*. In a **golden rectangle,** the ratio of the length to the width is approximately 1.6 to 1. The ratio is exactly

$$\frac{\text{length}}{\text{width}} = \frac{1 + \sqrt{5}}{2}$$

The early Greeks considered golden rectangles to be the most pleasing to the eye. Therefore, they used it extensively in their art and architecture. The Parthenon in Athens, Greece, exhibits many golden rectangles. It was built around 435 B.C. as a temple to the goddess Athena.

Mona Lisa by Leonardo da Vinci

The World Wide Web is a wonderful source of information about golden rectangles. Simply enter "golden rectangle" in a search engine. It will respond with thousands of websites where you can learn more about the use of golden rectangles in art, architecture, music, nature, and mathematics. Be sure to research Leonardo da Vinci's use of the golden rectangle in his painting *Mona Lisa*.

For online student resources, visit this textbook's website at **www.cengage.com/math.**

449

Lines and Angles

historical note

Geometry is one of the oldest branches of mathematics. Around 350 B.C., Euclid (yōō′klĭd) of Alexandria wrote *Elements,* which contained all of the known concepts of geometry. Euclid's contribution to geometry was to unify various concepts into a single deductive system that was based on a set of postulates. ∎

The word *geometry* comes from the Greek words for "earth" and "measure". In ancient Egypt, geometry was used by the Egyptians to measure land and to build structures such as the pyramids.

Today geometry is used in many fields, such as physics, medicine, and geology. Geometry is also used in applied fields such as mechanical drawing and astronomy. Geometric forms are used in art and design.

If you play a musical instrument, you know the meaning of the words *measure, rest, whole note,* and *time signature.* If you are a football fan, you have learned the terms *first down, sack, punt,* and *touchback.* Every field has its associated vocabulary. Geometry is no exception. We will begin by introducing two basic geometric concepts: point and line.

A **point** is symbolized by drawing a dot. A **line** is determined by two distinct points and extends indefinitely in both directions, as the arrows on the line at the right indicate. This line contains points A and B and is represented by $\overleftrightarrow{AB}$. A line can also be represented by a single letter, such as ℓ.

A **ray** starts at a point and extends indefinitely in *one* direction. The point at which a ray starts is called the **endpoint** of the ray. The ray shown at the right is denoted $\overrightarrow{AB}$. Point A is the endpoint of the ray.

A **line segment** is part of a line and has two endpoints. The line segment shown at the right is denoted by $\overline{AB}$.

QUESTION   *Classify each diagram as a line, a ray, or a line segment.*

a.   E ——————→ F

b.   C —————— D

c.   ←—— J —— K ——→

The distance between the endpoints of $\overline{AC}$ is denoted by AC. If B is a point on $\overline{AC}$, then AC (the distance from A to C) is the sum of AB (the distance from A to B) and BC (the distance from B to C).

$$AC = AB + BC$$

ANSWER   **a.** *Ray*   **b.** *Line segment*   **c.** *Line*

Given $AB = 22$ cm and $BC = 13$ cm, find AC.

Make a drawing and write an equation to represent the distances between the points on the line segment.

Substitute the given distances for AB and BC into the equation. Solve for AC.

$$AB + BC = AC$$
$$22 + 13 = AC$$
$$35 = AC$$
$$AC = 35 \text{ cm}$$

EXAMPLE 1 ■ Find a Distance on a Line Segment

Given $MN = 14$ mm, $NO = 17$ mm, and $OP = 15$ mm on $\overline{MP}$, find MP.

Solution

• Make a drawing.

$$MN + NO + OP = MP$$
• Write an equation to represent the distances on the line segment.

$$14 + 17 + 15 = MP$$
• Replace *MN* by **14**, *NO* by **17**, and *OP* by **15**.

$$46 = MP$$
• Solve for *MP*.

$MP = 46$ mm

CHECK YOUR PROGRESS 1   Given $QR = 28$ cm, $RS = 16$ cm, and $ST = 10$ cm on $\overline{QT}$, find QT.

Solution   *See page S29.*

EXAMPLE 2 ■ Use an Equation to Find a Distance on a Line Segment

X, Y, and Z are all on line ℓ. Given $XY = 9$ m and YZ is twice XY, find XZ.

Solution

$$XZ = XY + YZ$$
$$XZ = XY + 2(XY)$$
• *YZ* is twice *XY*.
$$XZ = 9 + 2(9)$$
• Replace *XY* by 9.
$$XZ = 9 + 18$$
• Solve for *XZ*.
$$XZ = 27$$

$XZ = 27$ m

CHECK YOUR PROGRESS 2   *A*, *B*, and *C* are all on line ℓ. Given $BC = 16$ ft and $AB = \frac{1}{4}(BC)$, find *AC*.

Solution   *See page S29.*

In this section, we are discussing figures that lie in a plane. A **plane** is a flat surface with no thickness and no boundaries. It can be pictured as a desktop or blackboard that extends forever. Figures that lie in a plane are called **plane figures.**

Lines in a plane can be intersecting or parallel. **Intersecting lines** cross at a point in the plane.

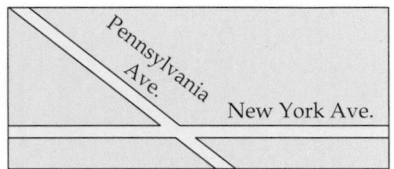

Parallel lines never intersect. The distance between them is always the same.

The symbol $\parallel$ means "is parallel to." In the figure at the right, $j \parallel k$ and $\overline{AB} \parallel \overline{CD}$. Note that *j* contains $\overline{AB}$ and *k* contains $\overline{CD}$. Parallel lines contain parallel line segments.

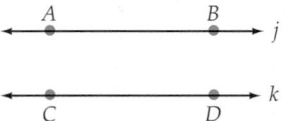

An **angle** is formed by two rays with the same endpoint. The **vertex** of the angle is the point at which the two rays meet. The rays are called the **sides** of the angle.

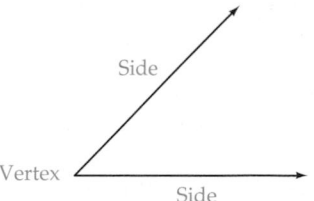

If *A* is a point on one ray of an angle, *C* is a point on the other ray, and *B* is the vertex, then the angle is called $\angle B$ or $\angle ABC$, where $\angle$ is the symbol for angle. Note that an angle can be named by the vertex, or by giving three points, where the second point listed is the vertex. $\angle ABC$ could also be called $\angle CBA$.

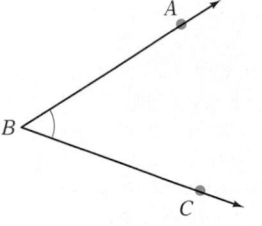

An angle can also be named by a variable written between the rays close to the vertex.

In the figure at the right, $\angle x$ and $\angle QRS$ are two different names for the same angle. $\angle y$ and $\angle SRT$ are two different names for the same angle. Note that in this figure, more than two rays meet at R. In this case, the vertex alone cannot be used to name $\angle QRT$.

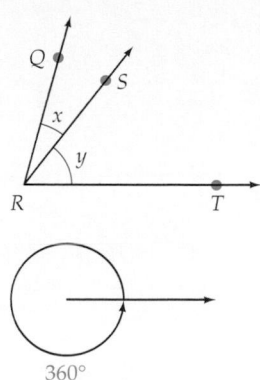

historical note

The Babylonians knew that Earth was in approximately the same position in the sky every 365 days. Historians suggest that the reason one complete revolution of a circle is 360° is that 360 is the closest number to 365 that is divisible by many natural numbers. ∎

An angle is often measured in **degrees.** The symbol for degrees is a small raised circle, °. The angle formed by rotating a ray through a complete circle has a measure of 360°.

360°

A **protractor** is often used to measure an angle. Place the line segment near the bottom edge of the protractor on BC as shown in the figure below. Make sure the center of the line segment on the protractor is directly over the vertex. $\angle ABC$ shown in the figure below measures 58°.

A 90° angle is called a **right angle.** The symbol ∟ represents a right angle.

90°

Perpendicular lines are intersecting lines that form right angles.

▼ **point of interest**

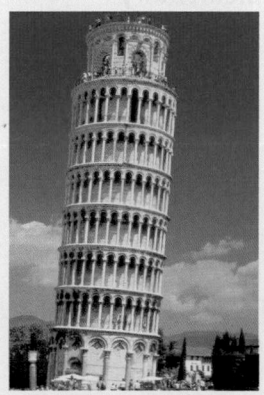

The Leaning Tower of Pisa is the bell tower of the Cathedral in Pisa, Italy. Its construction began on August 9, 1173 and continued for about 200 years. The Tower was designed to be vertical, but it started to lean during its construction. By 1350 it was 2.5° off from the vertical; by 1817, it was 5.1° off; and by 1990, it was 5.5° off. In 2001, work on the structure that returned its list to 5° was completed. (*Source: Time* magazine, June 25, 2001, pp. 34–35.)

The symbol $\perp$ means "is perpendicular to." In the figure at the right, $p \perp q$ and $\overline{AB} \perp \overline{CD}$. Note that line p contains $\overline{AB}$ and line q contains $\overline{CD}$. Perpendicular lines contain perpendicular line segments.

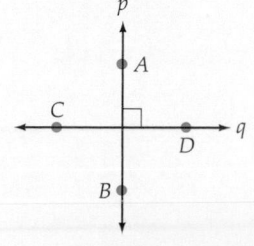

A **straight angle** is an angle whose measure is 180°. ∠AOB is a straight angle.

Straight angle

Complementary angles are two angles whose measures have the sum 90°.

∠A and ∠B at the right are complementary angles.

Supplementary angles are two angles whose measures have the sum 180°.

∠C and ∠D at the right are supplementary angles.

An **acute angle** is an angle whose measure is between 0° and 90°. ∠D above is an acute angle. An **obtuse angle** is an angle whose measure is between 90° and 180°. ∠C above is an obtuse angle.

The measure of ∠C is 110°. This is often written as $m\angle C = 110°$, where m is an abbreviation for "the measure of." This notation is used in Example 3.

EXAMPLE 3 ■ Determine If Two Angles are Complementary

Are angles E and F complementary angles?

Solution

$$m\angle E + m\angle F = 38° + 46° = 84°$$

The sum of the measures of ∠E and ∠F is not 90°. Therefore, angles E and F are not complementary angles.

CHECK YOUR PROGRESS 3 Are angles G and H supplementary angles?

Solution See page S29.

EXAMPLE 4 ■ Find the Measure of the Complement of an Angle

Find the measure of the complement of a 38° angle.

Solution

Complementary angles are two angles the sum of whose measures is 90°.
To find the measure of the complement, let x represent the complement of a 38° angle.
Write an equation and solve for x.

$$x + 38° = 90°$$
$$x = 52°$$

CHECK YOUR PROGRESS 4   Find the measure of the supplement of a 129° angle.

Solution   *See page S29.*

Adjacent angles are two angles that have a common vertex and a common side but have no interior points in common. In the figure at the right, $\angle DAC$ and $\angle CAB$ are adjacent angles.

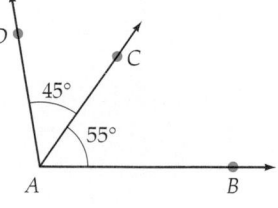

$$m\angle DAC = 45° \text{ and } m\angle CAB = 55°.$$
$$m\angle DAB = m\angle DAC + m\angle CAB$$
$$= 45° + 55° = 100°$$

In the figure at the right, $m\angle EDG = 80°$. The measure of $\angle FDG$ is three times the measure of $\angle EDF$. Find the measure of $\angle EDF$.

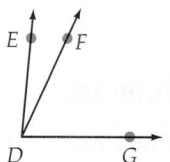

Let x = the measure of $\angle EDF$.
Then $3x$ = the measure of $\angle FDG$.
Write an equation and solve for x.

$$m\angle EDF + m\angle FDG = m\angle EDG$$
$$x + 3x = 80°$$
$$4x = 80°$$
$$x = 20°$$

$$m\angle EDF = 20°$$

EXAMPLE 5 ■ Solve a Problem Involving Adjacent Angles

Find the measure of $\angle x$.

Solution

To find the measure of $\angle x$, write an equation using the fact that the sum of the measures of $\angle x$ and 47° is 90°. Solve for $m\angle x$.

$$m\angle x + 47° = 90°$$
$$m\angle x = 43°$$

CHECK YOUR PROGRESS 5   Find the measure of $\angle a$.

Solution   *See page S29.*

Angles Formed by Intersecting Lines

Four angles are formed by the intersection of two lines. If the two lines are perpendicular, each of the four angles is a right angle.

If the two lines are not perpendicular, then two of the angles formed are acute angles and two of the angles formed are obtuse angles. The two acute angles are always opposite each other, and the two obtuse angles are always opposite each other.

In the figure at the right, $\angle w$ and $\angle y$ are acute angles. $\angle x$ and $\angle z$ are obtuse angles.

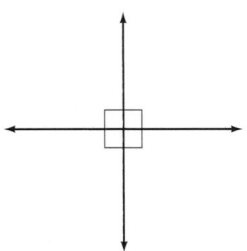

Two angles that are on opposite sides of the intersection of two lines are called **vertical angles.** Vertical angles have the same measure. $\angle w$ and $\angle y$ are vertical angles. $\angle x$ and $\angle z$ are vertical angles.

Recall that two angles that have a common vertex and a common side, but have no interior points in common, are called adjacent angles. For the figure shown above, $\angle x$ and $\angle y$ are adjacent angles, as are $\angle y$ and $\angle z$, $\angle z$ and $\angle w$, and $\angle w$ and $\angle x$. Adjacent angles of intersecting lines are supplementary angles.

Vertical angles have the same measure.

$$m\angle w = m\angle y$$
$$m\angle x = m\angle z$$

Adjacent angles formed by intersecting lines are supplementary angles.

$$m\angle x + m\angle y = 180°$$
$$m\angle y + m\angle z = 180°$$
$$m\angle z + m\angle w = 180°$$
$$m\angle w + m\angle x = 180°$$

EXAMPLE 6 ■ Solve a Problem Involving Intersecting Lines

In the diagram at the right, $m\angle b = 115°$. Find the measures of angles a, c, and d.

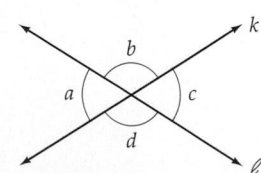

Solution

$m \angle a + m \angle b = 180°$ • $\angle a$ is supplementary to $\angle b$ because $\angle a$ and $\angle b$ are adjacent angles of intersecting lines.

$m \angle a + 115° = 180°$ • Replace $m \angle b$ with **115°**.

$\qquad m \angle a = 65°$ • Subtract 115° from each side of the equation.

$m \angle c = 65°$ • $m \angle c = m \angle a$ because $\angle c$ and $\angle a$ are vertical angles.

$m \angle d = 115°$ • $m \angle d = m \angle b$ because $\angle d$ and $\angle b$ are vertical angles.

$m \angle a = 65°$, $m \angle c = 65°$, and $m \angle d = 115°$.

CHECK YOUR PROGRESS 6

In the diagram at the right, $m \angle a = 35°$. Find the measures of angles b, c, and d.

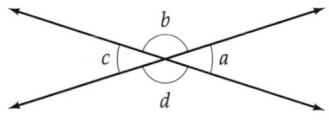

Solution   *See page S29.*

A line that intersects two other lines at different points is called a **transversal.**

If the lines cut by a transversal t are parallel lines and the transversal is perpendicular to the parallel lines, all eight angles formed are right angles.

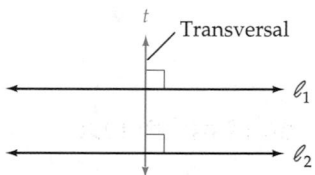

If the lines cut by a transversal t are parallel lines and the transversal is *not* perpendicular to the parallel lines, all four acute angles have the same measure and all four obtuse angles have the same measure. For the figure at the right:

$$m \angle b = m \angle d = m \angle x = m \angle z$$
$$m \angle a = m \angle c = m \angle w = m \angle y$$

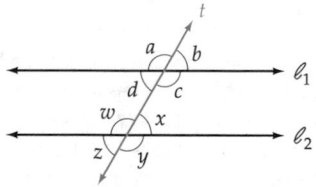

If two lines in a plane are cut by a transversal, then any two non-adjacent angles that are on opposite sides of the transversal and between the parallel lines are **alternate interior angles.** In the figure above, $\angle c$ and $\angle w$ are alternate interior angles; $\angle d$ and $\angle x$ are alternate interior angles. Alternate interior angles formed by two parallel lines cut by a transversal have the same measure.

If two lines in a plane are cut by a transversal, then any two non-adjacent angles that are on opposite sides of the transversal and outside the parallel lines are **alternate exterior angles.** In the figure at the top of the following page,

Two alternate interior angles formed by two parallel lines cut by a transversal have the same measure.

$$m \angle c = m \angle w$$
$$m \angle d = m \angle x$$

Two alternate exterior angles formed by two parallel lines cut by a transversal have the same measure.

$$m\angle a = m\angle y$$
$$m\angle b = m\angle z$$

$\angle a$ and $\angle y$ are alternate exterior angles; $\angle b$ and $\angle z$ are alternate exterior angles. Alternate exterior angles formed by two parallel lines cut by a transversal have the same measure.

If two lines in a plane are cut by a transversal, then any two angles that are on the same side of the transversal and are both acute angles or both obtuse angles are **corresponding angles.** For the figure at the right above, the following pairs of angles are corresponding angles: $\angle a$ and $\angle w$, $\angle d$ and $\angle z$, $\angle b$ and $\angle x$, $\angle c$ and $\angle y$. Corresponding angles formed by two parallel lines cut by a transversal have the same measure.

Two corresponding angles formed by two parallel lines cut by a transversal have the same measure.

$$m\angle a = m\angle w$$
$$m\angle d = m\angle z$$
$$m\angle b = m\angle x$$
$$m\angle c = m\angle y$$

QUESTION   Which angles in the diagram at the right above have the same measure as angle a? Which angles have the same measure as angle b?

EXAMPLE 7 ■ Solve a Problem Involving Parallel Lines Cut by a Transversal

In the diagram at the right, $\ell_1 \| \ell_2$ and $m\angle f = 58°$. Find the measures of $\angle a$, $\angle c$, and $\angle d$.

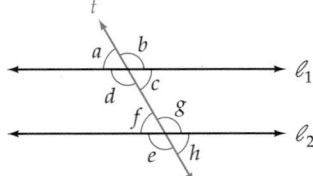

Solution

$m\angle a = m\angle f = 58°$ • $\angle a$ and $\angle f$ are corresponding angles.

$m\angle c = m\angle f = 58°$ • $\angle c$ and $\angle f$ are alternate interior angles.

$m\angle d + m\angle a = 180°$ • $\angle d$ is supplementary to $\angle a$.
$\quad\; m\angle d + 58° = 180°$ • Replace $m\angle a$ with **58°**.
$\qquad\qquad m\angle d = 122°$ • Subtract 58° from each side of the equation.

$m\angle a = 58°$, $m\angle c = 58°$, and $m\angle d = 122°$.

ANSWER   *Angles c, w, and y have the same measure as angle a. Angles d, x, and z have the same measure as angle b.*

CHECK YOUR PROGRESS 7

In the diagram at the right, $\ell_1 \parallel \ell_2$ and $m\angle g = 124°$. Find the measures of $\angle b$, $\angle c$, and $\angle d$.

Solution   *See page S29.*

Math Matters   The Principle of Reflection

When a ray of light hits a flat surface, such as a mirror, the light is reflected at the same angle at which it hit the surface. For example, in the diagram at the left, $m\angle x = m\angle y$.

This principle of reflection is in operation in a simple periscope. In a periscope light is reflected twice, with the result that light rays entering the periscope are parallel to the light rays at eye level.

The same principle is in operation on a billiard table. Assuming it has no "side spin," a ball bouncing off the side of the table will bounce off at the same angle at which it hit the side. In the figure below, $m\angle w = m\angle x$ and $m\angle y = m\angle z$.

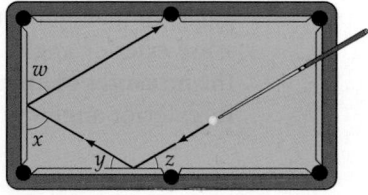

In the miniature golf shot illustrated below, $m\angle w = m\angle x$ and $m\angle y = m\angle z$.

Angles of a Triangle

If the lines cut by a transversal are not parallel lines, the three lines will intersect at three points. In the figure at the right, the transversal t intersects lines p and q. The three lines intersect at points A, B, and C. These three points define three line segments, $\overline{AB}$, $\overline{BC}$, and $\overline{AC}$. The plane figure formed by these three line segments is called a **triangle.**

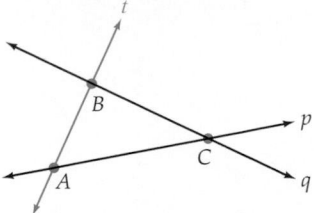

Each of the three points of intersection is the vertex of four angles. The angles within the region enclosed by the triangle are called **interior angles.** In the figure at the right, angles a, b, and c are interior angles. The sum of the measures of the interior angles of a triangle is 180°.

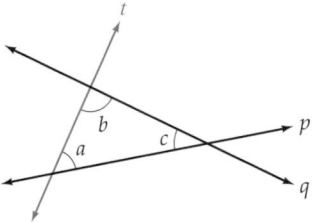

$$m\angle a + m\angle b + m\angle c = 180°$$

The Sum of the Measures of the Interior Angles of a Triangle

The sum of the measures of the interior angles of a triangle is 180°.

QUESTION   *Can the measures of the three interior angles of a triangle be 87°, 51°, and 43°?*

An **exterior angle of a triangle** is an angle which is adjacent to an interior angle of the triangle and is a supplement of the interior angle. In the figure at the right, angles m and n are exterior angles for angle a. **The sum of the measures of an interior angle and one of its exterior angles is 180°.**

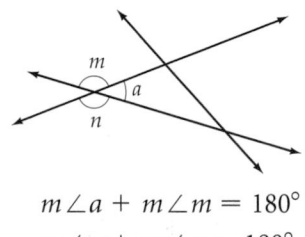

$$m\angle a + m\angle m = 180°$$
$$m\angle a + m\angle n = 180°$$

EXAMPLE 8 ■ Solve a Problem Involving the Angles of a Triangle

In the diagram at the right, $m\angle c = 40°$ and $m\angle e = 60°$. Find the measure of $\angle d$.

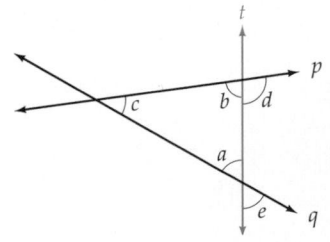

ANSWER   *No, because 87° + 51° + 43° = 181°, and the sum of the measures of the three interior angles of a triangle must be 180°.*

Solution

$m\angle a = m\angle e = 60°$ • $\angle a$ and $\angle e$ are vertical angles.

$m\angle c + m\angle a + m\angle b = 180°$ • The sum of the interior angles is **180°**.
$\quad 40° + 60° + m\angle b = 180°$ • Replace $m\angle c$ with **40°** and $m\angle a$ with **60°**.
$\qquad\quad 100° + m\angle b = 180°$ • Add $40° + 60°$.
$\qquad\qquad\qquad m\angle b = 80°$ • Subtract 100° from each side of the equation.

$m\angle b + m\angle d = 180°$ • $\angle b$ and $\angle d$ are supplementary angles.
$\quad 80° + m\angle d = 180°$ • Replace $m\angle b$ with **80°**.
$\qquad\qquad m\angle d = 100°$ • Subtract 80° from each side of the equation.

$m\angle d = 100°$

CHECK YOUR PROGRESS 8

In the diagram at the right, $m\angle c = 35°$ and $m\angle d = 105°$. Find the measure of $\angle e$.

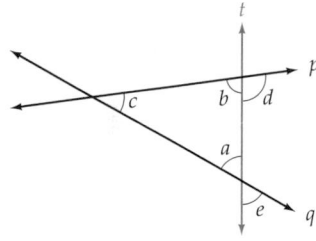

Solution   *See page S29.*

EXAMPLE 9 ■ Find the Measure of the Third Angle of a Triangle

Two angles of a triangle measure 43° and 86°. Find the measure of the third angle.

Solution

Use the fact that the sum of the measures of the interior angles of a triangle is 180°. Write an equation using x to represent the measure of the third angle. Solve the equation for x.

$x + 43° + 86° = 180°$
$\quad x + 129° = 180°$ • Add $43° + 86°$.
$\qquad\qquad x = 51°$ • Subtract 129° from each side of the equation.

The measure of the third angle is 51°.

CHECK YOUR PROGRESS 9   One angle in a triangle is a right angle, and one angle measures 27°. Find the measure of the third angle.

Solution   *See page S29.*

Excursion

Preparing a Circle Graph

On page 453, a protractor was used to measure angles. Preparing a circle graph requires the ability to use a protractor to draw angles.

To draw an angle of 142°, first draw a ray. Place a dot at the endpoint of the ray. This dot will be the vertex of the angle.

Place the line segment near the bottom edge of the protractor on the ray as shown in the figure at the right. Make sure the center of the bottom edge of the protractor is located directly over the vertex point. Locate the position of the 142° mark. Place a dot next to the mark.

Remove the protractor and draw a ray from the vertex to the dot at the 142° mark.

Here is an example of how to prepare a circle graph.

The revenues (in thousands of dollars) from four segments of a car dealership for the first quarter of a recent year were

New car sales:	$2100	Used car/truck sales:	$1500
New truck sales:	$1200	Parts/service:	$700

To draw a circle graph to represent the percent that each segment contributed to the total revenue from all four segments, proceed as follows:

Find the total revenue from all four segments.

$$2100 + 1200 + 1500 + 700 = 5500$$

Find what percent each segment is of the total revenue of $5500 thousand.

New car sales: $\dfrac{2100}{5500} \approx 38.2\%$

New truck sales: $\dfrac{1200}{5500} \approx 21.8\%$

Used car/truck sales: $\dfrac{1500}{5500} \approx 27.3\%$

Parts/service: $\dfrac{700}{5500} \approx 12.7\%$

(continued)

Each percent represents the part of the circle for that sector. Because the circle contains 360°, multiply each percent by 360° to find the measure of the angle for each sector. Round to the nearest degree.

New car sales: $0.382 \times 360° \approx 138°$
New truck sales: $0.218 \times 360° \approx 78°$
Used car/truck sales: $0.273 \times 360° \approx 98°$
Parts/service: $0.127 \times 360° \approx 46°$

Draw a circle and use a protractor to draw the sectors representing the percents that each segment contributed to the total revenue from all four segments.

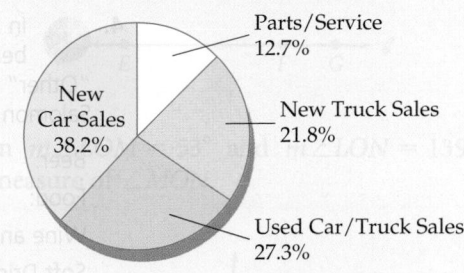

Parts/Service
12.7%

New Car Sales 38.2%

New Truck Sales 21.8%

Used Car/Truck Sales 27.3%

Excursion Exercises

Prepare a circle graph for the data provided in each exercise.

1. Shown below are American adults' favorite pizza toppings. (*Source:* Market Facts for Bolla wines)

Pepperoni:	43%
Sausage:	19%
Mushrooms:	14%
Vegetables:	13%
Other:	7%
Onions:	4%

2. According to a Pathfinder Research Group survey, more than 94% of American adults have heard of the Three Stooges. The choices of a favorite among those who have one are

Curly:	52%
Moe:	31%
Larry:	12%
Curly Joe:	3%
Shemp:	2%

(continued)

29.

30.

In Exercises 31–34, find the measure of ∠*a*.

31.

32.

33.

34.

In Exercises 35–40, find the value of *x*.

35.

36.

37.

38.

39.

40.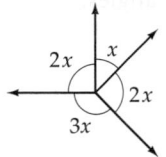

41. Given $m\angle a = 51°$, find the measure of ∠*b*.

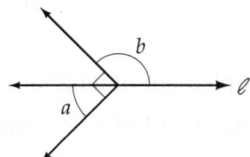

42. Given $m\angle a = 38°$, find the measure of ∠*b*.

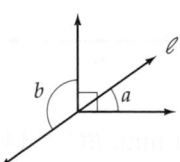

In Exercises 43 and 44, find the measure of ∠*x*.

43.

44.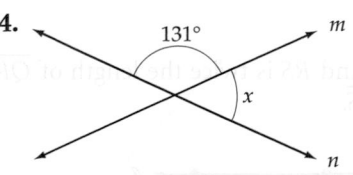

In Exercises 45 and 46, find the value of *x*.

45.

46.

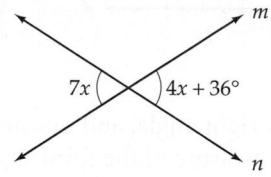

In Exercises 47–50, given that $\ell_1 \parallel \ell_2$, find the measures of angles *a* and *b*.

47.

48.

49.

50.

In Exercises 51–54, given that $\ell_1 \parallel \ell_2$, find *x*.

51.

52.

53.

54.

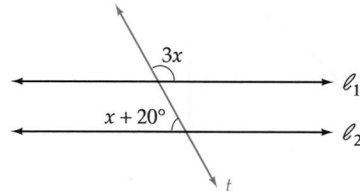

55. Given that $m\angle a = 95°$ and $m\angle b = 70°$, find the measures of angles *x* and *y*.

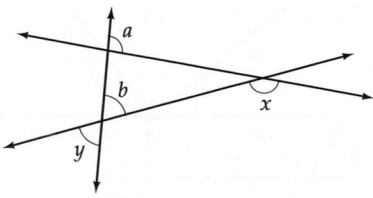

56. Given that $m\angle a = 35°$ and $m\angle b = 55°$, find the measures of angles *x* and *y*.

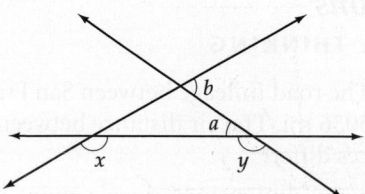

57. Given that $m \angle y = 45°$, find the measures of angles a and b.

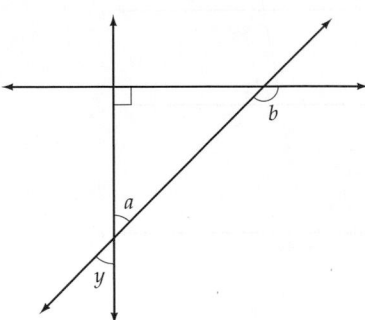

58. Given that $m \angle y = 130°$, find the measures of angles a and b.

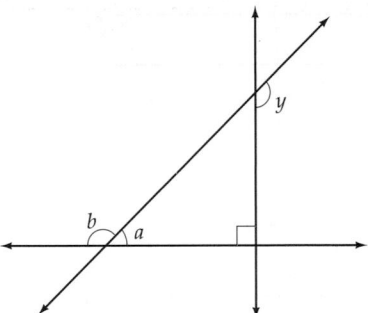

59. Given that $\overline{AO} \perp \overline{OB}$, express in terms of x the number of degrees in $\angle BOC$.

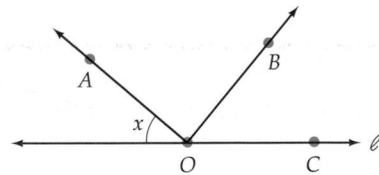

60. Given that $\overline{AO} \perp \overline{OB}$, express in terms of x the number of degrees in $\angle AOC$.

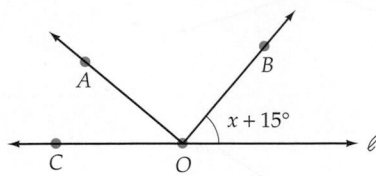

61. One angle in a triangle is a right angle, and one angle is equal to 30°. What is the measure of the third angle?

62. A triangle has a 45° angle and a right angle. Find the measure of the third angle.

63. Two angles of a triangle measure 42° and 103°. Find the measure of the third angle.

64. Two angles of a triangle measure 62° and 45°. Find the measure of the third angle.

65. A triangle has a 13° angle and a 65° angle. What is the measure of the third angle?

66. A triangle has a 105° angle and a 32° angle. What is the measure of the third angle?

67. Cut out a triangle and then tear off two of the angles, as shown below. Position the pieces you tore off so that angle a is adjacent to angle b and angle c is adjacent to angle b. Describe what you observe. What does this demonstrate?

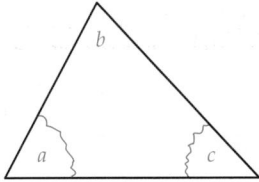

Extensions

CRITICAL THINKING

68. The road mileage between San Francisco, California and New York City is 3036 mi. The air distance between these two cities is 2571 mi. Why do the distances differ?

69. How many dimensions does a point have? a line? a line segment? a ray? an angle?

70. Which line segment is longer, $\overline{AB}$ or $\overline{CD}$?

COOPERATIVE LEARNING

71. For the figure at the right, find the sum of the measures of angles x, y, and z.

72. For the figure at the right, explain why $m\angle a + m\angle b = m\angle x$. Write a rule that describes the relationship between the measure of an exterior angle of a triangle and the sum of the measures of its two opposite interior angles (the interior angles that are non-adjacent to the exterior angle). Use the rule to write an equation involving angles a, c, and z.

73. If $\overline{AB}$ and $\overline{CD}$ intersect at point O, and $m\angle AOC = m\angle BOC$, explain why $\overline{AB} \perp \overline{CD}$.

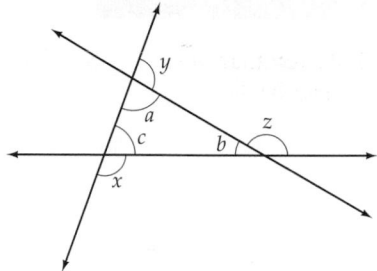

SECTION 8.2 | # Perimeter and Area of Plane Figures

Perimeter of Plane Geometric Figures

A **polygon** is a closed figure determined by three or more line segments that lie in a plane. The line segments that form the polygon are called its **sides.** The figures below are examples of polygons.

▼ **point of interest**

Although a polygon is described in terms of the number of its sides, the word actually comes from the Latin word *polygonum,* meaning "many *angles.*"

A   B   C   D   E

A **regular polygon** is one in which each side has the same length and each angle has the same measure. The polygons in Figures A, C, and D above are regular polygons.

The name of a polygon is based on the number of its sides. The table below lists the names of polygons that have from 3 to 10 sides.

Number of Sides	Name of Polygon
3	Triangle
4	Quadrilateral
5	Pentagon
6	Hexagon
7	Heptagon
8	Octagon
9	Nonagon
10	Decagon

The Pentagon in
Arlington, Virginia

Triangles and quadrilaterals are two of the most common types of polygons. Triangles are distinguished by the number of equal sides and also by the measures of their angles.

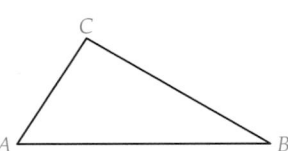

An **isosceles triangle** has exactly two sides of equal length. The angles opposite the equal sides are of equal measure.
$AC = BC$
$m\angle A = m\angle B$

The three sides of an **equilateral triangle** are of equal length. The three angles are of equal measure.
$AB = BC = AC$
$m\angle A = m\angle B$
$\quad\quad = m\angle C$

A **scalene triangle** has no two sides of equal length. No two angles are of equal measure.

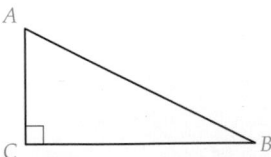

An **acute triangle** has three acute angles.

An **obtuse triangle** has one obtuse angle.

A **right triangle** has a right angle.

A **quadrilateral** is a four-sided polygon. Quadrilaterals are also distinguished by their sides and angles, as shown on the following page. Note that a rectangle, a square, and a rhombus are different forms of a parallelogram.

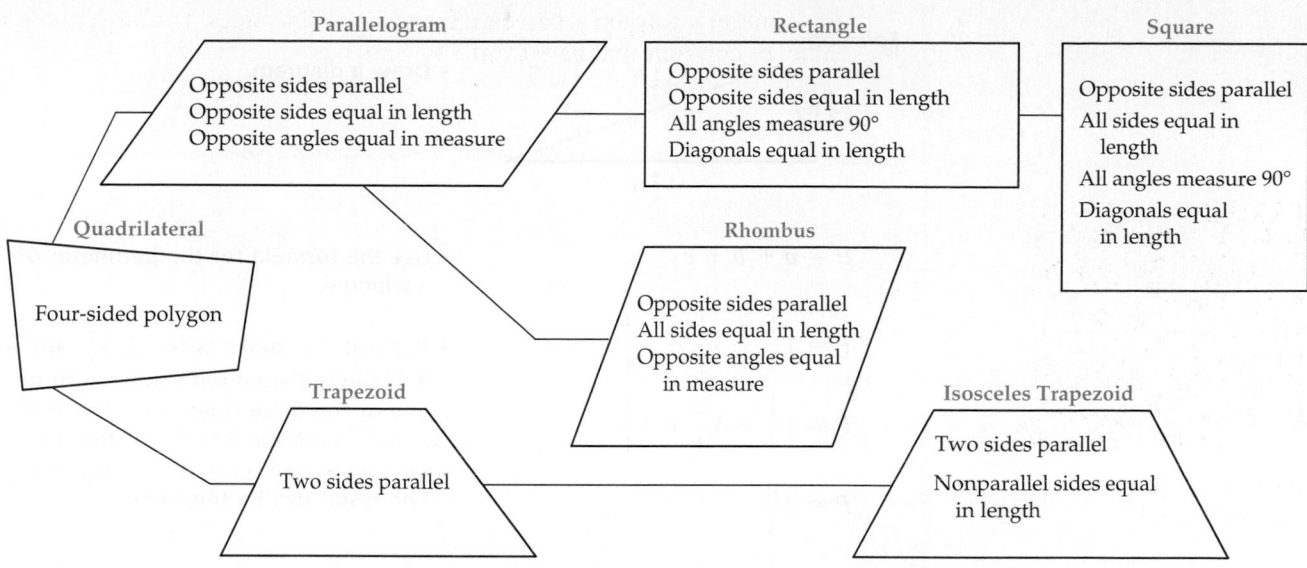

QUESTION   ***a.*** *What distinguishes a rectangle from other parallelograms?*

   b. *What distinguishes a square from other rectangles?*

The **perimeter** of a plane geometric figure is a measure of the distance around the figure. Perimeter is used when buying fencing for a garden or determining how much baseboard is needed for a room.

The perimeter of a triangle is the sum of the lengths of the three sides.

Perimeter of a Triangle

Let a, b, and c be the lengths of the sides of a triangle. The perimeter, P, of the triangle is given by $P = a + b + c$.

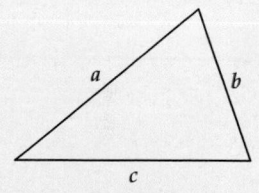

$$P = a + b + c$$

To find the perimeter of the triangle shown at the right, add the lengths of the three sides.

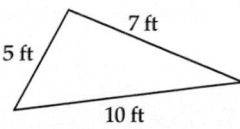

$$P = 5 + 7 + 10 = 22$$

The perimeter is 22 ft.

EXAMPLE 1 ■ Find the Perimeter of a Triangle

You want to sew bias binding along the edges of a cloth flag that has sides that measure $1\frac{1}{4}$ ft, $3\frac{1}{2}$ ft, and $3\frac{3}{4}$ ft. Find the length of bias binding needed.

ANSWER   ***a.*** *In a rectangle, all angles measure 90°.* ***b.*** *In a square, all sides are equal in length.*

Solution

• Draw a diagram.

$$P = a + b + c$$

• Use the formula for the perimeter of a triangle.

$$P = 1\frac{1}{4} + 3\frac{1}{2} + 3\frac{3}{4}$$

$$P = 1\frac{1}{4} + 3\frac{2}{4} + 3\frac{3}{4}$$

$$P = 7\frac{6}{4}$$

$$P = 8\frac{1}{2}$$

• Replace a, b, and c with $1\frac{1}{4}$, $3\frac{1}{2}$, and $3\frac{3}{4}$. You can replace a with the length of any of the three sides, and then replace b and c with the lengths of the other two sides. The order does not matter. The result will be the same.

• $7\frac{6}{4} = 7\frac{3}{2} = 7 + \frac{3}{2} = 7 + 1\frac{1}{2} = 8\frac{1}{2}$

You need $8\frac{1}{2}$ ft of bias binding.

CHECK YOUR PROGRESS 1   A bicycle trail in the shape of a triangle has sides that measure $4\frac{3}{10}$ mi, $2\frac{1}{10}$ mi, and $6\frac{1}{2}$ mi. Find the total length of the bike trail.

Solution   See page S29.

The perimeter of a quadrilateral is the sum of the lengths of its four sides.

A **rectangle** is a quadrilateral with all right angles and opposite sides of equal length. Usually the length, L, of a rectangle refers to the length of one of the longer sides of the rectangle and the width, W, refers to the length of one of the shorter sides. The perimeter can then be represented as
$P = L + W + L + W$.

The formula for the perimeter of a rectangle is derived by combining like terms.

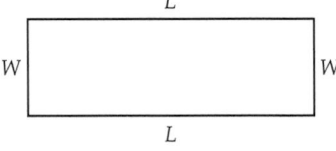

$$P = L + W + L + W$$
$$P = 2L + 2W$$

Perimeter of a Rectangle

Let L represent the length and W the width of a rectangle. The perimeter, P, of the rectangle is given by $P = 2L + 2W$.

EXAMPLE 2 ■ Find the Perimeter of a Rectangle

You want to trim a rectangular frame with a metal strip. The frame measures 30 in. by 20 in. Find the length of metal strip you will need to trim the frame.

Solution

• **Draw a diagram.**

$P = 2L + 2W$

• **Use the formula for the perimeter of a rectangle.**

$P = 2(30) + 2(20)$

• **The length is 30 in. Substitute 30 for** *L*. **The width is 20 in. Substitute 20 for** *W*.

$P = 60 + 40$

$P = 100$

You will need 100 in. of the metal strip.

CHECK YOUR PROGRESS 2   Find the length of decorative molding needed to edge the top of the walls in a rectangular room that is 12 ft long and 8 ft wide.

Solution   *See page S29.*

A **square** is a rectangle in which each side has the same length. Letting *s* represent the length of each side of a square, the perimeter of the square can be represented $P = s + s + s + s$.

The formula for the perimeter of a square is derived by combining like terms.

$P = s + s + s + s$

$P = 4s$

Perimeter of a Square

Let *s* represent the length of a side of a square. The perimeter, *P*, of the square is given by $P = 4s$.

EXAMPLE 3 ■ Find the Perimeter of a Square

Find the length of fencing needed to surround a square corral that measures 60 ft on each side.

Solution

• **Draw a diagram.**

$P = 4s$

• **Use the formula for the perimeter of a square.**

$P = 4(60)$

• **The length of a side is 60 ft. Substitute 60 for** *s*.

$P = 240$

240 ft of fencing is needed.

CHECK YOUR PROGRESS 3 A homeowner plans to fence in the area around the swimming pool in the back yard. The area to be fenced in is a square measuring 24 ft on each side. How many feet of fencing should the homeowner purchase?

Solution See page S30.

Figure $ABCD$ is a parallelogram. $\overline{BC}$ is the **base** of the parallelogram. Opposite sides of a parallelogram are equal in length, so $\overline{AD}$ is the same length as $\overline{BC}$, and $\overline{AB}$ is the same length as $\overline{CD}$.

Let b represent the length of the base and s the length of an adjacent side. Then the perimeter of a parallelogram can be represented as $P = b + s + b + s$.

$$P = b + s + b + s$$

The formula for the perimeter of a parallelogram is derived by combining like terms.

$$P = 2b + 2s$$

Perimeter of a Parallelogram

Let b represent the length of the base of a parallelogram and s the length of a side adjacent to the base. The perimeter, P, of the parallelogram is given by $P = 2b + 2s$.

EXAMPLE 4 ■ Find the Perimeter of a Parallelogram

You plan to trim the edge of a kite with a strip of red fabric. The kite is in the shape of a parallelogram with a base measuring 40 in. and a side measuring 28 in. Find the length of the fabric needed to trim the kite.

Solution

• Draw a diagram.

$$P = 2b + 2s$$

• Use the formula for the perimeter of a parallelogram.

$$P = 2(40) + 2(28)$$

• The base is **40** in. Substitute **40** for *b*. The length of a side is **28** in. Substitute **28** for *s*.

$$P = 80 + 56$$

• Simplify using the Order of Operations Agreement.

$$P = 136$$

To trim the kite, 136 in. of fabric is needed.

CHECK YOUR PROGRESS 4 A flower bed is in the shape of a parallelogram that has a base of length 5 m and a side of length 7 m. Wooden planks are used to edge the garden. Find the length of wooden planks needed to surround the garden.

Solution See page S30.

A **circle** is a plane figure in which all points are the same distance from point O, called the **center** of the circle.

A **diameter** of a circle is a line segment with endpoints on the circle and passing through the center. $\overline{AB}$ is a diameter of the circle at the right. The variable d is used to designate the length of a diameter of a circle.

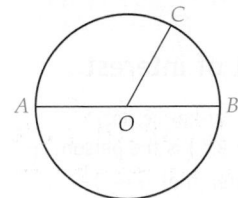

A **radius** of a circle is a line segment from the center of the circle to a point on the circle. $\overline{OC}$ is a radius of the circle at the right above. The variable r is used to designate the length of a radius of a circle.

The length of the diameter is twice the length of the radius.

$$d = 2r \quad \text{or} \quad r = \frac{1}{2}d$$

The distance around a circle is called the **circumference.** The formula for the circumference, C, of a circle is:

$$C = \pi d$$

Because $d = 2r$, the formula for the circumference can be written:

$$C = 2\pi r$$

> ### Circumference of a Circle
>
> The circumference, C, of a circle with diameter d and radius r is given by $C = \pi d$ or $C = 2\pi r$.

✔ TAKE NOTE

Recall that an irrational number is a number whose decimal representation never terminates and does not have a pattern of numerals that keep repeating.

The formula for circumference uses the number π (pi), which is an irrational number. The value of π can be approximated by a fraction or by a decimal.

$$\pi \approx 3\frac{1}{7} \quad \text{or} \quad \pi \approx 3.14$$

The π key on a scientific calculator gives a closer approximation of π than 3.14. A scientific calculator is used in this section to find approximate values in calculations involving π.

Find the circumference of a circle with a diameter of 6 m.

CALCULATOR NOTE

The π key on your calculator can be used to find decimal approximations to expressions that contain π. To perform the calculation at the right, enter

$6 \times \pi =$.

The diameter of the circle is given. Use the circumference formula that involves the diameter. $d = 6$.

$$C = \pi d$$
$$C = \pi(6)$$

The exact circumference of the circle is 6π m.

$$C = 6\pi$$

An approximate measure can be found by using the π key on a calculator.

An approximate circumference is 18.85 m.

$$C \approx 18.85$$

▼ **point of interest**

Archimedes (ar-kə-mē′dēz)
(c. 287–212 B.C.) is the person
who calculated that $\pi \approx 3\frac{1}{7}$.
He actually showed that
$3\frac{10}{71} < \pi < 3\frac{1}{7}$. The
approximation $3\frac{10}{71}$ is a more
accurate approximation of π
than $3\frac{1}{7}$, but it is more difficult
to use without a calculator.

EXAMPLE 5 ■ **Find the Circumference of a Circle**

Find the circumference of a circle with a radius of 15 cm. Round to the nearest hundredth of a centimeter.

Solution

$C = 2\pi r$	• The radius is given. Use the circumference formula that involves the radius.
$C = 2\pi(15)$	• Replace *r* with **15**.
$C = 30\pi$	• Multiply 2 times 15.
$C \approx 94.25$	• An approximation is asked for. Use the π key on a calculator.

The circumference of the circle is approximately 94.25 cm.

CHECK YOUR PROGRESS 5 Find the circumference of a circle with a diameter of 9 km. Give the exact measure.

Solution *See page S30.*

EXAMPLE 6 ■ **Application of Finding the Circumference of a Circle**

A bicycle tire has a diameter of 24 in. How many feet does the bicycle travel when the wheel makes 8 revolutions? Round to the nearest hundredth of a foot.

24 in.

Solution

24 in. = 2 ft	• The diameter is given in inches, but the answer must be expressed in feet. Convert the diameter (24 in.) to feet. There are 12 in. in 1 ft. Divide 24 by 12.
$C = \pi d$	• The diameter is given. Use the circumference formula that involves the diameter.
$C = \pi(2)$	• Replace *d* with **2**.
$C = 2\pi$	• This is the distance traveled in 1 revolution.
$8C = 8(2\pi) = 16\pi \approx 50.27$	• Find the distance traveled in **8 revolutions.**

The bicycle will travel about 50.27 ft when the wheel makes 8 revolutions.

CHECK YOUR PROGRESS 6 A tricycle tire has a diameter of 12 in. How many feet does the tricycle travel when the wheel makes 12 revolutions? Round to the nearest hundredth of a foot.

Solution *See page S30.*

CALCULATOR NOTE

To approximate $8(2\pi)$ on your calculator, enter

8 × 2 × π = .

Area of Plane Geometric Figures

Area is the amount of surface in a region. Area can be used to describe, for example, the size of a rug, a parking lot, a farm, or a national park. Area is measured in square units.

A square that measures 1 inch on each side has an area of 1 square inch, written 1 in^2.

A square that measures 1 centimeter on each side has an area of 1 square centimeter, written 1 cm^2.

1 in^2

1 cm^2

Larger areas are often measured in square feet (ft^2), square meters (m^2), square miles (mi^2), acres ($43{,}560 \text{ ft}^2$), or any other square unit.

QUESTION   **a.** *What is the area of a square that measures 1 yard on each side?*
b. *What is the area of a square that measures 1 kilometer on each side?*

The area of a geometric figure is the number of squares (each of area 1 square unit) that are necessary to cover the figure. In the figures below, two rectangles have been drawn and covered with squares. In the figure on the left, 12 squares, each of area 1 cm^2, were used to cover the rectangle. The area of the rectangle is 12 cm^2. In the figure on the right, six squares, each of area 1 in^2, were used to cover the rectangle. The area of the rectangle is 6 in^2.

4 cm

3 cm

The area of the rectangle is 12 cm^2.

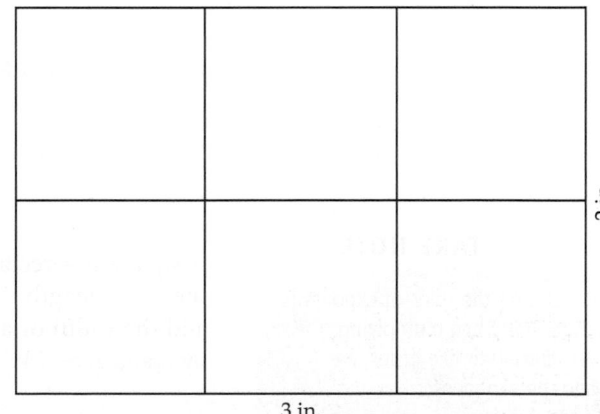

2 in.

3 in.

The area of the rectangle is 6 in^2.

Note from these figures that the area of a rectangle can be found by multiplying the length of the rectangle by its width.

Area of a Rectangle

Let L represent the length and W the width of a rectangle. The area, A, of the rectangle is given by $A = LW$.

QUESTION *How many squares, each 1 inch on a side, are needed to cover a rectangle that has an area of 18 in²?*

EXAMPLE 7 ■ **Find the Area of a Rectangle**

How many square feet of sod are needed to cover a football field? A football field measures 360 ft by 160 ft.

Solution

160 ft

360 ft

• Draw a diagram.

$A = LW$ • Use the formula for the area of a rectangle.

$A = 360(160)$ • The length is **360** ft. Substitute **360** for L. The width is **160** ft. Substitute **160** for W. Remember that LW means "L times W."

$A = 57{,}600$

$57{,}600$ ft² of sod is needed.   • Area is measured in square units.

CHECK YOUR PROGRESS 7   Find the amount of fabric needed to make a rectangular flag that measures 308 cm by 192 cm.

Solution   *See page S30.*

A square is a rectangle in which all sides are the same length. Therefore, both the length and the width of a square can be represented by s, and $A = LW = s \cdot s = s^2$.

s

$A = s \cdot s$

$A = s^2$

Area of a Square

Let s represent the length of a side of a square. The area, A, of the square is given by $A = s^2$.

ANSWER   *18 squares, each 1 inch on a side, are needed to cover the rectangle.*

EXAMPLE 8 ■ Find the Area of a Square

A homeowner wants to carpet the family room. The floor is square and measures 6 m on each side. How much carpet should be purchased?

Solution

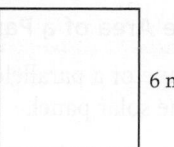

• Draw a diagram.

$A = s^2$

• Use the formula for the area of a square.

$A = 6^2$

• The length of a side is **6** m. Substitute **6** for *s*.

$A = 36$

36 m² of carpet should be purchased.

• Area is measured in square units.

CHECK YOUR PROGRESS 8   Find the area of the floor of a two-car garage that is in the shape of a square that measures 24 ft on a side.

Solution   *See page S30.*

Figure *ABCD* is a parallelogram. $\overline{BC}$ is the **base** of the parallelogram. $\overline{AE}$, perpendicular to the base, is the **height** of the parallelogram.

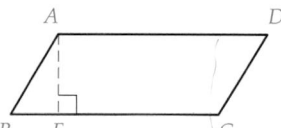

Any side of a parallelogram can be designated as the base. The corresponding height is found by drawing a line segment perpendicular to the base from the opposite side. In the figure at the right, $\overline{CD}$ is the base and $\overline{AE}$ is the height.

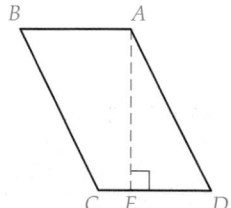

A rectangle can be formed from a parallelogram by cutting a right triangle from one end of the parallelogram and attaching it to the other end. The area of the resulting rectangle will equal the area of the original parallelogram.

Area of a Parallelogram

Let b represent the length of the base and h the height of a parallelogram. The area, A, of the parallelogram is given by $A = bh$.

EXAMPLE 9 ■ Find the Area of a Parallelogram

A solar panel is in the shape of a parallelogram that has a base of 2 ft and a height of 3 ft. Find the area of the solar panel.

Solution

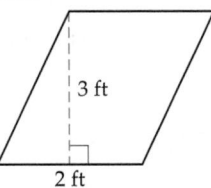

- Draw a diagram.

$A = bh$ — Use the formula for the area of a parallelogram.

$A = 2(3)$ — The base is **2** ft. Substitute **2** for *b*. The height is **3** ft. Substitute **3** for *h*. Remember that *bh* means "*b* times *h*."

$A = 6$

The area is 6 ft². — Area is measured in square units.

CHECK YOUR PROGRESS 9 A fieldstone patio is in the shape of a parallelogram that has a base measuring 14 m and a height measuring 8 m. What is the area of the patio?

Solution See page S30.

Figure ABC is a triangle. $\overline{AB}$ is the **base** of the triangle. $\overline{CD}$, perpendicular to the base, is the **height** of the triangle.

Any side of a triangle can be designated as the base. The corresponding height is found by drawing a line segment perpendicular to the base from the vertex opposite the base.

Consider triangle ABC with base b and height h shown at the right. By extending a line segment from C parallel to the base $\overline{AB}$ and equal in length to the base, a parallelogram is formed. The area of the parallelogram is bh and is twice the area of the original triangle. Therefore, the area of the triangle is one half the area of the parallelogram, or $\frac{1}{2}bh$.

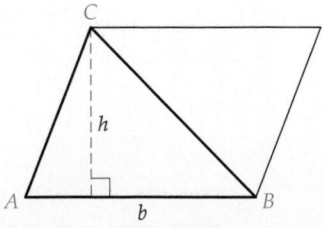

> **Area of a Triangle**
>
> Let b represent the length of the base and h the height of a triangle. The area, A, of the triangle is given by $A = \frac{1}{2}bh$.

EXAMPLE 10 ■ **Find the Area of a Triangle**

A riveter uses metal plates that are in the shape of a triangle with a base of 12 cm and a height of 6 cm. Find the area of one metal plate.

Solution

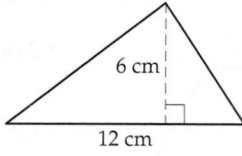

• Draw a diagram.

$A = \dfrac{1}{2}bh$ • Use the formula for the area of a triangle.

$A = \dfrac{1}{2}(12)(6)$ • The base is **12** cm. Substitute **12** for b. The height is **6** cm. Substitute **6** for h. Remember that bh means "b times h."

$A = 6(6)$

$A = 36$

The area is 36 cm². • Area is measured in square units.

CHECK YOUR PROGRESS 10   Find the amount of felt needed to make a banner that is in the shape of a triangle with a base of 18 in. and a height of 9 in.

Solution   *See page S30.*

✔ **TAKE NOTE**

The bases of a trapezoid are the parallel sides of the figure.

Figure *ABCD* is a *trapezoid*. $\overline{AB}$, with length b_1, is one **base** of the trapezoid and $\overline{CD}$, with length b_2, is the other base. $\overline{AE}$, perpendicular to the two bases, is the **height.**

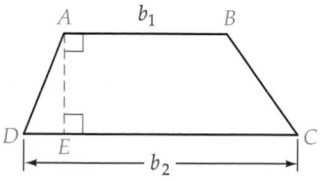

In the trapezoid at the right, the line segment $\overline{BD}$ divides the trapezoid into two triangles, ABD and BCD. In triangle ABD, b_1 is the base and h is the height. In triangle BCD, b_2 is the base and h is the height. The area of the trapezoid is the sum of the areas of the two triangles.

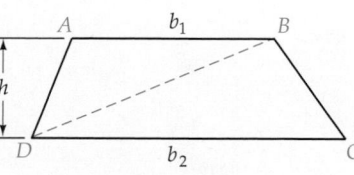

Area of trapezoid $ABCD$ = Area of triangle ABD + area of triangle BCD

$$= \frac{1}{2}b_1 h + \frac{1}{2}b_2 h = \frac{1}{2}h(b_1 + b_2)$$

Area of a Trapezoid

Let b_1 and b_2 represent the lengths of the bases and h the height of a trapezoid. The area, A, of the trapezoid is given by $A = \frac{1}{2}h(b_1 + b_2)$.

EXAMPLE 11 ■ Find the Area of a Trapezoid

A boat dock is built in the shape of a trapezoid with bases measuring 14 ft and 6 ft and a height of 7 ft. Find the area of the dock.

Solution

- Draw a diagram.

$$A = \frac{1}{2}h(b_1 + b_2)$$

- Use the formula for the area of a trapezoid.

$$A = \frac{1}{2} \cdot 7(14 + 6)$$

- The height is **7** ft. Substitute **7** for h. The bases measure **14** ft and **6** ft. Substitute **14** and **6** for b_1 and b_2.

$$A = \frac{1}{2} \cdot 7(20)$$

$$A = 70$$

The area is 70 ft².

- Area is measured in square units.

CHECK YOUR PROGRESS 11   Find the area of a patio that has the shape of a trapezoid with a height of 9 ft and bases measuring 12 ft and 20 ft.

Solution   *See page S30.*

The area of a circle is the product of π and the square of the radius.

$$A = \pi r^2$$

The Area of a Circle

The area, A, of a circle with radius of length r is given by $A = \pi r^2$.

Find the area of a circle that has a radius of 6 cm.

Use the formula for the area of a circle. $r = 6$.

$$A = \pi r^2$$
$$A = \pi(6)^2$$
$$A = \pi(36)$$

The exact area of the circle is 36π cm^2.

$$A = 36\pi$$

An approximate measure can be found by using the π key on a calculator.

$$A \approx 113.10$$

The approximate area of the circle is 113.10 cm^2.

EXAMPLE 12 ■ Find the Area of a Circle

Find the area of a circle with a diameter of 10 m. Round to the nearest hundredth of a square meter.

Solution

$r = \dfrac{1}{2}d = \dfrac{1}{2}(10) = 5$ • **Find the radius of the circle.**

$A = \pi r^2$ • **Use the formula for the area of a circle.**

$A = \pi(5)^2$ • **Replace r with 5.**

$A = \pi(25)$ • **Square 5.**

$A \approx 78.54$ • **An approximation is asked for. Use the π key on a calculator.**

The area of the circle is approximately 78.54 m^2.

CHECK YOUR PROGRESS 12   Find the area of a circle with a diameter of 12 km. Give the exact measure.

Solution   *See page S30.*

EXAMPLE 13 ■ Application of Finding the Area of a Circle

How large a cover is needed for a circular hot tub that is 8 ft in diameter? Round to the nearest tenth of a square foot.

Solution

$r = \dfrac{1}{2}d = \dfrac{1}{2}(8) = 4$ • **Find the radius of a circle with a diameter of 8 ft.**

$A = \pi r^2$ • **Use the formula for the area of a circle.**

$A = \pi(4)^2$ • **Replace r with 4.**

$A = \pi(16)$ • **Square 4.**

$A \approx 50.3$ • **Use the π key on a calculator.**

The cover for the hot tub must be 50.3 ft^2.

CHECK YOUR PROGRESS 13 How much material is needed to make a circular tablecloth that is to have a diameter of 4 ft? Round to the nearest hundredth of a square foot.

Solution *See page S30.*

Math Matters Möbius Bands

Cut out a long, narrow rectangular strip of paper.

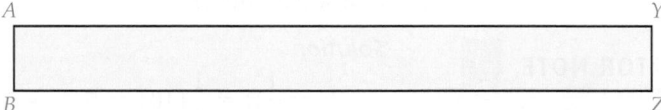

Give the strip of paper a half-twist.

Put the ends together so that *A* meets *Z* and *B* meets *Y*. Tape the ends together. The result is a *Möbius band.*

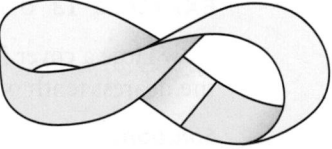

Make a Möbius band that is $1\frac{1}{2}$ in. wide. Use a pair of scissors to cut the Möbius band lengthwise down the middle, staying $\frac{3}{4}$ in. from each edge. Describe the result.

Make a Möbius band from plain white paper and then shade one side. Describe what remains unshaded on the Möbius band, and state the number of sides a Möbius band has.

Excursion

Slicing Polygons into Triangles[1]

Shown at the right is a triangle with three "slices" through it. Notice that the resulting pieces are six quadrilaterals and a triangle.

Excursion Exercises

1. Determine how you can slice a triangle so that all the resulting pieces are triangles. Use three slices. Each slice must cut all the way through the triangle.

2. Determine how you can slice each of the following polygons so that all the resulting pieces are triangles. Each slice must cut all the way through the figure. Record the number of slices required for each polygon. *Note:* There may be more than one solution for a figure.

   a. Quadrilateral   **b.** Pentagon   **c.** Hexagon   **d.** Heptagon

Using Patterns in Experimentation

3. Try to cut a pie into the greatest number of pieces with only five straight cuts of a knife. An illustration showing how five cuts can produce 13 pieces is shown below. The correct answer, however, yields more than thirteen pieces.

   A reasonable question is "How do I know when I have the maximum number of pieces?" To determine the answer, we suggest that you start with one cut, then two cuts, then three cuts, and so on. Try to discover a pattern for the greatest number of pieces that each successive cut can produce.

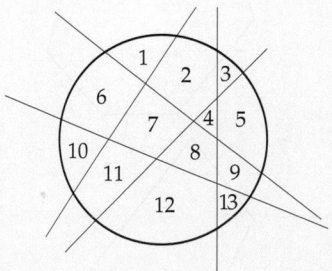

---

1. This activity is adapted from James Gary Propp's "The Slicing Game," *American Mathematical Monthly,* April 1996.

Exercise Set 8.2

1. Label the length of the rectangle L and the width of the rectangle W.

2. Label the base of the parallelogram b, the side s, and the height h.

3. What is wrong with each statement?

    a. The perimeter is 40 m².

    b. The area is 120 ft.

In Exercises 4–7, name each polygon.

4.   **5.**

6.   **7.**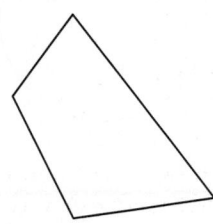

In Exercises 8–11, classify the triangle as isosceles, equilateral, or scalene.

8.   **9.**

10.   **11.**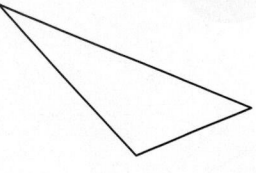

In Exercises 12–15, classify the triangle as acute, obtuse, or right.

12.   **13.**

14.   **15.**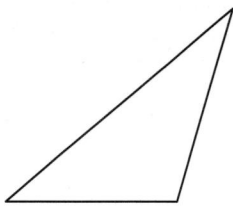

In Exercises 16–24, find (**a**) the perimeter and (**b**) the area of the figure.

16.
11 in.
7 in.

17.
10 m
5 m

18.
8 ft
6 ft

19.
4 cm
4 cm

20.
9 mi
9 mi

21.
10 km
10 km

22.

23.

24.

In Exercises 25–30, find (**a**) the circumference and (**b**) the area of the figure. Give both exact values and approximations to the nearest hundredth.

25.

26.

27.

28.

29.

30.

31. Fencing You need to fence in the triangular plot of land shown below. How many feet of fencing do you need?

32. Gardens A flower garden in the yard of a historical home is in the shape of a triangle, as shown below. The wooden beams lining the edge of the garden need to be replaced. Find the total length of wood beams that must be purchased in order to replace the old beams.

33. Yacht Racing The course of a yachting race is in the shape of a triangle with sides that measure $4\frac{3}{10}$ mi, $3\frac{7}{10}$ mi, and $2\frac{1}{2}$ mi. Find the total length of the course.

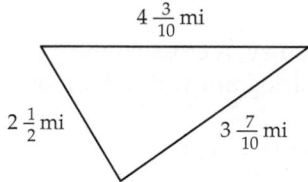

34. Physical Fitness An exercise course has stations set up along a path that is in the shape of a triangle with sides that measure $12\frac{1}{12}$ yd, $29\frac{1}{3}$ yd, and $26\frac{3}{4}$ yd. What is the entire length of the exercise course?

35. Fencing How many feet of fencing should be purchased to enclose a rectangular garden that is 20 ft long and 14 ft wide?

36. Sewing How many meters of binding are required to bind the edge of a rectangular quilt that measures 4 m by 6 m?

37. Perimeter Find the perimeter of a regular pentagon that measures 4 in. on each side.

38. **Interior Decorating** Wall-to-wall carpeting is installed in a room that is 15 ft long and 10 ft wide. The edges of the carpet are held down by tack strips. How many feet of tack-strip material are needed?

39. **Parks and Recreation** The length of a rectangular park is 62 yd. The width is 45 yd. How many yards of fencing are needed to surround the park?

40. **Perimeter** What is the perimeter of a regular hexagon that measures 9 cm on each side?

41. **Cross-Country** A cross-country course is in the shape of a parallelogram with a base of length 3 mi and a side of length 2 mi. What is the total length of the cross-country course?

42. **Parks and Recreation** A rectangular playground has a length of 160 ft and a width of 120 ft. Find the length of hedge that surrounds the playground.

43. **Sewing** Bias binding is to be sewn around the edge of a rectangular tablecloth measuring 68 in. by 42 in. If the bias binding comes in packages containing 15 ft of binding, how many packages of bias binding are needed for the tablecloth?

44. **Gardens** Find the area of a rectangular flower garden that measures 24 ft by 18 ft.

45. **Construction** What is the area of a square patio that measures 12 m on each side?

46. **Athletic Fields** Artificial turf is being used to cover a playing field. If the field is rectangular with a length of 110 yd and a width of 80 yd, how much artificial turf must be purchased to cover the field?

47. **Framing** The perimeter of a square picture frame is 36 in. Find the length of each side of the frame.

48. **Carpeting** A square rug has a perimeter of 24 ft. Find the length of each edge of the rug.

49. **Area** The area of a rectangle is 400 in². If the length of the rectangle is 40 in., what is the width?

50. **Area** The width of a rectangle is 8 ft. If the area is 312 ft², what is the length of the rectangle?

51. **Area** The area of a parallelogram is 56 m². If the height of the parallelogram is 7 m, what is the length of the base?

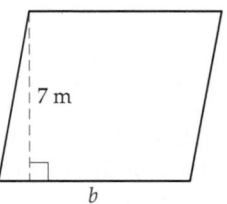

52. **Storage Units** You want to rent a storage unit. You estimate that you will need 175 ft² of floor space. In the Yellow Pages, you see the ad shown below. You want to rent the smallest possible unit that will hold everything you want to store. Which of the six units pictured in the ad should you select?

53. **Sailing** A sail is in the shape of a triangle with a base of 12 m and a height of 16 m. How much canvas was needed to make the body of the sail?

54. Gardens A vegetable garden is in the shape of a triangle with a base of 21 ft and a height of 13 ft. Find the area of the vegetable garden.

55. Athletic Fields How much artificial turf should be purchased to cover an athletic field that is in the shape of a trapezoid with a height of 15 m and bases that measure 45 m and 36 m?

56. Land Area A township is in the shape of a trapezoid with a height of 10 km and bases measuring 9 km and 23 km. What is the land area of the township?

57. Parks and Recreation A city plans to plant grass seed in a public playground that has the shape of a triangle with a height of 24 m and a base of 20 m. Each bag of grass seed will seed 120 m². How many bags of seed should be purchased?

58. Interior Decorating The family room of a home is on the third floor of the house. Because of the pitch of the roof, two walls of the room are in the shape of a

trapezoid with bases that measure 16 ft and 24 ft and a height of 8 ft. You plan to wallpaper the two walls. One roll of wallpaper will cover 40 ft². How many rolls of wallpaper should you purchase?

59. Home Maintenance You plan to stain the wooden deck at the back of your house. The deck is in the shape of a trapezoid with bases that measure 10 ft and 12 ft and a height of 10 ft. A quart of stain will cover 55 ft². How many quarts of stain should you purchase?

60. Interior Decorating A fabric wall hanging is in the shape of a triangle that has a base of 4 ft and a height of 3 ft. An additional 1 ft² of fabric is needed for hemming the material. How much fabric should be purchased to make the wall hanging?

61. Interior Decorating You want to tile your kitchen floor. The floor measures 10 ft by 8 ft. How many square tiles that measure 2 ft along each side should you purchase for the job?

62. Interior Decorating You are wallpapering two walls of a den, one measuring 10 ft by 8 ft and the other measuring 12 ft by 8 ft. The wallpaper costs $24 per roll, and each roll will cover 40 ft². What is the cost to wallpaper the two walls?

63. Gardens An urban renewal project involves reseeding a garden that is in the shape of a square, 80 ft on each side. Each bag of grass seed costs $8 and will seed 1500 ft². How much money should be budgeted for buying grass seed for the garden?

64. Carpeting You want to install wall-to-wall carpeting in the family room. The floor plan is drawn below. If the cost of the carpet you would like to purchase is $19 per square yard, what is the cost of carpeting your family room? Assume there is no waste. *Hint:* 9 ft² = 1 yd²

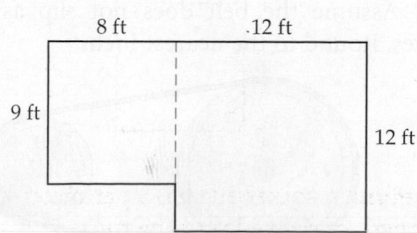

65. **Interior Decorating** You want to paint the walls of your bedroom. Two walls measure 16 ft by 8 ft, and the other two walls measure 12 ft by 8 ft. The paint you wish to purchase costs $17 per gallon, and each gallon will cover 400 ft² of wall. Find the total amount you will spend on paint.

66. **Landscaping** A walkway 2 m wide surrounds a rectangular plot of grass. The plot is 25 m long and 15 m wide. What is the area of the walkway?

67. **Draperies** The material used to make pleated draperies for a window must be twice as wide as the width of the window. Draperies are being made for four windows, each 3 ft wide and 4 ft high. Because the drapes will fall slightly below the window sill and extra fabric is needed for hemming the drapes, 1 ft must be added to the height of the window. How much material must be purchased to make the drapes?

68. **Fencing** How many feet of fencing should be purchased to enclose a circular flower garden that has a diameter of 18 ft? Round to the nearest tenth of a foot.

69. **Carpentry** Find the length of molding needed to put around a circular table that is 4.2 ft in diameter. Round to the nearest hundredth of a foot.

70. **Sewing** How much binding is needed to bind the edge of a circular rug that is 3 m in diameter? Round to the nearest hundredth of a meter.

71. **Gardens** Find the area of a circular flower garden that has a radius of 20 ft. Round to the nearest tenth of a square foot.

72. **Pulleys** A pulley system is diagrammed below. If pulley B has a diameter of 16 in. and is rotating at 240 revolutions per minute, how far does the belt travel each minute that the pulley system is in operation? Assume the belt does not slip as the pulley rotates. Round to the nearest inch.

73. **Bicycles** A bicycle tire has a diameter of 18 in. How many feet does the bicycle travel when the wheel makes 20 revolutions? Round to the nearest hundredth of a foot.

74. **Tricycles** The front wheel of a tricycle has a diameter of 16 in. How many feet does the tricycle travel when the wheel makes 15 revolutions? Round to the nearest hundredth of a foot.

75. **Telescopes** The lens located on an astronomical telescope has a diameter of 24 in. Find the exact area of the lens.

76. **Irrigation** An irrigation system waters a circular field that has a 50-foot radius. Find the exact area watered by the irrigation system.

77. **Pizza** How much greater is the area of a pizza that has a radius of 10 in. than the area of a pizza that has a radius of 8 in.? Round to the nearest hundredth of a square inch.

78. **Pizza** A restaurant serves a small pizza that has a radius of 6 in. The restaurant's large pizza has a radius that is twice the radius of the small pizza. How much larger is the area of the large pizza? Round to the nearest hundredth of a square inch. Is the area of the large pizza more or less than twice the area of the small pizza?

79. **Satellites** There are two general types of satellite systems that orbit our Earth: geostationary Earth orbit (GEO) and non-geostationary, primarily low Earth orbit (LEO). Geostationary satellite systems orbit at a distance of 36,000 km above Earth. An orbit at this altitude allows the satellite to maintain a fixed position in relation to Earth. What is the distance traveled by a GEO satellite in one orbit around Earth? The radius of Earth at the equator is 6380 km. Round to the nearest kilometer.

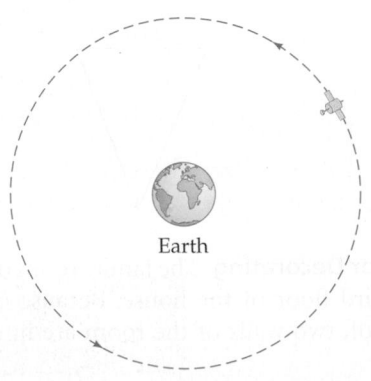

Earth

80. Ball Fields How much farther is it around the bases of a baseball diamond than around the bases of a softball diamond? *Hint:* Baseball and softball diamonds are squares.

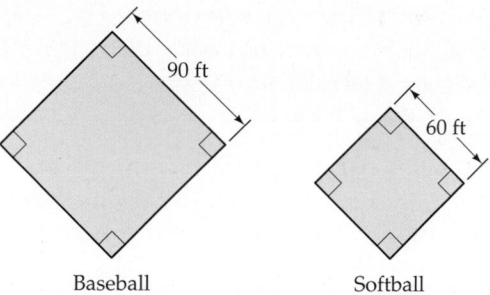

Baseball   Softball

81. Area Write an expression for the area of the shaded portion of the diagram. Leave the answer in terms of π and r.

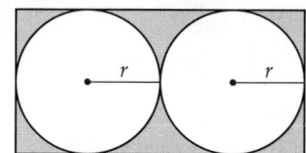

82. Area Write an expression for the area of the shaded portion of the diagram. Leave the answer in terms of π and r.

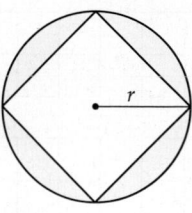

83. Area If both the length and width of a rectangle are doubled, how many times as large is the area of the resulting rectangle?

Extensions

CRITICAL THINKING

84. Determine whether the statement is always true, sometimes true, or never true.

a. Two triangles that have the same perimeter have the same area.

b. Two rectangles that have the same area have the same perimeter.

c. If two squares have the same area, then the sides of the squares have the same length.

85. Find the dimensions of a rectangle that has the same area as the shaded region in the diagram below. Write the dimensions in terms of the variable a.

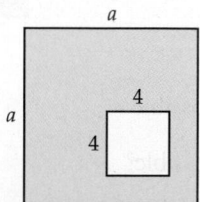

86. Find the dimensions of a rectangle that has the same area as the shaded region in the diagram below. Write the dimensions in terms of the variable x.

87. In the diagrams below, the length of one side of a square is 1 cm. Find the perimeter and the area of the eighth figure in the pattern.

    a.

    b.

    c.

EXPLORATIONS

88. The perimeter of the square at the right is 4 units.

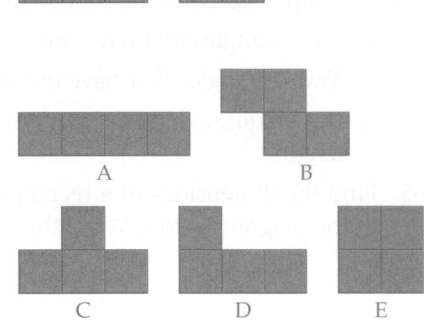

If two such squares are joined along one of the sides, the perimeter is 6 units. Note that it does not matter which sides are joined; the perimeter is still 6 units.

If three squares are joined, the perimeter of the resulting figure is 8 units for each possible placement of the squares.

Four squares can be joined in five different ways as shown. There are two possible perimeters: 10 units for A, B, C, and D, and 8 units for E.

    a. If five squares are joined, what is the maximum perimeter possible?

    b. If five squares are joined, what is the minimum perimeter possible?

    c. If six squares are joined, what is the maximum perimeter possible?

    d. If six squares are joined, what is the minimum perimeter possible?

89. Suppose a circle is cut into 16 equal pieces, which are then arranged as shown at the right. The figure formed resembles a parallelogram. What variable expression could describe the base of the parallelogram? What variable could describe its height? Explain how the formula for the area of a circle is derived from this approach.

SECTION 8.3	**Properties of Triangles**

▼ **point of interest**

Model trains are similar to actual trains. They come in a variety of sizes that manufacturers have agreed upon, so that, for example, an engine made by manufacturer A is able to run on a track made by manufacturer B. Listed below are three model railroad sizes by name, along with the ratio of model size to actual size.

Name	Ratio
Z	1:220
N	1:160
HO	1:87

Z Scale

N Scale

HO Scale

HO's ratio of 1:87 means that in every dimension, an HO scale model railroad car is $\frac{1}{87}$ the size of the real railroad car.

Similar Triangles

Similar objects have the same shape but not necessarily the same size. A tennis ball is similar to a basketball. A model ship is similar to an actual ship.

Similar objects have corresponding parts; for example, the rudder on the model ship corresponds to the rudder on the actual ship. The relationship between the sizes of each of the corresponding parts can be written as a ratio, and each ratio will be the same. If the rudder on the model ship is $\frac{1}{100}$ the size of the rudder on the actual ship, then the model wheelhouse is $\frac{1}{100}$ of the size of the actual wheelhouse, the width of the model is $\frac{1}{100}$ the width of the actual ship, and so on.

The two triangles ABC and DEF shown at the right are similar. Side $\overline{AB}$ corresponds to side $\overline{DE}$, side $\overline{BC}$ corresponds to side $\overline{EF}$, and side $\overline{AC}$ corresponds to side $\overline{DF}$. The ratios of the lengths of corresponding sides are equal.

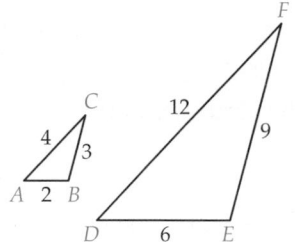

$$\frac{AB}{DE} = \frac{2}{6} = \frac{1}{3}, \quad \frac{BC}{EF} = \frac{3}{9} = \frac{1}{3}, \quad \text{and}$$

$$\frac{AC}{DF} = \frac{4}{12} = \frac{1}{3}$$

Because the ratios of corresponding sides are equal, several proportions can be formed.

$$\frac{AB}{DE} = \frac{BC}{EF}, \quad \frac{AB}{DE} = \frac{AC}{DF}, \quad \text{and} \quad \frac{BC}{EF} = \frac{AC}{DF}$$

The measures of corresponding angles in similar triangles are equal. Therefore,

$$m\angle A = m\angle D, \quad m\angle B = m\angle E, \quad \text{and}$$
$$m\angle C = m\angle F$$

Triangles ABC and DEF at the right are similar triangles. AH and DK are the heights of the triangles. The ratio of the heights of similar triangles equals the ratio of the lengths of corresponding sides.

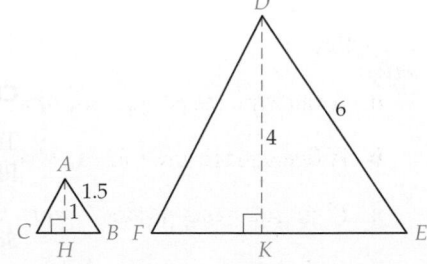

Ratio of corresponding sides $= \frac{1.5}{6} = \frac{1}{4}$

Ratio of heights $= \frac{1}{4}$

Properties of Similar Triangles

For similar triangles, the ratios of corresponding sides are equal. The ratio of corresponding heights is equal to the ratio of corresponding sides.

Triangles *ABC* and *DEF* are similar triangles. Find the area of triangle *ABC*.

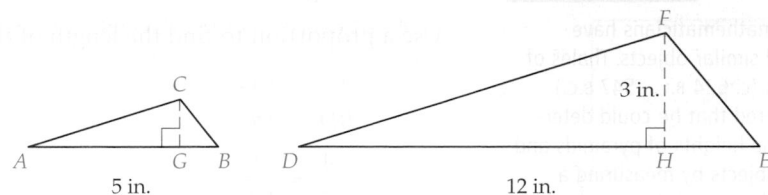

Solve a proportion to find the height of triangle *ABC*.

$$\frac{AB}{DE} = \frac{CG}{FH}$$

$$\frac{5}{12} = \frac{CG}{3}$$

$$12(CG) = 5(3)$$

$$12(CG) = 15$$

$$CG = 1.25$$

Use the formula for the area of a triangle.

$$A = \frac{1}{2}bh$$

The base is 5 in. The height is 1.25 in.

$$A = \frac{1}{2}(5)(1.25)$$

$$A = 3.125$$

The area of triangle *ABC* is 3.125 in².

If the three angles of one triangle are equal in measure to the three angles of another triangle, then the triangles are similar.

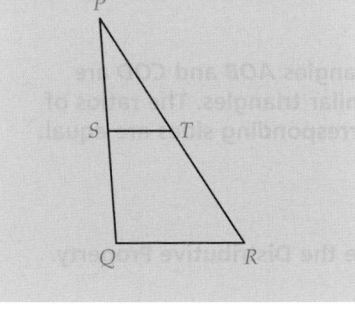
In triangle *ABC* at the right, line segment $\overline{DE}$ is drawn parallel to the base $\overline{AB}$. Because the measures of corresponding angles are equal, $m\angle x = m\angle r$ and $m\angle y = m\angle n$. We know that $m\angle C = m\angle C$. Thus the measures of the three angles of triangle *ABC* are equal, respectively, to the measures of the three angles of triangle *DEC*. Therefore, triangles *ABC* and *DEC* are similar triangles.

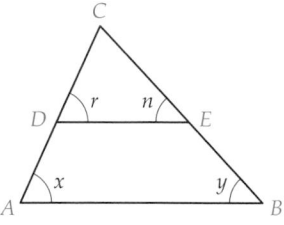

The sum of the measures of the three angles of a triangle is 180°. If two angles of one triangle are equal in measure to two angles of another triangle, then the third angles must be equal. Thus, we can say that if two angles of one triangle are equal in measure to two angles of another triangle, then the two triangles are similar.

In the figure at the right, $\overline{AB}$ intersects $\overline{CD}$ at point *O*. Angles *C* and *D* are right angles. Find the length of $\overline{DO}$.

First determine whether triangles *AOC* and *BOD* are similar.

$m\angle C = m\angle D$ because they are both right angles.

$m\angle x = m\angle y$ because vertical angles have the same measure.

Congruent Triangles

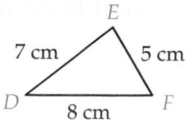

The two triangles at the right are **congruent.** They have the same shape and the same size.

Congruent and similar triangles differ in that the corresponding angles of congruent triangles have the same measure and the corresponding sides are equal in length, whereas for similar triangles, corresponding angles have the same measure but corresponding sides are not necessarily the same length.

The three major theorems used to determine whether two triangles are congruent are given below.

Side-Side-Side Theorem (SSS)

If the three sides of one triangle are equal in measure to the corresponding three sides of a second triangle, the two triangles are congruent.

In the triangles at the right, $AC = DE$, $AB = EF$, and $BC = DF$. The corresponding sides of triangles *ABC* and *DEF* are equal in measure. The triangles are congruent by the SSS Theorem.

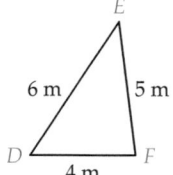

Side-Angle-Side Theorem (SAS)

If two sides and the included angle of one triangle are equal in measure to two sides and the included angle of a second triangle, the two triangles are congruent.

In the two triangles at the right, $AB = EF$, $AC = DE$, and $m\angle BAC = m\angle DEF$. The triangles are congruent by the SAS Theorem.

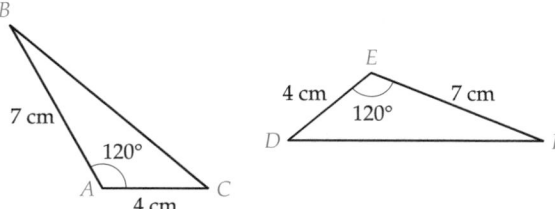

Angle-Side-Angle Theorem (ASA)

If two angles and the included side of one triangle are equal in measure to two angles and the included side of a second triangle, the two triangles are congruent.

For triangles *ABC* and *DEF* at the right, $m\angle A = m\angle F$, $m\angle C = m\angle E$, and $AC = EF$. The triangles are congruent by the ASA Theorem.

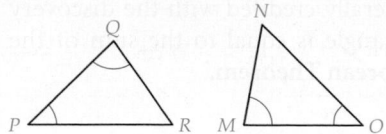

Given triangles *PQR* and *MNO*, do the conditions $m\angle P = m\angle O$, $m\angle Q = m\angle M$, and $PQ = MO$ guarantee that triangle *PQR* is congruent to triangle *MNO*?

Draw a sketch of the two triangles and determine whether one of the theorems for congruence is satisfied. See the figures at the left.

Because two angles and the included side of one triangle are equal in measure to two angles and the included side of the second triangle, the triangles are congruent by the ASA Theorem.

EXAMPLE 3 ■ Determine Whether Two Triangles Are Congruent

In the figure at the right, is triangle *ABC* congruent to triangle *DEF*?

Solution

To determine whether the triangles are congruent, determine whether one of the theorems for congruence is satisfied.

The triangles do not satisfy the SSS Theorem, the SAS Theorem, or the ASA Theorem.

The triangles are not necessarily congruent.

CHECK YOUR PROGRESS 3 In the figure at the right, is triangle *PQR* congruent to triangle *MNO*?

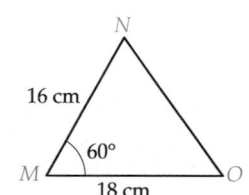

Solution   *See page S31.*

The Pythagorean Theorem

Recall that a right triangle contains one right angle. The side opposite the right angle is called the **hypotenuse.** The other two sides are called **legs.**

The angles in a right triangle are usually labeled with the capital letters *A*, *B*, and *C*, with *C* reserved for the right angle. The side opposite angle *A* is side *a*, the side opposite angle *B* is side *b*, and *c* is the hypotenuse.

The figure at the right is a right triangle with legs measuring 3 units and 4 units and a hypotenuse measuring 5 units. Each side of the triangle is also the side of a square. The number of square units in the area of the largest square is equal to the sum of the numbers of square units in the areas of the smaller squares.

Square of the   =   sum of the squares
hypotenuse   of the two legs

$$5^2 = 3^2 + 4^2$$

$$25 = 9 + 16$$

$$25 = 25$$

The Greek mathematician Pythagoras is generally credited with the discovery that the square of the hypotenuse of a right triangle is equal to the sum of the squares of the two legs. This is called the **Pythagorean Theorem.**

> **Pythagorean Theorem**
>
> If a and b are the lengths of the legs of a right triangle and c is the length of the hypotenuse, then $c^2 = a^2 + b^2$.

If the lengths of two sides of a right triangle are known, the Pythagorean Theorem can be used to find the length of the third side.

Consider a right triangle with legs that measure 5 cm and 12 cm. Use the Pythagorean Theorem, with $a = 5$ and $b = 12$, to find the length of the hypotenuse. (If you let $a = 12$ and $b = 5$, the result will be the same.) Take the square root of each side of the equation.

The length of the hypotenuse is 13 cm.

$$c^2 = a^2 + b^2$$
$$c^2 = 5^2 + 12^2$$
$$c^2 = 25 + 144$$
$$c^2 = 169$$
$$\sqrt{c^2} = \sqrt{169}$$
$$c = 13$$

✔ **TAKE NOTE**

The length of the side of a triangle cannot be negative. Therefore, we take only the principal, or positive, square root of 169.

EXAMPLE 4 ■ **Determine the Length of the Unknown Side of a Right Triangle**

The length of one leg of a right triangle is 8 in. The length of the hypotenuse is 12 in. Find the length of the other leg. Round to the nearest hundredth of an inch.

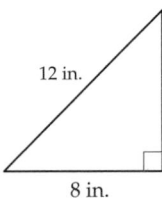

Solution

$$a^2 + b^2 = c^2$$ • Use the Pythagoran Theorem.
$$8^2 + b^2 = 12^2$$ • $a = \mathbf{8}$, $c = \mathbf{12}$
$$64 + b^2 = 144$$
$$b^2 = 80$$ • Solve for b^2. Subtract 64 from each side.
$$\sqrt{b^2} = \sqrt{80}$$ • Take the square root of each side of the equation.
$$b \approx 8.94$$ • Use a calculator to approximate $\sqrt{80}$.

The length of the other leg is approximately 8.94 in.

CHECK YOUR PROGRESS 4   The hypotenuse of a right triangle measures 6 m, and one leg measures 2 m. Find the measure of the other leg. Round to the nearest hundredth of a meter.

Solution   See page S31.

Excursion

Topology

In this section, we discussed similar figures—that is, figures with the same shape. The branch of geometry called *topology* is the study of even more basic properties of figures than their sizes and shapes. For example, look at the figures below. We could take a rubber band and stretch it into any one of these shapes.

All three of these figures are different shapes, but each can be turned into one of the others by stretching the rubber band.

In topology, figures that can be stretched, molded, or bent into the same shape *without puncturing or cutting* belong to the same family. They are called **topologically equivalent.**

Rectangles, triangles, and circles are topologically equivalent.

Line segments and wavy curves are topologically equivalent.

Note that the figures formed from a rubber band and those formed from a line segment are not topologically equivalent; to form a line segment from a rubber band, we would have to cut the rubber band.

In the following plane figures, the lines are joined where they cross. The figures are topologically equivalent. They are not topologically equivalent to any of the figures shown above.

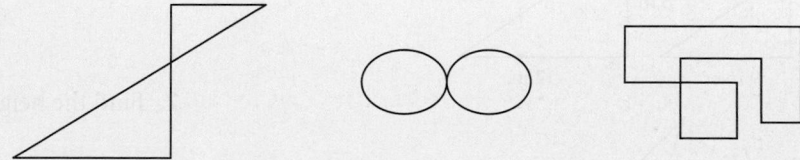

A **topologist** (a person who studies topology) is interested in identifying and describing different families of equivalent figures. Topology applies to solids as well as plane figures.

(continued)

For example, a topologist considers a brick, a potato, and a cue ball to be topologically equivalent to each other. Think of using modeling clay to form each of these shapes.

Excursion Exercises

Which of the figures listed is not topologically equivalent to the others?

1. a. Parallelogram   **b.** Square   **c.** Ray   **d.** Trapezoid

2. a. Wedding ring   **b.** Doughnut   **c.** Fork   **d.** Sewing needle

3. a.   **b.**   **c.**   **d.**   **e.**

Exercise Set 8.3

In Exercises 1–4, find the ratio of the lengths of corresponding sides for the similar triangles.

1.

2.

3.

4.

In Exercises 5–12, triangles *ABC* and *DEF* are similar triangles. Solve. Round to the nearest tenth.

5. Find side *DE.*

6. Find side *DE.*

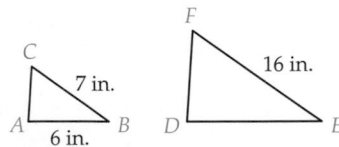

7. Find the height of triangle *DEF.*

8. Find the height of triangle *ABC*.

9. Find the perimeter of triangle *ABC*.

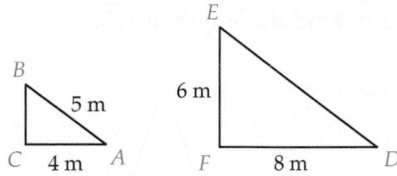

10. Find the perimeter of triangle *DEF*.

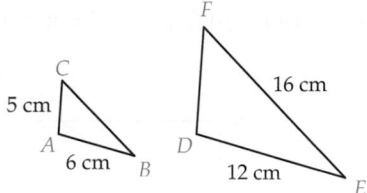

11. Find the perimeter of triangle *ABC*.

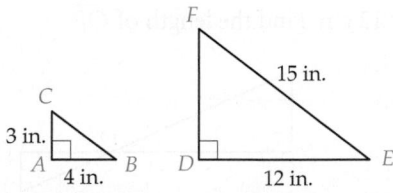

12. Find the area of triangle *DEF*.

In Exercises 13 and 14, triangles *ABC* and *DEF* are similar triangles. Solve. Round to the nearest tenth.

13. Find the area of triangle *ABC*.

14. Find the area of triangle *DEF*.

In Exercises 15–19, the given triangles are similar triangles. Use this fact to solve each exercise.

15. Find the height of the flagpole.

16. Find the height of the flagpole.

17. Find the height of the building.

18. Find the height of the building.

19. Find the height of the flagpole.

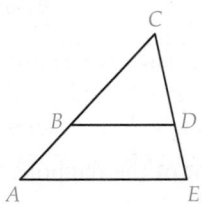

20. In the figure below, $\overline{BD} \parallel \overline{AE}$, BD measures 5 cm, AE measures 8 cm, and AC measures 10 cm. Find the length of $\overline{BC}$.

21. In the figure below, $\overline{AC} \parallel \overline{DE}$, BD measures 8 m, AD measures 12 m, and BE measures 6 m. Find the length of $\overline{BC}$.

22. In the figure below, $\overline{DE} \parallel \overline{AC}$, DE measures 6 in., AC measures 10 in., and AB measures 15 in. Find the length of $\overline{DA}$.

23. In the figure below, $\overline{AE} \parallel \overline{BD}$, $AB = 3$ ft, $ED = 4$ ft, and $BC = 3$ ft. Find the length of $\overline{CE}$.

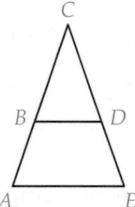

24. In the figure below, $\overline{MP}$ and $\overline{NQ}$ intersect at O, $NO = 25$ ft, $MO = 20$ ft, and $PO = 8$ ft. Find the length of $\overline{QO}$.

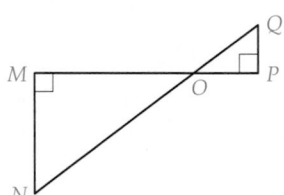

25. In the figure below, $\overline{MP}$ and $\overline{NQ}$ intersect at O, $NO = 24$ cm, $MN = 10$ cm, $MP = 39$ cm, and $QO = 12$ cm. Find the length of $\overline{OP}$.

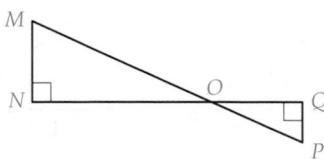

26. In the figure below, $\overline{MQ}$ and $\overline{NP}$ intersect at O, $NO = 12$ m, $MN = 9$ m, $PQ = 3$ m, and $MQ = 20$ m. Find the perimeter of triangle OPQ.

Surveying Surveyors use similar triangles to measure distances that cannot be measured directly. This is illustrated in Exercises 27 and 28.

27. The diagram below represents a river of width *CD*. Triangles *AOB* and *DOC* are similar. The distances *AB*, *BO*, and *OC* were measured and found to have the lengths given in the diagram. Find *CD*, the width of the river.

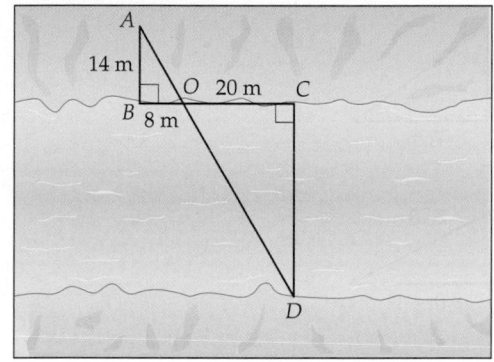

28. The diagram below shows how surveyors laid out similar triangles along the Winnepaugo River. Find the width, *d*, of the river.

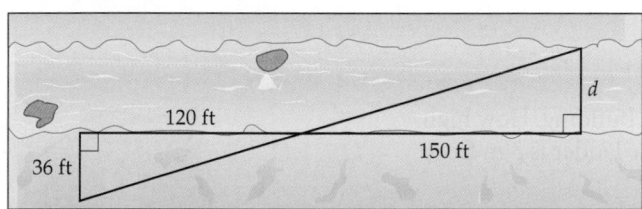

In Exercises 29–36, determine whether the two triangles are congruent. If they are congruent, state by what theorem (SSS, SAS, or ASA) they are congruent.

29.

30.

31.

32.

33.

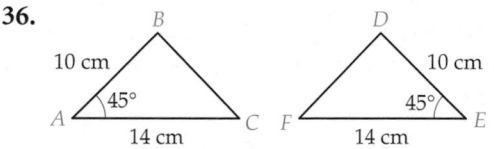

34.

35.

36.

37. Given triangle *ABC* and triangle *DEF*, do the conditions $m\angle C = m\angle E$, $AC = EF$, and $BC = DE$ guarantee that triangle *ABC* is congruent to triangle *DEF*? If they are congruent, by what theorem are they congruent?

38. Given triangle *PQR* and triangle *MNO*, do the conditions $PR = NO$, $PQ = MO$, and $QR = MN$ guarantee that triangle *PQR* is congruent to triangle *MNO*? If they are congruent, by what theorem are they congruent?

39. Given triangle *LMN* and triangle *QRS*, do the conditions $m\angle M = m\angle S$, $m\angle N = m\angle Q$, and $m\angle L = m\angle R$ guarantee that triangle *LMN* is congruent to triangle *QRS*? If they are congruent, by what theorem are they congruent?

40. Given triangle *DEF* and triangle *JKL*, do the conditions $m\angle D = m\angle K$, $m\angle E = m\angle L$, and $DE = KL$ guarantee that triangle *DEF* is congruent to triangle *JKL*? If they are congruent, by what theorem are they congruent?

41. Given triangle *ABC* and triangle *PQR*, do the conditions $m\angle B = m\angle P$, $BC = PQ$, and $AC = QR$ guarantee that triangle *ABC* is congruent to triangle *PQR*? If they are congruent, by what theorem are they congruent?

In Exercises 42–50, find the unknown side of the triangle. Round to the nearest tenth.

42.

3 in.

4 in.

43.

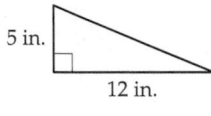

5 in.

12 in.

44.

5 cm

7 cm

45.

7 cm

9 cm

46.

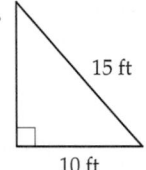

15 ft

10 ft

47.

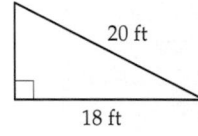

20 ft

18 ft

48.

4 cm   6 cm

49.

9 m   12 m

50.

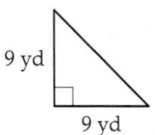

9 yd

9 yd

In Exercises 51–55, solve. Round to the nearest tenth.

51. Home Maintenance A ladder 8 m long is leaning against a building. How high on the building will the ladder reach when the bottom of the ladder is 3 m from the building?

8 m

3 m

52. Mechanics Find the distance between the centers of the holes in the metal plate.

3 cm

8 cm

53. Travel If you travel 18 mi east and then 12 mi north, how far are you from your starting point?

54. Perimeter Find the perimeter of a right triangle with legs that measure 5 cm and 9 cm.

55. Perimeter Find the perimeter of a right triangle with legs that measure 6 in. and 8 in.

Extensions

CRITICAL THINKING

56. Determine whether the statement is always true, sometimes true, or never true.

  a. If two angles of one triangle are equal to two angles of a second triangle, then the triangles are similar triangles.

  b. Two isosceles triangles are similar triangles.

  c. Two equilateral triangles are similar triangles.

  d. If an acute angle of a right triangle is equal to an acute angle of another right triangle, then the triangles are similar triangles.

57. **Home Maintenance** You need to clean the gutters of your home. The gutters are 24 ft above the ground. For safety, the distance a ladder reaches up a wall should be four times the distance from the bottom of the ladder to the base of the side of the house. Therefore, the ladder must be 6 ft from the base of the house. Will a 25-foot ladder be long enough to reach the gutters? Explain how you found your answer.

24 ft

6 ft

COOPERATIVE LEARNING

58. In the figure below, the height of a right triangle is drawn from the right angle perpendicular to the hypotenuse. (Recall that the hypotenuse of a right triangle is the side opposite the right angle.) Verify that the two smaller triangles formed are similar to the original triangle and similar to each other.

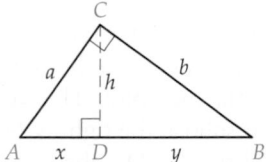

SECTION 8.4 | Volume and Surface Area

Volume

In Section 2 of this chapter, we developed the geometric concepts of perimeter and area. Perimeter and area refer to plane figures (figures that lie in a plane). We are now ready to introduce *volume* of geometric solids.

Geometric solids are figures in space. Figures in space include baseballs, ice cubes, milk cartons, and trucks.

Volume is a measure of the amount of space occupied by a geometric solid. Volume can be used to describe, for example, the amount of trash in a land fill, the amount of concrete poured for the foundation of a house, or the amount of water in a town's reservoir.

Five common geometric solids are rectangular solids, spheres, cylinders, cones, and pyramids.

A **rectangular solid** is one in which all six sides, called **faces,** are rectangles. The variable L is used to represent the length of a rectangular solid, W is used to represent its width, and H is used to represent its height. A shoe box is an example of a rectangular solid.

A **cube** is a special type of rectangular solid. Each of the six faces of a cube is a square. The variable s is used to represent the length of one side of a cube. A baby's block is an example of a cube.

A cube that is 1 ft on each side has a volume of 1 cubic foot, which is written 1 ft³. A cube that measures 1 cm on each side has a volume of 1 cubic centimeter, written 1 cm³.

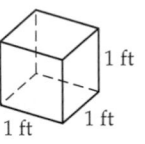

The volume of a solid is the number of cubes, each of volume 1 cubic unit, that are necessary to exactly fill the solid. The volume of the rectangular solid at the right is 24 cm³ because it will hold exactly 24 cubes, each 1 cm on a side. Note that the volume can be found by multiplying the length times the width times the height..

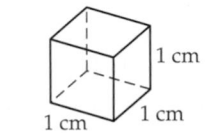

$4 \cdot 3 \cdot 2 = 24$

The volume of the solid is 24 cm³.

Volume of a Rectangular Solid

The volume, V, of a rectangular solid with length L, width W, and height H is given by $V = LWH$.

Volume of a Cube

The volume, V, of a cube with side of length s is given by $V = s^3$.

QUESTION   *Which of the following are rectangular solids: a juice box, a milk carton, a can of soup, a compact disc, a jewel box (plastic container) a compact disc is packaged in?*

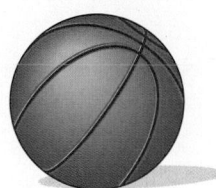

A **sphere** is a solid in which all points are the same distance from a point O, called the **center** of the sphere. A **diameter** of a sphere is a line segment with endpoints on the sphere and passing through the center. A **radius** is a line segment from the center to a point on the sphere. $\overline{AB}$ is a diameter and $\overline{OC}$ is a radius of the sphere shown at the right. A basketball is an example of a sphere.

If we let d represent the length of a diameter and r represent the length of a radius, then $d = 2r$ or $r = \frac{1}{2}d$.

$$d = 2r \quad \text{or} \quad r = \frac{1}{2}d$$

Volume of a Sphere

The volume, V, of a sphere with radius of length r is given by $V = \frac{4}{3}\pi r^3$.

Find the volume of a rubber ball that has a diameter of 6 in.

First find the length of a radius of the sphere.	$r = \frac{1}{2}d = \frac{1}{2}(6) = 3$
Use the formula for the volume of a sphere.	$V = \frac{4}{3}\pi r^3$
Replace r with 3.	$V = \frac{4}{3}\pi(3)^3$
	$V = \frac{4}{3}\pi(27)$
The exact volume of the sphere is 36π in³.	$V = 36\pi$
An approximate measure can be found by using the π key on a calculator.	$V \approx 113.10$

The volume of the rubber ball is approximately 113.10 in³.

ANSWER   *A juice box and a jewel box are rectangular solids.*

The most common cylinder, called a **right circular cylinder,** is one in which the bases are circles and are perpendicular to the height of the cylinder. The variable r is used to represent the length of the radius of a base of a cylinder, and h represents the height of the cylinder. In this text, only right circular cylinders are discussed.

Volume of a Right Circular Cylinder

The volume, V, of a right circular cylinder is given by $V = \pi r^2 h$, where r is the radius of the base and h is the height of the cylinder.

A **right circular cone** is obtained when one base of a right circular cylinder is shrunk to a point, called the **vertex,** V. The variable r is used to represent the radius of the base of the cone, and h represents the height of the cone. The variable l is used to represent the **slant height,** which is the distance from a point on the circumference of the base to the vertex. In this text, only right circular cones are discussed. An ice cream cone is an example of a right circular cone.

✔ TAKE NOTE

Note that πr^2 appears in the formula for the volume of a right circular cylinder and in the formula for a right circular cone. This is because, in each case, the base of the figure is a circle.

Volume of a Right Circular Cone

The volume, V, of a right circular cone is given by $V = \frac{1}{3}\pi r^2 h$, where r is the length of a radius of the circular base and h is the height of the cone.

✔ TAKE NOTE

Recall that an isosceles triangle has two sides of equal length.

The base of a **regular pyramid** is a regular polygon and the sides are isosceles triangles (two sides of the triangle are the same length). The height, h, is the distance from the vertex, V, to the base and is perpendicular to the base. The variable l is used to represent the **slant height,** which is the height of one of the isosceles triangles on the face of the pyramid. The regular square pyramid at the right has a square base. This is the only type of pyramid discussed in this text. Many Egyptian pyramids are regular square pyramids.

Pyramid at Giza

Volume of a Regular Square Pyramid

The volume, V, of a regular square pyramid is given by $V = \frac{1}{3}s^2 h$, where s is the length of a side of the base and h is the height of the pyramid.

QUESTION *Which of the following units could not be used to measure the volume of a regular square pyramid?*

   a. ft^3 ***b.*** m^3 ***c.*** yd^2 ***d.*** cm^3 ***e.*** *mi*

EXAMPLE 1 ■ Find the Volume of a Geometric Solid

Find the volume of a cube that measures 1.5 m on a side.

Solution

$V = s^3$ • Use the formula for the volume of a cube.

$V = 1.5^3$ • Replace *s* with **1.5**.

$V = 3.375$

The volume of the cube is 3.375 m³.

CHECK YOUR PROGRESS 1   The length of a rectangular solid is 5 m, the width is 3.2 m, and the height is 4 m. Find the volume of the solid.

Solution   *See page S31.*

EXAMPLE 2 ■ Find the Volume of a Geometric Solid

The radius of the base of a cone is 8 cm. The height of the cone is 12 cm. Find the volume of the cone. Round to the nearest hundredth of a cubic centimeter.

Solution

$V = \dfrac{1}{3}\pi r^2 h$ • Use the formula for the volume of a cone.

$V = \dfrac{1}{3}\pi (8)^2(12)$ • Replace *r* with **8** and *h* with **12**.

$V = \dfrac{1}{3}\pi (64)(12)$

$V = 256\pi$

$V \approx 804.25$ • Use the π key on a calculator.

The volume of the cone is approximately 804.25 cm³.

CHECK YOUR PROGRESS 2   The length of a side of the base of a regular square pyramid is 15 m and the height of the pyramid is 25 m. Find the volume of the pyramid.

Solution   *See page S31.*

ANSWER   *Volume is measured in cubic units. Therefore, the volume of a regular square pyramid could be measured in ft^3, m^3, or cm^3, but not in yd^2 or mi.*

EXAMPLE 3 ■ Find the Volume of a Geometric Solid

An oil storage tank in the shape of a cylinder is 4 m high and has a diameter of 6 m. The oil tank is two-thirds full. Find the number of cubic meters of oil in the tank. Round to the nearest hundredth of a cubic meter.

Solution

$r = \dfrac{1}{2}d = \dfrac{1}{2}(6) = 3$ • Find the radius of the base.

$V = \pi r^2 h$ • Use the formula for the volume of a cylinder.

$V = \pi(3)^2(4)$ • Replace *r* with **3** and *h* with **4**.

$V = \pi(9)(4)$

$V = 36\pi$

$\dfrac{2}{3}(36\pi) = 24\pi$ • Multiply the volume by $\dfrac{2}{3}$.

≈ 75.40 • Use the π key on a calculator.

There are approximately 75.40 m³ of oil in the storage tank.

CHECK YOUR PROGRESS 3 A silo in the shape of a cylinder is 16 ft in diameter and has a height of 30 ft. The silo is three-fourths full. Find the volume of the portion of the silo that is not being used for storage. Round to the nearest hundredth of a cubic foot.

Solution   *See page S31.*

Surface Area

The **surface area** of a solid is the total area on the surface of the solid. Suppose you want to cover a geometric solid with wallpaper. The amount of wallpaper needed is equal to the surface area of the figure.

When a rectangular solid is cut open and flattened out, each face is a rectangle. The surface area, S, of the rectangular solid is the sum of the areas of the six rectangles:

$$S = LW + LH + WH + LW$$
$$+ WH + LH$$

which simplifies to

$$S = 2LW + 2LH + 2WH$$

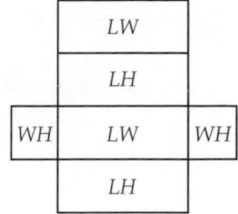

The surface area of a cube is the sum of the areas of the six faces of the cube. The area of each face is s^2. Therefore, the surface area S, of a cube is given by the formula $S = 6s^2$.

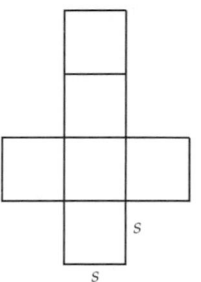

historical note

Pappus (păp'ŭs) of Alexandria (c. 290–350) was born in Egypt. We know the time period in which he lived because he wrote about his observation of the eclipse of the sun that took place in Alexandria on October 18, 320.

Pappas has been called the last of the great Greek geometers. His major work in geometry is *Synagoge,* or the *Mathematical Collection.* It consists of eight books. In Book V, Pappas proves that the sphere has a greater volume than any regular geometric solid with equal surface area. He also proves that if two regular solids have equal surface areas, the solid with the greater number of faces has the greater volume. ∎

When a cylinder is cut open and flattened out, the top and bottom of the cylinder are circles. The side of the cylinder flattens out to a rectangle. The length of the rectangle is the circumference of the base, which is $2\pi r$; the width is h, the height of the cylinder. Therefore, the area of the rectangle is $2\pi rh$. The surface area, S, of the cylinder is

$$S = \pi r^2 + 2\pi rh + \pi r^2$$

which simplifies to

$$S = 2\pi r^2 + 2\pi rh$$

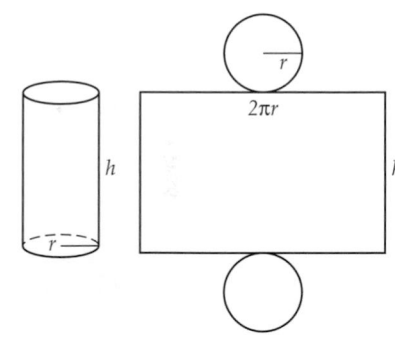

The surface area of a regular square pyramid is the area of the base plus the area of the four isosceles triangles. The length of a side of the square base is s; therefore, the area of the base is s^2. The slant height, l, is the height of each triangle, and s is the length of the base of each triangle. The surface area, S, of a regular square pyramid is

$$S = s^2 + 4\left(\frac{1}{2}sl\right)$$

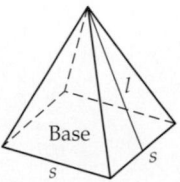

which simplifies to

$$S = s^2 + 2sl$$

Formulas for the surface areas of geometric solids are given below.

Surface Areas of Geometric Solids

The surface area, S, of a **rectangular solid** with length L, width W, and height H is given by $S = 2LW + 2LH + 2WH$.

The surface area, S, of a **cube** with sides of length s is given by $S = 6s^2$.

The surface area, S, of a **sphere** with radius r is given by $S = 4\pi r^2$.

The surface area, S, of a **right circular cylinder** is given by $S = 2\pi r^2 + 2\pi rh$, where r is the radius of the base and h is the height.

The surface area, S, of a **right circular cone** is given by $S = \pi r^2 + \pi rl$, where r is the radius of the circular base and l is the slant height.

The surface area, S, of a **regular square pyramid** is given by $S = s^2 + 2sl$, where s is the length of a side of the base and l is the slant height.

QUESTION   Which of the following units could not be used to measure the surface area of a rectangular solid?

    a. in^2 **b.** m^3 **c.** cm^2 **d.** ft^3 **e.** yd

Find the surface area of a sphere with a diameter of 18 cm.

First find the radius of the sphere. $r = \dfrac{1}{2}d = \dfrac{1}{2}(18) = 9$

Use the formula for the surface area of a sphere.

$$S = 4\pi r^2$$
$$S = 4\pi(9)^2$$
$$S = 4\pi(81)$$
$$S = 324\pi$$

The exact surface area of the sphere is 324π cm².

An approximate measure can be found by
using the π key on a calculator. $S \approx 1017.88$

The approximate surface area is 1017.88 cm².

ANSWER   *Surface area is measured in square units. Therefore, the surface area of a rectangular solid could be measured in in^2 or cm^2, but not in m^3, ft^3 or yd.*

EXAMPLE 4 ■ Find the Surface Area of a Geometric Solid

The diameter of the base of a cone is 5 m and the slant height is 4 m. Find the surface area of the cone. Round to the nearest hundredth of a square meter.

Solution

$r = \dfrac{1}{2}d = \dfrac{1}{2}(5) = 2.5$ • **Find the radius of the cone.**

$S = \pi r^2 + \pi r l$ • **Use the formula for the surface area of a cone.**

$S = \pi(2.5)^2 + \pi(2.5)(4)$ • **Replace *r* with 2.5 and *l* with 4.**

$S = \pi(6.25) + \pi(2.5)(4)$

$S = 6.25\pi + 10\pi$

$S = 16.25\pi$

$S \approx 51.05$

The surface area of the cone is approximately 51.05 m².

CHECK YOUR PROGRESS 4 The diameter of the base of a cylinder is 6 ft and the height is 8 ft. Find the surface area of the cylinder. Round to the nearest hundredth of a square foot.

Solution *See page S31.*

EXAMPLE 5 ■ Find the Surface Area of a Geometric Solid

Find the area of a label used to cover a soup can that has a radius of 4 cm and a height of 12 cm. Round to the nearest hundredth of a square centimeter.

Solution
The surface area of the side of a cylinder is given by $2\pi r h$.

Area of the label $= 2\pi r h$

$= 2\pi(4)(12)$

$= 96\pi$

≈ 301.59

The area of the label is approximately 301.59 cm².

CHECK YOUR PROGRESS 5 Which has a larger surface area, a cube with a side measuring 8 cm or a sphere with a diameter measuring 10 cm?

8 cm

10 cm

Solution *See page S31.*

Math Matters   Survival of the Fittest

The ratio of an animal's surface area to the volume of its body is a crucial factor in its survival. The more square units of skin for every cubic unit of volume, the more rapidly the animal loses body heat. Therefore, animals living in a warm climate benefit from a higher ratio of surface area to volume, whereas those living in a cool climate benefit from a lower ratio.

Excursion

Water Displacement

A recipe for peanut butter cookies calls for 1 cup of peanut butter. Peanut butter is difficult to measure. If you have ever used a measuring cup to measure peanut butter, you know that there tend to be pockets of air at the bottom of the cup. And trying to scrape all of the peanut butter out of the cup and into the mixing bowl is a challenge.

A more convenient method of measuring 1 cup of peanut butter is to fill a 2-cup measuring cup with 1 cup of water. Then add peanut butter to the water until the water reaches the 2-cup mark. (Make sure all the peanut butter is below the top of the water.) Drain off the water, and the one cup of peanut butter drops easily into the mixing bowl.

This method of measuring peanut butter works because when an object sinks below the surface of the water, the object displaces an amount of water that is equal to the volume of the object.

(continued)

A sphere with a diameter of 4 in. is placed in a rectangular tank of water that is 6 in. long and 5 in. wide. How much does the water level rise? Round to the nearest hundredth of an inch.

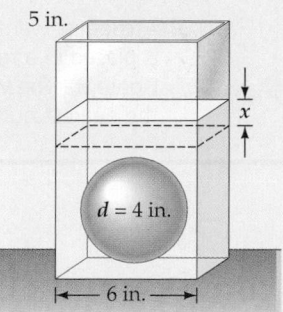

$V = \frac{4}{3}\pi r^3$ • Use the formula for the volume of a sphere.

$V = \frac{4}{3}\pi(2^3) = \frac{32}{3}\pi$ • $r = \frac{1}{2}d = \frac{1}{2}(4) = 2$

Let x represent the amount of the rise in water level. The volume of the sphere will equal the volume of the water displaced. As shown above, this volume is the rectangular solid with width 5 in., length 6 in., and height x in.

$V = LWH$ • Use the formula for the volume of a rectangular solid.

$\frac{32}{3}\pi = (6)(5)x$ • Substitute $\frac{32}{3}\pi$ for V, **6** for L, **5** for W, and x for H.

$\frac{32}{90}\pi = x$ • The exact height that the water will rise is $\frac{32}{90}\pi$.

$1.12 \approx x$ • Use a calculator to find an approximation.

The water will rise approximately 1.12 in.

Excursion Exercises

Figure 1   Figure 2   Figure 3

1. A cylinder with a 2-centimeter radius and a height of 10 cm is submerged in a tank of water that is 20 cm wide and 30 cm long (see Figure 1). How much does the water level rise? Round to the nearest hundredth of a centimeter.

(continued)

2. A sphere with a radius of 6 in. is placed in a rectangular tank of water that is 16 in. wide and 20 in. long (see Figure 2). The sphere displaces water until two-thirds of the sphere, with respect to its volume, is submerged. How much does the water level rise? Round to the nearest hundredth of an inch.

3. A chemist wants to know the density of a statue that weighs 15 lb. The statue is placed in a rectangular tank of water that is 12 in. long and 12 in. wide (see Figure 3). The water level rises 0.42 in. Find the density of the statue. Round to the nearest hundredth of a pound per cubic inch. *Hint:* Density = weight ÷ volume.

Exercise Set 8.4

In Exercises 1–6, find the volume of the figure. For calculations involving π, give both the exact value and an approximation to the nearest hundredth of a unit.

1.

6 in.
14 in.
10 in.

2.

14 ft
12 ft

3.

5 ft
3 ft
3 ft

4.

7.5 m
7.5 m
7.5 m

5.

3 cm

6.
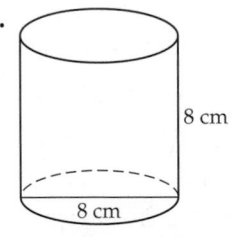
8 cm
8 cm

In Exercises 7–12, find the surface area of the figure. For calculations involving π, give both the exact value and an approximation to the nearest hundredth of a unit.

7.

3 m
5 m
4 m

8.

14 ft
14 ft
14 ft

9.
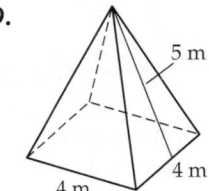
5 m
4 m
4 m

10.

2 cm

11.
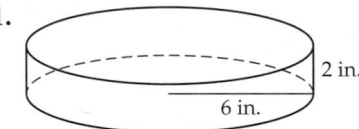
2 in.
6 in.

12.
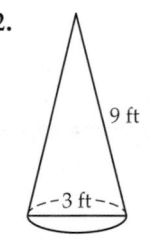
9 ft
3 ft

In Exercises 13–46, solve.

13. Volume A rectangular solid has a length of 6.8 m, a width of 2.5 m, and a height of 2 m. Find the volume of a solid.

14. Volume Find the volume of a rectangular solid that has a length of 4.5 ft, a width of 3 ft, and a height of 1.5 ft.

15. Volume Find the volume of a cube whose side measures 2.5 in.

16. Volume The length of a side of a cube is 7 cm. Find the volume of the cube.

17. **Volume** The diameter of a sphere is 6 ft. Find the exact volume of the sphere.

18. **Volume** Find the volume of a sphere that has a radius of 1.2 m. Round to the nearest hundredth of a cubic meter.

19. **Volume** The diameter of the base of a cylinder is 24 cm. The height of the cylinder is 18 cm. Find the volume of the cylinder. Round to the nearest hundredth of a cubic centimeter.

20. **Volume** The height of a cylinder is 7.2 m. The radius of the base is 4 m. Find the exact volume of the cylinder.

21. **Volume** The radius of the base of a cone is 5 in. The height of the cone is 9 in. Find the exact volume of the cone.

22. **Volume** The height of a cone is 15 cm. The diameter of the cone is 10 cm. Find the volume of the cone. Round to the nearest hundredth of a cubic centimeter.

23. **Volume** The length of a side of the base of a regular square pyramid is 6 in. and the height of the pyramid is 10 in. Find the volume of the pyramid.

24. **Volume** The height of a regular square pyramid is 8 m and the length of a side of the base is 9 m. What is the volume of the pyramid?

25. **The Statue of Liberty** The index finger of the Statue of Liberty is 8 ft long. The circumference at the second joint is 3.5 ft. Use the formula for the volume of a cylinder to approximate the volume of the index finger on the Statue of Liberty. Round to the nearest hundredth of a cubic foot.

26. **Surface Area** The height of a rectangular solid is 5 ft, the length is 8 ft, and the width is 4 ft. Find the surface area of the solid.

27. **Surface Area** The width of a rectangular solid is 32 cm, the length is 60 cm, and the height is 14 cm. What is the surface area of the solid?

28. **Surface Area** The side of a cube measures 3.4 m. Find the surface area of the cube.

29. **Surface Area** Find the surface area of a cube with a side measuring 1.5 in.

30. **Surface Area** Find the exact surface area of a sphere with a diameter of 15 cm.

31. **Surface Area** The radius of a sphere is 2 in. Find the surface area of the sphere. Round to the nearest hundredth of a square inch.

32. **Surface Area** The radius of the base of a cylinder is 4 in. The height of the cylinder is 12 in. Find the surface area of the cylinder. Round to the nearest hundredth of a square inch.

33. **Surface Area** The diameter of the base of a cylinder is 1.8 m. The height of the cylinder is 0.7 m. Find the exact surface area of the cylinder.

34. **Surface Area** The slant height of a cone is 2.5 ft. The radius of the base is 1.5 ft. Find the exact surface area of the cone. The formula for the surface area of a cone is given on page 514.

35. **Surface Area** The diameter of the base of a cone is 21 in. The slant height is 16 in. What is the surface area of the cone? The formula for the surface area of a cone is given on page 514. Round to the nearest hundredth of a square inch.

36. **Surface Area** The length of a side of the base of a pyramid is 9 in., and the pyramid's slant height is 12 in. Find the surface area of the pyramid.

37. **Surface Area** The slant height of a regular square pyramid is 18 m, and the length of a side of the base is 16 m. What is the surface area of the pyramid?

38. **Appliances** The volume of a freezer that is a rectangular solid with a length of 7 ft and a height of 3 ft is 52.5 ft^3. Find the width of the freezer.

39. **Aquariums** The length of an aquarium is 18 in. and the width is 12 in. If the volume of the aquarium is 1836 in^3, what is the height of the aquarium?

40. Surface Area The surface area of a rectangular solid is 108 cm². The height of the solid is 4 cm, and the length is 6 cm. Find the width of the rectangular solid.

41. Surface Area The length of a rectangular solid is 12 ft and the width is 3 ft. If the surface area is 162 ft², find the height of the rectangular solid.

42. Paint A can of paint will cover 300 ft² of surface. How many cans of paint should be purchased to paint a cylinder that has a height of 30 ft and a radius of 12 ft?

43. Ballooning A hot air balloon is in the shape of a sphere. Approximately how much fabric was used to construct the balloon if its diameter is 32 ft? Round to the nearest square foot.

44. Aquariums How much glass is needed to make a fish tank that is 12 in. long, 8 in. wide, and 9 in. high? The fish tank is open at the top.

45. Food Labels Find the area of a label used to completely cover the side of a cylindrical can of juice that has a diameter of 16.5 cm and a height of 17 cm. Round to the nearest hundredth of a square centimeter.

46. Surface Area The length of a side of the base of a regular square pyramid is 5 cm and the slant height of the pyramid is 8 cm. How much larger is the surface area of this pyramid than the surface area of a cone with a diameter of 5 cm and a slant height of 8 cm? Round to the nearest hundredth of a square centimeter.

In Exercises 47–52, find the volume of the figure. Round to the nearest hundredth of a unit.

47.

48.

49.

50.

51.

52.

In Exercises 53–58, find the surface area of the figure. Round to the nearest hundredth of a unit.

53.

54.

55.

56.

57.

58.

59. Oil Tanks A truck is carrying an oil tank, as shown in the figure below. If the tank is half full, how many cubic feet of oil is the truck carrying? Round to the nearest hundredth of a cubic foot.

60. Concrete The concrete floor of a building is shown in the following figure. At a cost of $3.15 per cubic foot,

find the cost of having the floor poured. Round to the nearest cent.

61. Swimming Pools How many liters of water are needed to fill the swimming pool shown below? (1 m^3 contains 1000 L.)

62. Paint A can of paint will cover 250 ft^2 of surface. Find the number of cans of paint that should be purchased to paint the exterior of the auditorium shown in the figure below.

63. Metallurgy A piece of sheet metal is cut and formed into the shape shown below. Given that there are 0.24 g in 1 cm^2 of the metal, find the total number of grams of metal used. Round to the nearest hundredth of a gram.

64. Plastering The walls of a room that is 25.5 ft long, 22 ft wide, and 8 ft high are being plastered. There are two doors in the room, each measuring 2.5 ft by 7 ft. Each of the six windows in the room measures 2.5 ft by 4 ft. At a cost of $.75 per square foot, find the cost of plastering the walls of the room.

65. Gold A solid sphere of gold with a radius of 0.5 cm has a value of $180. Find the value of a sphere of the same type of gold with a radius of 1.5 cm.

66. Swimming Pools A swimming pool is built in the shape of a rectangular solid. It holds 32,000 gal of water. If the length, width, and height of the pool are each doubled, how many gallons of water will be needed to fill the pool?

Extensions

CRITICAL THINKING

67. Half of a sphere is called a **hemisphere.** Derive formulas for the volume and surface area of a hemisphere.

68. a. Draw a two-dimensional figure that can be cut out and made into a right circular cone.

   b. Draw a two-dimensional figure that can be cut out and made into a regular square pyramid.

69. A sphere fits inside a cylinder as shown in the following figure. The height of the cylinder equals the diam-

eter of the sphere. Show that the surface area of the sphere equals the surface area of the side of the cylinder.

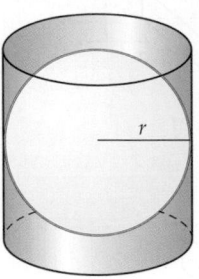

70. Determine whether the statement is always true, sometimes true, or never true.

   a. The slant height of a regular square pyramid is longer than the height.

   b. The slant height of a cone is shorter than the height.

   c. The four triangular faces of a regular square pyramid are equilateral triangles.

71. a. What is the effect on the surface area of a rectangular solid of doubling the width and height?

   b. What is the effect on the volume of a rectangular solid of doubling the length and width?

   c. What is the effect on the volume of a cube of doubling the length of each side of the cube?

   d. What is the effect on the surface area of a cylinder of doubling the radius and height?

EXPLORATIONS

72. Explain how you could cut through a cube so that the face of the resulting solid is

   a. a square.   **b.** an equilateral triangle.

   c. a trapezoid.   **d.** a hexagon.

| SECTION 8.5 | **Introduction to Trigonometry** |

Trigonometric Functions of an Acute Angle

Given the lengths of two sides of a right triangle, it is possible to determine the length of the third side by using the Pythagorean Theorem. In some situations, however, it may not be practical or possible to know the lengths of two of the sides of a right triangle.

Consider, for example, the problem of engineers trying to determine the distance across a ravine so that they can design a bridge that can be built connecting the two sides. Look at the triangle to the left.

It is fairly easy to measure the length of the side of the triangle that is on the land (100 feet), but the lengths of sides a and c cannot be measured easily because of the ravine.

The study of *trigonometry*, a term that comes from two Greek words meaning "triangle measurement," began about 2000 years ago, partially as a means of solving surveying problems such as the one above. In this section, we will examine *right triangle* trigonometry—that is, trigonometry that applies only to right triangles.

When working with right triangles, it is convenient to refer to the side *opposite* an angle and to the side *adjacent* to (next to) an angle. The hypotenuse of a right triangle is not adjacent to or opposite either of the acute angles in a right triangle.

TAKE NOTE

In trigonometry, it is common practice to use Greek letters for angles of a triangle. Here are some frequently used letters: α (alpha), β (beta), and θ (theta). The word *alphabet* is derived from the first two letters of the Greek alphabet, α and β.

Consider the right triangle in Figure 8.1 shown at the left. Six possible ratios can be formed using the lengths of the sides of the triangle.

$$\frac{\text{length of opposite side}}{\text{length of hypotenuse}} \qquad \frac{\text{length of hypotenuse}}{\text{length of opposite side}}$$

$$\frac{\text{length of adjacent side}}{\text{length of hypotenuse}} \qquad \frac{\text{length of hypotenuse}}{\text{length of adjacent side}}$$

$$\frac{\text{length of opposite side}}{\text{length of adjacent side}} \qquad \frac{\text{length of adjacent side}}{\text{length of opposite side}}$$

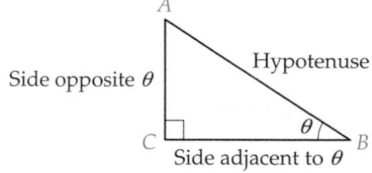

Figure 8.1

Each of these ratios defines a value of a trigonometric function of the acute angle θ. The functions are **sine** (sin), **cosine** (cos), **tangent** (tan), **cosecant** (csc), **secant** (sec), and **cotangent** (cot).

The Trigonometric Functions of an Acute Angle of a Right Triangle

If θ is an acute angle of a right triangle ABC, then

$$\sin \theta = \frac{\text{length of opposite side}}{\text{length of hypotenuse}} \qquad \csc \theta = \frac{\text{length of hypotenuse}}{\text{length of opposite side}}$$

$$\cos \theta = \frac{\text{length of adjacent side}}{\text{length of hypotenuse}} \qquad \sec \theta = \frac{\text{length of hypotenuse}}{\text{length of adjacent side}}$$

$$\tan \theta = \frac{\text{length of opposite side}}{\text{length of adjacent side}} \qquad \cot \theta = \frac{\text{length of adjacent side}}{\text{length of opposite side}}$$

As a convenience, we will write opp, adj, and hyp as abbreviations for *the length of the* opposite side, adjacent side, and hypotenuse, respectively. Using this convention, the definitions of the trigonometric functions are written

$$\sin \theta = \frac{\text{opp}}{\text{hyp}} \qquad \csc \theta = \frac{\text{hyp}}{\text{opp}}$$

$$\cos \theta = \frac{\text{adj}}{\text{hyp}} \qquad \sec \theta = \frac{\text{hyp}}{\text{adj}}$$

$$\tan \theta = \frac{\text{opp}}{\text{adj}} \qquad \cot \theta = \frac{\text{adj}}{\text{opp}}$$

All of the trigonometric functions have applications, but the sine, cosine, and tangent functions are used most frequently. For the remainder of this section, we will focus on those functions.

When working with trigonometric functions, be sure to draw a diagram and label the adjacent and opposite sides of an angle. For instance, in the definition above, if we had placed θ at angle A, then the triangle would have been labeled as shown at the left. The definitions of the functions remain the same.

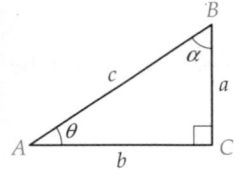

$$\sin \theta = \frac{\text{opp}}{\text{hyp}} \qquad \cos \theta = \frac{\text{adj}}{\text{hyp}} \qquad \tan \theta = \frac{\text{opp}}{\text{adj}}$$

QUESTION   *For the right triangle shown at the left, indicate which side is*

   a. adjacent to $\angle A$ *b. opposite θ*
   c. adjacent to α   *d. opposite $\angle B$*

EXAMPLE 1 ■ Find the Value of Trigonometric Functions

For the right triangle at the right, find the values of $\sin \theta$, $\cos \theta$, and $\tan \theta$.

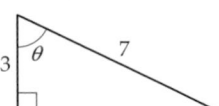

Solution
Use the Pythagorean Theorem to find the length of the side opposite θ.

$a^2 + b^2 = c^2$

$3^2 + b^2 = 7^2$ • $a = \mathbf{3}$, $c = \mathbf{7}$

$9 + b^2 = 49$

$b^2 = 40$

$b = \sqrt{40} = 2\sqrt{10}$

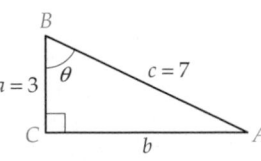

Using the definition of the trigonometric functions, we have

$$\sin \theta = \frac{\text{opp}}{\text{hyp}} = \frac{2\sqrt{10}}{7} \qquad \cos \theta = \frac{\text{adj}}{\text{hyp}} = \frac{3}{7} \qquad \tan \theta = \frac{\text{opp}}{\text{adj}} = \frac{2\sqrt{10}}{3}$$

CHECK YOUR PROGRESS 1   For the right triangle at the right, find the values of $\sin \theta$, $\cos \theta$, and $\tan \theta$.

Solution   *See page S31.*

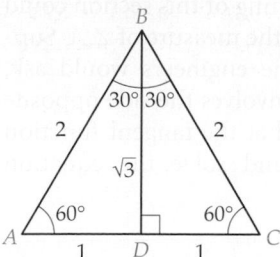

In Example 1, we gave the exact answers. In many cases, approximate values of trigonometric functions are given. The answers to Example 1, rounded to the nearest ten-thousandth, are

$$\sin \theta = \frac{2\sqrt{10}}{7} \approx 0.9035 \quad \cos \theta = \frac{3}{7} \approx 0.4286 \quad \tan \theta = \frac{2\sqrt{10}}{3} \approx 2.1082$$

There are many occasions when we will want to know the value of a trigonometric function for a given angle. Triangle ABC at the left is an equilateral triangle with sides of length 2 units and angle bisector $\overline{BD}$. Because $\overline{BD}$ bisects $\angle ABC$, the measures of $\angle ABD$ and $\angle DBC$ are both 30°. The angle bisector $\overline{BD}$ also bisects $\overline{AC}$. Therefore, $AD = 1$ and $DC = 1$. Using the Pythagorean Theorem, we can find the measure of BD.

$$(DC)^2 + (BD)^2 = (BC)^2$$
$$1^2 + (BD)^2 = 2^2$$
$$1 + (BD)^2 = 4$$
$$(BD)^2 = 3$$
$$BD = \sqrt{3}$$

Using the definitions of the trigonometric functions and triangle BCD, we can find the values of the sine, cosine, and tangent of 30° and 60°.

$$\sin 30° = \frac{\text{opp}}{\text{hyp}} = \frac{1}{2} = 0.5 \qquad \sin 60° = \frac{\text{opp}}{\text{hyp}} = \frac{\sqrt{3}}{2} \approx 0.8660$$

$$\cos 30° = \frac{\text{adj}}{\text{hyp}} = \frac{\sqrt{3}}{2} \approx 0.8660 \qquad \cos 60° = \frac{\text{adj}}{\text{hyp}} = \frac{1}{2} = 0.5$$

$$\tan 30° = \frac{\text{opp}}{\text{adj}} = \frac{1}{\sqrt{3}} \approx 0.5774 \qquad \tan 60° = \frac{\text{opp}}{\text{adj}} = \sqrt{3} \approx 1.732$$

The properties of an equilateral triangle enabled us to calculate the values of the trigonometric functions for 30° and 60°. Calculating values of the trigonometric functions for most other angles, however, would be quite difficult. Fortunately, many calculators have been programmed to allow us to estimate these values.

To use a TI-83/84 calculator to find tan 30°, confirm that your calculator is in "degree mode." Press the tan button and key in 30. Then press $\boxed{\text{ENTER}}$.

$$\tan 30° \approx 0.5774$$

Despite the fact that the values of many trigonometric functions are approximate, it is customary to use the equals sign rather than the approximately equals sign when writing these function values. Thus we write $\tan 30° = 0.5774$.

CALCULATOR NOTE

Just as distances can be measured in feet, miles, meters, and other units, angles can be measured in various units: degrees, radians, and grads. In this section, we use only degree measurements for angles, so be sure your calculator is in degree mode.

On a TI-83/84, press the $\boxed{\text{MODE}}$ key to determine whether the calculator is in degree mode.

EXAMPLE 2 ■ Use a Calculator to Find the Value of a Trigonometric Function

Use a calculator to find sin 43.8° to the nearest ten-thousandth.

Solution $\sin 43.8° = 0.6921$

CHECK YOUR PROGRESS 2 Use a calculator to find tan 37.1° to the nearest ten-thousandth.

Solution *See page S32.*

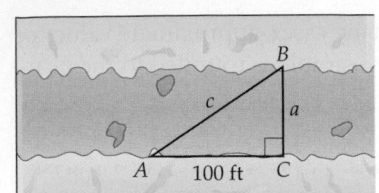

Using trigonometry, the engineers mentioned at the beginning of this section could determine the distance across the ravine after determining the measure of $\angle A$. Suppose the engineers measure the angle as $33.8°$. Now the engineers would ask, "Which trigonometric function, sine, cosine, or tangent, involves the side opposite an angle and the side adjacent to that angle?" Knowing that the tangent function is the required function, the engineers could write and solve the equation $\tan 33.8° = \dfrac{a}{100}$.

$$\tan 33.8° = \frac{a}{100}$$

$$100(\tan 33.8°) = a$$ • Multiply each side of the equation by **100**.

$$66.9 \approx a$$ • Use a calculator to find tan 33.8°. Multiply the result in the display by 100.

The distance across the ravine is approximately 66.9 feet.

EXAMPLE 3 ■ Find the Length of a Side of a Triangle

For the right triangle shown at the left, find the length of side a. Round to the nearest hundredth of a meter.

Solution
We are given the measure of $\angle A$ and the hypotenuse. We want to find the length of side a. Side a is opposite $\angle A$. The sine function involves the side opposite an angle and the hypotenuse.

$$\sin A = \frac{\text{opp}}{\text{hyp}}$$

$$\sin 26° = \frac{a}{24}$$ • $A = $ **26°**, hypotenuse $= $ **24** meters.

$$24(\sin 26°) = a$$ • Multiply each side by **24**.

$$10.52 \approx a$$ • Use a calculator to find sin 26°. Multiply the result in the display by 24.

The length of side a is approximately 10.52 meters.

CHECK YOUR PROGRESS 3 For the right triangle shown at the right, find the length of side a. Round to the nearest hundredth of a foot.

Solution See page S32.

Inverse Trigonometric Functions

Sometimes it is necessary to find one of the acute angles in a right triangle. For instance, suppose it is necessary to find the measure of $\angle A$ in the figure at the left. Because the side adjacent to $\angle A$ is known and the hypotenuse is known, we can write

$$\cos A = \frac{\text{adj}}{\text{hyp}}$$

$$\cos A = \frac{25}{27}$$

The solution of this equation is the angle whose cosine is $\frac{25}{27}$. This angle can be found by using the $\cos^{-1}$ key on a calculator.

$$\cos^{-1}\left(\frac{25}{27}\right) \approx 22.19160657$$

To the nearest tenth, the measure of $\angle A$ is $22.2°$.
The function $\cos^{-1}$ is called the *inverse cosine function*.

Definitions of the Inverse Sine, Inverse Cosine, and Inverse Tangent Functions

For $0° < x < 90°$:

$y = \sin^{-1}(x)$ can be read "y is the angle whose sine is x."
$y = \cos^{-1}(x)$ can be read "y is the angle whose cosine is x."
$y = \tan^{-1}(x)$ can be read "y is the angle whose tangent is x."

Note that $\sin^{-1}(x)$ is used to denote the inverse of the sine function. It is not the reciprocal of $\sin x$ but the notation used for its inverse. The same is true for $\cos^{-1}$ and $\tan^{-1}$.

EXAMPLE 4 ■ Evaluate an Inverse Trigonometric Function

Use a calculator to find $\sin^{-1}(0.9171)$. Round to the nearest tenth of a degree.

Solution

$\sin^{-1}(0.9171) \approx 66.5°$ • **The calculator must be in degree mode. Press the keys for the inverse sine function followed by .9171. Press** $\boxed{\text{ENTER}}$.

CHECK YOUR PROGRESS 4   Use a calculator to find $\tan^{-1}(0.3165)$. Round to the nearest tenth of a degree.

Solution   *See page S32.*

EXAMPLE 5 ■ Find the Measure of an Angle Using the Inverse of a Trigonometric Function

Given $\sin \theta = 0.7239$, find θ. Use a calculator. Round to the nearest tenth of a degree.

Solution
This is equivalent to finding $\sin^{-1}(0.7239)$. The calculator must be in the degree mode.

$$\sin^{-1}(0.7239) \approx 46.4°$$
$$\theta \approx 46.4°$$

CHECK YOUR PROGRESS 5   Given $\tan \theta = 0.5681$, find θ. Use a calculator. Round to the nearest tenth of a degree.

Solution   *See page S32.*

✔ TAKE NOTE

The expression $y = \sin^{-1}(x)$ is sometimes written $y = \arcsin(x)$. The two expressions are equivalent. The expressions $y = \cos^{-1}(x)$ and $y = \arccos(x)$ are equivalent, as are $y = \tan^{-1}(x)$ and $y = \arctan(x)$.

CALCULATOR NOTE

To find an inverse function on a calculator, usually the $\boxed{\text{INV}}$ or $\boxed{\text{2nd}}$ key is pressed prior to pushing the function key. Some calculators have $\sin^{-1}$, $\cos^{-1}$, and $\tan^{-1}$ keys. Consult the instruction manual for your calculator.

✔ TAKE NOTE

If
$\sin \theta = 0.7239$,
then
$\theta = \sin^{-1}(0.7239)$.

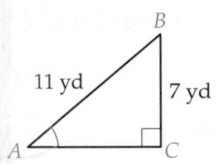

EXAMPLE 6 ■ Find the Measure of an Angle in a Right Triangle

For the right triangle shown at the left, find the measure of $\angle B$. Round to the nearest tenth of a degree.

Solution
We want to find the measure of $\angle B$, and we are given the lengths of the sides opposite $\angle B$ and adjacent to $\angle B$. The tangent function involves the side opposite an angle and the side adjacent to that angle.

$$\tan B = \frac{\text{opposite}}{\text{adjacent}}$$

$$\tan B = \frac{24}{16}$$

$$B = \tan^{-1}\left(\frac{24}{16}\right)$$

$$B \approx 56.3°$$ • Use the tan^{-1} key on a calculator.

The measure of $\angle B$ is approximately 56.3°.

CHECK YOUR PROGRESS 6   For the right triangle shown at the left, find the measure of $\angle A$. Round to the nearest tenth of a degree.

Solution See page S32.

Angles of Elevation and Depression

The use of trigonometry is necessary in a variety of situations. One application, called **line-of-sight problems,** concerns an observer looking at an object.

Angles of elevation and depression are measured with respect to a horizontal line. If the object being sighted is above the observer, the acute angle formed by the line of sight and the horizontal line is an **angle of elevation.** If the object being sighted is below the observer, the acute angle formed by the line of sight and the horizontal line is an **angle of depression.**

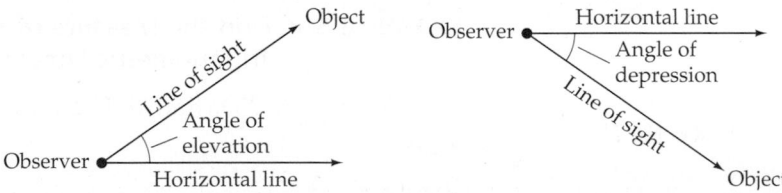

EXAMPLE 7 ■ Solve an Angle of Elevation Problem

The angle of elevation of the top of a flagpole 62 feet away is 34°. Find the height of the flagpole. Round to the nearest tenth of a foot.

Solution
Draw a diagram. To find the height, h, write a trigonometric function that relates the given information and the unknown side of the triangle.

$$\tan 34° = \frac{h}{62}$$
$$62(\tan 34°) = h \qquad \bullet \text{ Multiply each side by } \mathbf{62.}$$
$$41.8 \approx h \qquad \bullet \text{ Use a calculator to find } \tan 34°. \text{ Multiply}$$
the result in the display by 62.

The height of the flagpole is approximately 41.8 feet.

CHECK YOUR PROGRESS 7   The angle of depression from the top of a lighthouse that is 20 meters high to a boat on the water is 25°. How far is the boat from the base of the lighthouse? Round to the nearest tenth of a meter.

Solution See page S32.

Excursion

Approximating the Value of Trigonometric Functions

The value of a trigonometric function can be approximated by drawing a triangle with a given angle. To illustrate, we will choose an angle of 35°.

To find the tangent of 35° using the definitions given in this section, we can carefully construct a right triangle containing an angle of 35°. Because any two right triangles containing an angle of 35° are similar, *the value for tan 35° is the same no matter what triangle we draw.*

Excursion Exercises

1. Draw a horizontal line segment 10 cm long with left endpoint *A* and right endpoint *C*. See the diagram at the left.

2. Using a protractor, construct at *A* a 35° angle.

3. Draw at *C* a vertical line that intersects the terminal side of angle *A* at *B*. Your drawing should be similar to the one at the left.

4. Measure line segment *BC*.

5. What is the approximate value of tan 35°?

6. Using your value for *BC* and the Pythagorean Theorem, estimate *AB*.

7. Estimate sin 35° and cos 35°.

8. What are the values of sin 35°, cos 35°, and tan 35° as produced by a calculator? Round to the nearest ten-thousandth.

Exercise Set 8.5

1. Use the right triangle at the right and sides *a*, *b*, and *c* to do the following:

a. Name the ratio for the trigonometric function sin *A*.

b. Name the ratio for the trigonometric function sin *B*.

c. Name the ratio for the trigonometric function cos *A*.

d. Name the ratio for the trigonometric function cos *B*.

e. Name the ratio for the trigonometric function tan *A*.

f. Name the ratio for the trigonometric function tan *B*.

2. Explain the meaning of the notation $y = \sin^{-1}(x)$, $y = \cos^{-1}(x)$, and $y = \tan^{-1}(x)$.

In Exercises 3–10, find the values of sin θ, cos θ, and tan θ for the given right triangle. Give the exact values.

3.

4.

5.

6.

7.

8.

9.

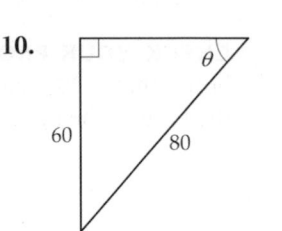

10.

In Exercises 11–26, use a calculator to estimate the value of each of the following. Round to the nearest ten-thousandth.

11. cos 47°   **12.** sin 62°   **13.** tan 55°

14. cos 11°   **15.** sin 85.6°   **16.** cos 21.9°

17. tan 63.4°   **18.** sin 7.8°   **19.** tan 41.6°

20. cos 73°   **21.** sin 57.7°   **22.** tan 39.2°

23. sin 58.3°   **24.** tan 35.1°   **25.** cos 46.9°

26. sin 50°

In Exercises 27–42, use a calculator. Round to the nearest tenth.

27. Given sin θ = 0.6239, find θ.

28. Given cos β = 0.9516, find β.

29. Find $\cos^{-1}(0.7536)$.

30. Find $\sin^{-1}(0.4478)$.

31. Given tan α = 0.3899, find α.

32. Given sin β = 0.7349, find β.

33. Find $\tan^{-1}(0.7815)$.

34. Find $\cos^{-1}(0.6032)$.

35. Given cos θ = 0.3007, find θ.

36. Given tan α = 1.588, find α.

37. Find $\sin^{-1}(0.0105)$.

38. Find $\tan^{-1}(0.2438)$.

39. Given sin β = 0.9143, find β.

40. Given cos θ = 0.4756, find θ.

41. Find $\cos^{-1}(0.8704)$.

42. Find $\sin^{-1}(0.2198)$.

For Exercises 43–56, draw a picture and label it. Set up an equation and solve it. Show all your work. Round an angle to the nearest tenth of a degree. Round the length of a side to the nearest hundredth of a unit.

43. Ballooning A balloon, tethered by a cable 997 feet long, was blown by a wind so that the cable made an angle of 57.6° with the ground. Find the height of the balloon off the ground.

997 ft
57.6°

44. Roadways A road is inclined at an angle of 9.8° with the horizontal. Find the distance that one must drive on this road in order to be elevated 14.8 feet above the horizontal.

45. Home Maintenance A ladder 30.8 feet long leans against a building. If the foot of the ladder is 7.25 feet from the base of the building, find the angle the top of the ladder makes with the building.

46. Aviation A plane takes off from a field and rises at an angle of 11.4° with the horizontal. Find the height of the plane after it has traveled a distance of 1250 feet.

47. Guy Wires A guy wire whose grounded end is 16 feet from the telephone pole it supports makes an angle of 56.7° with the ground. How long is the wire?

16 ft

48. Angle of Depression A lighthouse built at sea level is 169 feet tall. From its top, the angle of depression to a

boat below measures 25.1°. Find the distance from the boat to the foot of the lighthouse.

49. Angle of Elevation At a point 39.3 feet from the base of a tree, the angle of elevation of its top measures 53.4°. Find the height of the tree.

53.4°
39.3 ft

50. Angle of Depression An artillery spotter in a plane that is at an altitude of 978 feet measures the angle of depression of an enemy tank as 28.5°. How far is the enemy tank from the point on the ground directly below the spotter?

51. Home Maintenance A 15-foot ladder leans against a house. The ladder makes an angle of 65° with the ground. How far up the side of the house does the ladder reach?

65°

52. Angle of Elevation Find the angle of elevation of the sun when a tree 40.5 feet high casts a shadow 28.3 feet long.

53. Guy Wires A television transmitter tower is 600 feet high. If the angle between the guy wire (attached at the top) and the tower is 55.4°, how long is the guy wire?

54. Ramps A ramp used to load a racing car onto a flatbed carrier is 5.25 meters long, and its upper end is 1.74 meters above the lower end. Find the angle between the ramp and the road.

55. Angle of Elevation The angle of elevation of the sun is 51.3° at a time when a tree casts a shadow 23.7 yards long. Find the height of the tree.

56. Angle of Depression From the top of a building 312 feet tall, the angle of depression to a flower bed on the ground below is 12.0°. What is the distance between the base of the building and the flower bed?

Extensions

CRITICAL THINKING

57. Can the value of sin θ or cos θ ever be greater than 1? Explain your answer.

58. Can the value of tan θ ever be greater than 1? Explain your answer.

59. Let $\sin \theta = \dfrac{2}{3}$. Find the exact value of cos θ.

60. Let $\tan \theta = \dfrac{5}{4}$. Find the exact value of sin θ.

61. Let $\cos \theta = \dfrac{3}{4}$. Find the exact value of tan θ.

62. Let $\sin \theta = \dfrac{\sqrt{5}}{4}$. Find the exact value of tan θ.

63. Let sin θ = a, a > 0. Find cos θ.

64. Let tan θ = a, a > 0. Find sin θ.

EXPLORATIONS

As we noted in this section, angles can also be measured in *radians*. To define a radian, first consider a circle of radius *r* and two radii $\overline{OA}$ and $\overline{OB}$. The angle θ formed by the two radii is a **central angle**. The portion of the circle between *A* and *B* is an **arc** of the circle and is written $\overset{\frown}{AB}$. We say that $\overset{\frown}{AB}$ *subtends* the angle θ. The length of the arc is *s*. (See Figure 1 below.)

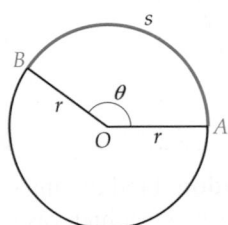

Figure 1

Definition of Radian

One **radian** is the measure of the central angle subtended by an arc of length *r*. The measure of θ in Figure 2 is 1 radian.

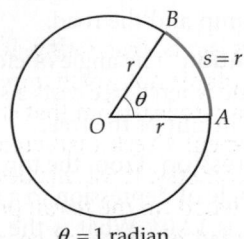

θ = 1 radian

Figure 2

To find the radian measure of an angle subtended by an arc of length *s*, use the following formula.

Radian Measure

Given an arc of length *s* on a circle of radius *r*, the measure of the central angle subtended by the arc is $\theta = \dfrac{s}{r}$ radians.

For example, to find the measure in radians of the central angle subtended by an arc of 9 in. in a circle of radius 12 in., divide the length of the arc (*s* = 9 in.) by the length of the radius (*r* = 12 in.). See Figure 3.

$$\theta = \frac{9 \text{ in.}}{12 \text{ in.}} \text{ radian}$$
$$= \frac{3}{4} \text{ radian}$$

Figure 3

65. Find the measure in radians of the central angle subtended by an arc of 12 cm in a circle of radius 3 cm.

66. Find the measure in radians of the central angle subtended by an arc of 4 cm in a circle of radius 8 cm.

67. Find the measure in radians of the central angle subtended by an arc of 6 in. in a circle of radius 9 in.

68. Find the measure in radians of the central angle subtended by an arc of 12 ft in a circle of radius 10 ft.

Recall that the circumference of a circle is given by C = 2πr. Therefore, the radian measure of the central angle subtended by the circumference is $\theta = \dfrac{2\pi r}{r} = 2\pi$.

In degree measure, the central angle has a measure of 360°. Thus we have 2π radians = 360°. Dividing each side of the equation by 2 gives π radians = 180°. From the last equation, we can establish the conversion factors $\dfrac{\pi \text{ radians}}{180°}$ and $\dfrac{180°}{\pi \text{ radians}}$. These conversion factors are used to convert between radians and degrees.

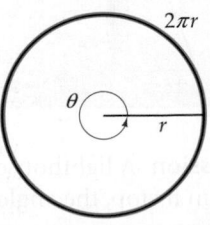

Conversion between Radians and Degrees

- To convert from degrees to radians, multiply by $\dfrac{\pi \text{ radians}}{180°}$.

- To convert from radians to degrees, multiply by $\dfrac{180°}{\pi \text{ radians}}$.

For instance, to convert 30° to radians, multiply 30° by $\dfrac{\pi \text{ radians}}{180°}$.

$$30° = 30°\left(\frac{\pi \text{ radians}}{180°}\right) \quad \bullet \text{ Exact answer}$$

$$= \frac{\pi}{6} \text{ radian} \quad \bullet \text{ Approximate answer}$$

$$\approx 0.5236 \text{ radian}$$

To convert 2 radians to degrees, multiply 2 by $\dfrac{180°}{\pi \text{ radians}}$.

$$2 \text{ radians} = 2\left(\frac{180°}{\pi \text{ radians}}\right) \bullet \text{ Exact answer}$$

$$= \left(\frac{360}{\pi}\right)° \quad \bullet \text{ Approximate answer}$$

$$\approx 114.5916°$$

69. What is the measure in degrees of 1 radian?

70. Is the measure of 1 radian larger or smaller than the measure of 1°?

In Exercises 71–76, convert degree measure to radian measure. Find an exact answer and an answer rounded to the nearest ten-thousandth.

71. 45°   **72.** 180°   **73.** 315°

74. 90°   **75.** 210°   **76.** 18°

In Exercises 77–82, convert radian measure to degree measure. For Exercises 80–82, find an exact answer and an answer rounded to the nearest ten-thousandth.

77. $\dfrac{\pi}{3}$ radians   **78.** $\dfrac{11\pi}{6}$ radians

79. $\dfrac{4\pi}{3}$ radians   **80.** 1.2 radians

81. 3 radians   **82.** 2.4 radians

SECTION 8.6 | **Non-Euclidean Geometry**

Euclidean Geometry versus Non-Euclidean Geometry

Learning to play a game by reading the rules can be frustrating. If the game has too many rules, you may decide that learning to play is not worth the effort. Most popular games are based on a few rules that are easy to learn but that still allow the game to develop into complex situations. The ancient Greek mathematician Euclid was immersed in the mathematical "game" of geometry. It was his desire to construct a substantial body of geometrical knowledge based on the *fewest* possible number of rules, which he called **postulates.** Euclid based his study of geometry on the following five postulates.

Euclid's Postulates

P1: A line segment can be drawn from any point to any other point.

P2: A line segment can be extended continuously in a straight line.

P3: A circle can be drawn with any center and any radius.

P4: All right angles are equal to one another.

P5: *The Parallel Postulate*   Through a given point not on a given line, exactly one line can be drawn parallel to the given line.

For many centuries, the truth of these postulates was felt to be self-evident. However, a few mathematicians suspected that the fifth postulate, known as the Parallel Postulate, could be deduced from the other postulates. Many individuals took on the task of proving the Parallel Postulate, but after more than 2000 years, the proof of the Parallel Postulate still remained unsolved.

Carl Friedrich Gauss (gaus′) (1777–1855) became interested in the problem of proving the Parallel Postulate as a teenager. After many failed attempts to establish the Parallel Postulate as a theorem, Gauss decided to take a different route. He came to the conclusion that the Parallel Postulate was an independent postulate and that it could be changed to produce a new type of geometry. This is analogous to changing one of the rules of a game to create a new game.

The diaries and letters written by Gauss show that he proposed the following alternative postulate.

Gauss's Alternative to the Parallel Postulate

Through a given point not on a given line, there are *at least two* lines parallel to the given line.

Thus Gauss was the first person to realize that non-Euclidean geometries could be created by merely changing or excluding the Parallel Postulate. It has been speculated that Gauss did not publish this result because he felt it would not be readily accepted by other mathematicians.

The idea of using an alternative postulate in place of the Parallel Postulate was first proposed *openly* by the Russian mathematician Nikolai Lobachevsky. In a lecture given in 1826, and in a series of monthly articles that appeared in the academic journal of the University of Kazan in 1829, Lobachevsky provided a detailed investigation into the problem of the Parallel Postulate. He proposed that a consistent new geometry could be developed by replacing the Parallel Postulate with the alternative postulate, which assumes that *more than one* parallel line can be drawn through a point not on a given line.

Lobachevsky described his geometry as *imaginary geometry*, because he could not comprehend a model of such a geometry. Independently of each other, Gauss and Lobachevsky had each conceived of the same idea; but whereas Gauss chose to keep the idea to himself, Lobachevsky professed the idea to the world. It is for this reason that we now refer to the geometry they each conceived as *Lobachevskian geometry*. Today Lobachevskian geometry is often called *hyperbolic geometry*.

The year 1826, in which Lobachevsky first lectured about a new non-Euclidean geometry, also marks the birth of the mathematician Bernhard Riemann. Although Riemann died of tuberculosis at age 39, he made major contributions in several areas of mathematics and physics, including the theory of functions of complex variables, electrodynamics, and non-Euclidean geometry. Riemann was the first person to consider a geometry in which the Parallel Postulate was replaced with the following postulate.

Riemann's Alternative to the Parallel Postulate

Through a given point not on a given line, there exist *no* lines parallel to the given line.

Unlike the geometry developed by Lobachevsky, which was not based on a physical model, the non-Euclidean geometry of Riemann was closely associated with a sphere and the remarkable idea that because a line is an undefined term, a line on the surface of a sphere can be different from a line on a plane. Even though a line on a sphere can be different from a line on a plane, it seems reasonable that "spherical lines" should retain some of the properties of lines on a plane. For example, on a plane, the shortest distance between two points is measured along the line that connects the points. The line that connects the points is an example of what is called a *geodesic*.

Definition of a Geodesic

A **geodesic** is a curve C on a surface S such that for any two points on C, the portion of C between these points is the shortest path on S that joins these points.

On a sphere, the geodesic between two points is a *great circle* that connects the points.

Definition of a Great Circle

A **great circle** of a sphere is a circle on the surface of the sphere whose center is at the center of the sphere. Any two points on a great circle divide the circle into two arcs. The shorter arc is the **minor arc** and the longer arc is the **major arc.**

In *Riemannian geometry,* which is also called *spherical geometry* or *elliptical geometry,* great circles, which are the geodesics of a sphere, are thought of as lines. Figure 8.2 shows a sphere and two of its great circles. Because all great circles of a sphere intersect, a sphere provides us with a model of a geometry in which there are no parallel lines.

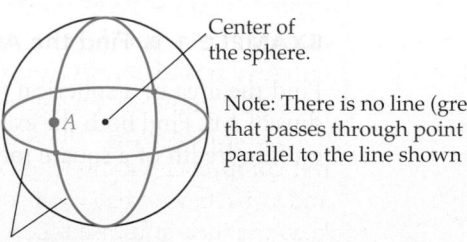

Center of the sphere.

Note: There is no line (great circle) that passes through point A that is parallel to the line shown in blue.

Two great circles of the sphere.

Figure 8.2 *A sphere and its great circles serve as a physical model for Riemannian geometry.*

2. Bell, E. T. *Men of Mathematics.* New York: Touchstone Books, Simon and Schuster, 1986.

In Riemannian geometry, a triangle may have as many as three right angles. Figure 8.3 illustrates a spherical triangle with one right angle, a spherical triangle with two right angles, and a spherical triangle with three right angles.

      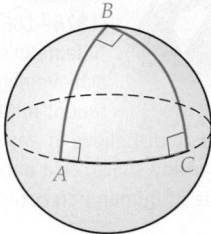

a. A spherical triangle with one right angle

b. A spherical triangle with two right angles

c. A spherical triangle with three right angles

Figure 8.3

In Euclidean geometry it is not possible to determine the area of a triangle from the measures of its angles alone.

In spherical geometry, however, any two triangles on the same sphere that are similar are also congruent. Therefore, in spherical geometry, the area of a triangle depends on the size of its angles and the radius of the sphere.

QUESTION   *In Euclidean geometry, are two similar triangles necessarily congruent triangles?*

The Spherical Triangle Area Formula

The area S of the spherical triangle ABC on a sphere with radius r is given by

$$S = (m\angle A + m\angle B + m\angle C - 180°) \cdot \left(\frac{\pi}{180°}\right)r^2$$

where each angle is measured in degrees.

EXAMPLE 1 ■ **Find the Area of a Spherical Triangle**

Find the area of a spherical triangle with three right angles on a sphere with a radius of 1 ft. Find both the exact area and the approximate area rounded to the nearest hundredth of a square foot.

ANSWER   *No.*

✔ **TAKE NOTE**

To check the result in Example 1, use the fact that the given triangle covers $\frac{1}{8}$ of the surface of the sphere. See Figure 8.3c. The total surface area of a sphere is $4\pi r^2$. In Example 1, $r = 1$ ft, so the sphere has a surface area of 4π ft^2. Thus the area of the spherical triangle in Example 1 should be

$$\left(\frac{1}{8}\right) \cdot (4\pi) = \frac{\pi}{2} \text{ ft}^2$$

Solution

Apply the spherical triangle area formula.

$$S = (m\angle A + m\angle B + m\angle C - 180°) \cdot \left(\frac{\pi}{180°}\right) r^2$$

$$= (90° + 90° + 90° - 180°) \cdot \left(\frac{\pi}{180°}\right)(1)^2$$

$$= (90°) \cdot \left(\frac{\pi}{180°}\right)$$

$$= \frac{\pi}{2} \text{ ft}^2 \qquad \bullet \text{ Exact area}$$

$$\approx 1.57 \text{ ft}^2 \qquad \bullet \text{ Approximate area}$$

CHECK YOUR PROGRESS 1 Find the area of the spherical triangle whose angles measure 200°, 90°, and 90° on a sphere with a radius of 6 in. Find both the exact area and the approximate area rounded to the nearest hundredth of a square inch.

Solution *See page S32.*

Mathematicians have not been able to create a three-dimensional model that *perfectly* illustrates all aspects of hyperbolic geometry. However, an infinite saddle surface can be used to visualize some of the basic aspects of hyperbolic geometry. Figure 8.4 shows a portion of an infinite saddle surface.

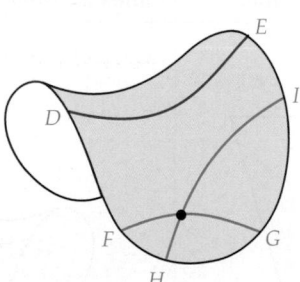

Figure 8.4 *A portion of an infinite saddle surface*

A line (geodesic) can be drawn through any two points on the saddle surface. Most lines on the saddle surface have a concave curvature as shown by $\overleftrightarrow{DE}$, $\overleftrightarrow{FG}$, and $\overleftrightarrow{HI}$. Keep in mind that the saddle surface is an infinite surface. Figure 8.4 shows only a portion of the surface.

Parallel lines on an infinite saddle surface are defined as two lines that do not intersect. In Figure 8.4, $\overleftrightarrow{FG}$ and $\overleftrightarrow{HI}$ are *not* parallel because they intersect at a point. The lines $\overleftrightarrow{DE}$ and $\overleftrightarrow{FG}$ are parallel because they do not intersect. The lines $\overleftrightarrow{DE}$ and $\overleftrightarrow{HI}$ are also parallel lines. Figure 8.4 provides a geometric model of a hyperbolic geometry because for a given line, *more than one* parallel line exists through a point not on the given line.

✔ **TAKE NOTE**

Several different physical models have been invented to illustrate hyperbolic geometry, but most of these models require advanced mathematics beyond the scope of this text.

Figure 8.5 shows a triangle drawn on a saddle surface. The triangle is referred to as a *hyperbolic triangle*. Due to the curvature of the sides of the hyperbolic triangle, the sum of the measures of the angles of the triangle is less than 180 degrees. This is true for all hyperbolic triangles.

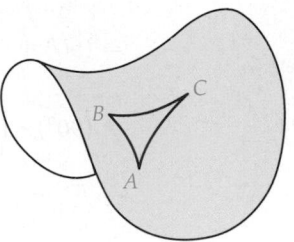

Figure 8.5 *A hyperbolic triangle*

The following chart compares and contrasts some of the properties of plane, hyperbolic, and spherical geometries.

Euclidean Geometry	Non-Euclidean Geometries	
Euclidean or Plane Geometry (circa 300 B.C.):	**Lobachevskian or Hyperbolic Geometry (1826):**	**Riemannian or Spherical Geometry (1855):**
Through a given point not on a given line, exactly one line can be drawn parallel to the given line.	*Through a given point not on a given line, there are at least two lines parallel to the given line.*	*Through a given point not on a given line, there exist no lines parallel to the given line.*
Geometry on a plane	Geometry on an infinite saddle surface	Geometry on a sphere
For any triangle *ABC*, $m \angle A + m \angle B + m \angle C = 180°$	For any triangle *ABC*, $m \angle A + m \angle B + m \angle C < 180°$	For any triangle *ABC*, $180° < m \angle A + m \angle B + m \angle C < 540°$
A triangle can have at most one right angle.	A triangle can have at most one right angle.	A triangle can have one, two, or three right angles.
The shortest path between two points is the line segment that connects the points.	The curves shown in the above figure illustrate some of the geodesics of an infinite saddle surface.	The shortest path between two points is the minor arc of a great circle that passes through the points.

Math Matters Curved Space

In 1915, Albert Einstein proposed a revolutionary theory. This theory is now called the *general theory of relativity*. One of the major ideas of this theory is that space is curved, or "warped," by the mass of stars and planets. The greatest curvature occurs around those stars with the largest mass. Light rays in space do not travel in a straight path, but rather follow the geodesics of this curved space. Recall that the shortest path that joins two points on a given surface is on a geodesic of the surface.

It is interesting to consider the paths of light rays in space from a different perspective, in which the light rays travel along straight paths, in a space that is non-Euclidean. To better understand this concept, consider an airplane that flies from Los Angeles to London. We say that the airplane flies on a straight path between the two cities. The path is not really a straight path if we use Euclidean geometry as our frame of reference, but if we think in terms of Reimannian geometry, then the path *is* straight. We can use Euclidean geometry or a non-Euclidean geometry as our frame of reference. It does not matter which we choose, but it does change our concept about what is a straight path and what is a curved path.

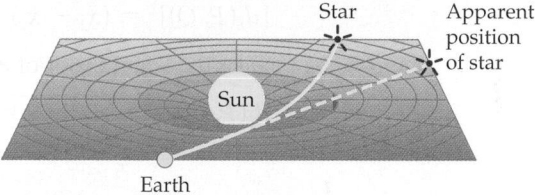

Light rays from a star follow the geodesics of space. Any light rays that pass near the sun are slightly bent. This causes some stars to appear to an observer on Earth to be in different positions than their actual positions.

City Geometry: A Contemporary Non-Euclidean Geometry

Consider the geometric model of a city shown in Figure 8.6. In this city, all of the streets run either straight north and south or straight east and west. The distance between adjacent north–south streets is 1 block, and the distance between adjacent east–west streets is 1 block. In a city it is generally not possible to travel from P to Q along a straight path. Instead, one must travel between P and Q by traveling along the streets. **As you travel from P to Q, we assume that you always travel in a direction that gets you closer to point Q.** Two such paths are shown by the red and the green dashed line segments in Figure 8.6.

We will use the notation $d_C(P, Q)$ to represent the *city distance* between the points P and Q. For P and Q as shown in Figure 8.6, $d_C(P, Q) = 7$ blocks. This distance can be determined by counting the number of blocks needed to travel along the streets from P to Q or by using the following formula.

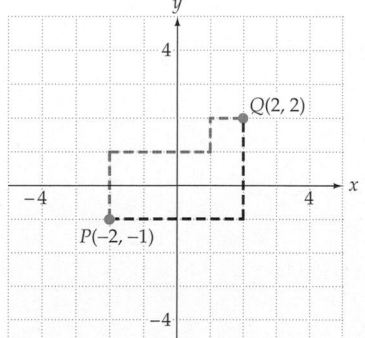

Figure 8.6 *Two city paths from P to Q*

point of interest

The city distance formula is also called the *Manhattan metric*. It first appeared in an article published by the mathematician Hermann Minkowski (1864–1909).

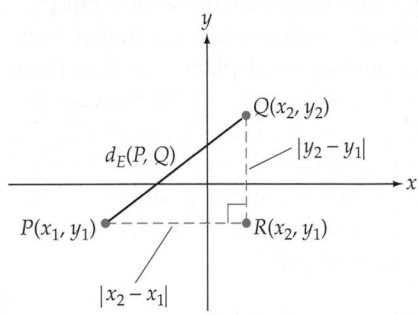

Figure 8.7

The City Distance Formula

If $P(x_1, y_1)$ and $Q(x_2, y_2)$ are two points in a city, then the **city distance** between P and Q is given by

$$d_C(P, Q) = |x_2 - x_1| + |y_2 - y_1|$$

In Euclidean geometry, the distance between the points P and Q is defined as the length of $\overline{PQ}$. To determine a *Euclidean distance formula* for the distance between $P(x_1, y_1)$ and $Q(x_2, y_2)$, we first locate the point $R(x_2, y_1)$. See Figure 8.7.

Note that R has the same x-coordinate as Q and that R has the same y-coordinate as P. The horizontal distance between P and R is $|x_2 - x_1|$, and the vertical distance between R and Q is $|y_2 - y_1|$. Apply the Pythagorean Theorem to the right triangle PRQ to produce

$$[d_E(P, Q)]^2 = |x_2 - x_1|^2 + |y_2 - y_1|^2$$

Because the square of a number cannot be negative, the absolute value signs are not necessary.

$$[d_E(P, Q)]^2 = (x_2 - x_1)^2 + (y_2 - y_1)^2$$

Take the square root of each side of the equation to produce

$$d_E(P, Q) = \sqrt{(x_2 - x_1)^2 + (y_2 - y_1)^2}$$

The Euclidean Distance Formula

If $P(x_1, y_1)$ and $Q(x_2, y_2)$ are two points in a plane, then the **Euclidean distance** between P and Q is given by

$$d_E(P, Q) = \sqrt{(x_2 - x_1)^2 + (y_2 - y_1)^2}$$

✔ **TAKE NOTE**

In Example 2 we have calculated the city distances by using the city distance formula. These distances can also be determined by counting the number of blocks needed to travel along the streets from P to Q on a rectangular coordinate grid.

EXAMPLE 2 ■ Find the Euclidean Distance and the City Distance Between Two Points

For each of the following, find $d_E(P, Q)$ and $d_C(P, Q)$. Assume that both $d_E(P, Q)$ and $d_C(P, Q)$ are measured in blocks. Round approximate results to the nearest tenth of a block.

a. $P(-4, -3)$, $Q(2, -1)$ **b.** $P(2, -3)$, $Q(-5, 4)$

Solution

a. $d_E(P, Q) = \sqrt{(x_2 - x_1)^2 + (y_2 - y_1)^2}$

$\qquad\qquad = \sqrt{[2 - (-4)]^2 + [(-1) - (-3)]^2}$

$\qquad\qquad = \sqrt{6^2 + 2^2}$

$\qquad\qquad = \sqrt{40} \approx 6.3$ blocks

$\quad d_C(P, Q) = |x_2 - x_1| + |y_2 - y_1|$

$\qquad\qquad = |2 - (-4)| + |(-1) - (-3)|$

$\qquad\qquad = |6| + |2|$

$\qquad\qquad = 8$ blocks

b. $d_E(P, Q) = \sqrt{(x_2 - x_1)^2 + (y_2 - y_1)^2}$
$\qquad\quad = \sqrt{[(-5) - 2]^2 + [4 - (-3)]^2}$
$\qquad\quad = \sqrt{(-7)^2 + 7^2}$
$\qquad\quad = \sqrt{98} \approx 9.9 \text{ blocks}$

$d_C(P, Q) = |x_2 - x_1| + |y_2 - y_1|$
$\qquad\quad = |(-5) - 2| + |4 - (-3)|$
$\qquad\quad = |-7| + |7|$
$\qquad\quad = 7 + 7$
$\qquad\quad = 14 \text{ blocks}$

CHECK YOUR PROGRESS 2   For each of the following, find $d_E(P, Q)$ and $d_C(P, Q)$. Assume that both $d_E(P, Q)$ and $d_C(P, Q)$ are measured in blocks. Round approximate results to the nearest tenth of a block.
a. $P(-1, 4), Q(3, 2)$ **b.** $P(3, -4), Q(-1, 5)$

Solution   *See page S32.*

Recall that a circle is a plane figure in which all points are the same distance from a given center point and the length of the radius r of the circle is the distance from the center point to a point on the circle. Figure 8.8 shows a *Euclidean circle* centered at $(0, 0)$ with a radius of 3 blocks. Figure 8.9 shows all the points in a city that are 3 blocks from the center point $(0, 0)$. These points form a *city circle* with a radius of 3 blocks.

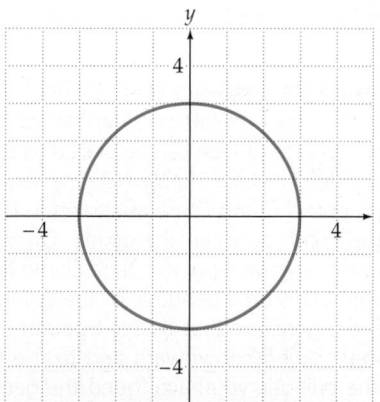

Figure 8.8   *A Euclidean circle with center (0, 0) and a radius of 3 blocks*

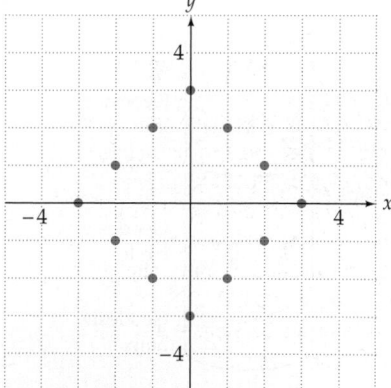

Figure 8.9   *A city circle with center (0, 0) and a radius of 3 blocks*

It is interesting to observe that the *city circle* shown in Figure 8.9 consists of just 12 points and that these points all lie on a square with vertices $(3, 0)$, $(0, 3)$, $(-3, 0)$, and $(0, -3)$.

Excursion

Finding Geodesics

Form groups of three or four students. Each group needs a roll of narrow tape or a ribbon and the two geometrical models shown at the right. The purpose of this Excursion is to use the tape (ribbon) to determine the geodesics of a surface.

Cylinder   Paper cup

The following three theorems can be used to determine the geodesics of a surface.

Geodesic Theorems

Theorem 1   If a surface is smooth with no edges or holes, then the shortest path between any two points is on a geodesic of the surface.

Theorem 2   *The Tape Test*   If a piece of tape is placed so that it lies flat on a smooth surface, then the center line of the tape is on a geodesic of the surface.

Theorem 3   *Inverse of the Tape Test*   If a piece of tape does not lie flat on a smooth surface, then the center line of the tape is not on a geodesic of the surface.

What are the geodesics of a cylinder? If two points *A* and *B* are as shown in Figure 8.10, then the vertical line segment between *A* and *B* is the shortest path between the points. A piece of tape can be placed so that it covers point *A* and point *B* and lies flat on the cylinder. Thus, by Theorem 2, line segment $\overline{AB}$ is on a geodesic of the cylinder.

If two points *C* and *D* are as shown in Figure 8.10, then the minor arc of a circle is the shortest path between the points. Once again we see that a piece of tape can be placed so that it covers points *C* and *D* and lies flat on the cylinder. Theorem 2 indicates that the arc $\overparen{CD}$ is on a geodesic of the cylinder.

To find a geodesic that passes through the two points *E* and *F*, start your tape at *E* and proceed slightly downward and to the right, toward point *F*. If your tape lies flat against the cylinder, you have found the geodesic for the two points. If your tape does not lie flat against the surface, then your path is not a geodesic and you need to experiment further. Eventually you will find the *circular helix* curve, shown in Figure 8.10, that allows the tape to lie flat on the cylinder.[3]

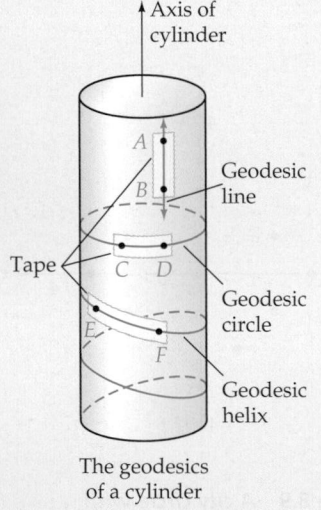

The geodesics of a cylinder

Figure 8.10   *The geodesics of a cylinder*

(continued)

---

3. The tread of a bolt is an example of a circular helix.

Axis of cup

Circle C

A B

Circle C is not a geodesic of the cup.

Figure 8.11

Additional experiments with the tape and the cylinder should convince you that a geodesic of a cylinder is either (a) a line parallel to the axis of the cylinder, (b) a circle with center on the axis of the cylinder and diameter perpendicular to the axis, or (c) a circular helix curve that has a constant slope and a center on the axis of the cylinder.

Excursion Exercises

1. **a.** Place two points A and B on a paper cup so that A and B are both at the same height, as in Figure 8.11. We know circle C that passes through A and B is *not* a geodesic of the cup because a piece of tape will not lie flat when placed directly on top of circle C. Experiment with a piece of tape to determine the *actual* geodesic that passes through A and B. Make a drawing that shows this geodesic and illustrate how it differs from circle C.

   b. Use a cup similar to the one in Figure 8.11 and a piece of tape to determine two other types of geodesics of the cup. Make a drawing that shows each of these two additional types of geodesics.

2. The only geodesics of a sphere are great circles. Write a sentence that explains how you can use a piece of tape to show that circle D in Figure 8.12 is not a geodesic of the sphere.

Circle D

Circle E

Figure 8.12   **Figure 8.13**

3. Write a sentence that explains how you know that circle E in Figure 8.13 is not a geodesic of the figure.

Excursion Exercises 4 to 6 require a world globe that shows the locations of major cities. We suggest that you use a thin ribbon, instead of tape, to determine the great circle routes in the following exercises, because tape may damage the globe.

4. A pilot flies a great circle route from Miami, Florida to Hong Kong. Which one of the following states will the plane fly over?

   a. California   **b.** Oregon

   c. Washington   **d.** Alaska

5. A pilot flies a great circle route from Los Angeles to London. Which one of the following cities will the plane fly over?

   a. New York   **b.** Chicago

   c. Godthaab, Greenland   **d.** Vancouver, Canada

(continued)

6. Washington, D.C. and Seoul, Korea both have a latitude of about 38°. How many miles (to the nearest 100 miles) will a pilot save by flying a great circle route between the cities as opposed to the route that follows the 38th parallel? *Hint:* Use a cloth measuring tape to measure the minor arc of the great circle that passes through the two cities. Use the scale on the globe to convert this distance to miles. Then use the measuring tape to determine the distance of the route that follows the 38th parallel.

7. **a.** The surface at the left below is called a *hyperboloid of one sheet*. Explain how you can determine that the blue circle is a geodesic of the hyperboloid, but the red circles are not geodesics of the hyperboloid.

   b. The saddle surface at the right below is called a *hyperbolic paraboloid*. Explain how you can determine that the blue parabola is a geodesic of the hyperbolic paraboloid, but the red parabolas are not geodesics of the hyperbolic paraboloid.

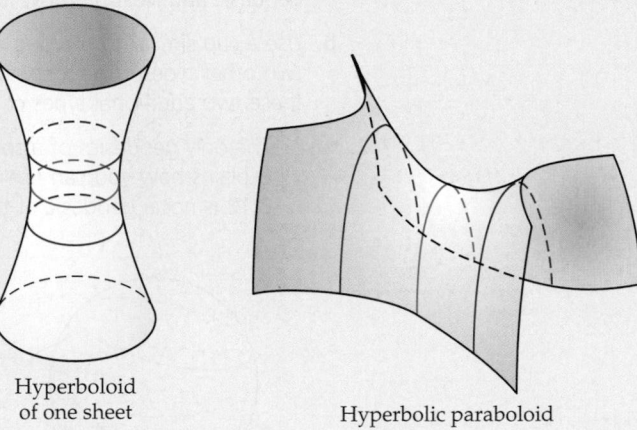

Hyperboloid of one sheet   Hyperbolic paraboloid

Exercise Set 8.6

1. State the parallel postulate for each of the following.
   a. Euclidean geometry
   b. Lobachevskian geometry
   c. Riemannian geometry

2. Name the mathematician who is called the Copernicus of Geometry.

3. Name the mathematician who was the first to consider a geometry in which Euclid's Parallel Postulate was replaced with "Through a given point not on a given line, there are *at least two* lines parallel to the given line."

4. Name the mathematician who was the first to create a non-Euclidean geometry using the postulate "Through a given point not on a given line, there exist no lines parallel to the given line."

5. What can be stated about the sum of the measures of the angles of a triangle in
   a. Euclidean geometry?
   b. Lobachevskian geometry?
   c. Riemannian geometry?

6. What is the maximum number of right angles a triangle can have in
   a. Euclidean geometry?
   b. Lobachevskian geometry?
   c. Riemannian geometry?

7. What name did Lobachevsky give to the geometry that he created?

8. Explain why great circles in Riemannian geometry are thought of as lines.

9. What is a geodesic?

10. In which geometry can two distinct lines be parallel to a third line but not parallel to each other?

11. What model was used in this text to illustrate hyperbolic geometry?

12. In which geometry do all perpendiculars to a given line intersect each other?

13. Find the exact area of a spherical triangle with angles of 150°, 120°, and 90° on a sphere with a radius of 1.

14. Find the area of a spherical triangle with three right angles on a sphere with a radius of 1980 mi. Round to the nearest ten thousand square miles.

A **spherical polygon** is a polygon on a sphere. Each side of a spherical polygon is an arc of a great circle. The area A of a spherical polygon of n sides on a sphere of radius r is given by

$$A = [\Sigma\theta - (n-2) \cdot 180°] \cdot \left(\frac{\pi}{180°}\right) r^2$$

where $\Sigma\theta$ is the sum of the measures of the angles of the polygon in degrees.

15. Use the above spherical polygon area formula to determine the area of a spherical quadrilateral with angles of 90°, 90°, 100°, and 100° on the planet Earth, which has a radius of 1980 mi. Round to the nearest ten thousand square miles.

16. Use the above spherical polygon area formula to determine the area of a spherical quadrilateral with angles of 90°, 90°, 120°, and 120° on the planet Earth, which has a radius of 1980 mi. Round to the nearest ten thousand square miles.

City Geometry In Exercises 17–24, find the Euclidean distance between the points and the city distance between the points. Assume that both $d_E(P, Q)$ and $d_C(P, Q)$ are measured in blocks. Round approximate results to the nearest tenth of a block.

17. $P(-3, 1)$, $Q(4, 1)$ **18.** $P(-2, 4)$, $Q(3, -1)$

19. $P(2, -3)$, $Q(-3, 5)$ **20.** $P(-2, 0)$, $Q(3, 7)$

21. $P(-1, 4)$, $Q(5, -2)$ **22.** $P(-5, 2)$, $Q(3, -4)$

23. $P(2, 0)$, $Q(3, -6)$ **24.** $P(2, -2)$, $Q(5, -2)$

A Distance Conversion Formula The following formula can be used to convert the Euclidean distance between the points P and Q to the city distance between P and Q. In this formula, the variable m represents the slope of the line segment $\overline{PQ}$.

$$d_C(P, Q) = \frac{1 + |m|}{\sqrt{1 + m^2}} d_E(P, Q)$$

In Exercises 25–30, use the above formula to find the city distance between P and Q.

25. $d_E(P, Q) = 5$ blocks, slope of $\overline{PQ} = \frac{3}{4}$

26. $d_E(P, Q) = \sqrt{29}$ blocks, slope of $\overline{PQ} = \frac{2}{5}$

27. $d_E(P, Q) = \sqrt{13}$ blocks, slope of $\overline{PQ} = -\frac{2}{3}$

28. $d_E(P, Q) = 2\sqrt{10}$ blocks, slope of $\overline{PQ} = -3$

29. $d_E(P, Q) = \sqrt{17}$ blocks, slope of $\overline{PQ} = \frac{1}{4}$

30. $d_E(P, Q) = 4\sqrt{2}$ blocks, slope of $\overline{PQ} = -1$

31. Explain why there is no formula that can be used to convert $d_C(P, Q)$ to $d_E(P, Q)$. Assume that no additional information is given other than the value of $d_C(P, Q)$.

32. a. If $d_E(P, Q) = d_E(R, S)$, must $d_C(P, Q) = d_C(R, S)$? Explain.

b. If $d_C(P, Q) = d_C(R, S)$, must $d_E(P, Q) = d_E(R, S)$? Explain.

33. Plot the points in the city circle with center $(-2, -1)$ and radius $r = 2$ blocks.

34. Plot the points in the city circle with center $(1, -1)$ and radius $r = 3$ blocks.

35. Plot the points in the city circle with center $(0, 0)$ and radius $r = 2.5$ blocks.

36. Plot the points in the city circle with center $(0, 0)$ and radius $r = 3.5$ blocks.

37. How many points are on the city circle with center $(0, 0)$ and radius $r = n$ blocks, where n is a natural number?

38. Which of the following city circles has the most points, a city circle with center (0, 0) and radius 4.5 blocks or a city circle with center (0, 0) and radius 5 blocks?

Extensions

CRITICAL THINKING

Apartment Hunting Use the following information to answer each of the questions in Exercises 39 and 40.

Amy and her husband Ryan are looking for an apartment located adjacent to a city street. Amy works at $P(-3, -1)$ and Ryan works at $Q(2, 3)$. Both Amy and Ryan plan to walk from their apartment to work along routes that follow the north–south and the east–west streets.

39. a. Plot the points where Amy and Ryan should look for an apartment if they wish the sum of the city distances they need to walk to work to be a minimum.

   b. Plot the points where Amy and Ryan should look for an apartment if they wish the sum of the city distances they need to walk to work to be a minimum and they both will walk the same distance. *Hint:* Find the intersection of the city circle with center *P* and radius of 4.5 blocks, and the city circle with center *Q* and radius of 4.5 blocks.

40. a. Plot the points where Amy and Ryan should look for an apartment if they wish the sum of the city distances they need to walk to work to be less than or equal to 10 blocks.

   b. Plot the points where Amy and Ryan should look for an apartment if they wish the sum of the city distances they need to walk to work to be less than or equal to 10 blocks and they both will walk the same distance. *Hint:* Find the intersection of the city circle with center *P* and radius of 5.5 blocks,

and the city circle with center *Q* and radius of 5.5 blocks.

41. A Finite Geometry Consider a finite geometry with the five points *A*, *B*, *C*, *D*, and *E*. In this geometry a line is any two of the five points. For example, the two points *A* and *B* together form the line denoted by *AB*. Parallel lines are defined as two lines that do not share a common point.

   a. How may lines are in this geometry?

   b. How many of the lines are parallel to line *AB*?

42. A Finite Geometry Consider a finite geometry with the six points *A*, *B*, *C*, *D*, *E*, and *F*. In this geometry a line is any two of the six points. Parallel lines are defined as two lines that do not share a common point.

   a. How many lines are in this geometry?

   b. How many of the lines are parallel to line *AB*?

EXPLORATIONS

43. **Janos Bolyai** The mathematician Janos Bolyai (bōl′yoi) (1802–1860) proposed a geometry that excluded Euclid's Parallel Postulate. Concerning the geometry he created, he remarked, "I have made such wonderful discoveries that I am myself lost in astonishment: Out of nothing I have created a strange new world." Use the Internet or a library to find information about Janos Bolyai and the mathematics he created. Write a report that summarizes the pertinent details concerning his work in the area of non-Euclidean geometry.

44. **Girolamo Saccheri** The mathematician Girolamo Saccheri (säk′kā-rē) (1667–1733) did important early work in non-Euclidean geometry. Use the Internet or a library to find information about Saccheri's work. Write a report that summarizes the pertinent details.

SECTION 8.7 | Fractals

Fractals—Endlessly Repeated Geometric Figures

Have you ever used a computer program to enlarge a portion of a photograph? Sometimes the result is a satisfactory enlargement; however, if the photograph is enlarged too much, the image may become blurred. For example, the photograph in Figure 8.14 on the following page is shown at its original size. The image in

Figure 8.15 is an enlarged portion of Figure 8.14. A computer monitor displays an image using small dots called *pixels*. If a computer image is enlarged using a program such as Adobe Photoshop™, the program must determine the color of each pixel in the enlargement. If the image file for the photograph cannot supply the needed color information for each pixel, then Photoshop determines the color of some pixels by *averaging* the numerical color values of neighboring pixels for which the image file has the color information. In the enlarged photograph in Figure 8.15, the image is somewhat blurred because some of the pixels do not provide accurate information about the original photograph. Figure 8.16 is an enlargement of a portion of Figure 8.15. The blurred image in Figure 8.16 provides even less detail than does Figure 8.15, because the colors of many of the pixels in this image were determined by averaging. If we continue to make enlargements of enlargements we will produce extremely blurred images that provide little information about the original photograph.

| **Figure 8.14** | **Figure 8.15** | **Figure 8.16** |

In the 1970s, the mathematician Benoit Mandelbrot discovered some remarkable methods that enable us to create geometric figures with a special property: if any portion of the figure is enlarged repeatedly, then additional details (not fewer details, as with the enlargement of a photograph) of the figure are displayed. Mandelbrot called these endlessly repeated geometric figures *fractals*. At the present time there is no universal agreement on the precise definition of a fractal, but the fractals that we will study in this lesson can be defined as follows. A **fractal** is a geometric figure in which a self-similar motif repeats itself on an ever-diminishing scale.

Fractals are generally constructed by using **iterative processes** in which the fractal is more closely approximated as a repeated cycle of procedures is performed. For example, a fractal known as the *Koch curve* is constructed as follows.

Construction of the Koch Curve

Step 0: Start with a line segment. This initial segment is shown as stage 0 in Figure 8.17. Stage 0 of a fractal is called the **initiator** of the fractal.

Step 1: On the middle third of the line segment, draw an equilateral triangle and remove its base. The resulting curve is stage 1 in Figure 8.17. Stage 1 of a fractal is called the **generator** of the fractal.

Stage 0

The zig-zag initiator

Stage 1

The zig-zag generator

Figure 8.20

CHECK YOUR PROGRESS 1 Draw stage 2 of the *zig-zag curve,* which is defined by the following iterative process.

Step 0: Start with a line segment. See stage 0 of Figure 8.20.

Step 1: Remove the middle half of the line segment and draw a zig-zag, as shown in stage 1 of Figure 8.20. Each of the six line segments in the generator is a $\frac{1}{4}$-scale replica of the initiator.

Step 2: Replace each initiator shape with the scaled version of the generator to produce the next stage. Repeat this step to produce additional stages.

Solution See page S32.

In each of the previous examples, the initiator was a line segment. In Example 2, we use a triangle and its interior as the initiator.

Stage 0 (the initiator)

Stage 1 (the generator)

Figure 8.21

EXAMPLE 2 ■ Draw Stages of a Fractal

Draw stage 2 and stage 3 of the *Sierpinski gasket* (also known as the *Sierpinski triangle*), which is defined by the following iterative process.

Step 0: Start with an equilateral triangle and its interior. This is stage 0 of the Sierpinski gasket. See Figure 8.21.

Step 1: Form a new triangle by connecting the midpoints of the sides of the triangle. Remove this center triangle. The result is the three blue triangles shown in stage 1 in Figure 8.21.

Step 2: Replace each initiator (green triangle) with a scaled version of the generator.

Solution
Two applications of step 2 of the above process produce stage 2 and stage 3 of the Sierpinski gasket, as shown in Figure 8.22.

Stage 2

Stage 3

Figure 8.22

CHECK YOUR PROGRESS 2 Draw stage 2 of the *Sierpinski carpet,* which is defined by the following process.

Step 0: Start with a square and its interior. See stage 0 in Figure 8.23.

Step 1: Subdivide the square into nine smaller congruent squares and remove the center square. This yields stage 1 (the generator) shown in Figure 8.23.

Step 2: Replace each initiator (tan square) with a scaled version of the generator. Repeat this step to create additional stages of the Sierpinski carpet.

Stage 0   Stage 1

Figure 8.23

Solution   *See page S33.*

Math Matters   Benoit Mandelbrot (1924–)

Benoit Mandelbrot is often called the Father of Fractal Geometry. He was not the first person to create a fractal, but he was the first person to discover how some of the ideas of earlier mathematicians such as Georg Cantor, Giuseppe Peano, Helge von Koch, Waclaw Sierpinski, and Gaston Julia could be united to form a new type of geometry. Mandelbrot also recognized that many fractals share characteristics with shapes and curves found in nature. For instance, the leaves of a fern, when compared with the whole fern, are almost identical in shape, only smaller. This self-similarity characteristic is evident (to some degree) in all fractals. The following quote by Mandelbrot is from his 1983 book, *The Fractal Geometry of Nature.*[4]

> Clouds are not spheres, mountains are not cones, coastlines are not circles, and bark is not smooth, nor does lightning travel in a straight line. More generally, I claim that many patterns of Nature are so irregular and fragmented, that, compared with Euclid—a term used in this work to denote all of standard geometry—Nature exhibits not simply a higher degree but an altogether different level of complexity.

4. Mandelbrot, Benoit B. *The Fractal Geometry of Nature.* New York: W. H. Freeman and Company, 1983, p. 1.

CHECK YOUR PROGRESS 4 Find the replacement ratio and the scaling ratio of the

a. Koch curve.   **b.** zig-zag curve.

Solution   *See page S33.*

Similarity Dimension

A number called the *similarity dimension* is used to quantify how densely a strictly self-similar fractal fills a region.

The **similarity dimension** D of a strictly self-similar fractal is given by

$$D = \frac{\log N}{\log r}$$

where N is the replacement ratio of the fractal and r is the scaling ratio.

EXAMPLE 5 ■ Find the Similarity Dimension of a Fractal

Find the similarity dimension, to the nearest thousandth, of the

a. Koch curve.   **b.** Sierpinski gasket.

Solution

a. Because the Koch curve is a strictly self-similar fractal, we can find its similarity dimension. Figure 8.17 on page 548 shows that stage 1 of the Koch curve consists of four line segments and stage 0 consists of only one line segment. Hence the replacement ratio is 4 : 1, or 4. The line segment in stage 0 is 3 times as long as each of the replica line segments in stage 1, so the scaling ratio is 3. Thus the Koch curve has a similarity dimension of

$$D = \frac{\log 4}{\log 3} \approx 1.262$$

b. In Example 4, we found that the Sierpinski gasket has a replacement ratio of 3 and a scaling ratio of 2. Thus the Sierpinski gasket has a similarity dimension of

$$D = \frac{\log 3}{\log 2} \approx 1.585$$

CHECK YOUR PROGRESS 5 Compute the similarity dimension, to the nearest thousandth, of the

a. box curve.   **b.** Sierpinski carpet.

Solution   *See page S33.*

✔ **TAKE NOTE**

Because the Koch snowflake is not a strictly self-similar fractal, we cannot compute its similarity dimension.

The results of Example 5 show that the Sierpinski gasket has a larger similarity dimension than the Koch curve. This means that the Sierpinski gasket fills a flat two-dimensional surface more densely than does the Koch curve.

Computers are used to generate fractals such as those shown in Figure 8.26. These fractals were *not* rendered by using an initiator and a generator, but they were rendered using iterative procedures.

a.   b.

c.   d.

Figure 8.26 *Computer-generated fractals*

Fractals have other applications in addition to being used to produce intriguing images. For example, computer scientists have recently developed fractal image compression programs based on self-transformations of an image. An image compression program is a computer program that converts an image file to a smaller file that requires less computer memory. In some situations these fractal compression programs outperform standardized image compression programs such as JPEG (*jay-peg*), which was developed by the Joint Photographic Experts Group.

During the past few years, some cellular telephones have been manufactured with internal antennas that are fractal in design. Figure 8.27 shows a cellular telephone with an internal antenna in the shape of a stage on the Sierpinski carpet fractal. The antenna in Figure 8.28 is in the shape of a stage of the Koch curve.

Draw another line segment of the same length as the original segment. Label the endpoint of this segment with a number that is 1 larger than the number used for the preceding vertex.

Step 2: Continue to repeat step 1 until you reach the last vertex. The last vertex of an n-stage Heighway dragon is the vertex numbered 2^n.

Excursion Exercises

1. Use a strip of paper and the folding procedure explained on pages 556 and 557 to create models of the first five stages (stage 0 through stage 4) of the Heighway dragon. Explain why it would be difficult to create the 10th stage of the Heighway dragon using the paper-folding procedure.

2. Use the left-right rule to draw stage 2 of the Heighway dragon.

3. Use the left-right rule to determine the direction in which to turn at vertex 7 of the Heighway dragon.

4. Use the left-right rule to determine the direction in which to turn at vertex 50 of the Heighway dragon.

5. Use the left-right rule to determine the direction in which to turn at vertex 64 of the Heighway dragon.

Exercise Set 8.7

In Exercises 1 and 2, use an iterative process to draw stage 2 and stage 3 of the fractal with the given initiator (stage 0) and the given generator (stage 1).

1. The Cantor point set

Stage 0

Stage 1

2. Lévy's curve

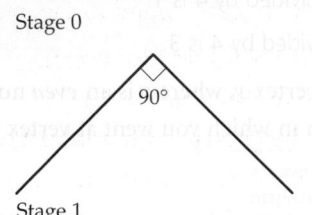

Stage 0

Stage 1

In Exercises 3–8, use an iterative process to draw stage 2 of the fractal with the given initiator (stage 0) and the given generator (stage 1).

3. The Sierpinski carpet, variation 1

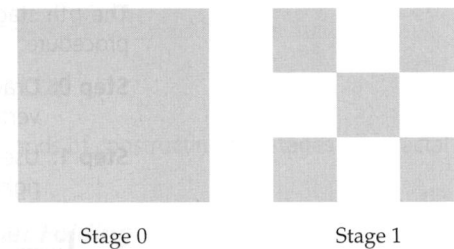

Stage 0   Stage 1

4. The Sierpinski carpet, variation 2

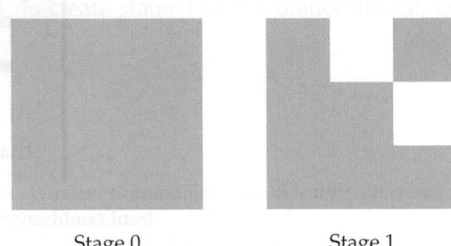

Stage 0   Stage 1

5. The river tree of Peano Cearo

Stage 0   Stage 1

6. Minkowski's fractal

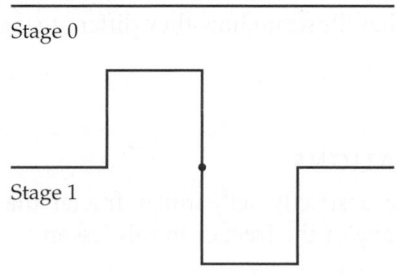

Stage 0

Stage 1

7. The square fractal

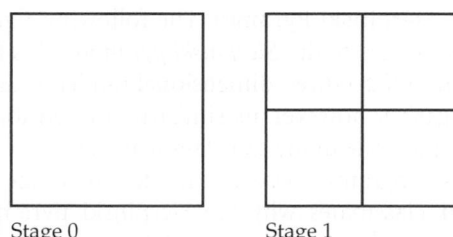

Stage 0   Stage 1

8. The cube fractal

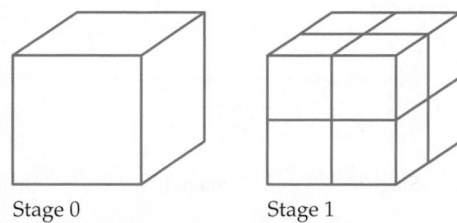

Stage 0   Stage 1

In Exercises 9 and 10, draw stage 3 and stage 4 of the fractal defined by the given iterative process.

9. The binary tree

Step 0: Start with a "⊤". This is stage 0 of the binary tree. The vertical line segment is the trunk of the tree and the horizontal line segment is the

branch of the tree. The branch is half the length of the trunk.

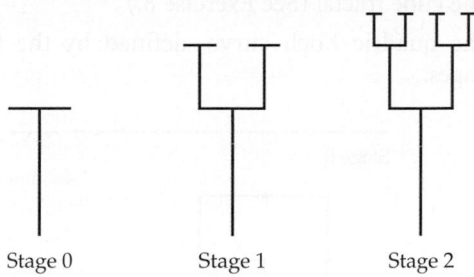

Stage 0   Stage 1   Stage 2

Step 1: At the ends of each branch, draw an upright ⊤ that is half the size of the ⊤ in the preceding stage.

Step 2: Continue to repeat step 1 to generate additional stages of the binary tree.

10. The I-fractal

Step 0: Start with the line segment shown as stage 0 below.

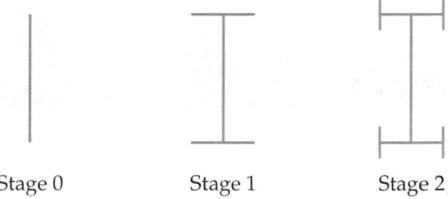

Stage 0   Stage 1   Stage 2

Step 1: At each end of the line segment, draw a crossbar that is half the length of the line segment it contacts. (This produces stage 1 of the I-fractal.)

Step 2: Use each crossbar from the preceding step as the connecting segment of a new "I." Attach new crossbars that are half the length of the connecting segment. Continue to repeat this step to generate additional stages of the I-fractal.

In Exercises 11–20, compute, if possible, the similarity dimension of the fractal. Round to the nearest thousandth.

11. The Cantor point set (See Exercise 1.)

12. Lévy's curve (See Exercise 2.)

13. The Sierpinski carpet, variation 1 (See Exercise 3.)

14. The Sierpinski carpet, variation 2 (See Exercise 4.)

15. The river tree of Peano Cearo (See Exercise 5.)

16. Minkowski's fractal (See Exercise 6.)

17. The square fractal (See Exercise 7.)

18. The cube fractal (See Exercise 8.)

19. The quadric Koch curve, defined by the following stages.

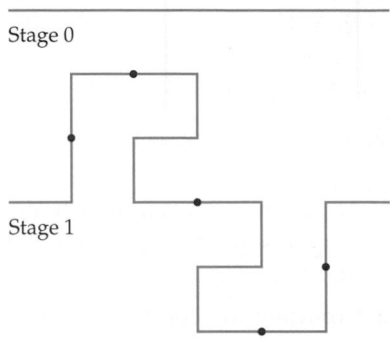

20. The Menger sponge, defined by the following stages.

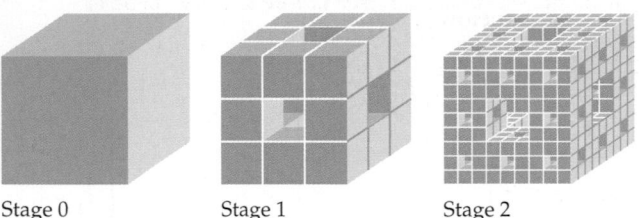

Stage 0   Stage 1   Stage 2

Extensions

CRITICAL THINKING

21. **a.** Rank, from largest to smallest, the similarity dimensions of the Sierpinski carpet; the Sierpinski carpet, variation 1 (see Exercise 3); and the Sierpinski carpet, variation 2 (see Exercise 4).

    b. Which of the three fractals is the most dense?

22. The *Peano curve* is defined by the following stages.

Stage 0   Stage 1

The arrows show the route used to trace the generator.

a. What is the similarity dimension of the Peano curve?

b. Explain why the Peano curve is referred to as a plane-filling curve.

23. Explain why the similarity dimension formula cannot be used to find the similarity dimension of the binary tree defined in Exercise 9.

24. Stage 0 and stage 1 of Lévy's curve (see Exercise 2) and the Heighway dragon (see page 556) are identical, but the fractals start to differ at stage 2. Make two drawings that illustrate how they differ at stage 2.

EXPLORATIONS

25. Create a strictly self-similar fractal that is different from any of the fractals in this lesson.

    a. Draw the first four stages of your fractal.

    b. Compute the replacement ratio, the scaling ratio, and the similarity dimension of your fractal.

26. **The Sierpinski Pyramid** The following figure shows three stages of the *Sierpinski pyramid*. This fractal has been called a three-dimensional model of the Sierpinski gasket; however, its similarity dimension is 2, not 3. Build scale models of stage 0 and stage 1 of the Sierpinski pyramid. Use the models to demonstrate to your classmates why the Sierpinski pyramid fractal has a similarity dimension of 2.

A triangular pyramid

Stage 0   Stage 1   Stage 2

The first three stages of the Sierpinski pyramid

CHAPTER 8   **Summary**

Key Terms

acute angle [p. 454]
acute triangle [p. 470]
adjacent angles [p. 455]
adjacent side [p. 523]
alternate exterior angles [p. 457]
alternate interior angles [p. 457]
angle [p. 452]
angle of depression [p. 528]
angle of elevation [p. 528]
area [p. 477]
base of a parallelogram [p. 474]
base of a trapezoid [p. 481]
box curve [p. 549]
center of a circle [p. 475]
center of a sphere [p. 509]
circle [p. 475]
circumference [p. 475]
city circle [p. 541]
complementary angles [p. 454]
corresponding angles [p. 458]
cosine [p. 523]
cosecant [p. 523]
cotangent [p. 523]
cube [p. 508]
degree [p. 453]
diameter [p. 475]
diameter of a sphere [p. 509]
endpoint [p. 450]
equilateral triangle [p. 470]
Euclidean circle [p. 541]
Euclidean geometry [p. 534]
exterior angle of a triangle [p. 460]
face of a rectangular solid [p. 508]
fractal [p. 547]
generator [p. 547]
geodesic [p. 535]
geometric solids [p. 507]
great circle [p. 535]
height of a parallelogram [p. 479]
height of a trapezoid [p. 481]
hyperbolic geometry [p. 534]
hyperbolic triangle [p. 538]
hypotenuse [p. 499]
imaginary geometry [p. 534]
initiator [p. 547]

interior angle of a triangle [p. 460]
intersecting lines [p. 452]
isosceles triangle [p. 470]
iterative process [p. 547]
Koch curve [p. 547]
Koch snowflake [p. 548]
legs of a right triangle [p. 499]
line [p. 450]
line segment [p. 450]
line of sight [p. 528]
Lobachevskian geometry [p. 534]
major/minor arc [p. 535]
non-Euclidean geometry [p. 534]
obtuse angle [p. 454]
obtuse triangle [p. 470]
opposite side [p. 523]
parallel lines [p. 452]
parallel lines on an infinite saddle surface [p. 537]
parallelogram [p. 471]
perimeter [p. 471]
perpendicular lines [p. 453]
plane [p. 452]
plane figure [p. 452]
point [p. 450]
polygon [p. 469]
postulate [p. 533]
protractor [p. 453]
quadrilateral [p. 470]
radius [p. 475]
radius of a sphere [p. 509]
ray [p. 450]
rectangle [p. 472]
rectangular solid [p. 508]
regular polygon [p. 469]
regular pyramid [p. 510]
replacement ratio [p. 553]
Riemmanian geometry [p. 535]
right angle [p. 453]
right circular cone [p. 510]
right circular cylinder [p. 510]
right triangle [p. 470]
scalene triangle [p. 470]
scaling ratio [p. 553]
secant [p. 523]
sides of an angle [p. 452]
sides of a polygon [p. 469]
Sierpinski carpet [p. 551]

Essential Concepts

- **Triangles**
  Sum of the measures of the interior angles $= 180°$
  Sum of the measures of an interior and a corresponding exterior angle $= 180°$

- **Perimeter Formulas**

Triangle:	$P = a + b + c$
Rectangle:	$P = 2L + 2W$
Square:	$P = 4s$
Parallelogram:	$P = 2b + 2s$
Circle:	$C = \pi d$ or $C = 2\pi r$

- **Area Formulas**

Triangle:	$A = \dfrac{1}{2}bh$
Rectangle:	$A = LW$
Square:	$A = s^2$
Circle:	$A = \pi r^2$
Parallelogram:	$A = bh$
Trapezoid:	$A = \dfrac{1}{2}h(b_1 + b_2)$

- **Volume Formulas**

Rectangular solid:	$V = LWH$
Cube:	$V = s^3$
Sphere:	$V = \dfrac{4}{3}\pi r^3$
Right circular cylinder:	$V = \pi r^2 h$
Right circular cone:	$V = \dfrac{1}{3}\pi r^2 h$
Regular pyramid:	$V = \dfrac{1}{3}s^2 h$

- **Surface Area Formulas**

Rectangular solid:	$S = 2LW + 2LH + 2WH$
Cube:	$S = 6s^2$
Sphere:	$S = 4\pi r^2$
Right circular cylinder:	$S = 2\pi r^2 + 2\pi rh$
Right circular cone:	$S = \pi r^2 + \pi rl$
Regular pyramid:	$S = s^2 + 2sl$

- **Similar Triangles**
  The ratios of corresponding sides are equal. The ratio of corresponding heights is equal to the ratio of corresponding sides.

- **Congruent Triangles**
  Side-Side-Side Theorem (SSS)

  If the three sides of one triangle are equal in measure to the corresponding three sides of a second triangle, the two triangles are congruent.

  Side-Angle-Side Theorem (SAS)

  If two sides and the included angle of one triangle are equal in measure to two sides and the included angle of a second triangle, the two triangles are congruent.

  Angle-Side-Angle Theorem (ASA)

  If two angles and the included side of one triangle are equal in measure to two angles and the included side of a second triangle, the two triangles are congruent.

- **Pythagorean Theorem**
  If a and b are the lengths of the legs of a right triangle and c is the length of the hypotenuse, then
  $$c^2 = a^2 + b^2.$$

■ **The Trigonometric Functions of an Acute Angle of a Right Triangle**
If θ is an acute angle of a right triangle ABC, then

$$\sin \theta = \frac{\text{length of opposite side}}{\text{length of hypotenuse}}$$

$$\cos \theta = \frac{\text{length of adjacent side}}{\text{length of hypotenuse}}$$

$$\tan \theta = \frac{\text{length of opposite side}}{\text{length of adjacent side}}$$

$$\csc \theta = \frac{\text{length of hypotenuse}}{\text{length of opposite side}}$$

$$\sec \theta = \frac{\text{length of hypotenuse}}{\text{length of adjacent side}}$$

$$\cot \theta = \frac{\text{length of adjacent side}}{\text{length of opposite side}}$$

■ **Definitions of the Inverse Sine, Inverse Cosine, and Inverse Tangent Functions**
For $0° < x < 90°$:

$y = \sin^{-1}(x)$ can be read "y is the angle whose sine is x."

$y = \cos^{-1}(x)$ can be read "y is the angle whose cosine is x."

$y = \tan^{-1}(x)$ can be read "y is the angle whose tangent is x."

■ **Parallel Postulates**
The Euclidean Parallel Postulate (*Plane Geometry*) Through a given point not on a given line, exactly one line can be drawn parallel to the given line.

Gauss's Alternative to the Parallel Postulate (*Hyperbolic Geometry*) Through a given point not on a given line, there are *at least two* lines parallel to the given line.

Riemann's Alternative to the Parallel Postulate (*Spherical Geometry*) Through a given point not on a given line, there exist *no* lines parallel to the given line.

■ **The Spherical Triangle Area Formula**
The area S of the spherical triangle ABC on a sphere with radius r is

$$S = (m\angle A + m\angle B + m\angle C - 180°) \cdot \left(\frac{\pi}{180°}\right) r^2$$

■ **City Distance Formula** The city distance between $P(x_1, y_1)$ and $Q(x_2, y_2)$ is given by

$$d_C(P, Q) = |x_2 - x_1| + |y_2 - y_1|$$

■ **Euclidean Distance Formula** The Euclidean distance between $P(x_1, y_1)$ and $Q(x_2, y_2)$ is given by

$$d_E(P, Q) = \sqrt{(x_2 - x_1)^2 + (y_2 - y_1)^2}$$

■ **Similarity Dimension of a Fractal**
The similarity dimension D of a strictly self-similar fractal is $D = \frac{\log N}{\log r}$, where N is the replacement ratio of the fractal and r is the scaling ratio.

CHAPTER 8   **Review Exercises**

1. Given that $m\angle a = 74°$ and $m\angle b = 52°$, find the measures of angles x and y.

2. Triangles ABC and DEF are similar. Find the perimeter of triangle ABC.

3. Find the volume of the geometric solid.

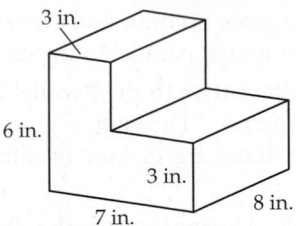

4. Find the measure of ∠x.

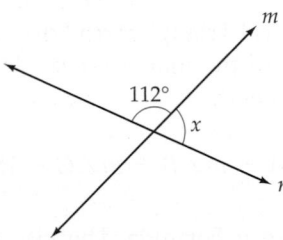

5. Find the surface area of the rectangular solid.

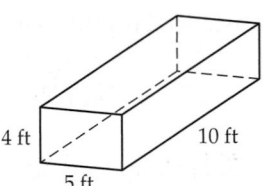

6. The length of a diameter of the base of a cylinder is 4 m, and the height of the cylinder is 8 m. Find the surface area of the cylinder. Give the exact value.

7. Given that $BC = 11$ cm and that AB is three times the length of BC, find the length of AC.

8. Find x.

9. Find the area of a parallelogram that has a base of 6 in. and a height of 4.5 in.

10. Find the volume of the square pyramid.

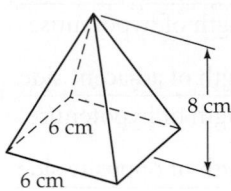

11. Find the circumference of a circle that has a diameter of 4.5 m. Round to the nearest hundredth of a meter.

12. Given that $\ell_1 \parallel \ell_2$, find the measures of angles a and b.

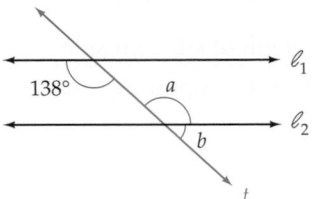

13. Find the supplement of a 32° angle.

14. Find the volume of a rectangular solid with a length of 6.5 ft, a width of 2 ft, and a height of 3 ft.

15. Two angles of a triangle measure 37° and 48°. Find the measure of the third angle.

16. The height of a triangle is 7 cm. The area of the triangle is 28 cm². Find the length of the base of the triangle.

17. Find the volume of a sphere that has a diameter of 12 mm. Give the exact value.

18. **Framing** The perimeter of a square picture frame is 86 cm. Find the length of each side of the frame.

19. **Paint** A can of paint will cover 200 ft² of surface. How many cans of paint should be purchased to paint a cylinder that has a height of 15 ft and a radius of 6 ft?

20. **Parks and Recreation** The length of a rectangular park is 56 yd. The width is 48 yd. How many yards of fencing are needed to surround the park?

21. **Patios** What is the area of a square patio that measures 9.5 m on each side?

22. **Landscaping** A walkway 2 m wide surrounds a rectangular plot of grass. The plot is 40 m long and 25 m wide. What is the area of the walkway?

23. Name the mathematician who was the first person to develop a non-Euclidean geometry, but chose not to publish his work.

24. Determine whether the two triangles are congruent. If they are congruent, state by what theorem they are congruent.

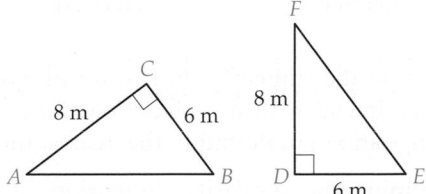

25. Find the unknown side of the triangle. Round to the nearest hundredth of a foot.

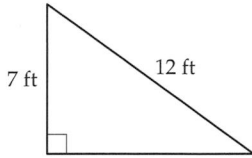

In Exercises 26 and 27, find the values of sin θ, cos θ, and tan θ for the given right triangle.

26.

27.

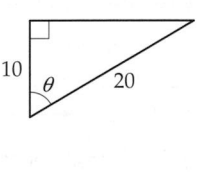

In Exercises 28–31, use a calculator. Round to the nearest tenth of a degree.

28. Find $\cos^{-1}(0.9013)$.

29. Find $\sin^{-1}(0.4871)$.

30. Given $\tan \beta = 1.364$, find β.

31. Given $\sin \theta = 0.0325$, find θ.

32. **Surveying** Find the distance across the marsh in the following figure. Round to the nearest tenth of a foot.

33. **Angle of Depression** The distance from a plane to a radar station is 200 miles, and the angle of depression is 40°. Find the number of ground miles from a point directly under the plane to the radar station. Round to the nearest tenth of a mile.

34. **Angle of Elevation** The angle of elevation from a point A on the ground to the top of a space shuttle is 27°. If point A is 110 feet from the base of the space shuttle, how tall is the space shuttle? Round to the nearest tenth of a foot.

35. **Name the mathematician** who called the geometry he developed "imaginary geometry."

36. What is another name for Riemannian geometry?

37. What is another name for Lobachevskian geometry?

38. Name a geometry in which the sum of the measures of the interior angles of a triangle is less than 180°.

39. Name a geometry in which there are no parallel lines.

In Exercises 40 and 41, determine the exact area of the spherical triangle.

40. Radius: 12 in.; angles: 90°, 150°, 90°

41. Radius: 5 ft; angles: 90°, 60°, 90°

City Geometry In Exercises 42–45, find the Euclidean distance and the city distance between the points. Assume that the distances are measured in blocks. Round approximate results to the nearest tenth of a block.

42. $P(-1, 1)$, $Q(3, 4)$

43. $P(-5, -2)$, $Q(2, 6)$

44. $P(2, 8)$, $Q(3, 2)$

45. $P(-3, 3)$, $Q(5, -2)$

46. Consider the points $P(1, 1)$, $Q(4, 5)$, and $R(-4, 2)$.

  a. Which two points are closest together if you use the Euclidean distance formula to measure distance?

  b. Which two points are closest together if you use the city distance formula to measure distance?

47. Draw stage 0, stage 1, and stage 2 of the Koch curve.

48. Draw stage 2 of the fractal with the following initiator and generator.

Stage 0
Initiator

Stage 1
Generator

49. Compute the similarity dimension of a strictly self-similar fractal with a replacement ratio of 5 and a scaling ratio of 4. Round to the nearest thousandth.

50. Determine the similarity dimension of the fractal defined in Exercise 48.

CHAPTER 8   Test

---

1. Find the volume of a cylinder with a height of 6 m and a radius of 3 m. Round to the nearest hundredth of a cubic meter.

2. Find the perimeter of a rectangle that has a length of 2 m and a width of 1.4 m.

3. Find the complement of a 32° angle.

4. Find the area of a circle that has a diameter of 2 m. Round to the nearest hundredth of a square meter.

5. In the figure below, lines ℓ_1 and ℓ_2 are parallel. Angle x measures 30°. Find the measure of angle y.

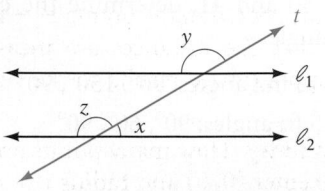

6. In the figure below, lines ℓ_1 and ℓ_2 are parallel. Angle x measures 45°. Find the measures of angles a and b.

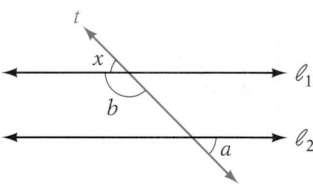

7. Find the area of a square that measures 2.25 ft on each side.

8. Find the volume of the figure. Give the exact value.

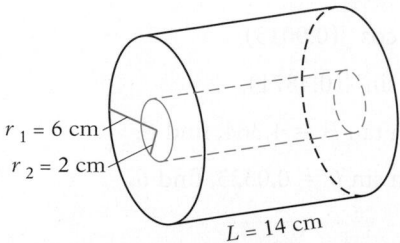

$r_1 = 6$ cm
$r_2 = 2$ cm
$L = 14$ cm

9. Triangles *ABC* and *DEF* are similar. Find side *BC*.

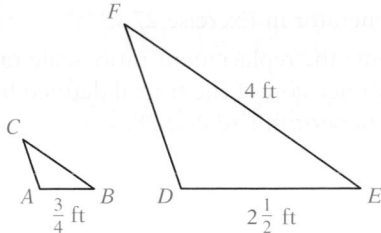

10. A right triangle has a 40° angle. Find the measures of the other two angles.

11. Find the measure of ∠*x*.

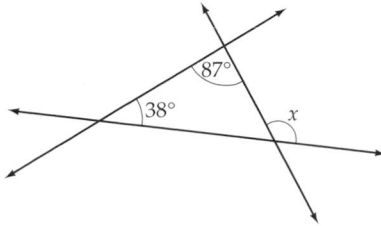

12. Find the area of the parallelogram shown below.

13. **Surveying** Find the width of the canal shown in the figure below.

14. **Pizza** How much more area is in a pizza with radius 10 in. than in a pizza with radius 8 in.? Round to the nearest hundredth of a square inch.

15. Determine whether the two triangles are congruent. If they are congruent, state by what theorem they are congruent.

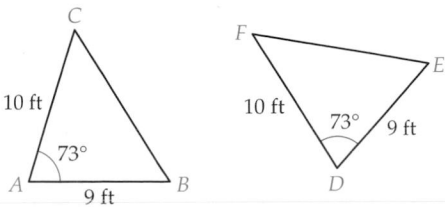

16. For the right triangle shown below, determine the length of side *BC*. Round to the nearest hundredth of a centimeter.

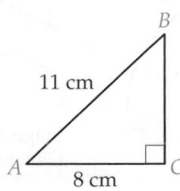

17. Find the values of sin θ, cos θ, and tan θ for the given right triangle.

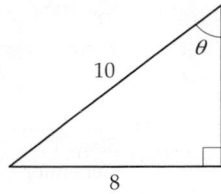

18. **Angle of Elevation** From a point 27 feet from the base of a Roman aqueduct, the angle of elevation to the top of the aqueduct is 78°. Find the height of the aqueduct. Round to the nearest foot.

19. **Trees** Find the cross-sectional area of a redwood tree that is 11 ft 6 in. in diameter. Round to the nearest hundredth of a square foot.

20. **Toolbox** A toolbox is 14 in. long, 9 in. wide, and 8 in. high. The sides and bottom of the toolbox are $\frac{1}{2}$ in. thick. The toolbox is open at the top. Find the volume of the interior of the toolbox in cubic inches.

21. **a.** State the Euclidean parallel postulate.

    b. State the parallel postulate used in Riemannian geometry.

22. What is the maximum number of right angles a triangle can have in

    a. Lobachevskian geometry?

    b. Riemannian geometry?

23. What is a great circle?

24. Find the area of a spherical triangle with a radius of 12 ft and angles of 90°, 100°, and 90°. Give the exact area and the area rounded to the nearest tenth of a square foot.

25. **City Geometry** Find the Euclidean distance and the city distance between the points $P(-4, 2)$ and $Q(5, 1)$. Assume that the distances are measured in blocks. Round approximate results to the nearest tenth of a block.

26. **City Geometry** How many points are on the city circle with center $(0, 0)$ and radius $r = 4$ blocks?

Introduction to Graphs

The acts of traveling the streets of a city, routing data through nodes on the Internet, and flying between cities have a common link. The goal of each of these tasks is to go from one place to another along a specified path. Efficient strategies to accomplish these goals can be studied using a branch of mathematics called *graph theory*.

For example, the diagram in Figure 9.1 could represent the flights available on a particular airline between a selection of cities. Each dot represents a city, and a line segment connecting two dots means there is a flight between the two cities. The line segments do not represent the actual paths the planes fly; they simply indicate a relationship between two cities (in this case, that a flight exists). If we wish to travel from San Francisco to New York, the diagram can help us examine the various possible routes. This type of diagram is called a *graph*. Note that this is a very different kind of graph from the graph of a function that we discussed in Chapter 6.

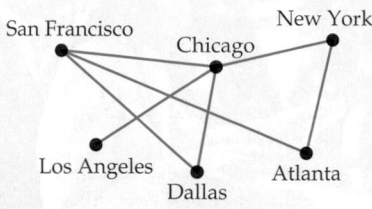

Figure 9.1

> **Definition of a Graph**
>
> A **graph** is a set of points called **vertices** and line segments or curves called **edges** that connect vertices.

Graphs can be used to represent many different scenarios. For instance, the three graphs in Figure 9.2 are the exact same graph as in Figure 9.1, but used in different contexts. In part (a), each vertex represents a baseball team, and an edge connecting two vertices might mean that the two teams played each other during the current season. Note that the placement of the vertices has nothing to do with geographical location; in fact, the vertices can be shown in any arrangement we choose. The important information is which vertices are connected by edges.

✔ **TAKE NOTE**

Vertices are always clearly indicated with a "dot." Edges that intersect with no marked vertex are considered to cross over each other without touching.

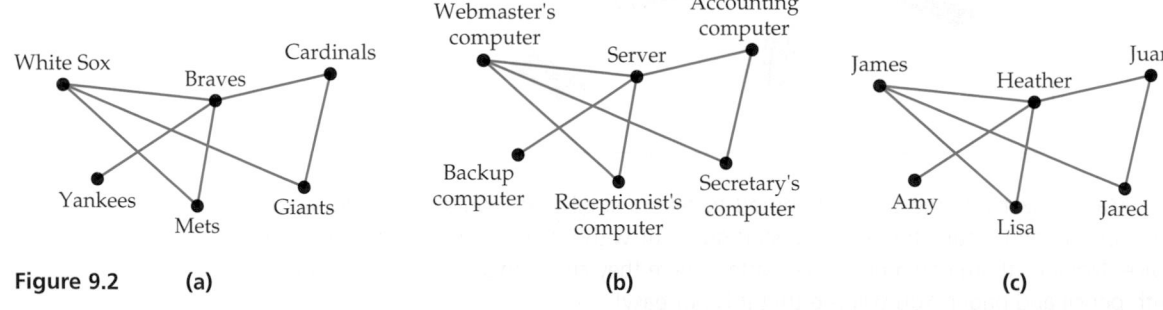

Figure 9.2   **(a)**   **(b)**   **(c)**

Figure 9.2(b) shows the computer network of a small business. Each vertex represents a computer, and the edges indicate which machines are directly connected to each other. The graph in Figure 9.2(c) could be used to indicate which students share a class together; each vertex represents a student, and an edge connecting two vertices means that those students share at least one class.

In general, graphs can contain vertices that are not connected to any edges, two or more edges that connect the same vertices (called **multiple edges**), or edges that loop back to the same vertex. We will usually deal with **connected graphs,** graphs in which any vertex can be reached from any other vertex by tracing along edges. (Essentially, the graph consists of only one "piece.") Several examples of graphs are shown below.

This graph has five vertices but no edges, and is referred to as a **null graph.** It is also an example of a *disconnected graph*.	This is a connected graph that has a pair of *multiple edges*. Notice that two edges cross in the center, but there is no vertex there. Unless a dot is drawn, the edges are considered to pass over each other without touching.	This graph is not connected; it consists of two different sections. It also contains a loop.	This is a connected graph in which every possible edge is drawn between vertices (without any multiple edges). Such a graph is called a **complete graph.**

Notice that it does not matter whether the edges are drawn straight or curved, and their lengths and positions are not important. Nor is the exact placement of the vertices important. The graph simply illustrates connections between vertices.

Consequently, the three graphs illustrated below are considered **equivalent graphs** because the edges form the same connections of vertices in each graph.

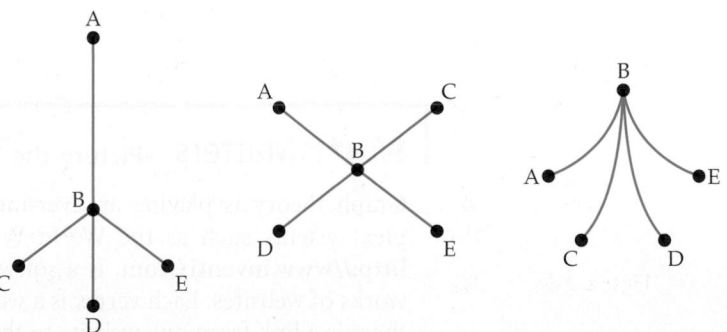

If you have difficulty seeing that these graphs are equivalent, use the labeled vertices to compare each graph. Notice that in each case, vertex B has an edge connecting it to each of the other four vertices, and no other edges exist.

EXAMPLE 1 ■ Equivalent Graphs

Determine whether the following two graphs are equivalent.

 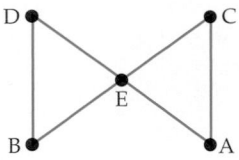

✔ **TAKE NOTE**

The order in which the vertices of an edge are given is not important; AC and CA represent the same edge.

Solution

Despite the fact that the two graphs have different arrangements of vertices and edges, they are equivalent. To illustrate, we examine the edges of each graph. The first graph contains six edges; we can list them by indicating which two vertices they connect. The edges are AC, AE, BD, BE, CE, and DE. If we do the same for the second graph, we get the exact same six edges. Because the two graphs represent the same connections among the vertices, they are equivalent.

CHECK YOUR PROGRESS 1   Determine whether the following two graphs are equivalent.

 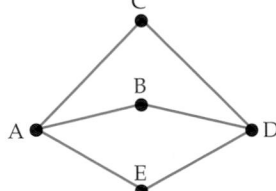

Solution   See page S33.

Math Matters   Picture the World Wide Web as a Graph

Graph theory is playing an ever-increasing role in the study of large and complex systems such as the World Wide Web. Internet Cartographer, available at **http://www.inventix.com,** is a software application that creates graphs from networks of websites. Each vertex is a website, and two vertices are joined by an edge if there is a link from one website to the other. The software was used to generate the image on the following page. You can imagine how large the graph would be if all the billions of existing web pages were included. The Internet search engine Google uses these relationships to rank its search results. Websites are ranked in

(continued)

part according to how many other sites link to them. In effect, the websites represented by the vertices of the graph with the most connected edges would appear first in Google's search results.

A graph of a network of websites. Each vertex represents a website, and an edge between vertices indicates that one site includes a link to the other.

Another example of an extremely large graph is the graph that uses vertices to represent telephone numbers. An edge connects two vertices if one number called the other. James Abello of AT&T Shannon Laboratories analyzed a graph formed from one day's worth of calls. The graph had over 53 million vertices and 170 million edges! Interestingly, although the graph was not a connected graph (it contained 3.7 million separate components), over 80% of the vertices were part of one large connected component. Within this component, any telephone could be linked to any other through a chain of 20 or fewer calls.

Euler Circuits

To solve the Königsberg bridges problem presented on page 569, we can represent the arrangement of land areas and bridges with a graph. Let each land area be represented by a vertex, and then connect two vertices if there is a bridge spanning the corresponding land areas. Then the geographical situation shown in Figure 9.3 on the following page becomes the graph shown in Figure 9.4.

Figure 9.3

Figure 9.4

In terms of a graph, the original problem can be stated as follows: Can we start at any vertex, move through each edge once (but not more than once), and return to the starting vertex? Again, try it with pencil and paper. Every attempt seems to end in failure.

Before we can examine how Euler proved this task impossible, we need to establish some terminology. A **walk** in a graph can be thought of as a movement from one vertex to another by traversing edges. We can refer to our movement by vertex letters. For example, in the graph in Figure 9.4, one walk would be A−B−A−C. If a walk ends at the same vertex it started at, it is considered a **closed walk,** or **circuit.** A circuit that uses every edge, but never uses the same edge twice, is called an **Euler circuit.** So an Euler circuit is a walk that starts and ends at the same vertex and uses every edge of the graph exactly once. (The walk may cross through vertices more than once.) If we could find an Euler circuit in the graph in Figure 9.4, we would have a solution to the Königsberg bridges problem: a path that crosses each bridge exactly once and returns to the starting point.

Euler essentially proved that the graph in Figure 9.4 cannot have an Euler circuit. He accomplished this by examining the number of edges that met at each vertex. This is called the **degree** of a vertex. He made the observation that in order to complete the desired walk, every time you approached a vertex you would then need to leave that vertex. If you traveled through that vertex again, you would again need an approaching edge and a departing edge. Thus, for an Euler circuit to exist, the degree of every vertex would have to be an even number. Furthermore, he was able to show that any graph that has even degree at every vertex must have an Euler circuit. Consequently, such graphs are called **Eulerian.** If we now look at the graph in Figure 9.4, we can see that it is not Eulerian. No Euler circuit exists because not every vertex has even degree.

Eulerian Graph Theorem

A connected graph is Eulerian if and only if every vertex of the graph is of even degree.

The Eulerian Graph Theorem guarantees that when all vertices of a graph have even degree, an Euler circuit exists, but it does not tell us how to find one. Because the graphs we will examine here are relatively small, we will rely on trial and error to find Euler circuits. There is a systematic method, called *Fluery's Algorithm,* that can be used to find an Euler circuit in graphs with a large number of vertices.

EXAMPLE 2 ■ Find an Euler Circuit

Determine whether the graph shown below is Eulerian. If it is, find an Euler circuit. If it is not, explain how you know. The number beside each vertex indicates the degree of the vertex.

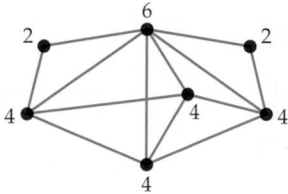

Solution

Each vertex has degree of either 2, 4, or 6, so by the Eulerian Graph Theorem, the graph is Eulerian. There are many possible Euler circuits in this graph. We do not have a formal method of locating one, so we just use trial and error. If we label the vertices as shown below, one Euler circuit is B–A–F–B–E–F–G–E–D–G–B–D–C–B.

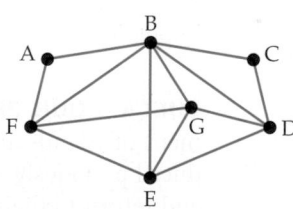

CHECK YOUR PROGRESS 2   Does the following graph have an Euler circuit? If so, find one. If not, explain why.

Solution   See page S33.

▼ point of interest

There are a number of instances in which finding an Euler circuit has practical implications. For example, in cities where it snows in the winter, the highway department must provide snow removal for the streets. The most efficient route is an Euler circuit. In this case, the snow plow leaves the maintenance garage, travels down each street only once, and returns to the garage. The situation becomes more complicated if one-way streets are involved; nonetheless, graph theory techniques can still help find the most efficient route to follow.

EXAMPLE 3 ■ An Application of Euler Circuits

The subway map below shows the tracks the subway trains traverse as well as the junctions where one can switch trains. Suppose an inspector needs to travel the full length of each track. Is it possible to plan a journey that traverses the tracks and returns to the starting point without traveling through any portion of a track more than once?

Solution

We can consider the subway map a graph, with a vertex at each junction. An edge represents a track that runs between two junctions. In order to find a travel route that does not traverse the same track twice, we need to find an Euler circuit in the graph. Notice, however, that the vertex representing the Civic Center junction has degree 3. Because a vertex has odd degree, the graph cannot be Eulerian, and it is impossible for the inspector not to travel at least one track twice.

CHECK YOUR PROGRESS 3   Suppose the city of Königsberg had the arrangement of islands and bridges pictured below instead of the arrangement we introduced previously. Would the citizens be able to complete a stroll across each bridge and return to their starting points without crossing the same bridge twice?

Solution   *See page S33.*

Euler Walks

Perhaps the Königsberg bridge problem would have a solution if we did not need to return to the starting point. Give it a try; you will still find it difficult to find a solution.

If we do not need to return to our starting point, then what we are looking for in Figure 9.4 on page 574 is a walk (not necessarily a circuit) that uses every edge once and only once. We call such a walk an **Euler walk.** Euler showed that even with this relaxed condition, the bridge problem still was not solvable. The general result of his argument is given in the following theorem.

Euler Walk Theorem

A connected graph contains an Euler walk if and only if the graph has two vertices of odd degree with all other vertices of even degree. Furthermore, every Euler walk must start at one of the vertices of odd degree and end at the other.

To see why this theorem is true, notice that the only places at which an Euler walk differs from an Euler circuit are the start and end vertices. If we never return to the starting vertex, only one edge meets there and the degree of the vertex is 1. If we do return, we cannot stop there. So we depart again, giving the vertex a degree of 3. Similarly, any return trip means that an additional two edges meet at the vertex. Thus the degree of the start vertex must be odd. By similar reasoning, the ending vertex must also have odd degree. All other vertices, just as in the case of an Euler circuit, must have even degree.

EXAMPLE 4 ■ An Application of Euler Walks

A photographer would like to travel across all of the roads shown on the map below. The photographer will rent a car that need not be returned to the same city, so the trip can begin in any city. Is it possible for the photographer to design a trip that traverses all of the roads exactly once?

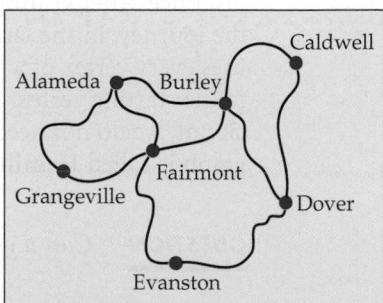

Solution

Looking at the map of roads as a graph, we see that a route that includes all of the roads but does not cover any road twice corresponds to an Euler walk of the graph. Notice that only two vertices have odd degree, the cities Alameda and Dover. Thus we know that an Euler walk exists, and so it is possible for the photographer to plan a route that travels each road once. Because (abbreviating the cities) A and D are vertices of odd degree, the photographer must start at one of these cities. With a little experimentation, we find that one Euler walk is A − B − C − D − B − F − A − G − F − E − D.

CHECK YOUR PROGRESS 4 A bicyclist wants to mountain bike through all the trails of a national park. A map of the park is shown below. Because the bicyclist will be dropped off in the morning by friends and picked up in the evening, she does not have a preference of where she begins and ends her ride. Is it possible for the cyclist to traverse all of the trails without repeating any portions of her trip?

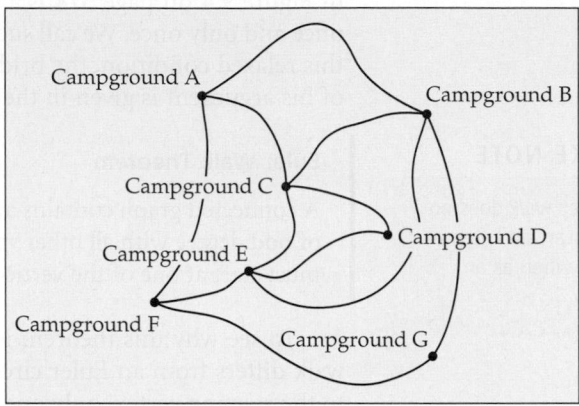

Solution See page S33.

Hamiltonian Circuits

In Example 4, we tried to find a route that traversed every road once without repeating any roads. Suppose our priority is to visit cities rather than travel roads. We do not care whether we use all the roads or not. Is there a route that visits each city once (without repeating any cities)?

You can verify that the route A–B–C–D–E–F–G visits each city in Example 4 just once. After visiting Grangeville, we could return to the starting city to complete the journey. In the language of graph theory, this route corresponds to a walk that uses every vertex of a (connected) graph, does not use any vertex twice, and returns to the starting vertex. Such a walk is called a **Hamiltonian circuit.** (Unlike an Euler circuit, we do not need to use every edge.) If a graph has a Hamiltonian circuit, the graph is called **Hamiltonian.**

QUESTION *Can a graph be both Eulerian and Hamiltonian?*

Because we found the Hamiltonian Circuit A–B–C–D–E–F–G–A in the map of cities in Example 4, we know that the graph is Hamiltonian. Unfortunately, we do not have a straightforward criterion to guarantee that a graph will be Hamiltonian, but we do have the following theorem.

ANSWER *Yes. For example, the graph shown here has an Euler circuit and a Hamiltonian circuit.*

Dirac's Theorem

Consider a connected graph with at least three vertices and no multiple edges. Let n be the number of vertices in the graph. If every vertex has degree of at least $n/2$, then the graph must be Hamiltonian.

We must be careful, however; if our graph does not meet the requirements of this theorem, it still might be Hamiltonian. Dirac's Theorem does not help us in this case.

EXAMPLE 5 ■ Apply Dirac's Theorem

The graph below shows the available flights of a popular airline. (An edge between two vertices in the graph means the airline has direct flights between the two corresponding cities.) Apply Dirac's Theorem to verify that the following graph is Hamiltonian. What does a Hamiltonian circuit represent in terms of flights?

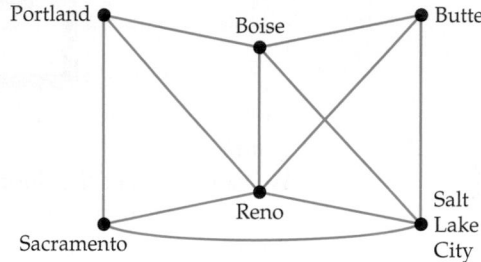

Solution

There are six vertices in the graph, so $n = 6$, and every vertex has degree of at least $n/2 = 3$. So, by Dirac's Theorem, the graph is Hamiltonian. This means the graph contains a circuit that visits each vertex once and returns to the starting vertex without visiting any vertex twice. Here, a Hamiltonian circuit represents a sequence of flights that visits each city and returns to the starting city without visiting any city twice. Notice that Dirac's Theorem does not tell us how to find the Hamiltonian circuit; it just guarantees that one exists.

CHECK YOUR PROGRESS 5 A large law firm has offices in seven major cities. The firm has overnight document deliveries scheduled every day between certain offices. In the graph below, an edge between vertices indicates that there is delivery service between the corresponding offices. Use Dirac's Theorem to answer the following question: Using the law firm's existing delivery service, is it possible to route a document to all the offices and return the document to its originating office without sending it through the same office twice?

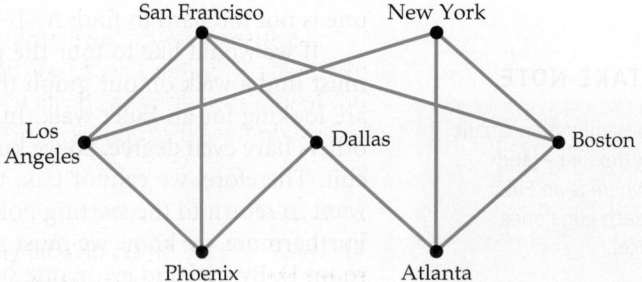

Solution   *See page S33.*

EXAMPLE 6 ■ An Application of Hamiltonian Circuits

The floor plan of an art gallery is pictured below. Draw a graph to represent the floor plan, where vertices correspond to rooms and edges correspond to doorways. Then use your graph to answer the following questions. Is it possible to take a walking tour through the gallery that visits every room and returns to the starting point without visiting any room twice? Is it possible to take a stroll that passes through every doorway without going through the same doorway twice? If so, does it matter whether we return to the starting point?

Solution

We can represent the floor plan by a graph if we let a vertex represent each room. Draw an edge between two vertices if there is a doorway between the two rooms, as shown in Figure 9.5.

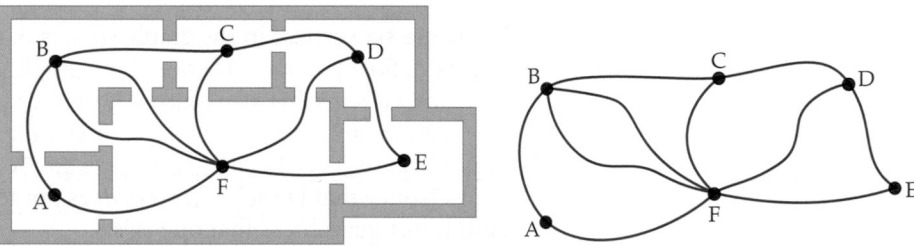

Figure 9.5   **Figure 9.6**

The graph in Figure 9.6 is equivalent to our floor plan. A walk through the gallery that visits each room just once and returns to the starting point corresponds to a visit to each vertex without visiting any vertex twice. In other words, we are looking for a Hamiltonian circuit. There are six vertices in the graph, and not all the vertices have degree of at least 3, so Dirac's Theorem does not guarantee that the graph is Hamiltonian. However, it is still possible that a Hamiltonian circuit exists. In fact, one is not too hard to find: A–B–C–D–E–F–A.

If we would like to tour the gallery and pass through every doorway once, we must find a walk on our graph that uses every edge once (and no more). Thus we are looking for an Euler walk. In the graph, two vertices have odd degree and the others have even degree. So we know that an Euler walk exists, but not an Euler circuit. Therefore, we cannot pass through each doorway once and only once if we want to return to the starting point, but we can do it if we end up somewhere else. Furthermore, we know we must start at a vertex of odd degree—either room C or room D. By trial and error, one such walk is C–B–F–B–A–F–E–D–C–F–D.

✓ **TAKE NOTE**

Recall that a Hamiltonian circuit visits each vertex once (and only once), whereas an Euler circuit uses each edge once (and only once).

CHECK YOUR PROGRESS 6   The floor plan of a warehouse is pictured below. Use a graph to represent the floor plan and answer the following questions. Is it possible to walk through the warehouse so that you pass through every doorway once but not twice? Does it matter whether you return to the starting point?

Solution   *See page S33.*

You may find it helpful to review the following key definitions from this section before proceeding.

walk	A path between vertices formed by traversing edges.
circuit	A walk that begins and ends at the same vertex.
Euler walk	A walk that uses every edge, but does not use any edge more than once.
Euler circuit	A walk that uses every edge, but does not use any edge more than once, and begins and ends at the same vertex.
Eulerian graph	A graph that contains an Euler circuit.
Hamiltonian circuit	A walk that uses every vertex, but does not use any vertex more than once, and begins and ends at the same vertex.
Hamiltonian graph	A graph that contains a Hamiltonian circuit.

Excursion

Pen-Tracing Puzzles

You may have seen puzzles before like this one: Can you draw the diagram at the right without lifting your pencil from the paper, and without tracing over the same segment twice?

(continued)

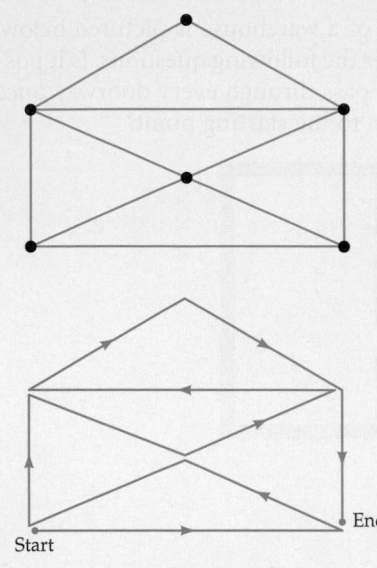

Start

End

Before reading on, try it for yourself. By trial and error, you may discover a tracing that works. Even though there are several possible tracings, you may notice that only certain starting points seem to allow a complete tracing. How do we know which point to start from? How do we even know that a solution exists?

Puzzles like this, called "pen-tracing puzzles," are actually problems in graph theory. If we imagine a vertex placed wherever two lines meet or cross over each other, then we have a graph. Our task is to start at a vertex and find a path that traverses every edge of the graph, without repeating any edges. In other words, we need an Euler walk! (An Euler circuit would work as well.)

As we learned in this section, a graph has an Euler walk only if two vertices are of odd degree and the remaining vertices are of even degree. Furthermore, the walk must start at one of the vertices of odd degree and end at the other. In the puzzle at the left, only two vertices are of odd degree—the two bottom corners. So we know that an Euler walk exists, and it must start from one of these two corners. At the left is one possible solution.

Of course, if every vertex is of even degree, we can solve the puzzle by finding an Euler circuit. If more than two vertices are of odd degree, then we know the puzzle cannot be solved.

Excursion Exercises

In Exercises 1–4, a pen-tracing puzzle is given. See if you can find a way to trace the shape without lifting your pen and without tracing over the same segment twice.

1.

2.

3.

4.

5. Explain why the following pen-tracing puzzle is impossible to solve.

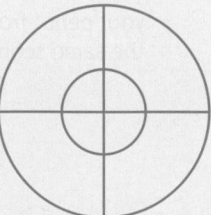

Exercise Set 9.1

In Exercises 1–4, (a) give the number of edges in the graph, (b) give the number of vertices in the graph, (c) determine the number of vertices that are of odd degree, (d) determine whether the graph is connected, and (e) determine whether the graph is a complete graph.

1.

2.

3.

4.

5. **Transportation** An "X" in the table below indicates a direct train route between the corresponding cities. Draw a graph to represent this information, in which each vertex represents a city and an edge connects two vertices if there is a train route between the corresponding cities.

	Springfield	Riverside	Greenfield	Watertown	Midland	Newhope
Springfield	—		X		X	
Riverside		—		X	X	X
Greenfield	X		—	X	X	X
Watertown		X	X	—		
Midland	X	X	X		—	X
Newhope		X	X		X	—

6. **Transportation** The table on the following page shows the nonstop flights offered by a small airline. Draw a graph to represent this information, where

each vertex represents a city and an edge connects two vertices if there is a non-stop flight between the corresponding cities.

	Newport	Lancaster	Plymouth	Auburn	Dorset
Newport	—	no	yes	no	yes
Lancaster	no	—	yes	yes	no
Plymouth	yes	yes	—	yes	yes
Auburn	no	yes	yes	—	yes
Dorset	yes	no	yes	yes	—

Architecture In Exercises 7 and 8, a floor plan of a museum is given. Draw a graph to represent the floor plan, where each vertex represents a room and an edge connects two vertices if there is a doorway between the two rooms.

 7.

 8.

9. **Social Network** A group of friends is represented by the graph at the right. An edge connecting two names means that the two friends have spoken to each other in the last week.

   a. Have John and Stacy talked to each other in the last week?

   b. How many of the friends in this group has Steve talked to in the last week?

   c. Among this group of friends, who has talked to the most people in the last week?

   d. Why would it not make sense for this graph to contain a loop?

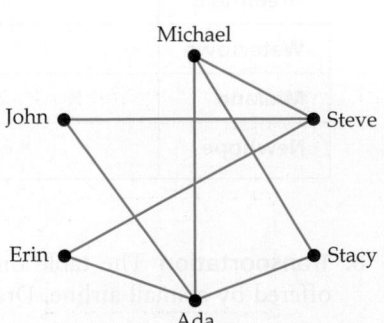

10. **Baseball** The local Little League baseball teams are represented by the graph at the right. An edge connecting two teams means that those teams have played a game against each other this season.

    a. Which team has played only one game this season?
    b. Which team has played the most games this season?
    c. Have any teams played each other twice this season?

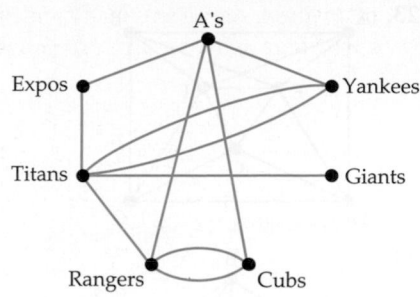

In Exercises 11–14, determine whether the two graphs are equivalent.

11.

12.

13.

14.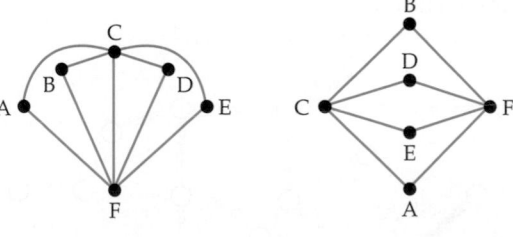

15. Explain why the following two graphs cannot be equivalent.

16. Label the vertices of the second graph so that it is equivalent to the first graph.

In Exercises 17–24, (a) determine whether the graph is Eulerian. If it is, find an Euler circuit. If it is not, explain why. (b) If the graph does not have an Euler circuit, does it have an Euler walk? If so, find one. If not, explain why.

17.   18.

19.   20.

21.   22.

23.

24.

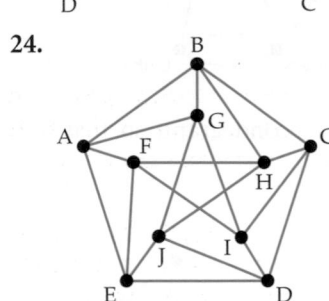

Parks In Exercises 25 and 26, a map of a park is shown with bridges connecting islands in a river to the banks.

a. Represent the map as a graph. See Figures 9.3 and 9.4 on page 574.

b. Is it possible to take a walk that crosses each bridge once and return to the starting point without crossing any bridge twice? If not, can you do it if you do not end at the starting point? Explain how you know.

25.

26.

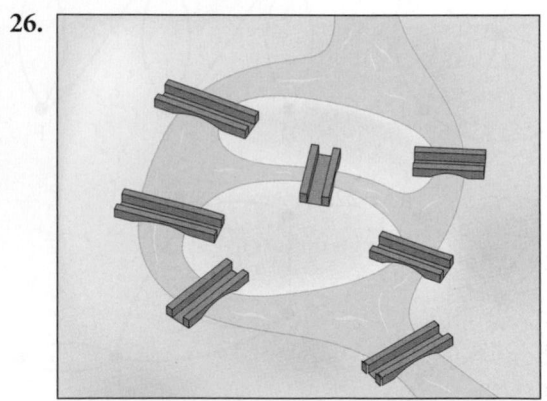

27. **Transportation** For the train routes given in Exercise 5, is it possible to travel along all of the train routes without traveling along any route twice? Explain how you reached your conclusion.

28. **Transportation** For the direct air flights given in Exercise 6, is it possible to start at one city and fly every route offered without repeating any flight if you return to the starting city? Explain how you reached your conclusion.

29. **Pets** The diagram below shows the arrangement of a Habitrail cage for a pet hamster. (Plastic tubes connect different cages.) Is it possible for a hamster to travel through every tube without going through the same tube twice? If so, find a route for the hamster to follow. Can the hamster return to its starting point without repeating any tube passages?

30. **Transportation** A subway map is shown below. Is it possible for a rider to travel the length of every subway route without repeating any segments? Justify your conclusion.

31. **Architecture** For the floor plan in Exercise 7, is it possible to walk through the museum and pass through each doorway without going through any doorway twice? Does it depend on whether you return to the room you started at? Justify your conclusion.

32. **Architecture** For the floor plan in Exercise 8, is it possible to walk through the museum and pass through each doorway without going through any doorway twice? Does it depend on whether you return to your starting point? Justify your conclusion.

In Exercises 33–36, use Dirac's Theorem to verify that the graph is Hamiltonian. Then find a Hamiltonian circuit.

33.

34.

35.

36.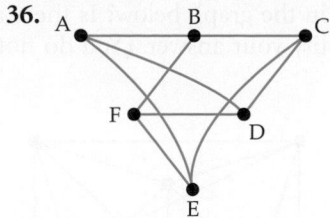

37. **Transportation** For the train routes given in Exercise 5, find a route that visits each city and returns to the starting city without visiting any city twice.

38. **Transportation** For the direct air flights given in Exercise 6, find a route that visits each city and returns to the starting city without visiting any city twice.

39. **Architecture** In Exercise 7, you were asked to draw a graph that represents a museum floor plan. Describe what a Hamiltonian circuit in the graph would correspond to in the museum.

40. **Transportation** Consider a subway map, like the one given in Exercise 30. If we draw a graph in which each vertex represents a train junction, and an edge between vertices means a train travels between those two junctions, what does a Hamiltonian circuit correspond to in regard to the subway?

Extensions

CRITICAL THINKING

41. **Route Planning** A security officer patrolling a city neighborhood needs to drive every street each night. The officer has drawn a graph to represent the neighborhood in which the edges represent the streets and the vertices correspond to street intersections. Would the most efficient way to drive the streets correspond to an Euler circuit, a Hamiltonian circuit, or neither? (The officer must return to the starting location when finished.) Explain your answer.

42. **Route Planning** A city engineer needs to inspect the traffic signs at each street intersection of a neighborhood. The engineer has drawn a graph to represent the neighborhood, where the edges represent the streets and the vertices correspond to street intersections. Would the most efficient route to drive correspond to an Euler circuit, a Hamiltonian circuit, or neither? (The engineer must return to the starting location when finished.) Explain your answer.

43. Is there an Euler circuit in the graph below? Is there an Euler walk? Is there a Hamiltonian circuit? Justify your answer. (You do not need to find any of the circuits or paths.)

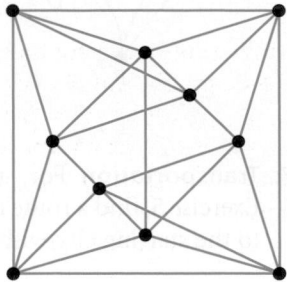

44. Is there an Euler circuit in the graph below? Is there an Euler walk? Is there a Hamiltonian circuit? Justify your answer. (You do not need to find any of the circuits or paths.)

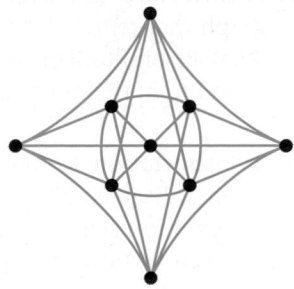

COOPERATIVE LEARNING

45. a. Draw a connected graph with six vertices that has no Euler circuits and no Hamiltonian circuits.

  b. Draw a graph with six vertices that has a Hamiltonian circuit but no Euler circuits.

  c. Draw a graph with five vertices that has an Euler circuit but no Hamiltonian circuits.

46. Travel A map of South America is shown at the right.

  a. Draw a graph in which the vertices represent the 13 countries of South America, and two vertices are joined by an edge if the corresponding countries share a common border.

  b. Two friends are planning a driving tour of South America. They would like to drive across every border on the continent. Is it possible to plan such a route that never crosses the same border twice? What would the route correspond to on the graph?

  c. Find a route the friends can follow that will start and end in Venezuela and that crosses every border while repeating the fewest number of borders possible. *Hint:* On the graph, add multiple edges corresponding to border crossings that allow an Euler circuit.

| **Efficient Routes**

Weighted Graphs

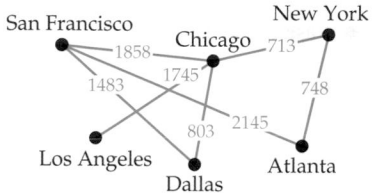

Figure 9.7

In Section 9.1, we examined the problem of finding a path that enabled us to visit all of the cities represented on a graph, and we saw that in many cases there were a number of different paths we could use. What if we are concerned with the distances we must travel between cities? If there is more than one route that brings us through all of the cities, chances are some of the routes will involve a longer total distance than others. If we hope to minimize the number of miles we must travel in order to see the cities, we would be interested in finding the best route among all the possibilities.

We can represent this situation with a *weighted graph*. A **weighted graph** is a graph in which each edge is associated with a value, called a **weight.** The value can represent any quantity we desire. In the case of distances between cities, we can label each edge with the number of miles between the corresponding cities. (Note that the length of an edge does not necessarily correlate to its weight.) For instance, the graph in Figure 9.7 is the graph of airline flights shown in Figure 9.1, but with the weights of the edges added. We now know at a glance the distances between cities.

We previously looked for routes that visited each city and returned to the starting city; in other words, a Hamiltonian circuit. For each such circuit we find in a weighted graph, we can compute the total weight of the circuit by finding the sum of the weights of the edges we traverse. In this case, the sum gives us the total distance traveled along our route. We can then compare different routes and find the one that requires the least total distance. This is an example of a famous problem called the *traveling salesman problem.*

TAKE NOTE

Remember that a Hamiltonian circuit in a graph is a closed walk that uses each vertex of the graph but does not use any vertex twice.

EXAMPLE 1 ■ Find Hamiltonian Circuits in a Weighted Graph

The table below lists the distances in miles between six popular cities that a particular airline flies to. Suppose a traveler would like to start in Chicago, visit the other five cities this airline flies to, and return to Chicago. Find three different routes that the traveler could follow, and find the total distance flown for each route.

	Chicago	New York	Washington, D.C.	Philadelphia	Atlanta	Dallas
Chicago	—	713	597	665	585	803
New York	713	—	no flights	no flights	748	1374
Washington, D.C.	597	no flights	—	no flights	544	1185
Philadelphia	665	no flights	no flights	—	670	1299
Atlanta	585	748	544	670	—	no flights
Dallas	803	1374	1185	1299	no flights	—

EXAMPLE 2 ■ The Greedy Algorithm

Use the Greedy Algorithm to find a Hamiltonian circuit in the weighted graph shown in Figure 9.9. Start at vertex A.

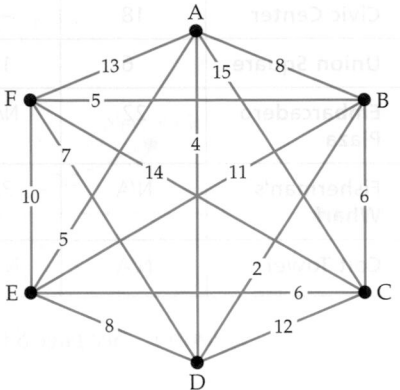

Figure 9.9

Solution

The edge at vertex A with the smallest weight is the edge to D, which has weight 4. From D, the edge with the smallest weight (besides the one we just traveled) has weight 2 and connects to B. The next edge, of weight 5, connects to vertex F. The edge from F of the least weight that has not yet been used is the edge to vertex D. However, we have already visited D, so we choose the edge with the next smallest weight, 10, to vertex E. The only remaining choice is the edge to vertex C, of weight 6, as all other vertices have been visited. Now we are at Step 3 of the algorithm, so we return to starting vertex A by traveling along the edge of weight 15. Thus our Hamiltonian circuit is A–D–B–F–E–C–A, with a total weight of

$$4 + 2 + 5 + 10 + 6 + 15 = 42$$

CHECK YOUR PROGRESS 2   Use the Greedy Algorithm to find a Hamiltonian circuit starting at vertex A in the weighted graph shown below.

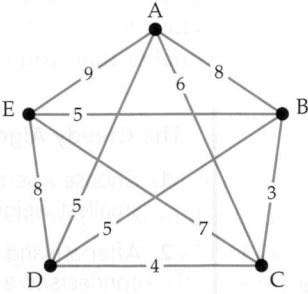

Solution   *See page S34.*

The Greedy Algorithm is so called because it has us choose the "cheapest" option at every chance we get. The next algorithm uses a different strategy to find an efficient route in a traveling salesman problem.

> **The Edge-Picking Algorithm**
>
> **1.** Mark the edge of smallest weight in the graph. (If two or more edges have the same weight, pick any one.)
>
> **2.** Mark the edge of next smallest weight in the graph, as long as it does not complete a circuit and does not add a third marked edge to a single vertex.
>
> **3.** Continue this process until you can no longer mark any edges. Then mark the final edge that completes the Hamiltonian circuit.

In Step 2 of the algorithm, we are instructed not to complete a circuit too early. Also, because a Hamiltonian circuit will always have exactly two edges at each vertex, we are warned not to mark an edge that would allow three edges to meet at one vertex. You can see the algorithm in action in the next example.

EXAMPLE 3 ■ The Edge-Picking Algorithm

Use the Edge-Picking Algorithm to find a Hamiltonian circuit in Figure 9.9.

Solution
The smallest weight appearing in the graph is 2, so we highlight the edge B–D of weight 2. The next smallest weight is 4, the weight of edge A–D.

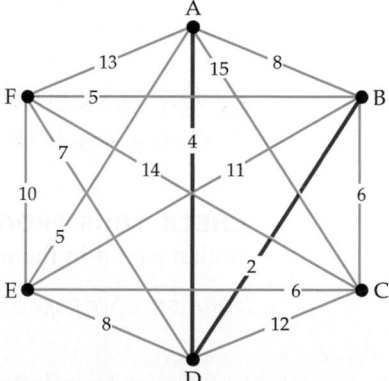

There are two edges of weight 5 (the next smallest weight), A–E and F–B, and we can highlight both of them. Next there are two edges of weight 6. However, we cannot use B–C because it would add a third marked edge to vertex B. We mark E–C.

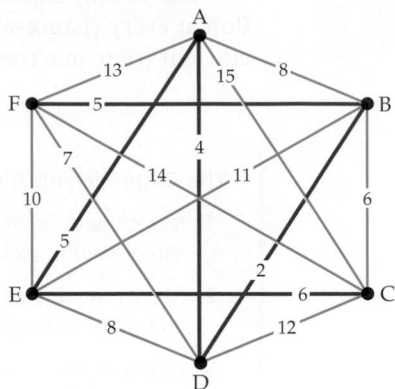

We are now at Step 3 of the algorithm; any edge we mark will either complete a circuit or add a third edge to a vertex. So we mark the final edge to complete the circuit, F–C.

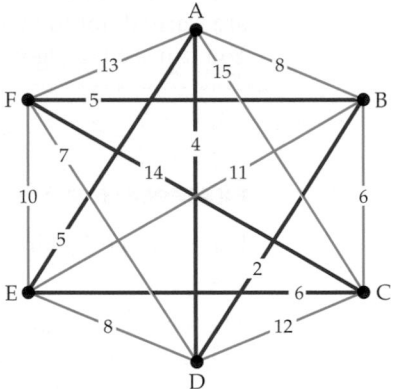

If we begin at vertex A, our Hamiltonian circuit is A–D–B–F–C–E–A. (In the reverse direction, an equivalent Hamiltonian circuit is A–E–C–F–B–D–A.) The total weight of the circuit is

$$4 + 2 + 5 + 14 + 6 + 5 = 36$$

CHECK YOUR PROGRESS 3 Use the Edge-Picking Algorithm to find a Hamiltonian circuit in the weighted graph in Check Your Progress 2.

Solution *See page S34.*

Notice from Examples 2 and 3 that the two algorithms gave different Hamiltonian circuits, and in this case the Edge-Picking Algorithm gave the more efficient route. Is this the best route? We mentioned before that there is no known efficient method for finding the very best circuit. In fact, the Hamiltonian circuit A–D–F–B–C–E–A in Figure 9.9 has a total weight of 33, which is smaller than the weights of both routes given by the algorithms. So when we use the algorithms, we have no guarantee that we are finding the best route, but we can be confident that we are finding a reasonably good solution.

QUESTION   *Can the Greedy Algorithm or the Edge-Picking Algorithm be used to identify a route to visit the cities in Example 1?*

Math Matters   Computers and Traveling Salesman Problems

The traveling salesman problem is a long-standing mathematical problem that has been analyzed since the 1920s by mathematicians, statisticians, and later, computer scientists. The algorithms given in this section can help us find good solutions, but they cannot guarantee that we will find the best solution.

At this point in time, the only way to find the optimal Hamiltonian circuit in a weighted graph is to find each and every possible circuit and compare the total weights of all circuits. Computers are well suited to such a task; however, as the number of vertices increases, the number of possible Hamiltonian circuits increases rapidly, and even computers are not fast enough to handle large graphs. There are so many possible circuits in a graph with a large number of vertices that finding them all could take hundreds or thousands of years, on even the fastest computers.

Computer scientists continue to improve their methods and produce more sophisticated algorithms. In 2004, five researchers (David Applegate, Robert Bixby, Vasek Chvátal, William Cook, and Keld Helsgaun) were able to find the optimal route to visit all 24,978 cities in Sweden. To accomplish this task, they used a network of 96 dual-processor workstation computers. The amount of computing time required was equivalent to a single-processor computer running for 84.8 years. You can see their resulting circuit on the map.

Applications of Weighted Graphs

In Example 1, we examined distances between cities. This is just one example of a weighted graph; the weight of an edge can be used to represent any quantity we like. For example, a traveler might be more interested in the cost of flights than the time

---

ANSWER   *No. Both algorithms apply only to complete graphs.*

or distance between cities. If we labeled each edge of the graph in Example 1 with the cost of traveling between the two cities, the total weight of a Hamiltonian circuit would be the total travel cost of the trip.

EXAMPLE 4 ■ An Application of the Greedy and Edge-Picking Algorithms

The cost of flying between various European cities is shown in the following table. Use both the Greedy Algorithm and the Edge-Picking Algorithm to find a low-cost route that visits each city just once and starts and ends in London. Which route is more economical?

	London, England	Berlin, Germany	Paris, France	Rome, Italy	Madrid, Spain	Vienna, Austria
London, England	—	$325	$160	$280	$250	$425
Berlin, Germany	$325	—	$415	$550	$675	$375
Paris, France	$160	$415	—	$495	$215	$545
Rome, Italy	$280	$550	$495	—	$380	$480
Madrid, Spain	$250	$675	$215	$380	—	$730
Vienna, Austria	$425	$375	$545	$480	$730	—

Solution

First we draw a weighted graph with vertices representing the cities and each edge labeled with the price of the flight between the corresponding cities.

To use the Greedy Algorithm, start at London and travel along the edge with the smallest weight, 160, to Paris. The edge of smallest weight leaving Paris is the edge to Madrid. From Madrid, the edge of smallest weight (that we have not already traversed) is the edge to London, of weight 250. However, we cannot use this edge, because it would bring us to a city we have already seen. We can take the next-smallest-weight edge to Rome. We cannot yet return to London, so the next available edge is to Vienna, then to Berlin, and finally back to London.

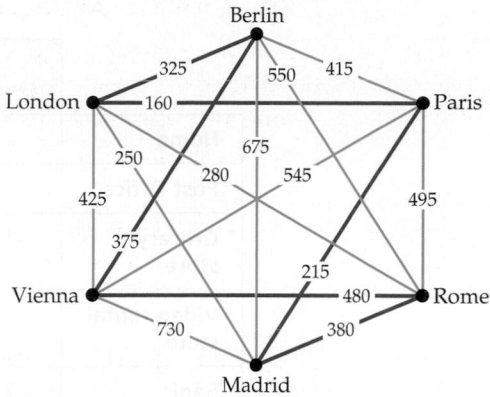

The total weight of the edges, and thus the total airfare for the trip, is

$$160 + 215 + 380 + 480 + 375 + 325 = \$1935$$

If we use the Edge-Picking Algorithm, the edges with the smallest weights that we can highlight are London–Paris and Madrid–Paris. The edge of next smallest weight is that of weight 250, but we cannot use this edge because it would complete a circuit. We can take the edge of next smallest weight, 280, from London to Rome. We cannot take the edge of next smallest weight, 325, because it would add a third edge to the London vertex, but we can take the edge Vienna–Berlin of weight 375. We must skip the edges of weights 380, 415, and 425, but we can take the edge of weight 480, which is the Vienna–Rome edge. There are no more edges we can mark that will meet the requirements of the algorithm, so we mark the last edge to complete the circuit, Berlin–Madrid.

The resulting route is London–Paris–Madrid–Berlin–Vienna–Rome–London, for a total cost of

$$160 + 215 + 675 + 375 + 480 + 280 = \$2185$$

(We could also travel this route in the reverse order.)

CHECK YOUR PROGRESS 4 Susan needs to mail a package at the Post Office, pick up several items at the grocery store, return a rented video, and make a deposit at her bank. The estimated driving time, in minutes, between each of these locations is given in the table below.

	Home	Post Office	Grocery store	Video rental store	Bank
Home	—	14	12	20	23
Post Office	14	—	8	12	21
Grocery store	12	8	—	17	11
Video rental store	20	12	17	—	18
Bank	23	21	11	18	—

Use both of the algorithms from this section to design routes for Susan to follow that will help minimize her total driving time. Assume she must start from home and return home when her errands are done.

Solution   *See page S34.*

A wide variety of problems are actually traveling salesman problems in disguise, and can be analyzed using the algorithms from this section. An example follows.

EXAMPLE 5 ■ An Application of the Edge-Picking Algorithm

A toolmaker needs to use one machine to create four different tools. The toolmaker needs to make adjustments to the machine before starting each different tool. However, since the tools have parts in common, the amount of adjustment required depends on which tool the machine was previously used to create. The table below lists the estimated time (in minutes) to readjust the machine from one tool to another. The machine is currently configured for Tool A, and should be returned to that state when all the tools are finished.

	Tool A	Tool B	Tool C	Tool D
Tool A	—	25	6	32
Tool B	25	—	18	9
Tool C	6	18	—	15
Tool D	32	9	15	—

Use the Edge-Picking Algorithm to determine a sequence for the creation of tools.

Solution

Draw a weighted graph in which each vertex represents a tool configuration of the machine, and the weight of each edge is the number of minutes required to adjust the machine from one tool to another.

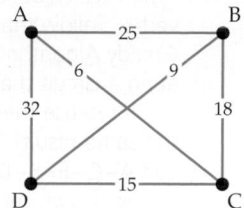

Using the Edge-Picking Algorithm, we first choose edge A–C, of weight 6. The next smallest weight is 9, or edge D–B, followed by edge D–C of weight 15. We end by completing the circuit with edge A–B. The final circuit, of total weight $25 + 9 + 15 + 6 = 55$, is A–B–D–C–A. So the machine starts with tool A, is reconfigured for tool B, then for tool D, then for tool C, and finally is returned to the settings used for tool A. (Notice that we can equivalently follow this sequence in the reverse order: from Tool A to C, to D, to B, and back to A.)

CHECK YOUR PROGRESS 5 Businesses often network their various computers. One option is to run wires from a central hub to each computer individually; another is to wire one computer to the next, and that one to the next, and so on until you return to the first computer. Thus the computers are all wired in a large loop. Suppose a company wishes to use the latter method, and the lengths of wire (in feet) required between computers are given in the table below.

	Computer A	Computer B	Computer C	Computer D	Computer E	Computer F	Computer G
Computer A	—	43	25	6	28	30	45
Computer B	43	—	26	40	37	22	25
Computer C	25	26	—	20	52	8	50
Computer D	6	40	20	—	30	24	45
Computer E	28	37	52	30	—	49	20
Computer F	30	22	8	24	49	—	41
Computer G	45	25	50	45	20	41	—

Use the Edge-Picking Algorithm to determine how the computers should be networked if the business wishes to use the least amount of wire possible.

Solution *See page S34.*

Excursion

Extending the Greedy Algorithm

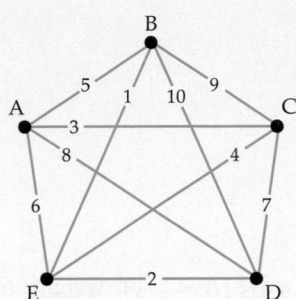

Figure 9.10

When we create a Hamiltonian circuit in a graph, it is a closed loop. We can start at any vertex, follow the path, and arrive back at the starting vertex. For instance, if we use the Greedy Algorithm to create a Hamiltonian circuit starting at vertex A, we are actually creating a circuit that could start at any vertex in the circuit.

If we use the Greedy Algorithm and start from different vertices, will we always get the same result? Try it on Figure 9.10 at the left. If we start at vertex A, we get the circuit A–C–E–B–D–A, with a total weight of 26 (see Figure 9.11). However, if we start at vertex B, we get B–E–D–C–A–B, with a total weight of 18 (see Figure 9.12). Even though we found the second circuit by starting at B, we could use the same circuit starting at A, namely A–B–E–D–C–A, or, equivalently, A–C–D–E–B–A. This circuit has a smaller total weight than the one we found by starting at A.

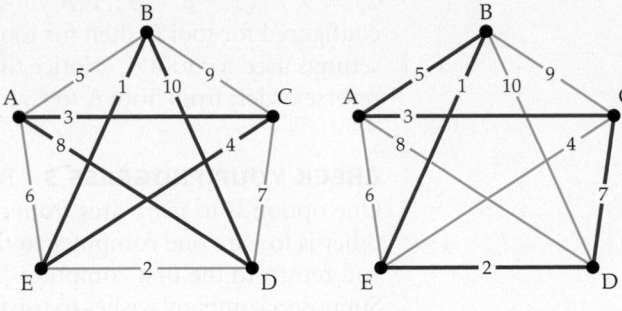

Figure 9.11   **Figure 9.12**

In other words, it may pay to try the Greedy Algorithm starting from different vertices, even when we know that we actually want to start from a particular vertex. To be thorough, we can extend the Greedy Algorithm by using it at each and every vertex, generating several different circuits. We then choose among these the circuit with the least total weight, and start at the vertex we want. The following exercises ask you to apply this approach for yourself.

Excursion Exercises

1. Continue investigating Hamiltonian circuits in Figure 9.10 by using the Greedy Algorithm starting at vertices C, D, and E. Then compare the various Hamiltonian circuits to identify the one with the smallest total weight.

2. Use the Greedy Algorithm and the weighted graph at the top of the following page to generate a Hamiltonian circuit starting from each vertex. Then compare the different circuits to find the one of smallest total weight.

(continued)

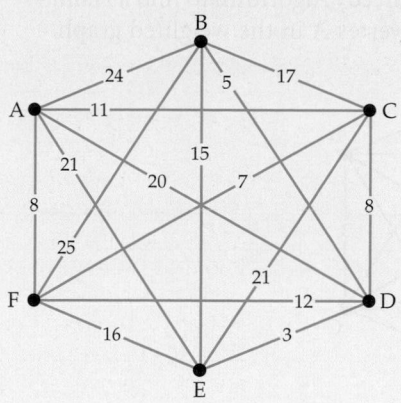

3. Use the Edge-Picking Algorithm to find a Hamiltonian circuit in the graph in Exercise 2. How does the weight of this circuit compare with the weights of the circuits found in Exercise 2?

Exercise Set 9.2

In Exercises 1–4, use trial and error to find two Hamiltonian circuits of different total weights, starting at vertex A in the weighted graph. Compute the total weight of each circuit.

1.

2.

3.

4.

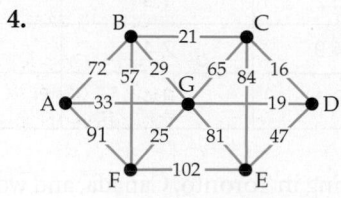

In Exercises 5–8, use the Greedy Algorithm to find a Hamiltonian circuit starting at vertex A in the weighted graph.

5.

6.

7.

8.

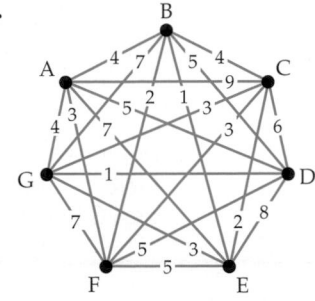

In Exercises 9–12, use the Edge-Picking Algorithm to find a Hamiltonian circuit in the indicated graph.

9. Graph in Exercise 5   **10.** Graph in Exercise 6

11. Graph in Exercise 7   **12.** Graph in Exercise 8

13. Travel A company representative lives in Louisville, Kentucky, and needs to visit offices in five different Indiana cities over the next few days. The representative wants to drive between cities and return to Louisville at the end of the trip. The estimated driving times, in hours, between cities are given in the table below. Represent the driving times by a weighted graph. Use the Greedy Algorithm to design an efficient route for the representative to follow.

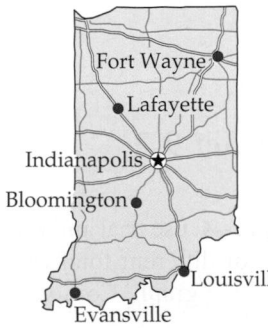

	Louisville	Bloomington	Fort Wayne	Indianapolis	Lafayette	Evansville
Louisville	—	3.6	6.4	3.2	4.9	3.1
Bloomington	3.6	—	4.5	1.3	2.4	3.4
Fort Wayne	6.4	4.5	—	3.3	3.0	8.0
Indianapolis	3.2	1.3	3.3	—	1.5	4.6
Lafayette	4.9	2.4	3.0	1.5	—	5.0
Evansville	3.1	3.4	8.0	4.6	5.0	—

14. Travel A tourist is staying in Toronto, Canada, and would like to visit four other Canadian cities by train. The visitor wants to go from one city to the next and return to Toronto while minimizing the total travel distance. The distances between cities, in kilometers, are given in the table on the following page. Represent the distances between the cities using a weighted graph. Use the Greedy Algorithm to plan a route for the tourist.

	Toronto	Kingston	Niagara Falls	Ottawa	Windsor
Toronto	—	259	142	423	381
Kingston	259	—	397	174	623
Niagara Falls	142	397	—	562	402
Ottawa	423	174	562	—	787
Windsor	381	623	402	787	—

15. **Travel** Use the Edge-Picking Algorithm to design a route for the company representative in Exercise 13.

16. **Travel** Use the Edge-Picking Algorithm to design a route for the tourist in Exercise 14.

17. **Travel** Nicole wants to tour Asia. She will start and end her journey in Tokyo and visit Hong Kong, Bangkok, Seoul, and Beijing. The airfares available to her between cities are given in the table. Draw a weighted graph that represents the travel costs between cities and use the Greedy Algorithm to find a low-cost route.

	Tokyo	Hong Kong	Bangkok	Seoul	Beijing
Tokyo	—	$845	$1275	$470	$880
Hong Kong	$845	—	$320	$515	$340
Bangkok	$1275	$320	—	$520	$365
Seoul	$470	$515	$520	—	$225
Beijing	$880	$340	$365	$225	—

18. **Travel** The prices to travel between five cities in Colorado by bus are given in the table below. Represent the travel costs between cities using a weighted graph. Use the Greedy Algorithm to find a low-cost route that starts and ends in Boulder and visits each city.

	Boulder	Denver	Colorado Springs	Grand Junction	Durango
Boulder	—	$16	$25	$49	$74
Denver	$16	—	$22	$45	$72
Colorado Springs	$25	$22	—	$58	$59
Grand Junction	$49	$45	$58	—	$32
Durango	$74	$72	$59	$32	—

19. **Travel** Use the Edge-Picking Algorithm to find a low-cost route for the traveler in Exercise 17.

20. **Travel** Use the Edge-Picking Algorithm to find a low-cost bus route in Exercise 18.

COOPERATIVE LEARNING

28. **Route Planning** Form a team of five classmates and, using a map, identify a driving route that will visit each home, return to the starting home, and that you believe would be the least total driving distance. Next determine the driving distances between the homes of the classmates. Represent these distances in a weighted graph, and then use the Edge-Picking Algorithm to determine a driving route that would visit each home and return to the starting home. Did the algorithm find a more efficient route than your first route?

Planarity

A puzzle that was posed some time ago goes something like this: Three utility companies each need to run pipes to three houses. Can they do so without crossing over each other's pipes at any point? It might be easier to think about the puzzle visually, as shown in Figure 9.13. Go ahead and try to draw pipes connecting each utility company to each house without letting any pipes cross over each other.

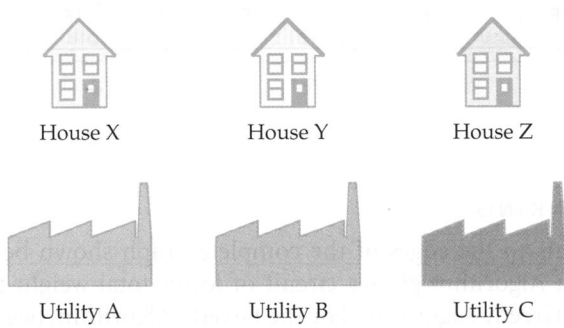

House X   House Y   House Z

Utility A   Utility B   Utility C

Figure 9.13

One way to approach the puzzle is to express the situation in terms of a graph. Each of the houses and utility companies will be represented by a vertex, and we will draw an edge between two vertices if a pipe needs to run from one building to the other. If we were not worried about pipes crossing, we could easily draw a solution, as in Figure 9.14.

To solve the puzzle, we need to draw an equivalent graph in which no edges cross over each other. Such a graph is called a *planar graph*.

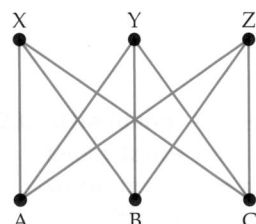

Figure 9.14 *The Utilities Graph*

Definition of a Planar Graph

A **planar graph** is a graph that can be drawn so that no edges intersect each other (except at vertices).

If the graph is drawn in such a way that no edges cross, we say that we have a **planar drawing** of the graph.

EXAMPLE 1 ■ Identify a Planar Graph

Show that the graph below is planar.

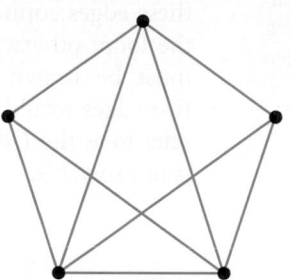

Solution

As the graph appears currently, several edges intersect each other. However, we can redraw the graph in an equivalent form in which no edges touch except at vertices by redrawing the two shaded edges shown below. To verify that the second graph is equivalent to the first, we can label the vertices and check that the edges join the same vertices in each graph. Because the given graph is equivalent to a graph whose edges do not intersect, the graph is planar.

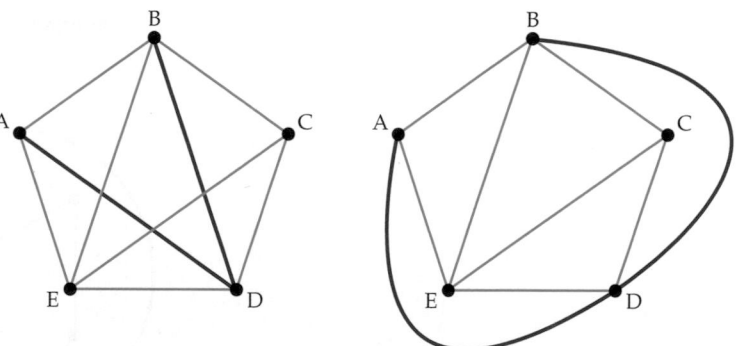

CHECK YOUR PROGRESS 1   Show that the following graph is planar.

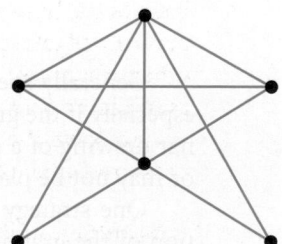

Solution   *See page S35.*

✔ **TAKE NOTE**

The strategy we used here to show that the graph in Figure 9.14 is not planar can often be used to make planar drawings of graphs that *are* planar. The basic strategy is: Find a Hamiltonian circuit, redraw this circuit in a circular loop, and then draw in the remaining edges.

Returning to the puzzle of connecting the utilities to the houses (Figure 9.13), how can we determine whether the graph in Figure 9.14 is planar? If we attempt to redraw the graph, we will find it difficult to do without having edges cross over each other. It turns out that, in fact, the graph in Figure 9.14 is not planar. To see why this is true, notice that the graph is Hamiltonian, and one Hamiltonian circuit is A−X−B−Y−C−Z−A. If we redraw the graph so that this circuit is drawn in a loop (see Figure 9.15), then we need to add the edges AY, BZ, and CX. All three of these edges connect opposite vertices. We can draw only one of these edges inside the loop; otherwise two edges would cross. This means that the other two edges must be drawn outside the loop, but as you can see in Figure 9.16, those two edges would then have to cross. Thus the graph in Figure 9.14, which we will refer to as the *Utilities Graph*, is by definition not planar, and so the utilities puzzle is not solvable.

Figure 9.15

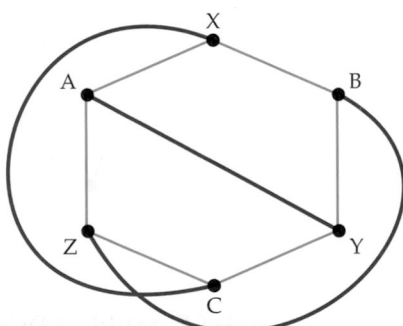

Figure 9.16

Generally speaking, it can be difficult to determine whether a graph is planar, especially if the graph has a large number of edges. Of course, if you can find a planar drawing of a graph, then you know it is planar. If not, however, the graph may or may not be planar.

One strategy we can use to show that a graph is *not* planar is to find a portion of the graph that we know by itself is not planar. The Utilities Graph in Figure 9.14 is a common pattern to watch for. Another graph that is not planar is the complete graph with five vertices, denoted K_5, shown in Figure 9.17. (We can prove that K_5 is not planar by using a strategy similar to the strategy used for the Utilities Graph.)

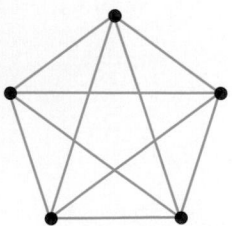

Figure 9.17 *The complete graph K_5*

What we are specifically looking for is a **subgraph**—a graph whose edges and vertices come from the given graph. Then the strategy is given by the following theorem.

> ### Theorem
>
> If a graph *G* has a subgraph that is not planar, then *G* is also not planar. In particular, if *G* contains the Utilities Graph or K_5 as a subgraph, *G* is not planar.

EXAMPLE 2 ■ Identify a Non-Planar Graph

Show that the following graph is not planar.

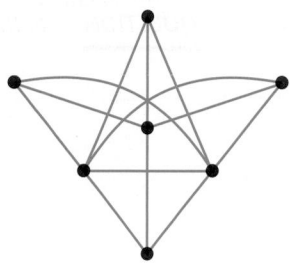

Solution

In the figure below, we have highlighted edges connecting the top six vertices. If we consider the highlighted edges and attached vertices as a subgraph, we can verify that the subgraph is the Utilities Graph. (The graph is slightly distorted compared with the version shown in Figure 9.14, but it is equivalent.) By the preceding theorem, we know that the graph is not planar.

CHECK YOUR PROGRESS 2   Show that the following graph is not planar.

Solution   See page S35.

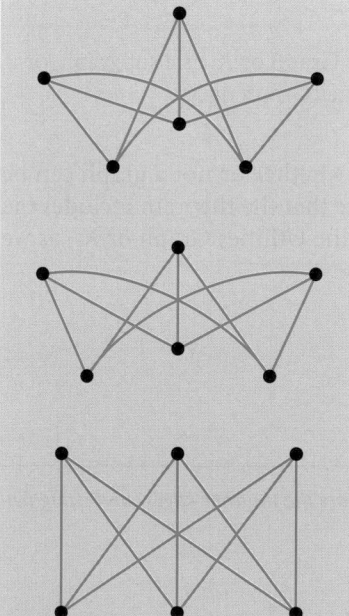

✔ TAKE NOTE

The figure below shows how the highlighted edges of the graph in Example 2 can be transformed into the Utilities Graph.

We can expand this strategy by considering *contractions* of a subgraph. A **contraction** of a graph is formed by "shrinking" an edge until the two vertices it connects come together and blend into one. If, in the process, the graph is left with any multiple edges, we merge them into one. The process is illustrated below.

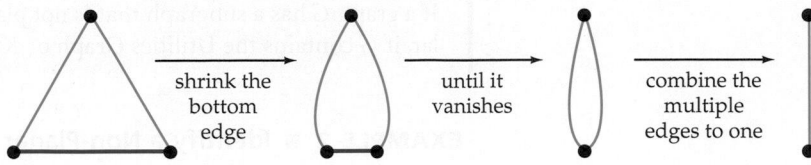

QUESTION   *Is the first graph below a contraction of the second graph?*

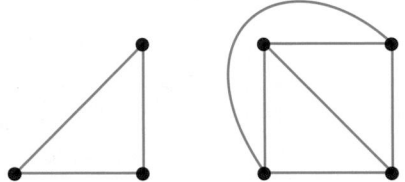

If we consider contractions, it turns out that the Utilities Graph and K_5 serve as building blocks for nonplanar graphs. In fact, it was proved in 1930 that any non-planar graph will always have a subgraph that is the Utilities Graph or K_5, or a subgraph that can be contracted to the Utilities Graph or K_5. We can then expand our strategy, as given by the following theorem.

> **Nonplanar Graph Theorem**
>
> A graph is nonplanar if and only if it has the Utilities Graph or K_5 as a subgraph, or it has a subgraph that can be contracted to the Utilities Graph or K_5.

This gives us a definite test that will determine whether or not a graph can be drawn in such a way as to avoid crossing edges. (Note that the theorem includes the case in which the entire graph can be contracted to the Utilities Graph or K_5, as we can consider the graph a subgraph of itself.)

ANSWER   *Yes. Contract the edge colored red, then eliminate the multiple edges (and straighten out the curved edge).*

EXAMPLE 3 ■ Identify a Non-Planar Graph

Show that the graph below is not planar.

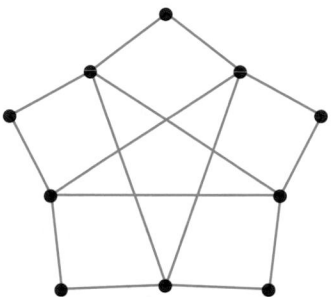

Solution

Notice that the graph looks similar to K_5. In fact, we can contract some edges and make the graph look like K_5. Choose a pair of adjacent outside edges and contract one of them, as shown in the figure below.

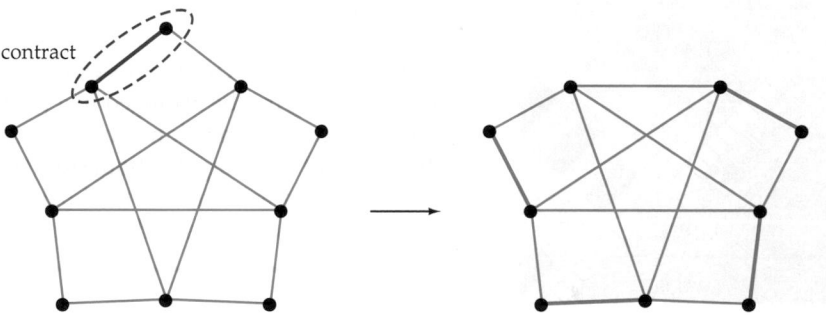

If we similarly contract the four edges colored green above, we arrive at the graph of K_5.

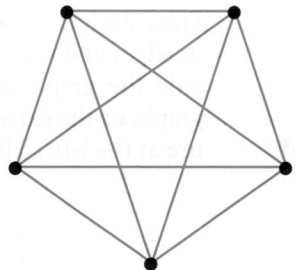

We were able to contract our graph to K_5, so by the Nonplanar Graph Theorem, the given graph is not planar.

5.

6.

7.

8.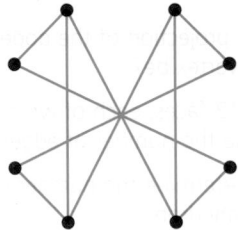

In Exercises 9–12, show that the graph is *not* planar.

9.

10.

11.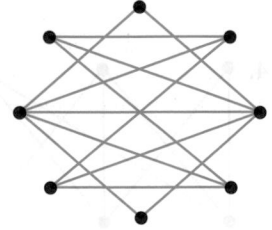

12.

13. Show that the following graph contracts to K_5.

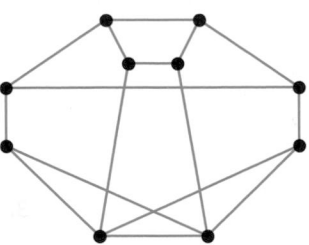

14. Show that the following graph contracts to the Utilities Graph.

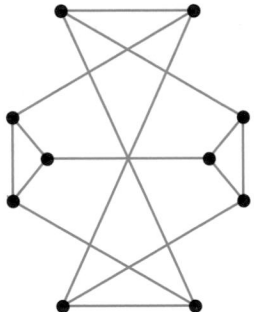

In Exercises 15 and 16, show that the graph is not planar by finding a subgraph whose contraction is the Utilities Graph or K_5.

15.

16.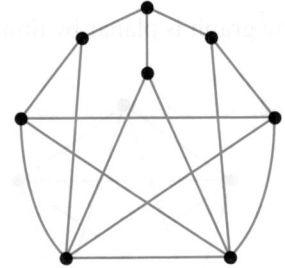

In Exercises 17–22, count the number of vertices, edges, and faces, and then verify Euler's Formula for the given graph.

17.   **18.**

19.   **20.**

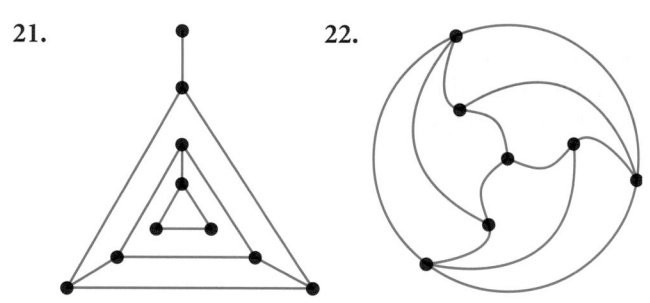

21.   **22.**

23. If a planar drawing of a graph has 15 edges and 8 vertices, how many faces does the graph have?

24. If a planar drawing of a graph has 100 vertices and 50 faces, how many edges are in the graph?

Extensions
CRITICAL THINKING

25. In a planar drawing of a graph, each face is bordered by a circuit. Make a planar drawing of a graph that is

equivalent to the graph shown, in which the faces are bordered by the same circuits as the given graph but where the face bordered by A–B–C–G–F–A is the infinite face.

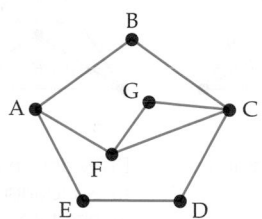

26. Make a planar drawing of a graph that is equivalent to the graph in Exercise 25, in which the faces are bordered by the same circuits as the graph in Exercise 25 but where the face bordered by C–F–G–C is the infinite face.

27. Sketch a planar graph (without multiple edges or loops) in which every vertex has degree 3.

28. Sketch a planar graph (without multiple edges or loops) in which every vertex has degree 4.

29. Explain why it is not possible to draw a planar graph that contains three faces and has the same number of vertices as edges.

30. If a planar drawing of a graph has twice as many edges as vertices, find a relationship between the number of faces and the number of vertices.

EXPLORATIONS

31. Dual Graph Every planar graph has what is called a *dual graph*. To form the dual graph, start with a planar drawing of the graph. With a different-color pen, draw a dot in each face (including the infinite face). These will be the vertices of the dual graph. Now, for every edge in the original graph, draw a new edge that crosses over it and connects the two new vertices in the faces on each side of the original edge. The resulting dual countries are neighbors—that is, if they share a common boundary. The result is shown in Figure 9.21.

Figure 9.21   **Figure 9.22**

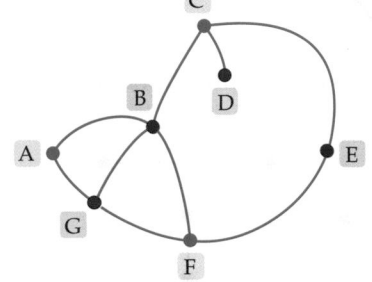

Figure 9.23

If we erase the boundaries of the countries, we are left with the graph in Figure 9.22. The resulting graph will always be a planar graph, because the edges simply connect neighboring countries. Our map-coloring question then becomes: Can we give each vertex of the graph in Figure 9.22 a color such that no two vertices connected by an edge share the same color? How many different colors will be required? If this can be accomplished using four colors, for instance, we will say that the graph is **4-colorable.** In fact, the graph in Figure 9.22 is actually *3-colorable.* One possible coloring is given in Figure 9.23.

We can now formally state the Four-Color Theorem.

Four-Color Theorem

Every planar graph is 4-colorable.

QUESTION   *The graph shown at the right requires five colors if we wish to color it such that no edge joins two vertices of the same color. Does this contradict the Four-Color Theorem?*

EXAMPLE 2 ■ Represent a Map as a Graph

The fictional map below shows the boundaries of countries on a rectangular continent. Represent the map as a graph, and then find a coloring of the graph using the least possible number of colors.

ANSWER   *No. This graph is not a planar graph, so the Four-Color Theorem does not apply.*

Solution
First draw a vertex in each country and then connect two vertices with an edge if the corresponding countries are neighbors. Now try to color the vertices of the resulting graph so that no edge connects two vertices of the same color. We know we will need at least two colors, so one strategy is to simply pick a starting vertex, give it a color, and then assign colors to the connected vertices one by one. Try to reuse the same colors, and use a new color only when there is no other option. For this graph we will need four colors. (The Four-Color Theorem guarantees that we will not need more than that.) To see why we will need four colors, notice that the one vertex colored green below connects to a ring of five vertices. Three different colors are required to color the five-vertex ring, and the green vertex connects to all these, so it must be colored a fourth color.

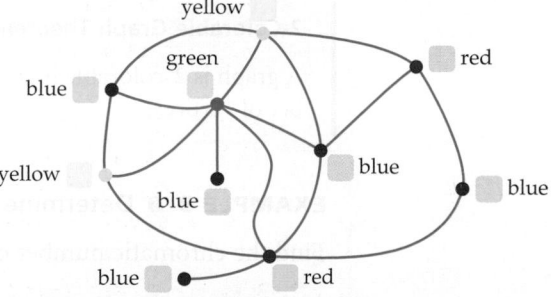

CHECK YOUR PROGRESS 2 Represent the fictional map of countries below as a graph, and then determine whether the graph is 2-colorable, 3-colorable, or 4-colorable by finding a suitable coloring of the graph.

Solution *See page S35.*

Math Matters   Proving the Four-Color Theorem

The Four-Color Theorem can be stated in a simple, short sentence, but proving it is anything but simple. The theorem was finally proved in 1976 by Wolfgang Haken and Kenneth Appel, two mathematicians at the University of Illinois. Mathematicians had long hunted for a short, elegant proof, but it turned out that the proof had to wait for the advent of computers to help sift through the many possible arrangements that can occur. The final proof used over 1000 hours of computer time (surely it would be less now!) and on paper came to several hundred pages that included some 10,000 diagrams.

The Chromatic Number of a Graph

We mentioned previously that representing a map as a graph always results in a planar graph. The Four-Color Theorem guarantees that we need only four colors to color a *planar* graph; however, if we wish to color a non-planar graph, we may need quite a few more than four colors. The smallest number of colors needed to color a graph so that no edge connects vertices of the same color is called the **chromatic number** of the graph. In general, there is no efficient method of finding the chromatic number of a graph, but we do have a theorem that can tell us whether a graph is 2-colorable.

> **2-Colorable Graph Theorem**
>
> A graph is 2-colorable if and only if it has no circuits that consist of an odd number of vertices.

EXAMPLE 3 ■ Determine the Chromatic Number of a Graph

Find the chromatic number of the Utilities Graph from Section 9.3.

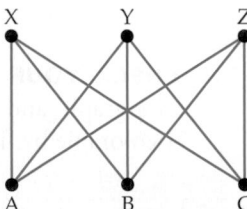

Solution

Notice that the graph contains circuits such as A−Y−C−Z−B−X−A with six vertices and A−Y−B−X−A with four vertices. Any circuit we find, in fact, seems to involve an even number of vertices. It is difficult to determine whether we have looked at all possible circuits, but our observations suggest that the graph may be 2-colorable. A little trial and error confirms this if we simply color vertices A, B, and C one color and the remaining vertices another. Thus the Utilities Graph has a chromatic number of 2.

CHECK YOUR PROGRESS 3 Determine whether the following graph is 2-colorable.

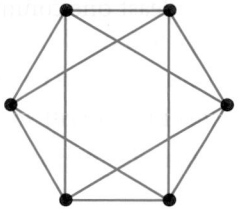

Solution   See page S35.

Applications of Graph Coloring

Determining the chromatic number of a graph and finding a corresponding coloring of the graph can solve a wide assortment of practical problems. One common application is in scheduling meetings or events. This is best shown by example.

EXAMPLE 4 ■ A Scheduling Application of Graph Coloring

Eight different school clubs want to schedule meetings on the last day of the semester. Some club members, however, belong to more than one of these clubs, so clubs that share members cannot meet at the same time. How many different time slots are required so that all members can attend all meetings? Clubs that have a member in common are indicated with an "X" in the table below.

	Ski club	Student government	Debate club	Honor society	Student newspaper	Community outreach	Campus Democrats	Campus Republicans
Ski club	—	X		X			X	X
Student government	X	—	X	X	X			
Debate club		X	—	X		X		X
Honor society	X	X	X	—	X	X		
Student newspaper		X		X	—	X	X	
Community outreach			X	X	X	—	X	X
Campus Democrats	X				X	X	—	
Campus Republicans	X		X			X		—

the second day classrooms 1 and 3, represented by the red vertices, will visit the zoo; and on the third day classroom 4, represented by the green vertex, will visit the zoo.

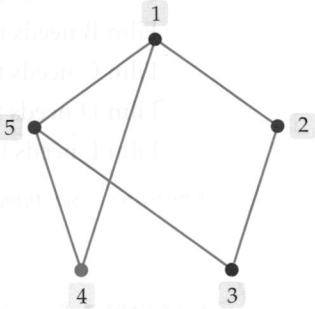

CHECK YOUR PROGRESS 5 Several delis in New York City have arranged deliveries to various buildings at lunchtime. The buildings' managements do not want more than one deli showing up at a particular building in one day, but the delis would like to deliver as often as possible. If they decide to agree on a delivery schedule, how many days will be required before each deli can return to the same building?

Deli A delivers to the Empire State Building, the Statue of Liberty, and Rockefeller Center.

Deli B delivers to the Chrysler Building, the Empire State Building, and the New York Stock Exchange.

Deli C delivers to the New York Stock Exchange, the American Stock Exchange, and the United Nations Building.

Deli D delivers to New York City Hall, the Chrysler Building, and Rockefeller Center.

Deli E delivers to Rockefeller Center, New York City Hall, and the United Nations Building.

Solution   *See page S36.*

Excursion

Modeling Traffic Lights with Graphs

Have you ever watched the cycles that traffic lights go through while you were waiting for a red light to turn green? Some intersections have lights that go through several stages, to allow all the different lanes of traffic to proceed safely.

Ideally, each stage of a traffic light cycle should allow as many lanes of traffic to proceed through the intersection as possible. We can design a traffic light cycle by modeling an intersection with a graph. Figure 9.24 shows a 3-way intersection where two

(continued)

2-way roads meet. Each direction of traffic has turn lanes, with left-turn lights. There are six different directions in which vehicles can travel, as indicated in the graph, and we have labeled each possibility with a letter.

Figure 9.24

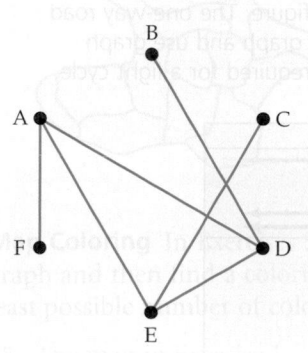

Figure 9.25

We can represent the traffic patterns with a graph; each vertex will represent one of the six possible traffic paths, and we will draw an edge between two vertices if the corresponding paths would allow vehicles to collide. The result is the graph shown in Figure 9.25. Because we do not want to allow vehicles to travel simultaneously along routes on which they could collide, any vertices connected by an edge can allow traffic to move only during different parts of the light cycle. We can represent each portion of the cycle by a color. Our job then is to color the graph using the fewest number of colors possible.

There is no 2-coloring of the graph because we have a circuit of length 3: A–D–E–A. We can, however, find a 3-coloring. One possibility is given in Figure 9.26.

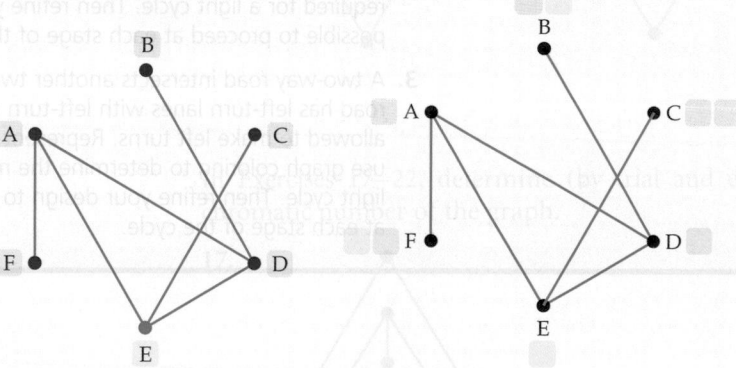

Figure 9.26   **Figure 9.27**

A 3-coloring of the graph means that the traffic lights at the intersection will have to go through a 3-stage cycle. One stage will allow the traffic routes corresponding to the red vertices to proceed, the next stage will let the paths corresponding to the blue vertices to proceed, and finally, the third stage will start path E, colored green, moving.

Although safety requires three stages for the lights, we can refine the design to allow more traffic to travel through the intersection. Notice that at the third stage, only one route, path E, is scheduled to be moving. However, there is no harm in allowing path B to move at the same time, since it is a right turn that doesn't conflict with route E. We could also allow path F to proceed at the same time. Adding these additional paths corresponds to adding colors to the graph in Figure 9.26. We do not want to use more than three colors, but we can add a second color to some of the vertices while maintaining

(continued)

19.   **20.**   **21.**   **22.**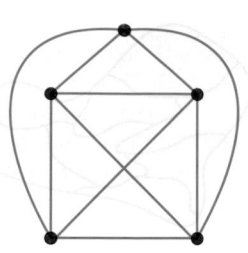

23. Scheduling Six student clubs need to hold meetings on the same day, but some students belong to more than one club. In order to avoid members missing meetings, the meetings need to be scheduled during different time slots. An "X" in the table below indicates that the two corresponding clubs share at least one member. Use graph coloring to determine the least number of time slots necessary to ensure that all club members can attend all meetings.

	Student newspaper	Honor society	Biology assoc.	Gaming club	Debate team	Engineering club
Student newspaper	—		X		X	
Honor society		—	X		X	X
Biology assoc.	X	X	—	X		
Gaming club			X	—	X	X
Debate team	X	X		X	—	
Engineering club		X		X		—

24. Scheduling Eight political committees must meet on the same day, but some members are on more than one committee. Thus any committees that have members in common cannot meet at the same time. An "X" in the table below indicates that the two corresponding committees share a member. Use graph coloring to determine the least number of meeting times that will be necessary so that all members can attend the appropriate meetings.

	Appropriations	Budget	Finance	Judiciary	Education	Health	Foreign affairs	Housing
Appropriations	—		X			X	X	
Budget		—		X		X		
Finance	X		—	X			X	X
Judiciary		X	X	—		X		X
Education					—		X	X
Health	X	X		X		—		
Foreign affairs	X		X		X		—	
Housing			X	X	X			—

25. **Scheduling** Six different groups of children would like to visit the zoo and feed different animals. (Assume each group will visit the zoo only one day.)

    Group 1 would like to feed the bears, dolphins, and gorillas.

    Group 2 would like to feed the bears, elephants, and hippos.

    Group 3 would like to feed the dolphins and elephants.

    Group 4 would like to feed the dolphins, zebras, and hippos.

    Group 5 would like to feed the bears and hippos.

    Group 6 would like to feed the gorillas, hippos, and zebras.

    Use graph coloring to find the minimum number of days that are required so that all groups can feed the animals they would like to feed but no animals will be fed twice on the same day. Design a schedule to accomplish this goal.

26. **Scheduling** Five different charity organizations send trucks on various routes to pick up donations that residents leave on their doorsteps.

    Charity A covers Main St., First Ave., and State St.

    Charity B covers First Ave., Second Ave., and Third Ave.

    Charity C covers State St., City Dr., and Country Lane.

    Charity D covers City Dr., Second Ave., and Main St.

    Charity E covers Third Ave., Country Lane, and Fourth Ave.

    Each charity has its truck travel down all three streets on its route on the same day, but no two charities wish to visit the same streets on the same day. Use graph coloring to design a schedule for the charities. Arrange their pickup routes so that no street is visited twice on the same day by different charities. The schedule should use the least possible number of days.

27. **Scheduling** Students in a film class have volunteered to form groups and create several short films. The class has three digital video cameras that may be checked out for one day only, and it is expected that each group will need the entire day to finish shooting. All members of each group must participate in the film they volunteered for, so a student cannot work on more than one film on any given day.

    Film 1 will be made by Brian, Angela, and Kate.

    Film 2 will be made by Jessica, Vince, and Brian.

    Film 3 will be made by Corey, Brian, and Vince.

    Film 4 will be made by Ricardo, Sarah, and Lupe.

    Film 5 will be made by Sarah, Kate, and Jessica.

    Film 6 will be made by Angela, Corey, and Lupe.

    Use graph coloring to design a schedule for loaning the cameras, using the least possible number of days, so that each group can shoot its film and all members can participate.

Extensions

CRITICAL THINKING

Maps In Exercises 28–30, draw a map of a fictional continent with country boundaries corresponding to the graph given.

28.

29.

30.

31. **Map Coloring** Draw a map of a fictional continent consisting of four countries, where the map cannot be colored with three or fewer colors without adjacent countries sharing a color.

32. If the chromatic number of a graph with five vertices is 1, what must the graph look like?

EXPLORATIONS

33. **Edge Coloring** In this section, we colored vertices of graphs so that no edge connected two vertices of the same color. We can also consider coloring edges, rather than vertices, so that no vertex connects to more than one edge of the same color. In parts a to d, assign each edge in the graph a color so that no vertex connects to two or more edges of the same color. Use the least number of colors possible.

a.   b.   c.   d.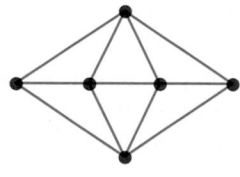

e. Explain why the number of colors required will always be at least the number of edges that meet at the vertex of highest degree in the graph.

34. **Scheduling** Edge colorings, as explained in Exercise 33, can be used to solve scheduling problems. For instance, suppose five players are competing in a tennis tournament. Each player needs to play every other player in a match (but not more than once). Each player will participate in no more than one game per day, and two matches can occur at the same time when possible. How many days will be required for the tournament? Represent the tournament as a graph, where each vertex corresponds to a player and an edge joins two vertices if the corresponding players will compete against each other in a match. Next color the edges, where each different color corresponds to a different day of the tournament. Because one player will not be in more than one match per day, no two edges of the same color can meet at the same vertex. If we can find an edge coloring of the graph that uses the least number of colors possible, it will correspond to the least number of days required for the tournament. Sketch a graph that represents the tournament, find an edge coloring using the least number of colors possible, and use your graph to design a schedule of matches for the tournament that minimizes the number of days required.

CHAPTER 9 **Summary**

Key Terms

4-colorable [p. 620]
algorithm [p. 591]
chromatic number [p. 622]
circuit or closed walk [p. 574]
complete graph [p. 571]
connected graph [p. 571]
contraction [p. 610]
degree [p. 574]
edge [p. 570]
equivalent graphs [p. 571]
Euler circuit [p. 574]
Euler walk [p. 577]
Eulerian graph [p. 574]
face [p. 612]
graph [p. 570]
Hamiltonian circuit [p. 578]
Hamiltonian graph [p. 578]
infinite face [p. 612]
K_5 [p. 608]
multiple edges [p. 571]
null graph [p. 571]
planar drawing [p. 607]
planar graph [p. 606]
subgraph [p. 609]
traveling salesman problem [p. 589]
Utilities Graph [p. 608]
vertex [p. 570]
walk [p. 574]
weight [p. 589]
weighted graph [p. 589]

Essential Concepts

- **Eulerian Graph Theorem**
  A connected graph is *Eulerian* if and only if every vertex of the graph is of even degree.

- **Euler Walk Theorem**
  A connected graph contains an Euler walk if and only if the graph has two vertices of odd degree and the remaining vertices are of even degree. Furthermore, every Euler walk must start at one of the vertices of odd degree and end at the other.

- **Hamiltonian Graphs and Dirac's Theorem**
  Dirac's Theorem states that in a connected graph with at least three vertices and with no multiple edges, if n is the number of vertices in the graph and every ver-

tex has degree of at least $n/2$, then the graph must be Hamiltonian. If it is not the case that every vertex has degree of at least $n/2$, then the graph may or may not be Hamiltonian.

- **The Greedy Algorithm**
  One method of finding a Hamiltonian circuit in a complete weighted graph is given by the following procedure.

  1. Choose a vertex to start at, then travel along the connected edge of smallest weight. (If two or more edges have the same weight, pick any one.)

  2. After arriving at the next vertex, travel along the edge of smallest weight that connects to a vertex not yet visited. Continue this process until you have visited all vertices.

  3. Return to the starting vertex.

  The Greedy Algorithm attempts to give a circuit of minimal total weight, although it does not always succeed.

- **The Edge-Picking Algorithm**
  A second method of finding a Hamiltonian circuit in a complete weighted graph consists of the following steps.

  1. Mark the edge of smallest weight in the graph. (If two or more edges have the same weight, pick any one.)

  2. Mark the edge of next smallest weight in the graph, as long as it does not complete a circuit and does not add a third marked edge to a single vertex.

  3. Continue this process until you can no longer mark any edges. Then mark the final edge that completes the Hamiltonian circuit.

- **Nonplanar Graph Theorem**
  A graph is nonplanar if and only if it has the Utilities Graph or K_5 as a subgraph, or it has a subgraph that can be contracted to the Utilities Graph or K_5.

- **Euler's Formula**
  In a connected planar graph drawn with no intersecting edges, let v be the number of vertices, e the number of edges, and f the number of faces. Then $v + f = e + 2$.

- **The Four-Color Theorem**
  Every planar graph is 4-colorable. (Note that fewer than four colors may be required; if the graph is not planar, more than four colors may be necessary.)

■ **Representing Maps as Graphs**
Draw a vertex in each region (country, state, etc.) of the map. Connect two vertices if the corresponding regions share a common border.

■ **2-Colorable Graph Theorem**
A graph is 2-colorable if and only if it has no circuits that consist of an odd number of vertices.

CHAPTER 9   **Review Exercises**

In Exercises 1 and 2, (a) give the number of edges in the graph, (b) find the number of vertices in the graph, (c) list the degree of each vertex, and (d) determine whether the graph is connected.

1.

2.
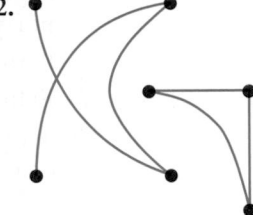

3. **Soccer** In the table below, an "X" indicates teams from a junior soccer league that have played each other in the current season. Draw a graph to represent the games by using a vertex to represent each team. Connect two vertices with an edge if the corresponding teams played a game against each other this season.

	Mariners	Scorpions	Pumas	Stingrays	Vipers
Mariners	—	X		X	X
Scorpions	X	—	X		
Pumas		X	—	X	X
Stingrays	X		X	—	
Vipers	X		X		—

4. Each vertex in the graph at the right represents a freeway in the Los Angeles area. An edge connects two vertices if the corresponding freeways have interchanges allowing drivers to transfer from one freeway to the other.

   a. Can drivers transfer from the 105 freeway to the 10?

   b. Among the freeways represented, how many have interchanges with the 5 freeway?

   c. Which freeways have interchanges to all the other freeways in the graph?

   d. Of the freeways represented in the graph, which has the least number of interchanges to the other freeways?

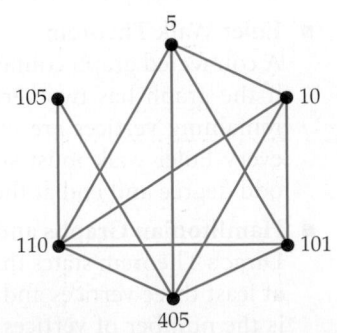

In Exercises 5 and 6, determine whether the two graphs are equivalent.

5.

6.

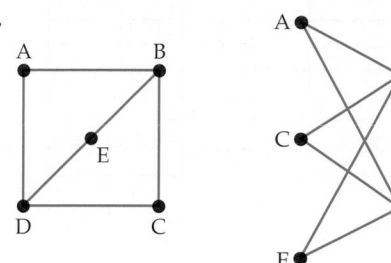

In Exercises 7–10, (a) find an Euler walk if possible, and (b) find an Euler circuit if possible.

7.

8.

9.

10.

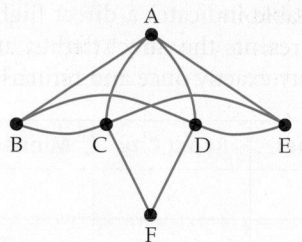

11. Parks The figure shows an arrangement of bridges connecting land areas in a park. Represent the map as a graph and then determine whether it is possible to stroll across each bridge exactly once and return to the starting position.

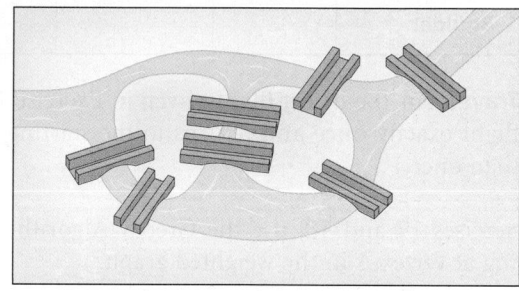

12. Architecture The floor plan of a sculpture gallery is shown. Is it possible to walk through each doorway exactly once? Is it possible to walk through each doorway exactly once and return to the starting point?

In Exercises 13 and 14, use Dirac's Theorem to verify that the graph is Hamiltonian, and then find a Hamiltonian circuit.

13.   **14.**

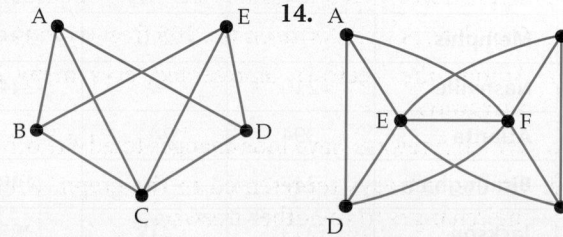

15. **Travel** An "X" in the table indicates a direct flight offered by a small airline. Draw a graph that represents the direct flights, and use your graph to find a route that visits each city exactly once and returns to the starting city.

	Casper	Rapid City	Minneapolis	Des Moines	Topeka	Omaha	Boulder
Casper	—	X					X
Rapid City	X	—	X				
Minneapolis		X	—	X	X		X
Des Moines			X	—	X		
Topeka			X	X	—	X	X
Omaha					X	—	X
Boulder	X		X		X	X	—

16. **Travel** For the direct flights given in Exercise 15, find a route that travels each flight exactly once and returns to the starting city. (You may visit cities more than once.)

In Exercises 17 and 18, use the Greedy Algorithm to find a Hamiltonian circuit starting at vertex A in the weighted graph.

17.

18.
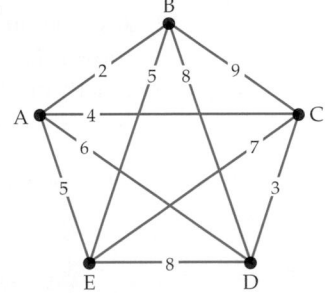

In Exercises 19 and 20, use the Edge-Picking Algorithm to find a Hamiltonian circuit starting at vertex A in the weighted graph.

19. The graph in Exercise 17

20. The graph in Exercise 18

21. **Efficient Route** The distances, in miles, between five different cities are given in the table. Sketch a weighted graph to represent the distances, and then use the Greedy Algorithm to design a route that starts in Memphis, visits each city, and returns to Memphis while attempting to minimize the total distance traveled.

	Memphis	Nashville	Atlanta	Birmingham	Jackson
Memphis	—	210	394	247	213
Nashville	210	—	244	189	418
Atlanta	394	244	—	148	383
Birmingham	247	189	148	—	239
Jackson	213	418	383	239	—

22. **Computer Networking** A small office needs to network five computers by connecting one computer to another and forming a large loop. The length of cable needed (in feet) between pairs of machines is given in the table. Use the Edge-Picking Algorithm to design a method to network the computers while attempting to use the least possible amount of cable.

	Computer A	Computer B	Computer C	Computer D	Computer E
Computer A	—	85	40	55	20
Computer B	85	—	35	40	18
Computer C	40	35	—	60	50
Computer D	55	40	60	—	30
Computer E	20	18	50	30	—

In Exercises 23 and 24, show that the graph is planar by finding a planar drawing.

23.

24.
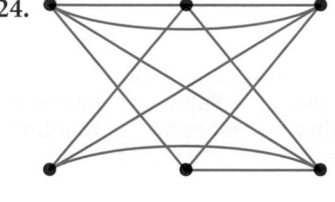

In Exercises 25 and 26, show that the graph is *not* planar.

25.

26.
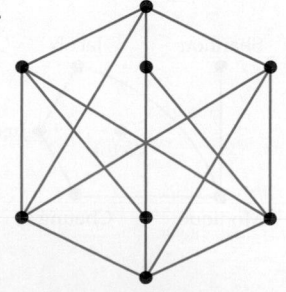

In Exercises 27 and 28, count the number of vertices, edges, and faces in the graph, and then verify Euler's Formula.

27.

28.
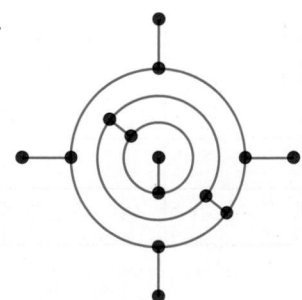

Map Coloring In Exercises 29 and 30, a fictional map is given showing the states of a country. Represent the map by a graph and find a coloring of the graph, using the least number of colors possible, such that no two neighboring countries share the same color.

29.

30.

In Exercises 31 and 32, show that the graph is 2-colorable by finding a 2-coloring, or explain why the graph is not 2-colorable.

In Exercises 33 and 34, determine (by trial and error) the chromatic number of the graph.

31.

32.

33.

34.

35. Scheduling A company has scheduled a retreat at a hotel resort. It needs to hold meetings the first day there, and several conference rooms are available. Some employees must attend more than one meeting, however, so the meetings cannot all be scheduled at the same time. An "X" in the table below indicates that at least one employee must attend both of the corresponding meetings, and so those two meetings must be held at different times. Draw a graph in which each vertex represents a meeting, and an edge joins two vertices if the corresponding meetings require the attendance of the same employee. Then use graph coloring to design a meeting schedule that uses the least number of different time slots possible.

	Budget meeting	Marketing meeting	Executive meeting	Sales meeting	Research meeting	Planning meeting
Budget meeting	—	X	X		X	
Marketing meeting	X	—		X		
Executive meeting	X		—		X	X
Sales meeting		X		—		X
Research meeting	X		X		—	X
Planning meeting			X	X	X	—

CHAPTER 9 **Test**

1. **Social Network** Each vertex in the graph to the right represents a student. An edge connects two vertices if the corresponding students have at least one class in common during the current term.

   a. Is there a class that both Jacob and Cheung are enrolled in?

   b. Who shares the most classes among the members of this group of students?

   c. How many classes does Victor have in common with the other students?

   d. Is this graph connected?

2. Determine whether the following two graphs are equivalent. Explain your reasoning.

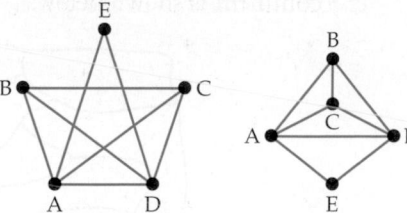

3. Answer the following questions for the graph shown to the right.

   a. Is the graph Eulerian? If so, find an Euler circuit. If not, explain how you know.

   b. Does the graph have an Euler walk? If so, find one. If not, explain how you know.

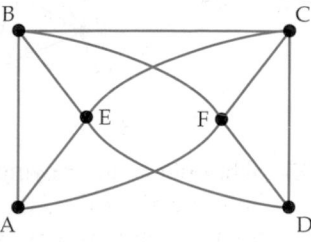

4. Recreation The illustration below depicts bridges connecting islands in a river to the banks. Can a person start at one location and take a stroll so that each bridge is crossed once, but no bridge is crossed twice? (The person does not need to return to the starting location.) Draw a graph to represent the land areas and bridges. Answer the question, using the graph to explain your reasoning.

5. a. What does Dirac's Theorem state? Explain how it guarantees that the graph to the right is Hamiltonian.

   b. Find a Hamiltonian circuit in the graph.

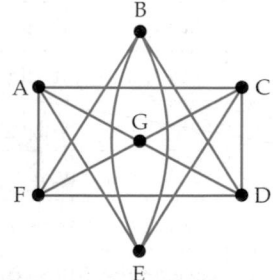

6. Low-Cost Route The table below shows the cost of direct train travel between various cities.

   a. Draw a weighted graph that represents the train fares.

   b. Use the Edge-Picking Algorithm to find a route that begins in Angora, visits each city, and returns to Angora. What is the total cost of this route?

   c. Is it possible to travel along each train route and return to the starting city without traveling any routes more than once? Explain how you know.

	Angora	Bancroft	Chester	Davenport	Elmwood
Angora	—	$48	$52	$36	$90
Bancroft	$48	—	$32	$42	$98
Chester	$52	$32	—	$76	$84
Davenport	$36	$42	$76	—	$106
Elmwood	$90	$98	$84	$106	—

7. Use the Greedy Algorithm to find a Hamiltonian circuit beginning at vertex A in the weighted graph shown.

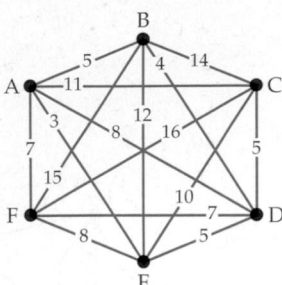

8. Sketch a planar drawing of the graph below.

9. Show that the graph below is not planar.

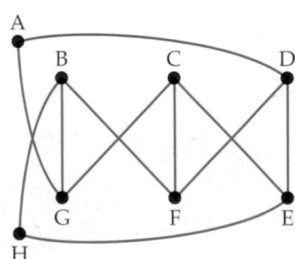

10. Answer the following questions for the graph shown below.

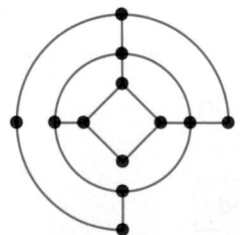

   a. How many vertices are of degree 3?
   b. How many faces does the graph consist of (including the infinite face)?
   c. Show that Euler's Formula is satisfied by this graph.

11. **Map Coloring** A fictional map of the countries of a continent is shown below.

   a. Represent the map by a graph in which the vertices correspond to countries and the edges indicate which countries share a common border.
   b. What is the chromatic number of your graph?
   c. Use your work from part b to color the countries of the map with the fewest number of colors possible so that no two neighboring countries share the same color.

12. For the graph shown below, find a 2-coloring of the vertices or explain why a 2-coloring is impossible.

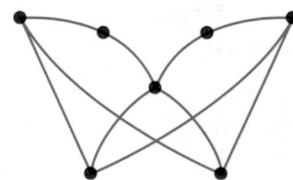

10 The Mathematics of Finance

10.1	Simple Interest
10.2	Compound Interest
10.3	Credit Cards and Consumer Loans
10.4	Stocks, Bonds, and Mutual Funds
10.5	Home Ownership

The table below shows the estimated annual expenses for a child born in 2003. The expenses are for the younger child in a two-child, two-parent home. From the table, we can see that the annual expense for a six-year-old child is $9730, and that $1670 of that amount is spent on food. Use the table to answer the following questions. (Answers are provided on the next page.)

1. Which age group has the highest annual expense? What might be some explanations for this age group having the highest annual expense?

2. For which ages is the annual cost of child care and education highest? Provide an explanation for this.

Estimated Annual Expenses for a Child Born in 2003							
Child's Age	Total	Housing	Food	Transportation	Clothing	Health Care	Child Care and Education	Miscellaneous
0–2	9510	3540	1130	1190	410	660	1570	1010
3–5	9780	3510	1310	1160	400	630	1740	1030
6–8	9730	3420	1670	1290	450	720	1110	1070
9–11	9600	3180	1960	1360	490	780	730	1100
12–14	10,350	3440	1980	1490	830	790	530	1290
15–17	10,560	2950	2200	1880	740	830	920	1040

Source: U.S. Department of Agriculture, Consumer Expenditure Survey Data

This table can also be used to estimate expenses for an only child by multiplying the total for any age group by 1.24.

3. Explain why the cost of raising an only child is greater than the cost of raising the second of two children.

4. What is the total estimated expense of raising an only child to the age of 18? And note that these data do not include the cost of college!

For online student resources, visit this textbook's website at **www.cengage.com/math.**

Given the cost of raising children, an understanding of the mathematics of finance is important for any parent. In this chapter, we will discuss the topics of simple interest, compound interest, consumer loans, investments, and home ownership.

| # Simple Interest

Simple Interest

When you deposit money in a bank—for example, in a savings account—you are permitting the bank to use your money. The bank may lend the deposited money to customers to buy cars or make renovations on their homes. The bank pays you for the privilege of using your money. The amount paid to you is called **interest.** If you are the one borrowing money from a bank, the amount you pay for the privilege of using that money is also called interest.

The amount deposited in a bank or borrowed from a bank is called the **principal.** The amount of interest paid is usually given as a percent of the principal. The percent used to determine the amount of interest is called the **interest rate.** If you deposit $1000 in a savings account paying 5% interest, $1000 is the principal and the interest rate is 5%.

Interest paid on the original principal is called **simple interest.** The formula used to calculate simple interest is given below.

> **Simple Interest Formula**
>
> The simple interest formula is
>
> $$I = Prt$$
>
> where I is the interest, P is the principal, r is the interest rate, and t is the time period.

In the simple interest formula, the time t is expressed in the same period as the rate. For example, if the rate is given as an annual interest rate, then the time is measured in years; if the rate is given as a monthly interest rate, then the time must be expressed in months.

Interest rates are most commonly expressed as annual interest rates. Therefore, unless stated otherwise, we will assume the interest rate is an annual interest rate.

Interest rates are generally given as percents. Before performing calculations involving an interest rate, write the interest rate as a decimal.

EXAMPLE 1 ■ Calculate Simple Interest

Calculate the simple interest earned in 1 year on a deposit of $1000 if the interest rate is 5%.

Solution
Use the simple interest formula. Substitute the following values into the formula: $P = 1000$, $r = 5\% = 0.05$, and $t = 1$.

$$I = Prt$$
$$I = 1000(0.05)(1)$$
$$I = 50$$

The simple interest earned is $50.

CHECK YOUR PROGRESS 1   Calculate the simple interest earned in 1 year on a deposit of $500 if the interest rate is 4%.

Solution   See page S36.

ANSWERS TO QUESTIONS ON PAGE 641

1. *15–17 years. For example, car insurance for teenage drivers.*

2. *3–5 years. For example, child care for preschoolers is an expense, whereas public school is free.*

3. *For example, no hand-me-downs.*

4. *$73,817.20*

EXAMPLE 2 ■ Calculate Simple Interest

Calculate the simple interest due on a three-month loan of $2000 if the interest rate is 6.5%.

Solution

Use the simple interest formula. Substitute the values $P = 2000$ and $r = 6.5\% = 0.065$ into the formula. Because the interest rate is an annual rate, the time must be measured in years: $t = \frac{3 \text{ months}}{1 \text{ year}} = \frac{3 \text{ months}}{12 \text{ months}} = \frac{3}{12}$.

$$I = Prt$$
$$I = 2000(0.065)\left(\frac{3}{12}\right)$$
$$I = 32.5$$

The simple interest due is $32.50.

CHECK YOUR PROGRESS 2   Calculate the simple interest due on a four-month loan of $1500 if the interest rate is 5.25%.

Solution   *See page S36.*

EXAMPLE 3 ■ Calculate Simple Interest

Calculate the simple interest due on a two-month loan of $500 if the interest rate is 1.5% per month.

Solution

Use the simple interest formula. Substitute the values $P = 500$ and $r = 1.5\% = 0.015$ into the formula. Because the interest rate is *per month*, the time period of the loan is expressed as the number of months: $t = 2$.

$$I = Prt$$
$$I = 500(0.015)(2)$$
$$I = 15$$

The simple interest due is $15.

CHECK YOUR PROGRESS 3   Calculate the simple interest due on a five-month loan of $700 if the interest rate is 1.25% per month.

Solution   *See page S36.*

Remember that in the simple interest formula, time t is measured in the same period as the interest rate. Therefore, if the time period of a loan with an annual interest rate is given in days, it is necessary to convert the time period of the loan to a fractional part of a year. There are two methods for converting time from days to years: the exact method and the ordinary method. Using the exact method, the number of days of the loan is divided by 365, the number of days in a year.

Exact method: $t = \dfrac{\text{number of days}}{365}$

TAKE NOTE

If you perform the computation in Example 2 by hand, then we recommend that you reduce the fraction $\frac{3}{12}$ to $\frac{1}{4}$. If you use a calculator to perform the computation, it is not necessary to take the time to reduce $\frac{3}{12}$ to $\frac{1}{4}$.

▼ point of interest

A PIRG (Public Interest Research Group) survey found that 29% of credit reports contained errors that could result in the denial of a loan. This is why financial advisors recommend that consumers check their credit ratings.

The ordinary method is based on there being an average of 30 days in a month and 12 months in a year (30 · 12 = 360). Using this method, the number of days of the loan is divided by 360.

Ordinary method: $t = \dfrac{\text{number of days}}{360}$

The ordinary method is used by most businesses. Therefore, unless otherwise stated, the ordinary method will be used in this text.

historical note

One explanation for the origin of the dollar sign is that the symbol evolved from the Mexican or Spanish letters P and S, for pesos or piastres or pieces of eight. The S gradually came to be written over the P. The $ symbol was widely used before the adoption of the U.S. dollar in 1785. ■

EXAMPLE 4 ■ Calculate Simple Interest

Calculate the simple interest due on a 45-day loan of $3500 if the annual interest rate is 8%.

Solution
Use the simple interest formula. Substitute the following values into the formula: $P = 3500$, $r = 8\% = 0.08$, and $t = \dfrac{\text{number of days}}{360} = \dfrac{45}{360}$.

$I = Prt$

$I = 3500(0.08)\left(\dfrac{45}{360}\right)$

$I = 35$

The simple interest due is $35.

CHECK YOUR PROGRESS 4   Calculate the simple interest due on a 120-day loan of $7000 if the annual interest rate is 5.25%.

Solution   See page S36.

The simple interest formula can be used to find the interest rate on a loan when the interest, principal, and time period of the loan are known. An example is given below.

EXAMPLE 5 ■ Calculate the Simple Interest Rate

The simple interest charged on a six-month loan of $3000 is $150. Find the simple interest rate.

Solution
Use the simple interest formula. Solve the equation for r.

$I = Prt$

$150 = 3000(r)\left(\dfrac{6}{12}\right)$

$150 = 1500r$ • $3000\left(\dfrac{6}{12}\right) = \mathbf{1500}$

$0.10 = r$ • **Divide each side of the equation by 1500.**

$r = 10\%$ • **Write the decimal as a percent.**

The simple interest rate on the loan is 10%.

CHECK YOUR PROGRESS 5   The simple interest charged on a six-month loan of $12,000 is $462. Find the simple interest rate.

Solution   *See page S37.*

MathMatters   Children Daydream about Being Rich

This chapter is about money, something everyone thinks about. But attitudes toward money differ. You might find it interesting to note that a survey of the world's six leading industrial nations revealed that about 62% of children aged 7 through 12 say that they think or daydream about "being rich." The breakdown by country is shown in the figure below.

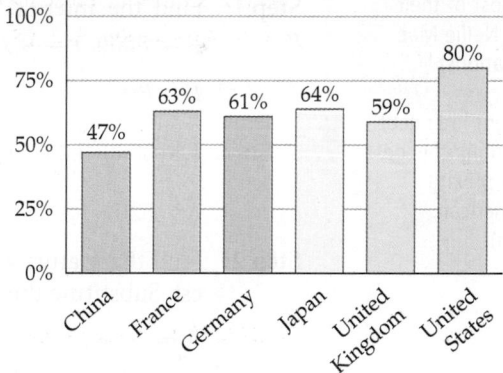

Percent of children aged 7–12 who say they think or daydream about "being rich"

Source: Roper Starch Worldwide for A. B. C. Research

Future Value and Maturity Value

point of interest

You may have heard the term *legal tender.* Section 102 of the Coinage Act of 1965 states, in part, that

All coins and currencies of the United States, regardless of when coins are issued, shall be legal tender for all debts, public and private, public charges, taxes, duties, and dues.

This means that when you offer U.S. currency to a creditor, you have made a valid and legal offer of payment of your debt.

When you borrow money, the total amount to be repaid to the lender is the sum of the principal and interest. This sum is calculated using the following future value or maturity value formula for simple interest.

Future Value or Maturity Value Formula for Simple Interest

The future or maturity value formula for simple interest is

$$A = P + I$$

where A is the amount after the interest, I, has been added to the principal, P.

This formula can be used for loans or investments. When used for a loan, A is the total amount to be repaid to the lender; this sum is called the **maturity value** of the loan. In Example 5, the simple interest charged on the loan of $3000 was $150. The maturity value of the loan is therefore $3000 + $150 = $3150.

For an investment, such as a deposit in a bank savings account, A is the total amount on deposit after the interest earned has been added to the principal. This sum is called the **future value** of the investment.

QUESTION   *Is the stated sum a maturity value or a future value?*

    a. *The sum of the principal and the interest on an investment*

    b. *The sum of the principal and the interest on a loan*

EXAMPLE 6 ■ Calculate a Maturity Value

Calculate the maturity value of a simple interest, eight-month loan of $8000 if the interest rate is 9.75%.

Solution

Step 1: Find the interest. Use the simple interest formula. Substitute the values $P = 8000$, $r = 9.75\% = 0.0975$, and $t = \frac{8}{12}$ into the formula.

$$I = Prt$$

$$I = 8000(0.0975)\left(\frac{8}{12}\right)$$

$$I = 520$$

Step 2: Find the maturity value. Use the maturity value formula for simple interest. Substitute the values $P = 8000$ and $I = 520$ into the formula.

$$A = P + I$$

$$A = 8000 + 520$$

$$A = 8520$$

The maturity value of the loan is $8520.

CHECK YOUR PROGRESS 6   Calculate the maturity value of a simple interest, nine-month loan of $4000 if the interest rate is 8.75%.

Solution   *See page S37.*

Recall that the simple interest formula states that $I = Prt$. We can substitute Prt for I in the future or maturity value formula, as follows.

$$A = P + I$$

$$A = P + Prt$$

$$A = P(1 + rt) \qquad \text{• Use the Distributive Property.}$$

In the final equation, A is the future value of an investment or the maturity value of a loan, P is the principal, r is the interest rate, and t is the time period.

ANSWER   *a.* *Future value*   *b.* *Maturity value*

We used the formula $A = P + I$ in Example 6. The formula $A = P(1 + rt)$ is used in Examples 7 and 8. Note that two steps were required to find the solution in Example 6, but only one step is required in Examples 7 and 8.

EXAMPLE 7 ■ Calculate the Maturity Value Using $A = P(1 + rt)$

Calculate the maturity value of a simple interest, three-month loan of $3800. The interest rate is 6%.

Solution

Substitute the following values into the formula $A = P(1 + rt)$: $P = 3800$, $r = 6\% = 0.06$, and $t = \frac{3}{12}$.

$$A = P(1 + rt)$$
$$A = 3800\left[1 + 0.06\left(\frac{3}{12}\right)\right]$$
$$A = 3800(1 + 0.015)$$
$$A = 3800(1.015)$$
$$A = 3857$$

The maturity value of the loan is $3857.

CHECK YOUR PROGRESS 7   Calculate the maturity value of a simple interest, one-year loan of $6700. The interest rate is 8.9%.

Solution   *See page S37.*

EXAMPLE 8 ■ Calculate the Future Value Using $A = P(1 + rt)$

Find the future value after 1 year of $850 in an account earning 8.2% simple interest.

Solution

Because $t = 1$, $rt = r(1) = r$. Therefore, $1 + rt = 1 + r = 1 + 0.082 = 1.082$.

$$A = P(1 + rt)$$
$$A = 850(1.082)$$
$$A = 919.7$$

The future value of the account after 1 year is $919.70.

CHECK YOUR PROGRESS 8   Find the future value after 1 year of $680 in an account earning 6.4% simple interest.

Solution   *See page S37.*

Recall that the formula $A = P + I$ states that A is the amount after the interest has been added to the principal. Subtracting P from each side of this equation yields the following formula.

$$I = A - P$$

This formula states that the amount of interest paid is equal to the total amount minus the principal. This formula is used in Example 9.

EXAMPLE 9 ■ Calculate the Simple Interest Rate

The maturity value of a three-month loan of $4000 is $4085. What is the simple interest rate?

Solution
First find the amount of interest paid. Subtract the principal from the maturity value.

$$I = A - P$$
$$I = 4085 - 4000$$
$$I = 85$$

Find the simple interest rate by solving the simple interest formula for r.

$$I = Prt$$
$$85 = 4000(r)\left(\frac{3}{12}\right)$$

$85 = 1000r$ • $4000\left(\dfrac{3}{12}\right) = \mathbf{1000}$

$0.085 = r$ • Divide each side of the equation by 1000.

$r = 8.5\%$ • Write the decimal as a percent.

The simple interest rate on the loan is 8.5%.

CHECK YOUR PROGRESS 9   The maturity value of a four-month loan of $9000 is $9240. What is the simple interest rate?

Solution   *See page S37.*

Exercise Set 10.1

1. Explain how to convert a number of months to a fractional part of a year.

2. Explain how to convert a number of days to a fractional part of a year.

3. Explain what each variable in the simple interest formula represents.

In Exercises 4–17, calculate the simple interest earned. Round to the nearest cent.

4. $P = \$2000$, $r = 6\%$, $t = 1$ year
5. $P = \$8000$, $r = 7\%$, $t = 1$ year
6. $P = \$3000$, $r = 5.5\%$, $t = 6$ months
7. $P = \$7000$, $r = 6.5\%$, $t = 6$ months
8. $P = \$4200$, $r = 8.5\%$, $t = 3$ months
9. $P = \$9000$, $r = 6.75\%$, $t = 4$ months
10. $P = \$12,000$, $r = 7.8\%$, $t = 45$ days
11. $P = \$3000$, $r = 9.6\%$, $t = 21$ days
12. $P = \$4000$, $r = 8.4\%$, $t = 33$ days
13. $P = \$7000$, $r = 7.2\%$, $t = 114$ days
14. $P = \$800$, $r = 1.5\%$ monthly, $t = 3$ months
15. $P = \$2000$, $r = 1.25\%$ monthly, $t = 5$ months
16. $P = \$3500$, $r = 1.8\%$ monthly, $t = 4$ months
17. $P = \$1600$, $r = 1.75\%$ monthly, $t = 6$ months

In Exercises 18–23, use the formula $A = P(1 + rt)$ to calculate the maturity value of the simple interest loan.

18. $P = \$8500$, $r = 6.8\%$, $t = 6$ months
19. $P = \$15,000$, $r = 8.9\%$, $t = 6$ months
20. $P = \$4600$, $r = 9.75\%$, $t = 4$ months
21. $P = \$7200$, $r = 7.95\%$, $t = 4$ months
22. $P = \$13,000$, $r = 1.4\%$ monthly, $t = 3$ months
23. $P = \$2800$, $r = 9.2\%$, $t = 3$ months

In Exercises 24–29, calculate the simple interest rate.

24. $P = \$8000$, $I = \$500$, $t = 1$ year
25. $P = \$1600$, $I = \$120$, $t = 1$ year
26. $P = \$4000$, $I = \$190$, $t = 6$ months
27. $P = \$2000$, $I = \$105$, $t = 6$ months
28. $P = \$500$, $I = \$10.25$, $t = 3$ months
29. $P = \$1200$, $I = \$37.20$, $t = 4$ months

30. **Simple Interest** Calculate the simple interest earned in 1 year on a deposit of $1900 if the interest rate is 8%.

31. **Simple Interest** Calculate the simple interest earned in 1 year on a deposit of $2300 if the interest rate is 7%.

32. **Simple Interest** Calculate the simple interest due on a three-month loan of $1400 if the interest rate is 7.5%.

33. **Simple Interest** You deposit $1500 in an account earning 10.4% interest. Calculate the simple interest earned in 6 months.

34. **Simple Interest** Calculate the simple interest due on a two-month loan of $800 if the interest rate is 1.5% per month.

35. **Simple Interest** Calculate the simple interest due on a 45-day loan of $1600 if the interest rate is 9%.

36. **Simple Interest** Calculate the simple interest due on a 150-day loan of $4800 if the interest rate is 7.25%.

37. **Maturity Value** Calculate the maturity value of a simple interest, eight-month loan of $7000 if the interest rate is 8.7%.

38. **Maturity Value** Calculate the maturity value of a simple interest, 10-month loan of $6600 if the interest rate is 9.75%.

39. **Maturity Value** Calculate the maturity value of a simple interest, one-year loan of $5200. The interest rate is 10.2%.

40. **Future Value** You deposit $880 in an account paying 9.2% simple interest. Find the future value of the investment after 1 year.

41. **Future Value** You deposit $750 in an account paying 7.3% simple interest. Find the future value of the investment after 1 year.

42. **Simple Interest Rate** The simple interest charged on a six-month loan of $6000 is $270. Find the simple interest rate.

43. Simple Interest Rate The simple interest charged on a six-month loan of $18,000 is $918. Find the simple interest rate.

44. Simple Interest Rate The maturity value of a four-month loan of $3000 is $3097. Find the simple interest rate.

45. Simple Interest Rate Find the simple interest rate on a three-month loan of $5000 if the maturity value of the loan is $5125.

46. Late Payments Your property tax bill is $1200. The county charges a penalty of 11% simple interest for late payments. How much do you owe if you pay the bill 2 months past the due date?

47. Late Payments Your electric bill is $132. You are charged 12% simple interest for late payments. How much do you owe if you pay the bill 1 month past the due date?

48. Certificate of Deposit If you withdraw part of your money from a certificate of deposit before the date of maturity, you must pay an interest penalty. Suppose you invested $5000 in a one-year certificate of deposit paying 8.5% interest. After 6 months, you decide to withdraw $2000. Your interest penalty is 3 months simple interest on the $2000. What interest penalty do you pay?

49. Maturity Value $10,000 is borrowed for 140 days at an 8% interest rate. Calculate the maturity value by the exact method and by the ordinary method. Which method yields the greater maturity value? Who benefits from using the ordinary method rather than the exact method, the borrower or the lender?

Extensions

CRITICAL THINKING

50. Interest has been described as a rental fee for money. Explain why this is an apt description of interest.

51. On July 31, at 4 P.M., you open a savings account that pays 5% interest, compounded daily, and you deposit $500 in the account. Your deposit is credited as of August 1. At the beginning of September, you receive a statement from the bank that shows that during the month of August, you received $2.15 in interest. The interest has been added to your account, bringing the total deposit to $502.15. At the beginning of October, you receive a statement from the bank that shows that during the month of September, you received $2.09 in interest on the $502.15 on deposit. Why did you receive less interest during the second month, when there was more money on deposit?

COOPERATIVE LEARNING

52. Simple Interest a. In the table below, the interest rate is an annual simple interest rate. Complete the table by calculating the simple interest due on the loan.

Loan Amount	Interest Rate	Period	Interest
$5000	6%	1 month	_____
$5000	6%	2 months	_____
$5000	6%	3 months	_____
$5000	6%	4 months	_____
$5000	6%	5 months	_____

Use the pattern of your answers in the table to find the simple interest due on a $5000 loan that has an annual simple interest rate of 6% for a period of:

b. 6 months   **c.** 7 months   **d.** 8 months   **e.** 9 months

Use your solutions to parts a through e to answer the following questions.

f. If you know the simple interest due on a one-month loan, explain how you can use that figure to calculate the simple interest due on a seven-month loan for the same principal and the same interest rate.

g. If the time period of a loan is doubled but the principal and interest rate remain the same, how many times as large is the simple interest due on the loan?

h. If the time period of a loan is tripled but the principal and interest rate remain the same, how many times as large is the simple interest due on the loan?

53. Simple Interest a. In the table below, the interest rate is an annual simple interest rate. Complete the table by calculating the simple interest due on the loan.

Loan Amount	Interest Rate	Period	Interest
$1000	6%	1 month	_____
$2000	6%	1 month	_____
$3000	6%	1 month	_____
$4000	6%	1 month	_____
$5000	6%	1 month	_____

Use the pattern of your answers in the table to determine the simple interest due on a one-month loan that has an annual simple interest rate of 6% when the principal is:

b. $6000   **c.** $7000   **d.** $8000   **e.** $9000

Use your solutions to parts a through e to answer the following questions.

f. If you know the simple interest due on a $1000 loan, explain how you can use that figure to calculate the simple interest due on an $8000 loan for the same time period and the same interest rate.

g. If the principal of a loan is doubled but the time period and interest rate remain the same, how many times as large is the simple interest due on the loan?

h. If the principal of a loan is tripled but the time period and interest rate remain the same, how many times as large is the simple interest due on the loan?

| SECTION 10.2 | **Compound Interest** |

Compound Interest

Simple interest is generally used for loans of 1 year or less. For loans of more than 1 year, the interest paid on the money borrowed is called *compound interest*. **Compound interest** is interest calculated not only on the original principal, but also on any interest that has already been earned.

To illustrate compound interest, suppose you deposit $1000 in a savings account earning 5% interest, compounded annually (once a year).

During the first year, the interest earned is calculated as follows.

$$I = Prt$$
$$I = \$1000(0.05)(1) = \$50$$

At the end of the first year, the total amount in the account is

$$A = P + I$$
$$A = \$1000 + \$50 = \$1050$$

During the second year, the interest earned is calculated using the amount in the account at the end of the first year.

$$I = Prt$$
$$I = \$1050(0.05)(1) = \$52.50$$

Note that the interest earned during the second year ($52.50) is greater than the interest earned during the first year ($50). This is because the interest earned during the first year was added to the original principal, and the interest for the second year was calculated using this sum. If the account earned simple interest rather than compound interest, the interest earned each year would be the same ($50).

At the end of the second year, the total amount in the account is the sum of the amount in the account at the end of the first year and the interest earned during the second year.

$$A = P + I$$
$$A = \$1050 + 52.50 = \$1102.50$$

The interest earned during the third year is calculated using the amount in the account at the end of the second year ($1102.50).

$$I = Prt$$
$$I = \$1102.50(0.05)(1) = \$55.125 \approx \$55.13$$

The interest earned each year keeps increasing. This is the effect of compound interest.

In this example, the interest is compounded annually. However, compound interest can be compounded semiannually (twice a year), quarterly (four times a year), monthly, or daily. The frequency with which the interest is compounded is called the **compounding period.**

If, in the preceding example, interest is compounded quarterly rather than annually, then the first interest payment on the $1000 in the account occurs after 3 months

$\left(t = \frac{3}{12} = \frac{1}{4}; \text{3 months is one-quarter of a year}\right)$. That interest is then added to the account, and the interest earned for the second quarter is calculated using that sum.

Western Currency Facility in Fort Worth, Texas

End of 1st quarter: $I = Prt = \$1000(0.05)\left(\frac{3}{12}\right) = \$12.50$

$$A = P + I = \$1000 + \$12.50 = \$1012.50$$

End of 2nd quarter: $I = Prt = \$1012.50(0.05)\left(\frac{3}{12}\right) = \$12.65625 \approx \$12.66$

$$A = P + I = \$1012.50 + \$12.66 = \$1025.16$$

End of 3rd quarter: $I = Prt = \$1025.16(0.05)\left(\frac{3}{12}\right) = \$12.8145 \approx \$12.81$

$$A = P + I = \$1025.16 + \$12.81 = \$1037.97$$

End of 4th quarter: $I = Prt = \$1037.97(0.05)\left(\frac{3}{12}\right) = \$12.974625 \approx \$12.97$

$$A = P + I = \$1037.97 + \$12.97 = \$1050.94$$

The total amount in the account at the end of the first year is $1050.94.

When the interest is compounded quarterly, the account earns more interest ($1050.94) than when the interest is compounded annually ($50). In general, an increase in the number of compounding periods results in an increase in the interest earned by an account.

In the example above, the formulas $I = Prt$ and $A = P + I$ were used to show the amount of interest added to the account each quarter. The formula $A = P(1 + rt)$ can be used to calculate A at the end of each quarter. For example, the amount in the account at the end of the first quarter is

$$A = P(1 + rt)$$
$$A = 1000\left[1 + 0.05\left(\frac{3}{12}\right)\right]$$
$$A = 1000(1.0125)$$
$$A = 1012.50$$

This amount, $1012.50, is the same as the amount calculated above using the formula $A = P + I$ to find the amount at the end of the first quarter.

The formula $A = P(1 + rt)$ is used in Example 1.

EXAMPLE 1 ■ Calculate Future Value

You deposit $500 in an account earning 6% interest, compounded semiannually. How much is in the account at the end of 1 year?

Solution

The interest is compounded every 6 months. Calculate the amount in the account after the first 6 months. $t = \frac{6}{12}$.

$$A = P(1 + rt)$$
$$A = 500\left[1 + 0.06\left(\frac{6}{12}\right)\right]$$
$$A = 515$$

Calculate the amount in the account after the second 6 months.

$$A = P(1 + rt)$$

$$A = 515\left[1 + 0.06\left(\frac{6}{12}\right)\right]$$

$$A = 530.45$$

The total amount in the account at the end of 1 year is $530.45.

CHECK YOUR PROGRESS 1 You deposit $2000 in an account earning 4% interest, compounded monthly. How much is in the account at the end of 6 months?

Solution See page S37.

In calculations that involve compound interest, the sum of the principal and the interest that has been added to it is called the **compound amount.** In Example 1, the compound amount is $530.45.

The calculations necessary to determine compound interest and compound amounts can be simplified by using a formula. Consider an amount P deposited into an account paying an annual interest rate r, compounded annually.

The interest earned during the first year is

$$I = Prt$$
$$I = Pr(1) \qquad \bullet\ t = 1.$$
$$I = Pr$$

The compound amount A in the account after 1 year is the sum of the original principal and the interest earned during the first year:

$$A = P + I$$
$$A = P + Pr$$
$$A = P(1 + r) \qquad \bullet\ \text{Factor } P \text{ from each term.}$$

During the second year, the interest is calculated on the compound amount at the end of the first year, $P(1 + r)$.

$$I = Prt$$
$$I = P(1 + r)r(1) \qquad \bullet\ \text{Replace } P \text{ with } P(1 + r);\ t = 1.$$
$$I = P(1 + r)r$$

The compound amount A in the account after 2 years is the sum of the compound amount at the end of the first year and the interest earned during the second year:

$$A = P + I$$
$$A = P(1 + r) + P(1 + r)r \qquad \bullet\ \text{Replace } P \text{ with } \mathbf{P(1 + r)} \text{ and } I \text{ with } \mathbf{P(1 + r)r}.$$

$$A = 1[P(1 + r)] + [P(1 + r)]r$$
$$A = P(1 + r)(1 + r) \qquad \bullet\ \text{Factor } P(1 + r) \text{ from each term.}$$
$$A = P(1 + r)^2 \qquad \bullet\ \text{Write } (1 + r)(1 + r) \text{ as } (1 + r)^2.$$

During the third year, the interest is calculated on the compound amount at the end of the second year, $P(1 + r)^2$.

$$I = Prt$$
$$I = P(1 + r)^2 r(1) \qquad \text{• Replace } P \text{ with } P(1 + r)^2; t = \mathbf{1}.$$
$$I = P(1 + r)^2 r$$

The compound amount A in the account after 3 years is the sum of the compound amount at the end of the second year and the interest earned during the third year:

$$A = P + I$$
$$A = P(1 + r)^2 + P(1 + r)^2 r \qquad \text{• Replace } P \text{ with } \mathbf{P(1 + r)^2} \text{ and } I \text{ with}$$
$$\mathbf{P(1 + r)^2 r}.$$
$$A = 1[P(1 + r)^2] + [P(1 + r)^2]r$$
$$A = P(1 + r)^2(1 + r) \qquad \text{• Factor } \mathbf{P(1 + r)^2} \text{ from each term.}$$
$$A = P(1 + r)^3 \qquad \text{• Write } \mathbf{(1 + r)^2(1 + r)} \text{ as } \mathbf{(1 + r)^3}.$$

Note that the compound amount at the end of each year is the previous year's compound amount multiplied by $(1 + r)$. The exponent on $(1 + r)$ is equal to the number of compounding periods. Generalizing from this, we can state that the compound amount after n years is $A = P(1 + r)^n$.

In deriving this equation, interest was compounded annually; therefore, $t = 1$. Applying a similar argument for more frequent compounding periods, we derive the following compound amount formula. This formula enables us to calculate the compound amount for any number of compounding periods per year.

Compound Amount Formula

The compound amount formula is

$$A = P(1 + i)^N$$

where A is the compound amount when P dollars are deposited at an interest rate of i per compounding period for N compounding periods.

Because i is the interest rate per compounding period and n is the number of compounding periods per year,

$$i = \frac{\text{annual interest rate}}{\text{number of compounding periods per year}} = \frac{r}{n}$$

$$N = (\text{number of compounding periods per year})(\text{number of years}) = nt$$

To illustrate how to calculate the values of i and N, consider an account earning 12% interest, compounded quarterly, for a period of 3 years.

The annual interest rate is 12%: $r = 12\%$.

When interest is compounded quarterly, there are four compounding periods per year: $n = 4$.

The time is 3 years: $t = 3$.

$$i = \frac{r}{n} = \frac{12\%}{4} = 3\%$$

$$N = nt = 4(3) = 12$$

▼ **point of interest**

It is believed that U.S. currency is green because at the time of the introduction of the smaller-size bills in 1929, green pigment was readily available in large quantities. The color was resistant to chemical and physical changes, and green was psychologically associated with strong, stable government credit. (*Source:* **www.moneyfactory.gov**)

✔ **TAKE NOTE**

The Compound Amount Formula can also be written as

$$A = P\left(1 + \frac{r}{n}\right)^{nt}.$$

The number of compounding periods in the 3 years is 12: $N = 12$. The account earns 3% interest per compounding period (per quarter): $i = 3\%$. Note that the interest rate per compounding period times the number of compounding periods per year equals the annual interest rate: $(3\%)(4) = 12\%$.

Recall that compound interest can be compounded annually (once a year), semiannually (twice a year), quarterly (four times a year), monthly, or daily. The possible values of n (the number of compounding periods per year) are recorded in the table below.

Values of n (number of compounding periods per year)

If interest is	then $n =$
compounded annually	1
compounded semiannually	2
compounded quarterly	4
compounded monthly	12
compounded daily	360

QUESTION *What is the value of i when the interest rate is 6%, compounded monthly?*

Recall that the future value of an investment is the value of the investment after the original principal has been invested for a period of time. In other words, it is the principal plus the interest earned. Therefore, it is the compound amount A in the compound amount formula.

EXAMPLE 2 ■ Calculate the Compound Amount

Calculate the compound amount when $10,000 is deposited in an account earning 8% interest, compounded semiannually, for 4 years.

Solution

Use the compound amount formula. $r = 8\% = 0.08$, $n = 2$, $t = 4$, $i = \frac{r}{n} = \frac{0.08}{2} = 0.04$, and $N = nt = 2(4) = 8$.

$$A = P(1 + i)^N$$
$$A = 10{,}000(1 + 0.04)^8$$
$$A = 10{,}000(1.04)^8$$
$$A \approx 10{,}000(1.368569)$$
$$A \approx 13{,}685.69$$

The compound amount after 4 years is approximately $13,685.69.

ANSWER $i = \dfrac{r}{n} = \dfrac{6\%}{12} = 0.5\% = 0.005.$

CALCULATOR NOTE

When using a scientific calculator to solve the compound amount formula for A, use the key-stroking sequence

$r \div n + 1 = y^x N \times P =$

When using a graphing calculator, use the sequence

$P (1 + r \div n) \wedge N$

CHECK YOUR PROGRESS 2   Calculate the compound amount when $4000 is deposited in an account earning 6% interest, compounded monthly, for 2 years.

Solution   *See page S38.*

EXAMPLE 3 ■ Calculate Future Value

Calculate the future value of $5000 earning 9% interest, compounded daily, for 3 years.

Solution

Use the compound amount formula. $r = 9\% = 0.09$, $t = 3$. Interest is compounded daily. Use the ordinary method. $n = 360$, $i = \frac{r}{n} = \frac{0.09}{360} = 0.00025$, $N = nt = 360(3) = 1080$

$$A = P(1 + i)^N$$
$$A = 5000(1 + 0.00025)^{1080}$$
$$A = 5000(1.00025)^{1080}$$
$$A \approx 5000(1.3099202)$$
$$A \approx 6549.60$$

The future value after 3 years is approximately $6549.60.

CHECK YOUR PROGRESS 3   Calculate the future value of $2500 earning 9% interest, compounded daily, for 4 years.

Solution   *See page S38.*

The formula $I = A - P$ was used in Section 10.1 to find the interest earned on an investment or the interest paid on a loan. This same formula is used for compound interest. It is used in Example 4 to find the interest earned on an investment.

EXAMPLE 4 ■ Calculate Compound Interest

How much interest is earned in 2 years on $4000 deposited in an account paying 6% interest, compounded quarterly?

Solution

Calculate the compound amount. Use the compound amount formula. $r = 6\% = 0.06$, $n = 4$, $t = 2$, $i = \frac{r}{n} = \frac{0.06}{4} = 0.015$, $N = nt = 4(2) = 8$

$$A = P(1 + i)^N$$
$$A = 4000(1 + 0.015)^8$$
$$A = 4000(1.015)^8$$
$$A \approx 4000(1.1264926)$$
$$A \approx 4505.97$$

Calculate the interest earned. Use the formula $I = A - P$.

$$I = A - P$$
$$I = 4505.97 - 4000$$
$$I = 505.97$$

The amount of interest earned is approximately $505.97.

▼ **point of interest**

The majority of Americans say their children should start saving for retirement earlier than they did. Here is the breakdown, by age, of when parents started saving for retirement. (*Source:* Lincoln Financial Group-Money Magazine Survey)

Under 20: 9%
20–24: 19%
25–29: 18%
30–39: 21%
40–49: 11%
50 and over: 6%
Don't know: 16%

CHECK YOUR PROGRESS 4   How much interest is earned in 6 years on $8000 deposited in an account paying 9% interest, compounded monthly?

Solution   *See page S38.*

An alternative to using the compound amount formula is to use a calculator that has finance functions built into it. The TI-83 and TI-84 graphing calculator is used in Example 5.

EXAMPLE 5 ■ Calculate Compound Interest

Use the finance feature of a calculator to determine the compound amount when $2000 is deposited in an account earning an interest rate of 12%, compounded quarterly, for 10 years.

Solution

On a TI-83 calculator, press [2nd] [Finance] to display the FINANCE CALC menu.

For the TI-83 Plus or TI-84, press [APPS] [ENTER].

Press [ENTER] to select 1: TVM Solver.

> After N =, enter 40.
>
> After I% =, enter 12.
>
> After PV =, enter −2000. (See the note below.)
>
> After PMT =, enter 0.
>
> After P/Y =, enter 4.
>
> After C/Y =, enter 4.

Use the up arrow key to place the cursor at FV =.

Press [ALPHA] [Solve].

The solution is displayed to the right of FV =.

The compound amount is $6524.08.

Note: For most financial calculators and financial computer programs such as Excel, money that is paid out (such as the $2000 that is being deposited in this example) is entered as a negative number.

CHECK YOUR PROGRESS 5   Use the finance feature of a calculator to determine the compound amount when $3500 is deposited in an account earning an interest rate of 6%, compounded semiannually, for 5 years.

Solution   *See page S38.*

CALCULATOR NOTE

On the TI-83/84 calculator screen below, the variable N is the number of compounding periods, I% is the interest rate, PV is the present value of the money, PMT is the payment, P/Y is the number of payments per year, C/Y is the number of compounding periods per year, and FV is the future value of the money. TVM represents Time Value of money.

Present value is discussed a little later in this section. Enter the principal for the present value amount.

"Solve" is above the [ENTER] key on the calculator.

```
N=40
I%=12
PV=-2000
PMT=0
■FV=6524.075584
P/Y=4
C/Y=4
PMT: END BEGIN
```

Math Matters   Federal Funds Rate

The Federal Reserve Board meets a number of times each year to decide, among other things, the federal funds rate. The **federal funds rate** is the interest rate banks charge one another for overnight loans. The Federal Reserve Board can decide to lower, raise, or leave unchanged the federal funds rate. Its decision has a significant effect on the economy. For example, if the board increases the rate, then banks have to pay more to borrow money. If banks must pay higher rates, they are going to charge their customers a higher rate to borrow money.

The graph below shows the federal funds rates from March 2001 through June 2004.

Chairman Greenspan

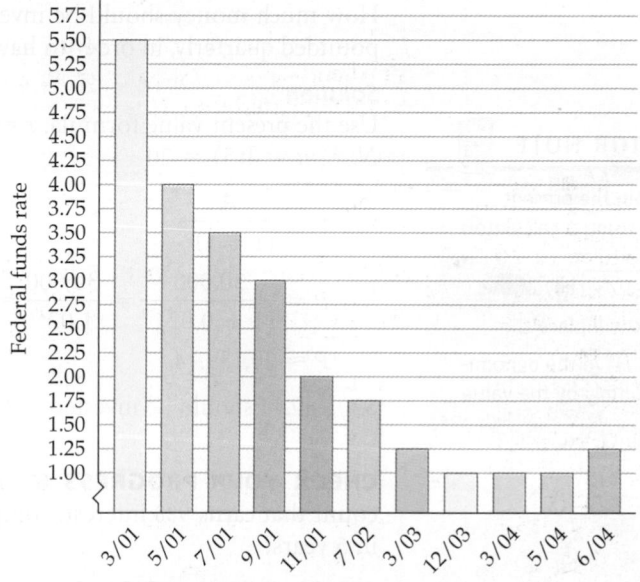

Present Value

The **present value** of an investment is the original principal invested, or the value of the investment before it earns any interest. Therefore, it is the principal, P, in the compound amount formula. Present value is used to determine how much money must be invested today in order for an investment to have a specific value at a future date.

The formula for the present value of an investment is found by solving the compound amount formula for P.

$$A = P(1 + i)^N$$

$$\frac{A}{(1 + i)^N} = \frac{P(1 + i)^N}{(1 + i)^N}$$ • **Divide each side of the equation by** $(1 + i)^N$.

$$\frac{A}{(1 + i)^N} = P$$

Present Value Formula

The present value formula is

$$P = \frac{A}{(1 + i)^N}$$

where P is the original principal invested at an interest rate of i per compounding period for N compounding periods, and A is the compound amount.

The present value formula is used in Example 6.

EXAMPLE 6 ■ Calculate Present Value

How much money should be invested in an account that earns 8% interest, compounded quarterly, in order to have $30,000 in 5 years?

Solution

Use the present value formula. $r = 8\% = 0.08$, $n = 4$, $t = 5$, $i = \frac{r}{n} = \frac{0.08}{4} = 0.02$, $N = nt = 4(5) = 20$

$$P = \frac{A}{(1 + i)^N}$$

$$P = \frac{30{,}000}{(1 + 0.02)^{20}} = \frac{30{,}000}{1.02^{20}} \approx \frac{30{,}000}{1.485947396}$$

$$P \approx 20{,}189.14$$

$20,189.14 should be invested in the account in order to have $30,000 in 5 years.

CHECK YOUR PROGRESS 6 How much money should be invested in an account that earns 9% interest, compounded semiannually, in order to have $20,000 in 5 years?

Solution *See page S38.*

CALCULATOR NOTE

To calculate P in the present value formula using a calculator, you can first calculate $(1 + i)^N$. Next use the $\boxed{1/x}$ key or the $\boxed{x^{-1}}$ key. This will place the value of $(1 + i)^N$ in the denominator. Then multiply by the value of A.

EXAMPLE 7 ■ Calculate Present Value

Use the finance feature of a calculator to determine how much money should be invested in an account that earns 7% interest, compounded monthly, in order to have $50,000 in 10 years.

Solution

On a TI-83 calculator, press $\boxed{2nd}$ [FINANCE] to display the FINANCE CALC menu. For the TI-83 Plus or TI-84, press $\boxed{APPS}$ $\boxed{ENTER}$.

Press $\boxed{ENTER}$ to select 1 TVM Solver.

After N =, enter 120.

After I% =, enter 7.

After PMT =, enter 0.

After FV =, enter 50000.

After P/Y =, enter 12.

After C/Y =, enter 12.

```
N=120
I%=7
PV=■
PMT=0
FV=50000
P/Y=12
C/Y=12
PMT: END BEGIN
```

```
N=120
I%=7
▮PV=-24879.81338
PMT=0
FV=50000
P/Y=12
C/Y=12
PMT: END BEGIN
```

Use the up arrow key to place the cursor at PV =.

Press ALPHA [Solve].

The solution is displayed to the right of PV =.

$24,879.81 should be invested in the account in order to have $50,000 in 10 years.

CHECK YOUR PROGRESS 7 Use the finance feature of a calculator to determine how much money should be invested in an account that earns 6% interest, compounded daily, in order to have $25,000 in 15 years.

Solution *See page S38.*

Inflation

We have discussed compound interest and its effect on the growth of an investment. After your money has been invested for a period of time in an account that pays interest, you will have more money than you originally deposited. But does that mean you will be able to buy more with the compound amount than you were able to buy with the original investment at the time you deposited the money? The answer is not necessarily, and the reason is the effect of inflation.

Suppose the price of a large-screen TV is $1500. You have enough money to purchase the TV, but decide to invest the $1500 in an account paying 6% interest, compounded monthly. After 1 year, the compound amount is $1592.52. But during that same year, the rate of inflation was 7%. The large-screen TV now costs

$$\$1500 \text{ plus } 7\% \text{ of } \$1500 = \$1500 + 0.07(\$1500)$$
$$= \$1500 + \$105$$
$$= \$1605$$

Because $1592.52 < $1605, you have actually lost purchasing power. At the beginning of the year, you had enough money to buy the large-screen TV; at the end of the year, the compound amount is not enough to pay for that same TV. Your money has actually lost value because it can buy less now than it could 1 year ago.

Inflation is an economic condition during which there are increases in the costs of goods and services. Inflation is expressed as a percent; for example, we speak of an annual inflation rate of 7%.

To calculate the effects of inflation, we use the same procedure we used to calculate compound amount. This process is illustrated in Example 8. Although inflation rates vary dramatically, in this section we will assume constant annual inflation rates, and we will use annual compounding in solving inflation problems. In other words, $n = 1$ for these exercises.

EXAMPLE 8 ■ Calculate the Effect of Inflation on Salary

Suppose your annual salary today is $35,000. You want to know what an equivalent salary will be in 20 years—that is, a salary that will have the same purchasing power. Assume a 6% inflation rate.

Solution

Use the compound amount formula. $r = 6\% = 0.06$. The inflation rate is an annual rate, so $n = 1$. $t = 20$, $i = \frac{r}{n} = \frac{0.06}{1} = 0.06$, $N = nt = 1(20) = 20$

$$A = P(1 + i)^N$$
$$A = 35{,}000(1 + 0.06)^{20}$$
$$A = 35{,}000(1.06)^{20}$$
$$A \approx 35{,}000(3.20713547)$$
$$A \approx 112{,}249.74$$

Twenty years from now, you need to earn an annual salary of approximately $112,249.74 in order to have the same purchasing power.

CHECK YOUR PROGRESS 8   Assume that the average new car sticker price in 2008 is $28,000. Use an annual inflation rate of 5% to estimate the average new car sticker price in 2025.

Solution   *See page S38.*

The present value formula can be used to determine the effect of inflation on the future purchasing power of a given amount of money. Substitute the inflation rate for the interest rate in the present value formula. The compounding period is 1 year. Again we will assume a constant rate of inflation.

EXAMPLE 9 ■ **Calculate the Effect of Inflation on Future Purchasing Power**

Suppose you purchase an insurance policy in 2010 that will provide you with $250,000 when you retire in 2045. Assuming an annual inflation rate of 8%, what will be the purchasing power of the $250,000 in 2045?

Solution

Use the present value formula. $r = 8\%$ and $t = 35$. The inflation rate is an annual rate, so $n = 1$. $i = \frac{r}{n} = \frac{8\%}{1} = 8\% = 0.08$, $N = nt = 1(35) = 35$

$$P = \frac{A}{(1 + i)^N}$$
$$P = \frac{250{,}000}{(1 + 0.08)^{35}}$$
$$P \approx \frac{250{,}000}{14.785344}$$
$$P \approx 16{,}908.64$$

In 2045, the purchasing power of $250,000 will be approximately $16,908.64.

CHECK YOUR PROGRESS 9   Suppose you purchase an insurance policy in 2010 that will provide you with $500,000 when you retire in 40 years. Assuming an annual inflation rate of 7%, what will be the purchasing power of half a million dollars in 2050?

Solution   *See page S39.*

Math Matters   The Rule of 72

The **Rule of 72** states that the number of years for prices to double is approximately equal to 72 divided by the annual inflation rate.

$$\text{Years to double} = \frac{72}{\text{annual inflation rate}}$$

For example, at an annual inflation rate of 6%, prices will double in approximately 12 years.

$$\text{Years to double} = \frac{72}{\text{annual inflation rate}} = \frac{72}{6} = 12$$

Effective Interest Rate

When interest is compounded, the annual rate of interest is called the **nominal rate.** The **effective rate** is the simple interest rate that would yield the same amount of interest after 1 year. When a bank advertises a "7% annual interest rate compounded daily and yielding 7.25%," the nominal interest rate is 7% and the effective rate is 7.25%.

QUESTION   *A bank offers a savings account that pays 2.75% annual interest, compounded daily and yielding 2.79%. What is the effective rate on this account? What is the nominal rate?*

Consider $100 deposited at 6%, compounded monthly, for 1 year.

The future value after 1 year is $106.17.

$$A = P(1 + i)^N$$
$$A = 100(1 + 0.005)^{12}$$
$$A \approx 106.17$$

The interest earned in 1 year is $6.17.

$$I = A - P$$
$$I = 106.17 - 100$$
$$I = 6.17$$

Now consider $100 deposited at an annual simple interest rate of 6.17%.

The interest earned in 1 year is $6.17.

$$I = Prt$$
$$I = 100(0.0617)(1)$$
$$I = 6.17$$

The interest earned on $100 is the same when it is deposited at 6% compounded monthly as when it is deposited at an annual simple interest rate of 6.17%. 6.17% is the effective annual rate of a deposit that earns 6% compounded monthly.

▼ **point of interest**

According to the Federal Reserve Board, the value of U.S. currency in circulation increased 100.4% from 1993 to 2003, to $690.2 billion.

ANSWER   *The effective rate is 2.79%. The nominal rate is 2.75%.*

In this example $100 was used as the principal. When we use $100 for *P* we multiply the interest rate by 100. Remember that the interest rate is written as a decimal in the equation $I = Prt$, and a decimal is written as a percent by multiplying by 100. Therefore, when $P = 100$, the interest earned on the investment ($6.17) is the same number as the effective annual rate (6.17%).

EXAMPLE 10 ■ Calculate the Effective Interest Rate

A credit union offers a certificate of deposit at an annual interest rate of 3%, compounded monthly. Find the effective rate. Round to the nearest hundredth of a percent.

Solution

Use the compound amount formula to find the future value of $100 after 1 year.

$r = 3\% = 0.03$, $n = 12$, $t = 1$, $i = \frac{r}{n} = \frac{0.03}{12} = 0.0025$, $N = nt = 12(1) = 12$

$$A = P(1 + i)^N$$
$$A = 100(1 + 0.0025)^{12}$$
$$A = 100(1.0025)^{12}$$
$$A \approx 100(1.030415957)$$
$$A \approx 103.04$$

Find the interest earned on the $100.

$$I = A - P$$
$$I = 103.04 - 100$$
$$I = 3.04$$

The effective interest rate is 3.04%.

CHECK YOUR PROGRESS 10   A bank offers a certificate of deposit at an annual interest rate of 4%, compounded quarterly. Find the effective rate. Round to the nearest hundredth of a percent.

Solution   *See page S39.*

To compare two investments or loan agreements, we could calculate the effective annual rate of each. However, a shorter method involves comparing the compound amounts of each. Because the value of $(1 + i)^N$ is the compound amount of $1, we can compare the value of $(1 + i)^N$ for each alternative.

EXAMPLE 11 ■ Compare Annual Yields

One bank advertises an interest rate of 5.5%, compounded quarterly, on a certificate of deposit. Another bank advertises an interest rate of 5.25%, compounded monthly. Which investment has the higher annual yield?

Solution

Calculate $(1 + i)^N$ for each investment.

$i = \dfrac{r}{n} = \dfrac{0.055}{4}$

$N = nt = 4(1) = 4$

$(1 + i)^N = \left(1 + \dfrac{0.055}{4}\right)^4$

≈ 1.0561448

$i = \dfrac{r}{n} = \dfrac{0.0525}{12}$

$N = nt = 12(1) = 12$

$(1 + i)^N = \left(1 + \dfrac{0.0525}{12}\right)^{12}$

≈ 1.0537819

Compare the two compound amounts.

$1.0561448 > 1.0537819$

An investment of 5.5% compounded quarterly has a higher annual yield than an investment that earns 5.25% compounded monthly.

CHECK YOUR PROGRESS 11   Which investment has the higher annual yield, one that earns 5% compounded quarterly or one that earns 5.25% compounded semiannually?

Solution   *See page S39.*

Math Matters   Saving for Retirement

The tables below show results of surveys in which workers were asked questions about saving for retirement.

How many workers fear they've fallen behind in saving				
	56 and older	47 – 55	37 – 46	25 and younger
On track to save enough for retirement	39%	30%	32%	33%
Ahead of schedule	6%	5%	5%	7%
A little behind schedule	21%	27%	24%	28%
A lot behind schedule	30%	37%	37%	30%

Source: 12th Annual Retirement Confidence Survey. Reprinted by permission of the Employee Benefits Research Institute.

Worker confidence in having enough money to live comfortably throughout their retirement years									
	1993	1994	1995	1996	1997	1998	1999	2000	2001
Very confident	18%	20%	21%	19%	24%	22%	22%	25%	22%
Somewhat confident	55%	45%	51%	41%	41%	45%	47%	47%	41%
Not too confident	19%	17%	19%	23%	19%	18%	21%	18%	18%
Not at all confident	6%	17%	8%	16%	15%	13%	9%	10%	17%

Source: 12th Annual Retirement Confidence Survey. Reprinted by permission of the Employee Benefits Research Institute.

Excursion

Consumer Price Index

An **index number** measures the change in a quantity, such as cost, over a period of time. One of the most widely used indexes is the Consumer Price Index (CPI). The CPI, which includes the selling prices of about 400 key consumer goods and services, indicates the relative change in the price of these items over time. It measures the effect of inflation on the cost of goods and services.

The main components of the Consumer Price Index, shown below, are the costs of housing, food and beverages, transportation, medical care, clothing, recreation, and education.

✔ **TAKE NOTE**

The category "Recreation" includes television sets, cable TV, pets and pet products, sports equipment, and admission tickets.

Other 5.3%
Education and Communication 4.8%
Recreation 5.9%
Apparel and Upkeep 4.5%
Medical Care 5.8%
Housing 40.0%
17.6%
16.2%
Transportation
Food and Drinks

The Components of the Consumer Price Index

Source: U.S. Bureau of Labor Statistics

✔ **TAKE NOTE**

You can obtain current and historical data on the Consumer Price Index by visiting the website of the Bureau of Labor Statistics at **www.bls.gov.**

The CPI is a measure of the cost of living for consumers. The government publishes monthly and annual figures on the Consumer Price Index.

The Consumer Price Index has a base period, 1982–1984, from which to make comparisons. The CPI for the base period is 100. The CPI for May 2004 was 189.1. This means that $100 in the period 1982–1984 had the same purchasing power as $189.10 in May of 2004.

An index number is actually a percent written without a percent sign. The CPI of 189.1 for May 2004 means that the average cost of consumer goods at that time was 189.1% of their cost in the 1982–84 period.

The table below gives the CPI for various products in 2003.

Product	CPI
All items	184.0
Food and beverages	180.5
Housing	184.8
Apparel	120.9
Transportation	157.6
Medical care	297.1
Recreation	110.7
Education and communication	109.8

The Consumer Price Index, 2003

Source: U.S. Bureau of Labor Statistics

(continued)

Excursion Exercises

Solve the following.

1. The CPI for 1990 was 130.7. What percent of the base period prices were the consumer prices in 1990?

2. The CPI for 2001 was 177.1. The percent increase in consumer prices from 2001 to 2002 was 2.8%. Find the CPI for 2002. Round to the nearest tenth.

3. The CPI for 1988 was 118.3. The CPI for 1989 was 124. Find the percent increase in consumer prices for this time period.

4. Of the items listed in the table on the previous page, are there any items that cost at least twice as much in 2003 as they cost during the base period? If so, which ones?

5. Of the items listed in the table on the previous page, are there any items that cost more than one-and-one-half times as much in 2003 as they cost during the base years, but less than twice as much as they cost during the base period? If so, which ones?

6. If the cost of textbooks for one semester was $120 in the base years, how much did similar textbooks cost in 2003?

7. If a movie ticket cost $9 in 2003, what would a comparable movie ticket have cost during the base years?

8. The base year for the consumer confidence index is 1985. The consumer confidence index in May of 2004 was 93.1. Were consumers more confident in 1985 or in May of 2004?

Exercise Set 10.2

 Use a calculator for Exercises 1–94.

In Exercises 1–8, calculate the compound amount. Use the compound amount formula and a calculator.

1. $P = \$1200$, $r = 7\%$ compounded semiannually, $t = 12$ years

2. $P = \$3500$, $r = 8\%$ compounded semiannually, $t = 14$ years

3. $P = \$500$, $r = 9\%$ compounded quarterly, $t = 6$ years

4. $P = \$7000$, $r = 11\%$ compounded quarterly, $t = 9$ years

5. $P = \$8500$, $r = 9\%$ compounded monthly, $t = 10$ years

6. $P = \$6400$, $r = 6\%$ compounded monthly, $t = 3$ years

7. $P = \$9600$, $r = 9\%$ compounded daily, $t = 3$ years

8. $P = \$1700$, $r = 9\%$ compounded daily, $t = 5$ years

In Exercises 9–14, calculate the compound amount. Use a calculator with a financial mode.

9. $P = \$1600$, $r = 8\%$ compounded quarterly, $t = 10$ years

10. $P = \$4200$, $r = 6\%$ compounded semiannually, $t = 8$ years

11. $P = \$3000$, $r = 12\%$ compounded monthly, $t = 5$ years

12. $P = \$9800$, $r = 10\%$ compounded quarterly, $t = 4$ years

13. $P = \$1700$, $r = 9\%$ compounded semiannually, $t = 3$ years

14. $P = \$8600$, $r = 11\%$ compounded semiannually, $t = 5$ years

In Exercises 15–20, calculate the future value.

15. $P = \$7500$, $r = 12\%$ compounded monthly, $t = 5$ years

16. $P = \$1800$, $r = 9.5\%$ compounded annually, $t = 10$ years

17. $P = \$4600$, $r = 10\%$ compounded semiannually, $t = 12$ years

18. $P = \$9000$, $r = 11\%$ compounded quarterly, $t = 3$ years

19. $P = \$22,000$, $r = 9\%$ compounded monthly, $t = 7$ years

20. $P = \$5200$, $r = 8.1\%$ compounded daily, $t = 9$ years

In Exercises 21–26, calculate the present value.

21. $A = \$25,000$, $r = 10\%$ compounded quarterly, $t = 12$ years

22. $A = \$20,000$, $r = 12\%$ compounded monthly, $t = 5$ years

23. $A = \$40,000$, $r = 7.5\%$ compounded annually, $t = 35$ years

24. $A = \$10,000$, $r = 11\%$ compounded semiannually, $t = 30$ years

25. $A = \$15,000$, $r = 8\%$ compounded quarterly, $t = 5$ years

26. $A = \$50,000$, $r = 18\%$ compounded monthly, $t = 5$ years

27. **Compound Amount** Calculate the compound amount when $8000 is deposited in an account earning 8% interest, compounded quarterly, for 5 years.

28. **Compound Amount** Calculate the compound amount when $3000 is deposited in an account earning 10% interest, compounded semiannually, for 3 years.

29. **Compound Amount** If you leave $2500 in an account earning 9% interest, compounded daily, how much money will be in the account after 4 years?

30. **Compound Amount** What is the compound amount when $1500 is deposited in an account earning an interest rate of 6%, compounded monthly, for 2 years?

31. **Future Value** What is the future value of $4000 earning 12% interest, compounded monthly, for 6 years?

32. **Future Value** Calculate the future value of $8000 earning 8% interest, compounded quarterly, for 10 years.

33. **Compound Interest** How much interest is earned in 3 years on $2000 deposited in an account paying 6% interest, compounded quarterly?

34. **Compound Interest** How much interest is earned in 5 years on $8500 deposited in an account paying 9% interest, compounded semiannually?

35. **Compound Interest** Calculate the amount of interest earned in 8 years on $15,000 deposited in an account paying 10% interest, compounded quarterly.

36. **Compound Interest** Calculate the amount of interest earned in 6 years on $20,000 deposited in an account paying 12% interest, compounded monthly.

37. **Compound Interest** How much money should be invested in an account that earns 6% interest, compounded monthly, in order to have $15,000 in 5 years?

38. **Compound Interest** How much money should be invested in an account that earns 7% interest, compounded quarterly, in order to have $10,000 in 5 years?

39. **Compound Interest** $1000 is deposited for 5 years in an account that earns 9% interest.

   a. Calculate the simple interest earned.

   b. Calculate the interest earned if interest is compounded daily.

   c. How much more interest is earned on the account when the interest is compounded daily?

40. **Compound Interest** $10,000 is deposited for 2 years in an account that earns 12% interest.

   a. Calculate the simple interest earned.

   b. Calculate the interest earned if interest is compounded daily.

   c. How much more interest is earned on the account when the interest is compounded daily?

41. **Future Value** $15,000 is deposited for 4 years in an account earning 8% interest.

   a. Calculate the future value of the investment if interest is compounded semiannually.

   b. Calculate the future value if interest is compounded quarterly.

   c. How much greater is the future value of the investment when the interest is compounded quarterly?

42. **Future Value** $25,000 is deposited for 3 years in an account earning 6% interest.

   a. Calculate the future value of the investment if interest is compounded annually.

   b. Calculate the future value if interest is compounded semiannually.

   c. How much greater is the future value of the investment when the interest is compounded semiannually?

43. **Compound Interest** $10,000 is deposited for 2 years in an account earning 8% interest.

   a. Calculate the interest earned if interest is compounded semiannually.

b. Calculate the interest earned if interest is compounded quarterly.

c. How much more interest is earned on the account when the interest is compounded quarterly?

44. Compound Interest $20,000 is deposited for 5 years in an account earning 6% interest.

a. Calculate the interest earned if interest is compounded annually.

b. Calculate the interest earned if interest is compounded semiannually.

c. How much more interest is earned on the account when the interest is compounded semiannually?

45. Loans To help pay your college expenses, you borrow $7000 and agree to repay the loan at the end of 5 years at 8% interest, compounded quarterly.

a. What is the maturity value of the loan?

b. How much interest are you paying on the loan?

46. Loans You borrow $6000 to help pay your college expenses. You agree to repay the loan at the end of 5 years at 10% interest, compounded quarterly.

a. What is the maturity value of the loan?

b. How much interest are you paying on the loan?

47. Present Value A couple plans to save for their child's college education. What principal must be deposited by the parents when their child is born in order to have $40,000 when the child reaches the age of 18? Assume the money earns 8% interest, compounded quarterly.

48. Present Value A couple plans to invest money for their child's college education. What principal must be deposited by the parents when their child turns 10 in order to have $30,000 when the child reaches the age of 18? Assume the money earns 8% interest, compounded quarterly.

49. Present Value You want to retire in 30 years with $1,000,000 in investments.

a. How much money would you have to invest today at 9% interest, compounded daily, in order to have $1,000,000 in 30 years?

b. How much will the $1,000,000 generate in interest each year if it is invested at 9% interest, compounded daily?

50. Present Value You want to retire in 40 years with $1,000,000 in investments.

a. How much money must you invest today at 8.1% interest, compounded daily, in order to have $1,000,000 in 40 years?

b. How much will the $1,000,000 generate in interest each year if it is invested at 8.1% interest, compounded daily?

51. Compound Amount You deposit $5000 in a two-year certificate of deposit (CD) earning 8.1% interest, compounded daily. At the end of the 2 years, you reinvest the compound amount in another two-year CD. The interest rate on the second CD is 7.2%, compounded daily. What is the compound amount when the second CD matures?

52. Compound Amount You deposit $7500 in a two-year certificate of deposit (CD) earning 9.9% interest, compounded daily. At the end of the 2 years, you reinvest the compound amount plus an additional $7500 in another two-year CD. The interest rate on the second CD is 10.8%, compounded daily. What is the compound amount when the second CD matures?

53. Inflation The average monthly rent for a three-bedroom apartment in San Luis Obispo, California, is $1686. Using an annual inflation rate of 7%, find the average monthly rent in 15 years.

54. Inflation The average cost of housing in Greenville, North Carolina, is $128,495. Using an annual inflation rate of 7%, find the average cost of housing in 10 years.

55. Inflation Suppose your salary in 2010 is $40,000. Assuming an annual inflation rate of 7%, what salary do you need to earn in 2015 in order to have the same purchasing power?

56. Inflation Suppose your salary in 2010 is $50,000. Assuming an annual inflation rate of 6%, what salary do you need to earn in 2020 in order to have the same purchasing power?

57. Inflation In 2009 you purchase an insurance policy that will provide you with $125,000 when you retire in 2049. Assuming an annual inflation rate of 6%, what will be the purchasing power of the $125,000 in 2049?

58. Inflation You purchase an insurance policy in the year 2010 that will provide you with $250,000 when you retire in 25 years. Assuming an annual inflation rate of 8%, what will be the purchasing power of the quarter-of-a-million dollars in 2035?

59. Inflation A retired couple have a fixed income of $3500 per month. Assuming an annual inflation rate of 7%, what is the purchasing power of their monthly income in 5 years?

60. Inflation A retired couple have a fixed income of $46,000 per year. Assuming an annual inflation rate of 6%, what is the purchasing power of their annual income in 10 years?

In Exercises 61–68, calculate the effective annual rate for an investment that earns the given rate of return. Round to the nearest hundredth of a percent.

61. 7.2% interest compounded quarterly

62. 8.4% interest compounded quarterly

63. 7.5% interest compounded monthly

64. 6.9% interest compounded monthly

65. 8.1% interest compounded daily

66. 6.3% interest compounded daily

67. 5.94% interest compounded monthly

68. 6.27% interest compounded monthly

Inflation In Exercises 69–76, you are given the 2004 price of an item. Use an inflation rate of 6% to calculate its price in 2009, 2014, and 2024. Round to the nearest cent.

69. Gasoline: $2.00 per gallon

70. Milk: $3.35 per gallon

71. Loaf of bread: $2.69

72. Sunday newspaper: $2.25

73. Ticket to a movie: $9

74. Paperback novel: $12.00

75. House: $275,000

76. Car: $24,000

In Exercises 77–82, calculate the purchasing power using an annual inflation rate of 7%. Round to the nearest cent.

77. $50,000 in 10 years

78. $25,000 in 8 years

79. $100,000 in 20 years

80. $30,000 in 15 years

81. $75,000 in 5 years

82. $20,000 in 25 years

83. a. Complete the table.

Nominal Rate	Effective Rate
4% annual compounding	
4% semiannual compounding	
4% quarterly compounding	
4% monthly compounding	
4% daily compounding	

b. As the number of compounding periods increases, does the effective rate increase or decrease?

84. Effective Interest Rate Beth Chipman has money in a savings account that earns an annual interest rate of 3%, compounded quarterly. What is the effective rate of interest on Beth's account? Round to the nearest hundredth of a percent.

85. Effective Interest Rate Blake Hamilton has money in a savings account that earns an annual interest rate of 3%, compounded monthly. What is the effective rate of interest on Blake's savings? Round to the nearest hundredth of a percent.

86. Annual Yield One bank advertises an interest rate of 6.6%, compounded quarterly, on a certificate of deposit. Another bank advertises an interest rate of 6.25%, compounded monthly. Which investment has the higher annual yield?

87. Annual Yield Which has the higher annual yield, 6% compounded quarterly or 6.25% compounded semiannually?

88. Annual Yield Which investment has the higher annual yield, one earning 7.8% compounded monthly or one earning 7.5% compounded daily?

89. Annual Yield One bank advertises an interest rate of 5.8%, compounded quarterly, on a certificate of deposit. Another bank advertises an interest rate of 5.6%, compounded monthly. Which investment has a higher annual yield?

Extensions

CRITICAL THINKING

90. Future Value a. Using an 8% interest rate with interest compounded quarterly, calculate the future value in 2 years of $1000, $2000, and $4000.

b. Based on your answers to part a, what is the future value if the investment is doubled again, to $8000?

91. Interest Rates The future value of $2000 deposited in an account for 25 years with interest compounded semiannually is $22,934.80. Find the interest rate.

92. Present Value You want to retire with an interest income of $12,000 per month. How much principal must be invested at an interest rate of 8%, compounded monthly, to generate this amount of monthly income? Round to the nearest hundred thousand.

COOPERATIVE LEARNING

93. **Saving for a Purchase** You want to buy a motorcycle costing $20,000. You have two options:

   a. You can borrow $20,000 at an effective annual rate of 8% for 1 year.

   b. You can save the money you would have made in loan payments during 1 year and purchase the motorcycle.

   If you decide to save your money for 1 year, you will deposit the equivalent of 1 month's loan payment ($1800) into your savings account at the end of each month, and you will earn 5% interest on the account. (In determining the amount of interest earned each month, assume that each month is $\frac{1}{12}$ of 1 year.) You will pay 28% of the interest earned on the savings account in income taxes. Also, an annual inflation rate of 7% will have increased the price of the motorcycle by 7%. If you choose the option of saving your money for 1 year, how much money will you have left after you pay the income tax and purchase the motorcycle?

EXPLORATIONS

94. **Continuous Compounding** In our discussion of compound interest, we used annual, semiannual, monthly, quarterly, and daily compounding periods. When interest is compounded daily, it is compounded 360 times a year. If interest were compounded twice daily, it would be compounded $360(2) = 720$ times a year. If interest were compounded four times a day, it would be compounded $360(4) = 1440$ times a year. Remember that the more frequent the compounding period, the more interest earned on the account. Therefore, if interest is compounded more frequently than daily, an investment will earn even more interest than if interest is compounded daily.

   Some banking institutions advertise **continuous compounding,** which means that the number of compounding periods per year gets very, very large. When compounding continuously, instead of using the compound amount formula $A = P(1 + i)^N$, the following formula is used.

   $$A = Pe^{rt}$$

   In this formula, A is the compound amount when P dollars are deposited at an annual interest rate of r percent compounded continuously for t years. The number e is approximately equal to 2.7182818.

   The number e is found in many real-world applications. It is an irrational number, so its decimal representation never terminates or repeats. Scientific calculators have an $\boxed{e^x}$ key for evaluating exponential expressions in which e is the base.

   To calculate the compound amount when $10,000 is invested for 5 years at an interest rate of 10%, compounded continuously, use the formula for continuous compounding. Substitute the following values into the formula: $P = 10,000$, $r = 10\% = 0.10$, and $t = 5$.

   $$A = Pe^{rt}$$
   $$A \approx 10,000(2.7182818)^{0.10(5)}$$
   $$A \approx 16,487.21$$

   The compound amount is $16,487.21.

In the following exercises, calculate the compound interest when interest is compounded continuously.

a. $P = \$5000$, $r = 8\%$, $t = 6$ years

b. $P = \$8000$, $r = 7\%$, $t = 15$ years

c. $P = \$12,000$, $r = 9\%$, $t = 10$ years

d. $P = \$7000$, $r = 6\%$, $t = 8$ years

e. $P = \$3000$, $r = 7.5\%$, $t = 4$ years

f. $P = \$9000$, $r = 8.6\%$, $t = 5$ years

Solve the following exercises.

g. Calculate the compound amount when $2500 is deposited in an account earning 11% interest, compounded continuously, for 12 years.

h. What is the future value of $15,000 earning 9.5% interest, compounded continuously, for 7 years?

i. How much interest is earned in 9 years on $6000 deposited in an account paying 10% interest, compounded continuously?

j. $25,000 is deposited for 10 years in an account that earns 8% interest. Calculate the future value of the investment if interest is compounded quarterly and if interest is compounded continuously. How much greater is the future value of the investment when interest is compounded continuously?

SECTION 10.3 | Credit Cards and Consumer Loans

Credit Cards

When a customer uses a credit card to make a purchase, the customer is actually receiving a loan. Therefore, there is frequently an added cost to the consumer who purchases on credit. This added cost may be in the form of an annual fee or interest charges on purchases. A **finance charge** is an amount paid in excess of the cash price; it is the cost to the customer for the use of credit.

Most credit card companies issue monthly bills. The due date on the bill is usually 1 month after the billing date (the date the bill is prepared and sent to the customer). If the bill is paid in full by the due date, the customer pays no finance charge. If the bill is not paid in full by the due date, a finance charge is added to the next bill.

Suppose a credit card billing date is the 10th day of each month. If a credit card purchase is made on April 15, then May 10 is the billing date (the 10th day of the month following April). The due date is June 10 (one month from the billing date). If the bill is paid in full before June 10, no finance charge is added. However, if the bill is not paid in full, interest charges on the outstanding balance will start to accrue (be added) on June 10, and any purchase made after June 10 will immediately start accruing interest.

The most common method of determining finance charges is the **average daily balance method**. Interest charges are based on the credit card's average daily balance, which is calculated by dividing the sum of the total amounts owed each day of the month by the number of days in the billing period.

Average Daily Balance

$$\text{Average daily balance} = \frac{\text{sum of the total amounts owed each day of the month}}{\text{number of days in the billing period}}$$

An example of calculating the average daily balance follows.

Suppose an unpaid bill for $315 had a due date of April 10. A purchase of $28 was made on April 12, and $123 was charged on April 24. A payment of $50 was made on April 15. The next billing date is May 10. The interest on the average daily balance is 1.5% per month. Find the finance charge on the May 10 bill.

To find the finance charge, first prepare a table showing the unpaid balance for each purchase, the number of days the balance is owed, and the product of these numbers. A negative sign in the Payments or Purchases column of the table indicates that a payment was made on that date.

Date	Payments or Purchases	Balance Each Day	Number of Days Until Balance Changes	Unpaid Balance Times Number of Days
April 10 – 11		$315	2	$630
April 12 – 14	$28	$343	3	$1029
April 15 – 23	– $50	$293	9	$2637
April 24 – May 9	$123	$416	16	$6656
Total				$10,952

The sum of the total amounts owed each day of the month is $10,952.

Find the average daily balance.

$$\text{Average daily balance} = \frac{\text{sum of the total amounts owed each day of the month}}{\text{number of days in the billing period}}$$
$$= \frac{10,952}{30} \approx 365.07$$

Find the finance charge.

$I = Prt$
$I = 365.07(0.015)(1)$
$I \approx 5.48$

The finance charge on the May 10 bill is $5.48.

EXAMPLE 1 ■ Calculate Interest on a Credit Card Bill

An unpaid bill for $620 had a due date of March 10. A purchase of $214 was made on March 15, and $67 was charged on March 30. A payment of $200 was made on March 22. The interest on the average daily balance is 1.5% per month. Find the finance charge on the April 10 bill.

Solution

First calculate the sum of the total amounts owed each day of the month.

Date	Payments or Purchases	Balance Each Day	Number of Days Until Balance Changes	Unpaid Balance times Number of Days
March 10 – 14		$620	5	$3100
March 15 – 21	$214	$834	7	$5838
March 22 – 29	– $200	$634	8	$5072
March 30 – April 9	$67	$701	11	$7711
Total				$21,721

The sum of the total amounts owed each day of the month is $21,721.

Find the average daily balance.

$$\text{Average daily balance} = \frac{\text{sum of the total amounts owed each day of the month}}{\text{number of days in the billing period}}$$

$$= \frac{21,721}{31} \approx \$700.68$$

Find the finance charge.

$$I = Prt$$
$$I = 700.68(0.015)(1)$$
$$I \approx 10.51$$

The finance charge on the April 10 bill is $10.51.

CHECK YOUR PROGRESS 1 A bill for $1024 was due on July 1. Purchases of $315 were made on July 7, and $410 was charged on July 22. A payment of $400 was made on July 15. The interest on the average daily balance is 1.2% per month. Find the finance charge on the August 1 bill.

Solution See page S39.

Math Matters   Credit Card Debt

The graph on the following page shows how long it would take you to pay off a credit card debt of $3000 and the amount of interest you would pay if you made the minimum monthly payment of 3% of the credit card balance each month.

If you have credit card debt and want to determine how long it will take you to pay off the debt, go to **http://www.cardweb.com.** There you will find a calculator

(continued)

that will calculate how long it will take to pay off the debt and the amount of interest you will pay. (*Source:* **CardWeb.com**)

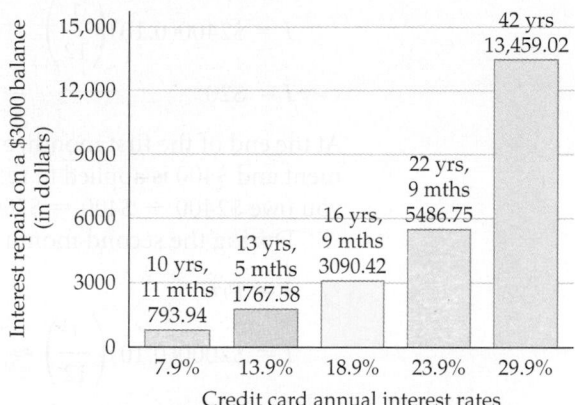

Source: **CardWeb.com,** reprinted by permission of Cardweb.com.

Annual Percentage Rate

Federal law, in the form of the Truth in Lending Act, requires that credit customers be made aware of the cost of credit. This law, passed by Congress in 1969, requires that a business issuing credit inform the consumer of all details of a credit transaction, including the true annual interest rate. The **true annual interest rate,** also called the **annual percentage rate (APR)** or **annual percentage yield (APY),** is the effective annual interest rate on which credit payments are based.

The idea behind the APR is that interest is owed only on the *unpaid balance* of the loan. For instance, suppose you decide to borrow $2400 from a bank that advertises a 10% *simple* interest rate. You want a six-month loan and agree to repay the loan in six equal monthly payments. The simple interest due on the loan is

$$I = Prt$$

$$I = \$2400(0.10)\left(\frac{6}{12}\right)$$

$$I = \$120$$

The total amount to be repaid to the bank is

$$A = P + I$$

$$A = \$2400 + \$120$$

$$A = \$2520$$

The amount of each monthly payment is

$$\text{Monthly payment} = \frac{2520}{6} = \$420$$

During the first month you owe $2400. The interest on that amount is

$$I = Prt$$

$$I = \$2400(0.10)\left(\frac{1}{12}\right)$$

$$I = \$20$$

At the end of the first month, of the $420 payment you make, $20 is the interest payment and $400 is applied to reducing the loan. Therefore, during the second month you owe $2400 − $400 = $2000.

During the second month you owe $2000. The interest on that amount is

$$I = Prt$$

$$I = \$2000(0.10)\left(\frac{1}{12}\right) \approx 16.667$$

$$I = \$16.67$$

At the end of the second month, of the $420 payment you make, $16.67 is the interest payment and $403.33 is applied to reducing the loan. Therefore, during the third month you owe $2000 − $403.33 = $1596.67.

The point of these calculations is to demonstrate that each month the amount you owe is decreasing, and not by a constant amount. From our calculations, the loan decreased by $400 the first month and by $403.33 the second month.

The Truth in Lending Act stipulates that the interest rate for a loan be calculated only on the amount owed at a particular time, not on the original amount borrowed. All loans must be stated according to this standard, thereby making it possible for a consumer to compare different loans.

We can use the following formula to estimate the annual percentage rate (APR) on a simple interest rate installment loan.

Approximate Annual Percentage Rate (APR) Formula for a Simple Interest Rate Loan

The annual percentage rate (APR) of a simple interest rate loan can be approximated by

$$APR \approx \frac{2Nr}{N + 1}$$

where N is the number of payments and r is the simple interest rate.

For the loan described above, $N = 6$ and $r = 10\% = 0.10$.

$$APR \approx \frac{2Nr}{N + 1}$$

$$\approx \frac{2(6)(0.10)}{6 + 1} = \frac{1.2}{7} \approx 0.171$$

The annual percentage rate on the loan is approximately 17.1%. Recall that the simple interest rate was 10%, much less than the actual rate. The Truth in Lending Act provides the consumer with a standard interest rate, APR, so that it is possible to compare loans. The 10% simple interest loan described above is equivalent to an APR loan of about 17%.

EXAMPLE 2 ■ Calculate a Finance Charge and an APR

You purchase a refrigerator for \$675. You pay 20% down and agree to repay the balance in 12 equal monthly payments. The finance charge on the balance is 9% simple interest.

a. Find the finance charge.

b. Estimate the annual percentage rate. Round to the nearest tenth of a percent.

Solution

a. To find the finance charge, first calculate the down payment.

$$\text{Down payment} = \text{percent down} \times \text{purchase price}$$
$$= 0.20 \times 675 = 135$$

$$\text{Amount financed} = \text{purchase price} - \text{down payment}$$
$$= 675 - 135 = 540$$

Calculate the interest owed on the loan.

$$\text{Interest owed} = \text{finance rate} \times \text{amount financed}$$
$$= 0.09 \times 540 = 48.60$$

The finance charge is \$48.60.

b. Use the APR formula to estimate the annual percentage rate.

$$\text{APR} \approx \frac{2Nr}{N+1}$$
$$\approx \frac{2(12)(0.09)}{12+1} = \frac{2.16}{13} \approx 0.166$$

The annual percentage rate is approximately 16.6%.

CHECK YOUR PROGRESS 2   You purchase a washing machine and dryer for \$750. You pay 20% down and agree to repay the balance in 12 equal monthly payments. The finance charge on the balance is 8% simple interest.

a. Find the finance charge.

b. Estimate the annual percentage rate. Round to the nearest tenth of a percent.

Solution   *See page S40.*

Consumer Loans: Calculating Monthly Payments

The stated interest rate for most consumer loans, such as a car loan, is normally the annual percentage rate, APR, as required by the Truth in Lending Act. The payment amount for these loans is given by the following formula.

Payment Formula for an APR Loan

The payment for a loan based on APR is given by

$$PMT = A\left(\frac{i}{1 - (1 + i)^{-n}}\right)$$

where PMT is the payment, A is the loan amount, i is the interest rate per payment period, and n is the total number of payments.

It is important to note that in this formula i is the interest rate *per payment period*. For instance, if the annual interest rate is 9% and payments are made monthly, then

$$i = \frac{\text{annual interest rate}}{\text{number of payments per year}} = \frac{0.09}{12} = 0.0075$$

QUESTION   *For a four-year loan repaid on a monthly basis, what is the value of n in the formula above?*

The payment formula given above is used to calculate monthly payments on most consumer loans. In Example 3 we calculate the monthly payment for a new television and in Example 4 we calculate the monthly payment for a car loan.

EXAMPLE 3 ■ Calculate a Monthly Payment

Integrated Visual Technologies is offering anyone who purchases a television an annual interest rate of 9.5% for 4 years. If Andrea Smyer purchases a 50-inch, rear projection television for $5995 from Integrated Visual Technologies, find her monthly payment.

Solution

To calculate the monthly payment, you will need a calculator. The following keystrokes will work on most scientific calculators.

First calculate i and store the result.

$$i = \frac{\text{annual interest rate}}{\text{number of payments per year}} = \frac{0.095}{12}$$

Keystrokes: 0.095 $\boxed{\div}$ 12 $\approx$ 0.00791667 $\boxed{STO}$

Calculate the monthly payment. For a four-year loan, $n = 4(12) = 48$.

$$PMT = A\left(\frac{i}{1 - (1 + i)^{-n}}\right)$$

$$= 5995\left(\frac{0.095/12}{1 - (1 + 0.095/12)^{-48}}\right) \approx 150.61$$

Keystrokes: 5995 $\boxed{\times}$ $\boxed{RCL}$ $\boxed{=}$ $\boxed{\div}$ $\boxed{(}$ 1 $\boxed{-}$ $\boxed{(}$ 1 $\boxed{+}$ $\boxed{RCL}$ $\boxed{)}$ $\boxed{y^x}$ 48 $\boxed{+/-}$ $\boxed{)}$ $\boxed{=}$

The monthly payment is $150.61.

ANSWER   *n = (number of years) × (number of payments per year) = 4 × 12 = 48*

CHECK YOUR PROGRESS 3   Carlos Menton purchases a new laptop computer from Knox Computer Solutions for $1499. If the sales tax is 4.25% of the purchase price and Carlos finances the total cost, including sales tax, for 3 years at an annual interest rate of 8.4%, find the monthly payment.

Solution   *See page S40.*

EXAMPLE 4 ■ Calculate a Car Payment

 A web page designer purchases a car for $18,395.

a. If the sales tax is 6.5% of the purchase price, find the amount of the sales tax.

b. If the car license fee is 1.2% of the purchase price, find the amount of the license fee.

c. If the designer makes a $2500 down payment, find the amount of the loan the designer needs.

d. Assuming the designer gets the loan in part c at an annual interest rate of 7.5% for 4 years, determine the monthly car payment.

Solution

a. Sales tax $= 0.065(18,395) = 1195.675$
The sales tax is $1195.68.

b. License fee $= 0.012(18,395) = 220.74$
The license fee is $220.74.

c. Loan amount = purchase price + sales tax + license fee − down payment
$$= 18,395 + 1195.68 + 220.74 - 2500$$
$$= 17,311.42$$
The loan amount is $17,311.42.

d. To calculate the monthly payment, you will need a calculator. The following keystrokes will work on most scientific calculators.
First calculate i and store the result.

$$i = \frac{\text{APR}}{12} = \frac{0.075}{12} = 0.00625$$

Keystrokes: 0.075 $\boxed{\div}$ 12 = 0.00625 $\boxed{\text{STO}}$

Calculate the monthly payment.

$$PMT = A\left(\frac{i}{1 - (1 + i)^{-n}}\right)$$

$$= 17,311.42\left(\frac{0.00625}{1 - (1 + 0.00625)^{-48}}\right) \approx 418.57$$

Keystrokes:
17311.42 $\boxed{\times}$ $\boxed{\text{RCL}}$ $\boxed{=}$ $\boxed{\div}$ $\boxed{(}$ 1 $\boxed{-}$ $\boxed{(}$ 1 $\boxed{+}$ $\boxed{\text{RCL}}$ $\boxed{)}$ $\boxed{y^x}$ 48 $\boxed{+/-}$ $\boxed{)}$ $\boxed{=}$

The monthly payment is $418.57.

CALCULATOR NOTE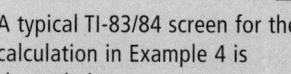

A typical TI-83/84 screen for the calculation in Example 4 is shown below.

```
N=48
I%=7.5
PV=17311.42
■PMT=-418.5711
FV=0
P/Y=12
C/Y=12
PMT: END BEGIN
```

The monthly payment is $418.57.

CHECK YOUR PROGRESS 4 A school superintendent purchases a new sedan for $26,788.

a. If the sales tax is 5.25% of the purchase price, find the amount of the sales tax.

b. The superintendent makes a $2500 down payment and the license fee is $145. Find the amount the superintendent must finance.

c. Assuming the superintendent gets the loan in part b at an annual interest rate of 8.1% for 5 years, determine the superintendent's monthly car payment.

Solution   See page S40.

Math Matters   Payday Loans

An ad reads

Get cash until payday! Loans of $100 or more available.

These ads refer to *payday* loans, which go by a variety of names, such as cash advance loans, check advance loans, post-dated check loans, or deferred deposit check loans. These types of loans are offered by finance companies and check-cashing companies.

Typically a borrower writes a personal check payable to the lender for the amount borrowed plus a *service fee.* The company gives the borrower the amount of the check minus the fee, which is normally a percent of the amount borrowed. The amount borrowed is usually repaid after payday, normally within a few weeks.

Under the Truth in Lending Act, the cost of a payday loan must be disclosed. Among other information, the borrower must receive, in writing, the APR for such a loan. To understand just how expensive these loans can be, suppose a borrower receives a loan for $100 for 2 weeks and pays a fee of $10. The APR for this loan can be calculated using the formula in this section or using a graphing calculator. Screens for a TI-83/84 calculator are shown below.

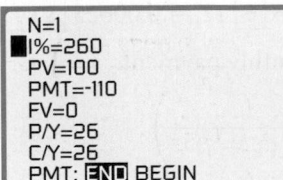

N = 1 (number of payments)
I% is unknown.
PV = 100 (amount borrowed)
PMT = −110 (the payment)
FV = 0 (no money is owed after all the payments)
P/Y = 26 (There are 26 two-week periods in 1 year.)
C/Y = 26

Place the cursor at I%=. Press ALPHA [SOLVE].

The annual interest rate is 260%.

To give you an idea of the enormity of a 260% APR, if the loan on the television set in Example 3, page 680, were based on a 260% interest rate, the monthly payment on the television set would be $1299.02!

The Federal Trade Commission (FTC) offers suggestions for consumers in need of credit. See **www.ftc.gov/bcp/conline/pubs/alerts/pdayalrt.htm.**

Consumer Loans: Calculating Loan Payoffs

Sometimes a consumer wants to pay off a loan before the end of the loan term. For instance, suppose you have a five-year car loan but would like to purchase a new car after owning your car for 4 years. Because there is still 1 year remaining on the loan, you must pay off the remaining loan before purchasing another car.

This is not as simple as just multiplying the monthly car payment by 12 to arrive at the payoff amount. The reason, as we mentioned earlier, is that each payment includes both interest and principal. By solving the Payment Formula for an APR Loan for A, the amount of the loan, we can calculate the payoff amount, which is just the remaining principal.

APR Loan Payoff Formula

The payoff amount for a loan based on APR is given by

$$A = PMT \left(\frac{1 - (1 + i)^{-n}}{i} \right)$$

where A is the loan payoff, PMT is the payment, i is the interest rate per payment period, and n is the number of *remaining* payments.

EXAMPLE 5 ■ Calculate a Payoff Amount

Allison Werke wants to pay off the loan on her jet ski that she has owned for 18 months. Allison's monthly payment is $284.67 on a two-year loan at an annual percentage rate of 8.7%. Find the payoff amount.

Solution

Because Allison has owned the jet ski for 18 months of a 24-month (two-year) loan, she has six payments remaining. Thus $n = 6$, the number of *remaining* payments. Here are the keystrokes to find the loan payoff.

Calculate i and store the result.

$$i = \frac{\text{annual interest rate}}{\text{number of payments per year}} = \frac{0.087}{12} = 0.00725$$

Keystrokes: 0.087 $\boxed{\div}$ 12 $\boxed{=}$ 0.00725 $\boxed{\text{STO}}$

Use the APR Loan Payoff Formula.

$$A = PMT \left(\frac{1 - (1 + i)^{-n}}{i} \right)$$

$$= 284.67 \left(\frac{1 - (1 + 0.00725)^{-6}}{0.00725} \right) \approx 1665.50$$

Keystrokes: 284.67 $\boxed{\times}$ $\boxed{(}$ 1 $\boxed{-}$ $\boxed{(}$ 1 $\boxed{+}$ $\boxed{\text{RCL}}$ $\boxed{)}$ $\boxed{y^x}$ 6 $\boxed{+/-}$ $\boxed{)}$ $\boxed{\div}$ $\boxed{\text{RCL}}$ $\boxed{=}$

The loan payoff is $1665.50.

CHECK YOUR PROGRESS 5 Aaron Jefferson has a five-year car loan based on an annual percentage rate of 8.4%. The monthly payment is $592.57. After 3 years, Aaron decides to purchase a new car and must pay off his car loan. Find the payoff amount.

Solution See page S40.

Car Leases

Leasing a car may result in lower monthly car payments. The primary reason for this is that at the end of the lease term, you do not own the car. Ownership of the car reverts to the dealer, who can then sell it as a used car and realize the profit from the sale.

The value of the car at the end of the lease term is called the **residual value** of the car. The residual value of a car is frequently based on a percent of the manufacturer's suggested retail price (MSRP) and normally varies between 40% and 60% of the MSRP, depending on the type of lease.

For instance, suppose the MSRP of a car is $18,500 and the residual value is 45% of the MSRP. Then

$$\text{Residual value} = 0.45 \cdot 18,500$$
$$= 8325$$

The residual value is $8325. This is the amount the dealer thinks the car will be worth at the end of the lease period. The person leasing the car, the lessee, usually has the option of purchasing the car at that price at the end of the lease.

In addition to the residual value of the car, the monthly lease payment for a car takes into consideration *net capitalized cost, the money factor, average monthly finance charge,* and *average monthly depreciation.* Each of these terms is defined below.

Net capitalized cost $=$ negotiated price $-$ down payment $-$ trade-in value

$$\textbf{Money factor} = \frac{\text{annual interest rate as a percent}}{2400}$$

Average monthly finance charge
$$= (\text{net capitalized cost} + \text{residual value}) \times \text{money factor}$$

$$\textbf{Average monthly depreciation} = \frac{\text{net capitalized cost} - \text{residual value}}{\text{term of the lease in months}}$$

Using these definitions, we have the following formula for a monthly lease payment.

> **Monthly Lease Payment Formula**
>
> The monthly lease payment formula is given by $P = F + D$, where P is the monthly lease payment, F is the average monthly finance charge, and D is the average monthly depreciation of the car.

EXAMPLE 6 ■ Calculate a Monthly Lease Payment for a Car

The director of human resources for a company decides to lease a car for 30 months. Suppose the annual interest rate is 8.4%, the negotiated price is $29,500, there is no trade-in, and the down payment is $5000. Find the monthly lease payment. Assume that the residual value is 55% of the MSRP of $33,400.

Solution
$$\text{Net capitalized cost} = \text{negotiated price} - \text{down payment} - \text{trade-in value}$$
$$= 29,500 - 5000 - 0 = 24,500$$

$$\text{Residual value} = 0.55(33,400) = 18,370$$

$$\text{Money factor} = \frac{\text{Annual interest rate as a percent}}{2400} = \frac{8.4}{2400} = 0.0035$$

✔ TAKE NOTE

When a person purchases a car, any state sales tax must be paid at the time of the purchase. However, with a lease, you make a state sales tax payment each month.

Suppose, for instance, that in Example 6 the state sales tax is 6% of the monthly lease payment. Then

Total monthly lease payment
$$= 354.38 + 0.06(354.38)$$
$$\approx 375.64$$

Average monthly finance charge
$$= (\text{net capitalized cost} + \text{residual value}) \times \text{money factor}$$
$$= (24{,}500 + 18{,}370) \times 0.0035$$
$$\approx 150.05$$

Average monthly depreciation $= \dfrac{\text{net capitalized cost} - \text{residual value}}{\text{term of the lease in months}}$
$$= \dfrac{24{,}500 - 18{,}370}{30}$$
$$\approx 204.33$$

Monthly lease payment
$$= \text{average monthly finance charge} + \text{average monthly depreciation}$$
$$= 150.05 + 204.33$$
$$= 354.38$$

The monthly lease payment is $354.38.

CHECK YOUR PROGRESS 6   Find the monthly lease payment for a car for which the negotiated price is $31,900, the annual interest rate is 8%, the length of the lease is 5 years, and the residual value is 40% of the MSRP of $33,395. There is no down payment or trade-in.

Solution   *See page S40.*

Excursion

Leasing versus Buying a Car

In July 2004, the MSRP for a 2005 Dodge Grand Caravan SE Plus was $24,500. We will use this information to analyze the results of leasing versus buying the car. To ensure that we are making valid comparisons, we will assume:

There is no trade-in, the negotiated price is the MSRP, and a down payment of $2500 is made.

The license fee is 1.1% of the negotiated price.

If you purchase a car, then the state sales tax is 5.5% of the negotiated price. If you lease the car, then you make a state tax payment every month. The amount of each of the monthly state tax payments is equal to 5.5% of the monthly lease payment.

The annual interest rate for both a loan and a lease is 6% and the term of the loan or the lease is 60 months.

The residual value when leasing the car is 45% of the MSRP.

1. Determine the loan amount to purchase the car.

2. Determine the monthly car payment to purchase the car.

3. How much will you have paid for the car (excluding maintenance) over the five-year term of the loan?

(continued)

4. At the end of 5 years, you sell the car for 45% of the original MSRP (the residual lease value). Your net car ownership cost is the amount you paid over the 5 years minus the amount you realized from selling the car. What is your net ownership cost?

5. Determine the net capitalized cost for the car.

6. Determine the lease payment. Remember to include the sales tax that must be paid each month.

7. How much will you have paid to lease the car for the five-year term? Because the car reverts to the dealer after 5 years, the net ownership cost is the total of all the lease payments for the 5 years.

8. Which option, buying or leasing, results in the smaller net ownership cost?

9. List some advantages and disadvantages of buying or leasing a car.

Exercise Set 10.3

In Exercises 1–4, calculate the finance charge for a credit card that has the given average daily balance and interest rate.

1. Average daily balance: $118.72; monthly interest rate: 1.25%

2. Average daily balance: $391.64; monthly interest rate: 1.75%

3. Average daily balance: $10,154.87; monthly interest rate: 1.5%

4. Average daily balance: $20,346.91; monthly interest rate: 1.25%

5. **Average Daily Balance** A credit card account had a $244 balance on March 5. A purchase of $152 was made on March 12, and a payment of $100 was made on March 28. Find the average daily balance if the billing date is April 5.

6. **Average Daily Balance** A credit card account has a $768 balance on April 1. A purchase of $316 was made on April 5, and a payment of $200 was made on April 18. Find the average daily balance if the new billing date is May 1.

7. **Finance Charges** A charge account had a balance of $944 on May 5. A purchase of $255 was made on May 17, and a payment of $150 was made on May 20. The interest on the average daily balance is 1.5% per month. Find the finance charge on the June 5 bill.

8. **Finance Charges** A charge account had a balance of $655 on June 1. A purchase of $98 was made on June 17, and a payment of $250 was made on June 15. The interest on the average daily balance is 1.2% per month. Find the finance charge on the July 1 bill.

9. **Finance Charges** On August 10, a credit card account had a balance of $345. A purchase of $56 was made on August 15, and $157 was charged on August 27. A payment of $75 was made on August 15. The interest on the average daily balance is 1.25% per month. Find the finance charge on the September 10 bill.

10. **Finance Charges** On May 1, a credit card account had a balance of $189. Purchases of $213 were made on May 5, and $102 was charged on May 21. A payment of $150 was made on May 25. The interest on the average daily balance is 1.5% per month. Find the finance charge on the June 1 bill.

In Exercises 11 and 12, you may want to use the spreadsheet program available at our web site at **www.cengage.com/math.** This spreadsheet automates the finance charge procedure shown in this section.

11. Finance Charges The activity date, company, and amount for a credit card bill are shown below. The due date of the bill is September 15. On August 15, there was an unpaid balance of $1236.43. Find the finance charge if the interest rate is 1.5% per month.

Activity Date	Company	Amount
August 15	Unpaid balance	1236.43
August 16	Vetenary clinic	125.00
August 17	Shell	23.56
August 18	Olive's restaurant	53.45
August 20	Seaside market	41.36
August 22	Monterey Hotel	223.65
August 25	Airline tickets	310.00
August 30	Bike 101	23.36
September 1	Trattoria Maria	36.45
September 9	Bookstore	21.39
September 12	Seaside Market	41.25
September 13	Credit card payment	−1345.00

12. Finance Charges The activity date, company, and amount for a credit card bill are shown below. The due date of the bill is July 10. On June 10, there was an unpaid balance of $987.81. Find the finance charge if the interest rate is 1.8% per month.

Activity Date	Company	Amount
June 10	Unpaid balance	987.81
June 11	Jan's Surf Shop	156.33
June 12	Albertson's	45.61
June 15	The Down Shoppe	59.84
June 16	NY Times Sales	18.54
June 20	Cardiff Delicatessen	23.09
June 22	The Olde Golf Mart	126.92
June 28	Lee's Hawaiian Restaurant	41.78
June 30	City Food Drive	100.00
July 2	Credit card payment	−1000.00
July 8	Safeway Stores	161.38

 Use a calculator for Exercises 13–42.

In Exercises 13–16, use the Approximate Annual Percentage Rate Formula.

13. APR Chuong Ngo borrows $2500 from a bank that advertises a 9% simple interest rate and repays the loan in three equal monthly payments. Estimate the APR. Round to the nearest tenth of a percent.

14. APR Charles Ferrara borrows $4000 from a bank that advertises an 8% simple interest rate. If he repays the loan in six equal monthly payments, estimate the APR. Round to the nearest tenth of a percent.

15. APR Kelly Ang buys a computer system for $2400 and makes a 15% down payment. If Kelly agrees to repay the balance in 24 equal monthly payments at an annual simple interest rate of 10%, estimate the APR for Kelly's loan.

16. **APR** Jill Richards purchases a stereo system for $1500. She makes a 20% down payment and agrees to repay the balance in 12 equal payments. If the finance charge on the balance is 7% simple interest, estimate the APR. Round to the nearest tenth of a percent.

17. **Monthly Payments** Arrowood's Camera Store advertises a Canon Power Shot 3.34-megapixel camera for $400, including taxes. If you finance the purchase of this camera for 1 year at an annual percentage rate of 6.9%, find the monthly payment.

18. **Monthly Payments** Optics Mart offers a Meade ETX Astro telescope for $1249, including taxes. If you finance the purchase of this telescope for 2 years at an annual percentage rate of 7.2%, what is the monthly payment?

19. **Buying on Credit** Alicia's Surf Shop offers its 9'4"-long Noge Rider surfboard for $649. The sales tax is 7.25% of the purchase price.
    a. What is the total cost, including sales tax?
    b. If you make a down payment of 25% of the total cost, find the down payment.
    c. Assuming you finance the remaining cost at an annual interest rate of 5.7% for six months, find the monthly payment.

20. **Buying on Credit** Waterworld marina offers a motorboat with a mercury engine for $38,250. The sales tax is 6.5% of the purchase price.
    a. What is the total cost, including sales tax?
    b. If you make a down payment of 20% of the total cost, find the down payment.
    c. Assuming you finance the remaining cost at an annual interest rate of 5.7% for three years, find the monthly payment.

21. **Buying on Credit** After becoming a commercial pilot, Lorna Kao decides to purchase a Cessna 182 for $64,995. Assuming the sales tax is 5.5% of the purchase price, find each of the following.
    a. What is the total cost, including sales tax?
    b. If Lorna makes a down payment of 20% of the total cost, find the down payment.
    c. Assuming Lorna finances the remaining cost at an annual interest rate of 7.15% for 10 years, find the monthly payment.

22. **Buying on Credit** Donald Savchenko purchased new living room furniture for $2488. Assuming the sales tax is 7.75% of the purchase price, find each of the following.
    a. What is the total cost, including sales tax?
    b. If Donald makes a down payment of 15% of the total cost, find the down payment.

    c. Assuming Donald finances the remaining cost at an annual interest rate of 8.16% for 2 years, find the monthly payment.

23. **Car Payments** Luis Mahla purchases a Porsche Boxster for $42,600 and finances the entire amount at an annual interest rate of 5.7% for 5 years. Find the monthly payment. Assume the sales tax is 6% of the purchase price and the license fee is 1% of the purchase price.

24. **Car Payments** Suppose you negotiate a selling price of $26,995 for a Ford Explorer. You make a down payment of 10% of the selling price and finance the remaining balance for 3 years at an annual interest rate of 7.5%. The sales tax is 7.5% of the selling price, and the license fee is 0.9% of the selling price. Find the monthly payment.

25. **Car Payments** Margaret Hsi purchases a late model Corvette for $24,500. She makes a down payment of $3000 and finances the remaining amount for 4 years at an annual interest rate of 8.5%. The sales tax is 5.5% of the selling price and the license fee is $331. Find the monthly payment.

26. **Car Payments** Chris Schmaltz purchases a Pontiac GTO for $34,119. Chris makes a down payment of $5000 and finances the remaining amount for 5 years at an annual interest rate of 7.6%. The sales tax is 6.25% of the selling price, and the license fee is $429. Find the monthly payment.

27. **Car Payments** Suppose you purchase a car for a total price of $25,445, including taxes and license fee, and finance that amount for 4 years at an annual interest rate of 8%.
    a. Find the monthly payment.
    b. What is the total amount of interest paid over the term of the loan?

28. **Car Payments** Adele Paolo purchased a Chevrolet Tracker for a total price of $21,425, including taxes and license fee, and financed that amount for 5 years at an annual interest rate of 7.8%.
    a. Find the monthly payment.
    b. What is the total amount of interest paid over the term of the loan?

29. **Loan Payoffs** Angela Montery has a five-year car loan for a Jeep Wrangler at an annual interest rate of 6.3% and a monthly payment of $603.50. After 3 years, Angela decides to purchase a new car. What is the payoff on Angela's loan?

30. **Loan Payoffs** Suppose you have a four-year car loan at an annual interest rate of 7.2% and a monthly payment of $587.21. After $2\frac{1}{2}$ years, you decide to purchase a new car. What is the payoff on your loan?

31. **Loan Payoffs** Suppose you have a four-year car loan at an annual interest rate of 8.9% and a monthly payment of $303.52. After 3 years, you decide to purchase a new car. What is the payoff on your loan?

32. **Loan Payoffs** Ming Li has a three-year car loan for a Mercury Sable at an annual interest rate of 9.3% and a monthly payment of $453.68. After 1 year, Ming decides to purchase a new car. What is the payoff on his loan?

33. **Car Leases** Suppose you decide to obtain a four-year lease for a car and negotiate a selling price of $28,990. The trade-in value of your old car is $3850. If you make a down payment of $2400, the money factor is 0.0027, and the residual value is $15,000, find each of the following.

   a. The net capitalized cost

   b. The average monthly finance charge

   c. The average monthly depreciation

   d. The monthly lease payment

34. **Car Leases** Marcia Scripps obtains a five-year lease for a Ford F-150 pickup and negotiates a selling price of $37,115. The trade-in value of her old car is $2950. Assuming she makes a down payment of $3000, the money factor is 0.0035, and the residual value is $16,500, find each of the following.

   a. The net capitalized cost

   b. The average monthly finance charge

   c. The average monthly depreciation

   d. The monthly lease payment

35. **Car Leases** Jorge Cruz obtains a three-year lease for a Dodge Stratus and negotiates a selling price of $22,100. The annual interest rate is 8.1%, the residual value is $15,000, and Jorge makes a down payment of $1000. Find each of the following.

   a. The net capitalized cost

   b. The money factor

   c. The average monthly finance charge

   d. The average monthly depreciation

   e. The monthly lease payment

36. **Car Leases** Suppose you obtain a five-year lease for a Porsche and negotiate a selling price of $165,000. The annual interest rate is 8.4%, the residual value is $85,000, and you make a down payment of $5000. Find each of the following.

   a. The net capitalized cost

   b. The money factor

   c. The average monthly finance charge

   d. The average monthly depreciation

   e. The monthly lease payment

Extensions

CRITICAL THINKING

37. Explain how the APR Loan Payoff Formula can be used to determine the selling price of a car when the monthly payment, the annual interest rate, and the term of the loan on the car are known. Using your process, determine the selling price of a car that is offered for $235 per month for 4 years if the annual interest rate is 7.2%.

COOPERATIVE LEARNING

38. **Car Trade-Ins** You may have heard advertisements from car dealerships that say something like "Bring in your car, paid for or not, and we'll take it as a trade-in for a new car." The advertisement does not go on to say that you have to pay off the remaining loan balance or that balance gets added to the price of the new car.

   a. Suppose you are making payments of $235.73 per month on a four-year car loan that has an annual interest rate of 8.4%. After making payments for 3 years, you decide to purchase a new car. What is the loan payoff?

   b. You negotiate a price, including taxes, of $18,234 for the new car. What is the actual amount you owe for the new car when the loan payoff is included?

   c. If you finance the amount in part b for 4 years at an annual interest rate of 8.4%, what is the new monthly payment?

39. Car Leases The residual value of a car is based on "average" usage. To protect a car dealership from abnormal usage, most car leases stipulate an average number of miles driven annually, that the tires be serviceable when the car is returned, and (in many cases) that all the manufacturer's recommended services be performed over the course of the lease. Basically, the dealership wants a car that can be put on the lot and sold as a used car without much effort.

Suppose you decide to lease a car for 4 years. The net capitalized cost is $19,788, the residual value is 55% of the MSRP of $28,990, and the interest rate is 5.9%. In addition, you must pay a mileage penalty of $.20 for each mile over 48,000 miles that the car is driven during the 4 years of the lease.

a. Determine the monthly lease payment using the Monthly Lease Payment Formula given below. This formula is used by some financing agencies to calculate a monthly lease payment.

> **Monthly Lease Payment Formula**
>
> The monthly lease payment is given by $P = \dfrac{Ai(1 + i)^n - Vi}{(1 + i)^n - 1}$, where P is the
>
> monthly lease payment, A is the net capitalized cost, V is the residual value, i is the interest rate per payment period as a decimal, and n is the number of lease payments.

b. If the odometer reads 87 miles when you lease the car and you return the car with 61,432 miles, what mileage penalty will you have to pay?

c. If your car requires new tires at a cost of $635, what is the total cost, excluding maintenance, of the lease for the 4 years?

EXPLORATIONS

40. Finance Charges For most credit cards, no finance charge is added to the bill if the full amount owed is paid by the due date. However, if you do not pay the bill in full, the unpaid amount *and* all current charges are subject to a finance charge. This is a point that is missed by many credit card holders.

To illustrate, suppose you have a credit card bill of $500 and you make a payment of $499, $1 less than the amount owed. Your credit card activity is as shown in the statement below.

Activity Date	Company	Amount
October 10	Unpaid balance	1.00
October 11	Rick's Tires	455.69
October 12	Costa's Internet Appliances	128.54
October 15	The Belgian Lion Restaurant	64.31
October 16	Verizon Wireless	33.57
October 20	Milton's Cake and Pie Shoppe	22.33
October 22	Fleming's Perfumes	65.00
October 24	Union 76	27.63
October 26	Amber's Books	42.31
November 2	Lakewood Meadows	423.88
November 8	Von's Grocery	55.64

a. Find the finance charge if the interest rate is 1.8% per month. Assume the due date of the bill is November 10. On October 10, the unpaid balance was the $1 you did not pay. You may want to use the spreadsheet program mentioned above Exercise 11.

b. Now assume that instead of paying $499, you paid $200, which is $299 less than the amount paid in part a. Calculate the finance charge.

c. How much more interest did you pay in part b than in part a?

d. If you took the $299 difference in payment and deposited it into an account that earned 1.8% simple interest (the credit card rate) for 1 month, how much interest would you earn?

e. Explain why the answers to parts c and d are the same.

41. a. **Car Leases** Use the formula in Exercise 39 to find the monthly lease payment, excluding sales tax, for a car for which the net capitalized cost is $23,488, the residual value is $12,500, the annual interest rate is 7%, and the term of the lease is 4 years.

b. Suppose you negotiate a net capitalized cost of $26,445 for a car and a residual value of $14,000. If the annual interest rate is 6.5% and the term of the lease is 5 years, find the monthly lease payment. The sales tax is 6.25% of the lease payment.

c. Use the formula in Exercise 39 to find the lease payment for Exercise 35. What is the difference between the payment calculated using this method and the payment calculated using the method in Exercise 35?

d. Use the formula in Exercise 39 to find the lease payment for Exercise 36. What is the difference between the payment calculated using this method and the payment calculated using the method in Exercise 36?

42. **Credit Card Debt** The APR Loan Payoff Formula can be used to determine how many months it will take to pay off a credit card debt if the minimum monthly payment is made each month. For instance, suppose you have a credit card bill of $620.50, the minimum payment is $13, and the interest rate is 18% per year. Using a graphing calculator, we can determine the number of months, n, it will take to pay off the debt. Enter the values shown on the calculator screen at the right. Move the cursor to N = and press ALPHA [SOLVE]. It will take over 84 months (or approximately 7 years) to pay off the credit card debt, assuming you do not make additional purchases.

```
N=84.53746933
■I%=18
PV=620.5
PMT=-13
FV=0
P/Y=12
C/Y=12
PMT: END BEGIN
```

a. Find the number of months it will take to pay off a credit card debt of $1283.34 if the minimum payment is $27 and the annual interest rate is 19.6%. Round to the nearest month.

b. How much interest will be paid on the credit card debt in part a?

c. If you have credit card debt, determine how many months it would take to pay off your debt by making the minimum monthly payments. How much interest would you pay? You may want to go to the website at **http://www.cardweb.com,** which was mentioned in the Math Matters on page 676, to determine the answers.

| SECTION 10.4 | Stocks, Bonds, and Mutual Funds |

Stocks

historical note

Have you heard the tongue-in-cheek advice for making a fortune in the stock market that goes something like "Buy low, sell high?" The phrase is adapted from a comment made by Hetty Green (1834–1916), who was also known as the Witch of Wall Street. She turned a $1 million inheritance into $100 million and became the richest woman in the world. In today's terms, that $100 million would be worth over $2 billion. When asked how she became so successful, she replied, "There is no secret in fortune making. All you have to do is buy cheap and sell dear, act with thrift and shrewdness, and be persistent." ∎

Stocks, bonds, and mutual funds are investment vehicles, but they differ in nature.

When owners of a company want to raise money, generally to expand their business, they may decide to sell part of the company to investors. An investor who purchases a part of the company is said to own *stock* in the company. Stock is measured in shares; a **share of stock** in a company is a certificate that indicates partial ownership in the company. The owners of the certificates are called **stockholders** or **shareholders.** As owners, the stockholders share in the profits or losses of the corporation.

A company may distribute profits to its shareholders in the form of **dividends.** A dividend is usually expressed as a per-share amount—for example, $.07 per share.

EXAMPLE 1 ■ Calculate Dividends Paid to a Stockholder

A stock pays an annual dividend of $.84 per share. Calculate the dividends paid to a shareholder who has 200 shares of the company's stock.

Solution

($.84 per share) × (200 shares) = $168

The shareholder receives $168 in dividends.

CHECK YOUR PROGRESS 1   A stock pays an annual dividend of $.72 per share. Calculate the dividends paid to a shareholder who has 550 shares of the company's stock.

Solution   *See page S40.*

The **dividend yield,** which is used to compare companies' dividends, is the amount of the dividend divided by the stock price and is expressed as a percent. Determining a dividend yield is similar to calculating the simple interest rate earned on an investment. You can think of the dividend as the interest earned, the stock price as the principal, and the yield as the interest rate.

▼ **point of interest**

Usually the dividends earned on shares of stock are sent to shareholders. However, in a **dividend reinvestment plan,** or DRIP, the dividends earned are applied toward the purchase of more shares.

EXAMPLE 2 ■ Calculate a Dividend Yield

A stock pays an annual dividend of $1.75 per share. The stock is trading at $70. Find the dividend yield.

Solution

$$I = Prt$$
$$1.75 = 70r(1)$$ • Let I = annual dividend and P = the stock price. The time is **1** year.

$$1.75 = 70r$$

$$0.025 = r \qquad \text{• Divide each side of the equation by 70.}$$

The dividend yield is 2.5%.

CHECK YOUR PROGRESS 2   A stock pays an annual dividend of $.82 per share. The stock is trading at $51.25. Find the dividend yield.

Solution   *See page S40.*

The **market value** of a share of stock is the price for which a stockholder is willing to sell a share of the stock and a buyer is willing to purchase it. Shares are always sold to the highest bidder. A **brokerage firm** is a dealer of stocks that acts as your agent when you want to buy or sell shares of stock. The **brokers** in the firm charge commissions for their service. Most trading of stocks happens on a stock exchange. **Stock exchanges** are businesses whose purpose it is to bring together buyers and sellers of stock. The largest stock exchange in the United States is the New York Stock Exchange. Shares of stock are also bought and sold through the National Association of Securities Dealers Automated Quotation System, which is commonly referred to as the NASDAQ. Every working day, each stock exchange provides financial institutions, Internet website hosts, newspapers, and other publications with data on the trading activity of all the stocks traded on that exchange. Table 10.2 is a portion of the stock table printed in the *Wall Street Journal* on August 4, 2004.

Table 10.2

YTD % CHG	52-WEEK HI	52-WEEK LO	STOCK (SYM)	DIV	YLD %	PE	VOL 100s	CLOSE	NET CHG
8.0	53.54	40.25 ♣PanPacProp **PNP**		2.17	4.2	21	1407	51.45	−0.28
−40.3	75.44	32.10	PanPharm **PRX**		...	10	7652	38.88	0.18
16.1	12.35	6.08	ParTch **PTC**		...	22	7	9.28	−0.10
−13.0	30.70	19	ParkElchm **PKE**	.24	1.0	43	1344	23.05	−0.56
36.5	4.49	1.65	ParkerDri **PKD**		...	dd	8091	3.48	−0.32
−3.4	61	43.90	ParkerHan **PH**	.76	1.3	20	4114	57.45	−0.63
5.4	48.70	36.80	ParkwyProp **PKY**	2.60	5.9	18	210	43.85	−0.45
−8.9	60.15	46.74 ♣PartnerRe **PRE**		1.36	2.6	6	2982	52.86	0.26
21.0	31.68	14.65	PatinaOil **POG** s	.20	.7	18	4810	29.65	−0.30
45.4	20	11.46	PaxarCp **PXR**		...	25	4144	19.48	0.34
−4.3	17.72	11.96	PaylessShoe **PSS**		...	...	9130	12.82	−0.25
33.9	58.34	28.61	Peabdy Egy **BTU**	.50	.9	31	3750	55.85	−0.22
0.5	12.80	9.17	Pearson ADS **PSO**	.45e	4.0	...	287	11.27	−0.08
15.7	71.62	37.50	PediatrixMed **PDX**		...	18	3743	63.75	0.50
▲ 3.2	15.05	14.40	Pengrowth n	.17p	...	...	5904	15.29	0.31
−2.0	16.10	11.46	PennAmGp **PNG**	.24	1.8	10	387	13	−0.02
1.2	21.58	12.85	PennEngrg **PNN**	.28	1.5	24	137	19.25	−0.54
−1.1	2.67	1.47	PennTreaty **PTA**		...	dd	609	1.82	0.08
34.8	40	19.83 ♣PennVirginia **PVA** s	.45	1.2	24	554	37.50	−0.05
9.6	39	27.25 ♣PennVARes **PVR**	2.16f	5.8	...	603	37.56	0.06
51.0	41.50	17.25	PenneyJC **JCP**	.50	1.3	dd	66959	39.69	−0.51
−2.7	37.87	30	♣PA Reit **PEI**	2.16	6.1	13	1027	35.31	−0.31
37.0	34.75	18.38	Pentair **PNR** s	.44f	1.4	19	7705	31.30	0.21
−6.3	46.03	38.50	PeopEngy **PGL**	2.16	5.5	16	2262	39.38	0.22
−13.8	29.38	14.05	PepBoys **PBY**	.27	1.4	dd	11159	19.71	−0.68
−5.8	21.71	16.70	PepcoHldg **POM**	1.00	5.4	17	3317	18.40	0.07
16.0	31.40	20.39	PepsiBttlng **PBG**	.20f	.7	17	11900	28.04	−0.15
10.1	21.67	13.03	PepsiAm **PAS**	.08	.4	15	3066	18.85	−0.05
9.8	55.71	43.35	PepsiCo **PEP**	.92	1.8	23	33068	51.20	0.12
44.3	25.26	8.34	Perdigao **ADS PDA**	.55e	2.2	...	32	25.04	0.29

YTD % CHG	52-WEEK HI	52-WEEK LO	STOCK (SYM)	DIV	YLD %	PE	VOL 100s	CLOSE	NET CHG
25.1	19.99	6.26	PeriniCp **PCR**		...	6	649	11.45	−0.12
0.4	22.59	13.96	PerkinElmer **PKI**	.28	1.6	29	4475	17.13	−0.27
▲ 35.7	11.12	7	PermRltyTr **PBT**	.83e	7.4	...	820	11.21	0.10
−11.1	14.76	9.67	PerotSys A **PER**		...	26	5341	11.99	−0.69
−11.1	14.32	7.37	Petrobrs ADS **PZE**		...	...	306	9.77	−0.08
−4.0	53.17	37.56	PetroCnda **PCZ**	.60g	...	...	641	47.35	0.55
−12.0	63.70	29.25	PtroChna ADS **PTR**	2.16e	4.3	...	2327	50.20	−0.20
▲ 41.7	32.88	12.80	Ptrokzkhstn A **PKZ**	.30eg	.9	7	5930	31.90	−0.83
−4.2	35.64	17.76	PetrlBra ADS **PBR**	1.76e	6.3	5	10196	28.02	0.03
−4.3	31.94	16.56	PtrlBras ADS A **PBRA**	1.76e	6.9	...	4861	25.52	−0.04
15.1	43.50	27	PfeiffrVac **PV**	.85e	2.1	...	9	40.32	1.42
−8.2	38.89	29.43	Pfizer **PFE**	.68	2.1	31	169915	32.45	0.25
1.3	90.52	41.11	PhelpDodg **PD**	.25e	.3	16	14948	77.08	−1.29
−0.1	25.57	23.20	PhilAuthInd **POB**	1.64	6.5	...	72	25.08	0.08
▲ 32.5	23.41	8.78	PhlpLngDst **PHI**		...	...	2246	23.09	0.48
−18.9	33.38	20.27	PhlpsEl **PHG**	.44e	1.9	...	14433	23.59	−0.54
3.4	19.95	13.72	PhillipsVanH **PVH**	.15	.8	dd	976	18.35	−0.38
−15.8	14.53	8.67	PhoenixCos **PNX**	.16e	1.6	14	3784	10.14	−0.32
−14.9	43.80	28.50	PhoenixCos un	1.81	5.6	...	2	32.11	−0.68
48.9	3.20	0.95	PhosphtRes **PLP**		...	dd	212	2.83	0.04
−4.1	43.95	37.23	PidmntNG **PNY**	1.72	4.1	...	1308	41.67	0.07
−19.9	26.44	16.82	Pier 1 **PIR**	.40	2.3	14	7163	17.52	−0.32
77.2	32.09	11.25	PilgrmPr **PPC**	.06	.2	20	3660	28.94	0.59
15.7	14.93	5.80	PinnacleEnt **PNK**		...	dd	1197	10.78	−0.51
1.9	41.50	32.87 ♣PinaclWCap **PNW**	1.80	4.4	14	2792	40.80	0.24
−23.9	31.25	20.85	PioneerCp **PIO**	.23e	1.1	...	263	21.44	−0.28
12.1	37.50	22.76	PionrNtrlRes **PXD**	.10e	.3	11	11662	35.78	0.52
−2.9	59.59	38.70	PiperJaffray **PJC** n		...	...	1259	40.35	−0.82
4.7	45.21	37.25	PitneyBws **PBI**	1.22	2.9	19	8263	42.51	−0.13
−8.8	19.23	12.23	PlacrDome **PDG**	.10g	.6	35	15195	16.33	0.20

The headings at the tops of the columns are repeated below, along with the information for Pier 1 (with stock symbol PIR).

YTD %CHG	52-WEEK HI	LO	STOCK (SYM)	DIV	YLD %	PE	VOL 100s	CLOSE	NET CHG
−19.9	26.44	16.82	Pier 1 (PIR)	.40	2.3	14	7163	17.52	−0.32

YTD % CHG The number −19.9 in the first column indicates that the price of a share of Pier 1 stock has decreased 19.9% so far this calendar year.

52-WEEK HI/LO The next two numbers show that in the last 52 weeks, the highest price a share of the stock sold for was $26.44, and the lowest price was $16.82.

DIV The number .40 under the column headed DIV means that the company is currently paying an annual dividend of $.40 per share of stock.

YLD% The current dividend yield on the company's stock is 2.3%. Thus the dividend of $.40 is 2.3% of the current purchase price of a share of the stock.

PE The heading PE refers to the price-to-earnings ratio, the purchase price per share divided by the earnings per share.

VOL 100s 7163 is the number of shares sold that day, in hundreds. $7163 \times 100 = 716{,}300$. 716,300 shares of Pier 1 were sold that day.

CLOSE The next number, 17.52, indicates that the closing price of the stock was $17.52. This means that in the final trade of the day, before the market closed, the price of a share of Pier 1 stock was $17.52 per share.

NET CHG The number −0.32 under the heading NET CHG indicates that the day's closing price was $.32 lower than that of the previous trading day.

▼ **point of interest**

Young adults age 18 to 34 make up 19% of the stock investors in this country. According to a survey of investors in this age group, 93% plan to use investment money for retirement, 52% are saving for a child's college education, 23% report that they will use proceeds to buy a home, and 19% have plans to start a business. (*Source:* Nasdaq Stock Market)

EXAMPLE 3 ■ **Calculate Profits or Losses and Expenses in Selling Stock**

Suppose you owned 500 shares of stock in J.C. Penney (which is listed as PenneyJC in Table 10.2). You purchased the shares at a price of $23.90 per share and sold them at the closing price of the stock given in Table 10.2.

a. Ignoring dividends, what was your profit or loss on the sale of the stock?

b. If your broker charges 2.4% of the total sale price, what was the broker's commission?

Solution

a. From Table 10.2, the selling price per share was $39.69.
The selling price per share is greater than the purchase price per share.
You made a profit on the sale of the stock.

$$\begin{aligned}
\text{Profit} &= \text{selling price} - \text{purchase price} \\
&= 500(\$39.69) - 500(\$23.90) \\
&= \$19,845 - \$11,950 \\
&= \$7895
\end{aligned}$$

The profit on the sale of the stock was $7895.

b. $$\begin{aligned}
\text{Commission} &= 2.4\%(\text{selling price}) \\
&= 0.024(\$19,845) \\
&= \$476.28
\end{aligned}$$

The broker's commission was $476.28.

CHECK YOUR PROGRESS 3   Use Table 10.2. Suppose you bought 300 shares of Pfizer at the 52-week low and sold the shares at the 52-week high.

a. Ignoring dividends, what was your profit or loss on the sale of the stock?

b. If your broker charges 2.1% of the total sale price, what was the broker's commission? Round to the nearest cent.

Solution   *See page S41.*

Bonds

When a corporation issues stock, it is *selling* part of the company to the stockholders. When it issues a **bond,** the corporation is *borrowing* money from the bondholders; a **bondholder** lends money to a corporation. Corporations, the federal government, government agencies, states, and cities all issue bonds. These entities need money to operate—for example, to fund the federal deficit, repair roads, or build a new factory—so they borrow money from the public by issuing bonds.

Bonds are usually issued in units of $1000. The price paid for the bond is the **face value.** The issuer promises to repay the bondholder on a particular day, called the **maturity date,** at a given rate of interest, called the **coupon.**

Assume that a bond with a $1000 face value has a 5% coupon and a 10-year maturity date. The bondholder collects interest payments of $50 in each of those 10 years. The payments are calculated using the simple interest formula, as shown below.

$$I = Prt$$
$$I = 1000(0.05)(1)$$
$$I = 50$$

At the end of the 10-year period, the bondholder receives from the issuer the $1000 face value of the bond.

▼ point of interest

Municipal bonds are issued by states, cities, counties, and other governments to raise money to build schools, highways, sewer systems, hospitals, and other projects for the public good. The income from many municipal bonds is exempt from federal and/or state taxes.

EXAMPLE 4 ■ Calculate Interest Payments on a Bond

A bond with a $10,000 face value has a 3% coupon and a 5-year maturity date. Calculate the total of the interest payments paid to the bondholder.

Solution

Use the simple interest formula to find the annual interest payments. Substitute the following values into the formula: $P = 10{,}000$, $r = 3\% = 0.03$, and $t = 1$.

$$I = Prt$$
$$I = 10{,}000(0.03)(1)$$
$$I = 300$$

Multiply the annual interest payments by the term of the bond.

$$300(5) = 1500$$

The total of the interest payments paid to the bondholder is $1500.

CHECK YOUR PROGRESS 4   A bond has a $15,000 face value, a 4-year maturity, and a 3.5% coupon. What is the total of the interest payments paid to the bondholder?

Solution   *See page S41.*

A key difference between stocks and bonds is that stocks make no promises about dividends or returns, whereas the issuer of a bond guarantees that, provided the issuer remains solvent, it will pay back the face value of the bond plus interest.

Mutual Funds

An **investment trust** is a company whose assets are stocks and bonds. The purpose of these companies is not to manufacture a product but to purchase stocks and bonds with the hope that their value will increase. A **mutual fund** is an example of an investment trust.

When investors purchase shares in a mutual fund, they are adding their money to a pool along with many other investors. The investments within a mutual fund are called the fund's portfolio. The investors in a mutual fund share the fund's profits or losses from the investments in the portfolio.

An advantage of owning shares of a mutual fund is that your money is managed by full-time professionals whose job it is to research and evaluate stocks; you own stocks without having to choose which individual stocks to buy or to decide when to sell them. Another advantage is that by owning shares in the fund, you have purchased shares of stock in many different companies. This diversification helps to reduce some of the risks of investing.

Because a mutual fund owns many different stocks, each share of the fund owns a fractional interest in each of the companies. Each day, the value of a share in the fund, called the **net asset value of the fund,** or **NAV,** depends on the performance of the stocks in the fund. It is calculated by the following formula.

Net Asset Value of a Mutual Fund

The net asset value of a mutual fund is given by

$$NAV = \frac{A - L}{N}$$

where A is the total fund assets, L is the total fund liabilities, and N is the number of shares outstanding.

EXAMPLE 5 ■ Calculate the Net Asset Value of, and the Number of, Shares Purchased in a Mutual Fund

A mutual fund has $600 million worth of stock, $5 million worth of bonds, and $1 million in cash. The fund's total liabilities amount to $2 million. There are 25 million shares outstanding. You invest $15,000 in this fund.

a. Calculate the NAV.

b. How many shares will you purchase?

Solution

a. $NAV = \dfrac{A - L}{N}$

$= \dfrac{606 \text{ million} - 2 \text{ million}}{25 \text{ million}}$
   • A = 600 million + 5 million + 1 million = 606 million, L = 2 million, N = 25 million

$= 24.16$

The NAV of the fund is $24.16.

b. $\dfrac{15,000}{24.16} \approx 620$ • Divide the amount invested by the cost per share of the fund. Round down to the nearest whole number.

You will purchase 620 shares of the mutual fund.

CHECK YOUR PROGRESS 5 A mutual fund has $750 million worth of stock, $750,000 in cash, and $1,500,000 in other assets. The fund's total liabilities amount to $1,500,000. There are 20 million shares outstanding. You invest $10,000 in this fund.

a. Calculate the NAV.

b. How many shares will you purchase?

Solution *See page S41.*

Math Matters   Growth of Mutual Funds

Where do Americans invest their money? You might correctly assume that the largest number of Americans invest in real estate, as every homeowner is considered to have an investment in real estate. But more and more Americans are investing their money in the stock market, and many of them are doing so by purchasing shares in mutual funds. The graph below shows the growth of mutual funds from 1985 to 2000. (*Source:* Investment Company Institute)

Year	Number of funds	Total Net Assets (in millions of dollars)	Number of Shareholder Accounts
1985	1528	495,385.1	34,098,401
1990	3079	1,065,190.2	61,947,955
1995	5725	2,811,292.2	131,219,221
2000	8155	6,964,667.0	244,748,546

Excursion

Treasury Bills

TAKE NOTE

You can obtain more information about the various Treasury securities at **http://www.publicdebt. treas.gov.** Using this site, investors can buy securities directly from the government, thereby avoiding the service fee charged by banks and brokerage firms.

The bonds issued by the United States government are called Treasuries. Some investors prefer to invest in Treasury Bills, rather than the stock market, because their investment is backed by the federal government. As such they are considered the safest of all investments. They are grouped into three categories.

U.S. Treasury bills have maturities of under 1 year.

U.S. Treasury notes have maturities ranging from 2 to 10 years.

U.S. Treasury bonds have maturities ranging from 10 to 30 years.

This Excursion will focus on Treasury bills.

The **face value** of a Treasury bill is the amount of money received on the maturity date of the bill. Treasury bills are sold on a **discount basis;** that is, the interest on the bill is computed and subtracted from the face value to determine its cost.

Suppose a company invests in a $50,000 United States Treasury bill at 3.35% interest for 28 days. The bank through which the bill is purchased charges a service fee of $15. What is the cost of the Treasury bill?

To find the cost, first find the interest. Use the simple interest formula.

$$I = Prt$$

$$= 50,000(0.0335)\left(\frac{28}{360}\right)$$

$$\approx 130.28$$

The interest earned is $130.28.

(continued)

Find the cost of the Treasury bill.

$$\text{Cost} = (\text{face value} - \text{interest}) + \text{service fee}$$
$$= (50,000 - 130.28) + 15$$
$$= 49,869.72 + 15$$
$$= 49,884.72$$

The cost of the Treasury bill is $49,884.72.

Excursion Exercises

1. The face value of a Treasury bill is $30,000. The interest rate is 2.32% and the bill matures in 182 days. The bank through which the bill is purchased charges a service fee of $15. What is the cost of the Treasury bill?

2. The face value of a 91-day Treasury bill is $20,000. The interest rate is 2.96%. The purchaser buys the bill through Treasury Direct and pays no service fee. Calculate the cost of the Treasury bill.

3. A company invests in a 29-day, $60,000 United States Treasury bill at 2.28% interest. The bank charges a service fee of $35. Calculate the cost of the Treasury bill.

4. A $40,000 United States Treasury bill, purchased at 1.96% interest, matures in 92 days. The purchaser is charged a service fee of $20. What is the cost of the Treasury bill?

Exercise Set 10.4

1. **Annual Dividends** A stock pays an annual dividend of $1.02 per share. Calculate the dividends paid to a shareholder who has 375 shares of the company's stock.

2. **Annual Dividends** A stock pays an annual dividend of $.58 per share. Calculate the dividends paid to a shareholder who has 1500 shares of the company's stock.

3. **Annual Dividends** Calculate the dividends paid to a shareholder who has 850 shares of a stock that is paying an annual dividend of $.63 per share.

4. **Annual Dividends** Calculate the dividends paid to a shareholder who has 400 shares of a stock that is paying an annual dividend of $.91 per share.

5. **Dividend Yield** Find the dividend yield for a stock that pays an annual dividend of $1.24 per share and has a current price of $49.375. Round to the nearest hundredth of a percent.

6. **Dividend Yield** The Blackburn Computer Company has declared an annual dividend of $.50 per share. The stock is trading at $40 per share. Find the dividend yield.

7. **Dividend Yield** A stock that pays an annual dividend of $.58 per share has a current price of $31.75. Find the dividend yield. Round to the nearest hundredth of a percent.

8. **Dividend Yield** The Moreau Corporation is paying an annual dividend of $.65 per share. If the price of a share of the stock is $81.25, what is the dividend yield on the stock?

Use the portion of the stock table shown below for Exercises 9 to 16. Round dollar amounts to the nearest cent when necessary.

YTD % CHG	52-WEEK HI	52-WEEK LO	STOCK (SYM)	DIV	YLD %	PE	VOL 100s	CLOSE	NET CHG
12.7	51.52	34.45	GallaherGp **GLH**	2.12e	4.4	...	415	47.95	−0.15
−0.7	19.05	12.52	GameStop A **GME**		...	14	3149	15.30	−0.38
−5.7	91.38	75.59♣	Gannett **GCI**	1.00	1.2	18	10658	84.06	−0.07
−4.2	25.72	16.99	Gap Inc **GPS**	.09	.4	19	37506	22.24	−0.35
15.9	30.30	19.95♣	GardnrDenvr **GDI**		...	18	530	27.66	0.08
8.5	13.75	8.86	Gartner **IT**		...	61	7366	12.27	−0.33
12.0	13.06	8.52	Gartner B **ITB**		...	61	2521	12.19	−0.33
−10.0	6.85	3.64	Gateway **GTW** ⌐		...	dd	12852	4.14	−0.25
−4.0	32.70	17.70	GaylEnt **GET**		...	dd	1248	28.66	−0.25
9.3	13.53	8.75	GenCorp **GY**	.12	1.0	dd	1987	11.77	−0.14
1.5	68.25	36.82	Genentech **DNA** s		...	74	28074	47.50	0.54
15.3	10.23	6.26	GenIClbl **BGC**		...	dd	2002	9.40	−0.26
9.1	101.94	75.59	GenDynam **GD**	1.44	1.5	18	4787	98.59	−1.44
6.1	34.57	27.18	GenElec **GE**	.80	2.4	21	157197	32.87	−0.39
12.7	35.30	21.82	GenGrthProp **GGP** s	1.20	3.8	25	6392	31.27	0.02
63.6	30.42	11.13	GenMaritime **GMR**		...	8	3176	28.80	−0.20
−0.8	49.17	43.75	GenMills **GIS**	1.24f	2.8	16	7247	44.92	−0.44
−19.3	55.55	36.11	GenMotor **GM**	2.00	4.6	6	57115	43.07	−0.23
36.9	25.67	14.30	Genesco **GCO** ♦		...	15	1688	20.71	−0.71
6.6	26.10	14	♣GeneseWY A **GWR** s		...	18	1085	22.38	−0.32
13.9	40.20	29.83	GenuinePart **GPC**	1.20	3.2	18	3739	37.80	−0.38
16.7	23.50	18.75	GnwrthFnl A **GNW** n	.68p	...	...	8890	22.76	0.04
10.8	29.18	25	GnwrthFnl un n	.33p	...	...	3122	28.15	...
−18.9	24.69	16.40♣	GeoGrp **GGI**		...	5	328	18.50	−0.25
↥ 23.9	35.99	20.71	GA Gulf **GGC**	.32	.9	22	3543	35.79	0.04
9.3	38.60	20.68♣	GA Pac **GP**	.50	1.5	15	8039	33.53	−0.32

9. **Stock Tables** For Gap, Inc. (GPS):

   a. What is the difference between the highest and lowest prices paid for this stock during the last 52 weeks?

   b. Suppose you own 750 shares of this stock. What dividend do you receive this year?

   c. How many shares of this stock were sold yesterday?

   d. Did the price of a share of this stock increase or decrease during the day shown in the table?

   e. What was the price of a share of this stock at the start of the trading day yesterday?

10. **Stock Tables** For General Motors (GM):

    a. What is the difference between the highest and lowest prices paid for this stock during the last 52 weeks?

    b. Suppose you own 750 shares of this stock. What dividend do you receive this year?

    c. How many shares of this stock were sold yesterday?

d. Did the price of a share of this stock increase or decrease during the day shown in the table?

e. What was the price of a share of this stock at the start of the trading day yesterday?

11. **Stock Purchases** At the closing price per share of General Dynamics (GD), how many shares of the stock can you purchase for $5000?

12. **Stock Purchases** At the closing price per share of GenCorp (GY), how many shares of the stock can you purchase for $2500?

13. **Stock Sale** Suppose you owned 1000 shares of stock in Gateway (GTW). You purchased the shares at a price of $3.85 per share and sold them at the closing price of the stock given in the table above.

    a. Ignoring dividends, what was your profit or loss on the sale of the stock?

    b. If your broker charges 1.9% of the total sale price, what was the broker's commission?

14. **Stock Sale** Gary Walters owned 400 shares of stock in General Electric (GE). He purchased the shares at a price of $27.80 per share and sold them at the closing price of the stock given in the table above.

    a. Ignoring dividends, what was Gary's profit or loss on the sale of the stock?

    b. If his broker charges 2.5% of the total sale price, what was the broker's commission?

15. **Stock Sale** Michelle Desjardins bought 800 shares of Genesco (GCO) at the 52-week low and sold the shares at the 52-week high shown in the table above.

    a. Ignoring dividends, what was Michelle's profit or loss on the sale of the stock?

    b. If her broker charges 2.3% of the total sale price, what was the broker's commission?

16. **Stock Sale** Suppose you bought 1200 shares of General Mills (GIS) at the 52-week low and sold the shares at the 52-week high shown in the table above.

    a. Ignoring dividends, what was your profit or loss on the sale of the stock?

    b. If your broker charges 2.25% of the total sale price, what was the broker's commission?

17. **Bonds** A bond with a face value of $6000 and a 4.2% coupon has a 5-year maturity. Find the annual interest paid to the bondholder.

18. **Bonds** The face value on a bond is $15,000. It has a 10-year maturity and a 3.75% coupon. What is the annual interest paid to the bondholder?

19. **Bonds** A bond with an $8000 face value has a 3.5% coupon and a 3-year maturity. What is the total of the interest payments paid to the bondholder?

20. **Bonds** A bond has a $12,000 face value, an 8-year maturity, and a 2.95% coupon. Find the total of the interest payments paid to the bondholder.

21. **Mutual Funds** A mutual fund has total assets of $50,000,000 and total liabilities of $5,000,000. There are 2,000,000 shares outstanding. Find the net asset value of the mutual fund.

22. **Mutual Funds** A mutual fund has total assets of $25,000,000 and total liabilities of $250,000. There are 1,500,000 shares outstanding. Find the net asset value of the mutual fund.

23. **Mutual Funds** A mutual fund has total assets of $15 million and total liabilities of $1 million. There are 2 million shares outstanding. You invest $5000 in this fund. How many shares will you purchase?

24. **Mutual Funds** A mutual fund has total assets of $12 million and total liabilities of $2 million. There are 1 million shares outstanding. You invest $2500 in this fund. How many shares will you purchase?

25. **Mutual Funds** A mutual fund has $500 million worth of stock, $500,000 in cash, and $1 million in other assets. The fund's total liabilities amount to $2 million. There are 10 million shares outstanding. You invest $12,000 in this fund. How many shares will you purchase?

26. **Mutual Funds** A mutual fund has $250 million worth of stock, $10 million worth of bonds, and $1 million in cash. The fund's total liabilities amount to $1 million. There are 13 million shares outstanding. You invest $10,000 in this fund. How many shares will you purchase?

Extensions

CRITICAL THINKING

27. **Load and No-Load Funds** All mutual funds carry fees. One type of fee is called a "load." This is an additional fee that generally is paid at the time you invest your money in the mutual fund. A no-load mutual fund does not charge this up-front fee.

    Suppose you invested $2500 in a 4% load mutual fund two years ago. The 4% fee was paid out of the $2500 invested. The fund has earned 8% during each of the past two years. There was a management fee of 0.015% charged at the end of each year. A friend of yours invested $2500 two years ago in a no-load fund that has earned 6% during each of the past two years. This fund charged a management fee of 0.15% at the end of each year. Find the difference between the values of the two investments now.

COOPERATIVE LEARNING

28. **Investing in the Stock Market** (This activity assumes that the instructor has assigned each student in the class to a group of three or four students.) Imagine that your group has $10,000 to invest in each of ten stocks. Use the stock table in today's paper or use the Internet to determine the price you would pay per share. Determine the number of shares of each stock you will purchase. Check the value of each stock every business day for the next four weeks. Assume that you sell your shares at the end of the fourth week. Calculate the group's profit or loss over the four-week period. Compare your profits or losses with those of the other groups in your class.

EXPLORATIONS

29. Find a mutual fund table in a daily newspaper. You can find one in the same section where the stock tables are printed. Explain the meaning of the heading of each column in the table.

Home Ownership

Initial Expenses

When you purchase a home, you generally make a down payment and finance the remainder of the purchase price with a loan obtained through a bank or savings and loan association. The amount of the down payment can vary, but it is normally between 10% and 30% of the selling price. The **mortgage** is the amount that is borrowed to buy the real estate. The amount of the mortgage is the difference between the selling price and the down payment.

Mortgage = selling price − down payment

This formula is used to find the amount of the mortgage. For example, suppose you buy a $240,000 home with a down payment of 25%. First find the down payment by computing 25% of the purchase price.

Down payment = 25% of 240,000 = 0.25(240,000)
= 60,000

Then find the mortgage by subtracting the down payment from the selling price.

Mortgage = selling price − down payment
= 240,000 − 60,000
= 180,000

The mortgage is $180,000.

The down payment is generally the largest initial expense in purchasing a home, but there are other expenses associated with the purchase. These payments are due at the closing, when the sale of the house is finalized, and are called **closing costs.** The bank may charge fees for attorneys, credit reports, loan processing, and title searches. There may also be a **loan origination fee.** This fee is usually expressed in **points.** One point is equal to 1% of the mortgage.

Suppose you purchase a home and obtain a loan for $180,000. The bank charges a fee of 1.5 points. To find the charge for points, multiply the loan amount by 1.5%.

Points = 1.5% of 180,000 = 0.015(180,000)
= 2700

The charge for points is $2700.

EXAMPLE 1 ■ Calculate a Down Payment and the Closing Costs

The purchase price of a home is $392,000. A down payment of 20% is made. The bank charges $450 in fees plus $2\frac{1}{2}$ points. Find the total of the down payment and the closing costs.

Solution
First find the down payment.

Down payment = 20% of 392,000 = 0.20(392,000)
= 78,400

The down payment is $78,400.

Next find the mortgage.

$$\text{Mortgage} = \text{selling price} - \text{down payment}$$
$$= 392{,}000 - 78{,}400$$
$$= 313{,}600$$

The mortgage is $313,600.

Then, calculate the charge for points.

$$\text{Points} = 2\frac{1}{2}\% \text{ of } 313{,}600 = 0.025(313{,}600) \qquad \bullet \; 2\frac{1}{2}\% = 2.5\% = 0.025$$
$$= 7840$$

The charge for points is $7840.

Finally, find the sum of the down payment and the closing costs.

$$78{,}400 + 450 + 7840 = 86{,}690$$

The total of the down payment and the closing costs is $86,690.

CHECK YOUR PROGRESS 1   The purchase price of a home is $410,000. A down payment of 25% is made. The bank charges $375 in fees plus 1.75 points. Find the total of the down payment and the closing costs.

Solution   *See page S41.*

Mortgages

When a bank agrees to provide you with a mortgage, you agree to pay off that loan in monthly payments. If you fail to make the payments, the bank has the right to **foreclose,** which means that the bank takes possession of the property and has the right to sell it.

There are many types of mortgages available to home buyers today, so the terms of mortgages differ considerably. Some mortgages are **adjustable rate mortgages (ARMs).** The interest rate charged on an ARM is adjusted periodically to more closely reflect current interest rates. The mortgage agreement specifies exactly how often and by how much the interest rate can change.

A **fixed rate mortgage,** or **conventional mortgage,** is one in which the interest rate charged on the loan remains the same throughout the life of the mortgage. For a fixed rate mortgage, the amount of the monthly payment also remains unchanged throughout the term of the loan.

The term of a mortgage can vary. Terms of 15, 20, 25, and 30 years are most common.

The monthly payment on a mortgage is the **mortgage payment.** The amount of the mortgage payment depends on the amount of the mortgage, the interest rate on the loan, and the term of the loan. This payment is calculated by using the Payment Formula for an APR Loan given in Section 10.3. We will restate the formula here.

> **Mortgage Payment Formula**
>
> The mortgage payment for a mortgage is given by
>
> $$PMT = A\left(\frac{i}{1 - (1 + i)^{-n}}\right)$$
>
> where PMT is the monthly mortgage payment, A is the amount of the mortgage, i is the interest rate per payment period, and n is the total number of payments.

EXAMPLE 2 ■ Calculate a Mortgage Payment

Suppose Allison Sommerset purchases a condominium and secures a loan of $134,000 for 30 years at an annual interest rate of 6.5%.

a. Find the monthly mortgage payment.
b. What is the total of the payments over the life of the loan?
c. Find the amount of interest paid on the loan over the 30 years.

Solution

a. First calculate i and store the result.

$$i = \frac{\text{annual interest rate}}{\text{number of payments per year}} = \frac{0.065}{12}$$

Keystrokes: 0.065 ÷ 12 ≈ 0.00541667 [STO]

Calculate the monthly payment. For a 30-year loan, $n = 30(12) = 360$.

$$PMT = A\left(\frac{i}{1 - (1 + i)^{-n}}\right)$$

$$= 134{,}000\left(\frac{0.065/12}{1 - (1 + 0.065/12)^{-360}}\right) \approx 846.97$$

Keystrokes:

134000 [×] [RCL] [=] [÷] [(] 1 [−] [(] 1 [+] [RCL] [)] [yˣ] 360 [+/−] [)] [=]

The monthly mortgage payment is $846.97.

b. To determine the total of the payments, multiply the number of payments (360) by the monthly payment ($846.97).

846.97(360) = 304,909.20

The total of the payments over the life of the loan is $304,909.20.

c. To determine the amount of interest paid, subtract the mortgage from the total of the payments.

304,909.20 − 134,000 = 170,909.20

The amount of interest paid over the life of the loan is $170,909.20.

CHECK YOUR PROGRESS 2 Suppose Antonio Scarletti purchases a home and secures a loan of $223,000 for 25 years at an annual interest rate of 7%.

a. Find the monthly mortgage payment.
b. What is the total of the payments over the life of the loan?
c. Find the amount of interest paid on the loan over the 25 years.

Solution See page S41.

A portion of a mortgage payment pays the current interest owed on the loan, and the remaining portion of the mortgage payment is used to reduce the principal owed on the loan. This process of paying off the principal and the interest, which is similar to paying a car loan, is called **amortizing the loan.**

In Example 2, the mortgage payment on a $134,000 mortgage at 6.5% for 30 years was $846.97. The amount of the first payment that is interest and the amount that is applied to the principal can be calculated using the simple interest formula.

$$I = Prt$$

$$= 134{,}000(0.065)\left(\frac{1}{12}\right)$$ • $P = 134{,}000$, the current loan amount; $r = 0.065$; $t = \frac{1}{12}$

$$\approx 725.83$$ • Round to the nearest cent.

Of the $846.97 mortgage payment, $725.83 is an interest payment. The remainder is applied toward reducing the principal.

$$\text{Principal reduction} = \$846.97 - \$725.83 = \$121.14$$

After the first month's mortgage payment, the balance on the loan (the amount that remains to be paid) is calculated by subtracting the principal paid on the mortgage from the mortgage.

$$\text{Loan balance after first month} = \$134{,}000 - \$121.14 = \$133{,}878.86$$

The portion of the second mortgage payment that is applied to interest and the portion that is applied to the principal can be calculated in the same manner. In the calculation, the figure used for the principal, P, is the current balance on the loan, $133{,}878.86$.

$$I = Prt$$

$$= 133{,}878.86(0.065)\left(\frac{1}{12}\right)$$ • $P = 133{,}878.86$, the current loan amount; $r = 0.065$; $t = \frac{1}{12}$

$$\approx 725.18$$ • Round to the nearest cent.

$$\text{Principal reduction} = \$846.97 - \$725.18 = \$121.79$$

Of the second mortgage payment, $725.18 is an interest payment and $121.79 is a payment toward the principal.

$$\text{Loan balance after second month} = \$133{,}878.86 - \$121.79 = \$133{,}757.07$$

The interest payment, principal payment, and balance on the loan can be calculated in this manner for all of the mortgage payments throughout the life of the loan—all 360 of them! Or a computer can be programmed to make these calculations and print out the information. The printout is called an **amortization schedule.** It lists, for each mortgage payment, the payment number, the interest payment, the amount applied toward the principal, and the resulting balance to be paid.

Each month, the amount of the mortgage payment that is an interest payment decreases and the amount applied toward the principal increases. This is because you are paying interest on a decreasing balance each month. Mortgage payments early in the life of a mortgage are largely interest payments; mortgage payments late in the life of a mortgage are largely payments toward the principal.

TAKE NOTE

You can find a spreadsheet at our website, **www.cengage.com/math,** that will enable you to obtain a complete amortization schedule for any fixed rate loan. Because car loans and home loans are calculated using the same formula, the spreadsheet can also be used to show the principal and interest payments on a car loan.

The partial amortization schedule below shows the breakdown for the first 12 months of the loan in Example 2.

Amortization Schedule

Loan Amount	$134,000.00
Interest Rate	6.50%
Term of Loan	30
Monthly Payment	$846.97

Month	Amount of Interest	Amount of Principal	New Loan Amount
1	$725.83	$121.14	$133,878.86
2	$725.18	$121.79	$133,757.07
3	$724.52	$122.45	$133,634.61
4	$723.85	$123.12	$133,511.50
5	$723.19	$123.78	$133,387.71
6	$722.52	$124.45	$133,263.26
7	$721.84	$125.13	$133,138.13
8	$721.16	$125.81	$133,012.32
9	$720.48	$126.49	$132,885.84
10	$719.80	$127.17	$132,758.66
11	$719.11	$127.86	$132,630.80
12	$718.42	$128.55	$132,502.25

QUESTION   *Using the amortization schedule above, how much of the loan has been paid off after 1 year?*

EXAMPLE 3 ■ Calculate Principal and Interest for a Mortgage Payment

You purchase a condominium for $98,750 and obtain a 30-year, fixed rate mortgage at 7.25%. After paying a down payment of 20%, how much of the second payment is interest and how much is applied toward the principal?

Solution

First find the down payment by multiplying the percent of the purchase price that is the down payment by the purchase price.

$0.20(98,750) = 19,750$

The down payment is $19,750.

Find the mortgage by subtracting the down payment from the purchase price.

$98,750 - 19,750 = 79,000$

The mortgage is $79,000.

ANSWER   *After 1 year (12 months), the loan amount is $132,502.25. The original loan was $134,000. The amount that has been paid off is*
$134,000 − $132,502.25 = $1497.75.

Calculate the mortgage payment.

$$i = \frac{\text{annual interest rate}}{\text{number of payments per year}} = \frac{0.0725}{12}$$

Keystrokes: 0.0725 $\boxed{\div}$ 12 $\approx$ 0.00604167 $\boxed{\text{STO}}$

Calculate the monthly payment. For a 30-year loan, $n = 30(12) = 360$.

$$PMT = A\left(\frac{i}{1 - (1 + i)^{-n}}\right)$$

$$= 79,000\left(\frac{0.0725/12}{1 - (1 + 0.0725/12)^{-360}}\right) \approx 538.92$$

Keystrokes:

79000 $\boxed{\times}$ $\boxed{\text{RCL}}$ $\boxed{=}$ $\boxed{\div}$ $\boxed{(}$ 1 $\boxed{-}$ $\boxed{(}$ 1 $\boxed{+}$ $\boxed{\text{RCL}}$ $\boxed{)}$ $\boxed{y^x}$ 360 $\boxed{+/-}$ $\boxed{)}$ $\boxed{=}$

The monthly payment is $538.92.

Find the amount of interest paid on the first mortgage payment by using the simple interest formula.

$$I = Prt$$

$$= 79,000(0.0725)\left(\frac{1}{12}\right)$$

• $P = $79,000, the current loan amount; $r = 0.0725$; $t = \dfrac{1}{12}$

$$\approx 477.29$$

• Round to the nearest cent.

Find the principal paid on the first mortgage payment by subtracting the interest paid from the monthly mortgage payment.

$$538.92 - 477.29 = 61.63$$

Calculate the balance on the loan after the first mortgage payment by subtracting the principal paid from the mortgage.

$$79,000 - 61.63 = 78,938.37$$

Find the amount of interest paid on the second mortgage payment.

$$I = Prt$$

$$= 78,938.37(0.0725)\left(\frac{1}{12}\right)$$

• $P = $78,938.37, the current loan amount; $r = 0.0725$; $t = \dfrac{1}{12}$

$$\approx 476.92$$

• Round to the nearest cent.

The interest paid on the second payment was $476.92.

Find the principal paid on the second mortgage payment.

$$538.92 - 476.92 = 62.00$$

The principal paid on the second payment was $62.

CHECK YOUR PROGRESS 3   You purchase a home for $295,000. You obtain a 30-year conventional mortgage at 6.75% after paying a down payment of 25% of the purchase price. Of the first month's payment, how much is interest and how much is applied toward the principal?

Solution   See page S41.

When a home is sold before the term of the loan has expired, the homeowner must pay the lender the remaining balance on the loan. To calculate that balance, we can use the APR Loan Payoff Formula from Section 10.3.

APR Loan Payoff Formula

The payoff amount for a mortgage is given by

$$A = PMT\left(\frac{1 - (1 + i)^{-n}}{i}\right)$$

where A is the loan payoff, PMT is the mortgage payment, i is the interest rate per payment period, and n is the number of *remaining* payments.

EXAMPLE 4 ■ Calculate a Mortgage Payoff

A homeowner has a monthly mortgage payment of $645.32 on a 30-year loan at an annual interest rate of 7.2%. After making payments for 5 years, the homeowner decides to sell the house. What is the payoff for the mortgage?

Solution

Use the APR Loan Payoff Formula. The homeowner has been making payments for 5 years, or 60 months. There are 360 months in a 30-year loan, so there are $360 - 60 = 300$ remaining payments.

$$A = PMT\left(\frac{1 - (1 + i)^{-n}}{i}\right)$$

$$= 645.32\left(\frac{1 - (1 + 0.006)^{-300}}{0.006}\right)$$

• $PMT = 645.32$; $i = \dfrac{0.072}{12} = 0.006$;

$$\approx 89,679.01$$

$n = 300$, the number of remaining payments

```
N=300
I%=7.2
■PV=89679.0079
PMT=-645.32
FV=0
P/Y=12
C/Y=12
PMT: END BEGIN
```

Here are the keystrokes to compute the payoff on a scientific calculator. The same calculation using a graphing calculator is shown at the left.

Calculate i: 0.072 [÷] 12 [=] 0.006 [STO]

Calculate the payoff: 645.32 [×] [(] [1] [−] [(] [1] [+] [RCL] [)] [y^x] 300 [+/−] [)] [÷] [RCL] [=]

The loan payoff is $89,679.01.

CHECK YOUR PROGRESS 4 Ava Rivera has a monthly mortgage payment of $846.82 on her condo. After making payments for 4 years, she decides to sell the condo. If she has a 25-year loan at an annual interest rate of 6.9%, what is the payoff for the mortgage?

Solution See page S41.

MathMatters   **Biweekly and Two-Step Mortgages**

A variation of the fixed rate mortgage is the *biweekly mortgage*. Borrowers make payments on a 30-year loan, but they pay half of a monthly payment every 2 weeks, which adds up to 26 half-payments a year, or 13 monthly payments. The extra monthly payment each year can result in the loan being paid off in about $17\frac{1}{2}$ years.

Another type of mortgage is the *two-step mortgage*. Its name is derived from the fact that the life of the loan has two stages. The first step is a low fixed rate for the first 7 years of the loan, and the second step is a different, and probably higher, fixed rate for the remaining 23 years of the loan. This loan is appealing to those homeowners who do not anticipate owning the home beyond the initial low-interest-rate period; they do not need to worry about the increased interest rate during the second step.

Ongoing Expenses

In addition to a monthly mortgage payment, there are other ongoing expenses associated with home ownership. Among these expenses are the costs of insurance, property tax, and utilities such as heat, electricity, and water.

Services such as schools, police and fire protection, road maintenance, and recreational services, which are provided by cities and counties, are financed by the revenue received from taxes levied on real property, or property taxes. Property tax is normally an annual expense that can be paid on a monthly, quarterly, semiannual, or annual basis.

Homeowners who obtain a mortgage must carry fire insurance. This insurance guarantees that the lender will be repaid in the event of a fire.

▼ **point of interest**

The home ownership rate in the United States for the first quarter of 2004 was 68.6%. The following list gives home owner-ship rates by region during the same quarter.

   Northeast: 65.1%
   Midwest: 73.5%
   South: 70.3%
   West: 63.7%

It is interesting to note that the home ownership rate in the United States in 1950 was 55.0%, significantly lower than it is today. (*Source:* U.S. Bureau of the Census)

EXAMPLE 5 ■ Calculate a Total Monthly Payment

A homeowner has a monthly mortgage payment of $1145.60 and an annual property tax bill of $1074. The annual fire insurance premium is $600. Find the total monthly payment for the mortgage, property tax, and fire insurance.

Solution
Find the monthly property tax bill by dividing the annual property tax bill by 12.

$$1074 \div 12 = 89.50$$

The monthly property tax bill is $89.50.

Find the monthly fire insurance bill by dividing the annual fire insurance bill by 12.

$$600 \div 12 = 50$$

The monthly fire insurance bill is $50.

Find the sum of the mortgage payment, the monthly property tax bill, and the monthly fire insurance bill.

$$1145.60 + 89.50 + 50.00 = 1285.10$$

The monthly payment for the mortgage, property tax, and fire insurance is $1285.10.

CHECK YOUR PROGRESS 5   A homeowner has a monthly mortgage payment of $1492.89, an annual property tax bill of $2332.80, and an annual fire insurance premium of $450. Find the total monthly payment for the mortgage, property tax bill, and fire insurance.

Solution   See page S42.

Excursion

Home Ownership Issues

There are a number of issues that a person must think about when purchasing a home. One such issue is the difference between the interest rate on which the loan payment is based and the APR. For instance, a bank may offer a loan at an annual interest rate of 6.5%, but then go on to say that the APR is 7.1%.

The discrepancy is a result of the Truth in Lending Act. This act requires that the APR be based on *all* loan fees. This includes points and other fees associated with the purchase. To calculate the APR, a computer or financial calculator is necessary.

Suppose you decide to purchase a home and you secure a 30-year, $285,000 loan at an annual interest rate of 6.5%.

1. Calculate the monthly payment for the loan.

2. If points are 1.5% of the loan amount, find the fee for points.

3. Add the fee for points to the loan amount. This is the modified mortgage on which the APR is calculated.

4. Using the result from Excursion Exercise 3 as the mortgage and the monthly payment from Excursion Exercise 1, determine the interest rate. (This is where the financial or graphing calculator is necessary. See page 679 for details.) The result is the APR required by the Truth in Lending Act. For this example we have included only points. In most situations, other fees would be included as well.

Another issue to research when purchasing a home is that of points and mortgage interest rates. Usually paying higher points results in a lower mortgage interest rate. The question for the homebuyer is: Should I pay higher points for a lower mortgage interest rate, or pay lower points for a higher mortgage interest rate? The answer to that question depends on many factors, one of which is the amount of time the homeowner plans on staying in the home.

Consider two typical situations for a 30-year, $100,000 mortgage. Option 1 offers an annual mortgage interest rate of 7.25% and a loan origination fee of 1.5 points. Option 2 offers an annual interest rate of 7% and a loan origination fee of 2 points.

5. Calculate the monthly payments for Option 1 and Option 2.

6. Calculate the loan origination fees for Option 1 and Option 2.

7. What is the total amount paid, including points, after 2 years for each option?

8. What is the total amount paid, including points, after 3 years for each option?

9. Which option is more cost effective if you stay in the home for 2 years or less? Which option is more cost effective if you stay in the home for 3 years or more? Explain your answer.

Exercise Set 10.5

1. **Mortgages** You buy a $258,000 home with a down payment of 25%. Find the amount of the down payment and the mortgage amount.

2. **Mortgages** Greg Walz purchases a home for $325,000 with a down payment of 10%. Find the amount of the down payment and the mortgage amount.

3. **Points** Clarrisa Madison purchases a home and secures a loan of $250,000. The bank charges a fee of 2.25 points. Find the charge for points.

4. **Points** Jerome Thurber purchases a home and secures a loan of $170,000. The bank charges a fee of $2\frac{3}{4}$ points. Find the charge for points.

5. **Closing Costs** The purchase price of a home is $309,000. A down payment of 30% is made. The bank charges $350 in fees plus 3 points. Find the total of the down payment and the closing costs.

6. **Closing Costs** The purchase price of a home is $243,000. A down payment of 20% is made. The bank charges $425 in fees plus 4 points. Find the total of the down payment and the closing costs.

7. **Closing Costs** The purchase price of a condominium is $121,500. A down payment of 25% is made. The bank charges $725 in fees plus $3\frac{1}{2}$ points. Find the total of the down payment and the closing costs.

8. **Closing Costs** The purchase price of a manufactured home is $159,000. A down payment of 20% is made. The bank charges $815 in fees plus 1.75 points. Find the total of the down payment and the closing costs.

9. **Mortgage Payments** Find the mortgage payment for a 25-year loan of $129,000 at an annual interest rate of 7.75%.

10. **Mortgage Payments** Find the mortgage payment for a 30-year loan of $245,000 at an annual interest rate of 6.5%.

11. **Mortgage Payments** Find the mortgage payment for a 15-year loan of $223,500 at an annual interest rate of 8.15%.

12. **Mortgage Payments** Find the mortgage payment for a 20-year loan of $149,900 at an annual interest rate of 8.5%.

13. **Mortgage Payments** Leigh King purchased a townhouse and obtained a 30-year loan of $152,000 at an annual interest rate of 7.75%.

    a. What is the mortgage payment?

    b. What is the total of the payments over the life of the loan?

    c. Find the amount of interest paid on the mortgage loan over the 30 years.

14. **Mortgage Payments** Richard Miyashiro purchased a condominium and obtained a 25-year loan of $199,000 at an annual interest rate of 8.25%.

    a. What is the mortgage payment?

    b. What is the total of the payments over the life of the loan?

    c. Find the amount of interest paid on the mortgage loan over the 25 years.

15. **Interest Paid** Ira Patton purchased a home and obtained a 15-year loan of $219,990 at an annual interest rate of 8.7%. Find the amount of interest paid on the loan over the 15 years.

16. **Interest Paid** Leona Jefferson purchased a home and obtained a 30-year loan of $437,750 at an annual interest rate of 7.5%. Find the amount of interest paid on the loan over the 30 years.

17. **Principal and Interest** Marcel Thiessen purchased a home for $208,500 and obtained a 15-year, fixed rate mortgage at 9% after paying a down payment of 10%. Of the first month's mortgage payment, how much is interest and how much is applied to the principal?

18. **Principal and Interest** You purchase a condominium for $173,000. You obtain a 30-year, fixed rate mortgage loan at 12% after paying a down payment of 25%. Of the second month's mortgage payment, how much is interest and how much is applied to the principal?

19. **Principal and Interest** You purchase a cottage for $185,000. You obtain a 20-year, fixed rate mortgage loan at 12.5% after paying a down payment of 30%. Of the second month's mortgage payment, how much is interest and how much is applied to the principal?

20. **Principal and Interest** Fay Nguyen purchased a second home for $183,000 and obtained a 25-year, fixed rate mortgage loan at 9.25% after paying a down payment of 30%. Of the second month's mortgage payment, how much is interest and how much is applied to the principal?

21. **Loan Payoffs** After making payments of $913.10 for 6 years on your 30-year loan at 8.5%, you decide to sell your home. What is the loan payoff?

22. **Loan Payoffs** Christopher Chamberlain has a 25-year mortgage loan at an annual interest rate of 7.75%. After making payments of $1011.56 for $3\frac{1}{2}$ years, Christopher decides to sell his home. What is the loan payoff?

23. **Loan Payoffs** Iris Chung has a 15-year mortgage loan at an annual interest rate of 7.25%. After making payments of $672.39 for 4 years, Iris decides to sell her home. What is the loan payoff?

24. **Loan Payoffs** After making payments of $736.98 for 10 years on your 30-year loan at 6.75%, you decide to sell your home. What is the loan payoff?

25. **Total Monthly Payment** A homeowner has a mortgage payment of $996.60, an annual property tax bill of $594, and an annual fire insurance premium of $300. Find the total monthly payment for the mortgage, property tax, and fire insurance.

26. **Total Monthly Payment** Malcolm Rothschild has a mortgage payment of $1753.46, an annual property tax bill of $1023, and an annual fire insurance premium of $780. Find the total monthly payment for the mortgage, property tax, and fire insurance.

27. **Total Monthly Payment** Baka Onegin obtains a 25-year mortgage loan of $259,500 at an annual interest rate of 7.15%. Her annual property tax bill is $1320 and her annual fire insurance premium is $642. Find the total monthly payment for the mortgage, property tax, and fire insurance.

28. **Total Monthly Payment** Suppose you obtain a 20-year mortgage loan of $198,000 at an annual interest rate of 8.4%. The annual property tax bill is $972 and the annual fire insurance premium is $486. Find the total monthly payment for the mortgage, property tax, and fire insurance.

29. **Mortgage Loans** Consider a mortgage loan of $150,000 at an annual interest rate of 8.125%.

   a. How much greater is the mortgage payment if the term is 15 years rather than 30 years?

   b. How much less is the amount of interest paid over the life of the 15-year loan than over the life of the 30-year loan?

30. **Mortgage Loans** Consider a mortgage loan of $359,960 at an annual interest rate of 7.875%.

   a. How much greater is the mortgage payment if the term is 15 years rather than 30 years?

   b. How much less is the amount of interest paid over the life of the 15-year loan than over the life of the 30-year loan?

31. **Mortgage Loans** The Mendez family is considering a mortgage loan of $349,500 at an annual interest rate of 6.75%.

   a. How much greater is their mortgage payment if the term is 20 years rather than 30 years?

   b. How much less is the amount of interest paid over the life of the 20-year loan than over the life of the 30-year loan?

32. **Mortgage Loans** Herbert Bloom is considering a mortgage loan of $322,495 at an annual interest rate of 7.5%.

   a. How much greater is his mortgage payment if the term is 20 years rather than 30 years?

   b. How much less is the amount of interest paid over the life of the 20-year loan than over the life of the 30-year loan?

33. **Affordability** A couple has saved $25,000 for a down payment on a home. Their bank requires a minimum down payment of 20%. What is the maximum price they can offer for a house in order to have enough money for the down payment?

34. **Affordability** You have saved $18,000 for a down payment on a house. Your bank requires a minimum down payment of 15%. What is the maximum price you can offer for a home in order to have enough money for the down payment?

35. **Affordability** You have saved $39,400 to make a down payment and pay the closing costs on your future home. Your bank informs you that a 15% down payment is required and that the closing costs should be $380 plus 4 points. What is the maximum price you can offer for a home in order to have enough money for the down payment and the closing costs?

Extensions

CRITICAL THINKING

36. **Amortization Schedules** Suppose you have a 30-year mortgage loan for $119,500 at an annual interest rate of 8.25%. For which monthly payment does the amount of principal paid first exceed the amount of interest paid? For this exercise, you will need a spreadsheet program for producing amortization schedules. You can find one at our website at **www.cengage.com/math.**

37. **Amortization Schedules** Does changing the amount of the loan in Exercise 36 change the number of the monthly payment for which the amount of principal paid first exceeds the amount of interest paid? For this exercise, you will need a spreadsheet program for producing amortization schedules. You can find one at our website at **www.cengage.com/math.**

38. **Amortization Schedules** Does changing the interest rate of the loan in Exercise 36 change the number of the monthly payment for which the amount of principal paid first exceeds the amount of interest paid? For this exercise, you will need a spreadsheet program for producing amortization schedules. You can find one at our website at **www.cengage.com/math.**

39. Suppose you are considering a mortgage loan for $250,000 at an annual interest rate of 8%. Explain why the monthly payment for a 15-year mortgage loan is not twice the monthly payment for a 30-year mortgage loan.

COOPERATIVE LEARNING

40. **Buying and Selling a Home** Suppose you buy a house for $208,750, make a down payment that is 30% of the purchase price, and secure a 30-year loan for the balance at an annual interest rate of 7.75%. The points on the loan are 1.5% and there are additional lender fees of $825.

a. How much is due at closing? Note that the down payment is due at closing.

b. After 5 years, you decide to sell your house. What is the loan payoff?

c. Because of inflation, you were able to sell your house for $248,000. Assuming the selling fees are 6% of the selling price, what are the proceeds of the sale after deducting selling fees? Do not include the interest paid on the mortgage. Remember to consider the loan payoff.

d. The percent return on an investment $= \dfrac{\text{proceeds from sale}}{\text{total closing costs}} \times 100$. Find the percent return on your investment. Round to the nearest percent.

41. **Affordability** Assume that you are a computer programmer for a company and that your gross pay is $72,000 per year. You are paid monthly and take home $4479.38 per month. You are considering purchasing a condominium and have looked at one you would like to buy. The purchase price is $134,000. The condominium development company will arrange financing for the purchase. A down payment of 20% of the selling price is required. The interest rate on the 30-year, fixed rate mortgage loan is 9%. The lender charges 2.5 points. The appraisal fee, title fee, and recording fee total $325. The property taxes on the condominium are currently $1152 per year.

The condominium management company charges a monthly maintenance fee for landscaping, trash removal, snow removal, maintenance on the buildings, management costs, and insurance on the property. The monthly fee is currently $120. This fee includes insurance on the buildings and land only, so you will need to purchase separate insurance coverage for your furniture and other personal possessions. You have talked to the insurance agent through whom you buy tenant homeowner's insurance (to cover the personal possessions in your apartment), and you were told that such coverage will cost you approximately $192 per year.

The condominium uses electricity for cooking, heating, and lighting. You have been informed that the unit will use approximately 8750 kilowatt-hours per year. The cost of electricity is currently $.07 per kilowatt-hour.

You have saved $36,000 in anticipation of buying a home, but you do not want your savings account balance to fall below $6000. (You want to have some funds to fall back on in case of an emergency.) You have $900 in your checking account, but you do not want your checking account balance to fall below $600.

a. Calculate the amount to be paid for the down payment and closing costs. Are you willing to take this much out of your accounts?

b. Determine the mortgage payment.

c. Calculate the total of the monthly payments related to ownership of the condominium (mortgage, maintenance fee, property tax, utilities, insurance).

d. Find the difference between your monthly take-home pay and the monthly expenses related to condominium ownership (part c). This figure indicates how much money is available to pay for all other expenses, including food, transportation, clothing, entertainment, dental bills, telephone bills, car bills, etc.

e. What percent of your monthly take-home pay are the condominium-related expenses (part c)? Round to the nearest tenth of a percent.

f. Do you think that, financially, you can handle the purchase of this condominium? Why?

CHAPTER 10 **Summary**

Key Terms

adjustable rate mortgage (ARM) [p. 703]
amortization schedule [p. 705]
amortize a loan [p. 705]
annual percentage rate (APR) [p. 677]
annual percentage yield (APY) [p. 677]
average daily balance [p. 674]
bond [p. 695]
bondholder [p. 695]
brokerage firm [p. 693]
closing costs [p. 702]
compound amount [p. 656]
compound interest [p. 654]
compounding period [p. 654]
conventional mortgage [p. 703]
coupon [p. 695]
dividend [p. 692]
dividend yield [p. 692]
effective interest rate [p. 665]
face value [p. 695]
finance charge [p. 674]
fixed rate mortgage [p. 703]
future value [p. 646]
inflation [p. 663]
interest [p. 642]
interest rate [p. 642]
investment trust [p. 696]
loan origination fee [p. 702]
market value [p. 693]
maturity date [p. 695]

maturity value [p. 645]
mortgage [p. 702]
mortgage payment [p. 703]
mutual fund [p. 696]
nominal interest rate [p. 665]
points [p. 702]
present value [p. 661]
principal [p. 642]
residual value [p. 684]
share of stock [p. 692]
simple interest [p. 642]
stock exchange [p. 693]
stockholders or shareholders [p. 692]

Essential Concepts

■ **Approximate Annual Percentage Rate (APR) Formula**

$$\text{APR} = \frac{2Nr}{N + 1}$$

N is the number of payments and r is the stated simple interest rate.

■ **APR Loan Payoff Formula**

$$A = PMT\left(\frac{1 - (1 + i)^{-n}}{i}\right)$$

A is the loan payoff, PMT is the payment, i is the interest rate per payment period, and n is the number of *remaining* payments.

- **Average Daily Balance Method**
  Average daily balance
  $$= \frac{\text{sum of the total amounts owed each day of the month}}{\text{number of days in the billing period}}$$

- **Compound Amount Formula**
  $A = P(1 + i)^N$
  A is the compound amount when P dollars are deposited at an interest rate i per compounding period for N compounding periods.
  $$i = \frac{\text{annual interest rate}}{\text{number of compounding periods per year}} = \frac{r}{n}$$
  $N = $ (number of compounding periods per year)
  $\times$ (number of years) $= nt$

- **Future Value/Maturity Value Formulas for Simple Interest**
  $A = P + I$
  $A = P(1 + rt)$

- **Monthly Lease Payment Formula**
  $P = F + D$
  P is the monthly lease payment, F is the average monthly finance charge, and D is the average monthly depreciation of the car, where:
  Net capitalized cost
  $\quad = $ negotiated price $-$ down payment
  $\quad\quad - $ trade-in value
  Money factor $= \dfrac{\text{annual interest rate as a percent}}{2400}$
  Average monthly finance charge
  $\quad = $ (net capitalized cost $+$ residual value)
  $\quad\quad \times$ money factor
  Average monthly depreciation
  $\quad = \dfrac{\text{net capitalized cost} - \text{residual value}}{\text{term of the lease in months}}$

- **Mortgage Amount**
  Mortgage $=$ selling price $-$ down payment

- **Net Asset Value of a Mutual Fund**
  $$NAV = \frac{A - L}{N}$$
  A is the total fund assets, L is the total fund liabilities, and N is the number of shares outstanding.

- **Payment Formula for an APR Loan**
  $$PMT = A\left(\frac{i}{1 - (1 + i)^{-n}}\right)$$
  PMT is the payment, A is the loan amount, i is the interest rate per payment period, and n is the total number of payments.

- **Present Value Formula**
  $$P = \frac{A}{(1 + i)^N}$$
  P is the original principal invested at an interest rate of i per compounding period for N compounding periods, and A is the compound amount.

- **Simple Interest Formula**
  $I = Prt$
  I is the interest, P is the principal, r is the interest rate, and t is the time period.

- **Time Period of a Loan: Converting from Days to Years**
  Exact method: $t = \dfrac{\text{number of days}}{365}$
  Ordinary method: $t = \dfrac{\text{number of days}}{360}$

CHAPTER 10   # Review Exercises

 Use a calculator for Exercises 1–33.

1. **Simple Interest** Calculate the simple interest due on a four-month loan of $2750 if the interest rate is 6.75%.

2. **Simple Interest** Find the simple interest due on an eight-month loan of $8500 if the interest rate is 1.15% per month.

3. **Simple Interest** What is the simple interest earned in 120 days on a deposit of $4000 if the interest rate is 6.75%?

4. **Maturity Value** Calculate the maturity value of a simple interest, 108-day loan of $7000 if the interest rate is 10.4%.

5. **Simple Interest Rate** The simple interest charged on a three-month loan of $6800 is $127.50. Find the simple interest rate.

6. **Compound Amount** Calculate the compound amount when $3000 is deposited in an account earning 6.6% interest, compounded monthly, for 3 years.

7. **Compound Amount** What is the compound amount when $6400 is deposited in an account earning an interest rate of 6%, compounded quarterly, for 10 years?

8. **Future Value** Find the future value of $6000 earning 9% interest, compounded daily, for 3 years.

9. **Compound Interest** Calculate the amount of interest earned in 4 years on $600 deposited in an account paying 7.2% interest, compounded daily.

10. **Present Value** How much money should be invested in an account that earns 8% interest, compounded semiannually, in order to have $18,500 in 7 years?

11. **Loans** To help pay your college expenses, you borrow $8000 and agree to repay the loan at the end of 5 years at 7% interest, compounded quarterly.

   a. What is the maturity value of the loan?

   b. How much interest are you paying on the loan?

12. **Present Value** A couple plans to save for their child's college education. What principal must be deposited by the parents when their child is born in order to have $80,000 when the child reaches the age of 18? Assume the money earns 8% interest, compounded quarterly.

13. **Dividend Yield** A stock pays an annual dividend of $.66 per share. The stock is trading at $60. Find the dividend yield.

14. **Bonds** A bond with a $20,000 face value has a 4.5% coupon and a 10-year maturity. Calculate the total of the interest payments paid to the bondholder.

15. **Inflation** In 2001, the price of 1 pound of red delicious apples was $1.29. Use an annual inflation rate of 6% to calculate the price of 1 pound of red delicious apples in 2011. Round to the nearest cent.

16. **Inflation** You purchase a bond that will provide you with $75,000 in 8 years. Assuming an annual inflation rate of 7%, what will be the purchasing power of the $75,000 in 8 years?

17. **Effective Interest Rate** Calculate the effective interest rate of 5.90% compounded monthly. Round to the nearest hundredth of a percent.

18. **Annual Yield** Which has the higher annual yield, 5.2% compounded quarterly or 5.4% compounded semiannually?

19. **Average Daily Balance** A credit card account had a $423.35 balance on March 11. A purchase of $145.50 was made on March 18, and a payment of $250 was made on March 29. Find the average daily balance if the billing date is April 11.

20. **Finance Charges** On September 10, a credit card account had a balance of $450. A purchase of $47 was made on September 20, and $157 was charged on September 25. A payment of $175 was made on September 28. The interest on the average daily balance is 1.25% per month. Find the finance charge on the October 10 bill.

21. **APR** Arlene McDonald borrows $1500 from a bank that advertises a 7.5% simple interest rate and repays the loan in six equal monthly payments.

   a. Find the monthly payment.

   b. Estimate the APR. Round to the nearest tenth of a percent.

22. **APR** Suppose you purchase a DVD player for $449, make a 10% down payment, and agree to repay the balance in 12 equal monthly payments. The finance charge on the balance is 7% simple interest.

   a. Find the monthly payment.

   b. Estimate the APR. Round to the nearest tenth.

23. **Monthly Payments** Photo Experts offers a Nikon camera for $999, including taxes. If you finance the purchase of this camera for 2 years at an annual interest rate of 8.5%, find the monthly payment.

24. **Monthly Payments** Abeni Silver purchases a plasma high-definition television for $9499. The sales tax is 6.25% of the purchase price.

   a. What is the total cost, including sales tax?

   b. If Abeni makes a down payment of 20% of the total cost, find the down payment.

   c. Assuming Abeni finances the remaining cost at an annual interest rate of 8% for 3 years, find the monthly payment.

25. **Car Payments** Suppose you decide to purchase a new car. You go to a credit union to get pre-approval for your loan. The credit union offers you an annual interest rate of 7.2% for 3 years. The purchase price of the car you select is $28,450, including taxes, and you make a 20% down payment. What is your monthly payment?

26. **Loan Payoffs** Dasan Houston obtains a $28,000, five-year car loan for a Windstar at an annual interest rate of 5.9%.

   a. Find the monthly payment.

   b. After 3 years, Dasan decides to purchase a new car. What is the payoff on his loan?

27. Car Leases Nami Coffey obtains a five-year lease for a Chrysler 300 and negotiates a selling price of $32,450. Assuming she makes a down payment of $3000, the money factor is 0.004, and the residual value is $16,000, find each of the following.

   a. The net capitalized cost

   b. The average monthly finance charge

   c. The average monthly depreciation

   d. The monthly lease payment using a sales tax rate of 7.5%

28. Stock Sale Suppose you purchased 500 shares of stock at a price of $28.75 per share and sold them for $39.40 per share.

   a. Ignoring dividends, what was your profit or loss on the sale of the stock?

   b. If your broker charges 1.3% of the total sale price, what was the broker's commission?

29. Mutual Funds A mutual fund has total assets of $34 million and total liabilities of $4 million. There are 2 million shares outstanding. You invest $3000 in this fund. How many shares will you purchase?

30. Closing Costs The purchase price of a seaside cottage is $459,000. A down payment of 20% is made. The bank charges $815 in fees plus 1.75 points. Find the total of the down payment and the closing costs.

31. Mortgage Payments Suppose you purchase a condominium and obtain a 30-year loan of $255,800 at an annual interest rate of 6.75%.

   a. What is the mortgage payment?

   b. What is the total of the payments over the life of the loan?

   c. Find the amount of interest paid on the mortgage loan over the 30 years.

32. Mortgage Payments and Loan Payoffs Garth Santacruz purchased a condominium and obtained a 25-year loan of $189,000 at an annual interest rate of 7.5%.

   a. What is the mortgage payment?

   b. After making payments for 10 years, Garth decides to sell his home. What is the loan payoff?

33. Total Monthly Payments Geneva Goldberg obtains a 15-year loan of $278,950 at an annual interest rate of 7%. Her annual property tax bill is $1134 and her annual fire insurance premium is $681. Find the total monthly payment for the mortgage, property tax, and fire insurance.

CHAPTER 10	**Test**

 Use a calculator for Exercises 1–22.

1. Simple Interest Calculate the simple interest due on a three-month loan of $5250 if the interest rate is 8.25%.

2. Simple Interest Find the simple interest earned in 180 days on a deposit of $6000 if the interest rate is 6.75%.

3. Maturity Value Calculate the maturity value of a simple interest, 200-day loan of $8000 if the interest rate is 9.2%.

4. Simple Interest Rate The simple interest charged on a two-month loan of $7600 is $114. Find the simple interest rate.

5. Compound Amount What is the compound amount when $4200 is deposited in an account earning an interest rate of 7%, compounded monthly, for 8 years?

6. Compound Interest Calculate the amount of interest earned in 3 years on $1500 deposited in an account paying 6.3% interest, compounded daily.

7. Maturity Value To help pay for a new truck, you borrow $10,500 and agree to repay the loan in 4 years at 9.5% interest, compounded monthly.

   a. What is the maturity value of the loan?

   b. How much interest are you paying on the loan?

8. Present Value A young couple wants to save money to buy a house. What principal must be deposited by the couple in order to have $30,000 in 5 years? Assume the money earns 6.25% interest, compounded daily.

9. Dividend Yield A stock that has a market value of $40 pays an annual dividend of $.48 per share. Find the dividend yield.

10. Bonds Suppose you purchase a $5000 bond that has a 3.8% coupon and a 10-year maturity. Calculate the total of the interest payments you will receive.

11. **Inflation** In 2002 the median value of a single-family house was $158,200. Use an annual inflation rate of 7% to calculate the median value of a single family house in 2022. (*Source:* moneycentral.msn.com)

12. **Effective Interest Rate** Calculate the effective interest rate of 6.25% compounded quarterly. Round to the nearest hundredth of a percent.

13. **Annual Yield** Which has the higher annual yield, 4.4% compounded monthly or 4.6% compounded semiannually?

14. **Finance Charges** On October 15, a credit card account had a balance of $515. A purchase of $75 was made on October 20, and a payment of $250 was made on October 28. The interest on the average daily balance is 1.8% per month. Find the finance charge on the November 15 bill.

15. **APR** Suppose you purchase a Joranda hand-held computer for $629, make a 15% down payment, and agree to repay the balance in 12 equal monthly payments. The finance charge on the balance is 9% simple interest.

   a. Find the monthly payment.

   b. Estimate the APR. Round to the nearest tenth of a percent.

16. **Monthly Payments** Technology Pro offers a new computer for $1899, including taxes. If you finance the purchase of this computer for 3 years at an annual percentage rate of 9.25%, find your monthly payment.

17. **Stock Sale** Suppose you purchased 800 shares of stock at a price of $31.82 per share and sold them for $25.70 per share.

   a. Ignoring dividends, what was your profit or loss on the sale of the stock?

   b. If your broker charges 1.1% of the total sale price, what was the broker's commission?

18. **Mutual Funds** A mutual fund has total assets of $42 million and total liabilities of $6 million. There are 3 million shares outstanding. You invest $2500 in this fund. How many shares will you purchase?

19. **Monthly Payments** Kalani Canfield purchases a high-speed color laser printer for $6575. The sales tax is 6.25% of the purchase price.

   a. What is the total cost, including sales tax?

   b. If Kalani makes a down payment of 20% of the total cost, find the down payment.

   c. Assuming Kalani finances the remaining cost at an annual interest rate of 7.8% for 3 years, find the monthly payment.

20. **Closing Costs** The purchase price of a house is $262,250. A down payment of 20% is made. The bank charges $815 in fees plus 3.25 points. Find the total of the down payment and the closing costs.

21. **Mortgage Payments and Loan Payoffs** Bernard Mason purchased a house and obtained a 30-year loan of $236,000 at an annual interest rate of 6.75%.

   a. What is the mortgage payment?

   b. After making payments for 5 years, Bernard decides to sell his home. What is the loan payoff?

22. **Total Monthly Payment** Zelda MacPherson obtains a 20-year loan of $312,000 at an annual interest rate of 7.25%. Her annual property tax bill is $1044 and her annual fire insurance premium is $516. Find the total monthly payment for the mortgage, property tax, and fire insurance.

CHAPTER

11 Combinatorics and Probability

11.1	The Counting Principle
11.2	Permutations and Combinations
11.3	Probability and Odds
11.4	Addition and Complement Rules
11.5	Conditional Probability
11.6	Expectation

The PowerBall lottery combines 27 states, the District of Columbia, and the Virgin Islands into a single lottery. To win this lottery, a player must select the five numbers from 1 to 53 and the one number from 1 to 42 that are chosen by the lottery commission. There are 120,526,770 different ways in which a player can make that selection. Thus the chances of winning the PowerBall lottery grand prize is 1 in 120,526,770. To put this in perspective, a person is 200 times more likely to be struck by lightning than to win the PowerBall lottery.

When no person selects the winning lottery numbers, the grand prize increases. As of May 2005, the largest Powerball jackpot was approximately $314.9 million, which was won on Christmas Day, 2002.

This chapter focuses on the mathematics necessary to calculate the number of ways in which certain events, such as selecting a winning lottery number, can happen. This is part of the study of combinatorics. Once the number of ways in which an event can occur is calculated, it is possible to determine the probability of that event. Probability is another topic covered in this chapter.

For online student resources, visit this textbook's website at **www.cengage.com/math.**

| # The Counting Principle

Counting by Making a List

Combinatorics is the study of counting the different outcomes of some task. For example, if a coin is flipped, the side facing upward will be a head or a tail. The outcomes can be listed as {H, T}. There are two possible outcomes.

If a regular six-sided die is rolled, the possible outcomes are ▯, ▯, ▯, ▯, ▯, ▯. The outcomes can also be listed as {1, 2, 3, 4, 5, 6}. There are six possible outcomes.

EXAMPLE 1 ■ Counting by Forming a List

List and then count the number of different outcomes that are possible when one letter from the word *Tennessee* is chosen.

Solution

The possible outcomes are {T, e, n, s}. There are four possible outcomes.

CHECK YOUR PROGRESS 1   List and then count the number of different outcomes that are possible when one letter is chosen from the word *Mississippi*.

Solution   *See page S42.*

In combinatorics, an **experiment** is an activity with an observable outcome. The set of all possible outcomes of an experiment is called the **sample space** of the experiment. Flipping a coin, rolling a die, and choosing a letter from the word *Tennessee* are experiments. The sample spaces are {H, T}, {1, 2, 3, 4, 5, 6}, and {T, e, n, s}, respectively.

An **event** is one or more of the possible outcomes of an experiment. Flipping a coin and having a head show on the upward face, rolling a 5 when a die is tossed, and choosing a T from one of the letters in the word *Tennessee* are all examples of events. An event is a *subset* of the sample space.

EXAMPLE 2 ■ Listing the Elements of an Event

One number is chosen from the sample space

$$S = \{1, 2, 3, 4, 5, 6, 7, 8, 9, 10, 11, 12, 13, 14, 15, 16, 17, 18, 19, 20\}$$

List the elements in the following events.

a. The number is even.

b. The number is divisible by 5.

c. The number is a prime number.

Solution

a. {2, 4, 6, 8, 10, 12, 14, 16, 18, 20}

b. {5, 10, 15, 20}

c. {2, 3, 5, 7, 11, 13, 17, 19}

CHECK YOUR PROGRESS 2   One digit is chosen from the digits 0 through 9. The sample space S is $\{0, 1, 2, 3, 4, 5, 6, 7, 8, 9\}$. List the elements in the following events.

a. The number is odd.

b. The number is divisible by 3.

c. The number is greater than 7.

Solution   *See page S42.*

Counting by Making a Table

Each of the experiments given above illustrates a *single-stage experiment*. A **single-stage experiment** is an experiment for which there is a single outcome. Some experiments have two, three, or more stages. Such experiments are called **multi-stage experiments.** To count the number of outcomes of such an experiment, a systematic procedure is helpful. Using a table to record results is one such procedure.

Consider the two-stage experiment of rolling two dice, one red and one green. How many different outcomes are possible? To determine the number of outcomes, make a table with the different outcomes of rolling the red die across the top and the different outcomes of rolling the green die down the side.

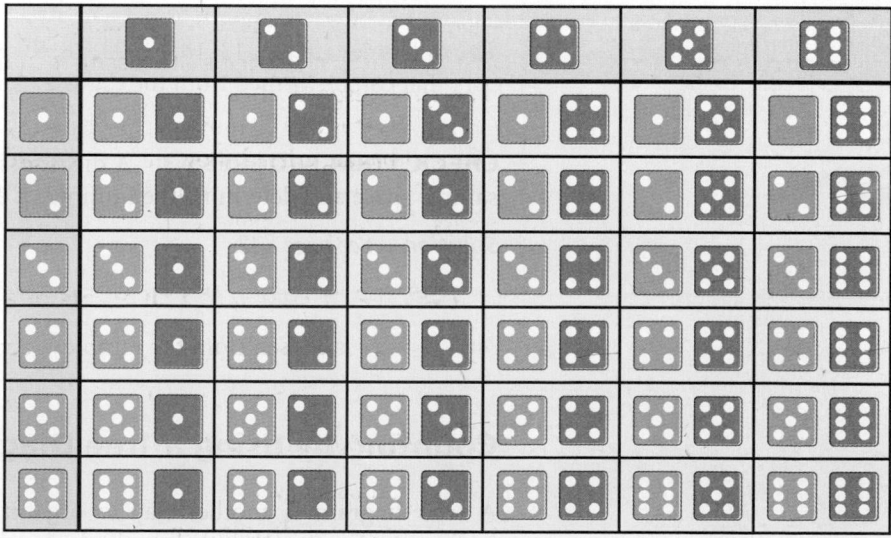

Outcomes of Rolling Two Dice

By counting the number of entries in the diagram above, we see that there are 36 different outcomes of the experiment of rolling two dice. The sample space is

From the table, several different events can be discussed.

- The sum of the pips (dots) on the upward faces is 7. There are six outcomes of this event. They are $\{$ ⚅ ⚀, ⚄ ⚁, ⚃ ⚂, ⚂ ⚃, ⚁ ⚄, ⚀ ⚅ $\}$.
- The sum of the pips on the upward faces is 11. There are two outcomes of this event. They are $\{$ ⚄ ⚅, ⚅ ⚄ $\}$.
- The number of pips on the upward faces are equal. There are six outcomes of this event. They are $\{$ ⚀ ⚀, ⚁ ⚁, ⚂ ⚂, ⚃ ⚃, ⚄ ⚄, ⚅ ⚅ $\}$.

EXAMPLE 3 ■ Counting Using a Table

Two-digit numbers are formed from the digits 1, 3, and 8. Find the sample space and determine the number of elements in the sample space.

Solution

Use a table to list all the different two-digit numbers that can be formed by using the digits 1, 3, and 8.

	1	3	8
1	11	13	18
3	31	33	38
8	81	83	88

The outcomes are $\{11, 13, 18, 31, 33, 38, 81, 83, 88\}$. There are nine two-digit numbers that can be formed from the digits 1, 3, and 8.

CHECK YOUR PROGRESS 3 A die is tossed and then a coin is flipped. Find the sample space and determine the number of elements in the sample space.

Solution See page S42.

Counting by Using a Tree Diagram

A **tree diagram** is another way to organize the outcomes of a multi-stage experiment. To illustrate the method, consider a computer store that offers a three-component computer system. The system consists of a central processing unit (CPU), a hard drive, and a monitor. If there are two CPUs, three hard drives, and two monitors from which to choose, how many different computer systems are possible?

We can organize the information by letting C_1 and C_2 represent the two CPUs; H_1, H_2, and H_3 represent the three hard drives; and M_1 and M_2 represent the two monitors (see Figure 11.1).

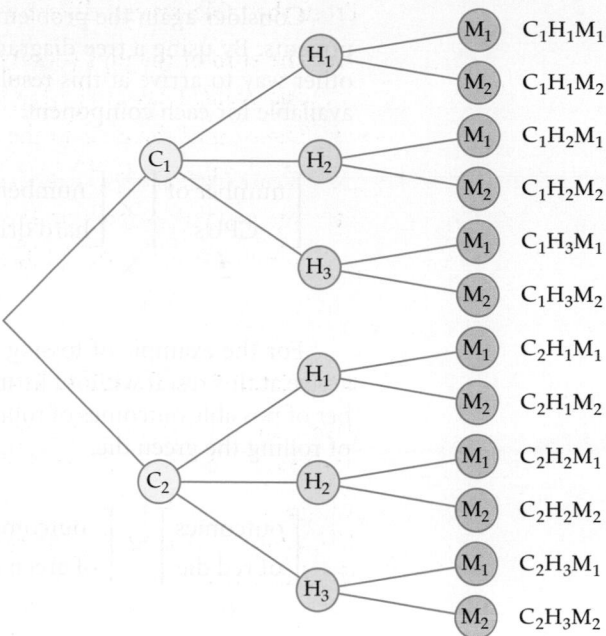

Figure 11.1

There are 12 possible computer systems.

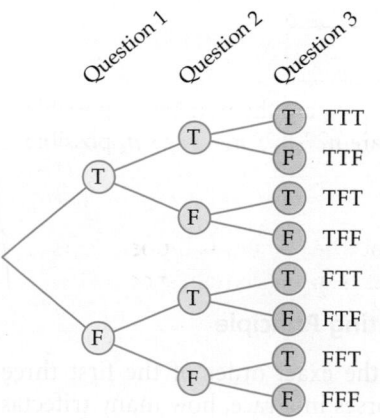

Figure 11.2

EXAMPLE 4 ■ Counting Using a Tree Diagram

A true/false test consists of 10 questions. Draw a tree diagram to show the number of ways to answer the first three questions.

Solution
See the tree diagram in Figure 11.2. There are eight possible ways to answer the first three questions.

CHECK YOUR PROGRESS 4   Draw a tree diagram to determine the sample space for Example 3.

Solution   See page S42.

The Counting Principle

For each of the previous problems, the possible outcomes were listed and then counted to determine the number of different outcomes. However, it is not always possible or practical to list and count outcomes. For example, the number of different five-card poker hands that can be drawn from a standard deck of 52 playing cards is 2,598,960. Trying to create a list of these hands would be quite time consuming.

Consider again the problem of selecting a computer system having three components. By using a tree diagram, we listed the 12 possible computer systems. Another way to arrive at this result is to find the product of the numbers of options available for each component.

$$
\begin{bmatrix} \text{number of} \\ \text{CPUs} \end{bmatrix} \times \begin{bmatrix} \text{number of} \\ \text{hard drives} \end{bmatrix} \times \begin{bmatrix} \text{number of} \\ \text{monitors} \end{bmatrix} = \begin{bmatrix} \text{number of} \\ \text{systems} \end{bmatrix}
$$
$$
\quad 2 \qquad\qquad \times \qquad 3 \qquad\qquad \times \qquad 2 \qquad = \qquad 12
$$

For the example of tossing two dice, there were 36 possible outcomes. We can arrive at this result without listing the outcomes by finding the product of the number of possible outcomes of rolling the red die and the number of possible outcomes of rolling the green die.

$$
\begin{bmatrix} \text{outcomes} \\ \text{of red die} \end{bmatrix} \times \begin{bmatrix} \text{outcomes} \\ \text{of green die} \end{bmatrix} = \begin{bmatrix} \text{number of} \\ \text{outcomes} \end{bmatrix}
$$
$$
\quad 6 \qquad\qquad \times \qquad 6 \qquad\qquad = \qquad 36
$$

This method of determining all of the outcomes of a multi-stage experiment without listing them is called the **counting principle.**

Counting Principle

Let E be a multi-stage experiment. If $n_1, n_2, n_3, \ldots, n_k$ are the number of possible outcomes of each of the k stages of E, then there are $n_1 \cdot n_2 \cdot n_3 \cdot \cdots \cdot n_k$ possible outcomes for E.

EXAMPLE 5 ■ Counting by Using the Counting Principle

In horse racing, a *trifecta* consists of choosing the exact order of the first three horses across the finish line. If there are eight horses in a race, how many trifectas are possible, assuming there are no ties?

Solution
Any one of the eight horses can be first, so $n_1 = 8$. Because a horse cannot finish both first and second, there are seven horses that can finish second; thus $n_2 = 7$. Similarly, there are six horses that can finish third; $n_3 = 6$. By the counting principle, there are $8 \cdot 7 \cdot 6 = 336$ possible trifectas.

CHECK YOUR PROGRESS 5   Nine runners are entered in a 100-meter dash for which a gold, silver, and bronze medal will be awarded for first, second, and third place finishes, respectively. In how many possible ways can the medals be awarded? (Assume there are no ties.)

Solution   See page S42.

✔ **TAKE NOTE**

The ISO (International Organization for Standardization) develops standards used in science, engineering, and commerce. ISO Latin 1 is one such standard that web browsers such as Internet Explorer, Safari, Mozilla, Netscape, Opera, and others use to display text in a browser. Because "International Organization for Standardization" would have different abbreviations in different languages ("IOS" in English; "OIN" in French, for *Organisation internationale de normalisation*), it was decided at the outset to use a word derived from the Greek *isos*, meaning "equal." [*Source:* www.iso.org]

Math Matters   Coding Characters for Web Pages

So that web pages look the same on computers all over the world, certain standards must be adopted and adhered to by web page developers. ISO Latin 1 (also called ISO 8859-1) is a standard character set used by many web browsers. Each upper- and lower-case letter, numeral, punctuation mark, and special symbol (for instance, &, %, and @) has a representation as an eight-digit binary code. Here are some examples:

Partial ISO Latin 1 Character Set

Letter or Symbol	Binary Code	Letter or Symbol	Binary Code
A	0100 0001	7	0101 0101
a	0110 0001	&	0010 0110
B	0100 0010	=	0110 0001

Symbols used in foreign languages are also available in the ISO Latin 1 character set. For instance, to display the word *español* (Spanish for "Spanish"), it is necessary to code the letter ñ. This letter is given by 1111 0001.

Using the counting principle, we can count the number of possible characters that can be represented by this scheme. Each of the eight digits in the binary number can be a 0 or a 1. Thus there are two choices for the first digit, two choices for the second digit, and so on until the eighth digit, for which there are two choices. By the counting principle, there are $2 \cdot 2 \cdot 2 \cdot 2 \cdot 2 \cdot 2 \cdot 2 \cdot 2 = 2^8 = 256$ possible characters that can be represented using the ISO Latin 1 method.

You can see which character set your browser is using by selecting Preferences and looking at the font characteristics being used by the browser.

Counting With and Without Replacement

Consider an experiment in which balls colored red, blue, and green are placed in a box. A person reaches into the box and repeatedly pulls out a colored ball, keeping note of the color picked. The sequence of colors that can result depends on whether or not the balls are returned to the box after each pick. This is referred to as performing the experiment *with replacement* or *without replacement*.

Consider the following two situations.

1. How many four-digit numbers can be formed from the digits 1 through 9 if no digit can be repeated?

2. How many four-digit numbers can be formed from the digits 1 through 9 if a digit can be used repeatedly?

In the first case, there are nine choices for the first digit ($n_1 = 9$). Because a digit cannot be repeated, the first digit chosen cannot be used again. Thus there are only eight choices for the second digit ($n_2 = 8$). Because neither of the first two digits can be used as the third digit, there are only seven choices for the third digit ($n_3 = 7$). Similarly, there are six choices for the fourth digit ($n_4 = 6$). By the counting principle there are $9 \cdot 8 \cdot 7 \cdot 6 = 3024$ four-digit numbers in which no digit is repeated.

In the second case, there are nine choices for the first digit ($n_1 = 9$). Because a digit can be used repeatedly, the first digit chosen can be used again. Thus there are nine choices for the second digit ($n_2 = 9$), and, similarly, there are nine choices for the third and fourth digits ($n_3 = 9$, $n_4 = 9$). By the counting principle, there are $9 \cdot 9 \cdot 9 \cdot 9 = 6561$ four-digit numbers when digits can be used repeatedly.

The set of four-digit numbers created without replacement includes numbers such as 3867, 7941, and 9128. For these numbers, no digit is repeated. However, numbers such as 6465, 9911, and 2222, each of which contains at least one repeated digit, can be created only with replacement.

QUESTION *Does a multi-stage experiment performed with replacement generally have more or fewer possible outcomes than the same experiment performed without replacement?*

✔ TAKE NOTE

Notice how significant the difference is in the number of outcomes of counting with replacement and counting without replacement. In Example 6 there are more than five times as many outcomes with replacement as there are without replacement.

EXAMPLE 6 ■ **Counting With and Without Replacement**

From the letters a, b, c, d, and e, how many four-letter groups can be formed if

a. a letter can be used more than once?

b. each letter can be used exactly once?

Solution

a. Because each letter can be repeated, there are $5 \cdot 5 \cdot 5 \cdot 5 = 625$ possible four-letter groups.

b. Because each letter can be used only once, there are $5 \cdot 4 \cdot 3 \cdot 2 = 120$ four-letter groups in which no letter is repeated.

CHECK YOUR PROGRESS 6 In how many ways can a mail carrier place three letters in five mailboxes if

a. each box may receive more than one letter?

b. each mailbox may receive no more than one letter?

Solution See page S42.

Excursion

Decision Trees

Decision trees are tree diagrams that are used to solve problems that involve many choices. To illustrate, we will consider a particular puzzle. Suppose we are given eight coins, one of which is counterfeit and slightly heavier than the other seven. Using a balance scale, we must find the counterfeit coin.

(continued)

ANSWER *More. Each stage of an experiment (after the first) performed without replacement will have fewer possible outcomes than the preceding stage. Performed with replacement, each stage of the experiment has the same number of outcomes.*

Designate the coins as c_1, c_2, c_3, c_4, c_5, c_6, c_7, and c_8. One way to determine the counterfeit coin is to weigh coins in pairs. This method is illustrated by the decision tree in Figure 11.3. In this case, it would take from one to four weighings to determine the counterfeit coin.

A second method is to divide the coins into two groups of four coins each, place each group on a pan of the balance scale, and take the coins from the side that goes down. Now divide these four coins into two groups of two coins each and weigh them on the balance scale. Again keep the coins from the heavier side. Weighing one of these coins against the other will reveal the counterfeit coin. The decision tree for this procedure is shown in Figure 11.4. Using this method, the counterfeit coin will be found in three weighings.

A third method is even more efficient. Divide the coins into three groups. Two of the groups contain three coins and the third group contains two coins. Place each of the three-coin groups on the balance scale. If they balance, the counterfeit coin is in the third group. Placing a coin from the third group on each of the balance pans will determine the counterfeit coin. If the three-coin groups do not balance, then weigh two of the coins in the pan that goes down. If these balance, the third coin is the counterfeit. If not, the counterfeit is the coin on the pan that goes down. This method requires only two weighings and is shown in the decision tree in Figure 11.5.

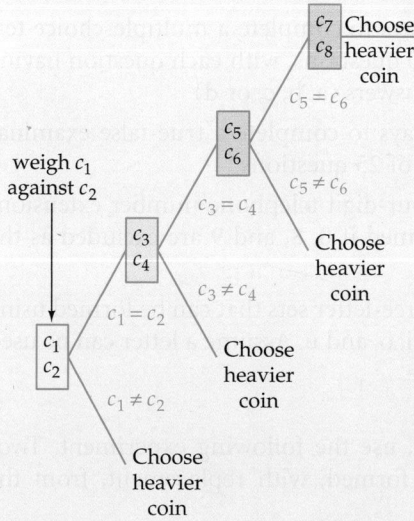

Figure 11.3

Using this method, it may take up to four weighings to determine which is the counterfeit coin.

Figure 11.4

Using this method, it will always take three weighings to determine which is the counterfeit coin.

*We are assuming that $c_1c_2c_3$ is heavier than $c_4c_5c_6$. If $c_4c_5c_6$ is heavier, use those coins in the final weighing.

Figure 11.5

Using this method, it will take only two weighings to determine which is the counterfeit coin.

Excursion Exercises

For each of the following problems, draw a decision tree and determine the minimum number of weighings necessary to identify the counterfeit coin.

1. In a stack of 12 identical-looking coins, one is counterfeit and is lighter than the remaining 11 coins. Using a balance scale, identify the counterfeit coin in as few weighings as possible.

2. In a stack of 13 identical-looking coins, one is counterfeit and is heavier than the remaining 12 coins. Using a balance scale, identify the counterfeit coin in as few weighings as possible.

Exercise Set 11.1

In Exercises 1–14, list the elements of the sample space defined by each experiment.

1. Select an even single-digit whole number.
2. Select an odd single-digit whole number.
3. Select one day from the days of the week.
4. Select one month from the months of the year.
5. Toss a coin twice.
6. Toss a coin three times.
7. Roll a single die and then toss a coin.
8. Toss a coin and then choose a digit from the digits 1 through 4.
9. Choose a complete dinner from a dinner menu that allows a customer to choose from two salads, three entrees, and two desserts.
10. Choose a car during a new car promotion that allows a buyer to choose from three body styles, two radios, and two interior color schemes.
11. Starting at A, find the paths that pass through each vertex of the square below exactly once.

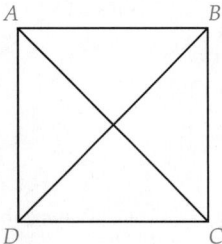

12. Starting at A, find the number of paths that pass through each vertex of the pentagon below exactly once.

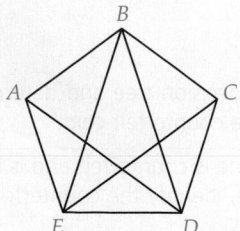

13. Three letters addressed to A, B, and C are randomly placed in three envelopes addressed to A, B, and C.

14. The first of three characters in a customer identification code is chosen from the first letters of North, South, East, and West. The second character is chosen from the digits 3 and 4 (for 2003 or 2004), and the third character is chosen from the first letters of Yes and No (to identify previous customers). Find the sample space of the beginning three characters of the identification codes for this company.

In Exercises 15–20, use the counting principle to determine the number of elements in the sample space.

15. Two digits are selected without replacement from the digits 1, 2, 3, and 4.
16. Two digits are selected with replacement from the digits 1, 2, 3, and 4.
17. The possible ways to complete a multiple-choice test consisting of 20 questions, with each question having four possible answers (a, b, c, or d)
18. The possible ways to complete a true-false examination consisting of 25 questions
19. The possible four-digit telephone number extensions that can be formed if 0, 8, and 9 are excluded as the first digit
20. The possible three-letter sets that can be formed using the vowels a, e, i, o, and u. Assume a letter can be used more than once.

In Exercises 21–26, use the following experiment. Two-digit numbers are formed, with replacement, from the digits 0 through 9.

21. How many two-digit numbers are possible?
22. How many two-digit even numbers are possible?
23. How many numbers are divisible by 5?
24. How many numbers are divisible by 3?
25. How many numbers are greater than 37?
26. How many numbers are less than 59?

In Exercises 27–30, use the following experiment. Four cards labeled A, B, C, and D are randomly placed in four boxes labeled A, B, C, and D. Each box receives exactly one card.

27. In how many ways can the cards be placed in the boxes?

28. Count the number of elements in the event that no box contains a card with the same letter as the box.

29. Count the number of elements in the event that *at least* one card is placed in the box with the corresponding letter.

30. If you add the answer for Exercise 28 and the answer for Exercise 29, is the sum the answer for Exercise 27? Why or why not?

Lotteries In Exercises 31–34, use the following experiment. A state lottery game consists of choosing one card from each of the four suits in a standard deck of playing cards. (There are 13 cards in each suit.)

31. Count the number of elements in the sample space.

32. Count the number of elements in the event that an ace, a king, a queen, and a jack are chosen.

33. Count the number of ways in which four aces can be chosen.

34. Count the number of ways in which four cards, each of a different face value, can be chosen.

35. Write a lesson that you could use to explain the meanings of the words *experiment, sample space,* and *event* as they apply to combinatorics.

36. Explain how a tree diagram is used to count the number of ways an experiment can be performed.

Extensions

CRITICAL THINKING

37. Computer Programming A main component of any computer programming language is its method of repeating a series of computations. Each programming language has its own syntax for performing those "loops." In one programming language, BASIC, the structure is similar to the display below.

```
FOR I = 1 TO 10          Starting with I = 1
    FOR J = 1 TO 15          Starting with J = 1
        SUM = I + J
    NEXT J               Increase J by 1 until J exceeds 15
NEXT I               Increase I by 1 until I exceeds 10
END
```

The program repeats each loop until the index variables, I and J in this case, exceed a certain value. After this program is executed, how many times will the instruction SUM = I + J have been executed? What is the final value of SUM?

38. Computer Programming One way in which a software engineer can write a program to sort a list of numbers from smallest to largest is to use a *bubble sort*. The following code segment, written in BASIC, will perform a bubble sort of n numbers. We have left out the details of how the numbers are sorted in the list.

```
FOR J = 1 TO n − 1
    FOR K = J + 1 TO n
        <Sorting takes place here.>
    NEXT K
NEXT J
END
```

a. If the list contains 10 numbers ($n = 10$), how many times will the program loop before reaching the END statement?

b. Suppose there are 20 numbers in the list. How many times will the program loop before reaching the END statement?

EXPLORATIONS

39. Use a tree diagram to display the relationships among the junior- and senior-level courses you must take for your major and their prerequisites.

40. Review the rules of the game checkers, and make a tree diagram that shows all of the first two moves that are possible by one player of a checker game. Assume that no moves are blocked by the opponent's checkers. (*Hint:* it may help to number the squares of the checkerboard.)

| SECTION 11.2 | **Permutations and Combinations** |

Factorial

Suppose four different colored squares are arranged in a row. One possibility is shown below.

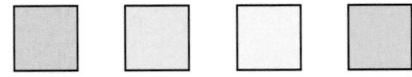

How many different ways are there to order the colors? There are four choices for the first square, three choices for the second square, two choices for the third square, and one choice for the fourth square. By the counting principle, there are $4 \cdot 3 \cdot 2 \cdot 1 = 24$ different arrangements of the four squares. Note from this example that the number of arrangements equals the product of the natural numbers n through 1, where n is the number of objects. This product is called a *factorial*.

Definition of *n* Factorial

***n* factorial** is the product of the natural numbers n through 1 and is symbolized by ***n*!**.

$$n! = n \cdot (n - 1) \cdot (n - 2) \cdot \cdots \cdot 3 \cdot 2 \cdot 1$$

Here are some examples.

$$5! = 5 \cdot 4 \cdot 3 \cdot 2 \cdot 1 = 120$$
$$8! = 8 \cdot 7 \cdot 6 \cdot 5 \cdot 4 \cdot 3 \cdot 2 \cdot 1 = 40{,}320$$
$$1! = 1$$

On some occasions it will be necessary to use 0! (zero factorial). Because it is impossible to define zero factorial in terms of a product of natural numbers, a standard definition is used.

CALCULATOR NOTE

The factorial of a number becomes quite large for even relatively small numbers. For instance, 58! is the approximate number of atoms in the known universe. The number 70! is greater than 10 with 100 zeros after it. This number is larger than most scientific calculators can handle.

Definition of Zero Factorial

$$0! = 1$$

A factorial can be written in terms of smaller factorials. This is useful when calculating large factorials. For example,

$$10! = 10 \cdot 9!$$
$$10! = 10 \cdot 9 \cdot 8!$$
$$10! = 10 \cdot 9 \cdot 8 \cdot 7!$$

EXAMPLE 1 ■ Simplify Factorials

Evaluate: **a.** $5! - 3!$ **b.** $\dfrac{9!}{6!}$

Solution

a. $5! - 3! = (5 \cdot 4 \cdot 3 \cdot 2 \cdot 1) - (3 \cdot 2 \cdot 1) = 120 - 6 = 114$

b. $\dfrac{9!}{6!} = \dfrac{9 \cdot 8 \cdot 7 \cdot \cancel{6!}}{\cancel{6!}} = 9 \cdot 8 \cdot 7 = 504$

CHECK YOUR PROGRESS 1   Evaluate: **a.** $7! + 4!$ **b.** $\dfrac{8!}{4!}$

Solution   See page S42.

Permutations

Determining the number of possible arrangements of distinct objects in a definite order, as we did with the squares earlier, is one application of the counting principle. Each arrangement of this type is called a *permutation*.

> **Definition of Permutation**
>
> A **permutation** is an arrangement of objects in a definite order.

For example, abc and cba are two different permutations of the letters a, b, and c. As a second example, 122 and 212 are two different permutations of the digits 1 and 2.

The counting principle is used to count the number of different permutations of any set of objects. We will begin our discussion with *distinct* objects. For instance, the objects a, b, c, d are distinct, whereas the objects ♥ ♥ ♠ ♦ are not all distinct.

Suppose there are two songs, *Intuition* and *Respect*, in a playlist, and you wish to play both on your music player. There are two ways to choose the first song; $n_1 = 2$. There is one way to choose the second song; $n_2 = 1$. By the counting principle, there are $2 \cdot 1 = 2! = 2$ permutations or orders in which you can play the two songs. Each permutation gives a different play list. These are

Permutation (playlist) 1	Permutation (playlist) 2
Intuition	*Respect*
Respect	*Intuition*

With three songs in a playlist, *Intuition*, *Respect*, and *Penny Lane*, there are three choices for the first song, two choices for the second song, and one choice for the third song. By the counting principle, there are $3 \cdot 2 \cdot 1 = 3! = 6$ permutations in which you can play the three songs.

Permutation 1	Permutation 2	Permutation 3	Permutation 4	Permutation 5	Permutation 6
Intuition	Intuition	Respect	Respect	Penny Lane	Penny Lane
Respect	Penny Lane	Intuition	Penny Lane	Intuition	Respect
Penny Lane	Respect	Penny Lane	Intuition	Respect	Intuition

▼ **point of interest**

When "shuffle mode" is selected on some CD players or music players such as an MP3 player, a program randomly selects one of the songs to play. After that song is played, the program randomly selects one of the remaining songs to play. This process is continued until all the songs have been played. From our discussion at the right, if a CD or MP3 player has 10 songs, there are 10! = 3,628,800 different orders in which the songs could be played.

With four songs in a playlist, there are $4 \cdot 3 \cdot 2 \cdot 1 = 4! = 24$ orders in which you could play the songs. In general, if there are n songs in a playlist, then there are $n!$ permutations or orders in which the songs could be played.

Suppose now that you have a playlist that consists of eight songs but you have time to listen to only three of the songs. You could choose any one of the eight songs to play first, then any one of the seven remaining songs to play second, and then any one of the remaining six songs to play third. By the counting principle, there are $8 \cdot 7 \cdot 6 = 336$ permutations in which the songs could be played.

The following formula can be used to determine the number of permutations of n distinct objects (songs in the examples above), of which k are selected.

Permutation Formula for Distinct Objects

The number of permutations of n distinct objects selected k at a time is

$$P(n, k) = \frac{n!}{(n - k)!}$$

Applying this formula to the situation above in which there were eight songs ($n = 8$), of which there was time to play only three songs ($k = 3$), we have

$$P(8, 3) = \frac{8!}{(8 - 3)!} = \frac{8!}{5!} = \frac{8 \cdot 7 \cdot 6 \cdot 5!}{5!} = 8 \cdot 7 \cdot 6 = 336$$

There are 336 permutations of playing the songs. This is the same answer we obtained using the counting principle.

EXAMPLE 2 ■ Counting Permutations

A university tennis team consists of six players who are ranked from 1 through 6. If a tennis coach has 10 players from which to choose, how many different tennis teams can the coach select?

Solution

Because the players on the tennis team are ranked from 1 through 6, a team with player A in position 1 is different from a team with player A in position 2. Therefore, the number of different teams is the number of permutations of 10 players selected six at a time.

$$P(10, 6) = \frac{10!}{(10 - 6)!} = \frac{10!}{4!} = \frac{10 \cdot 9 \cdot 8 \cdot 7 \cdot 6 \cdot 5 \cdot 4!}{4!}$$
$$= 10 \cdot 9 \cdot 8 \cdot 7 \cdot 6 \cdot 5 = 151,200$$

There are 151,200 possible tennis teams.

CHECK YOUR PROGRESS 2   A college golf team consists of five players who are ranked from 1 through 5. If a golf coach has eight players from which to choose, how many different golf teams can the coach select?

Solution   See page S42.

The Kentucky Derby

EXAMPLE 3 ■ Counting Permutations

 In 2004, the Kentucky Derby had 18 horses entered in the race. How many different finishes of first, second, third, and fourth place were possible?

Solution

Because the order in which the horses finish the race is important, the number of possible finishes of first, second, third, and fourth place is $P(18, 4)$.

$$P(18, 4) = \frac{18!}{(18-4)!} = \frac{18!}{14!} = \frac{18 \cdot 17 \cdot 16 \cdot 15 \cdot 14!}{14!}$$
$$= 18 \cdot 17 \cdot 16 \cdot 15 = 73{,}440$$

There were 73,440 possible finishes of first, second, third, and fourth places.

CHECK YOUR PROGRESS 3   There were 42 cars entered in the 2004 Daytona 500 NASCAR race. How many different ways could first, second, and third place prizes be awarded?

Solution   See page S42.

A Standard Deck of
Playing Cards

MathMatters   **How Many Shuffles?**

A standard deck of playing cards consists of 52 different cards divided into four suits: spades (♠), hearts (♥), diamonds (♦), and clubs (♣). Each shuffle of the deck results in a new arrangement of the cards. Another way of stating this is to say that each shuffle results in a new permutation of the cards. There are $P(52, 52) = 52! \approx 8 \times 10^{67}$ (that's 8 with 67 zeros after it) possible arrangements.

Suppose a deck has each of the four suits arranged in order from two through ace. How many shuffles are necessary to achieve a randomly ordered deck in which any card is equally likely to occur in any position in the deck?

Two mathematicians, Dave Bayer of Columbia University and Persi Diaconis of Harvard University, have shown that seven shuffles are enough. Their proof has many applications to complicated counting problems. One problem in particular is that of analyzing speech patterns. Solving this problem is critical to enabling computers to interpret human speech.

Applying Several Counting Techniques

The permutation formula is derived from the counting principle. This formula is just a convenient way to express the number of ways the items in an ordered list can be arranged. Some counting problems require using both the permutation formula and the counting principle.

EXAMPLE 4 ■ Counting Using Several Methods

Five women and four men are to be seated in a row of nine chairs. How many different seating arrangements are possible if

a. there are no restrictions on the seating arrangements?

b. the women sit together and the men sit together?

Solution

Because seating arrangements have a definite order, they are permutations.

a. If there are no restrictions on the seating arrangements, then the number of seating arrangements is $P(9, 9)$.

$$P(9, 9) = \frac{9!}{(9 - 9)!} = \frac{9!}{0!} = 9! = 362{,}880$$

There are 362,880 seating arrangements.

b. This is a multi-stage experiment, so both the permutation formula and the counting principle will be used. There are 5! ways to arrange the women and 4! ways to arrange the men. We must also consider that either the women or the men could be seated at the beginning of the row. There are two ways to do this. By the counting principle, there are $2 \cdot 5! \cdot 4!$ ways to seat the women together and the men together.

$$2 \cdot 5! \cdot 4! = 5760$$

There are 5760 arrangements in which women sit together and men sit together.

CHECK YOUR PROGRESS 4 There are seven tutors, three juniors and four seniors, who must be assigned to the seven hours that a math center is open each day. If each tutor works one hour per day, how many different tutoring schedules are possible if

a. there are no restrictions?

b. the juniors tutor during the first three hours and the seniors tutor during the last four hours?

Solution *See page S43.*

Permutations of Indistinguishable Objects

Up to this point we have been counting the number of permutations of *distinct* objects. We now look at the situation of arranging objects when some of them are identical. In the case of identical or indistinguishable objects, a modification of the permutation formula is necessary. The general idea for modifying the formula is to count the number of permutations as if all of the objects were distinct, and then remove the permutations that are not different in appearance.

Consider the permutations of the letters *bbbcc*. We first assume the letters are all different—for example, $b_1b_2b_3c_1c_2$. Using the permutation formula, there are $5! = 120$ permutations. Now we need to remove repeated permutations. Consider for a moment the letter b in the permutation $bbbc_1c_2$. If the b's are written as b_1, b_2, and b_3 (so that they are distinguishable), then

$$b_1b_2b_3c_1c_2 \quad b_1b_3b_2c_1c_2 \quad b_2b_1b_3c_1c_2 \quad b_2b_3b_1c_1c_2 \quad b_3b_2b_1c_1c_2 \quad b_3b_1b_2c_1c_2$$

are all distinct permutations that end with c_1c_2. There are six of these permutations. Note that $3! = 6$, where 3 is the number of b's.

However, because the b's are not distinct, each of these permutations of b's should have been counted only once. Thus there are six times too many permutations of b's for each arrangement of c_1 and c_2.

A similar argument applies to the c's. If the c's are identical, then c_1c_2bbb and c_2c_1bbb are the same permutation. For each arrangement of b's, there are two arrangements of c's that yield identical permutations. Note that there are two c's and that $2! = 2$, the number of identical permutations. Thus there are two times too many permutations of c's for each arrangement of b's.

Combining the results above, the number of permutations of $bbbcc$ is

$$\frac{5!}{3! \cdot 2!} = \frac{5 \cdot 4 \cdot 3 \cdot 2 \cdot 1}{(3 \cdot 2 \cdot 1) \cdot (2 \cdot 1)} = 10.$$

There are 10 distinct permutations of $bbbcc$.

Permutations of Objects, Some of Which are Identical

The number of distinguishable permutations of n objects of r different types, where k_1 identical objects are of one type, k_2 of another, and so on, is given by

$$\frac{n!}{k_1! \cdot k_2! \cdot \cdots \cdot k_r!}$$

where $k_1 + k_2 + \cdots + k_r = n$.

EXAMPLE 5 ■ Permutations of Identical Objects

If seven identical dice are rolled, find the number of ways two 4's, one 5, and four 6's can appear on the upward faces.

Solution

We are looking for the number of permutations of the digits 4456666. With $n = 7$ (number of dice), $k_1 = 2$ (number of 4's), $k_2 = 1$ (number of 5's), and $k_3 = 4$ (number of 6's), we have

$$\frac{7!}{2! \cdot 1! \cdot 4!} = 105$$

There are 105 permutations of the dice.

CHECK YOUR PROGRESS 5 Eight coins—three pennies, two nickels, and three dimes—are placed in a single stack. How many different stacks are possible if

a. there are no restrictions on the placement of the coins?

b. the dimes must stay together?

Solution   See page S43.

Combinations

For some arrangements of objects, the order of the arrangement is important. These are permutations. If a telephone extension is 2537, then the digits must be dialed in exactly that order. On the other hand, if you were to receive a one-dollar bill, a five-dollar bill, and a ten-dollar bill, you would have $16 regardless of the order in which you received the bills. A **combination** is a collection of objects for which the order is not important. The three-letter sequences acb and bca are *different* permutations but the *same* combination.

QUESTION *From a group of 45 applicants, five identical scholarships will be awarded. Is the number of ways in which the scholarships can be awarded determined by permutations or combinations?*

The formula for finding the number of combinations is derived in much the same manner as the formula for finding the number of permutations of identical objects. Consider the problem of finding the number of combinations possible when choosing three letters from the letters a, b, c, d, and e, without replacement. For each choice of three letters, there are 3! permutations. For example, choosing the letters a, d, and e gives the following six permutations.

ade   aed   dea   dae   ead   eda

Because there are six permutations and each permutation is the *same* combination, the number of permutations is six times the number of combinations. This is true each time three letters are selected. Therefore, to find the number of combinations of five objects chosen three at a time, divide the number of permutations by $3! = 6$. The number of combinations of five objects chosen 3 at a time is

$$\frac{P(5, 3)}{3!} = \frac{5!}{3! \cdot (5 - 3)!} = \frac{5!}{3! \cdot 2!} = \frac{5 \cdot 4 \cdot 3!}{3! \cdot 2!} = \frac{5 \cdot 4}{2 \cdot 1} = 10$$

Combination Formula

The number of combinations of n objects chosen k at a time is

$$C(n, k) = \frac{P(n, k)}{k!} = \frac{n!}{k! \cdot (n - k)!}$$

In Section 11.1, we stated that there were 2,598,960 possible five-card poker hands. This number was calculated using the combination formula. Because the five-card hand ace of hearts, king of diamonds, queen of clubs, jack of spades, ten of hearts is exactly the same as the five-card hand king of diamonds, jack of spades, queen of clubs, ten of hearts, ace of hearts, the order of the cards is not important and therefore the number of hands is a combination. The number of different five-card

ANSWER *Combinations. The order in which the scholarship winners are chosen is not important.*

poker hands is the combination of 52 cards chosen five at a time, which is given by $C(52, 5)$.

$$C(52, 5) = \frac{52!}{5! \cdot (52 - 5)!} = \frac{52!}{5! \cdot 47!} = \frac{52 \cdot 51 \cdot 50 \cdot 49 \cdot 48 \cdot 47!}{5! \cdot 47!}$$

$$= \frac{52 \cdot 51 \cdot 50 \cdot 49 \cdot 48}{5 \cdot 4 \cdot 3 \cdot 2 \cdot 1} = 2{,}598{,}960$$

EXAMPLE 6 ■ Counting Using the Combination Formula

A basketball team consists of 11 players. In how many different ways can a coach choose the five starting players, assuming the position of a player is not considered?

Solution

This is a combination problem, because the order in which the coach chooses the players is not important. The five starting players P_1, P_2, P_3, P_4, P_5 are the same as the five starting players P_3, P_5, P_1, P_2, P_4.

$$C(11, 5) = \frac{11!}{5! \cdot (11 - 5)!} = \frac{11!}{5! \cdot 6!} = \frac{11 \cdot 10 \cdot 9 \cdot 8 \cdot 7 \cdot 6!}{5! \cdot 6!}$$

$$= \frac{11 \cdot 10 \cdot 9 \cdot 8 \cdot 7}{5 \cdot 4 \cdot 3 \cdot 2 \cdot 1} = 462$$

There are 462 possible five-player starting teams.

CHECK YOUR PROGRESS 6   A softball team consists of 16 players. In how many ways can a coach choose the 9 starting players? (Assume the position of a player is not considered.)

Solution   *See page S43.*

Not considering the position of a player in Example 6 is an important assumption. If the positions center, left forward, right forward, left guard, and right guard are considered, then the problem is no longer a combination problem. If the coach chooses a team by position, then P_1 at center and P_2 at right guard would be a different team than P_1 at right guard and P_2 at center. In this case, because the position of a player is important, the number of teams is the permutations of 11 players chosen 5 at a time: $P(11, 5) = 55{,}440$.

EXAMPLE 7 ■ Counting Using the Combination Formula and the Counting Principle

A committee of five is chosen from five mathematicians and six economists. How many different committees are possible if the committee must include two mathematicians and three economists?

Solution

Because a committee of professors A, B, C, D, and E is exactly the same as a committee of professors B, D, E, A, and C, choosing a committee is an example of choosing a combination. There are five mathematicians from whom two are chosen, which is equivalent to $C(5, 2)$ combinations. There are six economists from whom three are chosen, which is equivalent to $C(6, 3)$ combinations. Therefore, by the counting principle, there are $C(5, 2) \cdot C(6, 3)$ ways to choose two mathematicians and three economists.

$$C(5, 2) \cdot C(6, 3) = \frac{5!}{2! \cdot 3!} \cdot \frac{6!}{3! \cdot 3!} = 10 \cdot 20 = 200$$

There are 200 possible committees consisting of two mathematicians and three economists.

CHECK YOUR PROGRESS 7   An IRS auditor randomly chooses five tax returns to audit from a stack of 10 tax returns, four of which are from corporations and six of which are from individuals. In how many different ways can the auditor choose the tax returns if the auditor wants to include three corporate and two individual returns?

Solution   *See page S43.*

Math Matters   Buying Every Possible Lottery Ticket

A lottery prize in Pennsylvania reached $65 million. A resident of the state suggested that it might be worth buying a ticket for every possible combination of numbers. To win the $65 million, a person needed to correctly select six of 50 numbers. Each ticket costs one dollar. Because the order of the numbers drawn is not important, the number of different possible tickets is $C(50, 6) = 15,890,700$. Thus it would cost the resident $15,890,700 to purchase tickets for every possible combination of numbers.

It might seem that an approximately $16 million investment to win $65 million is reasonable. Unfortunately, when prize levels reach such lofty heights, many more people play the lottery. This increases the chances that more than one person will select the winning combination of numbers. In fact, there were eight people with the winning numbers and each received approximately $8 million. Now the $16 million investment does not look very appealing.

Some of the problems in this section require a basic knowledge of what comprises a standard deck of playing cards. In a standard deck, there are four suits: spades, hearts, diamonds, and clubs. Each suit has 13 cards: 2 through 10, jack, queen, king, and ace. See the Math Matters on page 733.

EXAMPLE 8 ■ Counting Problems with Cards

From a standard deck of playing cards, five cards are chosen. How many five-card combinations contain

a. two kings and three queens?

b. five hearts?

c. five cards of the same suit?

Solution

a. There are $C(4, 2)$ ways of choosing two kings from four kings and $C(4, 3)$ ways of choosing three queens from four queens. By the counting principle, there are $C(4, 2) \cdot C(4, 3)$ ways of choosing two kings and three queens.

$$C(4, 2) \cdot C(4, 3) = \frac{4!}{2! \cdot 2!} \cdot \frac{4!}{3! \cdot 1!} = 6 \cdot 4 = 24$$

There are 24 ways of choosing two kings and three queens.

b. There are $C(13, 5)$ ways of choosing five hearts from 13 hearts.

$$C(13, 5) = \frac{13!}{5! \cdot 8!} = 1287$$

There are 1287 ways to choose five hearts from 13 hearts.

c. From part b, there would also be 1287 ways of choosing five spades from 13 spades, five clubs from 13 clubs, or five diamonds from 13 diamonds. Because there are four suits from which to choose and $C(13, 5)$ ways of choosing five cards from a suit, by the counting principle there are $4 \cdot C(13, 5)$ ways to choose five cards of the same suit.

$$4 \cdot C(13, 5) = 4 \cdot 1287 = 5148$$

There are 5148 ways of choosing five cards of the same suit from a standard deck of playing cards.

CHECK YOUR PROGRESS 8 From a standard deck of playing cards, five cards are chosen. How many five-card combinations contain four cards of the same suit?

Solution See page S43.

Five cards of the same suit is called a *flush* in poker.

Excursion

Choosing Numbers in Keno

A popular gambling game called Keno, first introduced in China over 2000 years ago, is played in many casinos. In Keno, there are 80 balls numbered from 1 to 80. The casino randomly chooses 20 balls from the 80 balls. These are "lucky balls" because if a gambler chooses some of the numbers on these balls, there is a possibility of winning money. The amount that is won depends on the number of lucky numbers the gambler has selected. The number of ways in which a casino can choose 20 balls from 80 is

$$C(80, 20) = \frac{80!}{20! \cdot 60!} \approx 3,535,000,000,000,000,000$$

Once the casino chooses the 20 lucky balls, the remaining 60 balls are unlucky for the gambler. A gambler who chooses five numbers will have from zero to five lucky numbers.

(continued)

A Keno card is used to mark the numbers chosen.

Let's consider the case in which two of the five numbers chosen by the gambler are lucky numbers. Because five numbers were chosen, there must be three unlucky numbers among the five numbers. The number of ways of choosing two lucky numbers from 20 lucky numbers is $C(20, 2)$. The number of ways of choosing three unlucky numbers from 60 unlucky numbers is $C(60, 3)$. By the counting principle, there are $C(20, 2) \cdot C(60, 3) = 190 \cdot 34{,}220 = 6{,}501{,}800$ ways to choose two lucky and three unlucky numbers.

Excursion Exercises

For each of the following exercises, assume that a gambler playing Keno has randomly chosen four numbers.

1. In how many ways can the gambler choose no lucky numbers?

2. In how many ways can the gambler choose exactly one lucky number?

3. In how many ways can the gambler choose exactly two lucky numbers?

4. In how many ways can the gambler choose exactly three lucky numbers?

5. In how many ways can the gambler choose four lucky numbers?

Exercise Set 11.2

In Exercises 1–36, evaluate each expression.

1. $8!$

2. $5!$

3. $9! - 5!$

4. $(9 - 5)!$

5. $(8 - 3)!$

6. $8! - 3!$

7. If $7! = 5040$, find $8!$.

8. If $9! = 362{,}880$, find $10!$.

9. If $6! = 720$, find $5!$.

10. If $11! = 39{,}916{,}800$, find $10!$.

11. If $P(n, 2) = 42$, find n.

12. If $P(n, 4) = 360$, find n.

13. $P(8, 5)$

14. $P(7, 2)$

15. $P(9, 7)$

16. $P(10, 5)$

17. $P(8, 0)$

18. $P(7, 0)$

19. $P(8, 8)$

20. $P(10, 10)$

21. $P(8, 2) \cdot P(5, 3)$

22. $\dfrac{P(10, 4)}{P(8, 4)}$

23. $\dfrac{P(6, 0)}{P(6, 6)}$

24. $\dfrac{P(6, 3) \cdot P(5, 2)}{P(4, 3)}$

25. $C(9, 2)$

26. $C(8, 6)$

27. $C(12, 0)$

28. $C(11, 11)$

29. $C(6, 2) \cdot C(7, 3)$

30. $C(8, 5) \cdot C(9, 4)$

31. $\dfrac{C(10, 4) \cdot C(5, 2)}{C(15, 6)}$

32. $\dfrac{C(4, 3) \cdot C(5, 2)}{C(9, 5)}$

33. $\dfrac{C(9, 7) \cdot C(5, 3)}{C(14, 10)}$

34. $3! \cdot C(8, 5)$

35. $4! \cdot C(10, 3)$

36. $5! \cdot C(18, 0)$

In Exercises 37–42, how many combinations are possible? Assume the items are distinct.

37. Seven items chosen five at a time

38. Eight items chosen three at a time

39. 12 items chosen seven at a time

40. Nine items chosen two at a time

41. 11 items chosen 11 at a time

42. 10 items chosen 10 at a time

43. Is it possible to calculate $C(7, 9)$? Think of your answer in terms of seven items chosen nine at a time.

44. Is it possible to calculate $C(n, k)$ where $k > n$? See Exercise 43 for some help.

45. **MP3 Player** A student downloaded five music files to a portable MP3 player. In how many different orders can the songs be played?

46. **Elections** The board of directors of a corporation must select a president, a secretary, and a treasurer. In how many possible ways can this be accomplished if there are 20 members on the board of directors?

47. **Elections** A committee of 16 students must select a president, a vice-president, a secretary, and a treasurer. In how many possible ways can this be accomplished?

48. **The Olympics** A gold, a silver, and a bronze medal are awarded in an Olympic event. In how many possible ways can the medals be awarded for a 200-meter sprint in which there are nine runners?

49. **Reading** A student must read three of seven books for an English class. How many different selections can the student make?

50. **Employment** The personnel director of a company must select four finalists from a group of 10 candidates for a job opening. How many different groups of four can the director select as finalists?

51. **Quality Control** A quality control inspector receives a shipment of 15 DVD players. How many different groups of three players can the inspector choose to test?

52. **Morse Code** In 1835, Samuel Morse, a professor of art at New York University, devised a code that could be transmitted over a wire by using an electric current. This was the invention of the telegraph. The code used is called Morse Code. It consists of a dot or a dash or a combination of up to five dots and/or dashes. For instance, the letter *c* is represented by — • — •, and • — represents the letter *a*. The numeral 0 is represented by five dashes, — — — — —. How many different symbols can be represented using Morse Code?

53. **15-Puzzles** The 15-puzzle consists of 15 numbered tiles and a blank space that, for mathematical analysis, is usually given the number 16. Assuming that any arrangement is possible, how many different arrangements of the 15-puzzle are possible? (*Note:* It is possible to prove that, starting with the puzzle as

shown, not every arrangement is possible. For instance, the arrangement 1 3 2 4 5 6 7 8 9 10 11 12 13 14 15 16 is not possible.)

54. **Signal Flags** The Coast Guard uses signal flags as a method of communicating between ships. If four different flags are available and the order in which the flags are raised is important, how many different signals are possible? Assume four flags are raised.

55. **Softball** How many games are necessary in a softball league consisting of eight teams if each team must play each of the other teams once?

56. **Test Banks** A math quiz is generated by randomly choosing five questions from a test bank consisting of 50 questions. How many different quizzes are possible?

57. **Football** A football league consists of six teams. How many games must be scheduled if each team must play each other team twice?

58. **Committee Selection** A committee of six people is chosen from eight women and eight men. How many different committees are possible that consist of three women and three men?

59. **Coin Tosses** Ten identical coins are tossed. How many possible arrangements of the coins include five heads and five tails?

60. **Coin Tosses** Twelve identical coins are tossed. How many possible arrangements of the coins include eight heads and four tails?

61. **Geometry** Seven points are drawn in a plane, no three of which are on the same straight line. How many different lines can be drawn through the seven points?

62. **Geometry** A pentagon is a five-sided plane figure. A diagonal is a line segment connecting any two non-adjacent vertices. How many diagonals are possible?

63. **Geometry** A hexagon is a six-sided plane figure. A diagonal is a line segment connecting any two nonadjacent vertices. How many diagonals are possible?

64. **Geometry** Seven distinct points are drawn on a circle. How many different triangles can be drawn in which each vertex of the triangle is at one of the seven points?

65. **Softball** Eighteen people decide to play softball. In how many ways can the 18 people be divided into two teams of nine people?

66. Bowling Fifteen people decide to form a bowling league. In how many ways can the 15 people be divided into three teams of five people each?

67. Committee Selection The "get-out-the-vote" committee of a political action group has 12 members. In how many ways can the 12 members be divided into groups of two people?

68. Pizza Toppings A restaurant offers a special pizza with any five toppings. If the restaurant has 12 toppings from which to choose, how many different special pizzas are possible?

69. Letter Arrangements How many different letter arrangements are possible using all the letters of the word *committee*?

70. Letter Arrangements How many different letter arrangements are possible using all the letters of the word *calculus*?

71. Firefighters At a certain fire station, one team of firefighters consists of 8 firefighters. If there are 24 firefighters qualified for a team, how many different teams are possible?

72. Platoons A typical platoon consists of 20 soldiers. If there are 30 soldiers available to create a platoon, how many different platoons are possible?

Exercises 73–78 refer to a standard deck of playing cards. Assume five cards are randomly chosen from the deck.

73. How many hands contain four aces?

74. How many hands contain two aces and two kings?

75. How many hands contain exactly three jacks?

76. How many hands contain exactly three jacks and two queens?

77. How many hands contain exactly two 7's?

78. How many hands contain exactly two 7's and two 8's?

79. Write a few sentences that explain the difference between a permutation and a combination of distinct objects. Give examples of each.

80. Francis Bacon, a contemporary of William Shakespeare, invented a cipher (a secret code) based on permutations of the letters *a* and *b*. Write an essay on Bacon's method and the intended use of his scheme.

Extensions

CRITICAL THINKING

81. If the expression $(x + y)^5$ is expanded, the result is initially 32 terms. The terms consist of every possible product of the form $a_1a_2a_3a_4a_5$ where each a_i is either x or y. After combining like terms, the expansion simplifies to 6 terms with variable parts x^5, x^4y, x^3y^2, x^2y^3, xy^4, and y^5. Use the formula for the arrangements of nondistinct objects to find the coefficient of each term and then write the expansion of $(x + y)^5$.

82. If the expression $(x + y)^6$ is expanded, the result is initially 64 terms. The terms consist of every possible product of the form $a_1a_2a_3a_4a_5a_6$ where each a_i is either x or y. After combining like terms, the expansion simplifies to 7 terms with variable parts x^6, x^5y, x^4y^2, x^3y^3, x^2y^4, xy^5, and y^6. Use the formula for the arrangements of nondistinct objects to find the coefficient of each term and then write the expansion of $(x + y)^6$.

EXPLORATIONS

83. Hamiltonian Circuits In Chapter 9, we examined the problem of determining certain paths through a network (or graph). One particular path, called a *Hamiltonian circuit,* visited each vertex (dot) of a graph exactly once and returned to the starting vertex. A Hamiltonian circuit is shown as the green path in the network below. The number associated with each line (edge) of the graph indicates the distance between two vertices. (The indicated distance does not match the physical distance in the drawing.) In most applications, the object is to find the *shortest* path. The green path shown here is the shortest path that visits each vertex exactly once and returns to the starting vertex.

One method of searching for the shortest Hamiltonian circuit is by trial and error. For a network with a small number of vertices, this procedure will work fine. As the number of vertices increases, the likelihood of finding a trial-and-error solution becomes extremely remote.

The counting principle can be used to find the number of possible paths through a network in which every pair of vertices possible is connected by a line. For the complete network with five vertices shown in the figure below, beginning at the home vertex labeled *H*, there are four choices for the next vertex to visit, three choices for the next, two choices for the next, and finally one choice that returns to *H*. By the counting principle, there are $4 \cdot 3 \cdot 2 \cdot 1 = 24$ possible circuits. Traveling circuit *HABCDH* is the same as traveling the circuit in the reverse order, *HDCBAH*. Thus there are $\frac{24}{2} = 12$ possible circuits. In general, there are $\frac{(n-1)!}{2}$ possible Hamiltonian circuits through a network of *n* vertices, where $n \geq 3$.

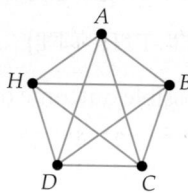

a. A network has eight vertices and each vertex is connected to the other vertices. How many Hamiltonian circuits are possible?

b. For the network at the right, find the number of possible Hamiltonian circuits.

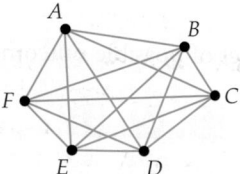

c. Suppose a network has 20 vertices (with every pair of vertices connected by a line segment) and a computer is available that can analyze one million paths per second. How many years would it take this computer to find all the possible Hamiltonian circuits of this network? (Assume a year is 365 days.)

d. Suppose a network has 40 vertices (with every pair of vertices connected by a line segment) and a computer is available that can analyze one trillion paths per second. How many years would it take this computer to find all the possible Hamiltonian circuits?

84. **Lotteries** The PowerBall multi-state lottery is played by choosing five numbers between 1 and 53 (regular numbers) and one number between 1 and 42 (bonus number). A player wins a prize under any of the following conditions:

   i) Only the bonus number is chosen correctly.

   ii) The bonus number and one regular number are chosen correctly.

   iii) The bonus number and two regular numbers are chosen correctly.

   iv) The bonus number and three regular numbers are chosen correctly.

   v) Three regular numbers are chosen correctly.

   vi) Four regular numbers are chosen correctly.

   vii) The bonus number and four regular numbers are chosen correctly.

   viii) Five regular numbers are chosen correctly.

   ix) The bonus number and five regular numbers are chosen correctly. This combination results in winning the jackpot.

   In how many different ways can a person who plays this game win a prize?

SECTION 11.3 | **Probability and Odds**

Introduction to Probability

In California, the likelihood of selecting the winning lottery numbers in the Super Lotto Plus game is approximately 1 chance in 41,000,000. In contrast, the likelihood of being struck by lightning is about 1 chance in 1,000,000. Comparing the likelihood of winning the Super Lotto Plus to the likelihood of being struck by lightning, you are 41 times more likely to be struck by lightning than to pick the winning California lottery numbers.

Which is more likely?

The likelihood of the occurrence of a particular event is described by a number between 0 and 1. (You can think of this as a percentage between 0% and 100%, inclusive.) This number is called the **probability** of the event. An event that is not very likely has a probability close to 0; an event that is very likely has a probability close to 1 (100%). For instance, the probability of being struck by lightning is close to 0. However, if you randomly choose a basketball player from the National Basketball Association, it is very likely that the player is over 6 feet tall, so the probability is close to 1.

Because any event has from a 0% to 100% chance of occurring, probabilities are always between 0 and 1, inclusive. If an event *must* occur, its probability is 1. If an event *cannot* occur, its probability is 0.

Probabilities can be calculated by considering the outcome of experiments. Here are some examples of experiments.

- Flip a coin and observe the outcome as a head or a tail.
- Select a company and observe its annual profit.
- Record the time a person spends at the checkout line in a supermarket.

The sample space of an experiment is the set of all possible outcomes of the experiment. For example, consider tossing a coin three times and observing the outcome as a head or a tail. Using H for head and T for tail, the sample space is

$$S = \{HHH, HHT, HTH, HTT, THH, THT, TTH, TTT\}$$

Note that the sample space consists of *every* possible outcome of tossing three coins.

EXAMPLE 1 ■ Find a Sample Space

A single die is rolled once. What is the sample space for this experiment?

Solution
The sample space is the set of possible outcomes of the experiment.

$$S = \{\;\boxed{\cdot}\;,\;\boxed{\because}\;,\;\boxed{\therefore}\;,\;\boxed{::}\;,\;\boxed{:\cdot:}\;,\;\boxed{:::}\;\}$$

CHECK YOUR PROGRESS 1   A coin is tossed twice. What is the sample space for this experiment?

Solution   See page S43.

Formally, an event is a subset of a sample space. Using the sample space of Example 1, here are some possible events:

- There are an even number of pips (dots) facing up. The event is

$$E_1 = \{\;\boxed{\because}\;,\;\boxed{::}\;,\;\boxed{:::}\;\}.$$

- The number of pips facing up is greater than 4. The event is $E_2 = \{\;\boxed{:\cdot:}\;,\;\boxed{:::}\;\}.$

- The number of pips facing up is less than 20. The event is

$$E_3 = \{\boxed{\cdot}, \boxed{\because}, \boxed{\therefore}, \boxed{::}, \boxed{\because\cdot}, \boxed{:::}\}.$$

Because the number of pips facing up is always less than 20, this event will always occur. The event and the sample space are the same.

- The number of pips facing up is greater than 15. The event is $E_4 = \emptyset$, the empty set. This is an impossible event; the number of pips facing up cannot be greater than 15.

Outcomes of some experiments are **equally likely,** which means that the chance of any one outcome is just as likely as the chance of another. For instance, if four balls of the same size but different colors—red, blue, green, and white—are placed in a box and a blindfolded person chooses one ball, the chance of choosing a green ball is the same as the chance of choosing any other color ball.

In the case of equally likely outcomes, the probability of an event is based on the number of elements in the event and the number of elements in the sample space. We will use $n(E)$ to denote the number of elements in the event E and $n(S)$ to denote the number of elements in the sample space S.

TAKE NOTE

As an example of an experiment whose outcomes are not equally likely, consider tossing a thumbtack and recording whether it lands with the point up or on its side. There are only two possible outcomes for this experiment, but the outcomes are not equally likely.

> **Probability of an Event**
>
> For an experiment with sample space S of *equally likely outcomes*, the probability $P(E)$ of an event E is given by
>
> $$P(E) = \frac{n(E)}{n(S)} = \frac{\text{number of elements in } E}{\text{total number of elements in sample space } S}$$

Because each outcome of rolling a fair die is equally likely, the probability of the events E_1 through E_4 described above can be determined from the formula for the probability of an event.

$$P(E_1) = \frac{3}{6} \quad \begin{array}{l} \longleftarrow \text{ Number of elements in } E_1 \\ \longleftarrow \text{ Number of elements in the sample space} \end{array}$$

$$= \frac{1}{2}$$

The probability of rolling an even number of pips on a single roll of one die is $\frac{1}{2}$ (or 50%).

$$P(E_2) = \frac{2}{6} \quad \begin{array}{l} \longleftarrow \text{ Number of elements in } E_2 \\ \longleftarrow \text{ Number of elements in the sample space} \end{array}$$

$$= \frac{1}{3}$$

The probability of rolling a number greater than 4 on a single roll of one die is $\frac{1}{3}$.

$$P(E_3) = \frac{6}{6} \quad \begin{array}{l} \longleftarrow \text{ Number of elements in } E_3 \\ \longleftarrow \text{ Number of elements in the sample space} \end{array}$$

$$= 1$$

The probability of rolling a number less than 20 on a single roll of one die is 1 (or 100%). Recall that the probability of any event that is certain to occur is 1.

$$P(E_4) = \frac{0}{6} \longleftarrow \text{Number of elements in } E_4$$
$$\phantom{P(E_4) = \frac{0}{6}} \longleftarrow \text{Number of elements in the sample space}$$
$$= 0$$

The probability of rolling a number greater than 15 on a single roll of one die is 0. (It is not possible to roll any number greater than 15.)

EXAMPLE 2 ■ Probability of Equally Likely Outcomes

A fair coin—one for which it is equally likely that heads or tails will result from a single toss—is tossed three times. What is the probability that two heads and one tail are tossed?

Solution
Determine the number of elements in the sample space. The sample space must include every possible toss of a head or a tail (in order) in three tosses of the coin.

$$S = \{HHH, HHT, HTH, HTT, THH, THT, TTH, TTT\}$$

The elements in the event are $E = \{HHT, HTH, THH\}$.

$$P(E) = \frac{n(E)}{n(S)} = \frac{3}{8}$$

The probability is $\frac{3}{8}$.

CHECK YOUR PROGRESS 2   If a fair die is rolled once, what is the probability that an odd number will show on the upward face?

Solution   *See page S43.*

TAKE NOTE

In Example 2, we calculated the probability as $\frac{3}{8}$. However, we could have expressed the probability as a decimal, 0.375, or as a percent, 37.5%. A probability can always be expressed as a fraction, a decimal, or a percent.

QUESTION   *Is it possible that the probability of some event could be 1.23?*

EXAMPLE 3 ■ Calculating Probabilities with Dice

Two fair dice are tossed, one after the other. What is the probability that the sum of the pips on the upward faces of the two dice equals 8?

ANSWER   *No. All probabilities must be between 0 and 1, inclusive.*

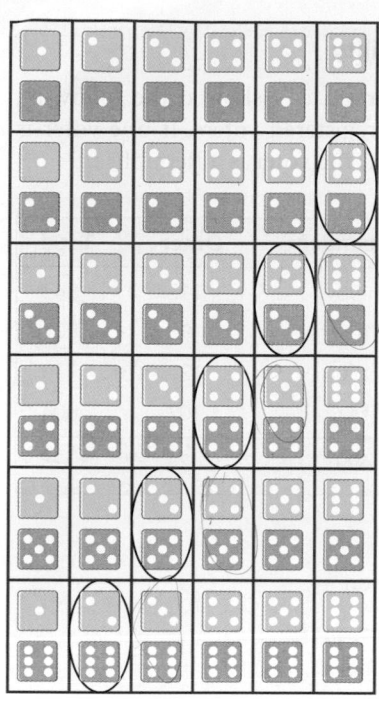

Figure 11.6

Outcomes of the roll of two dice

Point up	15
Side	85
Total	100

Solution

The dice must be considered as distinct, so there are 36 possible outcomes. (⚁ ⚄ and ⚄ ⚁ are considered different outcomes.) Therefore, $n(S) = 36$. The sample space is shown at the left. (See also Section 11.1.) Let E represent the event that the sum of the pips on the upward faces is 8. These outcomes are circled in Figure 11.6. By counting the number of circled pairs, $n(E) = 5$.

$$P(E) = \frac{n(E)}{n(S)} = \frac{5}{36}$$

The probability that the sum of the pips is 8 is $\frac{5}{36}$.

CHECK YOUR PROGRESS 3 Two fair dice are tossed. What is the probability that the sum of the pips on the upward faces of the two dice equals 7?

Solution *See page S43.*

Empirical Probability

Probabilities such as those calculated in the preceding examples are sometimes referred to as **theoretical probabilities.** In Example 2, we assume that, in theory, we have a perfectly balanced coin, and we calculate the probability based on the fact that each event is equally likely. Similarly, we assume the dice in Example 3 are equally likely to land with any of the six faces upward.

When a probability is based on data gathered from an experiment, it is called an **experimental probability** or an **empirical probability.** For instance, if we tossed a thumbtack 100 times and recorded the number of times it landed "point up," the results might be as shown in the table at the left. From this experiment, the empirical probability of "point up" is

$$P(\text{point up}) = \frac{15}{100} = 0.15$$

Empirical Probability of an Event

If an experiment is performed repeatedly and the occurrence of the event E is observed, the probability $P(E)$ of the event E is given by

$$P(E) = \frac{\text{number of times event } E \text{ occurred}}{\text{number of times the experiment was performed}}$$

EXAMPLE 4 ■ Calculate an Empirical Probability

A survey of the Registrar of Voters office in a certain city showed the following information on the ages and party affiliations of registered voters. If one voter is chosen from this survey, what is the probability that the voter is a Republican?

Age	Republican	Democrat	Independent	Other	Total
18–28	205	432	98	112	847
29–38	311	301	109	83	804
39–49	250	251	150	122	773
50+	272	283	142	107	804
Total	1038	1267	499	424	3228

Solution

Let R be the event that a Republican is selected. Then

$$P(R) = \frac{1038}{3228} \longleftarrow \text{ Number of Republicans in the survey}$$
$$\phantom{P(R) = \frac{1038}{3228}} \longleftarrow \text{ Total number of people surveyed}$$
$$\approx 0.32$$

The probability that the selected person is a Republican is approximately 0.32.

CHECK YOUR PROGRESS 4   Using the data from Example 4, what is the probability that a randomly selected person is between the ages of 39 and 49?

Solution   *See page S43.*

Application to Genetics

The Human Genome Project is a 13-year project designed to completely map the genetic make-up of *Homo sapiens.* Researchers hope to use this information to treat and prevent certain hereditary diseases.

The concept behind this project began with Gregor Mendel and his work on flower color and how it was transmitted from generation to generation. From his studies, Mendel concluded that flower color seems to be predictable in future generations by making certain assumptions about a plant's color "determiner." He concluded that red was a *dominant* determiner of color and that white was a *recessive* determiner. Today, geneticists talk about the *gene* for flower color and the *allele* of the gene. A gene consists of two dominant alleles (two red), a dominant and a recessive allele (red and white), or two recessive alleles (two white). Because red is the dominant allele, a flower will be white only if no dominant allele is present.

Later work by Reginald Punnett (1875–1967) showed how to determine the probability of certain flower colors by using a **Punnett square.** Using a capital letter for a dominant allele (R for red) and the corresponding lower-case letter for recessive allele (r for white), Punnett arranged the alleles of the parents in a square. A parent could be RR, Rr, or rr.

Math Matters   The Birth of Probability Theory

Pierre Fermat and Blaise Pascal are generally considered to be the founders of the study of probability. For many historians, the starting point of the formal discussion of probability is contained in a letter from Pascal to Fermat written in July of 1654.

> The Chevalier de Mere said to me that he found a falsehood in the theory of numbers for the following reason. If one wants to throw a six with a single die, there is an advantage in undertaking to do it in four throws, as the odds are 671 to 625. If one throws two sixes with a pair of dice, there is a disadvantage in having only 24 throws. However, 24 to 36 (which is the number of cases for two dice) is 4 to 6 (which is the number of cases on one die). This is the great "scandal" which makes him proclaim loftily that the theorems are not constant and Arithmetic is self-contradictory.

Basically (although it certainly isn't obvious from this letter), the Chevalier was claiming that there is better than a 50% chance of tossing a 6 in four rolls of a single die. By his reasoning, he concluded that there should be a better than 50% chance of rolling a pair of sixes in 24 tosses of two dice. However, the Chevalier tested his theory and found that 25 tosses were needed. From his tests, he concluded a "falsehood in the theory of numbers." In this letter, Pascal was mocking the inability of the Chevalier to correctly determine the probabilities involved.

Excursion

The Value of Pi by Simulation

A **simulation** is an activity designed to approximate a given situation. For instance, pilots fly a simulator to practice maneuvers that would be dangerous to try in an airplane. Chemists use computer programs to simulate chemical processes. This Excursion uses a simulation to approximate the value of π.

This Excursion will work better if four or five people work together. Get 25 toothpicks, and then tape several sheets of blank paper together to form a large rectangular shape. Use a large ruler to draw parallel lines on the paper such that the distance between the lines is the length of one toothpick. Then drop all of the toothpicks from approximately knee height onto the paper. (Make sure none of the toothpicks lands off the paper.) Record the number of toothpicks that cross any of the parallel lines. Repeat this process ten times for a total of 250 toothpicks dropped.[1]

Excursion Exercises

1. Using the recorded data, calculate the empirical probability that a dropped toothpick will cross a line.

2. The theoretical probability that a toothpick will cross a line is $\frac{2}{\pi}$. Use a calculator to find the value of $\frac{2}{\pi}$, rounded to four decimal places.

(continued)

Gre
(mĕ
(182
an A
mor
His
tran
traits from one ger
another was actua
confirm the prevail
the day that enviro
influenced the trait
However, his resear
suggest that plants
"determiners" that
characteristics of th
generation. Thus be
study of heredity. It
30 years for Mende
to be accepted in th
community. ■

---

1. See our website at **www.cengage.com/math** for a computer program that can be used to simulate the dropping of the toothpicks. This program will enable you to perform the experiment many thousands of times.

3. The experimental value you calculated in Exercise 1 should be close to the theoretical value you calculated in Exercise 2 (at least it should be if you dropped a toothpick around 1000 times). Calculate the percent error between the experimental value and the theoretical value. (The percent error can be determined by finding the difference between the two values and dividing it by the theoretical value.)

4. Explain how performing this experiment thousands of times could give you an approximate value for π.

5. Using your data, what approximate value for π do you calculate?

6. This experiment is based on a famous eighteenth century problem called the *Buffon Needle problem.* Look up "Buffon Needle problem" in the library or on the Internet and write a short essay about this problem and how it applies to this Excursion.

Exercise Set 11.3

In Exercises 1–6, list the elements of the sample space for each experiment.

1. A coin is flipped three times.

2. An even number between 1 and 11 is selected at random.

3. One day in the first two weeks of November is selected.

4. A current U.S. coin is selected from a piggybank.

5. A state is selected from the states in the U.S. whose name begins with the letter A.

6. A month is selected from the months that have exactly 30 days.

In Exercises 7–15, assume that it is equally likely for a child to be born a boy or a girl, and that the Lin family is planning on having three children.

7. List the elements of the sample space for the genders of the three children.

8. List the elements of the event that the Lins have two boys and one girl.

9. List the elements of the event that the Lins have at least two girls.

10. List the elements of the event that the Lins have no girls.

11. List the elements of the event that the Lins have at least one girl.

12. Compute the probability that the Lins will have two boys and one girl.

13. Compute the probability that the Lins will have at least two girls.

14. Compute the probability that the Lins will have no girls.

15. Compute the probability that the Lins will have at least one girl.

In Exercises 16–22, a coin is tossed four times. Assuming that the coin is equally likely to land on heads or tails, compute the probability of each event occurring.

16. Two heads and two tails

17. One head and three tails

18. All tails

19. All four coin tosses are identical

20. At least three heads

21. At least two tails

22. At least one head

In Exercises 23–26, a dodecahedral die (one with 12 sides numbered from 1 to 12) is tossed once. Find each of the following probabilities.

23. The number on the upward face is 12.

24. The number on the upward face is not 10.

25. The number on the upward face is divisible by 4.

26. The number on the upward face is less than 5 or greater than 9.

In Exercises 27–36, two regular six-sided dice are tossed. Compute the probability that the sum of the pips on the upward faces of the two dice is each of the following. (See Figure 11.6 on page 747 for the sample space of this experiment.)

27. 6   28. 11

29. 2   30. 12

31. 1   32. 14

33. At least 10   34. At most 5

35. An even number 36. An odd number

37. If two dice are rolled, compute the probability of rolling doubles (both dice show the same number of pips).

38. If two dice are rolled, compute the probability of *not* rolling doubles.

In Exercises 39–44, a card is selected at random from a standard deck of playing cards.

39. Compute the probability that the card is red.

40. Compute the probability that the card is a spade.

41. Compute the probability that the card is a 9.

42. Compute the probability that the card is a face card (jack, queen, or king).

43. Compute the probability that the card is between 5 and 9.

44. Compute the probability that the card is between 3 and 6.

Voter Characteristics In Exercises 45–50, use the data given in Example 4 to compute the probability that a randomly chosen voter from the survey will satisfy the following.

45. The voter is a Democrat.

46. The voter is not a Republican.

47. The voter is 50 years old or older.

48. The voter is under 39 years old.

49. The voter is between 39 and 49, and is registered as an Independent.

50. The voter is under 29 and is registered as a Democrat.

Education Levels In Exercises 51–54, a survey asked 850 respondents about their highest levels of completed education. The results are given in the following table.

Education completed	Number of respondents
No high school diploma	52
High school diploma	234
Associate's degree or two years of college	274
Bachelor's degree	187
Master's degree	67
Ph.D. or professional degree	36

If a respondent from the survey is selected at random, compute the probability of each of the following.

51. The respondent did not complete high school.

52. The respondent has an associate's degree or two years of college (but not more).

53. The respondent has a Ph.D. or professional degree.

54. The respondent has a degree beyond a bachelor's degree.

94. You can bet that the ball will land on any number from 1 to 12. If you win, the casino will pay you $2 for each dollar you bet. What is the probability of winning this bet?

95. You can bet that the ball will land on any particular number. If you win, the casino will pay you $35 for each dollar you bet. What is the probability of winning this bet?

96. You can bet that the ball will land on one of 0 or 00. If you win, the casino will pay you $17 for each dollar you bet. What is the probability of winning this bet?

97. You can bet that the ball will land on certain groups of six numbers (such as 1–6). If you win, the casino will pay you $5 for each dollar you bet. What is the probability of winning this bet?

| SECTION 11.4 | **Addition and Complement Rules** |

The Addition Rule for Probabilities

Suppose you draw a single card from a standard deck of playing cards. The sample space S consists of the 52 cards of the deck. Therefore, $n(S) = 52$. Now consider the events

$$E_1 = \text{a four is drawn} = \{♠4, ♥4, ♦4, ♣4\}$$
$$E_2 = \text{a spade is drawn}$$
$$= \{♠A, ♠2, ♠3, ♠4, ♠5, ♠6, ♠7, ♠8, ♠9, ♠10, ♠J, ♠Q, ♠K\}$$

It is possible, on one draw, to satisfy the conditions of both events: the ♠4 could be drawn. This card is an element of both E_1 and E_2.

Now consider the events

$$E_3 = \text{a five is drawn} = \{♠5, ♥5, ♦5, ♣5\}$$
$$E_4 = \text{a king is drawn} = \{♠K, ♥K, ♦K, ♣K\}$$

In this case, it is not possible to draw one card that satisfies the conditions of both events. There are no elements common to both sets. Two events that cannot both occur at the same time are called **mutually exclusive events.** The events E_3 and E_4 are mutually exclusive events, whereas E_1 and E_2 are not.

Mutually Exclusive Events

Two events A and B are mutually exclusive if they cannot occur at the same time. That is, A and B are mutually exclusive when $A \cap B = \varnothing$.

QUESTION   *A die is rolled once. Let E be the event that an even number is rolled and let O be the event that an odd number is rolled. Are the events E and O mutually exclusive?*

The probability of either of two mutually exclusive events occurring can be determined by adding the probabilities of the individual events.

ANSWER   *Yes. It is not possible to roll an even number and an odd number on a single roll of the die.*

Probability of Mutually Exclusive Events

If A and B are two mutually exclusive events, then the probability of A or B occurring is

$$P(A \text{ or } B) = P(A) + P(B)$$

EXAMPLE 1 ■ Probability of Mutually Exclusive Events

Suppose a single card is drawn from a standard deck of playing cards. Find the probability of drawing a five or a king.

Solution

Let $A = \{\spadesuit 5, \heartsuit 5, \diamondsuit 5, \clubsuit 5\}$ and $B = \{\spadesuit K, \heartsuit K, \diamondsuit K, \clubsuit K\}$. There are 52 cards in a standard deck of playing cards; thus $n(S) = 52$. Because the events are mutually exclusive, we can use the formula for the probability of mutually exclusive events.

$P(A \text{ or } B) = P(A) + P(B)$ • Formula for the probability of mutually exclusive events

$\qquad = \dfrac{1}{13} + \dfrac{1}{13} = \dfrac{2}{13}$ • $P(A) = \dfrac{4}{52} = \dfrac{1}{13}$, $P(B) = \dfrac{4}{52} = \dfrac{1}{13}$

The probability of drawing a five or a king is $\dfrac{2}{13}$.

CHECK YOUR PROGRESS 1   Two fair dice are tossed once. What is the probability of rolling a 7 or an 11? For the sample space for this experiment, see page 721.

Solution   *See page S44.*

Consider the experiment of rolling two dice. Let A be the event of rolling a sum of 8 and let B be the event of rolling a double (the same number on both dice).

$A = \{\boxed{\,\cdot\cdot\,}, \boxed{\,\cdot\cdot\,}, \boxed{\,\cdot\cdot\,}, \boxed{\,\cdot\cdot\,}, \boxed{\,\cdot\cdot\,}\}$
$B = \{\boxed{\,\cdot\cdot\,}, \boxed{\,\cdot\cdot\,}, \boxed{\,\cdot\cdot\,}, \boxed{\,\cdot\cdot\,}, \boxed{\,\cdot\cdot\,}, \boxed{\,\cdot\cdot\,}\}$

These events are *not* mutually exclusive because it is possible to satisfy the conditions of each event on one toss of the dice—a $\boxed{\,\cdot\cdot\,}\boxed{\,\cdot\cdot\,}$ could be rolled. Therefore, $P(A \text{ or } B)$, the probability of a sum of 8 or a double, cannot be calculated using the formula for the probability of mutually exclusive events. However, a modification of that formula can be used.

> ✓ **TAKE NOTE**
>
> The $P(A \text{ and } B)$ term in the Addition Rule for Probabilities is subtracted to compensate for the overcounting of the first two terms of the formula. If two events are mutually exclusive, then $A \cap B = \varnothing$. Therefore, $n(A \cap B) = 0$ and $P(A \text{ and } B) = \dfrac{n(A \cap B)}{n(S)} = 0$. For mutually exclusive events, the Addition Rule for Probabilities is the same as the formula for the probability of mutually exclusive events.

Addition Rule for Probabilities

Let A and B be two events in a sample space S. Then

$$P(A \text{ or } B) = P(A) + P(B) - P(A \text{ and } B)$$

Using this formula with

$A = \{\boxed{\,\cdot\cdot\,}, \boxed{\,\cdot\cdot\,}, \boxed{\,\cdot\cdot\,}, \boxed{\,\cdot\cdot\,}, \boxed{\,\cdot\cdot\,}\}$
$B = \{\boxed{\,\cdot\cdot\,}, \boxed{\,\cdot\cdot\,}, \boxed{\,\cdot\cdot\,}, \boxed{\,\cdot\cdot\,}, \boxed{\,\cdot\cdot\,}, \boxed{\,\cdot\cdot\,}\}$
$A \cap B = \{\boxed{\,\cdot\cdot\,}\}$

the probability of A or B can be calculated.

$$P(A \text{ or } B) = P(A) + P(B) - P(A \text{ and } B)$$

$$= \frac{5}{36} + \frac{6}{36} - \frac{1}{36} \quad \bullet P(A) = \frac{5}{36}, P(B) = \frac{6}{36}, P(A \cap B) = \frac{1}{36}$$

$$= \frac{10}{36} = \frac{5}{18}$$

On a single roll of two dice, the probability of rolling a sum of 8 or a double is $\frac{5}{18}$.

TAKE NOTE

Recall that the probability of an event A is $P(A) = \frac{n(A)}{n(S)}$. Therefore,

$$P(A \text{ and } B) = \frac{n(A \cap B)}{n(S)}.$$

	F	**No F**	**Total**
V	21	198	219
No V	76	195	271
Total	97	393	490

V: Vaccinated
F: Contracted the flu

EXAMPLE 2 ■ Use the Addition Rule for Probabilities

The table at the left shows data from an experiment conducted to test the effectiveness of a flu vaccine. If one person is selected from this population, what is the probability that the person was vaccinated or contracted the flu?

Solution

Let $V = \{\text{people who were vaccinated}\}$ and $F = \{\text{people who contracted the flu}\}$. These events are not mutually exclusive because there are 21 people who were vaccinated and who contracted the flu. The sample space S consists of the 490 people who participated in the experiment. From the table, $n(V) = 219$, $n(F) = 97$, and $n(V \text{ and } F) = 21$.

$$P(V \text{ or } F) = P(V) + P(F) - P(V \text{ and } F)$$

$$= \frac{219}{490} + \frac{97}{490} - \frac{21}{490}$$

$$= \frac{295}{490} \approx 0.602$$

The probability of selecting a person who was vaccinated or who contracted the flu is approximately 60.2%.

CHECK YOUR PROGRESS 2 The data in the table below show the starting salaries of college graduates with selected degrees. If one person is chosen from this population, what is the probability that the person has a degree in business or has a starting salary between $20,000 and $24,999?

	Degree			
Salary (in $)	**Engineering**	**Business**	**Chemistry**	**Psychology**
Less than 20,000	0	4	1	12
20,000–24,999	4	16	3	16
25,000–29,999	7	21	5	15
30,000–34,999	12	35	5	7
35,000 or more	12	22	4	5

Solution **See page S44.**

The Complement of an Event

Consider the experiment of tossing a single die once. The sample space is

$$S = \{ \boxed{\cdot}, \boxed{\because}, \boxed{\therefore}, \boxed{::}, \boxed{:\cdot:}, \boxed{:::} \}$$

Now consider the event $E = \{ \boxed{\therefore} \}$, that is, the event of tossing a $\boxed{\therefore}$. The probability of E is

$$P(E) = \frac{1}{6} \quad \longleftarrow \text{ Number of elements in } E$$
$$\quad \longleftarrow \text{ Number of elements in the sample space}$$

The **complement** of an event E, symbolized by E^c, is the "opposite" event of E. The complement includes all those outcomes of S that are not in E and excludes the outcomes in E. For the event E above, E^c is the event of not tossing a $\boxed{\therefore}$. Thus

$$E^c = \{ \boxed{\cdot}, \boxed{\because}, \boxed{::}, \boxed{:\cdot:}, \boxed{:::} \}$$

Notice that because E and E^c are opposite events, they are mutually exclusive, and their union is the entire sample space S. Thus $P(E) + P(E^c) = P(S)$. But $P(S) = 1$, so $P(E^c) = 1 - P(E)$.

Probability of the Complement of an Event

If E is an event and E^c is the complement of the event, then

$$P(E^c) = 1 - P(E)$$

Continuing our example, the probability of not tossing a $\boxed{\therefore}$ is given by

$$P\left(\text{not a } \boxed{\therefore}\right) = 1 - P\left(\boxed{\therefore}\right)$$
$$= 1 - \frac{1}{6} = \frac{5}{6}$$

You can also verify the probability of E^c directly:

$$P\left(\text{not a } \boxed{\therefore}\right) = \frac{5}{6} \quad \longleftarrow \text{ Number of elements in } E^c$$
$$\quad \longleftarrow \text{ Number of elements in the sample space}$$

EXAMPLE 3 ■ Find a Probability by the Complement Rule

The probability of tossing a sum of 11 on the toss of two dice is $\frac{1}{18}$. What is the probability of not tossing a sum of 11 on the toss of two dice?

Solution
Use the formula for the probability of the complement of an event. Let $E = \{\text{toss a sum of } 11\}$. Then $E^c = \{\text{toss a sum that is not } 11\}$.

$$P(E^c) = 1 - P(E)$$
$$= 1 - \frac{1}{18} = \frac{17}{18} \qquad \bullet \; P(E) = \frac{1}{18}$$

The probability of not tossing a sum of 11 is $\frac{17}{18}$.

CHECK YOUR PROGRESS 3   The probability that a person has type A blood is 34%. What is the probability that a person does not have type A blood?

Solution   *See page S44.*

Suppose we toss a coin three times and want to calculate the probability of having heads occur *at least once*. We could list all the possibilities of tossing three coins, as shown below, and then find the ones that contain at least one head.

$$\underbrace{\{\text{HHH, HHT, HTH, HTT, THH, THT, TTH,}}_{\text{at least one head}} \text{TTT}\}$$

The probability of at least one head is $\frac{7}{8}$.

Another way to calculate this result is to use the formula for the probability of the complement of an event. Let $E = \{\text{at least one head}\}$. From the list above, note that E contains every outcome except TTT (no heads). Thus $E^c = \{\text{TTT}\}$ and we have

$$P(E) = 1 - P(E^c)$$
$$= 1 - \frac{1}{8} = \frac{7}{8} \qquad \bullet \; P(E^c) = \frac{n(E^c)}{n(S)} = \frac{1}{8}$$

This is the same result that we calculated above. As we will see, sometimes working with a complement is much less work than proceeding directly.

In many cases, the principles of counting that were discussed in Sections 11.1 and 11.2 are part of the process of calculating a probability.

EXAMPLE 4 ■ Find a Probability by the Complement Rule

A die is tossed four times. What is the probability that a 🎲 will show on the upward face at least once?

Solution

Let $E = \{\text{at least one 6}\}$. Then $E^c = \{\text{no 6's}\}$. To calculate the number of elements in the sample space (all possible outcomes of tossing a die four times) and the number of items in E^c, we will use the counting principle.

Because on each toss of the die there are six possible outcomes,

$$n(S) = 6 \cdot 6 \cdot 6 \cdot 6 = 1296$$

On each toss of the die there are five numbers that are not 6's. Therefore,

$$n(E^c) = 5 \cdot 5 \cdot 5 \cdot 5 = 625$$
$$P(E) = 1 - P(E^c)$$
$$= 1 - \frac{625}{1296} = \frac{671}{1296}$$
$$\approx 0.518$$

When a die is tossed four times, the probability that a 🎲 will show on the upward face at least once is approximately 0.518.

CHECK YOUR PROGRESS 4   A pair of dice are rolled three times. What is the probability that a sum of 7 will occur at least once?

Solution   See page S44.

MathMatters   **The Monty Hall Problem**

A famous probability puzzle began with the game show *Let's Make a Deal*, of which Monty Hall was the host, and goes something like the following. (See also the Chapter 1 opener on page 1.) Suppose you appear on the show and are shown three closed curtains. Behind one of the curtains is the grand prize; behind the other two curtains are less desirable prizes (like a goat!). If you select the curtain hiding the grand prize, you win that prize. The probability of randomly choosing the grand prize, of course, is 1/3. After you choose a curtain, the show's host (who knows where the grand prize is) does not immediately open it to show you what you have won. Instead, he opens one of the other two curtains and reveals a goat. Obviously you are relieved that you did not choose that particular curtain, but he then asks if you would like to switch your choice to the third curtain. Should you stay with your original choice, or switch? Most people would say at first that it makes no difference. However, computer simulations that play the game over and over have shown that you *should* switch. In fact, you double your chances of winning the grand prize if you give up your first choice! See Exercise 56 on page 766 for a mathematical investigation, and then try a simulation of your own with Exercises 58 and 59.

Combinatoric Formulas and Probability

We end this section with another example of using counting principles in the calculation of a probability. In this case we will use the combination formula $C(n, r) = \frac{n!}{r!(n - r)!}$, which gives the number of ways r objects can be chosen from n objects.

EXAMPLE 5 ■ Find a Probability Using the Combination Formula

Every manufacturing process has the potential to produce a defective article. Suppose a manufacturing process for tableware produces 40 dinner plates, of which three are defective. (For instance, there is a paint flaw.) If five plates are randomly selected from the 40, what is the probability that at least one is defective?

Solution

Let $E = \{$at least one plate is defective$\}$. It is easier to work with the complement event, $E^c = \{$no plates are defective$\}$. To calculate the number of elements in the sample space (all possible outcomes of choosing five plates from 40), use the combination formula with $n = 40$ (the number of plates) and $r = 5$ (the number of plates that are chosen). Then

$$n(S) = C(40, 5) = \frac{40!}{5!(40 - 5)!} \qquad \bullet\ n = 40, r = 5$$

$$= \frac{40!}{5!\,35!} = 658{,}008$$

To find the number of outcomes that contain no defective plates, all of the plates chosen must come from the 37 nondefective plates. Therefore, we must calculate the number of ways five objects can be chosen from 37. Thus $n = 37$ (the number of nondefective plates) and $r = 5$ (the number of plates chosen).

$$n(E^c) = C(37, 5) = \frac{37!}{5!\,(37-5)!} \qquad \bullet\ n = 37, r = 5$$

$$= \frac{37!}{5!\,32!} = 435{,}897$$

$$P(E) = 1 - P(E^c)$$

$$= 1 - \frac{435{,}897}{658{,}008} = \frac{222{,}111}{658{,}008}$$

$$\approx 0.338$$

The probability is approximately 0.338, or 33.8%.

CHECK YOUR PROGRESS 5 The winner of a contest will be blindfolded and then allowed to reach into a hat containing 31 $1 bills and four $100 bills. The winner can remove four bills from the hat and keep the money. Find the probability that the winner will pull out at least one $100 bill.

Solution   See page S44.

Excursion

Keno Revisited

In Section 11.2 (see pages 739–740), we looked at the popular casino game Keno, in which a player chooses numbers from 1 to 80 and hopes that the casino will draw balls with the same numbers.

A player can choose only one number, or as many as 20. The casino will then pick 20 numbered balls from the 80 possible; if enough of the player's numbers match the lucky numbers the casino chooses, the player wins money. The amount won varies according to how many numbers were chosen and how many match.

Excursion Exercises

1. A gambler playing Keno has randomly chosen five numbers. What is the probability that the gambler will match at least one lucky number?

2. If five numbers are chosen, compute the probability of matching fewer than five lucky numbers.

3. If the Keno player chooses 15 numbers, bets $1, and matches 13 of the lucky numbers, the gambler will be paid $12,000. What is the probability of this occurring?

(continued)

4. If the Keno player chooses 15 numbers and matches five or six of the lucky numbers, the gambler gets the bet back but is not paid any extra. What is the probability of this occurring?

5. Some casinos will let you choose up to 20 numbers. In this case, if you don't match any of the lucky numbers, the casino pays you! Although this may seem unusual, it is actually more difficult not to match any of the lucky numbers than it is to match a few of them. Compute the probability of not matching any of the lucky numbers at all, and compare it to the probability of matching five lucky numbers.

6. If 20 numbers are chosen, find the probability of matching *at least one* lucky number.

Exercise Set 11.4

1. What are mutually exclusive events? How do you calculate the probability of mutually exclusive events?

2. Give an example of two mutually exclusive events and an example of two events that are not mutually exclusive.

In Exercises 3–6, first verify that the compound event consists of two mutually exclusive events, and then compute the probability of the compound event occurring.

3. A single card is drawn from a standard deck of playing cards. Find the probability of drawing a 4 or an ace.

4. A single card is drawn from a standard deck. Find the probability of drawing a heart or a club.

5. Two dice are rolled. Find the probability of rolling a 2 or a 10.

6. Two dice are rolled. Find the probability of rolling a 7 or an 8.

7. If $P(A) = 0.2$, $P(B) = 0.5$, and $P(A \text{ and } B) = 0.1$, find $P(A \text{ or } B)$.

8. If $P(A) = 0.6$, $P(B) = 0.4$, and $P(A \text{ and } B) = 0.2$, find $P(A \text{ or } B)$.

9. If $P(A) = 0.3$, $P(B) = 0.8$, and $P(A \text{ or } B) = 0.9$, find $P(A \text{ and } B)$.

10. If $P(A) = 0.7$, $P(A \text{ and } B) = 0.4$, and $P(A \text{ or } B) = 0.8$, find $P(B)$.

In Exercises 11–14, suppose you ask a friend to randomly choose an integer between 1 and 10, inclusive.

11. What is the probability that the number will be more than 6 or odd?

12. What is the probability that the number will be less than 5 or even?

13. What is the probability that the number will be even or prime?

14. What is the probability that the number will be prime or greater than 7?

In Exercises 15–20, two dice are rolled. Determine the probability of each of the following. ("Doubles" means both dice show the same number)

15. Rolling a 6 or doubles

16. Rolling a 7 or doubles

17. Rolling an even number or doubles

18. Rolling a number greater than 7 or doubles

19. Rolling an odd number or a number less than 6

20. Rolling an even number or a number greater than 9

In Exercises 21–26, a single card is drawn from a standard deck. Find the probability of each of the following events.

21. Drawing an 8 or a spade

22. Drawing an ace or a red card

23. Drawing a jack or a face card

24. Drawing a red card or a face card

25. Drawing a diamond or a black card

26. Drawing a spade or a red card

Employment In Exercises 27–30, use the data in the table below, which shows the employment status of individuals in a particular town by age group.

Age	Full-time	Part-time	Unemployed
0–17	24	164	371
18–25	185	203	148
26–34	348	67	27
35–49	581	179	104
50+	443	162	173

27. If a person is randomly chosen from the town's population, what is the probability that the person is aged 26–34 or is employed part-time?

28. If a person is randomly chosen from the town's population, what is the probability that the person is at least 50 years old or unemployed?

29. If a person is randomly chosen from the town's population, what is the probability that the person is under 18 or employed part-time?

30. If a person is randomly chosen from the town's population, what is the probability that the person is 18 or older or employed full-time?

31. **Contests** If the probability of winning a particular contest is 0.04, what is the probability of not winning the contest?

32. **Weather** Suppose the probability that it will rain tomorrow is 0.38. What is the probability that it will not rain tomorrow?

33. **Car Accidents** If there is a 1 in 2500 chance of an individual being involved in a car accident, find the probability of not being involved in a car accident.

34. **Elections** The odds in favor of a candidate winning an election are given as 3 to 5. What is the probability that the candidate will lose the election?

In Exercises 35–42, use the formula for the probability of the complement of an event.

35. Two dice are tossed. What is the probability of not tossing a 7?

36. Two dice are tossed. What is the probability of not getting doubles?

37. Two dice are tossed. What is the probability of getting a sum of at least 4?

38. Two dice are tossed. What is the probability of getting a sum of at most 11?

39. A single card is drawn from a deck. What is the probability of not drawing an ace?

40. A single card is drawn from a deck. What is the probability of not drawing a face card?

41. A coin is flipped four times. What is the probability of getting at least one tail?

42. A coin is flipped four times. What is the probability of getting at least two heads?

43. A single die is rolled three times. What is the probability that a 1 will show on the upward face at least once?

44. A single die is rolled four times. Find the probability that a 5 will be rolled at least once.

45. A pair of dice are rolled three times. What is the probability that a sum of 8 on the two dice will occur at least once?

46. A pair of dice are rolled four times. Compute the probability that a sum of 11 on the two dice will occur at least once.

47. A magician shuffles a standard deck of playing cards and allows an audience member to pull out a card, look at it, and replace it in the deck. Two additional people do the same. Find the probability that of the three cards drawn, at least one is a face card.

48. As in the preceding exercise, four audience members pull a card from a standard deck one-by-one and replace it. What is the probability that at least one ace is drawn?

49. If a person draws three cards from a standard deck (without replacing them), what is the probability that at least one of the cards is a face card?

50. If a person draws four cards from a standard deck (without replacing them), what is the probability that at least one of the cards is an ace?

51. **Video Rentals** A video rental store purchases 30 copies of a new movie. Unbenownst to the video store, four of the tapes are defective. If the store rents 12 of these videos the first day, what is the probability that at least one of the 12 renters will get a defective video?

52. **DVD Players** An electronics store currently has 28 new DVD players in stock, of which five are defective.

If customers buy three DVD players, what is the probability that at least one of them will be defective?

53. Prize Drawing Three employees of a restaurant each contributed one business card for a random drawing to win a prize. Forty-two business cards were received in all, and three cards will be drawn for prizes. Determine the probability that at least one of the restaurant employees will win a prize.

54. Coins A bag contains 44 U.S. quarters and six Canadian quarters. (The coins are identical in size.) If five quarters are randomly picked from the bag, what is the probability of getting at least one Canadian quarter?

Extensions

CRITICAL THINKING

55. Blackjack In the game blackjack, a player is dealt two cards from a standard deck of playing cards. The player has a blackjack if one card is an ace and the other card is a 10, a jack, a queen, or a king. In some casinos, blackjack is played with more than one standard deck of playing cards. Does using more than one deck of cards change the probability of getting a blackjack?

56. Monty Hall Problem The *Monty Hall problem* is described in the Math Matters on page 762. The question arises, "If the contestant changes his or her original choice of curtain, what is the probability of choosing the curtain hiding the grand prize?" To answer this question, complete the following.

a. What is the probability that the contestant will choose the grand prize on the first try?

b. What is the probability that the prize is not behind the curtain chosen by the contestant?

c. What is the probability that the person will choose the grand prize by switching?

57. Door Codes A planned community has 300 homes, each with an automatic garage door opener. The door opener has eight switches that a homeowner can set to 0 or 1. For example, a door opener code might be 01101001. Assuming all the homes in the community are sold, what is the probability that at least two homeowners will set their switches to the same code, and will therefore be able to open each other's garage doors?

COOPERATIVE LEARNING

58. Monty Hall Problem When someone is first presented with the Monty Hall problem in Exercise 56, there is a tendency for that person to think that switching his or her choice of curtain does not make any difference. You can actually simulate the Monty Hall game using playing cards and show that one is twice as likely to win by switching from the first choice. To do this you will need at least two people and three cards, say the ace of spades to represent the grand prize, and the two of hearts and the two of diamonds, which represent the other two prizes. Shuffle the cards and place them face down on the table. Choose one of the cards. The other player picks up the remaining two cards, removes one of the cards that is not the ace (it is possible that both cards will not be the ace), and places the other card face down on the table. Now you may either stay with your original selection or change to the remaining card. Perform this experiment 30 times staying with your original selection and thirty times where you change to the other card. Keep a record of how many times staying with your original selection resulted in selecting the ace and how many times switching cards resulted in choosing the ace. On the basis of your results, is staying or switching the better strategy?

59. Monty Hall Problem The benefit of switching curtains in the Monty Hall problem is even more dramatic if there are more hidden prizes from which to choose. Instead of using three cards as in Exercise 58, use five cards, the four 2's and the ace of spades. Shuffle them well, place them face down on a table, and choose one card. Another person then picks up the remaining four cards, removes three 2's, and places the remaining card face down on the table. Now you may either stay with your original selection or switch to the remaining card. Perform this experiment 30 times staying with your original selection and 30 where you change to the other card. Keep a record of how many times staying with your original selection resulted in selecting the ace and how many times changing resulted in choosing the ace. On the basis of your results, is staying or switching the better strategy? About how many more times did switching result in choosing the ace than did staying with your original choice?

EXPLORATIONS

60. **Poker** In five-card stud poker, a hand containing five cards of the same suit from a standard deck is called a flush. In this Exploration, you will compute the probability of getting a flush.

   a. How many five-card poker hands are possible?

   b. How many five-card poker hands are possible that contain all spades?

   c. What is the probability of getting a five-card poker hand containing all spades?

   d. What is the probability of getting a five-card poker hand containing all hearts? all diamonds? all clubs?

   e. Are the events of getting either five spades, five hearts, five diamonds, or five clubs mutually exclusive?

   f. What is the probability of getting a flush in five-card stud poker?

SECTION 11.5 | Conditional Probability

Conditional Probability

	F	No F	Total
V	21	198	219
No V	76	195	271
Total	97	393	490

V: Vaccinated
F: Contracted the flu

	F	No F	Total
V	21	198	219

In the preceding section, we discussed the effectiveness of a flu vaccination in preventing the onset of the flu. The table from that discussion is shown again at the left. From the table, we can calculate the probability that one person randomly selected from this population will have the flu.

$$P(F) = \frac{n(F)}{n(S)} = \frac{97}{490} \approx 0.198 \qquad \bullet \ n(F) = 97, \ n(S) = 490$$
(S denotes the sample space)

Now consider a slightly different situation. We could ask, "What is the probability that a person randomly chosen from this population will contract the flu *given* that the person received the flu vaccination?"

In this case we know that the person received a flu vaccination and we want to determine the probability that the person will contract the flu. Therefore, the only part of the table that is of concern to us is the top row. In this case, we have

$$P(F \text{ given } V) = \frac{21}{219} \approx 0.096$$

Thus the probability that an individual will contract the flu given that the individual has been vaccinated is about 0.096.

The probability of an event B occurring given that we know some other event A has already occurred is called a **conditional probability,** and is denoted $P(B \mid A)$.

> ### Conditional Probability Formula
>
> Let A and B be two events in a sample space S. Then the conditional probability of B given that A has occurred is
>
> $$P(B \mid A) = \frac{P(A \text{ and } B)}{P(A)}$$
>
> The symbol $P(B \mid A)$ is read "the probability of B given A."

To see how this formula applies to the flu data above, let

S = {all people participating in the test}
F = {people who contracted the flu}
V = {people who were vaccinated}

Then $F \cap V$ = {people who contracted the flu *and* were vaccinated}.

$$P(F \mid V) = \frac{P(F \text{ and } V)}{P(V)} = \frac{\dfrac{21}{490}}{\dfrac{219}{490}}$$

- $P(F \text{ and } V) = \dfrac{n(F \cap V)}{n(S)} = \dfrac{21}{490}$
- $P(V) = \dfrac{n(V)}{n(S)} = \dfrac{219}{490}$

$$= \frac{21}{219} \approx 0.096$$

The probability that one person selected from this population contracted the flu given that the person received the vaccination, $P(F \mid V)$, is about 0.096. Our answer agrees with the calculation we performed directly from the table, but the Conditional Probability Formula enables us to find conditional probabilities even when we cannot compute them directly.

QUESTION   *In the preceding example, what is the interpretation of $P(V \mid F)$?*

EXAMPLE 1 ■ Determine a Conditional Probability

The data in the table below show the results of a survey used to determine the number of adults who received financial help from their parents for certain purchases.

Age	College tuition	Buy a car	Buy a house	Total
18–28	405	253	261	919
29–39	389	219	392	1000
40–49	291	146	245	682
50–59	150	71	112	333
60+	62	15	98	175
Total	1297	704	1108	3109

If one person is selected from this survey, what is the probability that the person received financial help for purchasing a home, given that the person is between the ages of 29 and 39?

ANSWER   *$P(V \mid F)$ is the probability that a person selected from this population has been vaccinated, given that the person contracted the flu.*

Solution

Let $B = \{$adults who received financial help for a home purchase$\}$ and $A = \{$adults between 29 and 39$\}$. From the table, $n(A \cap B) = 392$, $n(A) = 1000$, and $n(S) = 3109$. Using the Conditional Probability Formula, we have

$$P(B \mid A) = \frac{P(A \text{ and } B)}{P(A)} = \frac{\dfrac{392}{3109}}{\dfrac{1000}{3109}}$$

• $P(A \text{ and } B) = \dfrac{n(A \cap B)}{n(S)} = \dfrac{392}{3109}$

• $P(A) = \dfrac{n(A)}{n(S)} = \dfrac{1000}{3109}$

$$= \frac{392}{1000} = 0.392$$

The probability that a person received financial help for purchasing a home, given that the person is between the ages of 29 and 39, is 0.392.

CHECK YOUR PROGRESS 1   Two dice are tossed, one after the other. What is the probability that the result is a sum of 6, given that the first die is not a 3?

Solution   *See page S44.*

Math Matters   Bertrand's Box Paradox

historical note

Thomas Bayes was born in London and became a Nonconformist minister who also dabbled in mathematics. Of the mathematical papers he wrote, only one was published in his lifetime, and that paper was published anonymously. His work on probability was not discovered until after his death. ∎

Bayes Theorem, named after Thomas Bayes (1702–1761), gives a method of computing conditional probabilities by knowing the reverse conditional probabilities. Consider the following problem, known as Bertrand's Box Paradox. Three boxes each contain two coins. One box has two gold coins, another has two silver coins, and the third box has one gold coin and one silver coin. A box is chosen at random, and a coin is pulled out (without looking at the other coin). If the coin that is taken out is gold, what is the probability that the other coin in the same box is also gold? Many people initially guess that the probability is $\frac{1}{2}$. To check, let B_1 be the event that the first box (with two gold coins) is chosen, B_2 the event that the second box (with two silver coins) is chosen, and B_3 the event that the third box (with one silver and one gold) is chosen. In addition, let G represent the event that a gold coin is pulled from a box, and S the event that a silver coin is chosen. The conditional probability of pulling a gold coin from a box, given that we know which box was chosen, is simple to compute. What we want to find, however, is the reverse: the conditional probability that we have chosen the first box, given that a gold coin was chosen, $P(B_1 \mid G)$. Bayes Theorem gives us a way to find this probability. In this case, the theorem states

$$P(B_1 \mid G) = \frac{P(G \mid B_1)P(B_1)}{P(G \mid B_1)P(B_1) + P(G \mid B_2)P(B_2) + P(G \mid B_3)P(B_3)}$$

$$= \frac{1 \cdot \dfrac{1}{3}}{1 \cdot \dfrac{1}{3} + 0 \cdot \dfrac{1}{3} + \dfrac{1}{2} \cdot \dfrac{1}{3}} = \frac{2}{3}$$

Thus, there is actually a $\frac{2}{3}$ chance that if a gold coin is pulled from a box, the other coin is also gold.

Product Rule for Probabilities

Suppose two cards are drawn, without replacement, from a standard deck of playing cards. Let A be the event that an ace is drawn on the first draw and B the event that an ace is drawn on the second draw. Then the probability that an ace is drawn on the first *and* second draw is $P(A \text{ and } B)$. To find this probability, we can solve the Conditional Probability Formula for $P(A \text{ and } B)$.

$$\frac{P(A \text{ and } B)}{P(A)} = P(B \mid A)$$

$$P(A) \cdot \frac{P(A \text{ and } B)}{P(A)} = P(A) \cdot P(B \mid A) \qquad \bullet \text{ Multiply each side by } P(A).$$

$$P(A \text{ and } B) = P(A) \cdot P(B \mid A)$$

This is called the Product Rule for Probabilities.

> **Product Rule for Probabilities**
>
> If A and B are two events from the sample space S, then
>
> $$P(A \text{ and } B) = P(A) \cdot P(B \mid A).$$

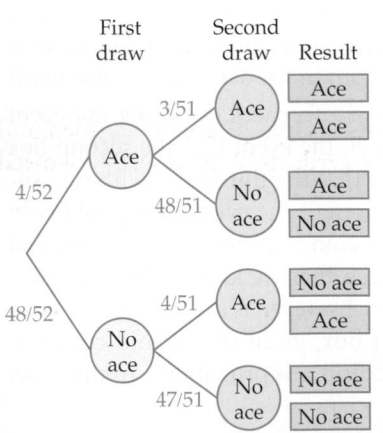

First draw   Second draw   Result

For the problem of drawing an ace from a standard deck of playing cards on the first and second draws, $P(A \text{ and } B)$ is the product of $P(A)$, the probability that the first drawn card is an ace, and $P(B \mid A)$, the probability of an ace on the second draw *given* that the first card drawn was an ace.

The tree diagram at the left shows the possible outcomes of drawing two cards from a deck without replacement. On the first draw, there are four aces in the deck of 52 cards. Therefore, $P(A) = \frac{4}{52} = \frac{1}{13}$. On the second draw, there are only 51 cards remaining and only three aces (an ace was drawn on the first draw). Therefore, $P(B \mid A) = \frac{3}{51} = \frac{1}{17}$. Putting these calculations together, we have

$$P(A \cap B) = P(A) \cdot P(B \mid A)$$

$$= \frac{1}{13} \cdot \frac{1}{17} = \frac{1}{221}$$

The probability of drawing an ace on the first and second draws is $\frac{1}{221}$.

The Product Rule for Probabilities can be extended to more than two events. The probability that a certain sequence of events will occur in succession is the product of the probabilities of each of the events *given* that the preceding events have occurred.

> **Probability of Successive Events**
>
> The probability of two or more events occurring in succession is the product of the conditional probabilities of each of the events.

EXAMPLE 2 ■ Find the Probability of Successive Events

A box contains four red, three white, and five green balls. Suppose three balls are randomly selected from the box in succession, without replacement.

a. What is the probability that first a red, then a white, and then a green ball are selected?

b. What is the probability that two white balls followed by one green ball are selected?

Solution

a. Let $A = \{$a red ball is selected first$\}$, $B = \{$a white ball is selected second$\}$, and $C = \{$a green ball is selected third$\}$. Then

$$P(A \text{ followed by } B \text{ followed by } C) = P(A) \cdot P(B \mid A) \cdot P(C \mid A \text{ and } B)$$

$$= \frac{4}{12} \cdot \frac{3}{11} \cdot \frac{5}{10}$$

$$= \frac{1}{22}$$

The probability of choosing a red, then a white, then a green ball is $\frac{1}{22}$.

b. Let $A = \{$a white ball is selected first$\}$, $B = \{$a white ball is selected second$\}$, and $C = \{$a green ball is selected third$\}$. Then

$$P(A \text{ followed by } B \text{ followed by } C) = P(A) \cdot P(B \mid A) \cdot P(C \mid A \text{ and } B)$$

$$= \frac{3}{12} \cdot \frac{2}{11} \cdot \frac{5}{10}$$

$$= \frac{1}{44}$$

The probability of choosing two white balls followed by one green ball is $\frac{1}{44}$.

CHECK YOUR PROGRESS 2 A standard deck of playing cards is shuffled and three cards are dealt. Find the probability that the cards dealt are a spade followed by a heart followed by another spade.

Solution   See page S45.

Independent Events

Earlier in this section we considered the probability of drawing two aces in a row from a standard deck of playing cards. Because the cards were drawn without replacement, the probability of an ace on the second draw *depended* on the result of the first draw.

Now consider the case of tossing a coin twice. The outcome of the first coin toss has no effect on the outcome of the second toss. So the probability of the coin flipping to a head or a tail on the second toss is not affected by the result of the first toss. When the outcome of a first event does not affect the outcome of a second event, the events are called *independent*.

✔ TAKE NOTE

In part a, there are originally 12 balls in the box. After a red ball is selected, there are only 11 balls remaining, of which three are white. Thus $P(B \mid A) = \frac{3}{11}$. After a red ball and a white ball are selected, there are 10 balls left, of which five are green. Thus $P(C \mid A \text{ and } B) = \frac{5}{10}$.

In part b, we have a similar situation. However, after a white ball is selected, there are 11 balls remaining, of which only two are white. Therefore, $P(B \mid A) = \frac{2}{11}$.

> **Independent Events**
>
> If A and B are two events in a sample space and $P(B\,|\,A) = P(B)$, then A and B are called **independent events**.

For a mathematical verification, consider tossing a coin twice. We can compute the probability that the second toss comes up heads, given that the first coin toss came up heads. If A is the event of a head on the first toss, then $A = \{HH, HT\}$. Let B be the event of a head on the second toss. Then $B = \{HH, TH\}$. The sample space is $S = \{HH, HT, TH, TT\}$. The conditional probability $P(B\,|\,A)$ (the probability of a head on the second toss given a head on the first toss) is

$$P(B\,|\,A) = \frac{P(A \text{ and } B)}{P(A)} = \frac{\frac{1}{4}}{\frac{1}{2}} = \frac{1}{2}$$

- $P(A \text{ and } B) = \dfrac{n(A \cap B)}{n(S)} = \dfrac{1}{4}$
- $P(A) = \dfrac{n(A)}{n(S)} = \dfrac{2}{4} = \dfrac{1}{2}$

Thus $P(B\,|\,A) = \frac{1}{2}$. Note, however, that $P(B) = \frac{n(B)}{n(S)} = \frac{2}{4} = \frac{1}{2}$. Therefore, in the case of tossing a coin twice, the probability of the second event does not depend on the outcome of the first event, and we have $P(B\,|\,A) = P(B)$.

In general, this result enables us to simplify the product rule when two events are independent; the probability of two independent events occurring in succession is simply the product of the probabilities of each of the individual events.

✔ **TAKE NOTE**

The Product Rule for Independent Events can be extended to more than two events. If E_1, E_2, E_3, and E_4 are independent events, then the probability that all four events will occur is $P(E_1) \cdot P(E_2) \cdot P(E_3) \cdot P(E_4)$.

> **Product Rule for Independent Events**
>
> If A and B are two independent events from the sample space S, then $P(A \text{ and } B) = P(A) \cdot P(B)$.

✔ **TAKE NOTE**

See page 747 for all the possible outcomes of the roll of two dice.

EXAMPLE 3 ■ **Find the Probability of Independent Events**

A pair of dice are tossed twice. What is the probability that the first roll is a sum of 7 and the second roll is a sum of 11?

Solution

The rolls of a pair of dice are independent; the probability of a sum of 11 on the second roll does not depend on the outcome of the first roll. Let $A = \{\text{sum of 7 on the first roll}\}$ and $B = \{\text{sum of 11 on the second roll}\}$. Then

$$P(A \text{ and } B) = P(A) \cdot P(B) = \frac{6}{36} \cdot \frac{2}{36} = \frac{1}{108}$$

CHECK YOUR PROGRESS 3 A coin is tossed three times. What is the probability that heads appears on all three tosses?

Solution See page S45.

Applications of Conditional Probability

Conditional probability is used in many real-world situations, such as to determine the efficacy of a drug test, to verify the accuracy of genetic testing, and to analyze evidence in legal proceedings.

EXAMPLE 4 ■ Drug Testing and Conditional Probability

Suppose that a company claims it has a test that is 95% effective in determining whether an athlete is using a steroid. That is, if an athlete is using a steroid, the test will be positive 95% of the time. In the case of a negative result, the company says its test is 97% accurate. That is, even if an athlete is not using steroids, it is possible that the test will be positive in 3% of the cases. Such an occurrence is called a **false positive.** Suppose this test is given to a group of athletes in which 10% of the athletes are using steroids. What is the probability that a randomly chosen athlete actually uses steroids, given that the athlete's test is positive?

Solution

Let S be the event that an athlete uses steroids and let T be the event that the test is positive. Then the probability we wish to determine is $P(S\,|\,T)$. Using the conditional probability formula, we have

$$P(S\,|\,T) = \frac{P(S\text{ and }T)}{P(T)}$$

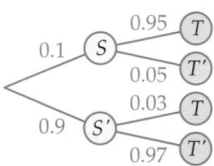

A tree diagram, shown at the left, can be used to calculate this probability. A positive test result can occur in two ways: either an athlete using steroids correctly tests positive, or an athlete not using steroids incorrectly tests positive. The probability of a positive test result, $P(T)$, corresponds to an athlete following path ST or path $S'T$ in the tree diagram. (S' symbolizes no steroid use and T' symbolizes a negative result.) $P(S\text{ and }T)$, the probability of using steroids and getting a positive test result, is path ST. Thus,

$$P(S\,|\,T) = \frac{P(S\text{ and }T)}{P(T)}$$

$$= \frac{(0.1)(0.95)}{(0.1)(0.95) + (0.9)(0.03)} \approx 0.779$$

Given that an athlete tests positive, the probability that the athlete actually uses steroids is approximately 77.9%.

This may be lower than you would expect, especially considering that the manufacturer claims that its test is 95% accurate. In fact, the prevalence of false-positive test results can be much more dramatic in cases of conditions that are present in a small percentage of the population. (See Exercise 61.)

▼ **point of interest**

The resulting calculation in Example 4 is actually an illustration of Bayes Theorem described in the Math Matters on page 769.

CHECK YOUR PROGRESS 4   A pharmaceutical company has a test that is 95% effective in determining whether a person has a certain genetic defect. It is possible, however, that the test may give a false positive result in 4% of cases. Suppose this particular genetic defect occurs in 2% of the population. Given that a person tests positive, what is the probability that the person actually has the defect?

Solution   See page S45.

Excursion

Sharing Birthdays

Have you ever been introduced to someone at a party or other social gathering and discovered that you share the same birthday? It seems like an amazing coincidence when it occurs. In fact, how rare is this?

As an example, suppose four people have gathered for a dinner party. We can determine the probability that at least two of the guests have the same birthday. (For simplicity, we will ignore the February 29th birthday from leap years.) Let E be the event that at least two people share a birthday. It is easier to look at the complement E^c, the event that no one shares the same birthday.

If we start with one of the guests, then the second guest cannot share the same birthday, so that person has 364 possible dates for his or her birthday from a total of 365. Thus the conditional probability that the second guest has a different birthday, given that we know the first person's birthday, is $\frac{364}{365}$. Similarly, the third person has 363 possible birthday dates that do not coincide with those of the first two guests. So the conditional probability that the third person does not share a birthday with either of the first two guests, given that we know the birthdays of the first two people, is $\frac{363}{365}$. The probability of the fourth guest having a distinct birthday is, similarly, $\frac{362}{365}$. We can use the Product Rule for Probabilities to find the probability that all of these conditions are met; that is, none of the four guests share a birthday.

$$P(E^c) = \frac{364}{365} \cdot \frac{363}{365} \cdot \frac{362}{365} \approx 0.984$$

Then $P(E) = 1 - P(E^c) \approx 0.016$, so there is about a 1.6% chance that in a group of four people, two or more will have the same birthday.

It would require 366 people gathered together to *guarantee* that two people in the group will have the same birthday. But how many people would be required to guarantee that the chance that at least two of them share the same birthday is at least 50/50? Make a guess before you proceed through the exercises. The results may surprise you!

Excursion Exercises

1. If eight people are present at a meeting, find the probability that at least two share a common birthday.

2. Compute the probability that at least two people among a group of 15 have the same birthday.

3. If 23 people are in attendance at a party, what is the probability that at least two share a birthday?

4. In a group of 40 people, what would you estimate to be the probability that at least two people share a birthday? If you have the patience, compute the probability to check your guess.

Exercise Set 11.5

1. What is a conditional probability?

2. Explain the difference between independent events and dependent events.

In Exercises 3–6, compute the conditional probabilities $P(A|B)$ and $P(B|A)$.

3. $P(A) = 0.7$, $P(B) = 0.4$, $P(A \text{ and } B) = 0.25$
4. $P(A) = 0.45$, $P(B) = 0.8$, $P(A \text{ and } B) = 0.3$
5. $P(A) = 0.61$, $P(B) = 0.18$, $P(A \text{ and } B) = 0.07$
6. $P(A) = 0.2$, $P(B) = 0.5$, $P(A \text{ and } B) = 0.2$

Employment In Exercises 7–10, use the data in the table below, which shows the employment status of individuals in a particular town by age group.

	Full-time	Part-time	Unemployed
0–17	24	164	371
18–25	185	203	148
26–34	348	67	27
35–49	581	179	104
50+	443	162	173

7. If a person in this town is selected at random, find the probability that the individual is employed part-time, given that he or she is between the ages of 35 and 49.

8. If a person in the town is randomly selected, what is the probability that the individual is unemployed, given that he or she is over 50 years old?

9. A person from the town is randomly selected; what is the probability that the individual is employed full-time, given that he or she is between 18 and 49 years of age?

10. A person from the town is randomly selected; what is the probability that the individual is employed part-time, given that he or she is at least 35 years old?

Video Games In Exercises 11–14, use the data in the following table, which shows the results of a survey of 2000 gamers about their favorite home video game systems, organized by age group. If a survey participant is selected at random, determine the probability of each of the following. Round to the nearest hundredth.

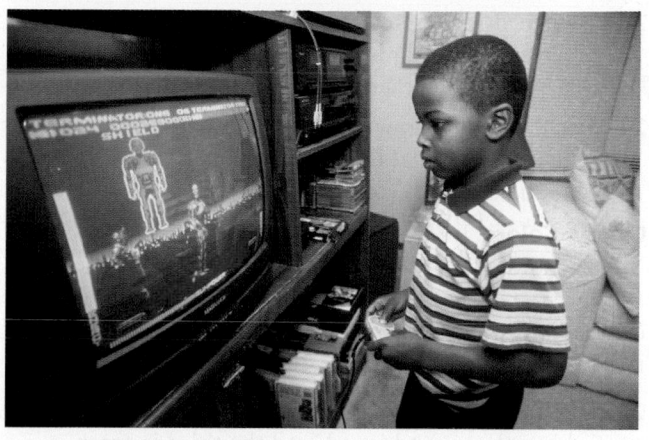

	Sony Play-station 3	Microsoft Xbox 360	Nintendo DS	Sega Dreamcast
0–12	63	84	55	51
13–18	105	139	92	113
19–24	248	217	83	169
25+	191	166	88	136

11. The participant prefers the Playstation 3 system.

12. The participant prefers the Xbox 360, given that the person is between the ages of 13 and 18.

13. The participant prefers Nintendo DS, given that the person is between the ages of 13 and 24.

14. The participant is under 12 years of age, given that the person prefers the Dreamcast machine.

15. A pair of dice are tossed. Find the probability that the sum on the two dice is 8, given that the sum is even.

16. A pair of dice are tossed. Find the probability that the sum on the two dice is 12, given that doubles are rolled.

17. A pair of dice are tossed. What is the probability that doubles are rolled, given that the sum on the two dice is less than 7?

18. A pair of dice are tossed. What is the probability that the sum on the two dice is 8, given that the sum is more than 6?

19. What is the probability of drawing two cards in succession (without replacement) from a standard deck and having them both be face cards?

20. Two cards are drawn from a standard deck without replacement. Find the probability that both cards are hearts.

21. Two cards are drawn from a standard deck without replacement. What is the probability that the first card is a spade and the second card is red?

22. Two cards are drawn from a standard deck without replacement. What is the probability that the first card is a king and the second card is not?

Candy Colors In Exercises 23–26, a snack-size bag of M&Ms candies is opened. Inside, there are 12 red candies, 12 blue, 7 green, 13 brown, 3 orange, and 10 yellow. Three candies are pulled from the bag in succession, without replacement.

23. Determine the probability that the first candy drawn is blue, the second is red, and the third is green.

24. Determine the probability that the first candy drawn is brown, the second is orange, and the third is yellow.

25. What is the probability that the first two candies drawn are green and the third is red?

26. What is the probability that the first candy drawn is orange, the second is blue, and the third is orange?

In Exercises 27–30, three cards are dealt from a shuffled standard deck of playing cards.

27. Find the probability that the first card dealt is red, the second is black, and the third is red.

28. Find the probability that the first two cards dealt are clubs and the third is a spade.

29. What is the probability that the three cards dealt are, in order, an ace, a face card, and an 8? (A face card is a jack, queen, or king.)

30. What is the probability that the three cards dealt are, in order, a red card, a club, and another red card?

Student Attendance In Exercises 31–34, the probability that a student enrolled at a local high school will be absent on a particular day is 0.04, assuming that the student was in attendance the previous school day. However, if a student is absent, the probability that he or she will be absent again the following day is 0.11. For each exercise, assume that the student was in attendance the previous day.

31. What is the probability that a student will be absent three days in a row?

32. What is the probability that a student will be absent two days in a row, but then show up on the third day?

33. Find the probability that a student will be absent, attend the next day, but then will be absent again the third day.

34. Find the probability that a student will be absent four days in a row.

In Exercises 35–38, determine whether the events are independent.

35. A single die is rolled and then rolled a second time.

36. Numbered balls are pulled from a bin one-by-one to determine the winning lottery numbers.

37. Numbers are written on slips of paper in a hat; one person pulls out a slip of paper without replacing it, then a second person pulls out a slip of paper.

38. In order to determine who goes first in a game, one person picks a number between 1 and 10, then a second person picks a number from the remaining 9 numbers.

In Exercises 39–44, a pair of dice are tossed twice.

39. Find the probability that both rolls give a sum of 8.

40. Find the probability that the first roll is a sum of 6 and the second roll is a sum of 12.

41. Find the probability that the first roll is a total of at least 10 and the second roll is a total of at least 11.

42. Find the probability that both rolls result in doubles.

43. Find the probability that both rolls give even sums.

44. Find the probability that both rolls give at most a sum of 4.

45. A fair coin is tossed four times in succession. Find the probability of getting two heads followed by two tails.

46. **Monopoly** In the game of Monopoly, a player is sent to jail if he or she rolls doubles with a pair of dice three times in a row. What is the probability of rolling doubles three times in succession?

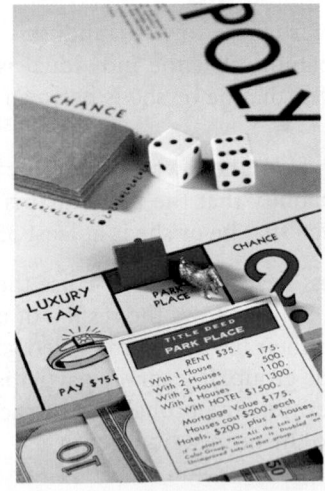

47. Find the probability of tossing a pair of dice three times in succession and getting a sum of at least 10 on all three tosses.

48. Find the probability of tossing a pair of dice three times in succession and getting a sum of at most 3 on all three tosses.

In Exercises 49–54, a card is drawn from a standard deck and replaced. After the deck is shuffled, another card is pulled.

49. What is the probability that both cards pulled are aces?

50. What is the probability that both cards pulled are face cards?

51. What is the probability that the first card drawn is a spade and the second card is a diamond?

52. What is the probability that the first card drawn is an ace and the second card is not an ace?

53. Find the probability that the first card drawn is a heart and the second card is a spade.

54. Find the probability that the first card drawn is a face card and the second card is black.

55. A standard deck of playing cards is shuffled and three people each choose a card. Find the probability that the first two cards chosen are diamonds and the third card is black if
   a. the cards are chosen *with* replacement.
   b. the cards are chosen *without* replacement.

56. A standard deck of playing cards is shuffled and three people each choose a card. Find the probability that all three cards are face cards if
   a. the cards are chosen *with* replacement.
   b. the cards are chosen *without* replacement.

57. A bag contains five red marbles, four green marbles, and eight blue marbles. Find the probability of pulling two red marbles followed by a green marble if the marbles are pulled from the bag
   a. with replacement.
   b. without replacement.

58. A box contains three medium t-shirts, five large t-shirts, and four extra-large t-shirts. If someone randomly chooses three t-shirts from the box, find the probability that the first t-shirt is large, the second is medium, and the third is large if the shirts are chosen
   a. with replacement.
   b. without replacement.

59. **Drug Testing** A company that performs drug testing guarantees that its test determines a positive result with 97% accuracy. However, the test also gives 6% false positives. If 5% of those being tested actually have the drug present in their bloodstream, find the probability that a person testing positive has actually been using drugs.

60. **Genetic Testing** A test for a genetic disorder can detect the disorder with 94% accuracy. However, the test will incorrectly report positive results for 3% of those without the disorder. If 12% of the population has the disorder, find the probability that a person testing positive actually has the genetic disorder.

61. **Disease Testing** A pharmaceutical company has developed a test for a rare disease that is present in 0.5% of the population. The test is 98% accurate in determining a positive result, and the chance of a false positive is 4%. What is the probability that someone who tests positive actually has the disease?

62. **HIV Testing** When used together, the ELISA and Western Blot tests for HIV are more than 99% accurate in determining a positive result. The chance of a false positive is between 1 and 5 for every 100,000 tests. If we assume a 99% accuracy rate for correctly identifying positive results and 5/100,000 false positives, find the probability that someone who tests positive has HIV. [The Centers for Disease Control and Prevention (CDC) estimate that about 0.3% of U.S. residents are infected with HIV.]

Extensions

CRITICAL THINKING

63. Suppose you are standing at a street corner and flip a coin to decide whether you will go north or south from your current position. When you reach the next intersection, you repeat the procedure. (This problem is a simplified version of what is called a *random walk* problem. Problems of this type are important in economics, physics, chemistry, biology, and other disciplines.)
   a. After performing this experiment three times, what is the probability that you will be three blocks north of your original position?
   b. After performing this experiment four times, what is the probability that you will be two blocks north of your original position?
   c. After performing this experiment four times, what is the probability that you will be back at your original position?

COOPERATIVE LEARNING

64. From a standard deck of playing cards, choose four red cards and four black cards. Deal the eight cards, face up, in two rows of four cards each. A good event is that each column contains a red and a black card. (The column can be red/black or black/red.) A bad event is any other situation. Although this problem is stated in terms of cards, it has a very practical application. If several proteins in a cell break (say, from radiation therapy) and then reattach, it is possible that the new protein is harmful to the cell.

   a. Perform this experiment 50 times and keep a record of the number of good events and bad events.

   b. Use your data to predict the probability of a good event.

   c. Repeat parts a and b again.

   d. Use your data from the complete 100 trials to predict the probability of a good event.

   e. Calculate the theoretical probability of a good event.

EXPLORATIONS

65. Monty Hall Problem This is another explanation, using conditional probability, of the Monty Hall problem discussed in Exercise 56 of the last section. Let the curtain chosen by the contestant be labeled A and the other two curtains be labeled B and C. In the following exercises, we will use A to represent the event that the grand prize is behind curtain A (and similarly for curtains B and C), and $\overline{A}$ to represent the event that Monty Hall opens curtain A (and similarly for curtains B and C).

   a. What is the probability that Monty Hall opens curtain B given that the grand prize is behind curtain A? This is $P(\overline{B}|A)$.

   b. What is the probability that Monty Hall opens curtain B given that the grand prize is behind curtain B? This is $P(\overline{B}|B)$.

   c. What is the probability that Monty Hall opens curtain B given that the grand prize is behind curtain C? This is $P(\overline{B}|C)$.

   d. The probability that the grand prize is behind curtain A given that curtain B is opened (you have not switched choices) is given by Bayes Theorem in the following form.

$$P(A|\overline{B}) = \frac{P(\overline{B}|A)P(A)}{P(\overline{B}|A)P(A) + P(\overline{B}|B)P(B) + P(\overline{B}|C)P(C)}$$

What is the probability?

   e. Find the probability of choosing the grand prize if you switch curtains. That is, find

$$P(C|\overline{B}) = \frac{P(\overline{B}|C)P(C)}{P(\overline{B}|A)P(A) + P(\overline{B}|B)P(B) + P(\overline{B}|C)P(C)}$$

   f. Is switching the better strategy?

SECTION 11.6 | # Expectation

Expectation

Suppose a barrel contains a large number of balls, half of which have the number 1000 painted on them and the other half of which have the number 500 painted on them. As the grand prize winner of a contest, you get to reach into the barrel (blindfolded, of course) and select 10 balls. Your prize is the sum of the numbers on the balls in cash.

   If you are very lucky, all of the balls will have 1000 painted on them and you will win $10,000. If you are very unlucky, all of the balls will have 500 painted on them and you will win $5000. Most likely, however, approximately one-half of the balls will have 1000 painted on them and one-half will have 500 painted on them. The amount of your winnings in this case will be $5(1000) + 5(500)$, or $7500. Because 10 balls were drawn, your amount of winnings per ball is $\frac{\$7500}{10} = \$750$.

The number $750 is called the *expected value* or the *expectation* of the game. You cannot win $750 on one draw, but if given the opportunity to draw many times, you will win, on average, $750 per ball.

<u>QUESTION</u>   *Can an expectation be negative?*

Another way we can calculate expectation is to use probabilities. For the game above, one-half of the balls have the number 1000 painted on them and one-half have the number 500 painted on them. Therefore, $P(1000) = \frac{1}{2}$ and $P(500) = \frac{1}{2}$. The expectation is calculated as follows.

Expectation
$= $ (probability of winning $1000) $\cdot$ $1000 $ + $ (probability of winning $500) $\cdot$ $500
$= P(1000) \cdot \$1000 + P(500) \cdot \$500$

$= \frac{1}{2} \cdot \$1000 + \frac{1}{2} \cdot \$500 = \$500 + \$250 = \$750$

The general result for experiments with numerical outcomes follows.

Expectation

Let $S_1, S_2, S_3, \ldots, S_n$ be the possible numerical outcomes of an experiment and let $P(S_1), P(S_2), P(S_3), \ldots, P(S_n)$ be the probabilities of those outcomes. Then the **expectation** of the experiment is

$$P(S_1) \cdot S_1 + P(S_2) \cdot S_2 + P(S_3) \cdot S_3 + \cdots + P(S_n) \cdot S_n$$

That is, to find the expectation of an experiment, multiply the probability of each outcome of the experiment by the outcome and then add the results.

EXAMPLE 1 ■ Expectation in Gambling

One of the wagers in roulette is to place a bet on one of the numbers from 0 to 36 or on 00. If that number comes up, the player wins 35 times the amount bet (and keeps the original bet). Suppose a player bets $1 on a number. What is the player's expectation?

<u>ANSWER</u>   *Yes. For instance, if the expected value of a gambling game is negative, it simply means that, in the long run, a person will lose that amount of money, on average, on each play.*

Solution

Let S_1 be the event that the player's number comes up and the player wins $35. Because there are 38 numbers from which to choose, $P(S_1) = \frac{1}{38}$. Let S_2 be the event that the player's number does not come up and the player therefore loses $1. Then $P(S_2) = 1 - \frac{1}{38} = \frac{37}{38}$.

$$\text{Expectation} = P(S_1) \cdot S_1 + P(S_2) \cdot S_2$$

$$= \frac{1}{38}(35) + \frac{37}{38}(-1) = -\frac{1}{19}$$

$$\approx -0.053$$

• The amount the player can win is entered as a positive number. The amount that can be lost is entered as a negative number.

The player's expectation is approximately $-$.053$. This means that, on average, the player will lose about $.05 every time this bet is made.

CHECK YOUR PROGRESS 1   In roulette it is possible to place a wager that one of the numbers between 1 and 12 (inclusive) will come up. If it does, the player wins twice the amount bet. Suppose a player bets $5 that a number between 1 and 12 will come up. What is the player's expectation?

Solution   *See page S45.*

In Example 1, the fact that the player is losing approximately 5 cents on each dollar bet means that the casino's expectation is positive 5 cents; it is earning (on average) 5 cents for every dollar spent making that particular bet at the roulette wheel. An individual player may get lucky, but over time the casino can plan on a predictable profit.

MathMatters   **A Bargain at Any Price?**

The Swiss mathematician Daniel Bernoulli discussed the following game in a paper he published in 1738. A fair coin is repeatedly tossed until the coin comes up tails. Let n = the number of total coin flips. When the coin comes up tails, you are paid 2^n dollars. Thus, if the first flip is tails, you are paid $2. If the coin comes up heads five times in a row and the sixth flip comes up tails, you are paid $2^6 = 64. How much would you pay to play such a game? $5? $20? The game becomes interesting when we compute the expected value:

$$\text{Expectation}$$
$$= P(\text{T}) \cdot 2^1 + P(\text{HT}) \cdot 2^2 + P(\text{HHT}) \cdot 2^3 + P(\text{HHHT}) \cdot 2^4 + \cdots$$
$$= \frac{1}{2} \cdot 2 + \frac{1}{4} \cdot 4 + \frac{1}{8} \cdot 8 + \frac{1}{16} \cdot 16 + \cdots$$
$$= 1 + 1 + 1 + 1 + \cdots$$

There is no maximum number of times the coin can be flipped, and the expectation is infinite! Theoretically, it would be worthwhile to play no matter how high the fee is.

Expectation in Insurance

When an insurance company sells a life insurance policy, the premium (the cost to purchase the policy) is based on many factors, but one of the most important is the probability that the insured person will outlive the term of the policy. Such probabilities are found in *mortality tables*, which give the probability that a person of a certain age will live one more year. For the life insurance company, it is very much like gambling. The company wants to know its expectation on a policy—that is, how much it will pay out, on average, for each policy it writes. Here is an example.

EXAMPLE 2 ■ Expectation in Insurance

According to mortality tables published in the National Vital Statistics Report, the probability that a 21-year-old will die within one year is approximately 0.000948. Suppose that the premium for a one-year, $25,000 life insurance policy for a 21-year-old is $32. What is the insurance company's expectation for this policy?

Solution

Let S_1 be the event that the person dies within one year. Then $P(S_1) = 0.000948$ and the company must pay out $25,000. Because the company charged $32 for the policy, the company's actual loss is $24,968. Let S_2 be the event that the policy holder does not die during the year of the policy. Then $P(S_2) = 0.999052$ and the company keeps the premium of $32. The expectation is

$$\text{Expectation} = P(S_1) \cdot S_1 + P(S_2) \cdot S_2$$
$$= 0.000948(-24{,}968) + 0.999052(32)$$
$$= 8.3$$

• The amount the company pays out is entered as a negative number. The amount the company receives is entered as a positive number.

The company's expectation is $8.30, so the company earns, on average, $8.30 for each policy sold.

CHECK YOUR PROGRESS 2   The probability that an 18-year-old will die within one year is approximately 0.000832. Suppose that the premium for a one-year, $10,000 life insurance policy for an 18-year-old is $45. What is the insurance company's expectation for this policy?

Solution   See page S45.

Expectation is also used when a company bids on a project. The company must try to predict the costs and amount of work involved to give a bid that allows it to make a profit from completing the project. At the same time, if the bid is too high, the client may reject the offer. Because it is impossible to predict in advance the exact requirements of the job, probabilities can be used to analyze the likelihood of making a profit, as the next example demonstrates.

EXAMPLE 3 ■ Expected Company Profits

Suppose a software company bids on a project to update the database program for an accounting firm. The software company assesses its potential profit as shown in the following table.

historical note

Edmond Halley (hăl´ē) (1656–1742), of Halley's comet fame, also created, for the city of Breslau, Germany, one of the first mortality tables, which he published in 1693. This was one of the first attempts to relate mortality and age in a population. ■

historical note

Pierre Simon Laplace (lə-pläs´) (1749–1827) made many important contributions to mathematics and astronomy. In 1812, he published his *Théorie Analytique des Probabilitiés*, in which he extended the theories of probability beyond analyzing games of chance and applied them to many practical and scientific problems. In his book he states, "The most important questions of life are indeed, for the most part, really only problems of probability." ■

Profit/Loss	Probability
$75,000	0.10
$50,000	0.25
$20,000	0.50
−$10,000	0.10
−$25,000	0.05

What is the profit expectation for the company?

Solution

The company's expected profit is

Expectation
$= 0.10(75,000) + 0.25(50,000) + 0.50(20,000) + 0.10(-10,000) + 0.05(-25,000)$
$= 7500 + 12,500 + 10,000 - 1000 - 1250 = 27,750$

The company's expected profit is $27,750.

CHECK YOUR PROGRESS 3   A road construction company bids on a project to build a new freeway. The company estimates its potential profit as shown in the table at the left. What is the profit expectation for the company?

Solution   See page S45.

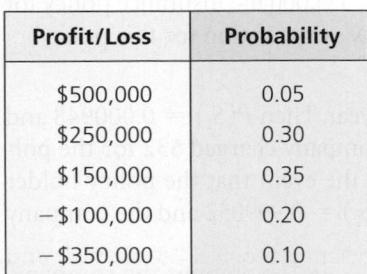

Profit/Loss	Probability
$500,000	0.05
$250,000	0.30
$150,000	0.35
−$100,000	0.20
−$350,000	0.10

Excursion

Chuck-a-luck

Chuck-a-luck is a game of chance in which three dice in a cage are tumbled. Bets can be placed on the values that the three dice will show. The table below shows the different bets and the amount won if $1 is wagered.

Numbers bet	Bet on a number from 1 through 6	
	if one die matches	Pays $1
	if two dice match	Pays $2
	if all three dice match	Pays $10
Field bet	Bet that the sum of the numbers showing on all three dice will be 5, 6, 7, 8, 13, 14, 15, or 16	Pays $1
Over 10	Bet that the sum of the numbers showing on all three dice will be more than 10	Pays $1
Under 11	Bet that the sum of the numbers showing on all three dice will be less than 11	Pays $1

(continued)

historical note

Chuck-a-luck, also known (sometimes with slight variations) as "Bird Cage," "Sic Bo," or "Sweat," is one of the oldest dice games. It was probably the most popular dice game played by the soldiers of the Civil War. The term *tinhorn gambler* is derived from the practice of using a metal chute in place of a cage to tumble the dice. ∎

Excursion Exercises

1. Compute the probability that if a bet is placed on the number 5, all three dice will show a 5.

2. What is the probability that *exactly* one die will show a 5?

3. What is the probability that two (but not three) dice will show a 5?

4. Find the probability that none of the dice will show a 5.

5. What is the expectation for a $1 bet placed on the number 5?

6. Determine the expectation for wagering $1 on the Over 10 bet.

7. Determine the expectation for wagering $1 on the Under 11 bet.

8. Which bet is most favorable for the player? Which is most favorable for the casino? (The expectation for a $1 Field bet is −4 cents.)

Exercise Set 11.6

1. The outcomes of an experiment and the probability of each outcome are given in the table below. Compute the expectation for this experiment.

Outcome	Probability
30	0.15
40	0.2
50	0.4
60	0.05
70	0.2

2. The outcomes of an experiment and the probability of each outcome are given in the table below. Compute the expectation for this experiment.

Outcome	Probability
5	0.4
6	0.3
7	0.1
8	0.08
9	0.07
10	0.05

3. **Roulette** One of the wagers in the game of roulette is to place a bet that the ball will land on a black number.

(Eighteen of the numbers are black, 18 are red, and two are green.) If the ball lands on a black number, the player wins the amount of his bet. If a player bets $1, find the player's expectation.

4. **Roulette** One of the wagers in roulette is to bet that the ball will stop on a number that is a multiple of 3. (Both 0 and 00 are not included.) If the ball stops on such a number, the player wins double the amount bet. If a player bets $1, compute the player's expectation.

Casino Games Many casinos have a game called the Big Six Money Wheel, in which a large wheel with various dollar amounts is spun. Players may bet on one or more denominations; if the wheel stops on that denomination, the player wins that amount for each dollar bet. The wheel has 54 slots; the number of slots marked with each denomination is given in the following table. Exercises 5 to 8 use this game.

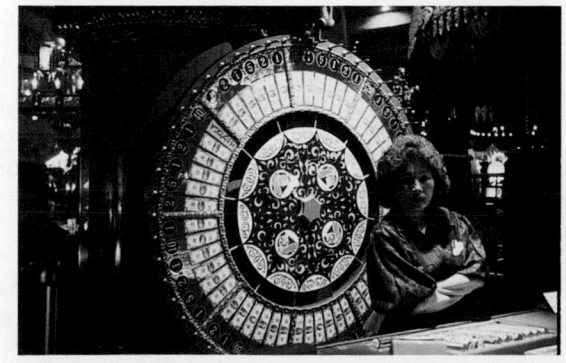

Denomination	Number of slots
$40	2
$20	2
$10	4
$5	8
$2	15
$1	23

5. If a player bets $1 on the $40 denomination, find the player's expectation.

6. If a player bets $1 on the $20 denomination, find the player's expectation.

7. If a player bets $1 on the $5 denomination, find the player's expectation.

8. If a player bets $1 on the $2 denomination, find the player's expectation.

9. **Life Insurance** The probability that a 22-year-old female in the U.S. will die within one year is approximately 0.00044. If an insurance company sells a one-year, $25,000 life insurance policy to such a person for $75, what is the company's expectation?

10. **Life Insurance** The probability that a 28-year-old male in the U.S. will die within one year is approximately 0.001395. If an insurance company sells a one-year, $20,000 life insurance policy to such a person for $155, what is the company's expectation?

11. **Life Insurance** The probability that an 80-year-old male in the U.S. will die within one year is approximately 0.069941. If an insurance company sells a one-year, $10,000 life insurance policy to such a person for $495, what is the company's expectation?

12. **Life Insurance** The probability that an 80-year-old female in the U.S. will die within one year is approximately 0.048711. If an insurance company sells a one-year, $15,000 life insurance policy to such a person for $860, what is the company's expectation?

13. **Life Insurance** The probability that a 30-year-old male in the U.S. will die within one year is about 0.001420. An insurance company is preparing to sell a 30-year-old male a one-year, $30,000 life insurance policy. How much should it charge for its premium in order to have a positive expectation for the policy?

14. **Life Insurance** The probability that a 25-year-old female in the U.S. will die within one year is about 0.000514. An insurance company is preparing to sell a 25-year-old female a one-year, $75,000 life insurance policy. How much should it charge for its premium in order to have a positive expectation for the policy?

15. **Construction** A construction company has been hired to build a custom home. The builder estimates the probabilities of potential profit (or loss) as shown in the table below. What is the profit expectation for the company?

Profit/Loss	Probability
$100,000	0.10
$60,000	0.40
$30,000	0.25
0	0.15
−$20,000	0.08
−$40,000	0.02

16. **Painting** A professional painter has been hired to paint a commercial building for $18,000. From this fee, the painter must buy supplies and pay employees.

The painter estimates the potential profit as shown in the table below. What is the profit expectation for the painter?

Profit/Loss	Probability
$10,000	0.15
$8,000	0.35
$5,000	0.2
$3,000	0.2
$1,000	0.1

17. Design Consultant A consultant has been hired to redesign a company's production facility. The consultant estimates the probabilities of her potential profit as shown in the table below. What is her profit expectation?

Profit/Loss	Probability
$40,000	0.05
$30,000	0.2
$20,000	0.5
$10,000	0.2
$5,000	0.05

18. Office Rentals A real estate company has purchased an office building with the intention of renting office space to small businesses. The company estimates the probabilities of potential profit (or loss) as shown in the table below. What is the profit expectation for the company?

Profit/Loss	Probability
$700,000	0.15
$400,000	0.25
$200,000	0.25
$50,000	0.20
−$100,000	0.10
−$250,000	0.05

19. Lotteries The Florida lottery game Mega Money is played by choosing four numbers from 1 to 44 and one number from 1 to 22. The table below shows the probability of winning the $2,000,000 jackpot on July 9, 2004, along with the amounts and probabilities of other prizes.

Match 4+Mega	$2,000,000	$\dfrac{1}{2,986,522}$
Match 4	$2164	$\dfrac{3}{426,646}$
Match 3+Mega	$440	$\dfrac{80}{1,493,261}$
Match 3	$70	$\dfrac{240}{213,323}$
Match 2+Mega	$27.50	$\dfrac{2340}{1,493,261}$
Match 2	$2.50	$\dfrac{7020}{213,323}$
Match 1+Mega	$3	$\dfrac{19,760}{1,493,261}$
Mega	$1	$\dfrac{45,695}{1,493,261}$

Assuming that the jackpot was not split among multiple winners, find the expectation for buying a $1 lottery ticket. Round to the nearest tenth of a cent.

20. **Lotteries** The Florida lottery game Lotto is played by choosing six numbers from 1 to 53. If these numbers match the ones drawn by the lottery commission, you win the jackpot. The table below shows the probability of winning the $26,000,000 jackpot on June 5, 2004, along with the amounts and probabilities of other prizes.

Match 6	$26,000,000	$\dfrac{1}{22,957,480}$
Match 5	$4273	$\dfrac{141}{11,478,740}$
Match 4	$64	$\dfrac{3243}{4,591,496}$
Match 3	$5	$\dfrac{16,215}{1,147,874}$

Assuming that the jackpot was not split among multiple winners, find the expectation for buying a $1 lottery ticket. Round to the nearest tenth of a cent.

Extensions

CRITICAL THINKING

21. If a pair of regular dice are tossed once, use the expectation formula to determine the expected sum of the numbers on the upward faces of the two dice.

22. Consider rolling a pair of unusual dice, for which the faces have the number of pips indicated.

Die 1: {1, 2, 3, 4, 5, 6}
Die 2: {0, 0, 0, 6, 6, 6}

a. List the sample space for the experiment.

b. Compute the probability of each possible sum of the upward faces on the dice.

c. What is the expected value of the sum of the numbers on the upward faces of the two dice?

23. Two dice, one labeled 1, 2, 2, 3, 3, 4 and the other labeled 1, 3, 4, 5, 6, 8, are rolled once. Use the formula for expectation to determine the expected sum of the numbers on the upward faces of the two dice. Dice such as these are called *Sicherman dice.*

24. Suppose you purchase a ticket for a prize and your expectation is −$1. What is the meaning of this expectation?

25. **Efron's dice** Suppose you are offered one of two pairs of dice, a red pair or a green pair, that are labeled as follows.

Red die 1: 0, 0, 4, 4, 4, 4

Red die 2: 2, 3, 3, 9, 10, 11

Green die 1: 3, 3, 3, 3, 3, 3

Green die 2: 0, 1, 7, 8, 8, 8

After you choose, your friend will receive the other pair. Which pair should you choose if you are going to play a game in which each of you rolls your dice and the player with the higher sum wins? Dice such as these are part of a set of four pairs of dice called *Efron's dice.* Explain why you chose the dice you did.

26. **Lotteries** The PowerBall lottery commission chooses five white balls from a drum containing 53 balls marked with the numbers 1 through 53, and one red ball from a separate drum containing 42 balls. The following table shows the odds of winning a certain prize if the numbers you choose match those chosen by the lottery commission.

Match	Prize	Approximate odds
⬤⬤⬤⬤⬤ + ⬤	Jackpot	1:120,526,770
⬤⬤⬤⬤⬤	$100,000	1:2,939,677
⬤⬤⬤⬤ + ⬤	$5,000	1:502,195
⬤⬤⬤⬤	$100	1:12,249
⬤⬤⬤ + ⬤	$100	1:10,685
⬤⬤⬤	$7	1:261
⬤⬤ + ⬤	$7	1:697
⬤ + ⬤	$4	1:124
⬤	$3	1:70

Overall odds: 1:35. Above odds based on $1 play.

Source: http://www.powerball.com/pbprizesNodds.shtm

a. Assuming that the jackpot for a certain drawing is $36,000,000, what is your expectation if you purchase one ticket for $1? Round to the nearest cent. Assume the jackpot is not split among multiple winners.

b. What is unusual about the two prizes for $7?

Summary

Key Terms

combination [p. 736]
combinatorics [p. 720]
complement of an event [p. 760]
conditional probability [p. 767]
counting with replacement [p. 725]
counting without replacement [p. 725]
counting principle [p. 724]
empirical probability (experimental probability) [p. 747]
equally likely outcomes [p. 745]
event [p. 720]
expectation [p. 779]
experiment [p. 720]
false positive [p. 773]
favorable outcome [p. 750]
independent events [p. 772]
multi-stage experiment [p. 721]
mutually exclusive events [p. 757]
n factorial, *n*! [p. 730]
odds [p. 750]
permutation [p. 731]
probability [p. 744]
Punett square [p. 748]
sample space [p. 720]
single-stage experiment [p. 721]
theoretical probability [p. 747]
tree diagram [p. 722]
unfavorable outcome [p. 750]

Essential Concepts

■ **Counting Principle**
Let E be a multi-stage experiment. If $n_1, n_2, n_3, \ldots, n_k$ are the number of possible outcomes of each of the k stages of E, then there are $n_1 \cdot n_2 \cdot n_3 \cdot \cdots \cdot n_k$ possible outcomes for E.

■ **Permutation Formula for Distinct Objects**
The number of permutations $P(n, k)$ of n distinct objects selected k at a time is

$$P(n, k) = \frac{n!}{(n-k)!}$$

■ **Permutations of Objects, Some of Which Are Identical**
The number of permutations of n objects of r different types, where k_1 identical objects are of one type, k_2 of another, and so on, is given by

$$\frac{n!}{k_1! \cdot k_2! \cdot \cdots \cdot k_r!}$$

where $k_1 + k_2 + \cdots + k_r = n$.

■ **Combination Formula**
The number of combinations of n objects chosen k at a time is

$$C(n, k) = \frac{n!}{k!\,(n-k)!}$$

■ **Probability of an Event**
For an experiment with sample space S of equally likely outcomes, the probability $P(E)$ of an event E is given by

$$P(E) = \frac{n(E)}{n(S)}$$

where $n(E)$ is the number of elements in the event and $n(S)$ is the number of elements in the sample space.

■ **Empirical Probability of an Event**
If an experiment is performed repeatedly and the occurrence of the event E is observed, the probability $P(E)$ of the event E is given by

$$P(E) = \frac{\text{number of times event } E \text{ occurred}}{\text{number of times the experiment was performed}}$$

■ **Odds of an Event**
Let E be an event in a sample space of equally likely outcomes. Then

$$\text{Odds in favor of } E = \frac{\text{number of favorable outcomes}}{\text{number of unfavorable outcomes}}$$

$$\text{Odds against } E = \frac{\text{number of unfavorable outcomes}}{\text{number of favorable outcomes}}$$

■ **Converting Odds to Probability**
Suppose E is an event in a sample space and that the *odds in favor* of E are $\frac{a}{b}$. Then $P(E) = \frac{a}{a+b}$.

- **Converting Probability to Odds**
  Suppose E is an event in a sample space. Then the *odds in favor* of E are $\frac{P(E)}{1 - P(E)}$.

- **Probability of Mutually Exclusive Events**
  Two events A and B are mutually exclusive if they cannot occur at the same time. That is, A and B are mutually exclusive when $A \cap B = \varnothing$. In this case, the probability of A or B occurring is
  $$P(A \text{ or } B) = P(A) + P(B)$$

- **Addition Rule for Probabilities**
  Let A and B be two events in a sample space S. Then
  $$P(A \text{ or } B) = P(A) + P(B) - P(A \text{ and } B)$$

- **Probability of the Complement of an Event**
  If E is an event and E^c is the complement of the event, then $P(E^c) = 1 - P(E)$.

- **Conditional Probability Formula**
  Let A and B be two events in a sample space S. Then the conditional probability of B given that A has occurred is
  $$P(B \mid A) = \frac{P(A \text{ and } B)}{P(A)}$$

- **Product Rule for Probabilities**
  If A and B are two events from the sample space S, then
  $$P(A \text{ and } B) = P(A) \cdot P(B \mid A)$$

- **Probability of Successive Events**
  The probability of two or more events occurring in succession is the product of the conditional probabilities of each of the events.

- **Product Rule for Independent Events**
  If A and B are two events in a sample space and $P(B \mid A) = P(B)$, then A and B are called independent events. In this case,
  $$P(A \text{ and } B) = P(A) \cdot P(B)$$

- **Expectation**
  Let $S_1, S_2, S_3, \ldots, S_n$ be the possible numerical outcomes of an experiment and let $P(S_1)$, $P(S_2)$, $P(S_3), \ldots, P(S_n)$ be the probabilities of those outcomes. Then the expectation of the experiment is
  $$P(S_1) \cdot S_1 + P(S_2) \cdot S_2 + P(S_3) \cdot S_3 + \cdots + P(S_n) \cdot S_n$$

CHAPTER 11 Review Exercises

In Exercises 1–4, list the elements of the sample space for the given experiment.

1. Two-digit numbers are formed, with replacement, from the digits 1, 2, and 3.

2. Two-digit numbers are formed, without replacement, from the digits 2, 6, and 8.

3. Use a tree diagram to list the number of outcomes that result from tossing four coins.

4. Use a table to list the number of two-character codes that can be formed from one of the digits 7, 8, or 9 followed by one of the letters A or B.

5. An athletic shoe store sells jogging shoes in three styles that come in four colors. Each color comes in six sizes. How many distinct shoes are available?

6. The combination for a lock to a bicycle chain contains four numbers chosen from the numbers 0 through 9. How many different combinations are possible?

7. **Serial Numbers** The Conn music company assigns the first four serial numbers to instruments in the following way. The first character is one of the letters G through K and indicates the decade in which the instrument is made: "G" for 1970s, "H" for 1980s, etc. The second character indicates the month of the year: "A" for January, "B" for February, etc. The third character is a number from 0 to 9 indicating the year in the decade a instrument is made, and the fourth character is a number from 0 to 9 indicating the type of instrument: 1 - cornet, 2 - trumpet, 3 - alto horn, 4 - French horn, 5 - mellophonium, 6 - valve trombone, 7 - slide trombone, 8 - euphonium, 9 - tuba, 0 - sousapone. How many four-character serial numbers are possible?

8. **Codes** A *biquinary code* is a code that consists of two distinct binary digits (a binary digit is a zero or one) followed by five binary digits for which there are no restrictions. How many biquinary codes are possible?

In Exercises 9–14, evaluate each expression.

9. $7!$ **10.** $8! - 4!$ **11.** $\dfrac{9!}{2!\,3!\,4!}$

12. $P(10, 6)$ **13.** $P(8, 3)$ **14.** $\dfrac{C(6, 2) \cdot C(8, 3)}{C(14, 5)}$

15. In how many different ways can seven people arrange themselves in a line to receive service from a bank teller?

16. A matching test has seven definitions that are to be paired with seven words. Assuming each word corresponds to exactly one definition, how many different matches are possible by random matching?

17. A matching test has seven definitions to be matched with five words. Assuming each word corresponds to exactly one definition, how many different matches are possible by random matching?

18. How many distinct arrangements are possible using the letters of the word *letter*?

19. Twelve identical coins are tossed. How many distinct arrangements are possible consisting of four heads and eight tails?

20. Three positions are open at a manufacturing plant: the day shift, the swing shift, and the night shift. In how many different ways can five people be assigned to the three shifts?

21. A professor assigns 25 homework problems, of which 10 will be graded. How many different sets of 10 problems can the professor choose to grade?

22. A stockbroker recommends 11 stocks to a client. If the client will invest in three of the stocks, how many different three-stock portfolios can be selected?

23. A quality control inspector receives a shipment of 15 computer monitors, of which three are defective. If the inspector randomly chooses five monitors, how many different sets can be formed that consist of three nondefective monitors and two defective monitors?

24. How many ways can nine people be seated in nine chairs if two of the people refuse to sit next to each other?

25. How many five-card poker hands consist of four of a kind (four aces, four kings, four queens, and so on)?

26. If it is equally likely that a child will be born a boy or a girl, compute the probability that a family of four children will have one boy and three girls.

27. If a coin is tossed three times, what is the probability of getting one head and two tails?

28. A large company currently employs 5739 men and 7290 women. If an employee is selected at random, what is the probability that the employee is a woman?

Enrollment In Exercises 29 and 30, use the table below, which shows the number of students at a university who are currently in each class level.

Class level	Number of students
first year	642
sophomore	549
junior	483
senior	445
graduate student	376

29. If a student is selected at random, what is the probability that the student is an upper-division undergraduate student (junior or senior)?

30. If a student is selected at random, what is the probability that the student is not a graduate student?

In Exercises 31–36, a pair of dice are tossed.

31. Find the probability that the sum of the pips on the two upward faces is 9.

32. Find the probability that the sum on the two dice is not 11.

33. Find the probability that the sum on the two dice is at least 10.

34. Find the probability that the sum on the two dice is an even number or a number less than 5.

35. What is the probability that the sum on the two dice is 9, given that the sum is odd?

36. What is the probability that the sum on the two dice is 8, given that doubles were rolled?

In Exercises 37–40, a single card is selected from a standard deck of playing cards.

37. What is the probability that the card is a heart or a black card?

38. What is the probability that the card is a heart or a jack?

39. What is the probability that the card is not a 3?

40. What is the probability that the card is red, given that it is not a club?

41. If a pair of dice are rolled, what are the odds in favor of getting a sum of 6?

42. If one card is drawn from a standard deck of playing cards, what are the odds that the card is a heart?

43. If the odds against an event occurring are 4 to 5, compute the probability of the event occurring.

44. Genotypes The hair length of a particular rodent is determined by a dominant allele H, corresponding to long hair, and a recessive allele h, corresponding to short hair. Draw a Punnett square for parents of genotypes Hh and hh, and compute the probability that the offspring of the parents will have short hair.

45. Two cards are drawn, without replacement, from a standard deck of playing cards. The probability that exactly one card is an ace is 0.145. The probability that exactly one card is a face card (jack, queen, or king) is 0.362, and the probability that a selection of two cards will contain an ace or a face card is 0.471. Find the probability that the two cards are an ace and a face card.

46. Surveys A recent survey asked 1000 people whether they liked cheese-flavored corn chips (642 people), jalapeno-flavored chips (487 people), or both (302 people). If one person is chosen from this survey, what is the probability that the person does not like either of the two flavors?

In Exercises 47–51, a box contains 24 different colored chips that are identical in size. Five are black, four are red, eight are white, and seven are yellow.

47. If a chip is selected at random, what is the probability that the chip will be yellow or white?

48. If a chip is selected at random, what are the odds in favor of getting a red chip?

49. If a chip is selected at random, find the probability that the chip is yellow given that it is not white.

50. If five chips are randomly chosen, without replacement, what is the probability that none of them is red?

51. If three chips are chosen without replacement, find the probability that the first one is yellow, the second is white, and the third is yellow.

Voting In Exercises 52–56, use the table below, which shows the number of voters in a city who voted for or against a proposition (or abstained from voting) according to their party affiliations. Round answers to the nearest hundredth.

	For	Against	Abstained
Democrat	8452	2527	894
Republican	2593	5370	1041
Independent	1225	712	686

52. If a voter is chosen at random, compute the probability that the person voted against the proposition.

53. If a voter is chosen at random, compute the probability that the person is a Democrat or an Independent.

54. If a voter is randomly chosen, what is the probability that the person abstained from voting on the proposition and is not a Republican?

55. A voter is randomly selected. What is the probability that the individual voted for the proposition, given that the voter is a registered Independent?

56. A voter is randomly selected. What is the probability that the individual is registered as a Democrat, given that the person voted against the proposition?

57. A single die is rolled three times in succession. What is the probability that each roll gives a 6?

58. A single die is rolled five times in succession. Find the probability that a 6 will be rolled at least once.

59. A single die is rolled five times in succession. Find the probability that exactly two of the rolls give a 6.

60. A person draws a card from a standard deck and replaces it; she then does this three more times. What is the probability that she drew a spade at least once?

61. Disease Testing A veterinarian uses a test to determine whether or not a dog has a disease that affects 7% of the dog population. The test correctly gives a positive result for 98% of dogs that have the disease, but gives false positives for 4% of dogs that do not have the disease. If a dog tests positive, what is the probability that the dog has the disease?

62. Weather Suppose that in your area in the wintertime, if it rains one day there is a 65% chance that it will rain the next day. If it does not rain on a given day, there is only a 15% chance that it will rain the following day. What is the probability that, if it didn't rain today, it will rain the next two days but not the following two?

63. **Batteries** About 1.2% of AA batteries produced by a particular manufacturer are defective. If a consumer buys a box of 12 of these batteries, what is the probability that at least one battery is defective?

64. Suppose it costs $4 to play a game in which a single die is rolled and you win the amount of dollars that the die shows. What is the expectation for the game?

65. I will flip two coins. If both coins come up tails, I will pay you $5. If one shows heads and one shows tails, you will pay me $2. If both coins come up heads, we will call it a draw. What is your expectation for this game?

66. **Raffle Tickets** For a fundraiser, an elementary school is selling 800 raffle tickets for $1 each. From these, five tickets will be drawn. One of the winners gets $200 and the others each get $75. If you buy one raffle ticket, what is your expectation?

67. If a pair of dice are rolled 65 times, on how many rolls can we expect to get a total of 4?

68. **Life Insurance** The probability that a 29-year-old female in the U.S. will die within one year is approximately 0.000616. If an insurance company sells a one-year, $40,000 life insurance policy to a 29-year-old for $320, what is the company's expectation?

69. **Life Insurance** The probability that a 19-year-old male in the U.S. will die within one year is approximately 0.001376. If an insurance company sells a one-year, $25,000 life insurance policy to a 19-year-old for $795, what is the company's expectation?

70. **Construction** A construction company has bid on a building renovation project. The company estimates the probabilities of potential profit (or loss) as shown in the table below. What is the profit expectation for the company?

Profit/loss	Probability
$25,000	0.20
$15,000	0.25
$10,000	0.20
$5,000	0.15
$0	0.10
−$5,000	0.10

Test

1. **Driver's License Numbers** A certain driver's license number begins with one of the letters A, D, G, or K and is followed by one of the digits 2, 3, or 4. List the elements in the sample space of the first two digits of this driver's license number.

2. **Computer Systems** A computer system can be configured using one of three processors of different speeds, one of four disk drives of different sizes, one of three monitors, and one of two graphics cards. How many different computer systems are possible?

3. **Transistors** In a very simple computer chip, 10 wires go from one transistor to a second transistor. For the computer to function, instructions must be sent between these two transistors. In how many ways can

four different instructions be sent between the two transistors if no two instructions can be sent along the same wire?

4. A matching test asks students to match 10 words with 15 definitions. If each word can be paired with only one definition, how many different pairs are possible?

5. **Computer Networks** Twenty computers are attached through a network to four printers. If any computer can be connected to any printer, how many different networks are possible?

6. A coin and a regular six-sided die are tossed together once. What is the probability that the coin shows a head or the die has a 5 on the upward face?

7. **Engineering** The probability that a certain brace A in a structure will break when a 1000-pound force is applied is 0.4. The probability that a brace B in the same structure will fail when the same force is applied is 0.5, and the probability that both braces will fail when the 1000-pound force is applied is 0.2. Are the events of A breaking and B breaking independent? Explain your answer.

8. What is the probability of drawing two cards in succession (without replacement) from a standard deck of playing cards and having them both be hearts?

9. Four cards are drawn from a standard deck of playing cards without replacement. What is the probability that none of them are 9's?

10. Three coins are tossed once. What are the odds in favor of the coins showing all heads?

11. **Disease Testing** A new medical test can determine whether or not a human has a disease that affects 5% of the population. The test correctly gives a positive result for 99% of people who have the disease, but gives a false positive for 3% of people who do not have the disease. If a person tests positive, what is the probability that the person has the disease?

12. **Advertising** The table below shows the number of men and the number of women who responded either positively or negatively to a new commercial. If one person is chosen from this group, find the probability that the person is a woman, given that the person responded negatively.

13. **Genotypes** Straight or curly hair for a hamster is determined by a dominant allele S, corresponding to straight hair, and a recessive allele s, which gives curly hair. If one parent is of genotype Ss and the other is of genotype ss, compute the probability that the offspring of the parents will have curly hair.

14. **Inventories** A software company is preparing a bid to create a new inventory program for an auto parts company. The software company estimates the probabilities of potential profit (or loss) as shown in the table below. What is the profit expectation for the company?

Profit/loss	Probability
$75,000	0.18
$50,000	0.36
$25,000	0.31
0	0.08
−$10,000	0.05
−$20,000	0.02

	Positive	Negative	Total
Men	684	736	1420
Women	753	642	1395
Total	1437	1378	2815

CHAPTER

12 Statistics

12.1 Measures of Central Tendency

12.2 Measures of Dispersion

12.3 Measures of Relative Position

12.4 Normal Distributions

12.5 Linear Regression and Correlation

The U.S. Census Bureau collects data on the population of the United States. It then issues *statistical* reports that indicate changes and trends in the U.S. population. For instance, in 2002 there were approximately 105 males for every 100 females between the ages of 5 and 17 years. However, in the category of people 85 years and older, there were approximately 46 men for every 100 women. See the graph below.

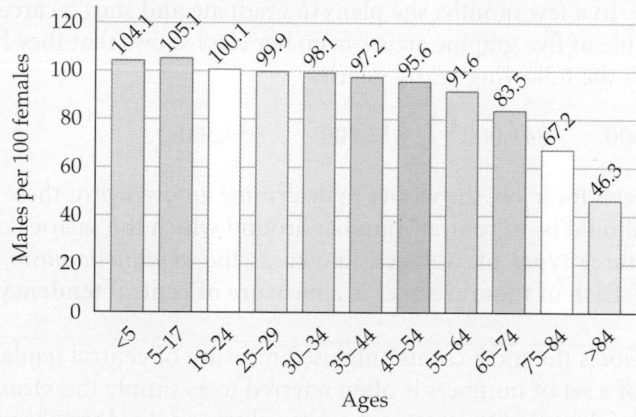

Source: U.S. Census Bureau, Current Population Survey, March 2002

Here are some other statistics from the Census Bureau.

- The *mean* (average) commuting time to work in the United States is approximately 25.5 minutes.

- In 1910, the mean annual family income in the U.S. was $687. In 2003, the mean annual family income was approximately $59,100.

However, the *median* annual family income was approximately $43,500. The difference between the mean and the median is one of the topics of this chapter.

For online student resources, visit this textbook's website at
www.cengage.com/math.

| SECTION 12.1 | **Measures of Central Tendency** |

The Arithmetic Mean

▼ **point of interest**

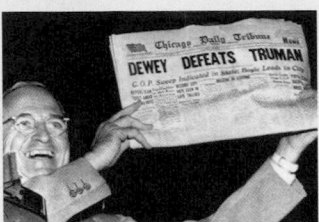

In the 1948 presidential election, the *Chicago Daily Tribune,* on the basis of incorrect information gathered from telephone polls on the night of the election, assumed that Thomas Dewey would defeat Harry Truman and published the headline shown in this photo. When all the votes were counted, Truman had won. Today, the use of cellular phones has caused pollsters to rethink how polls are conducted.

Statistics involves the collection, organization, summarization, presentation, and interpretation of data. The branch of statistics that involves the collection, organization, summarization, and presentation of data is called **descriptive statistics.** The branch that interprets and draws conclusions from the data is called **inferential statistics.**

Statisticians often collect data from small portions of a large group in order to determine information about the group. For instance, to determine who will be elected as the next president of the United States, an organization may poll a small group of voters. From the information it obtains from the small group, it will make conjectures about the voting preferences of the entire group of voters. In such situations the entire group under consideration is known as the **population,** and any subset of the population is called a **sample.**

Because of practical restraints such as time and money, it is common to apply descriptive statistical procedures to a sample of a population and then to make use of inferential statistics to deduce conclusions about the population. Obviously, some samples are more representative of the population than others.

One of the most basic statistical concepts involves finding *measures of central tendency* of a set of numerical data. Here is a scenario in which it would be helpful to find numerical values that locate, in some sense, the *center* of a set of data. Elle is a senior at a university. In a few months she plans to graduate and start a career as a graphic artist. A sample of five graphic artists from her class shows that they have received job offers with the following yearly salaries.

$34,000 $30,500 $41,000 $32,500 $39,500

Before Elle interviews for a job, she wishes to determine an *average* of these five salaries. This average should be a "central" number around which the salaries cluster. We will consider three types of averages, known as the *arithmetic mean*, the *median*, and the *mode*. Each of these averages is a **measure of central tendency** for numerical data.

The *arithmetic mean* is the most commonly used measure of central tendency. The arithmetic mean of a set of numbers is often referred to as simply the *mean*. To find the mean for a set of data, find the sum of the data values and divide by the number of data values. For instance, to find the mean of the five salaries listed above, Elle would divide the sum of the salaries by 5.

$$\text{Mean} = \frac{\$34,000 + \$30,500 + \$41,000 + \$32,500 + \$39,500}{5}$$

$$= \frac{\$177,500}{5} = \$35,500$$

The mean suggests that Elle can expect a job offer at a salary of $35,500.

In statistics it is often necessary to find the sum of a set of numbers. The traditional symbol used to indicate a summation is the Greek letter *sigma*, Σ. Thus the notation Σx, called **summation notation,** denotes the sum of all the numbers in a given set. The use of summation notation enables us to define the mean as follows.

> **Mean**
>
> The **mean** of n numbers is the sum of the numbers divided by n.
>
> $$\text{mean} = \frac{\Sigma x}{n}$$

It is traditional to denote the mean of a *sample* by $\bar{x}$ (which is read as "x bar") and to denote the mean of a *population* by the Greek letter μ (lower case mu).

EXAMPLE 1 ■ Find a Mean

Six friends in a biology class received test grades of

 92, 84, 65, 76, 88, and 90

Find the mean of these test scores.

Solution

$$\bar{x} = \frac{\Sigma x}{n} = \frac{92 + 84 + 65 + 76 + 88 + 90}{6} = \frac{495}{6} = 82.5$$

The mean of these test scores is 82.5.

CHECK YOUR PROGRESS 1 Four separate blood tests revealed that a patient had total blood cholesterol levels of

 245, 235, 220, and 210

Find the mean of the blood cholesterol levels.

Solution *See page S46.*

From a physical perspective, numerical data can be represented by weights on a seesaw. The mean of the data is represented by the balance point of the seesaw. For instance, the mean of 1, 3, 5, 5, 5, and 8 is 4.5. If equal weights are placed at the locations 1, 3, and 8 and three weights are placed at 5, then the seesaw will balance at 4.5.

A Physical Interpretation of the Mean

Balance point at 4.5

The Median

Another type of average is the *median*. Essentially, the median is the *middle number* or the *mean of the two middle numbers* in a list of numbers that have been arranged in numerical order from smallest to largest or from largest to smallest. Any list of numbers that is arranged in numerical order from smallest to largest or from largest to smallest is a **ranked list.**

> **Median**
>
> The **median** of a *ranked list* of n numbers is:
>
> ■ the middle number if n is odd.
>
> ■ the mean of the two middle numbers if n is even.

EXAMPLE 2 ■ **Find a Median**

Find the median for the data in the following lists.

a. 4, 8, 1, 14, 9, 21, 12   **b.** 46, 23, 92, 89, 77, 108

Solution

a. The list 4, 8, 1, 14, 9, 21, 12 contains seven numbers. The median of a list with an odd number of numbers is found by ranking the numbers and finding the middle number. Ranking the numbers from smallest to largest gives 1, 4, 8, 9, 12, 14, 21. The middle number is 9. Thus 9 is the median.

b. The list 46, 23, 92, 89, 77, 108 contains six numbers. The median of a list of data with an even number of numbers is found by ranking the numbers and computing the mean of the two middle numbers. Ranking the numbers from smallest to largest gives 23, 46, 77, 89, 92, 108. The two middle numbers are 77 and 89. The mean of 77 and 89 is 83. Thus 83 is the median of the data.

CHECK YOUR PROGRESS 2   Find the median for the data in the following lists.

a. 14, 27, 3, 82, 64, 34, 8, 51   **b.** 21.3, 37.4, 11.6, 82.5, 17.2

Solution   See page S46.

QUESTION   *The median of the ranked list 3, 4, 7, 11, 17, 29, 37 is 11. If the maximum value 37 is increased to 55, what effect will this have on the median?*

The Mode

A third type of average is the *mode.*

> **Mode**
>
> The **mode** of a list of numbers is the number that occurs most frequently.

ANSWER   *The median will remain the same because 11 will still be the middle number in the ranked list.*

Some lists of numbers do not have a mode. For instance, in the list 1, 6, 8, 10, 32, 15, 49, each number occurs exactly once. Because no number occurs more often than the other numbers, there is no mode.

A list of numerical data can have more than one mode. For instance, in the list 4, 2, 6, 2, 7, 9, 2, 4, 9, 8, 9, 7, the number 2 occurs three times and the number 9 occurs three times. Each of the other numbers occurs less than three times. Thus 2 and 9 are both modes for the data.

EXAMPLE 3 ■ Find a Mode

Find the mode for the data in the following lists.

a. 18, 15, 21, 16, 15, 14, 15, 21   **b.** 2, 5, 8, 9, 11, 4, 7, 23

Solution

a. In the list 18, 15, 21, 16, 15, 14, 15, 21, the number 15 occurs more often than the other numbers. Thus 15 is the mode.

b. Each number in the list 2, 5, 8, 9, 11, 4, 7, 23 occurs only once. Because no number occurs more often than the others, there is no mode.

CHECK YOUR PROGRESS 3   Find the mode for the data in the following lists.

a. 3, 3, 3, 3, 3, 4, 4, 5, 5, 5, 8   **b.** 12, 34, 12, 71, 48, 93, 71

Solution   *See page S46.*

The mean, the median, and the mode are all averages; however, they are generally not equal and they have different properties. The following summary illustrates some of the properties of each type of average.

Comparative Properties of the Mean, the Median, and the Mode

The *mean* of a set of data:

■ is the most sensitive of the averages. A change in any of the numbers changes the mean.

■ can be different from each of the numbers in the set.

■ can be changed drastically by changing an extreme value.

The *median* of a set of data:

■ is usually not changed by changing an extreme value.

■ is generally easy to compute.

The *mode* of a set of data:

■ may not exist, and when it does exist it may not be unique.

■ is one of the numbers in the set, provided a mode exists.

■ is generally not changed by changing an extreme value.

■ is generally easy to compute.

▼ **point of interest**

For some data, the mean and the median can differ by a large amount. For instance, during the 1994 baseball strike, the baseball team owners reported that the average (mean) player's salary was $1.2 million. This was true; however, the median salary was $500,000. (*Source: A Mathematician Reads the Newspaper*, 1995, by John Allen Paulos)

In the following example, we compare the mean, the median, and the mode for the salaries of five employees of a small company.

Salaries: $370,000 $60,000 $32,000 $16,000 $16,000

The sum of the five salaries is $494,000. Hence the mean is

$$\frac{\$494{,}000}{5} = \$98{,}800$$

The median is the middle number, $32,000. Because the $16,000 salary occurs the most, the mode is $16,000. The data contain one extreme value that is much larger than the other values. This extreme value makes the mean considerably larger than the median. Most of the employees of this company would probably agree that the median of $32,000 better represents the average of the salaries than does either the mean or the mode.

Math Matters   Average Rate for a Round Trip

Suppose you average 60 miles per hour on a one-way trip of 60 miles. On the return trip you average 30 miles per hour. You might be tempted to think that the average of 60 miles per hour and 30 miles per hour, which is 45 miles per hour, is the average rate for the entire trip. However, this is not the case. Because you were traveling more slowly on the return trip, the return trip took longer than the time spent going to your destination. More time was spent traveling at the slower speed. Thus the average rate for the round trip is less than the average (mean) of 60 miles per hour and 30 miles per hour.

To find the actual average rate for the round trip, use the formula

$$\text{Average rate} = \frac{\text{total distance}}{\text{total time}}$$

The total round-trip distance is 120 miles. The time spent going to your destination was 1 hour and the time spent on the return trip was 2 hours. The total time for the round trip was 3 hours. Thus

$$\text{Average rate} = \frac{\text{total distance}}{\text{total time}} = \frac{120}{3} = 40 \text{ miles per hour}$$

The Weighted Mean

A value called the *weighted mean* is often used when some data values are more important than others. For instance, many professors determine a student's course grade from the student's tests and the final examination. Consider the situation in which a professor counts the final examination score as two test scores. To find the weighted mean of the student's scores, the professor first assigns a weight to each score. In this case the professor could assign each of the test scores a weight of 1 and the final exam score a weight of 2. A student with test scores of 65, 70, and 75 and a final examination score of 90 has a weighted mean of

$$\frac{(65 \times 1) + (70 \times 1) + (75 \times 1) + (90 \times 2)}{5} = \frac{390}{5} = 78$$

Note that the numerator of the above weighted mean is the sum of the products of each test score and its corresponding weight. The number 5 in the denominator is the sum of all the weights ($1 + 1 + 1 + 2 = 5$). The above procedure can be generalized as follows.

The Weighted Mean

The **weighted mean** of the n numbers $x_1, x_2, x_3, \ldots, x_n$ with the respective assigned weights $w_1, w_2, w_3, \ldots, w_n$ is

$$\text{Weighted mean} = \frac{\Sigma(x \cdot w)}{\Sigma w}$$

where $\Sigma(x \cdot w)$ is the sum of the products formed by multiplying each number by its assigned weight, and Σw is the sum of all the weights.

EXAMPLE 4 ■ **Find a Weighted Mean**

point of interest

Grade point averages (GPA) can be determined by using the weighted mean formula. See Exercises 21 and 22 page 804.

An instructor determines a student's weighted mean from quizzes, tests, and a project. Each test counts as four quizzes and the project counts as eight quizzes. Larry has quiz scores of 70 and 55. His test scores are 90, 72, and 68. His project score is 85. Find Larry's weighted mean for the course.

Solution

If we assign each quiz score a weight of 1, then each test score will have a weight of 4, and the project will have a weight of 8. The sum of all the weights is 22.

Weighted mean

$$= \frac{(70 \times 1) + (55 \times 1) + (90 \times 4) + (72 \times 4) + (68 \times 4) + (85 \times 8)}{22}$$

$$= \frac{1725}{22} \approx 78.4$$

Larry's weighted mean is approximately 78.4.

CHECK YOUR PROGRESS 4   Find Larry's weighted mean in Example 4 if a test score counts as two quiz scores and the project counts as six quiz scores.

Solution   See page S46.

Data that have not been organized or manipulated in any manner are called **raw data.** A large collection of raw data may not provide much pertinent information that can be readily observed. A **frequency distribution,** which is a table that lists observed events and the frequency of occurrence of each observed event, is often used to organize raw data. For instance, consider the following table, which lists the number of cable television connections for each of 40 homes in a subdivision.

Table 12.1   *Numbers of Cable Television Connections per Household*

2	0	3	1	2	1	0	4
2	1	1	7	2	0	1	1
0	2	2	1	3	2	2	1
1	4	2	5	2	3	1	2
2	1	2	1	5	0	2	5

The frequency distribution in Table 12.2 below was constructed using the data from Table 12.1. The first column of the frequency distribution consists of the numbers 0, 1, 2, 3, 4, 5, 6, and 7. The corresponding frequency of occurrence, *f*, of each of the numbers in the first column is listed in the second column.

Table 12.2   *A Frequency Distribution for Table 12.1*

Observed event Number of cable television connections, *x*	Frequency Number of households, *f*, with *x* cable television connections
0	5
1	12
2	14
3	3
4	2
5	3
6	0
7	1
	40 total

This row indicates that there are 14 households with two cable television connections.

The formula for a weighted mean can be used to find the mean of the data in a frequency distribution. The only change is that the weights $w_1, w_2, w_3, \ldots, w_n$ are replaced with the frequencies $f_1, f_2, f_3, \ldots, f_n$. This procedure is illustrated in the next example.

EXAMPLE 5 ■ Find the Mean of Data Displayed in a Frequency Distribution

Find the mean of the data in Table 12.2.

Solution

The numbers in the right-hand column of Table 12.2 are the frequencies f for the numbers in the first column. The sum of all the frequencies is 40.

Mean

$$= \frac{\Sigma(x \cdot f)}{\Sigma f}$$

$$= \frac{(0 \cdot 5) + (1 \cdot 12) + (2 \cdot 14) + (3 \cdot 3) + (4 \cdot 2) + (5 \cdot 3) + (6 \cdot 0) + (7 \cdot 1)}{40}$$

$$= \frac{79}{40}$$

$$= 1.975$$

The mean number of cable connections per household for the homes in the subdivision is 1.975.

CHECK YOUR PROGRESS 5   A housing division consists of 45 homes. The following frequency distribution shows the number of homes in the subdivision that are two-bedroom homes, the number that are three-bedroom homes, the number that are four-bedroom homes, and the number that are five-bedroom homes. Find the mean number of bedrooms for the 45 homes.

Observed event Number of bedrooms, x	Frequency Number of homes with x bedrooms
2	5
3	25
4	10
5	5
	45 total

Solution   See page S46.

Excursion

Linear Interpolation and Animation

Linear interpolation is a method used to find a particular number between two given numbers. For instance, if a table lists the two entries 0.3156 and 0.8248, then the value exactly halfway between the numbers is the mean of the numbers, which is 0.5702. To find the number that is 0.2 of the way from 0.3156 to 0.8248, compute 0.2 times the difference between the numbers and, because the first number is smaller than the second number, add this result to the smaller number.

$$0.8248 - 0.3156 = 0.5092 \quad \longleftarrow \text{ Difference between the table entries}$$

$$0.2 \cdot (0.5092) = 0.10184 \quad \longleftarrow \text{ 0.2 of the above difference}$$

$$0.3156 + 0.10184 = 0.41744 \quad \longleftarrow \text{ Interpolated result, which is 0.2 of the way between the two table entries}$$

The above linear interpolation process can be used to find an intermediate number that is any specified fraction of the difference between two given numbers.

Excursion Exercises

1. Use linear interpolation to find the number that is 0.7 of the way from 1.856 to 1.972.

2. Use linear interpolation to find the number that is 0.3 of the way from 0.8765 to 0.8652. Note that because 0.8765 is larger than 0.8652, three-tenths of the difference between 0.8765 and 0.8652 must be subtracted from 0.8765 to find the desired number.

3. A calculator shows that $\sqrt{2} \approx 1.414$ and $\sqrt{3} \approx 1.732$. Use linear interpolation to estimate $\sqrt{2.4}$. *Hint:* Find the number that is 0.4 of the difference between 1.414 and 1.732 and add this number to the smaller number, 1.414. Round your estimate to the nearest thousandth.

4. We know that $2^1 = 2$ and $2^2 = 4$. Use linear interpolation to estimate $2^{1.2}$.

5. At the present time, a football player weighs 325 pounds. There are 90 days until the player needs to report to spring training at a weight of 290 pounds. The player wants to lose weight at a constant rate. That is, the player wants to lose the same amount of weight each day of the 90 days. What weight, to the nearest tenth of a pound, should the player attain in 25 days?

Graphic artists use computer drawing programs, such as Adobe Illustrator, to draw the intermediate frames of an animation. For instance, in the following figure, the artist drew the small green apple on the left and the large ripe apple on the right. The drawing program used interpolation procedures to draw the five apples between the two apples drawn by the artist.

(continued)

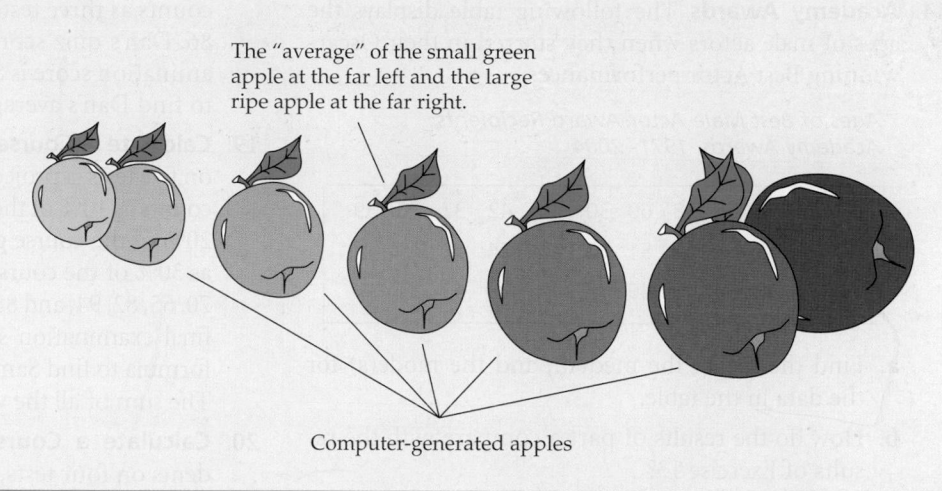

The "average" of the small green apple at the far left and the large ripe apple at the far right.

Computer-generated apples

Exercise Set 12.1

In Exercises 1–10, find the mean, the median, and the mode(s), if any, for the given data. Round noninteger means to the nearest tenth.

1. 2, 7, 5, 7, 14

2. 8, 3, 3, 17, 9, 22, 19

3. 11, 8, 2, 5, 17, 39, 52, 42

4. 101, 88, 74, 60, 12, 94, 74, 85

5. 2.1, 4.6, 8.2, 3.4, 5.6, 8.0, 9.4, 12.2, 56.1, 78.2

6. 5, 5, 5, 5, 5, 5, 5, 5, 5, 5, 5, 5, 5

7. 255, 178, 192, 145, 202, 188, 178, 201

8. 118, 105, 110, 118, 134, 155, 166, 166, 118

9. −12, −8, −5, −5, −3, 0, 4, 9, 21

10. −8.5, −2.2, 4.1, 4.1, 6.4, 8.3, 9.7

11. **a.** If one number in a set of data is changed, will this necessarily change the mean of the set? Explain.

b. If one number in a set of data is changed, will this necessarily change the median of the set? Explain.

12. If a set of data has a mode, then *must* the mode be one of the numbers in the set? Explain.

13. **Academy Awards** The following table displays the ages of female actors when they starred in their Oscar-winning Best Actor performances.

Ages of Best Female Actor Award Recipients, Academy Awards, 1971–2004

34	26	37	42	41	35	31	41	33	31	74	33
49	38	61	21	41	26	80	42	29	33	35	
45	49	39	34	26	25	33	35	35	28	30	

Find the mean, the median, and the mode(s) for the data in the table.

14. **Academy Awards** The following table displays the ages of male actors when they starred in their Oscar-winning Best Actor performances.

Ages of Best Male Actor Award Recipients, Academy Awards, 1971–2004

41	48	48	56	38	60	30	40	42	37	76	39
52	45	35	61	43	51	32	42	54	52	37	
38	31	45	60	46	40	36	47	29	43	37	

a. Find the mean, the median, and the mode(s) for the data in the table.

b. How do the results of part a compare with the results of Exercise 13?

15. **Dental Schools** Dental schools provide urban statistics to their students.

a. Use the following data to decide which of the two cities you would pick to set up your practice in.

Cloverdale: Population, 18,250;
median price of a home, $167,000;
dentists, 12; median age, 49;
mean number of patients, 1294.5

Barnbridge: Population, 27,840;
median price of a home, $204,400;
dentists, 17.5; median age, 53;
mean number of patients, 1148.7

b. ✎ Explain how you made your decision.

16. **Expense Reports** A salesperson records the following daily expenditures during a 10-day trip.

$185.34, $234.55, $211.86, $147.65, $205.60
$216.74, $1345.75, $184.16, $320.45, $88.12

✎ In your opinion, does the mean or the median of the expenditures best represent the salesperson's average daily expenditure? Explain your reasoning.

17. **Course Grades** A professor grades students on three tests, four quizzes, and a final examination. Each test counts as two quizzes and the final examination counts as two tests. Sara has test scores of 85, 75, and 90. Sara's quiz scores are 96, 88, 60, and 76. Her final examination score is 85. Use the weighted mean formula to find Sara's average for the course.

18. **Course Grades** A professor grades students on three tests, three quizzes, and a final examination. Each quiz counts as one-half a test and the final examination counts as three tests. Dan has test scores of 80, 65, and 86. Dan's quiz scores are 86, 80, and 60. His final examination score is 84. Use the weighted mean formula to find Dan's average for the course.

19. **Calculate a Course Grade** A professor grades students on five tests, a project, and a final examination. Each test counts as 10% of the course grade. The project counts as 20% of the course grade. The final examination counts as 30% of the course grade. Samantha has test scores of 70, 65, 82, 94, and 85. Samantha's project score is 92. Her final examination score is 80. Use the weighted mean formula to find Samantha's average for the course. *Hint:* The sum of all the weights is 100% = 1.

20. **Calculate a Course Grade** A professor grades students on four tests, a term paper, and a final examination. Each test counts as 15% of the course grade. The term paper counts as 20% of the course grade. The final examination counts as 20% of the course grade. Alan has test scores of 80, 78, 92, and 84. Alan received an 84 on his term paper. His final examination score was 88. Use the weighted mean formula to find Alan's average for the course.

Grade Point Average Many colleges use the four-point grading system: A = 4, B = 3, C = 2, D = 1, and F = 0. In Exercises 21 and 22, use the weighted mean formula to compute the grade point average for each student. *Hint:* The units represent the "weights" of the letter grades that the student received in a course.

21. *Dillon's Grades, Fall Semester*

Course	Course grade	Course units
English	B	4
History	A	3
Chemistry	D	3
Algebra	C	4

22. *Janet's Grades, Spring Semester*

Course	Course grade	Course units
Biology	A	4
Statistics	B	3
Business Law	C	3
Psychology	F	2
CAD	B	2

Measures of Central Tendency

In Exercises 23–26, find the mean, the median, and all modes for the data in the given frequency distribution.

23. *Points Scored by Lynn*

Points scored in a basketball game	Frequency
2	6
4	5
5	6
9	3
10	1
14	2
19	1

24. *Mystic Pizza Company*

Hourly pay rates for employees	Frequency
$8.00	14
$11.50	9
$14.00	8
$16.00	5
$19.00	2
$22.50	1
$35.00	1

25. *Quiz Scores*

Scores on a biology quiz	Frequency
2	1
4	2
6	7
7	12
8	10
9	4
10	3

26. *Ages of Science Fair Contestants*

Age	Frequency
7	3
8	4
9	6
10	15
11	11
12	7
13	1

Another measure of central tendency for a set of data is called the *midrange*. The **midrange** is defined as the value that is halfway between the minimum data value and the maximum data value. That is,

$$\text{Midrange} = \frac{\text{minimum value} + \text{maximum value}}{2}$$

The midrange is often stated as the *average* of a set of data in situations in which there are a large amount of data and the data are constantly changing. Many weather reports state the average daily temperature of a city as the midrange of the temperatures achieved during that day. For instance, if the minimum daily temperature of a city was 60° and the maximum daily temperature was 90°, then the midrange of the temperatures is $\frac{60° + 90°}{2} = 75°$.

27. Meteorology Find the midrange of the following daily temperatures, which were recorded at three-hour intervals.

52°, 65°, 71°, 74°, 76°, 75°, 68°, 57°, 54°

28. Meteorology Find the midrange of the following daily temperatures, which were recorded at three-hour intervals.

−6°, 4°, 14°, 21°, 25°, 26°, 18°, 12°, 2°

29. Meteorology During a 24-hour period on January 23–24, 1916, the temperature in Browning, Montana decreased from a high of 44°F to a low of −56°F. Find the midrange of the temperatures during this 24-hour period. (*Source: Time Almanac 2002,* page 609)

30. Meteorology During a two-minute period on January 22, 1943, the temperature in Spearfish, South Dakota increased from a low of −4°F to a high of 45°F. Find the mid-range of the temperatures during this two-minute period. (*Source: Time Almanac 2002,* page 609)

31. Test Scores After six biology tests, Ruben has a mean score of 78. What score does Ruben need on the next test to raise his average (mean) to 80?

32. **Test Scores** After four algebra tests, Alisa has a mean score of 82. One more 100-point test is to be given in this class. All of the test scores are of equal importance. Is it possible for Alisa to raise her average (mean) to 90? Explain.

33. **Baseball** For the first half of a baseball season, a player had 92 hits out of 274 times at bat. The player's batting average was $\frac{92}{274} \approx 0.336$. During the second half of the season, the player had 60 hits out of 282 times at bat. The player's batting average was $\frac{60}{282} \approx 0.213$.

    a. What is the average (mean) of 0.336 and 0.213?

    b. What is the player's batting average for the complete season?

    c. Does the answer in part a equal the average in part b?

34. **Commuting Times** Mark averaged 60 miles per hour during the 30-mile trip to college. Because of heavy traffic he was able to average only 40 miles per hour during the return trip. What was Mark's average speed for the round trip?

Extensions

CRITICAL THINKING

35. The mean of 12 numbers is 48. Removing one of the numbers causes the mean to decrease to 45. What number was removed?

36. Find eight numbers such that the mean, the median, and the mode of the numbers are all 45, and no more than two of the numbers are the same.

37. The average rate for a trip is given by

$$\text{Average rate} = \frac{\text{total distance}}{\text{total time}}$$

If a person travels to a destination at an average rate of r_1 miles per hour and returns over the same route to the original starting point at an average rate of r_2 miles per hour, then show that the average rate for the round trip is

$$r = \frac{2r_1 r_2}{r_1 + r_2}$$

38. Pick six numbers and compute the mean and the median of the numbers.

    a. Now add 12 to each of your original numbers and compute the mean and the median for this new set of numbers.

    b. How does the mean of the new set of data compare with the mean of the original set of data?

    c. How does the median of the new set of data compare with the median of the original set of data?

COOPERATIVE LEARNING

Consider the data in the following table.

Summary of Yards Gained in Two Football Games

	Game 1	Game 2	Combined statistics for both games
Warren	12 yards on 4 carries Average: 3 yards/carry	78 yards on 16 carries Average: 4.875 yards/carry	90 yards on 20 carries Average: 4.5 yards/carry
Barry	120 yards on 30 carries Average: 4 yards/carry	100 yards on 20 carries Average: 5 yards/carry	220 yards on 50 carries Average: 4.4 yards/carry

- In the first game Barry has the best average.
- In the second game Barry has the best average.
- If the statistics for the games are combined, Warren has the best average.

You may be surprised by the above results. After all, how can it be that Barry has the best average in game 1 and game 2, but he does not have the best average for both games? In statistics, an example such as this is known as a **Simpson's paradox**.

Form groups of three or four students to work Exercises 39 to 41.

39. Consider the following data.

Batting Statistics for Two Baseball Players

	First month	**Second month**	**Both months**
Dawn	2 hits; 5 at-bats Average: ?	19 hits; 49 at-bats Average: ?	? hits; ? at-bats Average: ?
Joanne	29 hits; 73 at-bats Average: ?	31 hits; 80 at-bats Average: ?	? hits; ? at-bats Average: ?

Is this an example of a Simpson's paradox? Explain.

40. Consider the following data.

Test Scores for Two Students

	English	**History**	**English and history combined**
Wendy	84, 65, 72, 91, 99, 84 Average: ?	66, 84, 75, 77, 94, 96, 81 Average: ?	Average: ?
Sarah	90, 74 Average: ?	68, 78, 98, 76, 68, 92, 88, 86 Average: ?	Average: ?

Is this an example of a Simpson's paradox? Explain.

EXPLORATIONS

41. Create your own example of a Simpson's paradox.

SECTION 12.2 | **Measures of Dispersion**

Table 12.3 *Test Scores*

Alan	Tara
55	80
80	76
97	77
80	83
68	84
100	80
Mean: 80	Mean: 80
Median: 80	Median: 80
Mode: 80	Mode: 80

The Range

In the preceding section we introduced the mean, the median, and the mode. Each of these statistics is a type of average that is designed to measure central tendencies of the data from which it was derived. Some characteristics of a set of data may not be evident from an examination of averages. For instance, consider the test scores for Alan and Tara, as shown in Table 12.3.

The mean, the median, and the mode of Alan's test scores and Tara's test scores are identical; however, an inspection of the test scores shows that Alan's scores are widely scattered, whereas all of Tara's scores are within a few units of the mean. This example shows that average values do not reflect the *spread* or *dispersion* of data. To measure the spread or dispersion of data, we must introduce statistical values known as the *range* and the *standard deviation*.

> **Range**
>
> The **range** of a set of data values is the difference between the largest data value and the smallest data value.

EXAMPLE 1 ■ Find a Range

Find the range of Alan's test scores in Table 12.3.

Solution

Alan's largest test score is 100 and his smallest test score is 55. The range of Alan's test scores is $100 - 55 = 45$.

CHECK YOUR PROGRESS 1   Find the range of Tara's test scores in Table 12.3.

Solution   *See page S46.*

Robert Wadlow

Math Matters   A World Record Range

The tallest man for whom there is irrefutable evidence was Robert Pershing Wadlow. On June 27, 1940, Wadlow was 8 feet 11.1 inches tall. The shortest man for whom there is reliable evidence is Gul Mohammad. On July 19, 1990, he was 22.5 inches tall. (*Source:* Guinness World Records 2001) The range of the heights of these men is $107.1 - 22.5 = 84.6$ inches.

The Standard Deviation

The range of a set of data is easy to compute, but it can be deceiving. The range is a measure that depends only on the two most extreme values, and as such it is very sensitive. For instance, the table at the left shows the times for two sprinters in six track meets. The range of times for the first sprinter is 0.7 second, and the range for the second sprinter is 1.7 seconds. If you consider only range values, then you might conclude that the first sprinter's times are more consistent than those of the second sprinter. However, a closer examination shows that if you exclude the time of 25.8 seconds by the second sprinter in the sixth race, then the second sprinter has a range of 0.1 second. On this basis one could argue that the second sprinter has a more consistent performance record.

220-Yard Dash (times in seconds)

Race	Sprinter 1	Sprinter 2
1	23.8	24.1
2	24.0	24.2
3	24.1	24.1
4	24.4	24.2
5	23.9	24.1
6	24.5	25.8
Range	0.7	1.7

The next measure of dispersion that we will consider is called the *standard deviation*. It is less sensitive to a change in an extreme value than is the range. The standard deviation of a set of numerical data makes use of the individual amount that each data value deviates from the mean. These deviations, represented by $(x - \bar{x})$, are positive when the data value x is greater than the mean $\bar{x}$, and are negative when x is less than the mean $\bar{x}$. The sum of all the deviations $(x - \bar{x})$ is 0 for all sets of data. For instance, consider the sample data 2, 6, 11, 12, 14. For these data, $\bar{x} = 9$. The individual deviation of each data value from the mean is shown in the table on the following page. Note that the sum of the deviations is 0.

Because the sum of all the deviations of the data values from the mean is *always* 0, we cannot use the sum of the deviations as a measure of dispersion for a set of data.

Deviations from the Mean

x	$x - \bar{x}$
2	$2 - 9 = -7$
6	$6 - 9 = -3$
11	$11 - 9 = 2$
12	$12 - 9 = 3$
14	$14 - 9 = 5$
Sum of the deviations ⟶	0

✔ **TAKE NOTE**

You may question why a denominator of $n - 1$ is used instead of n when we compute a sample standard deviation. The reason is that a sample standard deviation is often used to estimate the population standard deviation, and it can be shown mathematically that the use of $n - 1$ tends to yield better estimates.

What is needed is a procedure that can be applied to the deviations so that the sum of the numbers that are derived by adjusting the deviations is not always 0. The procedure that we will make use of *squares* each of the deviations $(x - \bar{x})$ to make each of them nonnegative. The sum of the squares of the deviations is then divided by a constant that depends on the number of data values. We then compute the square root of this result. The following definitions show that the formula for calculating the standard deviation of a population differs slightly from the formula used to calculate the standard deviation of a sample.

Standard Deviations for Samples and Populations

If $x_1, x_2, x_3, \ldots, x_n$ is a *population* of n numbers with a mean of μ, then the **standard deviation** of the population is $\sigma = \sqrt{\dfrac{\Sigma(x - \mu)^2}{n}}$ (1).

If $x_1, x_2, x_3, \ldots, x_n$ is a *sample* of n numbers with a mean of $\bar{x}$, then the **standard deviation** of the sample is $s = \sqrt{\dfrac{\Sigma(x - \bar{x})^2}{n - 1}}$ (2).

Most statistical applications involve a sample rather than a population, which is the complete set of data values. Sample standard deviations are designated by the lower-case letter *s*. In those cases in which we *do* work with a population, we designate the standard deviation of the population by σ, which is the lower-case Greek letter sigma. To calculate the standard deviation of n numbers, it is helpful to use the following procedure.

Procedure for Computing a Standard Deviation

1. Determine the mean of the n numbers.

2. For each number, calculate the deviation (difference) between the number and the mean of the numbers.

3. Calculate the square of each of the deviations and find the sum of these squared deviations.

4. If the data is a *population*, then divide the sum by n. If the data is a *sample*, then divide the sum by $n - 1$.

5. Find the square root of the quotient in Step 4.

EXAMPLE 2 ■ Find the Standard Deviation

The following numbers were obtained by sampling a population.

2, 4, 7, 12, 15

Find the standard deviation of the sample.

Solution

Step 1: The mean of the numbers is

$$\bar{x} = \frac{2 + 4 + 7 + 12 + 15}{5} = \frac{40}{5} = 8$$

Step 2: For each number, calculate the deviation between the number and the mean.

x	$x - \bar{x}$
2	$2 - 8 = -6$
4	$4 - 8 = -4$
7	$7 - 8 = -1$
12	$12 - 8 = 4$
15	$15 - 8 = 7$

Step 3: Calculate the square of each of the deviations in Step 2, and find the sum of these squared deviations.

x	$x - \bar{x}$	$(x - \bar{x})^2$
2	$2 - 8 = -6$	$(-6)^2 = 36$
4	$4 - 8 = -4$	$(-4)^2 = 16$
7	$7 - 8 = -1$	$(-1)^2 = 1$
12	$12 - 8 = 4$	$4^2 = 16$
15	$15 - 8 = 7$	$7^2 = \underline{49}$
		118 ⟵ The sum of the squared deviations

Step 4: Because we have a sample of $n = 5$ values, divide the sum 118 by $n - 1$, which is 4.

$$\frac{118}{4} = 29.5$$

Step 5: The standard deviation of the sample is $s = \sqrt{29.5}$. To the nearest hundredth, the standard deviation is $s = 5.43$.

CHECK YOUR PROGRESS 2 A student has the following quiz scores: 5, 8, 16, 17, 18, 20. Find the standard deviation for this population of quiz scores.

Solution See page S46.

In the next example we use standard deviations to determine which company produces batteries that are most consistent with regard to their life expectancy.

EXAMPLE 3 ■ Use Standard Deviations

A consumers group has tested a sample of eight size D batteries from each of three companies. The results of the tests are shown in the following table. According to these tests, which company produces batteries for which the values representing hours of constant use have the least standard deviation?

Company	Hours of Constant Use per Battery
EverSoBright	6.2, 6.4, 7.1, 5.9, 8.3, 5.3, 7.5, 9.3
Dependable	6.8, 6.2, 7.2, 5.9, 7.0, 7.4, 7.3, 8.2
Beacon	6.1, 6.6, 7.3, 5.7, 7.1, 7.6, 7.1, 8.5

Solution

The mean for each sample of batteries is 7 hours.
The batteries from EverSoBright have a standard deviation of

$$s_1 = \sqrt{\frac{(6.2 - 7)^2 + (6.4 - 7)^2 + \cdots + (9.3 - 7)^2}{7}}$$

$$= \sqrt{\frac{12.34}{7}} \approx 1.328 \text{ hours}$$

The batteries from Dependable have a standard deviation of

$$s_2 = \sqrt{\frac{(6.8 - 7)^2 + (6.2 - 7)^2 + \cdots + (8.2 - 7)^2}{7}}$$

$$= \sqrt{\frac{3.62}{7}} \approx 0.719 \text{ hours}$$

The batteries from Beacon have a standard deviation of

$$s_3 = \sqrt{\frac{(6.1 - 7)^2 + (6.6 - 7)^2 + \cdots + (8.5 - 7)^2}{7}}$$

$$= \sqrt{\frac{5.38}{7}} \approx 0.877 \text{ hours}$$

The batteries from Dependable have the *least* standard deviation. According to these results, the Dependable company produces the most consistent batteries with regard to life expectancy under constant use.

CHECK YOUR PROGRESS 3   A consumer testing agency has tested the strengths of three brands of $\frac{1}{8}$-inch rope. The results of the tests are shown in the following table. According to the sample test results, which company produces $\frac{1}{8}$-inch rope for which the breaking point has the least standard deviation?

Company	Breaking Point of $\frac{1}{8}$-inch Rope, in Pounds
Trustworthy	122, 141, 151, 114, 108, 149, 125
Brand X	128, 127, 148, 164, 97, 109, 137
NeverSnap	112, 121, 138, 131, 134, 139, 135

Solution   *See page S46.*

Many calculators have built-in features for calculating the mean and standard deviation of a set of numbers. The next example illustrates these features on a TI-83/84 graphing calculator.

EXAMPLE 4 ■ Use a Calculator to Find the Mean and Standard Deviation

 Use a graphing calculator to find the mean and standard deviation of the times in the following table. Because the table contains all the winning times for this race (up to the year 2004), the data set is a population.

Olympic Women's 400-Meter Dash Results, in Seconds, 1964–2004

52.0	52.0	51.08	49.29	48.88	48.83	48.65	48.83	48.25	49.11	49.41

Solution

On a TI-83/84 calculator, press STAT ENTER and then enter the above times into list **(L1)**. See the calculator display below. Press STAT ▶ ENTER ENTER. The calculator displays the mean and standard deviations shown below. Because we are working with a population, we are interested in the population standard deviation. From the calculator screen, $\bar{x} \approx 49.666$ and $\sigma x \approx 1.296$ seconds.

> ✔ **TAKE NOTE**
>
> Because the calculation of the population mean and the sample mean are the same, a graphing calculator uses the same symbol $\boxed{\bar{x}}$ for both. The symbols for the population standard deviation, $\boxed{\sigma x}$, and the sample standard deviation, $\boxed{s x}$, are different.

TI-83/84 Display of List 1

L1	L2	L3 1
52	------	------
52		
51.08		
49.29		
48.88		
48.83		
48.65		
L1(1) = 52		

TI-83/84 Display of $\bar{x}$, s and σ

```
1-Var Stats
 x̄=49.66636364        ← Mean
 Σx=546.33
 Σx²=27152.6879
 Sx=1.358802949       ← Sample standard
 σx=1.295567778          deviation
↓n=11                 ← Population standard
                         deviation
```

CHECK YOUR PROGRESS 4   Use a calculator to find the mean and the population standard deviation of the race times in the following table.

Olympic Men's 400-Meter Dash Results, in Seconds, 1896–2004

54.2	49.4	49.2	53.2	50.0	48.2	49.6	47.6	47.8
46.2	46.5	46.2	45.9	46.7	44.9	45.1	43.8	44.66
44.26	44.60	44.27	43.87	43.50	43.49	43.84	44.00	

Solution   *See page S47.*

The Variance

A statistic known as the *variance* is also used as a measure of dispersion. The **variance** for a given set of data is the square of the standard deviation of the data. The following chart shows the mathematical notations that are used to denote standard deviations and variances.

Notations for Standard Deviation and Variance

σ is the standard deviation of a population.

σ^2 is the variance of a population.

s is the standard deviation of a sample.

s^2 is the variance of a sample.

EXAMPLE 5 ■ Find the Variance

Find the variance for the sample given in Example 2.

Solution

In Example 2, we found $s = \sqrt{29.5}$. Variance is the square of the standard deviation. Thus the variance is $s^2 = \left(\sqrt{29.5}\right)^2 = 29.5$.

CHECK YOUR PROGRESS 5   Find the variance for the population given in Check Your Progress 2.

Solution   *See page S47.*

QUESTION   *Can the variance of a data set be smaller than the standard deviation of the data set?*

Although the variance of a set of data is an important measure of dispersion, it has a disadvantage that is not shared by the standard deviation: the variance does not have the same unit of measure as the original data. For instance, if a set of data consists of times measured in hours, then the variance of the data will be measured in *square* hours. The standard deviation of this data set is the square root of the variance, and as such it is measured in hours, which is a more intuitive unit of measure.

ANSWER   *Yes. The variance is smaller than the standard deviation whenever the standard deviation is less than 1.*

Excursion

A Geometric View of Variance and Standard Deviation[1]

The following geometric explanation of the variance and standard deviation of a set of data is designed to provide you with a deeper understanding of these important concepts.

Consider the data $x_1, x_2, \ldots, x_n$, which are arranged in ascending order. The average, or mean, of these data is

$$\mu = \frac{\Sigma x_i}{n}$$

and the variance is

$$\sigma^2 = \frac{\Sigma(x_i - \mu)^2}{n}$$

In the last formula, each term $(x_i - \mu)^2$ can be pictured as the area of a square whose sides are of length $|x_i - \mu|$, the distance between the ith data value and the mean. We will refer to these squares as *tiles*, denoting by T_i the area of the tile associated with the data value x_i. Thus $\sigma^2 = \frac{\Sigma T_i}{n}$, which means that the variance may be thought of as the *area of the averaged-sized tile* and the standard deviation σ as the length of a side of this averaged-sized tile. By drawing the tiles associated with a data set, as shown below, you can visually estimate an averaged-size tile and thus you can roughly approximate the variance and standard deviation.

TAKE NOTE

Up to this point we have used $\mu = \frac{\Sigma x}{n}$ as the formula for the mean. However, many statistics texts use the formula $\mu = \frac{\Sigma x_i}{n}$ for the mean. Letting the subscript i vary from 1 to n helps us to remember that we are finding the sum of all the numbers $x_1, x_2, \ldots, x_n$.

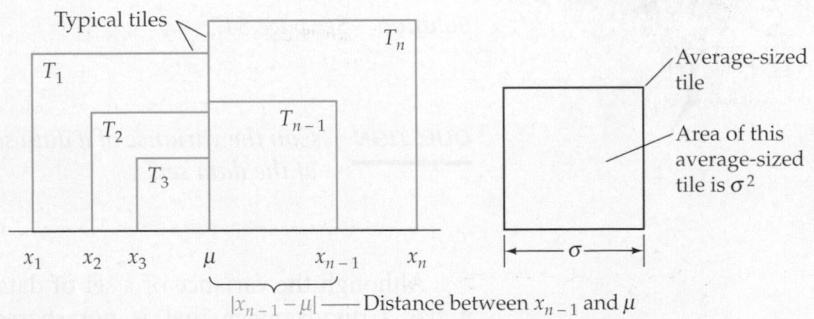

A typical data set, with its associated tiles and average-sized tile

These geometric representations of variance and standard deviation enable us to see visually how these values are used as measures of the dispersion of a set of data. If all of the data are bunched up near the mean, it is clear that the average-sized tile will be small and, consequently, so will its side length, which represents the standard deviation. But if even a small portion of the data lies far from the mean, the average-sized tile may be rather large, and thus its side length will also be large.

(continued)

---

1. Adapted with permission from "Chebyshev's Theorem: A Geometric Approach," *The College Mathematics Journal*, Vol. 26, No. 2, March 1995. Article by Pat Touhey, College Misericordia, Dallas, PA 18612.

Excursion Exercises

1. This exercise makes use of the geometric procedure just explained to calculate the variance and standard deviation of the population 2, 5, 7, 11, 15. The following figure shows the given set of data labeled on a number line, along with its mean, which is 8.

a. Draw the tile associated with each of the five data values 2, 5, 7, 11, and 15.

b. Label each tile with its area.

c. Find the sum of the areas of all the tiles.

d. Find the average (mean) of the areas of all five tiles.

e. To the right of the above number line, draw a tile whose area is the average found in part d.

f. What is the variance of the data? What geometric figure represents the variance?

g. What is the standard deviation of the data? What geometric figure represents the standard deviation?

2. a. to g. Repeat all of the steps described in Excursion Exercise 1 for the data set

$$6, 8, 9, 11, 16$$

h. Which of the data sets in these two Excursion Exercises has the larger mean? Which data set has the larger standard deviation?

Exercise Set 12.2

1. Meteorology During a 12-hour period on December 24, 1924, the temperature in Fairfield, Montana dropped from a high of 63°F to a low of −21°F. What was the range of the temperatures during this period? (*Source: Time Almanac 2002,* page 609)

2. Meteorology During a two-hour period on January 12, 1911, the temperature in Rapid City, South Dakota dropped from a high of 49°F to a low of −13°F. What was the range of the temperatures during this period? (*Source: Time Almanac 2002,* page 609)

In Exercises 3–12, find the range, the standard deviation, and the variance for the given *samples*. Round noninteger results to the nearest tenth.

3. 1, 2, 5, 7, 8, 19, 22

4. 3, 4, 7, 11, 12, 12, 15, 16

5. 2.1, 3.0, 1.9, 1.5, 4.8

6. 5.2, 11.7, 19.1, 3.7, 8.2, 16.3

7. 48, 91, 87, 93, 59, 68, 92, 100, 81

8. 93, 67, 49, 55, 92, 87, 77, 66, 73, 96, 54

9. 4, 4, 4, 4, 4, 4, 4, 4, 4, 4, 4, 4, 4, 4, 4, 4

10. 8, 6, 8, 6, 8, 6, 8, 6, 8, 6, 8, 6, 8

11. −8, −5, −12, −1, 4, 7, 11

12. −23, −17, −19, −5, −4, −11, −31

13. **Mountain Climbing** A mountain climber plans to buy some rope to use as a lifeline. Which of the following would be the better choice? Explain why you think your choice is the better choice.

Rope A: Mean breaking strength: 500 pounds; standard deviation of 300 pounds

Rope B: Mean breaking strength: 400 pounds; standard deviation of 40 pounds

14. **Lotteries** Which would you expect to be the larger: the standard deviation of five random numbers picked from 1 to 47 in the California Super Lotto, or the standard deviation of five random numbers picked from 1 to 51 in the multi-state PowerBall lottery?

15. **Heights of Students** Which would you expect to be the larger standard deviation: the standard deviation of the weights of 25 students in a first-grade class, or the standard deviation of the weights of 25 students in a college statistics course?

16. Evaluate the accuracy of the following statement: When the mean of a data set is large, the standard deviation will be large.

17. **Super Bowl** The following table lists the winning and losing scores for the Super Bowl games from 1972 through 2005.

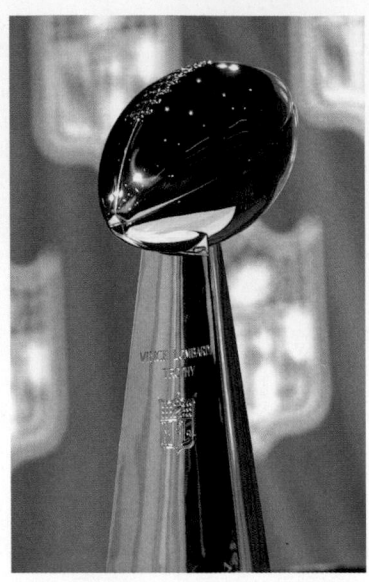

Super Bowl Results, 1972–2005

33–14	16–6	26–21	20–16	27–17
16–7	21–17	27–17	55–10	35–21
23–7	32–14	38–9	20–19	31–24
16–13	27–10	38–16	37–24	34–19
24–3	35–31	46–10	52–17	23–16
14–7	31–19	39–20	30–13	34–7
20–17	48–21	32–29	24–21	

a. Find the mean and the *population* standard deviation of the winning scores. Round each result to the nearest tenth.

b. Find the mean and the *population* standard deviation of the losing scores. Round each result to the nearest tenth.

c. Which of the two data sets has the larger mean? Which of the two data sets has the larger standard deviation?

18. **Academy Awards** The following tables list the ages of female and male actors when they starred in their Oscar-winning Best Actor performances.

Ages of Best Female Actor Award Recipients, Academy Awards, 1971–2004

34	26	37	42	41	35	31	41	33	31	74	33
49	38	61	21	41	26	80	42	29	33	35	
45	49	39	34	26	25	33	35	35	28	30	

Ages of Best Male Actor Award Recipients, Academy Awards, 1971–2004

41	48	48	56	38	60	30	40	42	37	76	39
52	45	35	61	43	51	32	42	54	52	37	
38	31	45	60	46	40	36	47	29	43	37	

a. Find the mean and the *sample* standard deviation of the ages of the female recipients. Round each result to the nearest tenth.

b. Find the mean and the *sample* standard deviation of the ages of the male recipients. Round each result to the nearest tenth.

c. Which of the two data sets has the larger mean? Which of the two data sets has the larger standard deviation?

19. **Baseball** The following tables list the numbers of home runs hit by the leaders in the National and American Leagues from 1971 to 2004.

Home Run Leaders, 1971–2004

National League

48	40	44	36	38	38	52	40	48	48	31	37
40	36	37	37	49	39	47	40	38	35	46	
43	40	47	49	70	65	50	73	49	47	48	

American League

33	37	32	32	36	32	39	46	45	41	22	39
39	43	40	40	49	42	36	51	44	43	46	
40	50	52	56	56	48	47	52	57	47	43	

a. Find the mean and the *population* standard deviation of the number of home runs hit by the leaders in the National League. Round each result to the nearest tenth.

b. Find the mean and the *population* standard deviation of the number of home runs hit by the leaders in the American League. Round each result to the nearest tenth.

c. Which of the two data sets has the larger mean? Which of the two data sets has the larger standard deviation?

20. **Triathlon** The following table lists the winning times for the men's and women's Ironman Triathlon World Championships, held in Kailua-Kona, Hawaii.

Ironman Triathlon World Championships (Winning times rounded to the nearest minute)

Men	(1980 – 2003)		Women	(1980 – 2003)	
9:25	8:31	8:04	11:21	9:01	9:07
9:38	8:09	8:33	12:01	9:01	9:32
9:08	8:28	8:24	10:54	9:14	9:24
9:06	8:19	8:17	10:44	9:08	9:13
8:54	8:09	8:21	10:25	8:55	9:26
8:51	8:08	8:31	10:25	8:58	9:29
8:29	8:20	8:30	9:49	9:20	9:08
8:34	8:21	8:23	9:35	9:17	9:12

a. Find the mean and the *population* standard deviation of the winning times of the female athletes. *Note:* Convert each time to hours. For instance, a time of 12:55 (12 hours 55 minutes) is equal to $12 + \frac{55}{60} = 12.91\overline{6}$ hours. Round each result to the nearest tenth.

b. Find the mean and the *population* standard deviation of the winning times of the male athletes. Round each result to the nearest tenth.

c. Which of the two data sets has the larger mean? Which of the two data sets has the larger standard deviation?

21. **Political Science** The table on the following page lists the U.S. presidents and their ages at inauguration. President Cleveland has two entries because he served two nonconsecutive terms.

Washington	57	J. Adams	61
Jefferson	57	Madison	57
Monroe	58	J. Q. Adams	57
Jackson	61	Van Buren	54
W. H. Harrison	68	Tyler	51
Polk	49	Taylor	64
Fillmore	50	Pierce	48
Buchanan	65	Lincoln	52
A. Johnson	56	Grant	46
Hayes	54	Garfield	49
Arthur	50	Cleveland	47, 55
B. Harrison	55	McKinley	54
T. Roosevelt	42	Taft	51
Wilson	56	Harding	55
Coolidge	51	Hoover	54
F. D. Roosevelt	51	Truman	60
Eisenhower	62	Kennedy	43
L. B. Johnson	55	Nixon	56
Ford	61	Carter	52
Reagan	69	G. H. W. Bush	64
Clinton	46	G. W. Bush	54

Source: The World Almanac and Book of Facts, 2005

Find the mean and the *population* standard deviation of the ages. Round each result to the nearest tenth.

22. **Political Science** The following table lists the deceased U.S. presidents as of November 2004, and their ages at death.

Washington	67	J. Adams	90
Jefferson	83	Madison	85
Monroe	73	J. Q. Adams	80
Jackson	78	Van Buren	79
W. H. Harrison	68	Tyler	71
Polk	53	Taylor	65
Fillmore	74	Pierce	64
Buchanan	77	Lincoln	56
A. Johnson	66	Grant	63
Hayes	70	Garfield	49
Arthur	56	Cleveland	71
B. Harrison	67	McKinley	58
T. Roosevelt	60	Taft	72
Wilson	67	Harding	57
Coolidge	60	Hoover	90
F. D. Roosevelt	63	Truman	88
Eisenhower	78	Kennedy	46
L. B. Johnson	64	Nixon	81
Reagan	93		

Source: The World Almanac and Book of Facts, 2005

Find the mean and the *population* standard deviation of the ages. Round each result to the nearest tenth.

Extensions

CRITICAL THINKING

23. Pick five numbers and compute the *population* standard deviation of the numbers.

   a. Add a nonzero constant c to each of your original numbers and compute the standard deviation of this new population.

   b. Use the results of part a and inductive reasoning to state what happens to the standard deviation of a population when a nonzero constant c is added to each data item.

24. Pick six numbers and compute the *population* standard deviation of the numbers.

   a. Double each of your original numbers and compute the standard deviation of this new population.

   b. Use the results of part a and inductive reasoning to state what happens to the standard deviation of a population when each data item is multiplied by a positive constant k.

25. a. All of the numbers in a sample are the same number. What is the standard deviation of the sample?

   b. If the standard deviation of a sample is 0, must all of the numbers in the sample be the same number?

   c. If two samples both have the same standard deviation, are the samples necessarily identical?

26. Under what condition would the variance of a sample be equal to the standard deviation of the sample?

EXPLORATIONS

27. a. [calculator icon] Use a calculator to compare the standard deviation of the population 1, 2, 3, 4, 5 and the value $\sqrt{\dfrac{5^2 - 1}{12}}$.

b. [calculator icon] Use a calculator to compare the standard deviation of the population 1, 2, 3, ..., 10 and the value $\sqrt{\dfrac{10^2 - 1}{12}}$.

c. [calculator icon] Use a calculator to compare the standard deviation of the population 1, 2, 3, ..., 15 and the value $\sqrt{\dfrac{15^2 - 1}{12}}$.

d. Make a conjecture about the standard deviation of the population 1, 2, 3, ..., n and the value $\sqrt{\dfrac{n^2 - 1}{12}}$.

28. Find, without using a calculator, the standard deviation of the population

$$3001, 3002, 3003, 3004, \ldots, 3010$$

Hint: Use your answer to part b of Exercise 23 and your conjecture from part d of Exercise 27.

SECTION 12.3 | # Measures of Relative Position

z-Scores

When you take a course in college, it is natural to wonder how you will do compared to the other students. Will you finish in the top 10% or will you be closer to the middle? One statistic that is often used to measure the position of a data value with respect to other values is known as the *z-score* or the *standard score*.

---

z-Score

The **z-score** for a given data value x is the number of standard deviations that x is above or below the mean of the data. The following formulas show how to calculate the *z*-score for a data value x in a population and in a sample.

$$\text{Population: } z_x = \frac{x - \mu}{\sigma} \qquad \text{Sample: } z_x = \frac{x - \bar{x}}{s}$$

QUESTION   *Must the z-score for a data value be a positive number?*

In the next example, we use a student's *z*-scores for two tests to determine how well the student did on each test in comparison to the other students.

ANSWER   *No. The z-score for a data value x is positive if x is greater than the mean, it is 0 if x is equal to the mean, and it is negative if x is less than the mean.*

EXAMPLE 1 ■ Compare z-Scores

Raul has taken two tests in his chemistry class. He scored 72 on the first test, for which the mean of all scores was 65 and the standard deviation was 8. He received a 60 on a second test, for which the mean of all scores was 45 and the standard deviation was 12. In comparison to the other students, did Raul do better on the first test or the second test?

Solution

Find the z-score for each test.

$$z_{72} = \frac{72 - 65}{8} = 0.875 \qquad z_{60} = \frac{60 - 45}{12} = 1.25$$

Raul scored 0.875 standard deviation above the mean on the first test and 1.25 standard deviations above the mean on the second test. These z-scores indicate that in comparison to his classmates, Raul scored better on the second test than he did on the first test.

CHECK YOUR PROGRESS 1   Cheryl has taken two quizzes in her history class. She scored 15 on the first quiz, for which the mean of all scores was 12 and the standard deviation was 2.4. Her score on the second quiz, for which the mean of all scores was 11 and the standard deviation was 2.0, was 14. In comparison to her classmates, did Cheryl do better on the first quiz or the second quiz?

Solution   See page S47.

The z-score equation $z_x = \dfrac{x - \bar{x}}{s}$ involves four variables. If the values of any three of the four variables are known, you can solve for the unknown variable. This procedure is illustrated in the next example.

EXAMPLE 2 ■ Use z-Scores

A consumers group tested a sample of 100 light bulbs. It found that the mean life expectancy of the bulbs was 842 hours, with a standard deviation of 90. One particular light bulb from the DuraBright Company had a z-score of 1.2. What was the life span of this light bulb?

Solution

Substitute the given values into the z-score equation and solve for x.

$$z_x = \frac{x - \bar{x}}{s}$$

$$1.2 = \frac{x - 842}{90}$$

$$108 = x - 842$$

$$950 = x$$

The light bulb had a life span of 950 hours.

CHECK YOUR PROGRESS 2   Roland received a score of 70 on a test for which the mean score was 65.5. Roland has learned that the z-score for his test is 0.6. What is the standard deviation for this set of test scores?

Solution   See page S47.

Percentiles

Most standardized examinations provide scores in terms of *percentiles*, which are defined as follows:

---

*p*th Percentile

A value x is called the **pth percentile** of a data set provided $p\%$ of the data values are less than x.

EXAMPLE 3 ■ Using Percentiles

According to the U.S. Department of Labor, the median annual salary in 2003 for a physical therapist was $57,720. If the 85th percentile for the annual salary of a physical therapist was $71,500, find the percent of physical therapists whose annual salary was

a. more than $57,720.

b. less than $71,500.

c. between $57,720 and $71,500.

Solution

a. By definition, the median is the 50th percentile. Therefore, 50% of the physical therapists earned more than $57,720 per year.

b. Because $71,500 is the 85th percentile, 85% of all physical therapists made less than $71,500.

c. From parts a and b, $85\% - 50\% = 35\%$ of the physical therapists earned between $57,720 and $71,500.

CHECK YOUR PROGRESS 3   According to the U.S. Department of Labor, the median annual salary in 2003 for a police dispatcher was $28,288. If the 30th percentile for the annual salary of a police dispatcher was $25,640, find the percent of police dispatchers whose annual salary was

a. less than $28,288.

b. more than $25,640.

c. between $25,640 and $28,288.

Solution   *See page S47.*

The following formula can be used to find the percentile that corresponds to a particular data value in a set of data.

Percentile for a Given Data Value

Given a set of data and a data value x,

$$\text{Percentile of score } x = \frac{\text{number of data values less than } x}{\text{total number of data values}} \cdot 100$$

EXAMPLE 4 ■ Find a Percentile

On a reading examination given to 900 students, Elaine's score of 602 was higher than the scores of 576 of the students who took the examination. What is the percentile for Elaine's score?

Solution

$$\text{Percentile} = \frac{\text{number of data values less than } 602}{\text{total number of data values}} \cdot 100$$

$$= \frac{576}{900} \cdot 100$$

$$= 64$$

Elaine's score of 602 places her at the 64th percentile.

CHECK YOUR PROGRESS 4   On an examination given to 8600 students, Hal's score of 405 was higher than the scores of 3952 of the students who took the examination. What is the percentile for Hal's score?

Solution   *See page S47.*

MathMatters   **Standardized Tests and Percentiles**

Standardized tests, such as the Scholastic Assessment Test (SAT), are designed to measure all students by a *single* standard. The SAT is used by many colleges as part of their admissions criteria. The SAT I is a three-hour examination that measures verbal and mathematical reasoning skills. Scores on each portion of the test range from 200 to 800 points. SAT scores are generally reported in points and percentiles. Sometimes students are confused by the percentile score. For instance, if a student scores 650 points on the mathematics portion of the SAT and is told that this score is in the 85th percentile, this *does not* indicate that the student answered 85% of the questions correctly. An 85th percentile score means that the student scored higher than 85% of the students who took the test. Consequently, the student scored lower than 15% (100% − 85%) of the students who took the test.

Quartiles

The three numbers Q_1, Q_2, and Q_3 that partition a data set into four (approximately) equal portions are called the **quartiles** of the data. For instance, for the data set below, the values $Q_1 = 11$, $Q_2 = 29$, and $Q_3 = 104$ are the quartiles of the data.

2, 5, 5, 8, 11, 12, 19, 22, 23, 29, 31, 45, 83, 91, 104, 159, 181, 312, 354

$$Q_1 \qquad\qquad Q_2 \qquad\qquad Q_3$$

The quartile Q_1 is called the *first quartile.* The quartile Q_2 is called the *second quartile.* It is the median of the data. The quartile Q_3 is called the *third quartile.* The following method of finding quartiles makes use of medians.

> **The Median Procedure for Finding Quartiles**
> 1. Rank the data.
> 2. Find the median of the data. This is the second quartile, Q_2.
> 3. The first quartile, Q_1, is the median of the data values smaller than Q_2. The third quartile, Q_3, is the median of the data values larger than Q_2.

EXAMPLE 5 ■ Use Medians to Find the Quartiles of a Data Set

The following table lists the calories per 100 milliliters of 25 popular beers. Find the quartiles for the data.

Calories, per 100 milliliters, of Selected Beers

43	37	42	40	53	62	36	32	50	49
26	53	73	48	45	39	45	48	40	56
41	36	58	42	39					

Solution

Step 1: Rank the data as shown in the following table.

1) 26	**2)** 32	**3)** 36	**4)** 36	**5)** 37	**6)** 39	**7)** 39	**8)** 40	**9)** 40
10) 41	**11)** 42	**12)** 42	**13)** 43	**14)** 45	**15)** 45	**16)** 48	**17)** 48	**18)** 49
19) 50	**20)** 53	**21)** 53	**22)** 56	**23)** 58	**24)** 62	**25)** 73		

Step 2: The median of these 25 data values has a rank of 13. Thus the median is 43. The second quartile Q_2 is the median of the data, so $Q_2 = 43$.

Step 3: There are 12 data values less than the median and 12 data values greater than the median. The first quartile is the median of the data values less than the median. Thus Q_1 is the mean of the data values with ranks of 6 and 7.

$$Q_1 = \frac{39 + 39}{2} = 39$$

The third quartile is the median of the data values greater than the median. Thus Q_3 is the mean of the data values with ranks of 19 and 20.

$$Q_3 = \frac{50 + 53}{2} = 51.5$$

CHECK YOUR PROGRESS 5   The following table lists the weights, in ounces, of 15 avocados in a random sample. Find the quartiles for the data.

Weights, in ounces, of Avocadoes

12.4	10.8	14.2	7.5	10.2	11.4	12.6	12.8	13.1	15.6
9.8	11.4	12.2	16.4	14.5					

Solution   *See page S47.*

Box-and-Whisker Plots

A **box-and-whisker plot** (sometimes called a **box plot**) is often used to provide a visual summary of a set of data. A box-and-whisker plot shows the median, the first and third quartiles, and the minimum and maximum values of a data set. See the figure below.

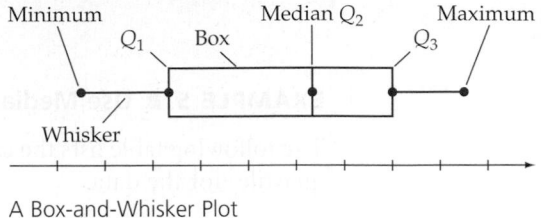

A Box-and-Whisker Plot

Construction of a Box-and-Whisker Plot

1. Draw a horizontal scale that extends from the minimum data value to the maximum data value.

2. Above the scale, draw a rectangle (box) with its left side at Q_1 and its right side at Q_3.

3. Draw a vertical line segment across the rectangle at the median, Q_2.

4. Draw a horizontal line segment, called a whisker, that extends from Q_1 to the minimum and another whisker that extends from Q_3 to the maximum.

EXAMPLE 6 ■ Construct a Box-and-Whisker Plot

Construct a box-and-whisker plot for the data set in Example 5.

Solution
For the data set in Example 5, we determined that $Q_1 = 39$, $Q_2 = 43$, and $Q_3 = 51.5$. The minimum data value for the data set is 26 and the maximum data value is 73. Thus the box-and-whisker plot is as shown below.

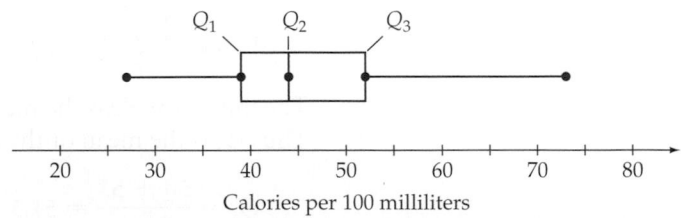

Figure 12.1 *A box-and-whisker plot of the data in Example 5*

historical note

John W. Tukey (1915–2000) made many important contributions to the field of statistics during his career at Princeton University and Bell Labs. He invented box plots when he was working on exploratory data analysis. ■

CHECK YOUR PROGRESS 6 Construct a box-and-whisker plot for the following data.

The Number of Rooms Occupied in a Resort During an 18-day Period

86	77	58	45	94	96	83	76	75
65	68	72	78	85	87	92	55	61

Solution See page S47.

Box plots have become popular because they are easy to construct and they illustrate several important features of a data set in a simple diagram. Note from Figure 12.1 that we can easily estimate

- the quartiles of the data.
- the range of the data.
- the position of the middle half of the data as shown by the length of the box.

Some graphing calculators, such as the TI-83/84, can be used to produce box-and-whisker plots. For instance, on a TI-83/84, you enter the data into a list as shown in Figure 12.2. The $\texttt{WINDOW}$ menu is used to enter appropriate boundaries that contain all the data. Use the key sequence $\boxed{\texttt{2nd}}\ \boxed{\texttt{[STAT PLOT]}}\ \boxed{\texttt{ENTER}}$ and choose from the $\texttt{Type}$ menu the box-and-whisker plot icon. The $\boxed{\texttt{GRAPH}}$ key is then used to display the box-and-whisker plot. After the calculator displays a box-and-whisker plot, the $\boxed{\texttt{TRACE}}$ key and the $\boxed{\blacktriangleright}$ key enable you to view Q_1, Q_2, Q_3, and the minimum and maximum of your data set.

TAKE NOTE

The following data was used to produce the box plot shown to the right.

21.2, 20.5, 17.0, 16.8, 16.8,
16.5, 16.2, 14.0, 13.7, 13.3,
13.1, 13.0, 12.4, 12.1, 12.0

Figure 12.2 *TI-83/84 Screen Displays*

Excursion

Stem-and-Leaf Diagrams

The relative position of each data value in a small set of data can be graphically displayed by using a *stem-and-leaf diagram*. For instance, consider the following history test scores:

65, 72, 96, 86, 43, 61, 75, 86, 49, 68, 98, 74, 84, 78, 85, 75, 86, 73

In the stem-and-leaf diagram on the following page, we have organized the history test scores by placing all of the scores that are in the 40s in the top row, the scores that are

(continued)

A Stem-and-Leaf Diagram of a Set of History Test Scores

Stems	Leaves
4	3 9
5	
6	1 5 8
7	2 3 4 5 5 8
8	4 5 6 6 6
9	6 8

Legend: 8 | 6 represents 86

in the 50s in the second row, the scores that are in the 60s in the third row, and so on. The tens digits of the scores have been placed to the left of the vertical line. In this diagram they are referred to as *stems*. The ones digits of the test scores have been placed in the proper row to the right of the vertical line. In this diagram they are the *leaves*. It is now easy to make observations about the distribution of the scores. Only two of the scores are in the 90s. Six of the scores are in the 70s, and none of the scores are in the 50s. The lowest score is 43 and the highest is 98.

Steps in the Construction of a Stem-and-Leaf Diagram

1. Determine the stems and list them in a column from smallest to largest or largest to smallest.

2. List the remaining digit of each stem as a leaf to the right of the stem.

3. Include a *legend* that explains the meaning of the stems and the leaves. Include a *title* for the diagram.

The choice of how many leading digits to use as the stem will depend on the particular data set. For instance, consider the following data set, in which a travel agent has recorded the amount spent by customers for a cruise.

Amount Spent for a Cruise, Summer of 2005

$3600	$4700	$7200	$2100	$5700	$4400	$9400
$6200	$5900	$2100	$4100	$5200	$7300	$6200
$3800	$4900	$5400	$5400	$3100	$3100	$4500
$4500	$2900	$3700	$3700	$4800	$4800	$2400

One method of choosing the stems is to let each thousands digit be a stem and each hundreds digit be a leaf. If the stems and leaves are assigned in this manner, then the notation 2|1, with a stem of 2 and a leaf of 1, represents a cost of $2100, and 5|4 represents a cost of $5400. A stem-and-leaf diagram can now be constructed by writing all of the stems in a column from smallest to largest to the left of a vertical line, and writing the corresponding leaves to the right of the line.

Amount Spent for a Cruise

Stems	Leaves
2	1 1 4 9
3	1 1 6 7 7 8
4	1 4 5 5 7 8 8 9
5	2 4 4 7 9
6	2 2
7	2 3
8	
9	4

Legend:
7 | 3 represents $7300

(continued)

Sometimes two sets of data can be compared by using a *back-to-back stem-and-leaf diagram,* in which common stems are listed in the middle column of the diagram. Leaves from one data set are displayed to the right of the stems, and leaves from the other data set are displayed to the left. For instance, the back-to-back stem-and-leaf diagram below shows the test scores for two classes that took the same test. It is easy to see that the 8 A.M. class did better on the test because it had more scores in the 80s and 90s and fewer scores in the 40s, 50s, and 60s. The number of scores in the 70s was the same for both classes.

Biology Test Scores

8 A.M. class		10 A.M. class
2	4	5 8
7	5	6 7 9 9
5 8	6	2 3 4 8
1 2 3 3 3 7 8	7	1 3 3 5 5 6 8
4 4 5 5 6 8 8 9	8	2 3 6 6 6
2 4 5 5 8	9	4 5

Legend: 3|7
represents 73

Legend: 8|2
represents 82

Excursion Exercises

1. The following table lists the ages of customers who purchased a cruise. Construct a stem-and-leaf diagram for the data.

Ages of Customers Who Purchased a Cruise

32	45	66	21	62	68	72
61	55	23	38	44	77	64
46	50	33	35	42	45	51
51	28	40	41	52	52	33

2. Construct a back-to-back stem-and-leaf diagram for the winning and losing scores given in Exercise 17 of Section 12.2 (page 816). What information is revealed by your diagram?

3. Construct a back-to-back stem-and-leaf diagram for the data given in the two tables in Exercise 18 of Section 12.2 (pages 816–817). What information is revealed by your diagram?

4. Construct a back-to-back stem-and-leaf diagram for the data given in the two tables in Exercise 19 of Section 12.2 (page 817). What information is revealed by your diagram?

Exercise Set 12.3

In Exercises 1–4, round each z-score to the nearest hundredth.

1. A data set has a mean of $\bar{x} = 75$ and a standard deviation of 11.5. Find the z-score for each of the following.

   a. $x = 85$ b. $x = 95$

   c. $x = 50$ d. $x = 75$

2. A data set has a mean of $\bar{x} = 212$ and a standard deviation of 40. Find the z-score for each of the following.

   a. $x = 200$ b. $x = 224$

   c. $x = 300$ d. $x = 100$

3. A data set has a mean of $\bar{x} = 6.8$ and a standard deviation of 1.9. Find the z-score for each of the following.

   a. $x = 6.2$ b. $x = 7.2$

   c. $x = 9.0$ d. $x = 5.0$

4. A data set has a mean of $\bar{x} = 4010$ and a standard deviation of 115. Find the z-score for each of the following.

   a. $x = 3840$ b. $x = 4200$

   c. $x = 4300$ d. $x = 4030$

5. **Blood Pressure** A blood pressure test was given to 450 women ages 20 to 36. It showed that their mean systolic blood pressure was 119.4 mm Hg, with a standard deviation of 13.2 mm Hg.

   a. Determine the z-score, to the nearest hundredth, for a woman who had a systolic blood pressure reading of 110.5 mm Hg.

   b. The z-score for one woman was 2.15. What was her systolic blood pressure reading?

6. **Fruit Juice** A random sample of 1000 oranges showed that the mean amount of juice per orange was 7.4 fluid ounces, with a standard deviation of 1.1 fluid ounces.

   a. Determine the z-score, to the nearest hundredth, of an orange that produced 6.6 fluid ounces of juice.

   b. The z-score for one orange was 3.15. How much juice was produced by this orange? Round to the nearest tenth of a fluid ounce.

7. **Cholesterol** A test involving 380 men ages 20 to 24 found that their blood cholesterol levels had a mean of 182 mg/dl and a standard deviation of 44.2 mg/dl.

   a. Determine the z-score, to the nearest hundredth, for one of the men who had a blood cholesterol level of 214 mg/dl.

   b. The z-score for one man was −1.58. What was his blood cholesterol level? Round to the nearest hundredth.

8. **Tire Wear** A random sample of 80 tires showed that the mean mileage per tire was 41,700 miles, with a standard deviation of 4300 miles.

   a. Determine the z-score, to the nearest hundredth, for a tire that provided 46,300 miles of wear.

   b. The z-score for one tire was −2.44. What mileage did this tire provide? Round your result to the nearest hundred miles.

9. **Test Scores** Which of the following three test scores is the highest relative score?

   a. A score of 65 on a test with a mean of 72 and a standard deviation of 8.2

   b. A score of 102 on a test with a mean of 130 and a standard deviation of 18.5

   c. A score of 605 on a test with a mean of 720 and a standard deviation of 116.4

10. **Physical Fitness** Which of the following fitness scores is the highest relative score?

    a. A score of 42 on a test with a mean of 31 and a standard deviation of 6.5

    b. A score of 1140 on a test with a mean of 1080 and a standard deviation of 68.2

    c. A score of 4710 on a test with a mean of 3960 and a standard deviation of 560.4

11. **Reading Test** On a reading test, Shaylen's score of 455 was higher than the scores of 4256 of the 7210 students who took the test. Find the percentile, rounded to the nearest percent, for Shaylen's score.

12. **Placement Exams** On a placement examination, Rick scored lower than 1210 of the 12,860 students who took the exam. Find the percentile, rounded to the nearest percent, for Rick's score.

13. **Test Scores** Kevin scored at the 65th percentile on a test given to 9840 students. How many students scored lower than Kevin?

14. **Test Scores** Rene scored at the 84th percentile on a test given to 12,600 students. How many students scored higher than Rene?

15. **Median Income** In 2004, the median family income in the United States was $57,500. (*Source:* U.S. Department of Housing and Urban Development) If the 88th percentile for the 2004 median four-person family income was $70,400, find the percentage of families whose 2004 income was

    a. more than $57,500.   b. more than $70,400.

    c. between $57,500 and $70,400.

16. **Monthly Rents** A recent survey by the U.S. Census Bureau determined that the median monthly housing rent was $632. If the first quartile for monthly housing rent was $497, find the percent of monthly housing rents that were

    a. more than $497.   b. less than $632.

    c. between $497 and $632.

17. **Commute to School** A survey was given to 18 students. One question asked about the one-way distance the student had to travel to attend college. The results, in miles, are shown in the following table. Use the median procedure for finding quartiles to find the first, second, and third quartiles for the data.

Distance Traveled to Attend College								
12	18	4	5	26	41	1	8	10
10	3	28	32	10	85	7	5	15

18. **Prescriptions** The following table shows the number of prescriptions a doctor wrote each day for a 36-day period. Use the median procedure for finding quartiles to find the first, second, and third quartiles for the data.

Number of Prescriptions Written per Day					
8	12	14	10	9	16
7	14	10	7	11	16
11	12	8	14	13	10
9	14	15	12	10	8
10	14	8	7	12	15
14	10	9	15	10	12

19. ✏ **Earned Run Average** The following table shows the earned run averages (ERAs) for the baseball teams in the American League and the National League during the 2004 season. Draw box-and-whisker plots for the teams' ERAs in each league. Place one plot above the other so that you can compare the data.

Write a few sentences that explain any differences you found by using the box-and-whisker plots.

Team Pitching Statistics, 2004 Regular Season Earned Run Averages (ERAs)

American League		National League	
Minnesota	4.04	Atlanta	3.75
Oakland	4.17	St. Louis	3.75
Boston	4.19	Chicago	3.83
Anaheim	4.28	Los Angeles	4.01
Texas	4.54	San Diego	4.03
New York	4.69	Houston	4.05
Baltimore	4.71	Florida	4.10
Seattle	4.76	New York	4.10
Tampa Bay	4.82	Milwaukee	4.26
Cleveland	4.82	Pittsburgh	4.31
Chicago	4.91	Montréal	4.33
Toronto	4.93	San Francisco	4.34
Detroit	4.93	Philadelphia	4.47
Kansas City	5.16	Arizona	4.98
		Cincinnati	5.21
		Colorado	5.54

Source: STATS, Inc.

20. ✏ **Super Bowl** The following data are the points scored during the regular season by the two teams that played in the 2004 Super Bowl.

Points scored by New England Patriots							
0	31	23	17	38	17	19	9
30	12	23	38	12	27	21	31

Points scored by Carolina Panthers							
24	12	23	19	23	17	23	10
27	20	20	16	14	20	20	37

Draw a box-and-whiskers plot of each set of data, placing one plot over the other. Write a few sentences explaining any differences you found between the two plots.

21. ✎ **Salary Comparison** The table below shows the median weekly salaries for women and men for selected occupations. Draw box-and-whiskers plots for these data. For each occupation, place one plot above the other so that you can compare the data. Write a few sentences that explain any differences you found.

Occupation	Women's Median Weekly Earnings	Men's Median Weekly Earnings
Chief executive	$1243	$1736
Operations manager	$966	$1170
Systems manager	$904	$1271
Financial manager	$1280	$1437
Human resource dir.	$823	$1314
Purchasing manager	$844	$1297
Education administrator	$878	$1172
Medical Services mgr.	$954	$1149
Property manager	$638	$849
Claims adjuster	$648	$868
Management analyst	$977	$1267
Auditor	$756	$1041

Source: U.S. Department of Labor, September 2004.

22. ✎ **Home Sales** The following table shows the median sales prices of existing single-family homes in the United States in the four regions of the country for the years 1993 through 2003. Prices have been rounded to the nearest hundred.

a. Draw a box-and-whisker plot of the data for each of the four regions. Write a few sentences that explain any differences you found.

b. Use the Internet to find the median price of a single-family home in your region of the United States for the current year. How does this median price compare with the 2003 median price shown in the following table?

Median Prices of Homes Sold in the United States, 1993–2003

Year	Northeast	Midwest	South	West
1993	162,600	125,000	115,000	135,000
1994	169,000	132,900	116,900	140,400
1995	180,000	134,000	124,500	141,000
1996	186,900	137,500	125,000	153,900
1997	190,000	149,900	129,600	160,000
1998	200,000	157,500	135,800	163,500
1999	210,500	164,000	145,900	173,700
2000	227,400	169,700	148,000	196,400
2001	246,400	172,600	155,400	213,600
2002	264,300	178,000	163,400	238,500
2003	264,500	184,300	168,100	260,900

Source: National Association of REALTORS.

Extensions

CRITICAL THINKING

23. a. The population 3, 4, 9, 14, and 20 has a mean of 10 and a standard deviation of 6.356. The z-scores for each of the five data values are $z_3 \approx -1.101$, $z_4 \approx -0.944$, $z_9 \approx -0.157$, $z_{14} \approx 0.629$, and $z_{20} \approx 1.573$. Find the mean and the standard deviation of these z-scores.

b. The population 2, 6, 12, 17, 22, and 25 has a mean of 14 and a standard deviation of 8.226. The z-scores for each of the six data values are $z_2 \approx -1.459$, $z_6 \approx -0.973$, $z_{12} \approx -0.243$, $z_{17} \approx 0.365$, $z_{22} \approx 0.973$, and $z_{25} \approx 1.337$. Find the mean and the standard deviation of these z-scores.

c. Use the results of part a and part b to make a conjecture about the mean and standard deviation of the z-scores for any set of data.

24. For each of the following, determine whether the statement is true or false.

a. For any given set of data, the median of the data equals the mean of Q_1 and Q_3.

b. For any given set of data, $Q_3 - Q_2 = Q_2 - Q_1$.

c. A z-score for a given data value x in a set of data can be a negative number.

d. If a student answers 75% of the questions on a test correctly, then the student's score on the test will place the student at the 75th percentile.

EXPLORATIONS

25. Some data sets include values so large or so small that they differ significantly from the rest of the data. Such data values are referred to as **outliers.** An outlier may be the result of an error, such as an incorrect measurement or a recording error, or it may be a legitimate data value. Consult a statistics text to find the mathematical formula that is used to determine whether a given data value in a set of data is an outlier. Use the formula to find all outliers for the data set in Exercise 17 page 829.

SECTION 12.4 | Normal Distributions

Frequency Distributions and Histograms

Large sets of data are often displayed using a *grouped frequency distribution* or a *histogram.* For instance, consider the following situation. An Internet service provider (ISP) has installed new computers. To estimate the new download times its subscribers will experience, the ISP surveyed 1000 of its subscribers to determine the time required for each subscriber to download a particular file from the Internet site **music.net.** The results of that survey are summarized in the table below.

Table 12.4 *A grouped frequency distribution with 12 classes*

Download time (in seconds)	Number of subscribers
0–5	6
5–10	17
10–15	43
15–20	92
20–25	151
25–30	192
30–35	190
35–40	149
40–45	90
45–50	45
50–55	15
55–60	10

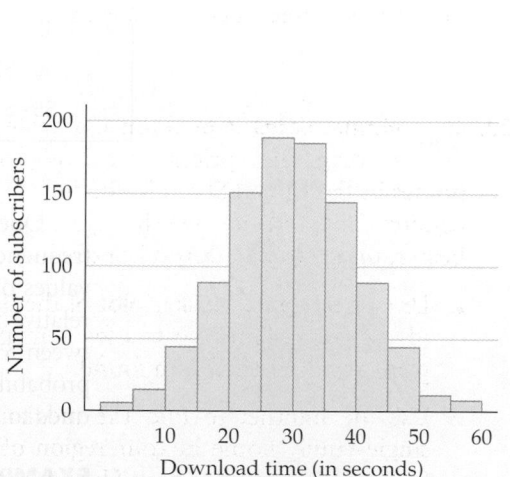

Figure 12.3 *A histogram for the frequency distribution in Table 12.4*

Table 12.4 is called **a grouped frequency distribution.** It shows how often (frequently) certain events occurred. Each interval, 0–5, 5–10, and so on, is called a **class.** This distribution has 12 classes. For the 10–15 class, 10 is the **lower class**

boundary and 15 is the **upper class boundary.** Any data value that lies on a common boundary is assigned to the higher class. The *graph* of a frequency distribution is called a **histogram.** A histogram provides a pictorial view of how the data are distributed. In Figure 12.3 on the previous page, the height of each bar of the histogram indicates how many subscribers experienced the download times shown by the class on the base of the bar.

Examine the distribution in Table 12.5. It shows the *percent* of subscribers that are in each class, as opposed to the frequency distribution in Table 12.4 on the previous page, which shows the *number* of customers in each class. The type of frequency distribution that lists the *percent* of data in each class is called a **relative frequency distribution.** The **relative frequency histogram** in Figure 12.4 was drawn by using the data in the relative frequency distribution. It shows the *percent* of subscribers along its vertical axis.

Table 12.5 *A relative frequency distribution*

Download time (in seconds)	Percent of subscribers
0–5	0.6
5–10	1.7
10–15	4.3
15–20	9.2
20–25	15.1
25–30	19.2
30–35	19.0
35–40	14.9
40–45	9.0
45–50	4.5
50–55	1.5
55–60	1.0

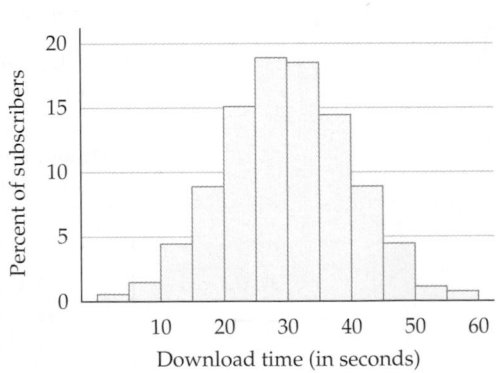

Figure 12.4 *A relative frequency histogram*

One advantage of using a relative frequency distribution instead of a grouped frequency distribution is that there is a direct correspondence between the percent values of the relative frequency distribution and probabilities. For instance, in the relative frequency distribution in Table 12.5, the percent of the data that lies between 35 and 40 seconds is 14.9%. Thus, if a subscriber is chosen at random, the probability that the subscriber will require at least 35 seconds but less than 40 seconds to download the music file is 0.149.

EXAMPLE 1 ■ Use a Relative Frequency Distribution

Use the relative frequency distribution in Table 12.5 to determine the

a. *percent* of subscribers who required at least 25 seconds to download the file.

b. *probability* that a subscriber chosen at random will require at least 5 but less than 20 seconds to download the file.

Solution

a. The percent of data in all the classes with a lower boundary of 25 seconds or more is the sum of the percents for all of the classes highlighted in red in the distribution below. Thus the percent of subscribers who required at least 25 seconds to download the file is 69.1%. See Table 12.6.

Table 12.6

Download time (in seconds)	Percent of subscribers	
0–5	0.6	
5–10	1.7	Sum is 15.2%
10–15	4.3	
15–20	9.2	
20–25	15.1	
25–30	19.2	
30–35	19.0	
35–40	14.9	
40–45	9.0	Sum is 69.1%
45–50	4.5	
50–55	1.5	
55–60	1.0	

b. The percent of data in all the classes with a lower boundary of at least 5 seconds and an upper boundary of 20 seconds or less is the sum of the percents in all of the classes highlighted in blue in the distribution above. Thus the percent of subscribers who required at least 5 but less than 20 seconds to download the file is 15.2%. The probability that a subscriber chosen at random will require at least 5 but less than 20 seconds to download the file is 0.152. See Table 12.6.

CHECK YOUR PROGRESS 1 Use the relative frequency distribution in Table 12.5 to determine the

a. *percent* of subscribers who required less than 25 seconds to download the file.

b. *probability* that a subscriber chosen at random will require at least 10 seconds but less than 30 seconds to download the file.

Solution   *See page S47.*

There is a geometric analogy between percent of data and probabilities and the relative frequency histogram for the data. For instance, the percent of data described in part a of Example 1 corresponds to the *area* represented by the red bars in the histogram in Figure 12.5. The percent of data described in part b of Example 1 corresponds to the area represented by the blue bars in the histogram in Figure 12.6.

Figure 12.5

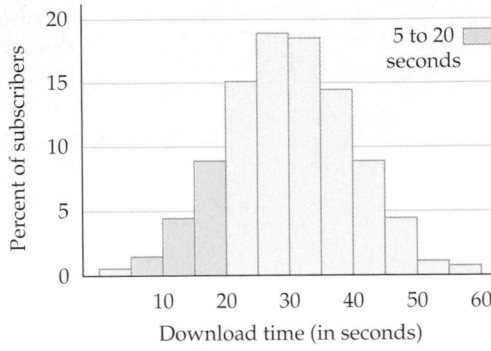

Figure 12.6

Normal Distributions and The Empirical Rule

A histogram of a set of data provides us with a tool that can indicate patterns or trends in the distribution of the data. The terms *uniform, bimodal, symmetrical, skewed* and *normal* are used to describe the distribution of sets of data.

A **uniform distribution,** shown in the figure below, occurs when all of the observed events occur with the same frequency. The graph of a uniform distribution remains at the same height over the range of the data. Some random processes produce distributions that are uniform or nearly uniform. For example, if the spinner below is used to generate numbers, then in the *long run* each of the numbers 1, 2, 3, ..., 8 will be generated with approximately the same frequency.

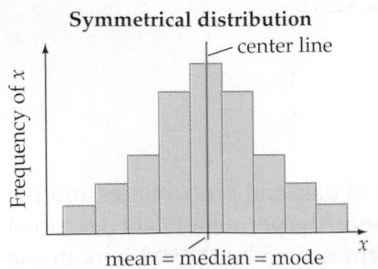

A **bimodal distribution,** shown in the histogram at the left, is produced when two *nonadjacent* classes occur more frequently than any of the other classes. Bimodal distributions are often produced by a sample that contains data from two very different populations.

A **symmetrical distribution,** shown at the left, is symmetrical about a vertical center line. If you fold a symmetrical distribution along the center line, the right side of the distribution will match the left side. The following sets of data are examples of distributions that are nearly symmetrical: the weights of all male students, the heights of all teenage females, the prices of a gallon of regular gasoline in a large city, the mileages for a particular type of automobile tire, and the amounts of soda dispensed by a vending machine per day. In a symmetrical distribution, the mean, the median, and the mode are all equal and are located at the center of the distribution.

Skewed distributions, shown in the figures below, can be identified by the fact that their distributions have a longer *tail* on one side of the distribution and a shorter tail on the other side. A distribution is skewed to the *left* if it has a longer tail on the left and is skewed to the *right* if it has a longer tail on the right. In a distribution that is skewed to the left, the mean is less than the median, which is less than the mode. In a distribution that is skewed to the right, the mode is less than the median, which is less than the mean.

Skewed distributions

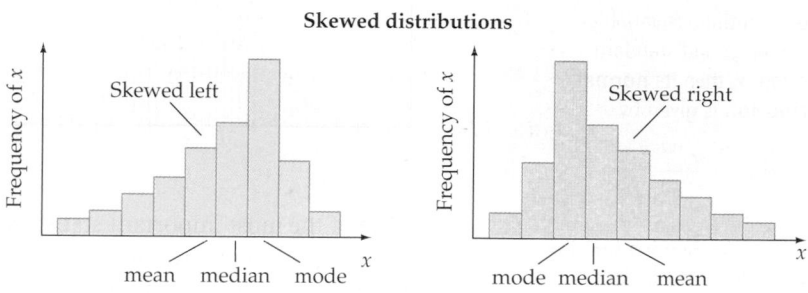

Many examinations yield test scores that have skewed distributions. For instance, if a test designed for students in the sixth grade is given to students in a ninth-grade class, most of the scores will be high. The distribution of the test scores will be skewed to the left, as shown above.

Discrete data are separated from each other by an increment, or "space." For instance, only whole numbers are used to record the number of points that a basketball player scores in a game. The possible points that the player can score, which we will represent by s, is restricted to 0, 1, 2, 3, 4, ... The variable s is a **discrete variable.** Different scores are separated from each other by at least 1. A variable that is based on counting procedures is a discrete variable. Histograms are generally used to show the distributions of discrete variables.

Continuous data can take on the values of all real numbers in some interval. For example, the possible times that it takes to drive to the grocery store are continuous data. The times are not restricted to natural numbers such as 4 minutes or 5 minutes. In fact, the time may be any part of a minute, or even of a second, if we care to measure that precisely. A variable such as the time t, that is based on *measuring* with smaller and smaller units, is called a **continuous variable.** Continuous curves, rather than histograms, are used to show the distributions of continuous variables.

Distributions of Continuous Variables

In some cases we use a continuous curve to display the distribution of a set of discrete data. For instance, in those cases in which we have a large set of data and very small class intervals, the shape of the top of the histogram approaches a smooth curve. See the two figures below. When graphing the distributions of very large sets of data with very small class intervals, it is common practice to replace the histogram with a smooth continuous curve.

A histogram for discrete data A continuous distribution curve

One of the most important statistical distributions is known as a *normal distribution*. The precise mathematical definition of a normal distribution is given by the equation in the Take Note at the left. However, for many applied problems, it is sufficient to know that all normal distributions have the following properties.

Properties of a Normal Distribution

The distribution of data in a normal distribution has a bell shape that is symmetrical about a vertical line through its center. The mean, the median, and the mode of a normal distribution are all equal and they are located at the center of the distribution.

A normal distribution

The Empirical Rule: In a normal distribution, about

68.2% of the data lie within 1 standard deviation of the mean.
95.4% of the data lie within 2 standard deviations of the mean.
99.7% of the data lie within 3 standard deviations of the mean.

The Empirical Rule can be used to solve many applied problems.

EXAMPLE 2 ■ Use the Empirical Rule to Solve an Application

A survey in 2004 of 1000 U.S. gas stations found that the price charged for a gallon of regular gas could be closely approximated by a normal distribution with a mean of $1.88 and a standard deviation of $0.20. How many of the stations charge

a. between $1.48 and $2.28 for a gallon of regular gas?

b. less than $2.08 for a gallon of regular gas?

c. more than $2.28 for a gallon of regular gas?

Solution

a. The $1.48 per gallon price is 2 standard deviations below the mean. The $2.28 price is 2 standard deviations above the mean. In a normal distribution, 95.4% of all data lie within 2 standard deviations of the mean. See Figure 12.7. Therefore, approximately

$$(95.4\%)(1000) = (0.954)(1000) = 954$$

of the stations charge between $1.48 and $2.28 for a gallon of regular gas.

b. The $2.08 price is 1 standard deviation above the mean. See Figure 12.8. In a normal distribution, 34.1% of all data lie between the mean and 1 standard deviation above the mean. Thus, approximately

$$(34.1\%)(1000) = (0.341)(1000) = 341$$

of the stations charge between $1.88 and $2.08 for a gallon of regular gasoline. Half of the stations charge less than the mean. Therefore, about $341 + 500 = 841$ of the stations charge less than $2.08 for a gallon of regular gas.

c. The $2.28 price is 2 standard deviations above the mean. In a normal distribution, 95.4% of all data are within 2 standard deviations of the mean. This means that the other 4.6% of the data will lie either above 2 standard deviations of the mean or below 2 standard deviations of the mean. We are interested only in the data that are more than 2 standard deviations above the mean, which is $\frac{1}{2}$ of 4.6%, or 2.3%, of the data. See Figure 12.9. Thus about $(2.3\%)(1000) = (0.023)(1000) = 23$ of the stations charge more than $2.28 for a gallon of regular gas.

Figure 12.7

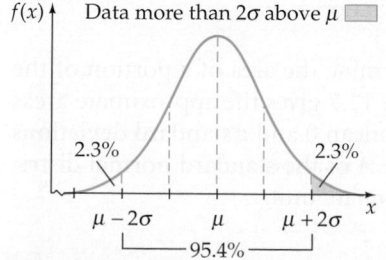

Figure 12.8

CHECK YOUR PROGRESS 2   A vegetable distributor knows that during the month of August, the weights of its tomatoes are normally distributed with a mean of 0.61 pound and a standard deviation of 0.15 pound.

a. What percent of the tomatoes weigh less than 0.76 pound?

b. In a shipment of 6000 tomatoes, how many tomatoes can be expected to weigh more than 0.31 pound?

c. In a shipment of 4500 tomatoes, how many tomatoes can be expected to weigh from 0.31 pound to 0.91 pound?

Solution   *See page S47.*

Figure 12.9

QUESTION   *Can the Empirical Rule be applied to all data sets?*

The Standard Normal Distribution

It is often helpful to convert the values of a continuous variable x to z-scores, as we did in the previous section by using the z-score formulas:

$$z_x = \frac{x - \bar{x}}{s} \quad \text{or} \quad z_x = \frac{x - \mu}{\sigma}$$

If the original distribution of x values is a normal distribution, then the corresponding distribution of z-scores will also be a normal distribution. This normal distribution of z-scores is called the *standard normal distribution*. See Figure 12.10. It has a mean of 0 and a standard deviation of 1, and it was first used by the French mathematician Abraham De Moivre (1667–1754).

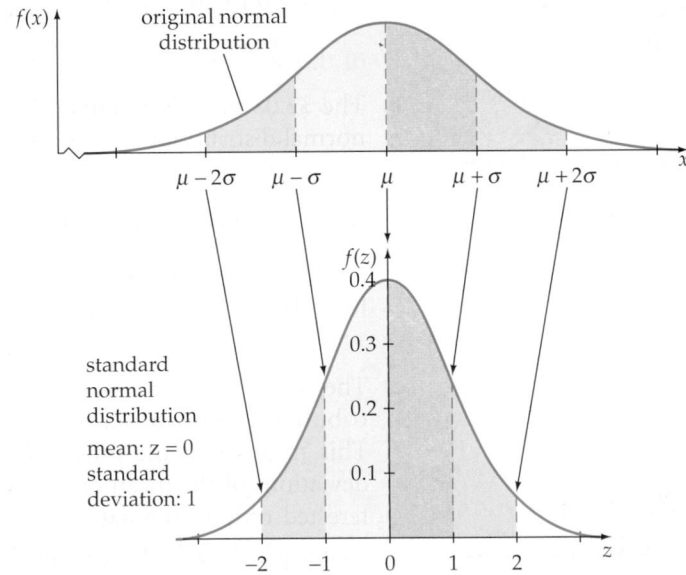

Figure 12.10 *Conversion of a normal distribution to the standard normal distribution*

The Standard Normal Distribution

The **standard normal distribution** is the normal distribution for the continuous variable z that has a mean of 0 and a standard deviation of 1.

Tables and calculators are often used to determine the area of a portion of the standard normal distribution. For example, Table 12.7 gives the approximate areas of the standard normal distribution between the mean 0 and z standard deviations from the mean. Table 12.7 indicates that the area A of the standard normal distribution from the mean 0 up to $z = 1.34$ is 0.410 square unit.

ANSWER   *No. The Empirical Rule can only be applied to normal distributions.*

Table 12.7 *Area Under the Standard Normal Curve*

z	A	z	A	z	A	z	A	z	A	z	A
.00	.000	.56	.212	1.12	.369	1.68	.454	2.24	.487	2.80	.497
.01	.004	.57	.216	1.13	.371	1.69	.454	2.25	.488	2.81	.498
.02	.008	.58	.219	1.14	.373	1.70	.455	2.26	.488	2.82	.498
.03	.012	.59	.222	1.15	.375	1.71	.456	2.27	.488	2.83	.498
.04	.016	.60	.226	1.16	.377	1.72	.457	2.28	.489	2.84	.498
.05	.020	.61	.229	1.17	.379	1.73	.458	2.29	.489	2.85	.498
.06	.024	.62	.232	1.18	.381	1.74	.459	2.30	.489	2.86	.498
.07	.028	.63	.236	1.19	.383	1.75	.460	2.31	.490	2.87	.498
.08	.032	.64	.239	1.20	.385	1.76	.461	2.32	.490	2.88	.498
.09	.036	.65	.242	1.21	.387	1.77	.462	2.33	.490	2.89	.498
.10	.040	.66	.245	1.22	.389	1.78	.462	2.34	.490	2.90	.498
.11	.044	.67	.249	1.23	.391	1.79	.463	2.35	.491	2.91	.498
.12	.048	.68	.252	1.24	.393	1.80	.464	2.36	.491	2.92	.498
.13	.052	.69	.255	1.25	.394	1.81	.465	2.37	.491	2.93	.498
.14	.056	.70	.258	1.26	.396	1.82	.466	2.38	.491	2.94	.498
.15	.060	.71	.261	1.27	.398	1.83	.466	2.39	.492	2.95	.498
.16	.064	.72	.264	1.28	.400	1.84	.467	2.40	.492	2.96	.498
.17	.067	.73	.267	1.29	.401	1.85	.468	2.41	.492	2.97	.499
.18	.071	.74	.270	1.30	.403	1.86	.469	2.42	.492	2.98	.499
.19	.075	.75	.273	1.31	.405	1.87	.469	2.43	.492	2.99	.499
.20	.079	.76	.276	1.32	.407	1.88	.470	2.44	.493	3.00	.499
.21	.083	.77	.279	1.33	.408	1.89	.471	2.45	.493	3.01	.499
.22	.087	.78	.282	1.34	.410	1.90	.471	2.46	.493	3.02	.499
.23	.091	.79	.285	1.35	.411	1.91	.472	2.47	.493	3.03	.499
.24	.095	.80	.288	1.36	.413	1.92	.473	2.48	.493	3.04	.499
.25	.099	.81	.291	1.37	.415	1.93	.473	2.49	.494	3.05	.499
.26	.103	.82	.294	1.38	.416	1.94	.474	2.50	.494	3.06	.499
.27	.106	.83	.297	1.39	.418	1.95	.474	2.51	.494	3.07	.499
.28	.110	.84	.300	1.40	.419	1.96	.475	2.52	.494	3.08	.499
.29	.114	.85	.302	1.41	.421	1.97	.476	2.53	.494	3.09	.499
.30	.118	.86	.305	1.42	.422	1.98	.476	2.54	.494	3.10	.499
.31	.122	.87	.308	1.43	.424	1.99	.477	2.55	.495	3.11	.499
.32	.126	.88	.311	1.44	.425	2.00	.477	2.56	.495	3.12	.499
.33	.129	.89	.313	1.45	.426	2.01	.478	2.57	.495	3.13	.499
.34	.133	.90	.316	1.46	.428	2.02	.478	2.58	.495	3.14	.499
.35	.137	.91	.319	1.47	.429	2.03	.479	2.59	.495	3.15	.499
.36	.141	.92	.321	1.48	.431	2.04	.479	2.60	.495	3.16	.499
.37	.144	.93	.324	1.49	.432	2.05	.480	2.61	.495	3.17	.499
.38	.148	.94	.326	1.50	.433	2.06	.480	2.62	.496	3.18	.499
.39	.152	.95	.329	1.51	.434	2.07	.481	2.63	.496	3.19	.499
.40	.155	.96	.331	1.52	.436	2.08	.481	2.64	.496	3.20	.499
.41	.159	.97	.334	1.53	.437	2.09	.482	2.65	.496	3.21	.499
.42	.163	.98	.336	1.54	.438	2.10	.482	2.66	.496	3.22	.499
.43	.166	.99	.339	1.55	.439	2.11	.483	2.67	.496	3.23	.499
.44	.170	1.00	.341	1.56	.441	2.12	.483	2.68	.496	3.24	.499
.45	.174	1.01	.344	1.57	.442	2.13	.483	2.69	.496	3.25	.499
.46	.177	1.02	.346	1.58	.443	2.14	.484	2.70	.497	3.26	.499
.47	.181	1.03	.348	1.59	.444	2.15	.484	2.71	.497	3.27	.499
.48	.184	1.04	.351	1.60	.445	2.16	.485	2.72	.497	3.28	.499
.49	.188	1.05	.353	1.61	.446	2.17	.485	2.73	.497	3.29	.499
.50	.191	1.06	.355	1.62	.447	2.18	.485	2.74	.497	3.30	.500
.51	.195	1.07	.358	1.63	.448	2.19	.486	2.75	.497	3.31	.500
.52	.198	1.08	.360	1.64	.449	2.20	.486	2.76	.497	3.32	.500
.53	.202	1.09	.362	1.65	.451	2.21	.486	2.77	.497	3.33	.500
.54	.205	1.10	.364	1.66	.452	2.22	.487	2.78	.497		
.55	.209	1.11	.367	1.67	.453	2.23	.487	2.79	.497		

✔ **TAKE NOTE**

In Table 12.7, the entries below *A* give the area under the standard normal curve from 0 to the *z*-value listed to the left of the *A* value. The *A* values have been rounded to the nearest thousandth.

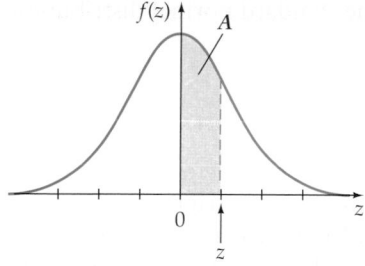

Figure 12.11 *A is the area of the shaded region*

✔ **TAKE NOTE**

To find the *A* value for the *z*-score 0.382, round 0.382 to the nearest hundredth to produce 0.38. Then use Table 12.7 to find that $A \approx 0.148$.

Because the standard normal distribution is symmetrical about the mean of 0, we can also use Table 12.7 to find the area of a region that is located to the left of the mean. This process is explained in Example 3.

EXAMPLE 3 ■ Use Symmetry to Determine an Area

Find the area of the standard normal distribution between $z = -1.44$ and $z = 0$.

Solution
Because the standard normal distribution is symmetrical about the center line $z = 0$, the area of the standard normal distribution between $z = -1.44$ and $z = 0$ is equal to the area between $z = 0$ and $z = 1.44$. See Figure 12.12. The entry in Table 12.7 associated with $z = 1.44$ is 0.425. Thus the area of the standard normal distribution between $z = -1.44$ and $z = 0$ is 0.425 square unit.

Figure 12.12 *Symmetrical region*

CHECK YOUR PROGRESS 3   Find the area of the standard normal distribution between $z = -0.67$ and $z = 0$.

Solution   *See page S48.*

In Figure 12.13, the region to the right of $z = 0.82$ is called a *tail region*. A **tail region** is a region of the standard normal distribution to the right of a positive z-value or to the left of a negative z-value. To find the area of a tail region, we subtract the entry in Table 12.7 from 0.500. This procedure is illustrated in the next example.

EXAMPLE 4 ■ Find the Area of a Tail Region

Find the area of the standard normal distribution to the right of $z = 0.82$.

Solution
Table 12.7 indicates that the area from $z = 0$ to $z = 0.82$ is 0.294 square unit. The area to the right of $z = 0$ is 0.500 square unit. Thus the area to the right of $z = 0.82$ is $0.500 - 0.294 = 0.206$ square unit. See Figure 12.13.

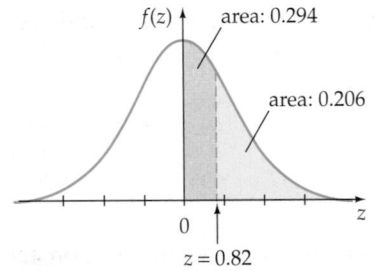

Figure 12.13 *Area of a tail region*

CHECK YOUR PROGRESS 4   Find the area of the standard normal distribution to the left of $z = -1.47$.

Solution   *See page S48.*

The Standard Normal Distribution, Areas, Percentages, and Probabilities

In the standard normal distribution, the *area* of the distribution from $z = a$ to $z = b$ represents

■ the *percentage* of z-values that lie in the interval from a to b.

■ the *probability* that z lies in the interval from a to b.

Because the area of a portion of the standard normal distribution can be interpreted as a percentage of the data or as a probability that the variable lies in an interval, we can use the standard normal distribution to solve many application problems.

EXAMPLE 5 ■ Solve an Application

A soda machine dispenses soda into 14-ounce cups. Tests show that the actual amount of soda dispensed is normally distributed, with a mean of 12 ounces and a standard deviation of 0.8 ounce.

a. What percent of cups will receive less than 11 ounces of soda?

b. What percent of cups will receive between 10.8 ounces and 12.2 ounces of soda?

c. If a cup is chosen at random, what is the probability that the machine will overflow the cup?

Solution

a. The *z*-score for 11 ounces is

$$z_{11} = \frac{11 - 12}{0.8} = -1.25$$

Table 12.7 indicates that 0.394 (39.4%) of the data in a normal distribution are between $z = 0$ and $z = 1.25$. Because the data are normally distributed, 39.4% of the data is also between $z = 0$ and $z = -1.25$. The percent of data to the left of $z = -1.25$ is 50% − 39.4% = 10.6%. See Figure 12.14. Thus 10.6% of the cups filled by the soda machine will receive less than 11 ounces of soda.

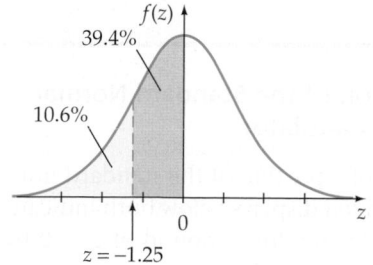

Figure 12.14 *Portion of data to the left of $z = -1.25$*

b. The *z*-score for 12.2 ounces is

$$z_{12.2} = \frac{12.2 - 12}{0.8} = 0.25$$

Table 12.7 indicates that 0.099 (9.9%) of the data in a normal distribution is between $z = 0$ and $z = 0.25$.

The *z*-score for 10.8 ounces is

$$z_{10.8} = \frac{10.8 - 12}{0.8} = -1.5$$

Table 12.7 indicates that 0.433 (43.3%) of the data in a normal distribution are between $z = 0$ and $z = 1.5$. Because the data are normally distributed, 43.3% of the data is also between $z = 0$ and $z = -1.5$. See Figure 12.15. Thus the percent of the cups that the vending machine will fill with between 10.8 ounces and 12.2 ounces of soda is

43.3% + 9.9% = 53.2%

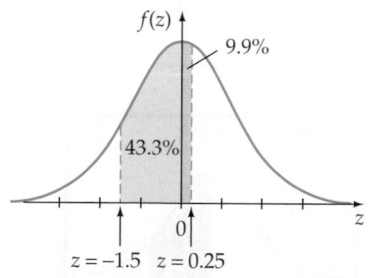

Figure 12.15 *Portion of data between two z-scores*

c. A cup will overflow if it receives more than 14 ounces of soda. The *z*-score for 14 ounces is

$$z_{14} = \frac{14 - 12}{0.8} = 2.5$$

Table 12.7 indicates that 0.494 (49.4%) of the data in the standard normal distribution are between $z = 0$ and $z = 2.5$. The percent of data to the right of $z = 2.5$ is determined by subtracting 49.4% from 50%. See Figure 12.16. Thus 0.6% of the time the machine produces an overflow, and the probability that a cup chosen at random will overflow is 0.006.

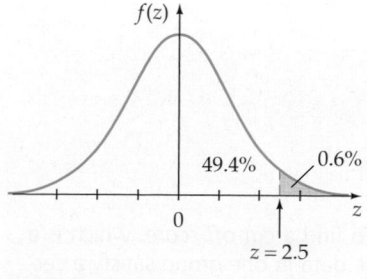

Figure 12.16 *Portion of data to the right of $z = 2.5$*

CHECK YOUR PROGRESS 5   A study of the careers of professional football players shows that the lengths of their careers are nearly normally distributed, with a mean of 6.1 years and a standard deviation of 1.8 years.

a. What percent of professional football players have a career of more than 9 years?

b. If a professional football player is chosen at random, what is the probability that the player will have a career of between 3 and 4 years?

Solution   See page S48.

Math Matters   **Find the Area of a Portion of the Standard Normal Distribution by Using a Calculator**

Some calculators can be used to find the area of a portion of the standard normal distribution. For instance, the TI-83/84 screen displays below both indicate that the area of the standard normal distribution from a lower bound of $z = 0$ to an upper bound of $z = 1.34$ is about 0.409877 square unit. This is a more accurate value than the entry given in Table 12.7, which is 0.410.

Select the `normalcdf(` function from the `DISTR` menu. Enter your lower bound, followed by your upper bound. Press `ENTER`.

The `ShadeNorm` instruction in the `DISTR`, `DRAW` menu draws the standard normal distribution and shades the area between your lower bound and your upper bound.

Figure 12.17 *TI-83/84 screen displays*

Excursion

Cut-Off Scores

There are many applications for which it is necessary to find a *cut-off score,* which is a score that separates data into two groups such that the data in one group satisfy a certain requirement and the data in the other group do not satisfy the requirement. If the data are normally distributed, then we can find a cut-off score by the method shown in the following example.

(continued)

EXAMPLE

The OnTheGo company manufactures laptop computers. A study indicates that the life spans of their computers are normally distributed, with a mean of 4.0 years and a standard deviation of 1.2 years. How long should the company warrant its computers if the company wishes less than 4% of its computers to fail during the warranty period?

Solution

Figure 12.18 shows a standard normal distribution with 4% of the data to the left of some unknown z-score and 46% of the data to the right of the z-score but to the left of the mean of 0. Using Table 12.7, we find that the z-score associated with an area of $A = 0.46$ is 1.75. Our unknown z-score is to the left of 0, so it must be negative. Thus $z_x = -1.75$. If we let x represent the time in years that a computer is in use, then x is related to the z-scores by the formula

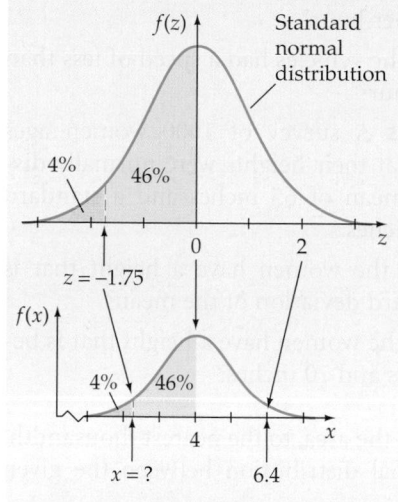

Figure 12.18 *Finding a cut-off score*

$$z_x = \frac{x - \bar{x}}{s}$$

Solving for x with $\bar{x} = 4.0$, $s = 1.2$, and $z = -1.75$ gives us

$$-1.75 = \frac{x - 4.0}{1.2}$$

$$(-1.75)(1.2) = x - 4.0$$

$$x = 4.0 - 2.1$$

$$x = 1.9 \qquad \text{The cut-off score}$$

Hence the company can provide a 1.9-year warranty and expect less than 4% of its computers to fail during the warranty period.

Excursion Exercises

1. A professor finds that the grades in a large class are normally distributed. The mean of the grades is 64 and the standard deviation is 10. If the professor decides to give an A grade to the students in the top 9% of the class, what is the cut-off score for an A?

2. The results of a statewide examination of the reading skills of sixth-grade students were normally distributed, with a mean score of 104 and a standard deviation of 16. The students in the top 10% are to receive an award, and those in the bottom 14% will be required to take a special reading class.

   a. What score does a student need in order to receive an award?

   b. What is the cut-off score that will be used to determine whether a student will be required to take the special reading class?

3. A secondary school system finds that the 440-yard dash times of its female students are normally distributed, with an average time of 72 seconds and a standard deviation of 5.5 seconds. What time does a runner need in order to be in the 9% of the runners with the best times? Round to the nearest hundredth of a second.

Exercise Set 12.4

1. **Physician Income** The 2003 median income for family practice physicians was $130,000. (*Source: American Academy of Family Physicians,* © 2004). The distribution of the physicians' incomes is skewed to the right. Is the mean of these incomes greater or less than $130,000?

2. **Testing** At a university, 500 law students took an examination. One student completed the exam in 24 minutes; however, the mode for the times is 50 minutes. The distribution of the times the students took to complete the exam is skewed to the left. Is the mean of these times greater or less than 50 minutes?

In Exercises 3–8, use the Empirical Rule to answer each question.

3. In a normal distribution, what percent of the data lie
   a. within 2 standard deviations of the mean?
   b. above 1 standard deviation of the mean?
   c. between 1 standard deviation below the mean and 2 standard deviations above the mean?

4. In a normal distribution, what percent of the data lie
   a. within 3 standard deviations of the mean?
   b. below 2 standard deviations of the mean?
   c. between 2 standard deviations below the mean and 3 standard deviations above the mean?

5. **Shipping** During 1 week an overnight delivery company found that the weights of its parcels were normally distributed, with a mean of 24 ounces and a standard deviation of 6 ounces.
   a. What percent of the parcels weighed between 12 ounces and 30 ounces?
   b. What percent of the parcels weighed more than 42 ounces?

6. **Baseball** A baseball franchise finds that the attendance at its home games is normally distributed, with a mean of 16,000 and a standard deviation of 4000.
   a. What percent of the home games have an attendance between 12,000 and 20,000 people?
   b. What percent of the home games have an attendance of less than 8000 people?

7. **Traffic** A highway study of 8000 vehicles that passed by a checkpoint found that their speeds were normally distributed, with a mean of 61 miles per hour and a standard deviation of 7 miles per hour.
   a. How many of the vehicles had a speed of more than 68 miles per hour?
   b. How many of the vehicles had a speed of less than 40 miles per hour?

8. **Women's Heights** A survey of 1000 women ages 20 to 30 found that their heights were normally distributed, with a mean of 65 inches and a standard deviation of 2.5 inches.
   a. How many of the women have a height that is within 1 standard deviation of the mean?
   b. How many of the women have a height that is between 60 inches and 70 inches?

In Exercises 9–16, find the area, to the nearest thousandth, of the standard normal distribution between the given z-scores.

9. $z = 0$ and $z = 1.5$
10. $z = 0$ and $z = 1.9$
11. $z = 0$ and $z = -1.85$
12. $z = 0$ and $z = -2.3$
13. $z = 1$ and $z = 1.9$
14. $z = 0.7$ and $z = 1.92$
15. $z = -1.47$ and $z = 1.64$
16. $z = -0.44$ and $z = 1.82$

In Exercises 17–24, find the area, to the nearest thousandth, of the indicated region of the standard normal distribution.

17. The region where $z > 1.3$
18. The region where $z > 1.92$
19. The region where $z < -2.22$
20. The region where $z < -0.38$
21. The region where $z > -1.45$
22. The region where $z < 1.82$
23. The region where $z < 2.71$
24. The region where $z < 1.92$

In Exercises 25–30, find the z-score, to the nearest hundredth, that satisfies the given condition.

25. 0.200 square unit of the standard normal distribution is to the right of z.
26. 0.227 square unit of the standard normal distribution is to the right of z.

27. 0.184 square unit of the standard normal distribution is to the left of z.

28. 0.330 square unit of the standard normal distribution is to the left of z.

29. 0.363 square unit of the standard normal distribution is to the right of z.

30. 0.440 square unit of the standard normal distribution is to the left of z.

In Exercises 31–40, use Table 12.7 to answer each question. *Note:* Round z-scores to the nearest hundredth and then find the required A values using Table 12.7 on page 839.

31. A population is normally distributed with a mean of 44.8 and a standard deviation of 12.4.

  a. What percent of the data are greater than 51.0?

  b. What percent of the data are between 47.9 and 63.4?

32. A population is normally distributed with a mean of 6.8 and a standard deviation of 1.2.

  a. What percent of the data are less than 7.2?

  b. What percent of the data are between 7.1 and 9.5?

33. A population is normally distributed with a mean of 580 and a standard deviation of 160.

  a. What percent of the data are less than 404?

  b. What percent of the data are between 460 and 612?

34. A population is normally distributed with a mean of 3010 and a standard deviation of 640.

  a. What percent of the data are greater than 2818?

  b. What percent of the data are between 2562 and 4162?

35. Cereal Weight The weights of all the boxes of corn flakes filled by a machine are normally distributed, with a mean weight of 14.5 ounces and a standard deviation of 0.4 ounce. What percent of the boxes will

  a. weigh less than 14 ounces?

  b. weigh between 13.5 ounces and 15.5 ounces?

36. Telephone Calls A telephone company has found that the lengths of its long distance telephone calls are normally distributed, with a mean of 225 seconds and a standard deviation of 55 seconds. What percent of its long distance calls are

  a. longer than 340 seconds?

  b. between 200 and 300 seconds?

37. Rope Strength The breaking point of a particular type of rope is normally distributed, with a mean of 350 pounds and a standard deviation of 24 pounds.

What is the probability that a piece of this rope chosen at random will have a breaking point of

  a. less than 320 pounds?

  b. between 340 and 370 pounds?

38. Tire Mileage The mileage for WearEver tires is normally distributed, with a mean of 48,000 miles and a standard deviation of 7400 miles. What is the probability that the WearEver tires you purchase will provide a mileage of

  a. more than 60,000 miles?

  b. between 40,000 and 50,000 miles?

39. Bank Lines The amount of time customers spend waiting in line at a bank is normally distributed, with a mean of 2.5 minutes and a standard deviation of 0.75 minute. Find the probability that the time a customer spends waiting is

  a. less than 3 minutes.

  b. less than 1 minute.

40. IQ Tests A psychologist finds that the intelligence quotients of a group of patients are normally distributed, with a mean of 102 and a standard deviation of 16. Find the percent of the patients with IQs

  a. above 114.

  b. between 90 and 118.

41. Heights Consider the data set of the heights of all babies born in the United States during a particular year. Do you think this data set is nearly normally distributed? Explain.

42. Weights Consider the data set of the weights of all Valencia oranges grown in California during a particular year. Do you think this data set is nearly normally distributed? Explain.

Extensions

CRITICAL THINKING

In Exercises 43–52, determine whether the given statement is true or false.

43. The standard normal distribution has a mean of 0.

44. Every normal distribution is a bell-shaped distribution.

45. In a normal distribution, the mean, the median, and the mode of the distribution are all located at the center of the distribution.

46. If a distribution is symmetrical about a vertical line down its center, then it is a normal distribution.

47. The mean of a normal distribution is always larger than the standard deviation of the distribution.

48. The standard deviation of the standard normal distribution is 1.

49. If a data value x from a normal distribution is positive, then its z-score must also be positive.

50. All normal distributions have a mean of 0.

51. Let x be the number of people who attended a baseball game today. The variable x is a discrete variable.

52. The time of day, d, in the lobby of a bank is measured with a digital clock. The variable d is a continuous variable.

53. **a.** How does the area of the standard normal distribution for $0 \leq z < 1$ compare with the area of the standard normal distribution for $0 \leq z \leq 1$?

    b. Explain the reasoning you used to answer part a.

54. **a.** Make a sketch of two normal distributions that have the same standard deviation but different means.

    b. Make a sketch of two normal distributions that have the same mean but different standard deviations.

55. Determine the two z-scores that bound the middle 60% of the data in a normal distribution.

56. Determine the approximate z-scores for the first quartile and the third quartile of the standard normal distribution.

EXPLORATIONS

57. The mathematician Pafnuty Chebyshev (cha-bĭ´shôf) (1821–1894) is well known for a theorem that concerns the distribution of data in any data set. This theorem is known as Chebyshev's Theorem. Consult a statistics text or the Internet to find information on Chebyshev's Theorem. Write a statement of Chebyshev's Theorem and use the theorem to find the minimum percent of data in any data set that must be within 2 standard deviations of the mean.

SECTION 12.5 | Linear Regression and Correlation

Linear Regression

In many applications, scientists try to determine whether two variables are related. If they are related, the scientists then try to find an equation that can be used to *model* the relationship. For instance, the zoology professor R. McNeill Alexander wanted to determine whether the *stride length* of a dinosaur, as shown by its fossilized footprints, could be used to estimate the speed of the dinosaur. Stride length for an animal is defined as the distance l from a particular point on a footprint to that same point on the next footprint of the same foot. (See the figure at the left.) Because no dinosaurs were available, he and fellow scientist A. S. Jayes carried out experiments with many types of animals, including adult men, dogs, camels, ostriches, and elephants. The results of these experiments tended to support the idea that the speed s of an animal is related to the animal's stride length l. To better understand this relationship, examine the data in Table 12.8, which is similar to, but less extensive than, the data collected by Alexander and Jayes.

Table 12.8 *Speed for Selected Stride Lengths*

a. Adult men

Stride length (meters)	2.5	3.0	3.3	3.5	3.8	4.0	4.2	4.5
Speed (meters per second)	3.4	4.9	5.5	6.6	7.0	7.7	8.3	8.7

b. Dogs

Stride length (meters)	1.5	1.7	2.0	2.4	2.7	3.0	3.2	3.5
Speed (meters per second)	3.7	4.4	4.8	7.1	7.7	9.1	8.8	9.9

c. Camels

Stride length (meters)	2.5	3.0	3.2	3.4	3.5	3.8	4.0	4.2
Speed (meters per second)	2.3	3.9	4.4	5.0	5.5	6.2	7.1	7.6

A graph of the ordered pairs in Table 12.8 is shown in Figure 12.19. In this graph, which is called a **scatter diagram** or **scatter plot,** the horizontal axis represents the stride lengths in meters and the vertical axis represents the average speeds in meters per second. The scatter diagram seems to indicate that for each of the three species, a larger stride length generally produces a faster speed. Also notice that for each species, a straight line can be drawn such that all of the points for that species lie on or very close to the line. Thus the relationship between speed and stride length appears to be a linear relationship.

Figure 12.19 *Scatter diagram for Table 12.8*

After a relationship between paired data, which are referred to as **bivariate data,** has been discovered, a scientist tries to model the relationship with an equation. One method of determining a linear relationship for bivariate data is called **linear regression.** To see how linear regression is carried out, let us concentrate on the bivariate data for the dogs, which is shown by the green points in Figures 12.19

and 12.20. There are many lines that can be drawn such that the data points lie close to the line; however, scientists are generally interested in the line called the *line of best fit* or the *least-squares regression line.*

Definition of the Least-Squares Regression Line

The **least-squares regression line** for a set of data is the line that minimizes the sum of the squares of the vertical deviations from each data point to the line.

Figure 12.20 *Vertical deviations*

The least-squares regression line is also called the **least-squares line.** The approximate equation of the least-squares line for the bivariate data for the dogs is $\hat{y} = 3.2x - 1.1$. Figure 12.20 shows the graph of these data and the graph of $\hat{y} = 3.2x - 1.1$. In Figure 12.20, the vertical deviations from the ordered pairs to the graph of $\hat{y} = 3.2x - 1.1$ are $0, -0.06, 0.5, -0.52, -0.16, -0.6, 0.34$ and 0.2.

It is traditional to use the symbol $\hat{y}$ (pronounced *y*-hat) in place of *y* in the equation of a least-squares line. This also helps us differentiate the line's *y*-values from the *y*-values of the given ordered pairs.

The next theorem can be used to determine the equation of the least-squares line for a given set of ordered pairs.

The Formula for the Least-Squares Line

The equation of the least-squares line for the *n* ordered pairs

$$(x_1, y_1), (x_2, y_2), (x_3, y_3), \ldots, (x_n, y_n)$$

is $\hat{y} = ax + b$, where

$$a = \frac{n\Sigma xy - (\Sigma x)(\Sigma y)}{n\Sigma x^2 - (\Sigma x)^2} \quad \text{and} \quad b = \bar{y} - a\bar{x}$$

In the above theorem, Σx represents the sum of all the *x* values, Σy represents the sum of all the *y* values, and Σxy represents the sum of the *n* products $x_1 y_1, x_2 y_2, \ldots, x_n y_n$. The notation $\bar{x}$ represents the mean of the *x* values, and $\bar{y}$ represents the mean of the *y* values. The following example illustrates a procedure that can be used to calculate efficiently the sums needed to find the equation of the least-squares line for a given set of data.

EXAMPLE 1 ■ Find the Equation of a Least-Squares Line

Find the equation of the least-squares line for the ordered pairs in Table 12.8a.

Solution
The ordered pairs are

$$(2.5, 3.4), (3.0, 4.9), (3.3, 5.5), (3.5, 6.6), (3.8, 7.0), (4.0, 7.7), (4.2, 8.3), (4.5, 8.7)$$

The number of ordered pairs is $n = 8$. Organize the data in four columns, as shown in Table 12.9. Then find the sum of each column.

Table 12.9

x	y	x^2	xy
2.5	3.4	6.25	8.50
3.0	4.9	9.00	14.70
3.3	5.5	10.89	18.15
3.5	6.6	12.25	23.10
3.8	7.0	14.44	26.60
4.0	7.7	16.00	30.80
4.2	8.3	17.64	34.86
4.5	8.7	20.25	39.15
$\Sigma x = 28.8$	$\Sigma y = 52.1$	$\Sigma x^2 = 106.72$	$\Sigma xy = 195.86$

Find the slope a.

$$a = \frac{n\Sigma xy - (\Sigma x)(\Sigma y)}{n\Sigma x^2 - (\Sigma x)^2}$$

$$= \frac{(8)(195.86) - (28.8)(52.1)}{(8)(106.72) - (28.8)^2}$$

$$\approx 2.7303$$

Find $\bar{x}$ and $\bar{y}$.

$$\bar{x} = \frac{\Sigma x}{n} = \frac{28.8}{8} = 3.6 \qquad \bar{y} = \frac{\Sigma y}{n} = \frac{52.1}{8} = 6.5125$$

Find the y-intercept b.

$$b = \bar{y} - a\bar{x}$$

$$\approx 6.5125 - (2.7303)(3.6)$$

$$= -3.31658$$

If a and b are each rounded to the nearest tenth, to reflect the accuracy of the original data, then we have as our equation of the least-squares line:

$$\hat{y} = ax + b$$

$$\hat{y} \approx 2.7x - 3.3$$

See Figure 12.21.

CHECK YOUR PROGRESS 1   Find the equation of the least-squares line for the stride length and speed of camels given in Table 12.8c.

Solution   *See page S48.*

Once the equation of the least-squares line is found, it can be used to make predictions. This procedure is illustrated in the next example.

✔ **TAKE NOTE**

It can be proved that for any set of ordered pairs, the graph of the ordered pair $(\bar{x}, \bar{y})$ is a point on the least-squares line for the ordered pairs. This can serve as a check. If you have calculated the least-squares line for a set of ordered pairs and you find that, within rounding limits, $(\bar{x}, \bar{y})$ is not a point on your least-squares line, then you know that you have made an error.

Figure 12.21 *Least-squares line for speed versus stride length in adult men*

EXAMPLE 2 ■ **Use a Least-Squares Line to Make a Prediction**

Use the equation of the least-squares line from Example 1 to predict the average speed of an adult man for each of the following stride lengths. Round your results to the nearest tenth of a meter per second (mps).

a. 2.8 meters   **b.** 4.8 meters

Solution

a. In Example 1, we found the equation of the least-squares line to be $\hat{y} = 2.7x - 3.3$. Substituting 2.8 for x gives

$$\hat{y} = 2.7(2.8) - 3.3 = 4.26$$

Rounding 4.26 to the nearest tenth produces 4.3. Thus 4.3 meters per second is the predicted average speed for an adult man with a stride length of 2.8 meters.

b. In Example 1, we found the equation of the least-squares line to be $\hat{y} = 2.7x - 3.3$. Substituting 4.8 for x gives

$$\hat{y} = 2.7(4.8) - 3.3 = 9.66$$

Rounding 9.66 to the nearest tenth produces 9.7. Thus 9.7 meters per second is the predicted average speed for an adult man with a stride length of 4.8 meters.

CHECK YOUR PROGRESS 2 Use the equation of the least-squares line from Check Your Progress 1 to predict the average speed of a camel for each of the following stride lengths. Round your results to the nearest tenth of a meter per second.

a. 2.7 meters   **b.** 4.5 meters

Solution *See page S48.*

✔ **TAKE NOTE**

Sometimes values predicted by extrapolation are not reasonable. For instance, if we wish to predict the speed of a man with a stride length of $x = 20$ meters, the least-squares equation $\hat{y} = 2.7x - 3.3$ gives us a speed of 50.7 meters per second. Because the maximum stride length of adult men is considerably less than 20 meters, we should not trust this prediction.

The procedure in Example 2a made use of an equation to determine a point between given data points. This procedure is referred to as **interpolation**. In Example 2b, an equation was used to determine a point to the right of the given data points. The process of using an equation to determine a point to the right or left of given data points is referred to as **extrapolation**. See Figure 12.22.

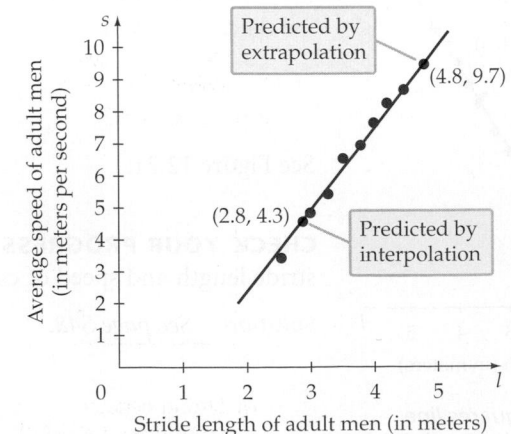

Figure 12.22 *Interpolation and extrapolation*

Linear Correlation Coefficient

To determine the strength of a linear relationship between two variables, statisticians use a statistic called the *linear correlation coefficient*, which is denoted by the variable r and is defined as follows.

> **Linear Correlation Coefficient**
>
> For the n ordered pairs (x_1, y_1), (x_2, y_2), (x_3, y_3), ..., (x_n, y_n), the **linear correlation coefficient** r is given by
>
> $$r = \frac{n(\Sigma xy) - (\Sigma x)(\Sigma y)}{\sqrt{n(\Sigma x^2) - (\Sigma x)^2} \cdot \sqrt{n(\Sigma y^2) - (\Sigma y)^2}}$$

historical note

Karl Pearson (pîr′sən) spent most of his career as a mathematics professor at University College, London. Some of his major contributions concerned the development of statistical procedures such as regression analysis and correlation. He was particularly interested in applying these statistical concepts to the study of heredity. The term *standard deviation* was invented by Pearson, and because of his work in the area of correlation, the formal name given to the linear correlation coefficient is the *Pearson product moment coefficient of correlation.* Pearson was a co-founder of the statistical journal *Biometrika.* ■

If the linear correlation coefficient r is positive, the relationship between the variables has a **positive correlation.** In this case, if one variable increases, the other variable also tends to increase. If r is negative, the linear relationship between the variables has a **negative correlation.** In this case, if one variable increases, the other variable tends to decrease.

Figure 12.23 shows some scatter diagrams along with the type of linear correlation that exists between the x and y variables. If r is positive, then the closer r is to 1 the stronger the linear relationship between the variables. If r is negative, then the closer r is to -1 the stronger the linear relationship between the variables.

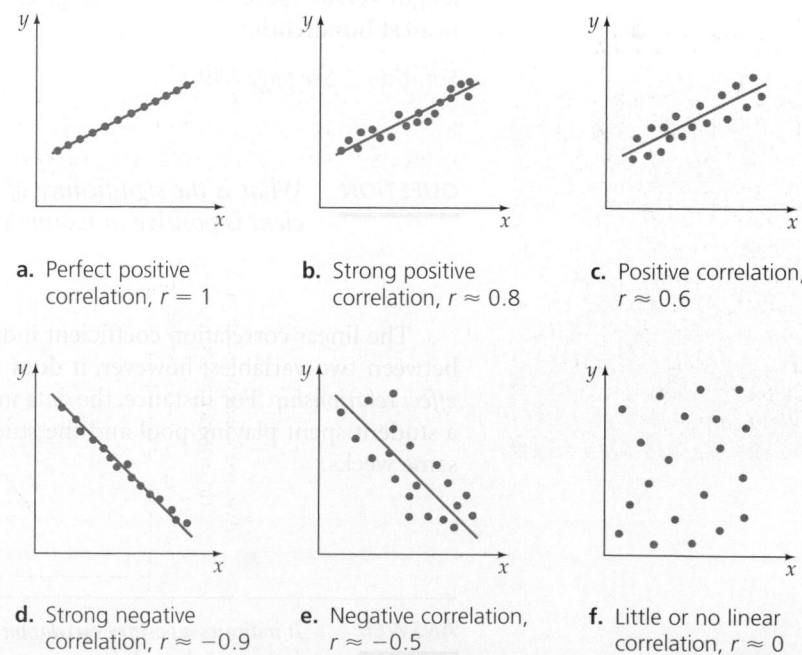

a. Perfect positive correlation, $r = 1$

b. Strong positive correlation, $r \approx 0.8$

c. Positive correlation, $r \approx 0.6$

d. Strong negative correlation, $r \approx -0.9$

e. Negative correlation, $r \approx -0.5$

f. Little or no linear correlation, $r \approx 0$

Figure 12.23 *Linear correlation*

EXAMPLE 3 ■ Find a Linear Correlation Coefficient

Find the linear correlation coefficient for stride length versus speed of an adult man. Use the data in Table 12.8a. Round your result to the nearest hundredth.

Solution

The ordered pairs are

$$(2.5, 3.4), (3.0, 4.9), (3.3, 5.5), (3.5, 6.6), (3.8, 7.0), (4.0, 7.7), (4.2, 8.3), (4.5, 8.7)$$

The number of ordered pairs is $n = 8$. In Table 12.9 on page 849 we found:

$$\Sigma x = 28.8 \qquad \Sigma y = 52.1 \qquad \Sigma x^2 = 106.72 \qquad \Sigma xy = 195.86$$

The only additional value that is needed is

$$\Sigma y^2 = 3.4^2 + 4.9^2 + 5.5^2 + 6.6^2 + 7.0^2 + 7.7^2 + 8.3^2 + 8.7^2$$
$$= 362.25$$

Substituting the above values into the equation for the linear correlation coefficient gives us

$$r = \frac{n(\Sigma xy) - (\Sigma x)(\Sigma y)}{\sqrt{n(\Sigma x^2) - (\Sigma x)^2} \cdot \sqrt{n(\Sigma y^2) - (\Sigma y)^2}}$$

$$= \frac{8(195.86) - (28.8)(52.1)}{\sqrt{8(106.72) - (28.8)^2} \cdot \sqrt{8(362.25) - (52.1)^2}}$$

$$\approx 0.993715$$

To the nearest hundredth, the linear correlation coefficient is 0.99.

CHECK YOUR PROGRESS 3   Find the linear correlation coefficient for stride length versus speed of a camel as given in Table 12.8c. Round your result to the nearest hundredth.

Solution   See page S49.

QUESTION   *What is the significance of the fact that the linear correlation coefficient is positive in Example 3?*

The linear correlation coefficient indicates the strength of a linear relationship between two variables; however, it does *not* indicate the presence of a *cause-and-effect relationship*. For instance, the data in Table 12.10 show the hours per week that a student spent playing pool and the student's weekly algebra test scores for those same weeks.

ANSWER   *It indicates a positive correlation between a man's stride length and his speed. That is, as a man's stride length increases, his speed also increases.*

Table 12.10 *Algebra Test Scores vs. Hours Spent Playing Pool*

Hours per week spent playing pool	4	5	7	8	10
Weekly algebra test score	52	60	72	79	83

The linear correlation coefficient for the ordered pairs in the table is $r \approx 0.98$. Thus there is a strong positive linear relationship between the student's algebra test scores and the time the student spent playing pool. This does not mean that the higher algebra test scores were caused by the increased time spent playing pool. The fact that the student's test scores increased with the increase in the time spent playing pool could be due to many other factors or it could just be a coincidence.

In your work with applications that involve the linear correlation coefficient r, it is important to remember the following properties of r.

Properties of the Linear Correlation Coefficient

1. The linear correlation coefficient r is always a real number between 1 and -1, inclusive. In the case in which

   ■ all of the ordered pairs lie on a line with positive slope, r is 1.

   ■ all of the ordered pairs lie on a line with negative slope, r is -1.

2. For any set of ordered pairs, the linear correlation coefficient r and the slope of the least-squares line both have the same sign.

3. Interchanging the variables in the ordered pairs does not change the value of r. Thus the value of r for the ordered pairs (x_1, y_1), (x_2, y_2), ..., (x_n, y_n) is the same as the value of r for the ordered pairs (y_1, x_1), (y_2, x_2), ..., (y_n, x_n).

4. The value of r does not depend on the units used. You can change the units of a variable from, for example, feet to inches and the value of r will remain the same.

Math Matters   Use a Calculator to Find the Equation of the Least-Squares Line and the Linear Correlation Coefficient

Calculators can be used to estimate the slope and y-intercept of the least-squares line for bivariate data. Many calculators will also estimate the linear correlation coefficient. A **TI-83/84 calculator displays the linear correlation coefficient only if you have used the** DiagnosticOn **command, which is found in the** CATALOG **menu.** Press 2nd [CATALOG], scroll down to the DiagnosticOn command, and press ENTER . Now enter the first components of the ordered pairs into list L1 and the second components into list L2, as shown in Figure 12.24 on the following page. The key sequence STAT ▶ 4 VARS ▶ ENTER ENTER ENTER stores the equation for the least-squares line in Y1 and produces the LinReg display in which a is the slope of the least-squares line, b is the y-intercept of the least-squares line, and r is the linear correlation coefficient.

(continued)

1. Enter the data.

2. LinReg(ax + b) display

Slope of the least-squares line

y-intercept of the least-squares line

Linear correlation coefficient

3. The equation of the least-squares line is stored in the Y= menu.

Figure 12.24 *TI-83/84 Screen Displays*

To display a scatter diagram of the ordered pairs and a graph of the least-squares line, use the WINDOW menu to enter appropriate values for Xmin, Xmax, Ymin, and Ymax. Use the key sequence 2nd [STAT PLOT] to display the STAT PLOT menu. Select the scatter diagram icon and enter L1 to the right of Xlist: and L2 to the right of Ylist:. See Figure 12.25. Press the GRAPH key to display the scatter diagram of the data and the least-squares line.

1. Enter window settings.

2. Use the STAT PLOT menu to choose settings.

3. Press GRAPH to display the scatter diagram and least-squares line.

Figure 12.25 *TI-83/84 Screen Displays*

Excursion

An Application of Linear Regression

At this point, the work by Alexander and Jayes presented in this lesson cannot be used to estimate the speed of a dinosaur because for each animal species, we calculated a different least-squares regression line. Also, no dinosaurs are available to provide data for

(continued)

stride lengths and speeds. Motivated by a strong desire to find a mathematical model that could be used to estimate the speed of any animal from its stride length, Alexander came up with the idea of using *relative stride lengths*. A **relative stride length** is the number obtained by dividing the stride length of an animal by the animal's leg length. That is,

$$\text{Relative stride length} = \frac{\text{stride length}}{\text{leg length}} \qquad \text{(I)}$$

Thus a person with a leg length of 0.9 meter (distance from the hip to the ground) who runs steadily with a stride length of 4.5 meters has a relative stride length of (4.5 meters) ÷ (0.9 meters) = 5. Note that a relative stride length is a dimensionless quantity.

Because Alexander found it helpful to convert stride length to a dimensionless quantity (relative stride length), it was somewhat natural for him also to convert speed to a dimensionless quantity. His definition of *dimensionless speed* is

$$\text{Dimensionless speed} = \frac{\text{speed}}{\sqrt{\text{leg length} \times g}} \qquad \text{(II)}$$

where g is the gravitational acceleration constant of 9.8 meters per second per second. At this point you may feel that things are getting a bit complicated and that you weren't really all that interested in the speed of a dinosaur anyway. However, once Alexander and Jayes converted stride lengths to *relative* stride lengths and speeds to *dimensionless* speeds, they discovered that many graphs of their data, even for different species, were nearly linear! To illustrate this concept, examine Table 12.11, in which the ordered pairs were formed by converting each ordered pair of Table 12.8 (page 847) from the form (stride length, speed) to the form (relative stride length, dimensionless speed). The conversions were calculated by using leg lengths of 0.8 meter for the adult men, 0.5 meter for the dogs, and 1.2 meters for the camels.

Table 12.11 *Dimensionless Speed for Relative Stride Lengths*

a. Adult men

Relative stride length (x)	3.1	3.8	4.1	4.4	4.8	5.0	5.3	5.6
Dimensionless speed (y)	1.2	1.8	2.0	2.4	2.5	2.8	3.0	3.1

b. Dogs

Relative stride length (x)	3.0	3.4	4.0	4.8	5.4	6.0	6.4	7.0
Dimensionless speed (y)	1.7	2.0	2.2	3.2	3.5	4.1	4.0	4.5

c. Camels

Relative stride length (x)	2.1	2.5	2.7	2.8	2.9	3.2	3.3	3.5
Dimensionless speed (y)	0.7	1.1	1.3	1.5	1.6	1.8	2.1	2.2

(continued)

A scatter diagram of the data in Table 12.11 is shown in Figure 12.26. The scatter diagram shows a strong linear correlation. (You didn't expect a perfect linear correlation, did you? After all, we are working with camels, dogs, and adult men.) Although we have considered only three species, Alexander and Jayes were able to show a strong linear correlation for several species.

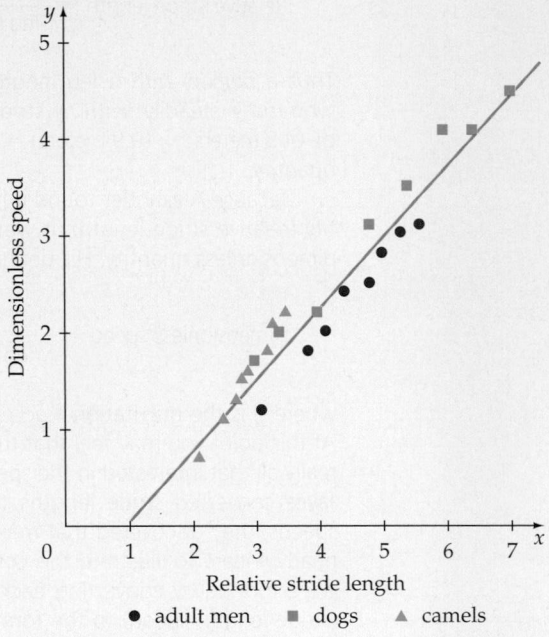

● adult men   ■ dogs   ▲ camels

Figure 12.26

Finally it is time to estimate the speed of a dinosaur. Consider a large theropod with a leg length of 2.5 meters. If the theropod's fossilized footprints show a stride length of 5 meters, then its relative stride length is $\frac{5 \text{ m}}{2.5 \text{ m}} = 2$. The least-squares regression line in Figure 12.26 shows that a relative stride length of 2 has a dimensionless speed of about 0.8. If we use 2.5 meters for the leg length and 0.8 for dimensionless speed and solve equation (II) (page 855) for speed, we get

$$\text{Speed} = (\text{dimensionless speed})\sqrt{\text{leg length} \times g}$$
$$= (0.8)\sqrt{2.5 \times 9.8}$$
$$\approx 4.0 \text{ meters per second}$$

For more information about estimating the speeds of dinosaurs, consult the following article by Alexander and Jayes: "A dynamic similarity hypothesis for the gaits of quadrupedal mammals." *Journal of Zoology* 201:135–152, 1983.

Excursion Exercises

1. **a.** Use a calculator to find the equation of the least-squares regression line for *all* of the data in Table 12.11.

    b. Find the linear correlation coefficient for the least-squares line in part a.

(continued)

sauropod

pachycephalosaur

2. The photograph at the right shows a set of sauropod tracks and a set of tracks made by a carnivore. These tracks were discovered by Roland Bird in 1938 in the Paluxy River bed, near the town of Glen Rose, Texas. Measurements of the sauropod tracks indicate an average stride length of about 4.0 meters. Assume that the sauropod that made the tracks had a leg length of 3.0 meters. Use the equation of the least-squares regression line from Excursion Exercise 1 to estimate the speed of the sauropod that produced the tracks.

3. A pachycephalosaur has an estimated leg length of 1.4 meters, and its footprints show a stride length of 3.1 meters. Use the equation of the least-squares regression line from Excursion Exercise 1 to estimate the speed of this pachycephalosaur.

Exercise Set 12.5

1. Which of the scatter diagrams below suggests the

  a. strongest positive linear correlation between the x and y variables?

  b. strongest negative linear correlation between the x and y variables?

2. Which of the scatter diagrams below suggests

  a. a near perfect positive linear correlation between the x and y variables?

  b. little or no linear correlation between the x and y variables?

a.

b.

c.

d.

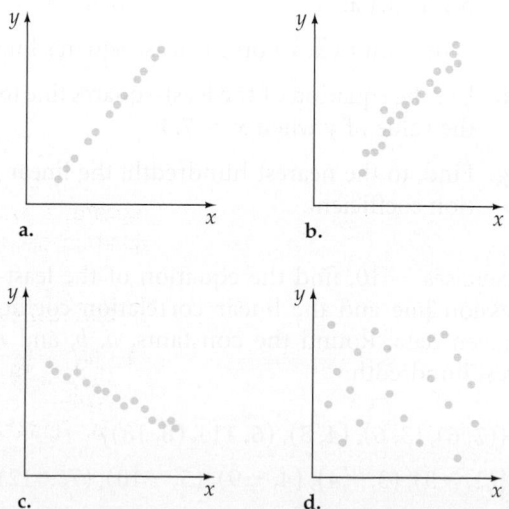

a.

b.

c.

d.

3. Given the bivariate data:

x	1	2	3	5	6
y	7	5	3	2	1

  a. Draw a scatter diagram for the data.

  b. Find n, Σx, Σy, Σx^2, $(\Sigma x)^2$, and Σxy.

  c. Find a, the slope of the least-squares line, and b, the y-intercept of the least-squares line.

  d. Draw the least-squares line on the scatter diagram from part a.

  e. Is the point $(\bar{x}, \bar{y})$ on the least-squares line?

  f. Use the equation of the least-squares line to predict the value of y when $x = 3.4$.

  g. Find, to the nearest hundredth, the linear correlation coefficient.

4. Given the bivariate data:

x	3	4	5	6	7
y	2	3	3	5	5

  a. Draw a scatter diagram for the data.

  b. Find n, Σx, Σy, Σx^2, $(\Sigma x)^2$, and Σxy.

  c. Find a, the slope of the least-squares line, and b, the y-intercept of the least-squares line.

  d. Draw the least-squares line on the scatter diagram from part a.

  e. Is the point $(\bar{x}, \bar{y})$ on the least-squares line?

  f. Use the equation of the least-squares line to predict the value of y when $x = 7.3$.

  g. Find, to the nearest hundredth, the linear correlation coefficient.

In Exercises 5–10, find the equation of the least-squares regression line and the linear correlation coefficient for the given data. Round the constants, a, b, and r, to the nearest hundredth.

5. $\{(2, 6), (3, 6), (4, 8), (6, 11), (8, 18)\}$

6. $\{(2, -3), (3, -4), (4, -9), (5, -10), (7, -12)\}$

7. $\{(-3, 11.8), (-1, 9.5), (0, 8.6), (2, 8.7), (5, 5.4)\}$

8. $\{(-7, -11.7), (-5, -9.8), (-3, -8.1), (1, -5.9),$ $(2, -5.7)\}$

9. $\{(1, 4.1), (2, 6.0), (4, 8.2), (6, 11.5), (8, 16.2)\}$

10. $\{(2, 5), (3, 7), (4, 8), (6, 11), (8, 18), (9, 21)\}$

11. **Value of a Corvette** The following table gives the retail value of a 2004 Corvette Z06 for various odometer readings. (*Source*: Kelley Blue Book website, November 3, 2004)

Odometer Reading	Retail Value
13,000	$46,100
18,000	$44,600
20,000	$43,300
25,000	$41,975
29,000	$40,975
32,000	$39,750

  a. Find the least-squares regression line for the data. Round constants to the nearest thousandth.

  b. Use the equation from part a to predict the retail price of the model car with an odometer reading of 30,000.

  c. Find the linear correlation coefficient for these data.

  d. What is the significance of the fact that the linear correlation coefficient is negative for these data?

12. **Paleontology** The table on the following page shows the length, in centimeters, of the humerus and the total wingspan, in centimeters, of several pterosaurs, which are extinct flying reptiles. (*Source*: Southwest Educational Development Laboratory)

Pterosaur Data

Humerus	Wingspan	Humerus	Wingspan
24	600	20	500
32	750	27	570
22	430	15	300
17	370	15	310
13	270	9	240
4.4	68	4.4	55
3.2	53	2.9	50
1.5	24		

a. Find the equation of the least-squares regression line for the data. Round constants to the nearest hundredth.

b. Use the equation from part a to determine, to the nearest centimeter, the projected wingspan of a pterosaur if its humerus is 54 centimeters.

13. **Health** The U.S. Centers for Disease Control and Prevention (CDC) use a measure called body mass index (BMI) to determine whether a person is overweight. A BMI between 25.0 and 29.9 is considered overweight and 30.0 or more is considered obese. The following table shows the percent of United States males 18 years old or older who were overweight in the years indicated, judging on the basis of BMI. (*Source:* CDC, November 5, 2003)

Year	Percent Obese
1995	16.3
1996	16.3
1997	17.1
1998	18.4
1999	19.9
2000	20.6
2001	21.2
2002	23.1

a. Using 0 for 1995, 1 for 1996, and so on, find the least-squares regression line for the data.

b. Use the equation from part a to predict the percent of overweight males in 2005.

14. **Health** The U.S. Centers for Disease Control and Prevention (CDC) use a measure called body mass index (BMI) to determine whether a person is overweight. A BMI between 25.0 and 29.9 is considered overweight and 30.0 or more is considered obese. The following table shows the percent of United States females 18 years old or older who were overweight in the years indicated, judging on the basis of BMI. (*Source:* CDC, November 5, 2003)

Year	Percent Obese
1995	14.7
1996	16.8
1997	16.5
1998	18.3
1999	19.7
2000	19.8
2001	20.8
2002	21.4

a. Using 0 for 1995, 1 for 1996, and so on, find the least-squares regression line for the data.

b. Use the equation from part a to predict the percent of overweight females in 2005.

15. **Cellular Phone** The following table shows the approximate number of cellular telephone subscriptions in the United States for recent years.

U.S. Cellular Telephone Subscriptions

Year	1998	1999	2000	2001	2002	2003
Subscriptions, in millions	69	86	109	128	141	159

Source: CTIA Semiannual Wireless Survey. Data extracted from *The World Almanac and Book of Facts 2005*, page 398.

a. Find the linear correlation coefficient for the data.

b. On the basis of the value of the linear correlation coefficient, would you conclude, at the $|r| > 0.9$ level, that the data can be reasonably modeled by a linear equation? Explain.

16. **Life Expectancy** The average remaining lifetimes for men in the United States are given in the following table. (*Source:* National Institute of Health)

Average Remaining Lifetimes for Men

Age	Years	Age	Years
0	73.6	65	15.9
15	59.4	75	9.9
35	40.8		

Use the linear correlation coefficient to determine whether there is a strong correlation, at the $|r| > 0.9$ level, between a man's age and the average remaining lifetime for that man.

17. **Median Incomes** The following table lists the median weekly earnings, in dollars, for women and men for selected years from 1980 to 2002. (*Source:* U.S. Department of Labor, Bureau of Labor Statistics)

Median Weekly Earnings

	1980	1985	1990	1995	2000	2002
Women (x)	415	442	462	476	513	530
Men (y)	540	547	550	561	601	609

a. Find, to the nearest hundredth, the linear correlation coefficient for the data.

b. On the basis of your answer to part a, would you say that there is a strong linear relationship, at the $|r| > 0.9$ level, between the median weekly earnings of women and the median weekly earnings of men?

18. **Life Expectancy** The average remaining lifetimes for women in the United States are given in the following table. (*Source:* National Institute of Health)

Average Remaining Lifetimes for Women

Age	Years	Age	Years
0	79.4	65	19.2
15	65.1	75	12.1
35	45.7		

a. Find the equation of the least-squares regression line for the data.

b. Use the equation from part a to estimate the remaining lifetime of a woman of age 25.

19. **Temperature** The data given in the following table shows equivalent temperatures on the Celsius temperature scale and the Fahrenheit temperature scale.

Celsius (x°)	−40	0	100
Fahrenheit (y°)	−40	32	212

a. Find the linear correlation coefficient for the data.

b. What is the significance of the value found in part a?

c. Find the equation of the least-squares regression line.

d. Use the equation of the least-squares line from part c to predict the Fahrenheit temperature that corresponds to a Celsius temperature of 35°.

e. Is the procedure in part d an example of interpolation or extrapolation?

20. **Fitness** An aerobic exercise instructor remembers the data given in the following table, which shows the recommended maximum exercise heart rates for individuals of the given ages.

Age (x years)	20	40	60
Maximum heart rate (y beats per minute)	170	153	136

a. Find the linear correlation coefficient for the data.

b. What is the significance of the value found in part a?

c. Find the equation of the least-squares regression line.

d. Use the equation of the least-squares line from part c to predict the maximum exercise heart rate for a person who is 72.

e. Is the procedure in part d an example of interpolation or extrapolation?

Extensions

CRITICAL THINKING

21. **Tuition** The following table shows the average annual tuition and fees of private and public 4-year colleges for the school years 1998–1999 through 2003–2004. (*Source:* The College Board. Extracted from *The New York Times Almanac, 2005*, page 354.)

Tuition and Fees

Year	Private	Public
1998–1999	14,709	3247
1999–2000	15,518	3362
2000–2001	16,233	3487
2001–2002	17,272	3725
2002–2003	18,273	4081
2003–2004	19,710	4694

Is there a linear relationship, at the $|r| > 0.9$ level, between average tuition at public 4-year colleges and that at private 4-year colleges?

22. Fuel Efficiency The following table shows the average fuel efficiency, in miles per gallon (mpg), of all cars sold in the United States during the years 1999 through 2004. (*Source:* Environmental Protection Agency. Extracted from *The World Almanac and Book of Facts, 2005*, page 237.)

Fuel Efficiency

Year	Miles per Gallon
1999	24.1
2000	24.1
2001	24.3
2002	24.5
2003	24.7
2004	24.6

Is there a linear relation, at the $|r| > 0.9$ level, between year and average miles per gallon?

EXPLORATIONS

23. Another linear model that can be used to model data is called the *median-median line*. Use a statistics text or the Internet to read about the median-median line.

a. Find the equation of the median-median line for the data given in Exercise 13.

b. Explain the type of situation in which it would be better to model data using the median-median line than it would be to model the data using the least-squares line.

24. Search for bivariate data (in a magazine, a newspaper, an almanac, or on the Internet) that can be closely modeled by a linear equation.

a. Draw a scatter diagram of the data.

b. Find the equation of the least-squares line and the linear correlation coefficient for the data.

c. Graph the least-squares line on the scatter diagram in part a.

d. Use the equation of the least-squares line to predict a range value for a specific domain value.

CHAPTER 12 **Summary**

Key Terms

bimodal distribution [p. 834]
bivariate data [p. 847]
box-and-whisker plot [p. 824]
class [p. 831]

continuous data [p. 835]
continuous variable [p. 835]
descriptive statistics [p. 794]
discrete data [p. 835]

Essential Concepts

- The *mean* of n numbers is the sum of the numbers divided by n. The mean of a sample is denoted by $\bar{x}$ and the mean of a population is denoted by μ.

- The *median* of a *ranked list* of n numbers is the middle number if n is odd and the mean of the two middle numbers if n is even.

- The *mode* of a list of numbers is the number that occurs most frequently.

- The *weighted mean* of the n numbers $x_1, x_2, x_3, \ldots, x_n$ with the respective assigned weights $w_1, w_2, w_3, \ldots, w_n$ is $\frac{\Sigma(x \cdot w)}{\Sigma w}$, where $\Sigma(x \cdot w)$ is the sum of the products formed by multiplying each number by its assigned weight, and Σw is the sum of all the weights.

- The *range* of a set of data values is the difference between the largest data value and the smallest data value.

- The *standard deviation* of the *sample* $x_1, x_2, x_3, \ldots, x_n$ with a mean of $\bar{x}$ is $s = \sqrt{\dfrac{\Sigma(x - \bar{x})^2}{n - 1}}$.

- The *standard deviation* of the *population* $x_1, x_2, x_3, \ldots, x_n$ with a mean of μ is
$$\sigma = \sqrt{\dfrac{\Sigma(x - \mu)^2}{n}}.$$

- The *z-score* for a given data value x is the number of standard deviations that x lies above or below the mean of the data.

  Population: $z_x = \dfrac{x - \mu}{\sigma}$ Sample: $z_x = \dfrac{x - \bar{x}}{s}$

- A value x is called the *pth percentile* of a data set provided $p\%$ of the data is less than x.

- **The Empirical Rule**
  In a normal distribution, about
  68.2% of the data lie within 1 standard deviation of the mean.
  95.4% of the data lie within 2 standard deviations of the mean.
  99.7% of the data lie within 3 standard deviations of the mean.

- The *standard normal distribution* is the normal distribution for the continuous variable z that has a mean of 0 and a standard deviation of 1.

- In the standard normal distribution, the *area* of the distribution from $z = a$ to $z = b$ represents the percentage of z-values that lie in the interval from a to b and the probability that z lies in the interval from a to b.

- The *least-squares regression line* is the line that minimizes the sum of the squares of the vertical deviations from each data point to the line.

- The equation of the *least-squares line* for the n ordered pairs $(x_1, y_1), (x_2, y_2), (x_3, y_3), \ldots, (x_n, y_n)$ is
$\hat{y} = ax + b$, where $a = \dfrac{n\Sigma xy - (\Sigma x)(\Sigma y)}{n\Sigma x^2 - (\Sigma x)^2}$ and
$b = \bar{y} - a\bar{x}$.

- For the n ordered pairs $(x_1, y_1), (x_2, y_2), (x_3, y_3), \ldots, (x_n, y_n)$, the *linear correlation coefficient* r is given by
$$r = \dfrac{n(\Sigma xy) - (\Sigma x)(\Sigma y)}{\sqrt{n(\Sigma x^2) - (\Sigma x)^2} \cdot \sqrt{n(\Sigma y^2) - (\Sigma y)^2}}.$$

Review Exercises

1. Find the mean, the median, and the mode for the following data. Round noninteger values to the nearest tenth.

$$12, 17, 14, 12, 8, 19, 21$$

2. A set of data has a mean of 16, a median of 15, and a mode of 14. Which of these numbers must be a value in the data set?

3. Write a set of data with five data values for which the mean, median, and mode are all 55.

4. State whether the mean, the median, or the mode is being used.

   a. In 2002, there were as many people aged 25 and younger in the world as there were people aged 25 and older.

   b. The majority of full-time students carry a load of 15 credit hours per semester.

   c. The average annual return on an investment is 6.5%.

5. **Bridges** The lengths of cantilever bridges in the United States are shown below. Find the mean, the median, the mode, and the range of the data.

   Bridge Length (in feet)
   Baton Rouge (Louisiana), 1235
   Commodore John Barry (Pennsylvania), 1644
   Greater New Orleans (Louisiana), 1576
   Longview (Washington), 1200
   Patapsco River (Maryland), 1200
   Queensboro (New York), 1182
   Tappan Zee (New York), 1212
   Transbay Bridge (California), 1400

6. **Average Speed** Cleone traveled 45 miles to her sister's house in 1 hour. The return trip took 1.5 hours. What was Cleone's average rate for the entire trip?

7. **Grade Point Average** In a 4.0 grading system, each letter grade has the following numerical value.

A = 4.00	B− = 2.67	D+ = 1.33
A− = 3.67	C+ = 2.33	D = 1.00
B+ = 3.33	C = 2.00	D− = 0.67
B = 3.00	C− = 1.67	F = 0.00

Use the weighted mean formula to find the grade point average for a student with the following grades. Round to the nearest hundredth.

Course	Credits	Grade
Mathematics	3	A
English	3	C+
Computer	2	B−
Biology	4	B
Art	1	A

8. **Test Scores** A teacher finds that the test scores of a group of 40 students have a mean of 72 and a standard deviation of 8.

   a. If Ann has a test score of 82, what is Ann's z-score?

   b. Assuming the data is normally distributed, what is Ann's percentile score?

9. **Airline Industry** An airline recorded the times it took for a ground crew to unload the baggage from an airplane. The recorded times, in minutes, were 12, 18, 20, 14, and 16. Find the *sample* standard deviation and the variance of these times. Round your results to the nearest hundredth of a minute.

10. **Ticket Prices** The following table gives the average annual admission prices to U.S. movie theaters for the years 1994 to 2003.

Average Annual Admission Price

1994	$4.08	1999	$5.08
1995	$4.35	2000	$5.39
1996	$4.42	2001	$5.65
1997	$4.59	2002	$5.80
1998	$4.69	2003	$6.03

Source: NATO average ticket price based on Ernst & Young survey; MPAA Worldwide Market Research

Find the mean, the median, and the standard deviation for this *sample* of admission prices.

11. **Test Scores** One student received test scores of 85, 92, 86, and 89. A second student received scores of 90, 97, 91, and 94 (exactly five points more on each test).

    a. What is the relationship between the means of the two students' test scores?

    b. What is the relationship between the standard deviations of the two students' test scores?

12. A *population* data set has a mean of 81 and a standard deviation of 5.2. Find the z-scores for each of the following. Round to the nearest hundredth.

    a. $x = 72$

    b. $x = 84$

13. **Cholesterol Levels** The cholesterol levels for 10 adults are shown below. Draw a box-and-whiskers plot of the data.

    Cholesterol Levels

310	185	254	221	170
214	172	208	164	182

14. **Test Scores** The following histogram shows the distribution of the test scores for a history test.

    a. How many students scored at least 84 on the test?

    b. How many students took the test?

    c. What is the uniform class width?

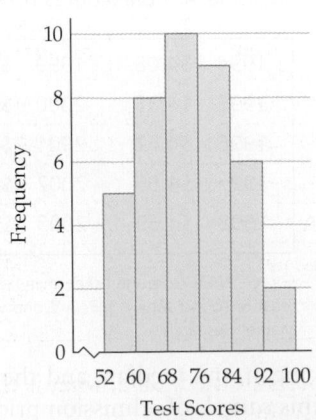

15. **Teacher Salaries** Use the following relative frequency distribution to determine the

    a. *percent* of the states that paid an average teacher salary of at least $44,000.

    b. *probability, as a decimal,* that a state selected at random paid an average teacher salary of at least $41,000 but less than $50,000.

Average Salaries of Public School Teachers, 2002–2003

Average Salary, s	Number of States	Relative Frequency
$32,000 ≤ s < $35,000	4	8%
$35,000 ≤ s < $38,000	7	14%
$38,000 ≤ s < $41,000	13	26%
$41,000 ≤ s < $44,000	7	14%
$44,000 ≤ s < $47,000	7	14%
$47,000 ≤ s < $50,000	3	6%
$50,000 ≤ s < $53,000	5	10%
$53,000 ≤ s < $56,000	4	8%
$56,000 ≤ s < $59,000	1	2%

Source: NEA Research, Estimation Data Base (2004).

16. **Cellular Phone Prevalence** The following table shows the percent of households that had a cellular phone in selected years. (*Source:* Consumer Electronics Association. Extracted from *The World Almanac and Book of Facts, 2005,* page 398.)

Percent of Cellular Phones in U.S. Households

Year	Percent
1990	5
1995	29
2000	60
2002	68
2003	70

Is there a linear relationship, at the $|r| > 0.9$ level, that would allow you to conclude the data could be modeled by a linear equation?

17. 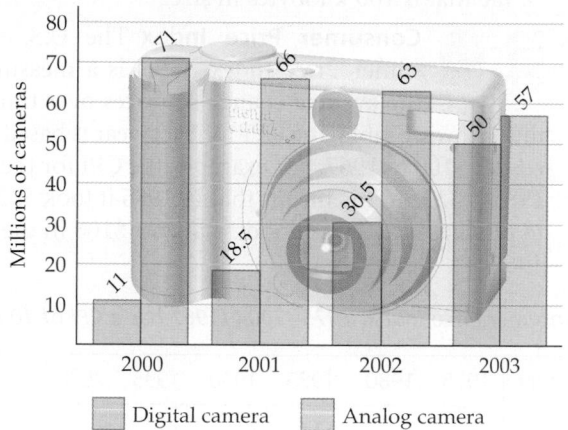 **Camera Sales** The following double-bar graph shows the sales, in millions of cameras, of analog and digital still cameras.

Worldwide Camera Sales

Values shown: 71, 66, 63, 57, 50, 30.5, 18.5, 11

Millions of cameras (y-axis: 10–80)
Years: 2000, 2001, 2002, 2003

☐ Digital camera   ☐ Analog camera

Source: Digital Photography Review, dpreview.com
August 27, 2004.

a. Determine the linear regression equation of the number of sales of digital cameras as a function of the year. Use 0 for 2000, 1 for 2001, etc.

b. Determine the linear regression equation of the number of sales of analog cameras as a function of the year.

c. Judging on the basis of the linear models found in parts a and b, will digital camera sales be greater than or less than analog camera sales in 2005?

18. Test Scores A professor gave a final examination to 110 students. Eighteen students had examination scores that were more than one standard deviation above the mean. With this information, can you conclude that 18 of the students had examination scores that were less than one standard deviation below the mean? Explain.

19. Waiting Time The amount of time customers spend waiting in line at the ticket counter of an amusement park is normally distributed, with a mean of 6.5 minutes and a standard deviation of 1 minute. Find the probability that the time a customer will spend waiting is:

a. less than 8 minutes.   **b.** less than 6 minutes.

20. Pet Food The weights of all the sacks of dog food filled by a machine are normally distributed, with an average weight of 50 pounds and a standard deviation of 0.5 pound. What percent of the sacks will

a. weigh less than 49.6 pounds?

b. weigh between 49 and 51 pounds?

21. Telecommunication A telephone company finds that the life spans of its telephones are normally distributed, with a mean of 6.5 years and a standard deviation of 0.5 year.

a. What percent of its telephones will last at least 7.25 years?

b. What percent of its telephones will last between 5.8 years and 6.8 years?

c. What percent of its telephones will last less than 6.9 years?

22. Astronomy The following table gives the distances, in millions of miles, of Earth from the sun for selected times.

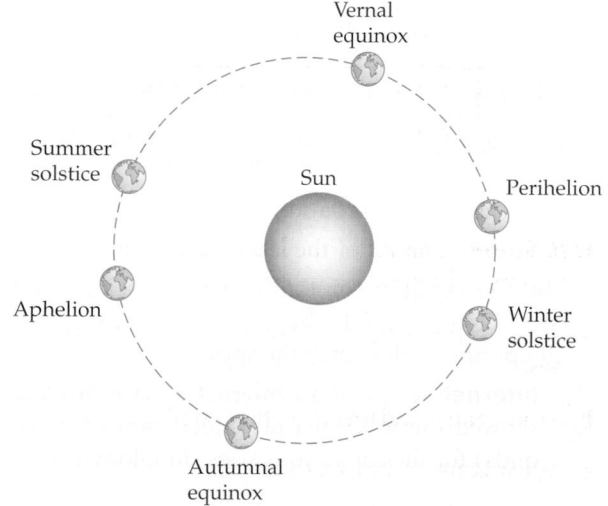

Position	Distance (millions of miles)
Perihelion	91.4
Vernal equinox	92.6
Summer solstice	94.5
Aphelion	94.6
Autumnal equinox	94.3
Winter solstice	91.5

On the basis of these data, what is the mean distance of Earth from the sun?

23. Given the bivariate data

x	10	12	14	15	16
y	8	7	5	4	1

  a. Draw a scatter diagram for the data.

  b. Find n, Σx, Σy, Σx^2, $(\Sigma x)^2$, and Σxy.

  c. Find a, the slope of the least-squares regression line, and b, the y-intercept of the least-squares line.

  d. Draw the least-squares line on the scatter diagram from part a.

  e. Is the point $(\bar{x}, \bar{y})$ on the least-squares line?

  f. Use the equation of the least-squares line to predict the value of y for $x = 8$.

  g. Find the linear correlation coefficient.

24. **Physics** A student has recorded the data in the following table, which shows the distance a spring stretches in inches for a given weight in pounds.

Weight, x	80	100	110	150	170
Distance, y	6.2	7.4	8.3	11.1	12.7

  a. Find the linear correlation coefficient.

  b. Find the equation of the least-squares line.

  c. Use the equation of the least-squares line from part b to predict the distance a weight of 195 pounds will stretch the spring.

25. **Internet** A test of an Internet service provider showed the following download times (in seconds) for files of various sizes (in kilobytes).

Size	Time	Size	Time
10.5	0.20	110	2.01
12.9	0.24	156	2.68
15	0.27	163	2.87
20	0.36	175	3.10
60	1.09	200	3.64
75	1.42	250	4.61

Download Times

  a. Find the equation of the least-squares line for these data.

  b. On the basis of the value of the linear correlation coefficient, is a linear model of these data a reasonable model?

  c. Use the equation of the least-squares line from part a to predict the expected download time of a file that is 100 kilobytes in size.

26. **Consumer Price Index** The U.S. Consumer Price Index (CPI) is a measure of the average change in prices over time. In the following table, the CPI for each year is based on a cost of $100 in 1967. For example, the CPI for the year 1985 is 322.2. This means that in 1985 it took $322.20 to purchase the same goods that cost $100 in the year 1967.

Consumer Price Index, 1975–2004 (1967 has a CPI of 100)

Year	1975	1980	1985	1990	1995	2000	2004*
CPI	161.2	248.8	322.2	391.4	456.5	515.8	562.0

*Average for first half of 2004
Source: Bureau of Labor Statistics, U.S. Dept. of Labor. Data taken from *The World Almanac and Book of Facts 2005,* page 109.

  a. Find the equation of the least-squares regression line and the linear correlation coefficient for the data in the table. Let the year 1970 be represented by $x = 0$, 1975 by $x = 5$, and so on. Round constants to the nearest hundredth.

  b. Use the equation of the least-squares regression line to predict the CPI for the year 2007. Round to the nearest tenth.

1. Find the mean, the median, and the mode for the following data. Round noninteger values to the nearest tenth.

$$3, 7, 11, 12, 7, 9, 15$$

2. **Test Scores** A professor grades students on three tests, two quizzes, and a final examination. Each quiz counts as one-half a test and the final examination counts as two tests. Pam has test scores of 90, 75, and 84. Pam's quiz scores are 86 and 50. Her final examination score is 88. Use the weighted mean formula to find Pam's average for the course. Round to the nearest tenth.

3. Find the range, the standard deviation, and the variance for the following sample data.

$$7, 11, 12, 15, 31, 22$$

4. A *sample* data set has a mean of $\bar{x} = 65$ and a standard deviation of 10.2. Find the z-scores for each of the following. Round to the nearest hundredth.

   a. $x = 77$ **b.** $x = 60$

5. **Basketball** Draw a box-and-whiskers plot for the following data.

   Points Scored by Top 20 Women's National Basketball Association Players in 2004

634	598	578	568	526	520	517
494	488	464	460	459	446	445
440	439	437	434	432	413	

6. **Movie Attendance** Use the following frequency distribution to estimate what *percent* of the movie attendees were

   a. at least 40 years of age.

   b. at least 21 but less than 40 years of age.

   Movie Attendance by Age Group, 2003

Age Group	Percent of Total Yearly Admissions
12–15	11%
16–20	16%
21–24	12%
25–29	9%
30–39	19%
40–49	14%
50–59	11%
60+	8%

   Source: MPA Worldwide Market Research

7. During 1 month, an overnight delivery company found that the weights of its parcels were normally distributed, with a mean of 34 ounces and a standard deviation of 10 ounces. Use the Empirical Rule to determine

   a. what percent of the parcels weighed between 34 ounces and 54 ounces.

   b. what percent of the parcels weighed less than 24 ounces.

8. **Box Weights** The weights of all the boxes of cake mix filled by a machine are normally distributed, with a mean weight of 18.0 ounces and a standard deviation of 0.8 ounce. What percent of the boxes will

   a. weigh less than 17 ounces?

   b. weigh between 18.4 and 19.0 ounces?

9. **Camera Sales** The following double-bar graph shows the sales, in millions of cameras, of analog and digital still cameras.

   ■ Digital camera   ■ Analog camera

   Source: Digital Photography Review, dpreview.com August 27, 2004.

   Is there a linear relationship, at the $|r| > 0.9$ level, to suggest there is a linear equation that models the sale of analog cameras as a function of the year?

10. **Nutrition** The following table shows the percent of water and the number of calories in various canned soups to which 100 grams of water are added.

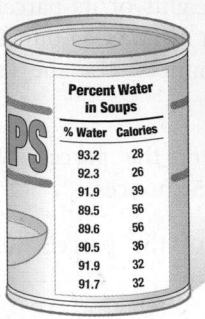

Percent Water in Soups

% Water	Calories
93.2	28
92.3	26
91.9	39
89.5	56
89.6	56
90.5	36
91.9	32
91.7	32

a. Find the equation of the least-squares regression line for the data. Round constants to the nearest hundredth.

b. Use the equation in part a to find the expected number of calories in a soup that is 89% water. Round to the nearest whole number.

CHAPTER

13 Apportionment and Voting

- **13.1** Introduction to Apportionment
- **13.2** Introduction to Voting
- **13.3** Weighted Voting Systems

In this chapter, we discuss two of the most fundamental principles of democracy: the right to vote and the value of that vote. The U.S. Constitution, in Article I, Section 2, states in part that

> The House of Representatives shall be composed of members chosen every second year by the people of the several states, and the electors in each state shall have the qualifications requisite for electors of the most numerous branch of the state legislature. . . . Representatives and direct taxes shall be apportioned among the several states which may be included within this union, according to their respective numbers. . . . The actual Enumeration shall be made within three years after the first meeting of the Congress of the United States, and within every subsequent term of ten years, in such manner as they shall by law direct. The number of Representatives shall not exceed one for every thirty thousand, but each state shall have at least one Representative; . . .

This article of the Constitution requires that "Representatives . . . be *apportioned* [our italics] among the several states . . . according to their respective numbers. . . ." That is, the number of representatives each state sends to Congress should be based on its population. Because populations change over time, this article also requires that the number of people within a state should be counted "within every subsequent term of ten years." This is why we have a census every 10 years.

The way representatives are *apportioned* has been a contentious issue since the founding of the United States. The first presidential veto was issued by George Washington in 1792 because he did not approve of the way the House of Representatives decided to apportion the number of representatives each state would have. Ever since that first veto, the issue of how to apportion membership in the House of Representatives among the states has been revisited many times.

 For online student resources, visit this textbook's website at **www.cengage.com/math.**

Introduction to Apportionment

historical note

The original Article I, Section 2 of the U.S. Constitution included wording as to how to count citizens. According to this article, the numbers "shall be determined by adding to the whole number of free persons, including those bound to service for a term of years, and excluding Indians not taxed, three fifths of all other Persons." The "three fifths of all other Persons" meant that a slave was counted as only $\frac{3}{5}$ of a person. This article was modified by Section 1 of the 14th Amendment to the Constitution, which, in part, states that "All persons born or naturalized in the United States, and subject to the jurisdiction thereof, are citizens of the United States and of the state wherein they reside...." ∎

The mathematical investigation into **apportionment,** which is a method of dividing a whole into various parts, has its roots in the U.S. Constitution. (See the chapter opener.) Since 1790, when the House of Representatives first attempted to apportion itself, various methods have been used to decide how many voters would be represented by each member of the House. The two competing plans in 1790 were put forward by Alexander Hamilton and Thomas Jefferson.

To illustrate how the Hamilton and Jefferson plans were used to calculate the number of representatives each state should have, we will consider the fictitious country of Andromeda, with a population of 20,000 and five states. The population of each state is given in the table at the right.

Andromeda's constitution calls for 25 representatives to be chosen from these states. The number of representatives is to be apportioned according to the states' respective populations.

Andromeda

State	Population
Apus	11,123
Libra	879
Draco	3518
Cephus	1563
Orion	2917
Total	20,000

The Hamilton Plan

Under the Hamilton plan, the total population of the country (20,000) is divided by the number of representatives (25). This gives the number of citizens represented by each representative. The number is called the *standard divisor.*

Standard Divisor

$$\text{Standard divisor} = \frac{\text{total population}}{\text{number of people to apportion}}$$

✓ **TAKE NOTE**

Today apportionment is applied to situations other than a population of people. For instance, *population* could refer to the number of math classes offered at a college or the number of fire stations in a city. Nonetheless, the definition of *standard divisor* is still given as though people were involved.

For Andromeda, we have

$$\text{Standard divisor} = \frac{\text{total population}}{\text{number of people to apportion}} = \frac{20,000}{25} = 800$$

QUESTION *What is the meaning of the number 800 calculated above?*

Now divide the population of each state by the standard divisor and round the quotient *down* to a whole number. For example, both 15.1 and 15.9 would be rounded to 15. Each whole number quotient is called a *standard quota.*

ANSWER *It is the number of citizens represented by each representative.*

Standard Quota

The **standard quota** is the whole number part of the quotient of a population divided by the standard divisor.

State	Population	Quotient	Standard quota
Apus	11,123	$\dfrac{11{,}123}{800} \approx 13.904$	13
Libra	879	$\dfrac{879}{800} \approx 1.099$	1
Draco	3518	$\dfrac{3518}{800} \approx 4.398$	4
Cephus	1563	$\dfrac{1563}{800} \approx 1.954$	1
Orion	2917	$\dfrac{2917}{800} \approx 3.646$	3
		Total	22

From the calculations in the above table, the total number of representatives is 22, not 25 as required by Andromeda's constitution. When this happens, the Hamilton plan calls for revisiting the calculation of the quotients and assigning an additional representative to the state with the largest decimal remainder. This process is continued until the number of representatives equals the number required by the constitution. For Andromeda, we have

TAKE NOTE

Additional representatives are assigned according to the largest decimal remainders. Because the sum of the standard quotas came to only 22 representatives, we must add three more representatives. The states with the three highest decimal remainders are Cephus (1.<u>954</u>), Apus (13.<u>904</u>), and Orion (3.<u>646</u>). Thus each of these states gets an additional representative.

State	Population	Quotient	Standard quota	Number of representatives
Apus	11,123	$\dfrac{11{,}123}{800} \approx 13.904$	13	14
Libra	879	$\dfrac{879}{800} \approx 1.099$	1	1
Draco	3518	$\dfrac{3518}{800} \approx 4.398$	4	4
Cephus	1563	$\dfrac{1563}{800} \approx 1.954$	1	2
Orion	2917	$\dfrac{2917}{800} \approx 3.646$	3	4
		Total	22	25

The Jefferson Plan

As we saw with the Hamilton plan, dividing by the standard divisor and then rounding down does not always yield the correct number of representatives. In the previous example, we were three representatives short. The Jefferson plan attempts to overcome this difficulty by using a *modified standard divisor*. This number is chosen, by trial and error, so that the sum of the standard quotas is the total number of representatives. In a specific apportionment calculation, there may be more than one number that can serve as the modified standard divisor. In the following apportionment calculation, we used 740 as our modified standard divisor. However, 741 also can be used as the modified standard divisor.

State	Population	Quotient	Standard quota	Number of representatives
Apus	11,123	$\dfrac{11{,}123}{740} \approx 15.031$	15	15
Libra	879	$\dfrac{879}{740} \approx 1.188$	1	1
Draco	3518	$\dfrac{3518}{740} \approx 4.754$	4	4
Cephus	1563	$\dfrac{1563}{740} \approx 2.112$	2	2
Orion	2917	$\dfrac{2917}{740} \approx 3.942$	3	3
		Total	25	25

The table below shows how the results of the Hamilton and Jefferson apportionment methods differ. Note that each method assigns a different number of representatives to certain states.

State	Population	Hamilton plan	Jefferson plan
Apus	11,123	14	15
Libra	879	1	1
Draco	3518	4	4
Cephus	1563	2	2
Orion	2917	4	3
	Total	25	25

Although we have applied apportionment to allocating representatives to a congress, there are other applications of apportionment. For instance, nurses can be assigned to hospitals according to the number of patients requiring care; police officers can be assigned to precincts based on the number of reported crimes; math classes can be scheduled based on student demand for those classes. These are only some of the ways apportionment can be used.

Ruben County

City	Population
Cardiff	7020
Solana	2430
Vista	1540
Pauma	3720
Pacific	5290

EXAMPLE 1 ■ Apportioning Board Members Using the Hamilton and Jefferson Methods

Suppose the 18 members on the board of the Ruben County environmental agency are selected according to the populations of the five cities in the county, as shown in the table at the left.

a. Use the Hamilton method to determine the number of board members each city should have.

b. Use the Jefferson method to determine the number of board members each city should have.

Solution

a. First find the total population of the counties.

$$7020 + 2430 + 1540 + 3720 + 5290 = 20,000$$

Now calculate the standard divisor.

$$\text{Standard divisor} = \frac{\text{population of county}}{\text{number of board members}} = \frac{20,000}{18} \approx 1111.11$$

Use the standard divisor to find the standard quota for each city.

City	Population	Quotient	Standard quota	Number of board members
Cardiff	7020	$\frac{7020}{1111.11} \approx 6.318$	6	6
Solana	2430	$\frac{2430}{1111.11} \approx 2.187$	2	2
Vista	1540	$\frac{1540}{1111.11} \approx 1.386$	1	2
Pauma	3720	$\frac{3720}{1111.11} \approx 3.348$	3	3
Pacific	5290	$\frac{5290}{1111.11} \approx 4.761$	4	5
		Total	16	18

The sum of the standard quotas is 16, so we must add two more members. The two cities with the largest decimal remainders are Pacific and Vista. Each of these two cities gets one additional board member. Thus the composition of the environmental board using the Hamilton method is Cardiff: 6, Solana: 2, Vista: 2, Pauma: 3, Pacific: 5.

b. To use the Jefferson method, we must find a *modified* standard divisor that is less than the standard divisor we calculated in part a. We must do this by trial and error. For instance, if we choose 925 as the modified standard divisor, we have the following result.

City	Population	Quotient	Standard quota	Number of board members
Cardiff	7020	$\frac{7020}{925} \approx 7.589$	7	7
Solana	2430	$\frac{2430}{925} \approx 2.627$	2	2
Vista	1540	$\frac{1540}{925} \approx 1.665$	1	1
Pauma	3720	$\frac{3720}{925} \approx 4.022$	4	4
Pacific	5290	$\frac{5290}{925} \approx 5.719$	5	5
		Total	19	19

This result yields too many board members. Thus we must increase the modified standard divisor. By experimenting with different divisors, we find that 950 is a possible modified standard divisor. Using 950 as the standard divisor gives the results shown in the table below.

City	Population	Quotient	Standard quota	Number of board members
Cardiff	7020	$\frac{7020}{950} \approx 7.389$	7	7
Solana	2430	$\frac{2430}{950} \approx 2.558$	2	2
Vista	1540	$\frac{1540}{950} \approx 1.621$	1	1
Pauma	3720	$\frac{3720}{950} \approx 3.916$	3	3
Pacific	5290	$\frac{5290}{950} \approx 5.568$	5	5
		Total	18	18

Thus the composition of the environmental board using the Jefferson method is Cardiff: 7, Solana: 2, Vista: 1, Pauma: 3, Pacific: 5.

European Countries'
Populations, 2004

Country	Population
France	60,400,000
Germany	82,400,000
Italy	58,000,000
Spain	40,000,000
Belgium	10,300,000

Source: The World Almanac and Book of Facts, 2005, pages 848–849

CHECK YOUR PROGRESS 1 Suppose the 20 members of a committee from five European countries are selected according to the populations of the five countries, as shown in the table at the left.

a. Use the Hamilton method to determine the number of representatives each country should have.

b. Use the Jefferson method to determine the number of representatives each country should have.

Solution See page S49.

Suppose that the environmental agency in Example 1 decides to add one more member to the board even though the population of each city remains the same. The total number of members is now 19 and we must determine how the members of the board will be apportioned.

The standard divisor is now $\frac{20,000}{19} \approx 1052.63$. Using Hamilton's method, the calculations necessary to apportion the board members are shown below.

City	Population	Quotient	Standard quota	Number of board members
Cardiff	7020	$\frac{7020}{1052.63} \approx 6.669$	6	7
Solana	2430	$\frac{2430}{1052.63} \approx 2.309$	2	2
Vista	1540	$\frac{1540}{1052.63} \approx 1.463$	1	1
Pauma	3720	$\frac{3720}{1052.63} \approx 3.534$	3	4
Pacific	5290	$\frac{5290}{1052.63} \approx 5.026$	5	5
		Total	17	19

The table below summarizes the number of board members each city would have if the board consisted of 18 members (Example 1) or 19 members.

City	Hamilton apportionment with 18 board members	Hamilton apportionment with 19 board members
Cardiff	6	7
Solana	2	2
Vista	2	1
Pauma	3	4
Pacific	5	5
Total	18	19

Notice that although one more board member was added, Vista lost a board member, even though the populations of the cities did not change. This is called the **Alabama paradox** and has a negative effect on fairness. In the interest of fairness, an apportionment method should not exhibit the Alabama paradox. (See the Math Matters below for other paradoxes.)

Math Matters   Apportionment Paradoxes

The Alabama paradox, although it was not given that name until later, was first noticed after the 1870 census. At the time, the House of Representatives had 270 seats. However, when the number of representatives in the House was increased to 280 seats, Rhode Island lost a representative.

After the 1880 census, C. W. Seaton, the chief clerk of the U.S. Census Office, calculated the number of representatives each state would have if the number were set at some number between 275 and 300. He noticed that when the number of representatives was increased from 299 to 300, Alabama lost a representative.

There are other paradoxes that involve apportionment methods. Two of them are the *population paradox* and the *new states paradox*. It is possible for the population of one state to be increasing faster than that of another state and for the state still to lose a representative. This is an example of the **population paradox.**

In 1907, when Oklahoma was added to the Union, the size of the House was increased by five representatives to account for Oklahoma's population. However, when the complete apportionment of the Congress was recalculated, New York lost a seat and Maine gained a seat. This is an example of the **new states paradox.**

Fairness in Apportionment

To decide which plan—the Hamilton or the Jefferson—is better, we might try to determine which plan is fairer. Of course, *fair* can be quite a subjective term, so we will try to state conditions by which an apportionment plan is judged fair. One criterion of fairness for an apportionment plan is that it should satisfy the *quota rule*.

> **Quota Rule**
>
> The number of representatives apportioned to a state is the standard quota or one more than the standard quota.

We can show that the Jefferson plan does not satisfy the quota rule by calculating the standard quota of Apus (see page 872).

$$\text{Standard quota} = \frac{\text{population of Apus}}{\text{standard divisor}} = \frac{11{,}123}{800} \approx 13$$

The standard quota of Apus is 13. However, the Jefferson plan assigns 15 representatives to that state (see page 872), two more than its standard quota. Therefore, the Jefferson method violates the quota rule.

As we have seen, the choice of apportionment method affects the number of representatives a state will have. Given that fact, mathematicians and others have tried to work out an apportionment method that is fair. The difficulty lies in trying to define what is fair.

Another measure of fairness is *average constituency*. This is the population of a state divided by the number of representatives from the state and then rounded to the nearest whole number.

> **Average Constituency**
>
> $$\text{Average constituency} = \frac{\text{population of a state}}{\text{number of representatives from the state}}$$

Consider the two states Hampton and Shasta in the table below.

State	Population	Representatives	Average constituency
Hampton	16,000	10	$\frac{16,000}{10} = 1600$
Shasta	8340	5	$\frac{8340}{5} = 1668$

✔ TAKE NOTE

The idea of average constituency is an essential aspect of our democracy. To understand this, suppose state *A* has an average constituency of 1000 and state *B* has an average constituency of 10,000. When a bill is voted on in the House of Representatives, each vote has equal weight. However, a vote from a representative from state *A* would represent 1000 people, but a vote from a representative from state *B* would represent 10,000 people. Consequently, in this situation, we do not have "equal representation."

Because the average constituencies are approximately equal, it seems natural to say that both states are equally represented. See the Take Note to the left.

QUESTION *Although the average constituencies of Hampton and Shasta are approximately equal, which state has the more favorable representation?*

Now suppose that one representative will be added to one of the states. Which state is more deserving of the new representative? In other words, to be fair, which state should receive the new representative?

The changes in the average constituency are shown below.

State	Average constituency (old)	Average constituency (new)
Hampton	$\frac{16,000}{10} = 1600$	$\frac{16,000}{11} \approx 1455$
Shasta	$\frac{8340}{5} = 1668$	$\frac{8340}{6} = 1390$

From the table, there are two possibilities for adding one representative. If Hampton receives the representative, its average constituency will be 1455 and Shasta's will remain at 1668. The difference in the average constituencies is $1668 - 1455 = 213$. This difference is called the *absolute unfairness of the apportionment.*

ANSWER *Because Hampton's average constituency is smaller than Shasta's, Hampton has the more favorable representation.*

Absolute Unfairness of an Apportionment

The **absolute unfairness of an apportionment** is the absolute value of the difference between the average constituency of state A and the average constituency of state B.

$$|\text{Average constituency of } A - \text{average constituency of } B|$$

If Shasta receives the representative, its average constituency will be 1390 and Hampton's will remain at 1600. The absolute unfairness of apportionment is $1600 - 1390 = 210$. This is summarized below.

	Hampton's average constituency	Shasta's average constituency	Absolute unfairness of apportionment
Hampton receives the new representative	1455	1668	213
Shasta receives the new representative	1600	1390	210

Because the smaller absolute unfairness of apportionment occurs if Shasta receives the new representative, it might seem that Shasta should receive the representative. However, this is not necessarily true.

To understand this concept, let's consider a somewhat different situation. Suppose an investor makes two investments, one of \$10,000 and another of \$20,000. One year later, the first investment is worth \$11,000 and the second investment is worth \$21,500. This is shown in the table below.

	Original investment	One year later	Increase
Investment A	\$10,000	\$11,000	\$1000
Investment B	\$20,000	\$21,500	\$1500

Although there is a larger increase in investment B, the increase per dollar of the original investment is $\frac{1500}{20,000} = 0.075$. On the other hand, the increase per dollar of investment A is $\frac{1000}{10,000} = 0.10$. Another way of saying this is that each \$1 of investment A produced a return of 10 cents (0.10), whereas each \$1 of investment B produced a return of 7.5 cents (0.075). Therefore, even though the increase in investment A was less than the increase in investment B, investment A was more productive.

A similar process is used when deciding which state should receive another representative. Rather than look at the difference in the absolute unfairness in apportionment, we determine the *relative unfairness* of adding the representative.

Relative Unfairness of an Apportionment

The **relative unfairness of an apportionment** is the quotient of the absolute unfairness of apportionment and the average constituency of the state receiving the new representative.

$$\frac{\text{Absolute unfairness of the apportionment}}{\text{Average constituency of the state receiving the new representative}}$$

EXAMPLE 2 ■ Determine the Relative Unfairness of an Apportionment

Determine the relative unfairness of an apportionment that gives a new representative to Hampton rather than Shasta.

Solution

Using the table for Hampton and Shasta shown on the previous page, we have

Relative unfairness of the apportionment

$$= \frac{\text{absolute unfairness of the apportionment}}{\text{average constituency of Hampton with a new representative}}$$

$$= \frac{213}{1455} \approx 0.146$$

The relative unfairness of the apportionment is approximately 0.146.

CHECK YOUR PROGRESS 2 Determine the relative unfairness of an apportionment that gives a new representative to Shasta rather than Hampton.

Solution *See page S50.*

The relative unfairness of an apportionment is used in the following way.

Apportionment Principle

When adding a new representative to a state, the representative is assigned to the state in such a way as to give the smallest relative unfairness of apportionment.

From Example 2, the relative unfairness of adding a representative to Hampton is approximately 0.146. From Check Your Progress 2, the relative unfairness of adding a representative to Shasta is approximately 0.151. Because the smaller relative unfairness results from adding the representative to Hampton, that state should receive the new representative.

Although we have focused on assigning representatives to states, the apportionment principle can be used in many other situations.

EXAMPLE 3 ■ Use the Apportionment Principle

The table below shows the number of paramedics and the annual number of paramedic calls for two cities. If a new paramedic is hired, use the apportionment principle to determine to which city the paramedic should be assigned.

	Paramedics	Annual paramedic calls
Tahoe	125	17,526
Erie	143	22,461

Solution

Calculate the relative unfairness of the apportionment that assigns the paramedic to Tahoe and the relative unfairness of the apportionment that assigns the paramedic to Erie. In this case, average constituency is the annual paramedic calls divided by the number of paramedics.

	Tahoe's annual paramedic calls per paramedic	Erie's annual paramedic calls per paramedic	Absolute unfairness of apportionment
Tahoe receives a new paramedic	$\dfrac{17{,}526}{125 + 1} \approx 139$	$\dfrac{22{,}461}{143} \approx 157$	$157 - 139 = 18$
Erie receives a new paramedic	$\dfrac{17{,}526}{125} \approx 140$	$\dfrac{22{,}461}{143 + 1} \approx 156$	$156 - 140 = 16$

If Tahoe receives the new paramedic, the relative unfairness of the apportionment is

Relative unfairness of the apportionment

$$= \frac{\text{absolute unfairness of the apportionment}}{\text{Tahoe's average constituency with a new paramedic}}$$

$$= \frac{18}{139} \approx 0.129$$

If Erie receives the new paramedic, the relative unfairness of the apportionment is

Relative unfairness of the apportionment

$$= \frac{\text{absolute unfairness of the apportionment}}{\text{Erie's average constituency with a new paramedic}}$$

$$= \frac{16}{156} \approx 0.103$$

Because the smaller relative unfairness results from adding the paramedic to Erie, that city should receive the paramedic.

CHECK YOUR PROGRESS 3   The table below shows the number of first and second grade teachers in a school district and the number of students in each of those grades. If a new teacher is hired, use the apportionment principle to determine to which grade the teacher should be assigned.

	Number of teachers	Number of students
First grade	512	12,317
Second grade	551	15,439

Solution   See page S50.

historical note

According to the U.S. Bureau of the Census, methods of apportioning the House of Representatives have changed over time.

1790–1830: Jefferson method

1840: Webster method (See the paragraph following Exercise 24, page 888.)

1850–1900: Hamilton method

1910, 1930: Webster method

Note that 1920 is missing. In direct violation of the U.S. Constitution, the House of Representatives failed to reapportion the House in 1920.

1940–2000: Method of equal proportions or the Huntington-Hill method

All apportionment plans enacted by the House have created some controversy. For instance, the constitutionality of the Huntington-Hill method was challenged by Montana in 1992 because it lost a seat to Washington after the 1990 census. For more information on this subject, see **http://www.census.gov/ population/www/censusdata/ apportionment/history.html.** ■

Huntington-Hill Apportionment Method

As we mentioned earlier, the members of the House of Representatives are apportioned among the states every 10 years. The present method used by the House is based on the apportionment principle and is called the *method of equal proportions* or the *Huntington-Hill method*. This method has been used since 1940.

The Huntington-Hill method is implemented by calculating what is called a *Huntington-Hill number*. This number is derived from the apportionment principle. See Exercise 35, page 890.

Huntington-Hill Number

The value of $\dfrac{(P_A)^2}{a(a+1)}$, where P_A is the population of state A and a is the current number of representatives from state A, is called the **Huntington-Hill number** for state A.

When the Huntington-Hill method is used to apportion representatives between two states, the state with the greater Huntington-Hill number receives the next representative. This method can be extended to more than two states.

Huntington-Hill Apportionment Principle

When there is a choice of adding one representative to a number of states, the representative should be added to the state with the greatest Huntington-Hill number.

EXAMPLE 4 ■ Use the Huntington-Hill Apportionment Principle

The table below shows the numbers of lifeguards that are assigned to three different beaches and the numbers of rescues made by lifeguards at those beaches. Use the Huntington-Hill apportionment principle to determine to which beach a new lifeguard should be assigned.

Beach	Number of lifeguards	Number of rescues
Mellon	37	1227
Donovan	51	1473
Ferris	24	889

Solution

Calculate the Huntington-Hill number for each of the beaches. In this case, the population is the number of rescues and the number of representatives is the number of lifeguards.

Mellon: Donovan: Ferris:

$$\frac{1227^2}{37(37+1)} \approx 1071 \qquad \frac{1473^2}{51(51+1)} \approx 818 \qquad \frac{889^2}{24(24+1)} \approx 1317$$

Ferris has the greatest Huntington-Hill number. Thus, according to the Huntington-Hill Apportionment Principle, the new lifeguard should be assigned to Ferris.

✔ TAKE NOTE

The advantage of using the Huntington-Hill apportionment principle, rather than calculating relative unfairness, occurs when there are many states that could receive the next representative. For instance, if we were to use relative unfairness to determine which of four states should receive a new representative, it would be necessary to compute the relative unfairness for every possible pairing of the states—a total of 24 computations. However, using the Huntington-Hill method, we need only calculate the Huntington-Hill number for each state—a total of four calculations. In a sense, the Huntington-Hill number provides a short cut for applying the relative unfairness method.

CHECK YOUR PROGRESS 4   A university has a president's council that is composed of students from each of the undergraduate classes. If a new student representative is added to the council, use the Huntington-Hill apportionment principle to determine which class the new student council member should represent.

Class	Number of representatives	Number of students
First year	12	2015
Second year	10	1755
Third year	9	1430
Fourth year	8	1309

Solution   *See page S51.*

Now that we have looked at various apportionment methods, it seems reasonable to ask which is the best method. Unfortunately, all apportionment methods have some flaws. This was proved by Michael Balinski and H. Peyton Young.

Balinski-Young Impossibility Theorem

Any apportionment method either will violate the quota rule or will produce paradoxes such as the Alabama paradox.

Although there is no perfect apportionment method, Balinski and Young went on to present a strong case that the Webster method (following Exercise 24 on page 888) is the system that most closely satisfies the goal of one person, one vote. However, political expediency sometimes overrules mathematical proof. Some historians have suggested that although the Huntington-Hill apportionment method was better than some of the previous methods, President Franklin Roosevelt chose this method in 1941 because it alloted one more seat to Arkansas and one less to Michigan. This essentially meant that the House of Representatives would have one more seat for the Democrats, Roosevelt's party.

Excursion

Apportioning the 1790 House of Representatives

The first apportionment of the House of Representatives, using the 1790 census, is given in the following table. This apportionment was calculated by using the Jefferson method. (See our website at **www.cengage.com** for an Excel spreadsheet that will help with the computations.)

(continued)

historical note

According to the U.S. Constitution, each state must have at least one representative to the House of Representatives. The remaining representatives are then assigned to the states using, since 1941, the Huntington-Hill apportionment principle. ■

point of interest

For most states, the population shown in the table is not the actual population of the state because slaves were counted as only three-fifths of a person. (See the Historical Note on page 870.) For instance, the actual population of Connecticut was 237,946, of which 2764 were slaves. For apportionment purposes, the number of slaves was subtracted, and then $\frac{3}{5}$ of that population was added back.

$$237,946 - 2764 + \frac{3}{5}(2764) \approx 236,841$$

Apportionment Using the Jefferson Method, 1790

State	Population	Number of representatives
Connecticut	236,841	7
Delaware	55,540	1
Georgia	70,835	2
Maryland	278,514	8
Massachusetts	475,327	14
Kentucky	68,705	2
New Hampshire	141,822	4
Vermont	85,533	2
New York	331,591	10
New Jersey	179,570	5
Pennsylvania	432,879	13
North Carolina	353,523	10
South Carolina	206,236	6
Virginia	630,560	19
Rhode Island	68,446	2

Source: U.S. Census Bureau

Excursion Exercises

1. Verify this apportionment using the Jefferson method. You will have to experiment with various modified divisors until you reach the given representation. See the Calculator Note on page 874.

2. Find the apportionment that would have resulted if the Hamilton method had been used.

3. Give each state one representative. Use the Huntington-Hill method with $n = 1$ to determine the state that receives the next representative. The Calculator Note in this section will help. With the populations stored in L1, enter 2nd L1 x^2 ÷ 2 STO 2nd L2 ENTER. Now scroll through L2 to find the largest number.

4. Find the apportionment that would have resulted if the Huntington-Hill method (the one used for the 2000 census) had been used in 1790. See our website at **www.cengage.com/math** for a spreadsheet that will help with the calculations.

Exercise Set 13.1

1. Explain how to calculate the standard divisor of an apportionment for a total population p with n items to apportion.

2. **Teacher Aides** A total of 25 teacher aides are to be apportioned among seven classes at a new elementary school. The enrollment in each of the seven classes is shown in the following table.

Class	Number of students
Kindergarten	38
First grade	39
Second grade	35
Third grade	27
Fourth grade	21
Fifth grade	31
Sixth grade	33
Total	224

a. Determine the standard divisor. What is the meaning of the standard divisor in the context of this exercise?

b. Use the Hamilton method to determine the number of teacher aides to be apportioned to each class.

c. Use the Jefferson method to determine the number of teacher aides to be apportioned to each class. Is this apportionment in violation of the quota rule?

d. How do the apportionment results produced using the Jefferson method compare with the results produced using the Hamilton method?

3. In the Hamilton apportionment method, explain how to calculate the standard quota for a particular state (group).

4. What is the quota rule?

5. The following table shows how the average constituency changes for two regional governing boards, Joshua and Salinas, when a new representative is added to each board.

	Joshua's average constituency	Salinas's average constituency
Joshua receives new board member	1215	1547
Salinas receives new board member	1498	1195

a. Determine the relative unfairness of an apportionment that gives a new board member to Joshua rather than to Salinas. Round to the nearest thousandth.

b. Determine the relative unfairness of an apportionment that gives a new board member to Salinas rather than to Joshua. Round to the nearest thousandth.

c. Using the apportionment principle, determine which regional governing board should receive the new board member.

6. The table below shows how the average constituency changes when two different national parks, Evergreen State Park and Rust Canyon Preserve, add a new forest ranger.

	Evergreen State Park's average constituency	Rust Canyon Preserve's average constituency
Evergreen receives new forest ranger	466	638
Rust Canyon receives new forest ranger	650	489

a. Determine the relative unfairness of an apportionment that gives a new forest ranger to Evergreen rather than to Rust Canyon. Round to the nearest thousandth.

b. Determine the relative unfairness of an apportionment that gives a new forest ranger to Rust Canyon rather than to Evergreen. Round to the nearest thousandth.

c. Using the apportionment principle, determine which national park should receive the new forest ranger.

7. The table below shows the number of sales associates and the average number of customers per day visiting a store at a company's two department stores. The company is planning to add a new sales associate to one of the stores. Use the apportionment principle to determine which store should receive the new employee.

Shopping mall location	Number of sales associates	Average number of customers per day
Summer Hill Galleria	587	5289
Seaside Mall Galleria	614	6215

8. The table below shows the number of interns and the average number of patients admitted each day to two different hospitals. The hospital administrator is planning to add a new intern to one of the hospitals. Use the apportionment principle to determine which hospital should receive the new intern.

Hospital location	Number of interns	Average number of patients admitted per day
South Coast Hospital	128	518
Rainer Hospital	145	860

9. **House of Representatives** The U.S. House of Representatives currently has 435 members to represent the 281,424,177 citizens of the U.S. as determined by the 2000 census.

a. Calculate the standard divisor for the apportionment of these representatives and explain the meaning of this standard divisor in the context of this exercise.

b. According to the 2000 census, the population of Delaware was 785,068. Delaware currently has only one representative in the House of Representatives. Is Delaware currently overrepresented or underrepresented in the House of Representatives? Explain.

c. According to the 2000 census, the population of Vermont was 609,890. Vermont currently has only one representative in the House of Representatives. Is Vermont currently overrepresented or underrepresented in the House of Representatives? Explain.

10. **College Enrollment** The following table shows the enrollment for each of the four divisions of a college. The four divisions are liberal arts, business, humanities, and science. There are 180 new computers that are to be apportioned among the divisions based on the enrollments.

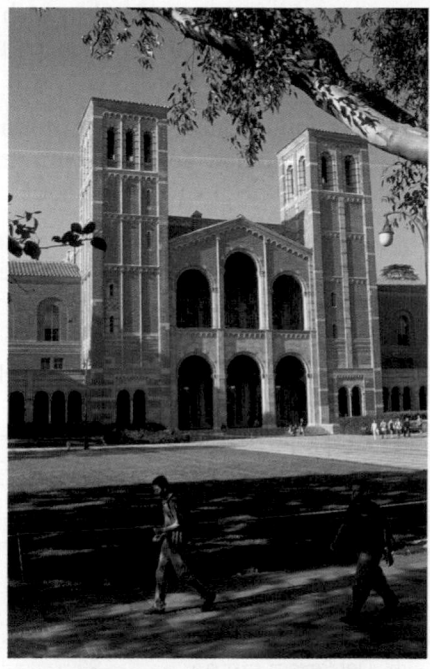

Division	Enrollment
Liberal arts	3455
Business	5780
Humanities	1896
Science	4678
Total	15,809

a. What is the standard divisor for an apportionment of the computers? What is the meaning of the standard divisor in the context of this exercise?

b. Use the Hamilton method to determine the number of computers to be apportioned to each division.

c. ✎ If the computers are to be apportioned using the Jefferson method, explain why neither 86 nor 87 can be used as a modified standard divisor. Explain why 86.5 can be used as a modified standard divisor.

d. ✎ Explain why the modified standard divisor used in the Jefferson method cannot be larger than the standard divisor.

e. Use the Jefferson method to determine the number of computers to be apportioned to each division. Is this apportionment in violation of the quota rule?

f. How do the apportionment results produced using the Jefferson method compare with the results produced using the Hamilton method?

11. Medical Care A hospital district consists of six hospitals. The district administrators have decided that 48 new nurses should be apportioned based on the number of beds in each of the hospitals. The following table shows the number of beds in each hospital.

Hospital	Number of beds
Sharp	242
Palomar	356
Tri-City	308
Del Raye	190
Rancho Verde	275
Bel Aire	410
Total	1781

a. ✎ Determine the standard divisor. What is the meaning of the standard divisor in the context of this exercise?

b. Use the Hamilton method to determine the number of nurses to be apportioned to each hospital.

c. Use the Jefferson method to determine the number of nurses to be apportioned to each hospital.

d. How do the apportionment results produced using the Jefferson method compare with the results produced using the Hamilton method?

12. ✎ What is the Alabama paradox?

13. ✎ What is the population paradox?

14. ✎ What is the new states paradox?

15. ✎ What is the Balinski-Young Impossibility Theorem?

16. Apportionment of Projectors Consider the apportionment of 27 projectors for a school district with four campus locations labeled *A*, *B*, *C*, and *D*. The following table shows the apportionment of the projectors using the Hamilton method.

Campus	A	B	C	D
Enrollment	840	1936	310	2744
Apportionment of 27 projectors	4	9	1	13

a. If the number of projectors to be apportioned increases from 27 to 28, what will be the apportionment if the Hamilton method is used? Did the Alabama paradox occur? Explain.

b. If the number of projectors to be apportioned using the Hamilton method increases from 28 to 29, will the Alabama paradox occur? Explain.

17. Hotel Management A company operates four resorts. The CEO of the company decides to use the Hamilton method to apportion 115 new flat-screen digital television sets to the resorts based on the number of guest rooms at each resort.

Resort	A	B	C	D
Number of guest rooms	23	256	182	301
Apportionment of 115 televisions	4	39	27	45

a. If the number of television sets to be apportioned by the Hamilton method increases from 115 to 116, will the Alabama paradox occur?

b. If the number of television sets to be apportioned by the Hamilton method increases from 116 to 117, will the Alabama paradox occur?

c. If the number of television sets to be apportioned by the Hamilton method increases from 117 to 118, will the Alabama paradox occur?

18. College Security A college apportions 40 security personnel among three education centers according to their enrollments. The following table shows the present enrollments at each of the centers.

Center	A	B	C
Enrollment	356	1054	2590

a. Use the Hamilton method to apportion the security personnel.

b. ✏ After a semester, the centers have the following enrollments.

Center	A	B	C
Enrollment	370	1079	2600

Center A has an increased enrollment of 14 students, which is an increase of $\frac{14}{356} \approx 0.039 = 3.9\%$. Center B has an increased enrollment of 25 students, which is an increase of $\frac{25}{1054} \approx 0.024 = 2.4\%$.

If the security personnel are reapportioned using the Hamilton method, will the population paradox occur? Explain.

19. Management Scientific Research Corporation has offices in Boston and Chicago. The number of employees at each office is shown in the following table. There are 22 vice presidents to be apportioned between the offices.

Office	Boston	Chicago
Employees	151	1210

a. Use the Hamilton method to find each office's apportionment of vice presidents.

b. ✏ The corporation opens an additional office in San Francisco with 135 employees and decides to have a total of 24 vice presidents. If the vice presidents are reapportioned using the Hamilton method, will the new states paradox occur? Explain.

20. Education The science division of a college consists of the three departments: mathematics, physics, and chemistry. The number of students enrolled in each department is shown in the following table. There are 19 clerical assistants to be apportioned among the departments.

Department	Math	Physics	Chemistry
Student enrollment	4325	520	1165

a. Use the Hamilton method to find each department's apportionment of clerical assistants.

b. ✏ The division opens a new computer science department with a student enrollment of 495. The division decides to have a total of 20 clerical assistants. If the clerical assistants are reapportioned using the Hamilton method, will the new states paradox occur? Explain.

21. Education The following table shows the number of fifth and sixth grade teachers in a school district and the number of students in each of those grades. The number of teachers for each of the grade levels was determined by using the Huntington-Hill apportionment method.

	Number of teachers	Number of students
Fifth grade	19	604
Sixth grade	21	698

The district has decided to hire a new teacher for either the fifth or sixth grade.

a. Use the apportionment principle to determine to which grade the new teacher should be assigned.

b. Use the Huntington-Hill apportionment principle to determine to which grade the new teacher should be assigned. How does this result compare with the result in part a?

22. Social Workers The following table shows the number of social workers and the number of cases (the case load) handled by the social workers for two offices. The number of social workers for each office was determined by using the Huntington-Hill apportionment method.

	Number of social workers	Case load
Hill Street office	20	584
Valley office	24	712

A new social worker is to be hired for one of the offices.

a. Use the apportionment principle to determine to which office the social worker should be assigned.

b. Use the Huntington-Hill apportionment principle to determine to which office the new social worker should be assigned. How does this result compare with the result in part a?

c. The results of part b indicate that the new social worker should be assigned to the Valley office. At this moment the Hill Street office has 20 social workers and the Valley office has 25 social workers. Use the Huntington-Hill apportionment principle to determine to which office the *next* new social worker should be assigned. Assume the case loads remain the same.

23. Computer Usage The table below shows the number of computers that are assigned to four different schools and the number of students in those schools. Use the Huntington-Hill apportionment principle to determine to which school a new computer should be assigned.

School	Number of computers	Number of students
Rose	26	625
Lincoln	22	532
Midway	26	620
Valley	31	754

24. ✎ **House of Representatives** Currently, the U.S. House of Representatives has 435 members who have been apportioned by the Huntington-Hill apportionment method. If the number of representatives were to be increased to 436, then, according to the 2000 census figures, Utah would be given the new representative. How must Utah's 2000 census Huntington-Hill number compare with the 2000 census Huntington-Hill numbers for the other 49 states? Explain.

The *Webster method of apportionment* is similar to the Jefferson method except that quotas are rounded up when the decimal remainder is 0.5 or greater and down when the decimal remainder is less than 0.5. This method of rounding is referred to as **rounding to the nearest integer.** For instance, using the Jefferson method, a quotient of 15.91 would be rounded to 15; using the Webster method, it would be rounded to 16. A quotient of 15.49 would be rounded to 15 in both methods.

To use the Webster method you must still experiment to find a *modified standard divisor* for which the sum of the quotas rounded to the nearest integer equals the number of items to be apportioned. Webster's method is similar to Jefferson's method; however, Webster's method is generally more difficult to apply because the modified divisor may be less than, equal to, or more than the standard divisor.

A calculator can be very helpful in testing a possible modified standard divisor md when applying the Webster method of apportionment. For instance, on a TI-83/84 calculator, first store the populations in L1. Then enter

$$\text{iPart}(\text{L1}/md + .5) \rightarrow \text{L2}$$

where md is the modified divisor. Then press the ENTER key. Now scroll through L2 to view the quotas rounded to the *nearest integer*. If the sum of these quotas equals the total number of items to be apportioned, then you have the Webster apportionment. If the sum of the quotas in L2 is less than the total number of items to be apportioned, try a smaller modified standard divisor. If the sum of the quotas in L2 is greater than the total number of items to be apportioned, try a larger modified standard divisor.

25. **Computer Usage** Use the Webster method to apportion the computers in Exercise 10, page 885. How do the apportionment results produced using the Webster method compare with the results produced using the

   a. Hamilton method?

   b. Jefferson method?

26. **Demographics** The table below shows the populations of five European countries. A committee of 20 people from these countries is to be formed using the Webster method of apportionment.

Country	Population
France	60,400,000
Germany	82,400,000
Italy	58,000,000
Spain	40,000,000
Belgium	10,300,000
Total	251,100,000

Source: World Almanac and Book of Facts, 2005, pages 845–849

   a. Explain why 12,600,000 *cannot* be used as a modified standard divisor.

   b. Explain why 12,700,000 *can* be used as a modified standard divisor.

   c. Use the Webster apportionment method to determine the apportionment of the 20 committee members.

27. Which of the following apportionment methods can violate the quota rule?

   ■ Hamilton method

   ■ Jefferson method

   ■ Webster method

   ■ Huntington-Hill method

28. According to Michael Balinski and H. Peyton Young, which of the apportionment methods most closely satisfies the goal of one person, one vote?

29. What method is presently used to apportion the members of the U.S. House of Representatives?

Extensions

CRITICAL THINKING

30. According to the 2000 census, what is the population of your state? How many representatives does your state have in the U.S. House of Representatives? Is your state underrepresented or overrepresented in the House of Representatives? Explain. (*Hint:* The result of Exercise 9a on page 885 shows that the ratio of representatives to citizens is about $\frac{1}{646,952}$.) How does your state's current number of representatives compare with the number of representatives it had after the 1990 census?

31. Create an apportionment problem in which the Hamilton, Jefferson, and Webster methods produce the same apportionment.

EXPLORATIONS

32. John Quincy Adams, the sixth president of the United States, proposed an apportionment method. Research this method, which is known as the Adams method of apportionment. Describe how this method works. Also indicate whether it satisfies the quota rule and whether it is susceptible to any paradoxes.

33. In the Huntington-Hill method of apportionment, each state is first given one representative and then additional representatives are assigned, one at a time, to the state currently having the highest Huntington-Hill number. This way of implementing the Huntington-Hill apportionment method is time consuming. Another process for implementing the Huntington-Hill apportionment method consists of using a modified divisor and a special rounding procedure that involves the *geometric mean* of two consecutive integers. Research this process for implementing the Huntington-Hill apportionment method. Apply this process to apportion 22 new security vehicles to each of the following schools, based on their student populations.

School	Number of students	Number of security vehicles
Del Mar	5230	?
Wheatly	12,375	?
West	8568	?
Mountain View	14,245	?

34. It can be shown that the results of the rounding procedure used in the Huntington-Hill method described in Exercise 33 differ only slightly from the results of the rounding procedure used in the Webster apportionment method. Thus both methods often produce the same apportionment. Verify that for Exercise 33, the Webster method produces the same apportionment as the Huntington-Hill method.

35. The Huntington-Hill number is derived by using the apportionment principle. Let P_A = population of state A, a = number of representatives from state A, P_B = population of state B, and b = number of representatives from state B. Complete the following to derive the Huntington-Hill number.

   a. Write the fraction that gives the average constituency of state A when it receives a new representative.

   b. Write the fraction that gives the average constituency of state B without a new representative.

   c. Express the relative unfairness of apportionment by giving state A the new representative in terms of the fractions from parts a and b.

   d. Express the relative unfairness of apportionment by giving state B the new representative.

   e. According to the apportionment principle, state A should receive the next representative instead of state B if the relative unfairness of giving the new representative to state A is *less than* the relative unfairness of giving the new representative to state B. Express this inequality in terms of the expressions in parts c and d.

   f. Simplify the inequality and you will have the Huntington-Hill number.

Introduction to Voting

Plurality Method of Voting

One of the most revered privileges of those of us who live in a democracy is the right to vote for our representatives. Sometimes, however, we are puzzled by the fact that the best candidate did not get elected. Unfortunately, because of the way our *plurality* voting system works, it is possible to elect someone or pass a proposition that has less than *majority support*. As we proceed through this section, we will look at the problems with plurality voting and alternatives to this system. We start with a definition.

> **The Plurality Method of Voting**
>
> Each voter votes for one candidate, and the candidate with the most votes wins. The winning candidate does not have to have a majority of the votes.

EXAMPLE 1 ■ Determine the Winner Using Plurality Voting

Fifty people were asked to rank their preferences of five varieties of chocolate candy, using 1 for their favorite and 5 for their least favorite. This type of ranking of choices is called a **preference schedule**. The results are shown in the table below.

	Rankings					
Caramel center	5	4	4	4	2	4
Vanilla center	1	5	5	5	5	5
Almond center	2	3	2	1	3	3
Toffee center	4	1	1	3	4	2
Solid chocolate	3	2	3	2	1	1
Number of voters:	17	11	9	8	3	2

According to the table (see the column in blue), 3 voters ranked solid chocolate first, caramel centers second, almond centers third, toffee centers fourth, and vanilla centers fifth. According to this table, which variety of candy would win the taste test using the plurality voting system?

Solution

To answer the question, we will make a table showing the number of first-place votes for each candy.

	First-place votes
Caramel center	0
Vanilla center	17
Almond center	8
Toffee center	11 + 9 = 20
Solid chocolate	3 + 2 = 5

Because toffee centers received 20 first-place votes, this type of candy wins the plurality taste test.

CHECK YOUR PROGRESS 1 According to the table in Example 1, which variety of candy would win second place using the plurality voting system?

Solution *See page S51.*

Example 1 can be used to show the difference between plurality and majority. There were 20 first-place votes for toffee-centered chocolate, so it wins the taste test. However, toffee-centered chocolate was the first choice of only 40% $\left(\frac{20}{50} = 40\%\right)$ of the people voting. Thus less than half of the people voted for toffee-centered chocolate as number one, so it did not receive a majority vote.

▼ **point of interest**

Another anomaly in the presidential election of 1824 was that William Crawford actually had fewer popular votes than Henry Clay but more electoral votes. By the Twelfth Amendment, the candidates with the top three *electoral* votes get forwarded to the House of Representatives for consideration. Thus Adams, Jackson, and Crawford were the candidates forwarded to the House for consideration.

Math Matters   Gubernatorial and Presidential Elections

In 1998, in a three-party race, plurality voting resulted in the election of former wrestler Jesse Ventura as governor of Minnesota, despite the fact that over 60% of the state's voters did not vote for him. In fact, he won the governor's race with only 37% of the voters choosing him. Ventura won not because the majority of voters chose him, but because of the plurality voting method.

There are many situations that can be cited to show that plurality voting can lead to unusual results. When plurality voting is mixed with other voting methods, even the plurality winner may not win. One way this can happen is in U.S. presidential elections. The president of the United States is elected not directly by popular vote but by the Electoral College.

In the 1824 presidential election, the approximate percent of the *popular* vote received by each candidate was: John Quincy Adams, 31%; Andrew Jackson, 43%; William Crawford, 13%; and Henry Clay, 13%. The vote in the Electoral College was John Quincy Adams, 84; Andrew Jackson, 99; William Crawford, 41; and Henry Clay, 37. Because none of the candidates had received 121 electoral votes (the number needed to win in 1824), by the Twelfth Amendment to the U.S. Constitution, the House of Representatives decided the election. The House elected John Quincy Adams, thereby electing a president who had less than one-third of the popular vote.

There have been three other instances when the candidate with the most popular vote in a presidential election was not elected president: 1876, Hayes versus Tilden; 1888, Harrison versus Cleveland; and 2000, Bush versus Gore.

Borda Count Method of Voting

historical note

The issue of whether plurality voting methods are fair has been around for over 200 years. Jean C. Borda (1733–1799) was a member of the French Academy of Sciences when he first started thinking about the way in which people were elected to the Academy. He was concerned that the plurality method of voting might not result in the best candidate being elected. The Borda Count method was born out of these concerns. It was the first attempt to mathematically quantify voting systems. ∎

The problem with plurality voting is that alternative choices are not considered. For instance, the result of the Minnesota governor's contest might have been quite different if voters had been asked, "Choose the candidate you prefer, but if that candidate does not receive a *majority* of the votes, which candidate would be your second choice?"

To see why this might be a reasonable alternative to plurality voting, consider the following situation. Thirty-six senators are considering an educational funding measure. Because the senate leadership wants an educational funding measure to pass, the leadership first determined that the senators preferred measure A for $50 million over measure B for $30 million. However, because of an unexpected dip in state revenues, measure A was removed from consideration and a new measure C, for $15 million, was proposed. The senate leadership determined that senators favored measure B over measure C. In summary, we have

A majority of senators favor measure A over measure B.

A majority of senators favor measure B over measure C.

From these results, it seems reasonable to think that a majority of senators would prefer Measure A over Measure C. However, when the senators were asked about their preferences between the two measures, Measure C was preferred over Measure A. To understand how this could happen, consider the preference schedule for the senators shown in the following table.

	Rankings		
Measure A: $50 million	1	2	3
Measure B: $30 million	2	3	1
Measure C: $15 million	3	1	2
Number of senators:	15	12	9

Notice that 15 senators prefer Measure A over Measure C, but $12 + 9 = 21$ senators, a majority of the 36 senators, prefer Measure C over Measure A. This means that if all three measures were on the ballot, A would come in first, B would come in second, and C would come in third. However, if just A and C were on the ballot, C would win over A. This paradoxical result was first discussed by Jean C. Borda in 1770.

In an attempt to remove such paradoxical results from voting, Borda proposed that voters rank their choices by giving each choice a certain number of points.

✔ **TAKE NOTE**

Paradoxes occur in voting only when there are three or more candidates or issues on a ballot. If there are only two candidates in a race, then the candidate receiving the majority of the votes cast is the winner. In a two-candidate race, the majority and the plurality are the same.

The Borda Count Method of Voting

If there are n candidates or issues in an election, each voter ranks the candidates or issues by giving n points to the voter's first choice, $n - 1$ points to the voter's second choice, and so on, with the voter's least favorite choice receiving 1 point. The candidate or issue that receives the most total points is the winner.

Applying the Borda Count method to the education measures, a measure receiving a first-place vote receives 3 points. (There are three different measures.) Each measure receiving a second-place vote receives 2 points, and each measure receiving a third-place vote receives 1 point. This is summarized in the table below.

▼ **point of interest**

One way to see the difference between a plurality voting system (sometimes called a "winner-take-all" method) and the Borda Count method is to consider grades earned in school. Suppose a student is going to be selected for a scholarship based on grades. If one student has 10 A's and 20 F's and another student has five A's and 25 B's, it would seem that the second student should receive the scholarship. However, if the scholarship is awarded by the plurality of A's, the first student will get the scholarship. The Borda Count method is closely related to the method used to calculate grade-point average (GPA).

Points per vote

Measure A: 15 first-place votes:	$15 \cdot 3 = 45$
12 second-place votes:	$12 \cdot 2 = 24$
9 third-place votes:	$9 \cdot 1 = 9$
Total:	78
Measure B: 9 first-place votes:	$9 \cdot 3 = 27$
15 second-place votes:	$15 \cdot 2 = 30$
12 third-place votes:	$12 \cdot 1 = 12$
Total:	69
Measure C: 12 first-place votes:	$12 \cdot 3 = 36$
9 second-place votes:	$9 \cdot 2 = 18$
15 third-place votes:	$15 \cdot 1 = 15$
Total:	69

Using the Borda Count method, measure A is the clear winner. Notice also that measure A is the plurality winner, although it does not always happen that the Borda Count method and the plurality method yield the same winner.

EXAMPLE 2 ■ Use the Borda Count Method

The members of a club are going to elect a president from four nominees using the Borda Count method. If the 100 members of the club mark their ballots as shown in the table below, who will be elected president?

	Rankings					
Avalon	2	2	2	2	3	2
Branson	1	4	4	4	2	1
Columbus	3	3	1	3	1	3
Dunkirk	4	1	3	1	4	4
Number of voters:	30	24	18	12	10	6

Solution

Using the Borda Count method, each first-place vote receives 4 points, each second-place vote receives 3 points, each third-place vote receives 2 points, and each last-place vote receives 1 point. The summary for each candidate is shown below.

Avalon:	0 first-place votes	$0 \cdot 4 =$	0
	90 second-place votes	$90 \cdot 3 =$	270
	10 third-place votes	$10 \cdot 2 =$	20
	0 fourth-place votes	$0 \cdot 1 =$	0
		Total	290

Branson:	36 first-place votes	$36 \cdot 4 =$	144
	10 second-place votes	$10 \cdot 3 =$	30
	0 third-place votes	$0 \cdot 2 =$	0
	54 fourth-place votes	$54 \cdot 1 =$	54
		Total	228

Columbus:	28 first-place votes	$28 \cdot 4 =$	112
	0 second-place votes	$0 \cdot 3 =$	0
	72 third-place votes	$72 \cdot 2 =$	144
	0 fourth-place votes	$0 \cdot 1 =$	0
		Total	256

Dunkirk:	36 first-place votes	$36 \cdot 4 =$	144
	0 second-place votes	$0 \cdot 3 =$	0
	18 third-place votes	$18 \cdot 2 =$	36
	46 fourth-place votes	$46 \cdot 1 =$	46
		Total	226

✔ **TAKE NOTE**

Notice in Example 2 that Avalon was the winner even though that candidate did not receive any first-place votes. The Borda Count method was devised to allow voters to say, "If my first choice does not win, then consider my second choice."

Avalon has the largest total score. By the Borda Count method, Avalon is elected president.

CHECK YOUR PROGRESS 2   The preference schedule given earlier for the 50 people who were asked to rank their preferences of five varieties of chocolate candy is shown again below.

	Rankings					
Caramel center	5	4	4	4	2	4
Vanilla center	1	5	5	5	5	5
Almond center	2	3	2	1	3	3
Toffee center	4	1	1	3	4	2
Solid chocolate	3	2	3	2	1	1
Number of voters:	17	11	9	8	3	2

Determine the taste test favorite using the Borda Count method.

Solution   *See page S51.*

Plurality with Elimination

A variation of the plurality method of voting is called *plurality with elimination*. Like the Borda Count method, the method of plurality with elimination considers a voter's alternate choices.

Suppose that 30 members of a regional planning board must decide where to build a new airport. The airport consultants to the regional board have recommended four different sites. The preference schedule for the board members is shown in the table below.

✔ **TAKE NOTE**

When the second round of voting occurs, the two ballots that listed Bremerton as the first choice must be adjusted. The second choice on those ballots becomes the first, the third choice becomes the second, and the fourth choice becomes the third. The order of preference does not change. Similar adjustments must be made to the 12 ballots that listed Bremerton as the second choice. Because that choice is no longer available, Apple Valley becomes the second choice and Del Mar becomes the third choice. This also applies to the 11 ballots that listed Bremerton as the third choice. The fourth choice of those ballots, Del Mar, becomes the third choice.

	Rankings			
Apple Valley	3	1	2	3
Bremerton	2	3	3	1
Cochella	1	2	4	2
Del Mar	4	4	1	4
Number of ballots:	12	11	5	2

Using the plurality with elimination method, the board members first eliminate the site with the fewest number of first-place votes. If two or more of these alternatives have the same number of first-place votes, all are eliminated unless that would eliminate all alternatives. In that case, a different method of voting must be used. From the table above, Bremerton is eliminated because it received only two first-place votes. Now a vote is retaken using the following important assumption: *Voters do not change their preferences from round to round.* This means that after Bremerton is deleted, the twelve people in the first column would adjust their preference so that Apple Valley becomes their second choice, Cochella remains their first choice,

▼ **point of interest**

Plurality with elimination is used to choose the city to host the Olympic games.

A variation of this method is also used to select the Academy Award nominees.

and Del Mar becomes their third choice. For the eleven voters in the second column, Apple Valley remains their first choice, Cochella remains their second choice, and Del Mar becomes their third choice. Similar adjustments are made by the remaining voters. The new preference schedule is

	Rankings			
Apple Valley	2	1	2	2
Cochella	1	2	3	1
Del Mar	3	3	1	3
Number of ballots:	12	11	5	2

The board members now repeat the process and eliminate the site with the fewest first-place votes. In this case it is Del Mar. The new adjusted preference schedule is

	Rankings			
Apple Valley	2	1	1	2
Cochella	1	2	2	1
Number of ballots:	12	11	5	2

From this table, Apple Valley has 16 first-place votes and Cochella has 14 first-place votes. Therefore, Apple Valley is the selected site for the new airport.

EXAMPLE 3 ■ Use the Plurality with Elimination Voting Method

A university wants to add a new sport to its existing program. To help ensure that the new sport will have student support, the students of the university are asked to rank the four sports under consideration. The results are shown in the table below.

	Rankings					
Lacrosse	3	2	3	1	1	2
Squash	2	1	4	2	3	1
Rowing	4	3	2	4	4	4
Golf	1	4	1	3	2	3
Number of ballots:	326	297	287	250	214	197

Use the plurality with elimination method to determine which of these sports should be added to the university's program.

TAKE NOTE

Remember to shift the preferences at each stage of the elimination method. The 297 students who chose rowing as their third choice and golf as their fourth choice now have golf as their third choice. Check each preference schedule and update it as necessary.

Solution

Because rowing received no first-place votes, it is eliminated from consideration. The new preference schedule is shown below.

	Rankings					
Lacrosse	3	2	2	1	1	2
Squash	2	1	3	2	3	1
Golf	1	3	1	3	2	3
Number of ballots:	326	297	287	250	214	197

From this table, lacrosse has 464 first-place votes, squash has 494 first-place votes, and golf has 613 first-place votes. Because lacrosse has the fewest first-place votes, it is eliminated. The new preference schedule is shown below.

	Rankings					
Squash	2	1	2	1	2	1
Golf	1	2	1	2	1	2
Number of ballots:	326	297	287	250	214	197

From this table, squash received 744 first-place votes and golf received 827 first-place votes. Therefore, golf is added to the sports program.

CHECK YOUR PROGRESS 3   A service club is going to sponsor a dinner to raise money for a charity. The club has decided to serve Italian, Mexican, Thai, Chinese, or Indian food. The members of the club were surveyed to determine their preferences. The results are shown in the table below.

	Rankings				
Italian	2	5	1	4	3
Mexican	1	4	5	2	1
Thai	3	1	4	5	2
Chinese	4	2	3	1	4
Indian	5	3	2	3	5
Number of ballots:	33	30	25	20	18

Use the plurality with elimination method to determine the food preference of the club members.

Solution   *See page S52.*

Pairwise Comparison Voting Method

The *pairwise comparison* method of voting is sometimes referred to as the "head-to-head" method. In this method, each candidate is compared one-on-one with each of the other candidates. A candidate receives 1 point for a win, 0.5 points for a tie, and 0 points for a loss. The candidate with the greatest number of points wins the election.

A voting method that elects the candidate who wins all head-to-head matchups is said to satisfy the Condorcet criterion.

Condorcet criterion

A candidate who wins all possible head-to-head matchups should win an election when all candidates appear on the ballot.

This is one of the *fairness criteria* that a voting method should exhibit. We will discuss other fairness criteria later in this section.

EXAMPLE 4 ■ Use the Pairwise Comparison Voting Method

There are four proposals for the name of a new football stadium at a college: Panther Stadium, after the team mascot; Sanchez Stadium, after a large university contributor; Mosher Stadium, after a famous alumnus known for humanitarian work; and Fritz Stadium, after the college's most winning football coach. The preference schedule cast by alumni and students is shown below.

	Rankings				
Panther Stadium	2	3	1	2	4
Sanchez Stadium	1	4	2	4	3
Mosher Stadium	3	1	4	3	2
Fritz Stadium	4	2	3	1	1
Number of ballots:	752	678	599	512	487

Use the pairwise comparison voting method to determine the name of the stadium.

Solution

We will create a table to keep track of each of the head-to-head comparisons. Before we begin, note that a matchup between, say, Panther and Sanchez is the same as the matchup between Sanchez and Panther. Therefore, we will shade the duplicate cells and the cells between the same candidates. This is shown below.

versus	Panther	Sanchez	Mosher	Fritz
Panther				
Sanchez				
Mosher				
Fritz				

To complete the table, we will place the name of the winner in the cell of the head-to-head match. For instance, for the Panther–Sanchez matchup,

✓ Panther was favored over Sanchez on $678 + 599 + 512 = 1789$ ballots.
   Sanchez was favored over Panther on $752 + 487 = 1239$ ballots.

The winner of this matchup is Panther, so that name is placed in the Panther versus Sanchez cell. Do this for each of the matchups.

✓ Panther was favored over Mosher on $752 + 599 + 512 = 1863$ ballots.
   Mosher was favored over Panther on $678 + 487 = 1165$ ballots.

   Panther was favored over Fritz on $752 + 599 = 1351$ ballots.
✓ Fritz was favored over Panther on $678 + 512 + 487 = 1677$ ballots.

   Sanchez was favored over Mosher on $752 + 599 = 1351$ ballots.
✓ Mosher was favored over Sanchez on $678 + 512 + 487 = 1677$ ballots.

   Sanchez was favored over Fritz on $752 + 599 = 1351$ ballots.
✓ Fritz was favored over Sanchez on $678 + 512 + 487 = 1677$ ballots.

   Mosher was favored over Fritz on $752 + 678 = 1430$ ballots.
✓ Fritz was favored over Mosher on $599 + 512 + 487 = 1598$ ballots.

versus	Panther	Sanchez	Mosher	Fritz
Panther		Panther	Panther	Fritz
Sanchez			Mosher	Fritz
Mosher				Fritz
Fritz				

From the above table, Fritz has three wins, Panther has two wins, and Mosher has one win. Using pairwise comparison, Fritz Stadium is the winning name.

CHECK YOUR PROGRESS 4   One hundred restaurant critics were asked to rank their favorite restaurants from a list of four. The preference schedule for the critics is shown in the table below.

	Rankings				
Sanborn's Fine Dining	3	1	4	3	1
The Apple Inn	4	3	3	2	4
May's Steak House	2	2	1	1	3
Tory's Seafood	1	4	2	4	2
Number of ballots:	31	25	18	15	11

Use the pairwise voting method to determine the critics' favorite restaurant.

Solution   See page S52.

Fairness of Voting Methods and Arrow's Theorem

Kenneth J. Arrow

Now that we have examined various voting options, we will stop to ask which of these options is the *fairest*. To answer that question, we must first determine what we mean by fair.

In 1948, Kenneth J. Arrow was trying to develop material for his Ph.D. dissertation. As he studied, it occurred to him that he might be able to apply the principles of order relations to problems in social choice or voting. (An example of an order relation for real numbers is "less than.") His investigation led him to outline various criteria for a fair voting system. A paraphrasing of four fairness criteria is given below.

Fairness Criteria

1. *Majority criterion:* The candidate who receives a majority of the first-place votes is the winner.

2. *Monotonicity criterion:* If candidate *A* wins an election, then candidate *A* will also win the election if the only change in the voters' preferences is that supporters of a different candidate change their votes to support candidate *A*.

3. *Condorcet criterion:* A candidate who wins all possible head-to-head matchups should win an election when all candidates appear on the ballot.

4. *Independence of irrelevant alternatives:* If a candidate wins an election, the winner should remain the winner in any recount in which losing candidates withdraw from the race.

There are other criteria, such as the *dictator criterion,* which we will discuss in the next section. However, what Kenneth Arrow was able to prove is that no matter what kind of voting system we devise, it is impossible for it to satisfy the fairness criteria.

Arrow's Impossibility Theorem

There is no voting method involving three or more choices that satisfies the fairness criteria.

By Arrow's Impossibility Theorem, none of the voting methods we have discussed are fair. Not only that, but we *cannot* construct a fair voting system for three or more candidates. We will now give some examples of each of the methods we have discussed and show which of the fairness criteria are not satisfied.

EXAMPLE 5 ■ Show That the Borda Count Method Violates the Majority Criterion

Suppose the preference schedule for three candidates, Alpha, Beta, and Gamma, is given by the table below.

	Rankings		
Alpha	1	3	3
Beta	2	1	2
Gamma	3	2	1
Number of ballots:	55	50	3

Show that using the Borda Count method violates the majority criterion.

Solution

The calculations for Borda's method are shown below.

Alpha

55 first-place votes	$55 \cdot 3 = 165$
0 second-place votes	$0 \cdot 2 = 0$
53 third-place votes	$53 \cdot 1 = 53$
	Total 218

Beta

50 first-place votes	$50 \cdot 3 = 150$
58 second-place votes	$58 \cdot 2 = 116$
0 third-place votes	$0 \cdot 1 = 0$
	Total 266

Gamma

3 first-place votes	$3 \cdot 3 = 9$
50 second-place votes	$50 \cdot 2 = 100$
55 third-place votes	$55 \cdot 1 = 55$
	Total 164

From these calculations, Beta should win the election. However, Alpha has the majority (more than 50%) of the first-place votes. This result violates the majority criterion.

CHECK YOUR PROGRESS 5   Using the table in Example 5, show that the Borda Count method violates the Condorcet criterion.

Solution   *See page S52.*

QUESTION   *Does the pairwise comparison voting method satisfy the Condorcet criterion?*

EXAMPLE 6 ■ Show that Plurality with Elimination Violates the Monotonicity Criterion

Suppose the preference schedule for three candidates, Alpha, Beta, and Gamma, is given by the table below.

	Rankings			
Alpha	2	3	1	1
Beta	3	1	2	3
Gamma	1	2	3	2
Number of ballots:	25	20	16	10

ANSWER   *Yes. The pairwise comparison voting method elects the person who wins all head-to-head matchups.*

a. Show that, using plurality with elimination voting, Gamma wins the election.
b. Suppose that the 10 people who voted for Alpha first and Gamma second changed their votes such that they all voted for Alpha second and Gamma first. Show that, using plurality with elimination voting, Beta will now be elected.
c. Explain why this result violates the montonicity criterion.

Solution

a. Beta received the fewest first-place votes, so Beta is eliminated. The new preference schedule is

	Rankings			
Alpha	2	2	1	1
Gamma	1	1	2	2
Number of ballots:	25	20	16	10

From this schedule, Gamma has 45 first-place votes and Alpha has 26 first-place votes, so Gamma is the winner.

b. If the 10 people who voted for Alpha first and Gamma second changed their votes such that they all voted for Alpha second and Gamma first, the preference schedule would be

	Rankings			
Alpha	2	3	1	2
Beta	3	1	2	3
Gamma	1	2	3	1
Number of ballots:	25	20	16	10

From this schedule, Alpha has the fewest first-place votes and is eliminated. The new preference schedule is

	Rankings			
Beta	2	1	1	2
Gamma	1	2	2	1
Number of ballots:	25	20	16	10

From this schedule, Gamma has 35 first-place votes and Beta has 36 first-place votes, so Beta is the winner.

c. This result violates the monotonicity criterion because Gamma, who won the first election, loses the second election even though Gamma received a larger number of first-place votes.

CHECK YOUR PROGRESS 6   The table below shows the preferences for three new car colors.

	Rankings		
Radiant silver	1	3	3
Electric red	2	2	1
Lightning blue	3	1	2
Number of votes:	30	27	2

Show that the Borda Count method violates the independence of irrelevant alternatives criterion.

Solution   *See page S52.*

Excursion

Variations of the Borda Count Method

Sixty people were asked to select their preferences among plain ice tea, lemon-flavored ice tea, and raspberry-flavored ice tea. The preference schedule is shown in the table below.

	Rankings		
Plain ice tea	1	3	3
Lemon ice tea	2	2	1
Raspberry ice tea	3	1	2
Number of ballots:	25	20	15

1. Using the Borda method of voting, which flavor of ice tea is preferred by this group? Which is second? Which is third?

2. Instead of using the normal Borda method, suppose the Borda method used in Exercise 1 of this Excursion assigned 1 point for first, 0 points for second, and −1 point for third place. Does this alter the preferences you found in Exercise 1?

3. Suppose the Borda method used in Exercise 1 of this Excursion assigned 10 points for first, 5 points for second, and 0 points for third place. Does this alter the preferences you found in Exercise 1?

4. Suppose the Borda method used in Exercise 1 of this Excursion assigned 20 points for first, 5 points for second, and 0 points for third place. Does this alter the preferences you found in Exercise 1?

(continued)

5. Suppose the Borda method used in Exercise 1 of this Excursion assigned 25 points for first, 5 points for second, and 0 points for third place. Does this alter the preferences you found in Exercise 1?

6. Can the assignment of points for first, second, and third place change the preference order when the Borda method of voting is used?

7. Suppose the assignment of points for first, second, and third place for the Borda method of voting are consecutive integers. Can the value of the starting integer change the outcome of the preferences?

Exercise Set 13.2

1. What is the difference between a majority and a plurality? Is it possible to have one without the other?

2. Explain why the plurality voting system may not be the best system to use in some situations.

3. Explain how the Borda Count method of voting works.

4. Explain how the plurality with elimination voting method works.

5. Explain how the pairwise comparison voting method works.

6. What does the Condorcet criterion say?

7. Is there a "best" voting method? Is one method more fair than the others?

8. Explain why, if only two candidates are running, the plurality and Borda Count methods will determine the same winner.

9. Presidential Election The table below shows the popular vote and the Electoral College vote for the major candidates in the 2000 presidential election.

Candidate	Popular vote	Electoral College vote
George Bush	50,456,002	271
Al Gore	50,999,897	266
Ralph Nader	2,882,955	0

Source: *Encyclopaedia Britannica* Online

a. Which candidate received the plurality of the popular vote?

b. Did any candidate receive a majority of the popular vote?

c. Who won the election?

10. Breakfast Cereal Sixteen people were asked to rank three breakfast cereals in order of preference. Their responses are given below.

Corn Flakes	3	1	1	2	3	3	2	2	1	3	1	3	1	2	1	2
Raisin Bran	1	3	2	3	1	2	1	1	2	1	2	2	3	1	3	3
Mini Wheats	2	2	3	1	2	1	3	3	3	2	3	1	2	3	2	1

13.2 • Introduction to Voting   905

If the plurality method of voting is used, which cereal is the group's first preference?

11. **Cartoon Characters** A kindergarten class was surveyed to determine the childrens' favorite cartoon characters among Mickey Mouse, Bugs Bunny, and Scooby Doo. The students ranked the characters in order of preference; the results are shown in the preference schedule below.

	Rankings					
Mickey Mouse	1	1	2	2	3	3
Bugs Bunny	2	3	1	3	1	2
Scooby Doo	3	2	3	1	2	1
Number of students:	6	4	6	5	6	8

a. How many students are in the class?

b. How many votes are required for a majority?

c. Using plurality voting, which character is the childrens' favorite?

12. **Catering** A 15-person committee is having lunch catered for a meeting. Three caterers, each specializing in a different cuisine, are available. In order to choose a caterer for the group, each member is asked to rank the cuisine options in order of preference. The results are given in the preference schedule below.

	Rankings				
Italian	1	1	2	3	3
Mexican	2	3	1	1	2
Japanese	3	2	3	2	1
Number of votes:	2	4	1	5	3

Using plurality voting, which caterer should be chosen?

13. **Movies** Fifty consumers were surveyed about their movie watching habits. They were asked to rank the likelihood that they would participate in each listed activity. The results are summarized in the table below.

	Rankings				
Go to a theater	2	3	1	2	1
Rent a video or DVD	3	1	3	1	2
Watch pay-per-view	1	2	2	3	3
Number of votes:	8	13	15	7	7

Using the Borda Count method of voting, which activity is the most popular choice among this group of consumers?

14. **Breakfast Cereal** Use the Borda Count method of voting to determine the preferred breakfast cereal in Exercise 10.

15. **Cartoons** Use the Borda Count method of voting to determine the childrens' favorite cartoon character in Exercise 11.

16. **Catering** Use the Borda Count method of voting to determine which caterer the committee should hire in Exercise 12.

17. **Class Election** A senior high school class held an election for class president. Instead of just voting for one candidate, the students were asked to rank all four candidates in order of preference. The results are shown below.

	Rankings					
Raymond Lee	2	3	1	3	4	2
Suzanne Brewer	4	1	3	4	1	3
Elaine Garcia	1	2	2	2	3	4
Michael Turley	3	4	4	1	2	1
Number of votes:	36	53	41	27	31	45

Using the Borda Count method, which student should be class president?

18. **Cell Phone Usage** A journalist reviewing various cellular phone services surveyed 200 customers and asked each one to rank four service providers in order of preference. The group's results are shown below.

	Rankings				
Verizon	3	4	2	3	4
Sprint PCS	1	1	4	4	3
Cingular	2	2	1	2	1
Nextel	4	3	3	1	2
Number of votes:	18	38	42	63	39

Using the Borda Count method, which provider is the favorite of these customers?

19. **Baseball** A Little League baseball team must choose the colors for its uniforms. The coach offered four different choices, and the players ranked them in order of preference, as shown in the table below.

	Rankings			
Red and white	2	3	3	2
Green and yellow	4	1	4	1
Red and blue	3	4	2	4
Blue and white	1	2	1	3
Number of votes:	4	2	5	4

Using the plurality with elimination method, what color should the uniforms be?

20. **Radio Station** A number of college students were asked to rank four radio stations in order of preference. The responses are given in the table below.

	Rankings				
WNNX	3	1	1	2	4
WKLS	1	3	4	1	2
WWVV	4	2	2	3	1
WSTR	2	4	3	4	3
Number of votes:	57	72	38	61	15

Use plurality with elimination to determine the students' favorite radio station among the four.

21. **Class Election** Use plurality with elimination to choose the class president in Exercise 17.

22. **Cell Phone Usage** Use plurality with elimination to determine the preferred cellular phone service in Exercise 18.

23. **Campus Club** A campus club has money left over in its budget and must spend it before the school year ends. The members arrived at five different possibilities, and each member ranked them in order of preference. The results are shown in the table below.

	Rankings				
Establish a scholarship	1	2	3	3	4
Pay for several members to travel to a convention	2	1	2	1	5
Buy new computers for the club	3	3	1	4	1
Throw an end-of-year party	4	5	5	2	2
Donate to charity	5	4	4	5	3
Number of votes:	8	5	12	9	7

a. Using the plurality voting system, how should the club spend the money?

b. Use the plurality with elimination method to determine how the money should be spent.

c. Using the Borda Count method of voting, how should the money be spent?

d. In your opinion, which of the previous three methods seems most appropriate in this situation? Why?

24. **Recreation** A company is planning its annual summer retreat and has asked its employees to rank five different choices of recreation in order of preference. The results are given in the table below.

	Rankings				
Picnic in a park	1	2	1	3	4
Water skiing at a lake	3	1	2	4	3
Amusement park	2	5	5	1	2
Riding horses at a ranch	5	4	3	5	1
Dinner cruise	4	3	4	2	5
Number of votes:	10	18	6	28	16

a. Using the plurality voting system, what activity should be planned for the retreat?

b. Use the plurality with elimination method to determine which activity should be chosen.

c. Using the Borda Count method of voting, which activity should be planned?

25. **Star Wars Movies** Fans of the *Star Wars* movies have been debating, on a website, regarding which of the films is the best. To see what the overall opinion is, visitors to the website can rank the four films in order of preference. The results are shown in the preference schedule below.

	Rankings			
Star Wars	1	2	1	3
The Empire Strikes Back	4	4	2	1
Return of the Jedi	2	1	3	2
The Phantom Menace	3	3	4	4
Number of votes:	429	1,137	384	582

Using pairwise comparison, which film is the favorite of the visitors to the website who voted?

26. **Family Reunion** The Nelson family is trying to decide where to hold a family reunion. They have asked all their family members to rank four choices in order of preference. The results are shown in the preference schedule below.

	Rankings				
Grand Canyon	3	1	2	3	1
Yosemite	1	2	3	4	4
Bryce Canyon	4	4	1	2	2
Yellowstone	2	3	4	1	3
Number of votes:	7	3	12	8	13

Use the pairwise comparison method to determine the best choice for the reunion.

27. **School Mascot** A new college needs to pick a mascot for its football team. The students were asked to rank four choices in order of preference; the results are tallied below.

	Rankings				
Bulldog	3	4	4	1	3
Panther	2	1	2	4	2
Hornet	4	2	1	2	4
Bobcat	1	3	3	3	1
Number of votes:	638	924	525	390	673

Using the pairwise comparison method of voting, which mascot should be chosen?

28. **Election** Five candidates are running for president of a charity organization. Interested persons were asked to rank the candidates in order of preference. The results are given below.

	Rankings				
P. Gibson	5	1	2	1	2
E. Yung	2	4	5	5	3
R. Allenbaugh	3	2	1	3	5
T. Meckley	4	3	4	4	1
G. DeWitte	1	5	3	2	4
Number of votes:	16	9	14	9	4

Use the pairwise comparison method to determine the president of the organization.

29. Use the pairwise comparison method to choose the colors for the Little League uniforms in Exercise 19.

30. Use the pairwise comparison method to determine the favorite radio station in Exercise 20.

31. Does the winner in Exercise 11c satisfy the Condorcet criterion?

32. Does the winner in Exercise 12 satisfy the Condorcet criterion?

33. Does the winner in Exercise 23c satisfy the Condorcet criterion?

34. Does the winner in Exercise 24c satisfy the Condorcet criterion?

35. Does the winner in Exercise 17 satisfy the majority criterion?

36. Does the winner in Exercise 20 satisfy the majority criterion?

37. Election Three candidates are running for mayor. A vote was taken in which the candidates were ranked in order of preference. The results are shown in the preference schedule below.

	Rankings		
John Lorenz	1	3	3
Marcia Beasley	3	1	2
Stephen Hyde	2	2	1
Number of votes:	2691	2416	237

a. Use the Borda Count method to determine the winner of the election.

b. Verify that the majority criterion has been violated.

c. Identify a candidate who wins all head-to-head comparisons.

d. Explain why the Condorcet criterion has been violated.

e. If Marcia Beasley drops out of the race for mayor (and voter preferences remain the same), determine the winner of the election again, using the Borda Count method.

f. Explain why the independence of irrelevant alternatives criterion has been violated.

38. Film Competition Three films have been selected as finalists in a national student film competition. Seventeen judges have viewed each of the films and ranked them in order of preference. The results are given in the preference schedule below.

	Rankings			
Film A	1	3	2	1
Film B	2	1	3	3
Film C	3	2	1	2
Number of votes:	4	6	5	2

a. Using the plurality with elimination method, which film should win the competition?

b. Suppose the first vote is declared invalid and a revote is taken. All of the judges' preferences remain the same except for the votes represented by the last column of the table. The judges who cast these votes both decide to switch their first place vote to Film C, so their preference now is C first, then A, and then B. Which film now wins using the plurality with elimination method?

c. Has the monotonicity criterion been violated?

Extensions

CRITICAL THINKING

39. Election A campus club needs to elect four officers: a president, a vice president, a secretary, and a treasurer. The club has five volunteers. Rather than vote individually for each position, the club members will rank the candidates in order of preference. The votes will then be tallied using the Borda Count method. The candidate receiving the highest number of points will be president, the candidate receiving the next highest number of points is vice president, the candidate receiving the next highest number of points is secretary, and the candidate receiving the next highest number of points will be treasurer. For the preference schedule shown below, determine who wins each position in the club.

	Rankings				
Cynthia	4	2	5	2	3
Andrew	2	3	1	4	5
Jen	5	1	2	3	2
Hector	1	5	4	1	4
Medin	3	4	3	5	1
Number of votes:	22	10	16	6	27

40. Election Use the plurality with elimination method of voting to determine the four officers in Exercise 39. Is your result the same as the result you arrived at using the Borda Count method?

41. Scholarship Awards The members of a scholarship committee have ranked four finalists competing for a scholarship in order of preference. The results are shown in the preference schedule below.

	Rankings			
Francis Chandler	3	4	4	1
Michael Huck	1	2	3	4
David Chang	2	3	1	2
Stephanie Owen	4	1	2	3
Number of votes:	9	5	7	4

If you are one of the voting members and you want David Chang to win the scholarship, which voting method would you suggest that the committee use?

COOPERATIVE LEARNING

42. Restaurants Suppose you and three friends, David, Sara, and Cliff, are trying to decide on a pizza restaurant. You like Pizza Hut best, Round Table pizza is acceptable to you, and you definitely do not want to get pizza from Domino's. Domino's is David's favorite, and he also likes Round Table, but he won't eat pizza from Pizza Hut. Sara says she will only eat Round Table pizza. Cliff prefers Domino's, but he will also eat Round Table pizza. He doesn't like Pizza Hut.

   a. Given the preferences of the four friends, which pizza restaurant would be the best choice?

   b. If you use the plurality system of voting to determine which pizza restaurant to go to, which restaurant wins? Does this seem like the best choice for the group?

   c. If you use the pairwise comparison method of voting, which pizza restaurant wins?

   d. Does one of the four voting methods discussed in this section give the same winner as your choice in part a? Does the method match your reasoning in making your choice?

EXPLORATIONS

43. Another method of voting is to assign a "weight," or score, to each candidate rather than ranking the candidates in order. All candidates must receive a score, and two or more candidates can receive the same score from a voter. A score of 5 represents the strongest endorsement of a candidate. The scores range down to 1, which corresponds to complete disapproval of a candidate. A score of 3 represents indifference. The candidate with the most total points wins the election. The results of a sample election are given in the table.

	Rankings							
Candidate A	2	1	2	5	4	2	4	5
Candidate B	5	3	5	3	2	5	3	2
Candidate C	4	5	4	1	4	3	2	1
Candidate D	1	3	2	4	5	1	3	2
Number of votes:	26	42	19	33	24	8	24	33

   a. Find the winner of the election.

   b. If plurality were used (assuming that a person's vote would go to the candidate that he or she gave the highest score to), verify that a different winner would result.

44. *Approval voting* is a system in which voters may vote for more than one candidate. Each vote counts equally, and the candidate with the most total votes wins the election. Many feel that this is a better system for large elections than simple plurality because it considers a voter's second choices and is a stronger measure of overall voter support for each candidate. Some organizations use approval voting to elect their officers. The United Nations uses this method to elect the secretary-general.

a. Suppose a math class is going to show a film involving mathematics or mathematicians on the last day of class. The options are *Stand and Deliver, Good Will Hunting, A Beautiful Mind, Pi,* and *Contact.* The students vote using approval voting. The results are as follows.

8 students vote for all five films.

8 students vote for *Good Will Hunting, A Beautiful Mind,* and *Contact.*

8 students vote for *Stand and Deliver, Good Will Hunting,* and *Contact.*

8 students vote for *A Beautiful Mind* and *Pi.*

8 students vote for *Stand and Deliver* and *Pi.*

8 students vote for *Good Will Hunting* and *Contact.*

1 student votes for *Pi.*

Which film will be chosen for the last day of class screening?

b. Use approval voting in Exercise 42 to determine the pizza restaurant the group of friends should choose. Does your result agree with your answer to part a of Exercise 42?

SECTION 13.3 | # Weighted Voting Systems

Biased Voting Systems

A **weighted voting system** is one in which some voters have more weight on the outcome of an election. Examples of weighted voting systems are fairly common. A few examples are the stockholders of a company, the Electoral College, the United Nations Security Council, and the European Union.

MathMatters   **The Electoral College**

As mentioned in the Historical Note on the following page, the Electoral College elects the president of the United States. The number of electors representing each state is equal to the sum of the number of senators (2) and the number of members in the House of Representatives for that state. The original intent of the framers of the Constitution was to protect the smaller states. We can verify this by computing the number of people represented by each elector. In the 2004 election, each Vermont elector represented about 203,000 people; each California elector represented about

(continued)

historical note

The U.S. Constitution, Article 2, Section 1 states that the members of the Electoral College elect the president of the United States. The original article directed members of the College to vote for two people. However, it did not stipulate that one name was for president and the other name was for vice president. The article goes on to state that the person with the greatest number of votes becomes president and the one with the next highest number of votes becomes vice president. In 1800, Thomas Jefferson and Aaron Burr received exactly the same number of votes even though they were running on a Jefferson for president, Burr for vice president ticket. Thus the House of Representatives was asked to select the president. It took 36 different votes by the House before Jefferson was elected president. In 1804, the Twelfth Amendment to the Constitution was ratified to prevent a recurrence of the 1800 election problems. ∎

616,000 people. To see how this gives a state with a smaller population more *power* (a word we will discuss in more detail later in this section), note that three electoral votes from Vermont represent approximately the same size population as does one electoral vote from California. Each vote does not represent the same number of people.

Another peculiarity related to the Electoral College system is that it is very sensitive to small vote swings. For instance, in the 2000 election, if an additional 0.01% of the voters in Florida had cast their votes for Al Gore instead of George Bush, Gore would have won the presidential election.

Consider a small company with a total of 100 shares of stock and three stockholders, A, B, and C. Suppose that A owns 45 shares of the stock (which means A has 45 votes), B owns 45 shares, and C owns 10 shares. If a vote of 51 or greater is required to approve any measure before the owners, then a measure cannot be passed without two of the three owners voting for the measure. Even though C has only 10 shares, C has the same voting power as A and B.

Now suppose that a new stockholder is brought into the company and the shares of the company are redistributed so that A has 27 shares, B has 26 shares, C has 25 shares, and D has 22 shares. Note, in this case, that any two of A, B, or C can pass a measure, but D paired with any of the other shareholders cannot pass a measure. D has virtually no power even though D has only three shares less than C.

The number of votes that are required to pass a measure is called a **quota.** For the two stockholder examples above, the quota was 51. The **weight of a voter** is the number of votes controlled by the voter. In the case of the company whose stock was split $A-27$ shares, $B-26$ shares, $C-25$ shares, and $D-22$ shares, the weight of A is 27, the weight of B is 26, the weight of C is 25, and the weight of D is 22. Rather than write out in sentence form the quota and weight of each voter, we use the notation

Quota ——⌐   Weights

$$\{51: 27, 26, 25, 22\}$$

• The four numbers after the colon indicate that there are a total of four voters in this system.

This notation is very convenient. We state its more general form in the definition below.

Weighted Voting System

A weighted voting system of n voters is written $\{q: w_1, w_2, \ldots, w_n\}$, where q is the quota and w_1 through w_n represent the weights of each of the n voters.

Using this notation, we can describe various voting systems.

- **One person, one vote:** For instance, $\{5: 1, 1, 1, 1, 1, 1, 1, 1, 1\}$. In this system, each person has one vote and five votes, a majority, are required to pass a measure.

- **Dictatorship:** For instance, $\{20: 21, 6, 5, 4, 3\}$. In this system, the person with 21 votes can pass any measure. Even if the remaining four people get together, their votes do not total the quota of 20.

■ **Null system:** For instance, {28: 6, 3, 5, 2}. If all the members of this system vote for a measure, the total number of votes is 16, which is less than the quota. Therefore, no measure can be passed.

■ **Veto power system:** For instance, {21: 6, 5, 4, 3, 2, 1}. In this case, the sum of all the votes is 21, the quota. Therefore, if any one voter does not vote for the measure, it will fail. Each voter is said to have **veto power.** In this case, this means that even the voter with one vote can veto a measure (cause the measure not to pass). If at least one voter in a voting system has veto power, the system is a veto power system.

UN Security Council Chamber

Math Matters   UN Security Council: An Application of Inequalities

The United Nations Security Council consists of five permanent members (United States, China, France, Great Britain, and Russia) and 10 members that are elected by the General Assembly for a two-year term. In 2005, the 10 nonpermanent members were Algeria, Argentina, Belize, Brazil, Denmark, Germany, Japan, Philippines, Romania, and United Republic of Tanzania.

For a resolution to pass the Security Council,

1. Nine countries must vote for the resolution; and

2. If one of the five permanent members votes against the resolution, it fails.

This situation can be described using inequalities. Let x be the weight of the vote of one permanent member of the Council and let q be the quota for a vote to pass. Then, by condition 1, $q \leq 5x + 4$. (The weights of the five votes of the permanent members plus the single votes of four nonpermanent members must be greater than or equal to the quota.)

By condition 2, we have $4x + 10 < q$. (If one of the permanent members opposes the resolution, it fails even if all of the nonpermanent members vote for it.)

Combining the inequalities from condition 1 and condition 2, we have

$$4x + 10 < 5x + 4$$
$$10 < x + 4 \quad \bullet \text{ Subtract } 4x \text{ from each side.}$$
$$6 < x \quad \bullet \text{ Subtract 4 from each side.}$$

The smallest whole number greater than 6 is 7. Therefore, the weight of each permanent member is 7. Substituting 7 into $q \leq 5x + 4$ and $4x + 10 < q$, we find that $q = 39$. Thus the weighted voting system of the Security Council is given by {39: 7, 7, 7, 7, 7, 1, 1, 1, 1, 1, 1, 1, 1, 1, 1, 1}.

QUESTION   *Is the UN Security Council voting system a veto power system?*

In a weighted voting system, a **coalition** is a set of voters each of whom votes the same way, either for or against a resolution. A **winning coalition** is a set of voters the sum of whose votes is greater than or equal to the quota. A **losing coalition**

ANSWER   *Yes. If any of the permanent members votes against a resolution, the resolution cannot pass.*

is a set of voters the sum of whose votes is less than the quota. A voter who leaves a winning coalition and thereby turns it into a losing coalition is called a **critical voter**.

As shown in the next theorem, for large numbers of voters, there are many possible coalitions.

Number of Possible Coalitions of *n* Voters

The number of possible coalitions of *n* voters is $2^n - 1$.

As an example, if all electors of each state to the Electoral College cast their ballots for one candidate, then there are $2^{51} - 1 \approx 2.25 \times 10^{15}$ possible coalitions (the District of Columbia is included). The number of *winning* coalitions is far less. For instance, any coalition of 10 or fewer states cannot be a winning coalition because the largest 10 states do not have enough electoral votes to elect the president. As we proceed through this section, we will not attempt to list all the coalitions, only the winning coalitions.

✔ **TAKE NOTE**

The number of coalitions of *n* voters is the number of subsets that can be formed from *n* voters. From Chapter 2, this is 2^n. Because a coalition must contain at least one voter, the empty set is not a possible coalition. Therefore, the number of coalitions is $2^n - 1$.

EXAMPLE 1 ■ **Determine Winning Coalitions in a Weighted Voting System**

Suppose that the four owners of a company, Ang, Bonhomme, Carmel, and Diaz, own, respectively, 500 shares, 375 shares, 225 shares, and 400 shares. The weighted voting system for this company is {751: 500, 375, 225, 400}.

a. Determine the winning coalitions.

b. For each winning coalition, determine the critical voters.

Solution

a. A winning coalition must represent at least 751 votes. We will list these coalitions in the table below, in which we use *A* for Ang, *B* for Bonhomme, *C* for Carmel, and *D* for Diaz.

✔ **TAKE NOTE**

The coalition {A, C} is not a winning coalition because the total number of votes for that coalition is 725, which is less than 751.

Winning coalition	Number of votes
{A, B}	875
{A, D}	900
{B, D}	775
{A, B, C}	1100
{A, B, D}	1275
{A, C, D}	1125
{B, C, D}	1000
{A, B, C, D}	1500

b. A voter who leaves a winning coalition and thereby creates a losing coalition is a critical voter. For instance, for the winning coalition {A, B, C}, if A leaves, the number of remaining votes is 600, which is not enough to pass a resolution. If B leaves, the number of remaining votes is 725—again, not enough to pass a resolution. Therefore, A and B are critical voters for the coalition {A, B, C} and C is not a critical voter. The table below shows the critical voters for each winning coalition.

Winning coalition	Number of votes	Critical voters
{A, B}	875	A, B
{A, D}	900	A, D
{B, D}	775	B, D
{A, B, C}	1100	A, B
{A, B, D}	1275	None
{A, C, D}	1125	A, D
{B, C, D}	1000	B, D
{A, B, C, D}	1500	None

CHECK YOUR PROGRESS 1   Many countries must govern by forming coalitions from among many political parties. Suppose a country has five political parties named A, B, C, D, and E. The numbers of votes, respectively, for each party are 22, 18, 17, 10, and 5.

a. Determine the winning coalitions if 37 votes are required to pass a resolution.

b. For each winning coalition, determine the critical voters.

Solution   *See page S53.*

QUESTION   *Is the voting system in Example 1 a dictatorship? What is the total number of possible coalitions in Example 1?*

Banzhaf Power Index

There are a number of measures of the *power* of a voter. For instance, as we saw from the Electoral College example, some electors represent fewer people and therefore their votes may have more power. As an extreme case, suppose that two electors, A and B, each represent 10 people and that a third elector, C, represents 1000 people. If a measure passes when two of the three electors vote for the measure, then A and B voting together could pass a resolution even though they represent only 20 people.

ANSWER   *No. There is no one shareholder who has 751 or more shares of stock. The number of possible coalitions is $2^4 - 1 = 15$.*

Another measure of power, called the *Banzhaf power index*, was derived by John F. Banzhaf III in 1965. The purpose of this index is to determine the power of a voter in a weighted voting system.

Banzhaf Power Index

The **Banzhaf power index** of a voter v, symbolized by $BPI(v)$, is given by

$$BPI(v) = \frac{\text{number of times voter } v \text{ is a critical voter}}{\text{number of times any voter is a critical voter}}$$

Consider four people A, B, C, and D and the one-person, one-vote system given by $\{3: 1, 1, 1, 1\}$.

Winning coalition	Number of votes	Critical voters
{A, B, C}	3	A, B, C
{A, B, D}	3	A, B, D
{A, C, D}	3	A, C, D
{B, C, D}	3	B, C, D
{A, B, C, D}	4	None

To find $BPI(A)$, we look under the critical voters column and find that A is a critical voter three times. The number of times any voter is a critical voter, the denominator of the Banzhaf power index, is 12. (A is a critical voter three times, B is a critical voter three times, C is a critical voter three times, and D is a critical voter three times. The sum is $3 + 3 + 3 + 3 = 12$.) Thus

$$BPI(A) = \frac{3}{12} = 0.25$$

Similarly, we can calculate the Banzhaf power index for each of the other voters.

$$BPI(B) = \frac{3}{12} = 0.25 \qquad BPI(C) = \frac{3}{12} = 0.25 \qquad BPI(D) = \frac{3}{12} = 0.25$$

In this case, each voter has the same power. This is expected in a voting system in which each voter has one vote.

Now suppose that three people A, B, and C belong to a dictatorship given by $\{3: 3, 1, 1\}$.

Winning coalition	Number of votes	Critical voters
{A}	3	A
{A, B}	4	A
{A, C}	4	A
{A, B, C}	5	A

The sum of the critical voters in all winning coalitions is 4. To find $BPI(A)$, we look under the critical voters column and find that A is a critical voter four times. Thus

$$BPI(A) = \frac{4}{4} = 1 \qquad BPI(B) = \frac{0}{4} = 0 \qquad BPI(C) = \frac{0}{4} = 0$$

Thus A has all the power. This is expected in a dictatorship.

EXAMPLE 2 ■ Compute the BPI for a Weighted Voting System

Suppose the stock in a company is held by five people, A, B, C, D, and E. The voting system for this company is {626: 350, 300, 250, 200, 150}. Determine the Banzhaf power index of A and E.

Solution

Determine all of the winning coalitions and the critical voters in each coalition.

Winning coalition	Critical voters	Winning coalition	Critical voters
{A, B}	A, B	{B, C, E}	B, C, E
{A, B, C}	A, B	{B, D, E}	B, D, E
{A, B, D}	A, B	{A, B, C, D}	None
{A, B, E}	A, B	{A, B, C, E}	None
{A, C, D}	A, C, D	{A, B, D, E}	None
{A, C, E}	A, C, E	{A, C, D, E}	A
{A, D, E}	A, D, E	{B, C, D, E}	B
{B, C, D}	B, C, D	{A, B, C, D, E}	None

The number of times all voters are critical is 28. To find $BPI(A)$, we look under the critical voters columns and find that A is a critical voter eight times. Thus

$$BPI(A) = \frac{8}{28} \approx 0.29$$

To find $BPI(E)$, we look under the critical voters columns and find that E is a critical voter four times. Thus

$$BPI(E) = \frac{4}{28} \approx 0.14$$

CHECK YOUR PROGRESS 2 Suppose that a government is composed of four political parties, A, B, C, and D. The voting system for this government is {26: 18, 16, 10, 6}. Determine the Banzhaf power index of A and D.

Solution   See page S53.

In many cities, the only time the mayor votes on a resolution is when there is a tie vote by the members of the city council. This is also true of the United States Senate. The vice president only votes when there is a tie vote by the senators.

In Example 3, we will calculate the Banzhaf power index for a voting system in which one voter votes only to break a tie.

EXAMPLE 3 ■ Use the BPI to Determine a Voter's Power

Suppose a city council consists of four members, A, B, C, and D, and a mayor M. The mayor votes only when there is a tie vote among the members of the council. In all cases, a resolution receiving three or more votes passes. Show that the Banzhaf power index for the mayor is the same as the Banzhaf power index for each city council member.

Solution
We first list all of the winning coalitions that do not include the mayor. To this list, we add the winning coalitions in which the mayor votes to break a tie.

Winning coalition (without mayor)	Critical voters	Winning coalition (mayor voting)	Critical voters
{A, B, C}	A, B, C	{A, B, M}	A, B, M
{A, B, D}	A, B, D	{A, C, M}	A, C, M
{A, C, D}	A, C, D	{A, D, M}	A, D, M
{B, C, D}	B, C, D	{B, C, M}	B, C, M
{A, B, C, D}	None	{B, D, M}	B, D, M
		{C, D, M}	C, D, M

By examining the table, we see that A, B, C, D, and M each occur in exactly six winning coalitions. The total number of critical voters in all winning coalitions is 30. Therefore, each member of the council and the mayor have the same Banzhaf power index, which is $\frac{6}{30} = 0.2$.

CHECK YOUR PROGRESS 3 The European Economic Community (EEC) was founded in 1958 and originally consisted of Belgium, France, Germany, Italy, Luxembourg, and the Netherlands. The weighted voting system was {12: 2, 4, 4, 4, 1, 2}. Find the Banzhaf power index for each country.

Solution See page S54.

▼ **point of interest**

In 2005, 25 countries were full members of the organization known as the European Union (EU), which at one time was referred to as the Common Market or the European Economic Community (EEC). (See Check Your Progress 3.)

By working Check Your Progress 3, you will find that the Banzhaf power index for the original EEC gave little power to Belgium and the Netherlands and no power to Luxembourg. However, there was an implicit understanding among the countries that a resolution would not pass unless all countries voted for it, thereby effectively giving each country veto power.

Excursion

Blocking Coalitions and the Banzhaf Power Index

The four members A, B, C, and D of an organization adopted the weighted voting system {6: 4, 3, 2, 1}. The table below shows the winning coalitions.

Winning coalition	Number of votes	Critical voters
{A, B}	7	A, B
{A, C}	6	A, C
{A, B, C}	9	A
{A, B, D}	8	A, B
{A, C, D}	7	A, C
{B, C, D}	6	B, C, D
{A, B, C, D}	10	None

Using the Banzhaf power index, we have $BPI(A) = \frac{5}{12}$.

A **blocking coalition** is a group of voters who can prevent passage of a resolution. In this case, a critical voter is one who leaves a blocking coalition, thereby producing a coalition that is no longer capable of preventing the passage of a resolution. For the voting system above, we have

Blocking coalition	Number of votes	Number of remaining votes	Critical voters
{A, B}	7	3	A, B
{A, C}	6	4	A, C
{A, D}	5	5	A, D
{B, C}	5	5	B, C
{A, B, C}	9	1	None
{A, B, D}	8	2	A
{A, C, D}	7	3	A
{B, C, D}	6	4	B, C

If we count the number of times A is a critical voter in a winning or blocking coalition, we find what is called the *Banzhaf index*. In this case, the Banzhaf index is 10 and we write $BI(A) = 10$. Using both the winning coalition and the blocking coalition tables, we find that

(continued)

$BI(B) = 6$, $BI(C) = 6$, and $BI(D) = 2$. This information can be used to create an alternative definition of the Banzhaf power index.

Banzhaf Power Index—Alternative Definition

$$BPI(A) = \frac{BI(A)}{\text{sum of all Banzhaf indices for the voting system}}$$

Applying this definition to the voting system given above, we have

$$BPI(A) = \frac{BI(A)}{BI(A) + BI(B) + BI(C) + BI(D)} = \frac{10}{10 + 6 + 6 + 2} = \frac{10}{24} = \frac{5}{12}$$

Excursion Exercises

1. Using the data in Example 1 on page 916, list all blocking coalitions.

2. For the data in Example 1 on page 916, calculate the Banzhaf power indices for A, B, C, and D using the alternative definition.

3. Using the data in Check Your Progress 3 on page 920, list all blocking coalitions.

4. For the data in Check Your Progress 3 on page 920, calculate the Banzhaf power indices for Belgium and Luxembourg using the alternative definition.

5. Create a voting system with three members that is a dictatorship. Calculate the Banzhaf power index of each voter for this system using the alternative definition.

6. Create a voting system with four members in which one member has veto power. Calculate the Banzhaf power index for this system using the alternative definition.

7. Create a voting system with five members that meets the one-person, one-vote rule. Calculate the Banzhaf power index for this system using the alternative definition.

Exercise Set 13.3

In each of the following exercises, the weighted voting systems for the voters A, B, C, ... are given in the form $\{q: w_1, w_2, w_3, w_4, \ldots, w_n\}$. The weight of voter A is w_1, the weight of voter B is w_2, the weight of voter C is w_3, and so on.

1. A weighted voting system is given by $\{6: 4, 3, 2, 1\}$.
   a. What is the quota?
   b. How many voters are in this system?
   c. What is the weight of voter B?
   d. What is the weight of the coalition $\{A, C\}$?

e. Is $\{A, D\}$ a winning coalition?

f. Which voters are critical voters in the coalition $\{A, C, D\}$?

g. How many coalitions can be formed?

h. How many coalitions consist of exactly two voters?

2. A weighted voting system is given by $\{16: 8, 7, 4, 2, 1\}$.
   a. What is the quota?
   b. How many voters are in this system?
   c. What is the weight of voter C?
   d. What is the weight of the coalition $\{B, C\}$?

    e. Is {B, C, D, E} a winning coalition?

    f. Which voters are critical voters in the coalition {A, B, D}?

    g. How many coalitions can be formed?

    h. How many coalitions consist of exactly three voters?

In Exercises 3–12, calculate, if possible, the Banzhaf power index for each voter. Round to the nearest hundredth.

  3. {6: 4, 3, 2}

  4. {10: 7, 6, 4}

  5. {10: 7, 3, 2, 1}

  6. {14: 7, 5, 1, 1}

  7. {19: 14, 12, 4, 3, 1}

  8. {3: 1, 1, 1, 1}

  9. {18: 18, 7, 3, 3, 1, 1}

10. {14: 6, 6, 4, 3, 1}

11. {80: 50, 40, 30, 25, 5}

12. {85: 55, 40, 25, 5}

13. Which, if any, of the voting systems in Exercises 3 to 12 is

    a. a dictatorship?

    b. a veto power system? *Note:* A voting system is a veto power system if any of the voters have veto power.

    c. a null system?

    d. a one-person, one-vote system?

14. Explain why it is impossible to calculate the Banzhaf power index for any voter in the null system {8: 3, 2, 1, 1}.

15. **Music Education** A music department consists of a band director and a music teacher. Decisions on motions are made by voting. If both members vote in favor of a motion, it passes. If both members vote against a motion, it fails. In the event of a tie vote, the principal of the school votes to break the tie. For this voting scheme, determine the Banzhaf power index for each department member and for the principal. *Hint:* See Example 3, page 920.

16. Four voters A, B, C, and D make decisions by using the voting scheme {4: 3, 1, 1, 1}, except when there is a tie. In the event of a tie, a fifth voter E casts a vote to break the tie. For this voting scheme, determine the Banzhaf power index for each voter, including voter E. *Hint:* See Example 3, page 920.

17. **Criminal Justice** In a criminal trial, each of the 12 jurors has one vote and all of the jurors must agree to reach a verdict. Otherwise the judge will declare a mistrial.

    a. Write the weighted voting system, in the form {q: w_1, w_2, w_3, w_4, ..., w_{12}}, used by these jurors.

    b. Is this weighted voting system a one-person, one-vote system?

    c. Is this weighted voting system a veto power system?

    d. Explain an easy way to determine the Banzhaf power index for each voter.

18. **Criminal Justice** In California civil court cases, each of the 12 jurors has one vote and at least nine of the jury members must agree to reach a verdict.

    a. Write the weighted voting system, in the form {q: w_1, w_2, w_3, w_4, ..., w_{12}}, used by these jurors.

    b. Is this weighted voting system a one-person, one-vote system?

    c. Is this weighted voting system a veto power system?

    d. Explain an easy way to determine the Banzhaf power index for each voter.

A voter who has a weight that is greater than or equal to the quota is called a **dictator.** In a weighted voting system, the dictator has all the power. A voter who is never a critical voter has no power and is referred to as a **dummy.** This term is not meant to be a comment on the voter's intellectual powers. It just indicates that the voter has no ability to influence an election.

In Exercises 19–22, identify any dictator and all dummies for each weighted voting system.

19. {16: 16, 5, 4, 2, 1}

20. {15: 7, 5, 3, 2}

21. {19: 12, 6, 3, 1}

22. {45: 40, 6, 2, 1}

23. **Football** At the beginning of each football season, the coaching staff at Vista High School must vote to decide which players to select for the team. They use the weighted voting system $\{4: 3, 2, 1\}$. In this voting system, the head coach A has a weight of 3, the assistant coach B has a weight of 2, and the junior varsity coach C has a weight of 1.

a. Compute the Banzhaf power index for each of the coaches.

b. ✎ Explain why it seems reasonable that the assistant coach and the junior varsity coach have the same Banzhaf power index in this voting system.

24. **Football** The head coach in Exercise 23 has decided that next year the coaching staff should use the weighted voting system $\{5: 4, 3, 1\}$. The head coach is still voter A, the assistant coach is still voter B, and the junior varsity coach is still voter C.

a. Compute the Banzhaf power index for each coach under this new system.

b. How do the Banzhaf power indices for this new voting system compare with the Banzhaf power indices in Exercise 23? Did the head coach gain any power, according to the Banzhaf power indices, with this new voting system?

25. Consider the weighted voting system $\{60: 4, 56, 58\}$.

a. Compute the Banzhaf power index for each voter in this system.

b. ✎ Voter B has a weight of 56 compared to only 4 for voter A, yet the results of part a show that voter A and voter B both have the same Banzhaf power index. Explain why it seems reasonable, in this voting system, to assign voters A and B the same Banzhaf power index.

Extensions
CRITICAL THINKING

26. It can be proved that for any natural number constant c, the weighted voting systems $\{q: w_1, w_2, w_3, w_4, \ldots, w_n\}$ and $\{cq: cw_1, cw_2, cw_3, cw_4, \ldots, cw_n\}$ both have the same Banzhaf power index distribution. Verify that this theorem is true for the weighted voting system $\{14: 8, 7, 6, 3\}$ and the constant $c = 2$.

27. Consider the weighted voting system $\{q: 8, 3, 3, 2\}$, with q an integer and $9 \le q \le 16$.

a. For what values of q is there a dummy?

b. For what values of q do all voters have the same power?

c. If a voter is a dummy for a given quota, must the voter be a dummy for all larger quotas?

28. ✎ Consider the weighted voting system $\{17: 7, 7, 7, 2\}$.

a. Explain why voter D is a dummy in this system.

b. Explain an *easy* way to compute the Banzhaf power indices for this system.

29. In a weighted voting system, two voters have the same weight. Must they also have the same Banzhaf power index?

30. In a weighted voting system, Voter A has a larger weight than voter B. Must the Banzhaf power index for voter A be larger than the Banzhaf power index for voter B?

31. ✎ Consider the one-person, one-vote strict majority system $\{2: 1, 1, 1\}$ and the weighted voting system $\{5: 3, 3, 3\}$. Explain why the systems are essentially equivalent.

32. Consider the voting system $\{7: 3, 2, 2, 2, 2\}$. A student has determined that the Banzhaf power index for voter A is $\frac{5}{13}$.

a. Explain an *easy* way to calculate the Banzhaf power index for each of the other voters.

b. If the given voting system were changed to $\{8: 3, 2, 2, 2, 2\}$, which voters, if any, would lose power according to the Banzhaf power index?

EXPLORATIONS

33. ✎ **Shapley-Shubik Power Index** Another index that is used to measure the power of voters in a weighted voting system is the *Shapley-Shubik power*

index. Write a short report on the Shapley-Shubik power index. Explain how to calculate the Shapley-Shubik power index for each voter in the weighted voting system {6: 4, 3, 2}. How do these Shapley-Shubik power indices compare with the Banzhaf power indices for this voting system? (See your results from Exercise 3.) Explain under what circumstances you would choose to use the Shapley-Shubik power index over the Banzhaf power index.

34. **UN Security Council** The United Nations Security Council consists of five permanent members and 10 members that are elected for a two-year term. (See the *Math Matters* on page 915.) The weighted voting system of the Security Council is given by

$$\{39: 7, 7, 7, 7, 7, 1, 1, 1, 1, 1, 1, 1, 1, 1, 1\}$$

In this system, each permanent member has a voting weight of 7 and each elected member has a voting weight of 1.

a. Use the program "BPI" at the website **www.math.temple.edu/~cow/bpi.html** to compute the Banzhaf power index distribution for the members of the Security Council.

b. According to the Banzhaf power index distribution from part a, each permanent member has about how many times more power than an elected member?

c. Some people think that the voting system used by the United Nations Security Council gives too much power to the permanent members. A weighted voting system that would reduce the power of the permanent members is given by

$$\{30: 5, 5, 5, 5, 5, 1, 1, 1, 1, 1, 1, 1, 1, 1, 1\}$$

In this new system, each permanent member has a voting weight of 5 and each elected member has a voting weight of 1. Use the program "BPI" at **www.math.temple.edu/~cow/bpi.html** to compute the Banzhaf power indices for the members of the Security Council under this voting system.

d. According to the Banzhaf power indices from part c, each permanent member has about how many times more power than an elected member under this new voting system?

35. **European Community** The European Community 2005 consists of 25 countries. Issues are decided by the weighted voting system

$$\{232: 29, 29, 29, 29, 27, 27, 13, 12, 12, 12, 12, 12, 10, \\ 10, 7, 7, 7, 7, 7, 7, 4, 4, 4, 4, 4, 4\}$$

The following table shows the weights for each country. (*Source:* **http://news.bbc.co.uk**)

Germany, United Kingdom, France, Italy	29
Spain, Poland	27
Netherlands	13
Greece, Portugal, Belgium, Czech Republic, Hungary	12
Sweden, Austria	10
Slovakia, Denmark, Finland, Ireland, Lithuania	7
Latvia, Slovenia, Estonia, Cyprus, Luxembourg, Malta	4

a. Use the program "BPI" on the website at **www.math.temple.edu/~cow/bpi.html** to compute the Banzhaf power indices for the countries in the European Community 2005.

b. According to the Banzhaf power indices from part a, how many times more voting power does Italy have than Luxembourg? Round to the nearest tenth.

CHAPTER 13   **Summary**

Key Terms

absolute unfairness of an apportionment [p. 878]
Alabama paradox [p. 876]
apportionment [p. 870]
apportionment principle [p. 879]
Arrow's Impossibility Theorem [p. 900]
average constituency [p. 877]
Balinski-Young Impossibility Theorem [p. 882]
Banzhaf power index [p. 918]
Borda Count method of voting [p. 892]
coalition [p. 915]
Condorcet criterion [p. 898]
critical voter [p. 916]
dictatorship [p. 914]
fairness criteria [p. 900]
Hamilton-plan/method [p. 870]
Huntington-Hill apportionment principle [p. 881]
Huntington-Hill method [p. 881]
Huntington-Hill number [p. 881]
independence of irrelevant alternatives [p. 900]
Jefferson plan/method [p. 872]
losing coalition [p. 915]
majority [p. 890]
majority criterion [p. 900]
modified standard divisor [p. 872]
monotonicity criterion [p. 900]
new state paradox [p. 876]
null system [p. 915]
one-person, one-vote system [p. 914]
pairwise comparison method of voting [p. 898]
plurality method of voting [p. 890]
plurality with elimination method [p. 895]
population paradox [p. 876]
preference schedule [p. 891]
quota [p. 914]
quota rule [p. 876]
relative unfairness of an appointment [p. 878]
standard divisor [p. 870]
standard quota [p. 871]
veto power [p. 915]
weight of a voter [p. 914]
weighted voting system [p. 914]
winning coalition [p. 915]

Essential Concepts

- **Standard Divisor**

$$\text{Standard divisor} = \frac{\text{total population}}{\text{number of items to apportion}}$$

- **Standard Quota**

  The *standard quota* is the whole number part of the quotient of a population and the standard divisor.

- **Quota Rule**

  The number of representatives apportioned to a state is the standard quota or one more than the standard quota.

- **Huntington-Hill Number**

  The value of $\dfrac{(P_A)^2}{a(a+1)}$, where P_A is the population of state A and a is the current number of representatives from state A, is called the Huntington-Hill number for state A.

- **Balinski-Young Impossibility Theorem**

  Any apportionment method will either violate the quota rule or will produce paradoxes such as the Alabama paradox.

- **Plurality Method of Voting**

  Each voter votes for one candidate, and the candidate with the most votes wins.

- **Borda Count Method of Voting**

  With n candidates in an election, each voter ranks the candidates by giving n points to the voter's first choice, $n-1$ points to the voter's second choice, and so on. The candidate who receives the most total points is the winner.

- **Plurality with Elimination Method of Voting**

  Eliminate the candidate with the fewest number of first-place votes. Retake a vote, keeping the same ranking preferences, and eliminate the candidate with the fewest number of first-place votes. Continue until only one candidate remains.

- **Pairwise Comparison Method of Voting**

  Compare each candidate head-to-head with each other candidate. Award 1 point for a win, 0.5 point for a tie, and 0 points for a loss. The candidate with the greatest number of points wins the election.

- **Majority Criterion**

  The candidate who receives a majority of the first-place votes is the winner.

■ **Monotonicity Criterion**

If candidate A wins the election, then candidate A will also win the election if the only change in the voters' preferences is that supporters of a different candidate change their votes to support candidate A.

■ **Condorcet Criterion**

A candidate who wins all possible head-to-head matchups should win an election when all candidates appear on the ballot.

■ **Independence of Irrelevant Alternatives Criterion**

If a candidate wins an election, the winner should remain the winner in any recount in which losing candidates withdraw from the race.

■ **Arrow's Impossibility Theorem**

There is no voting method for an election with three or more candidates that satisfies all four fairness criteria.

■ **Banzhaf Power Index**

The Banzhaf power index of a voter v, symbolized by $BPI(v)$, is given by

$$BPI(v) = \frac{\text{number of times voter } v \text{ is a critical voter}}{\text{number of times any voter is a critical voter}}$$

■ **Number of Possible Coalitions of n Voters**

The number of possible coalitions of n voters is $2^n - 1$.

CHAPTER 13   **Review Exercises**

1. **Airline Industry** The table below shows how the average constituency changes when two different airports, High Desert Airport and Eastlake Airport, add a new air traffic controller.

	High Desert Airport average constituency	Eastlake Airport average constituency
High Desert Airport receives new controller	297	326
Eastlake Airport receives new controller	302	253

a. Determine the relative unfairness of an apportionment that gives a new air traffic controller to High Desert Airport rather than to Eastlake Airport. Round to the nearest thousandth.

b. Determine the relative unfairness of an apportionment that gives a new air traffic controller to Eastlake Airport rather than to High Desert Airport. Round to the nearest thousandth.

c. Using the apportionment principle, determine which airport should receive the new air traffic controller.

2. **Education** The following table shows the number of English professors and the number of students taking English at two campuses of a state university. The university is planning to add a new English professor to one of the campuses. Use the apportionment principle to determine which campus should receive the new professor.

University campus	Number of English professors	Number of students taking English
Morena Valley	38	1437
West Keyes	46	1504

3. **Education** The following table shows the enrollments for each of the four divisions of a college. There are 50 new overhead projectors that are to be apportioned among the divisions based on the enrollments.

Division	Enrollment
Health	1280
Business	3425
Engineering	1968
Science	2936
Total	9609

a. Use the Hamilton method to determine the number of projectors to be apportioned to each division.

b. Use the Jefferson method to determine the number of projectors to be apportioned to each division.

c. Use the Webster method to determine the number of projectors to be apportioned to each division.

4. **Airline Industry** The following table shows the numbers of ticket agents at five airports for a small airline company. The company has hired 35 new security employees who are to be apportioned among the airports based on the number of ticket agents at each airport.

Airport	Number of ticket agents
Newark	28
Cleveland	19
Chicago	34
Philadelphia	13
Detroit	16
Total	110

a. Use the Hamilton method to apportion the new security employees among the airports.

b. Use the Jefferson method to apportion the new security employees among the airports.

c. Use the Webster method to apportion the new security employees among the airports.

5. **Technology** A company has four offices. The president of the company uses the Hamilton method to apportion 66 new computer printers among the offices based on the number of employees at each office.

Office	A	B	C	D
Number of employees	19	195	308	402
Apportionment of 66 printers	1	14	22	29

a. If the number of printers to be apportioned by the Hamilton method increases from 66 to 67, will the Alabama paradox occur? Explain.

b. If the number of printers to be apportioned by the Hamilton method increases from 67 to 68, will the Alabama paradox occur? Explain.

6. **Automobile Sales** Consider the apportionment of 27 automobiles to the sales departments of a business with five regional centers labeled *A*, *B*, *C*, *D*, and *E*. The following table shows the Hamilton apportionment of the automobiles based on the number of sales personnel at each center.

Center	A	B	C	D	E
Number of sales personnel	31	108	70	329	49
Apportionment of 27 automobiles	2	5	3	15	2

a. If the number of automobiles to be apportioned increases from 27 to 28, what will be the apportionment if the Hamilton method is used? Does the Alabama paradox occur? Explain.

b. If the number of automobiles to be apportioned using the Hamilton method increases from 28 to 29, will the Alabama paradox occur? Explain.

7. **Music Company** MusicGalore.net has offices in Los Angeles and Newark. The number of employees at each office is shown in the following table. There are 11 new computer file servers to be apportioned between the offices according to the number of employees.

Office	Los Angeles	Newark
Employees	1430	235

a. Use the Hamilton method to find each office's apportionment of file servers.

b. The corporation opens an additional office in Kansas City with 111 employees and decides to have a total of 12 file servers. If the file servers are reapportioned using the Hamilton method, will the new states paradox occur? Explain.

8. **Building Inspectors** A city apportions 34 building inspectors among three regions according to their populations. The following table shows the present population of each region.

Region	A	B	C
Population	14,566	3321	29,988

a. Use the Hamilton method to apportion the inspectors.

b. After a year the regions have the following populations.

Region	A	B	C
Population	15,008	3424	30,109

Region A has an increase in population of 442, which is an increase of 3.03%. Region B has an increase in population of 103, which is an increase of 3.10%. Region C has an increase in population of 121, which is an increase of 0.40%. If the inspectors are reapportioned using the Hamilton method, will the population paradox occur? Explain.

9. Is the Hamilton apportionment method susceptible to the population paradox?

10. Is the Jefferson apportionment method susceptible to the new states paradox?

11. **Corporate Security** The Huntington-Hill apportionment method has been used to apportion 86 security guards among each of three corporate office buildings according to the number of employees at each building. See the following table.

Building	Number of security guards	Number of employees
A	25	414
B	43	705
C	18	293

The corporation has decided to hire a new security guard.

a. Use the Huntington-Hill apportionment principle to determine to which building the new security guard should be assigned.

b. If another security guard is hired, bringing the total number of guards to 88, to which building should this guard be assigned?

12. **Homecoming Queen** Three high school students are running for Homecoming Queen. Students at the school were allowed to rank the candidates in order of preference. The results are shown in the preference schedule below.

	Rankings		
Cynthia L.	3	2	1
Hannah A.	1	3	3
Shannon M.	2	1	2
Number of votes:	112	97	11

a. Use the Borda Count method to find the winner.

b. Find a candidate who wins all head-to-head comparisons.

c. Explain why the Condorcet criterion has been violated.

d. Who wins using the plurality voting system?

e. Explain why the majority criterion has been violated.

13. **Homecoming Queen** In Exercise 12, suppose Cynthia L. withdraws from the Homecoming Queen election.

a. Assuming voter preferences between the remaining two candidates remain the same, who will be crowned Homecoming Queen using the Borda Count method?

b. Explain why the independence of irrelevant alternatives criterion has been violated.

14. **Scholarship Awards** A scholarship committee must choose a winner from three finalists, Jean, Margaret, and Terry. Each member of the committee ranked the three finalists and Margaret was selected winner using the plurality with elimination method. This vote was later declared invalid and a new vote was taken. All members voted using the same rankings except one, who changed her first choice from Terry to Margaret. This time Jean won the scholarship using the same voting method. Which fairness criterion was violated, and why?

15. A weighted voting system for the voters A, B, C, and D is given by {18: 12, 7, 6, 1}. The weight of voter A is 12, the weight of voter B is 7, the weight of voter C is 6, and the weight of voter D is 1.

a. What is the quota?

b. What is the weight of the coalition {A, C}?

c. Is {A, C} a winning coalition?

d. Which voters are critical voters in the coalition {A, C, D}?

e. How many coalitions can be formed?

f. How many coalitions consist of exactly two voters?

16. A weighted voting system for the voters A, B, C, D, and E is given by {35: 29, 11, 8, 4, 2}. The weight of voter A is 29, the weight of voter B is 11, the weight of voter C is 8, the weight of voter D is 4, and the weight of voter E is 2.

a. What is the quota?

b. What is the weight of the coalition {A, D, E}?

c. Is {A, D, E} a winning coalition?

d. Which voters are critical voters in the coalition {A, C, D, E}?

e. How many coalitions can be formed?

f. How many coalitions consist of exactly two voters?

17. Calculate the Banzhaf power indices for the voters A, B, and C in the weighted voting system {9: 6, 5, 3}.

18. Calculate the Banzhaf power indices for the voters A, B, C, D, and E in the one-person, one-vote system {3: 1, 1, 1, 1, 1}.

19. Calculate the Banzhaf power indices for the voters A, B, C, and D in the weighted voting system {31: 19, 15, 12, 10}. Round to the nearest hundredth.

20. Calculate the Banzhaf power indices for the voters A, B, C, D, and E in the weighted voting system {35: 29, 11, 8, 4, 2}. Round to the nearest hundredth.

In Exercises 21 and 22, identify any dictator and all dummies for each weighted voting system.

21. Voters A, B, C, D, and E: {15: 15, 10, 2, 1, 1}

22. Voters A, B, C, and D: {28: 19, 6, 4, 2}

23. Four voters A, B, C, and D make decisions by using the weighted voting system {5: 4, 2, 1, 1}. In the event of a tie, a fifth voter E casts a vote to break the tie. For this voting scheme, determine the Banzhaf power index for each voter, including voter E.

24. Four finalists are competing in an essay contest. Judges have read and ranked each essay in order of preference. The results are shown in the preference schedule below.

	Rankings			
Crystal Kelley	3	2	2	1
Manuel Ortega	1	3	4	3
Peter Nisbet	2	4	1	2
Sue Toyama	4	1	3	4
Number of votes:	8	5	4	6

 a. Using the plurality voting system, who is the winner of the essay contest?

 b. Does this winner have a majority?

 c. Use the Borda Count method of voting to determine the winner of the essay contest.

25. **Ski Club** A campus ski club is trying to decide where to hold its winter break ski trip. The members of the club were surveyed and asked to rank five choices in order of preference. Their responses are tallied in the following table.

	Rankings				
Aspen	1	1	3	2	3
Copper Mountain	5	4	2	4	4
Powderhorn	3	2	5	1	5
Telluride	4	5	4	5	2
Vail	2	3	1	3	1
Number of votes:	14	8	11	18	12

 a. Use the plurality method of voting to determine which resort the club should choose.

 b. Use the Borda Count method to choose the ski resort the club should visit.

26. **Campus Election** Four students are running for the Activities Director position on campus. Students were asked to rank the four candidates in order of preference. The results are shown in the table below.

	Rankings			
G. Reynolds	2	3	1	3
L. Hernandez	1	4	4	2
A. Kim	3	1	2	1
J. Schneider	4	2	3	4
Number of votes:	132	214	93	119

Use the plurality with elimination method to determine the winner of the election.

27. **Consumer Preferences** A group of consumers were surveyed about their favorite candy bars. Each participant was asked to rank four candy bars in order of preference. The results are given in the table below.

	Rankings				
Nestle Crunch	1	4	4	2	3
Snickers	2	1	2	4	1
Milky Way	3	2	1	1	4
Twix	4	3	3	3	2
Number of votes:	15	38	27	16	22

Use the plurality with elimination method to determine the group's favorite candy bar.

28. Use the pairwise comparison method of voting to choose the winner of the election in Exercise 26.

29. Use the pairwise comparison method of voting to choose the group's favorite candy bar in Exercise 27.

1. Postal Service The table below shows the number of mail carriers and the population for two cities, Spring Valley and Summerville. The postal service is planning to add a new mail carrier to one of the cities. Use the apportionment principle to determine which city should receive the new mail carrier.

City	Number of mail carriers	Population
Spring Valley	158	67,530
Summerville	129	53,950

2. Computer Allocation The following table shows the number of employees for each of the four divisions of a corporation. There are 85 new computers that are to be apportioned among the divisions based on the number of employees in each division.

Division	Number of employees
Sales	1008
Advertising	234
Service	625
Manufacturing	3114
Total	4981

a. Use the Hamilton method to determine the number of computers to be apportioned to each division.

b. Use the Jefferson method to determine the number of computers to be apportioned to each division. Does this particular apportionment violate the quota rule?

3. High School Counselors The following table shows the number of counselors and the number of students for each of two high schools. The current number of counselors for each school was determined using the Huntington-Hill apportionment method.

School	Number of counselors	Number of students
Cedar Falls	9	2646
Lake View	7	1984

A new counselor is to be hired for one of the schools.

a. Calculate the Huntington-Hill number for each of the schools. Round to the nearest whole number.

b. Use the Huntington-Hill apportionment principle to determine to which school the new counselor should be assigned.

4. A weighted voting system for the voters A, B, C, D, and E is given by {33: 21, 14, 12, 7, 6}.

a. What is the quota?

b. What is the weight of the coalition {B, C}?

c. Is {B, C} a winning coalition?

d. Which voters are critical voters in the coalition {A, C, D}?

e. How many coalitions can be formed?

f. How many coalitions consist of exactly two voters?

5. Consumer Preference One hundred consumers ranked three brands of bottled water in order of preference. The results are shown in the preference schedule below.

	Rankings				
Arrowhead	2	3	1	3	2
Evian	3	2	2	1	1
Aquafina	1	1	3	2	3
Number of votes:	22	17	31	11	19

a. Using the plurality system of voting, which brand of bottled water is the preferred brand?

b. Does the winner have a majority?

c. Use the Borda Count method of voting to determine the favored brand of water.

6. Executives' Preferences A company with offices across the country will hold its annual executive meeting in one of four locations. All of the executives were asked to rank the locations in order of preference. The results are shown in the table below.

	Rankings			
New York	3	1	2	2
Dallas	2	3	1	4
Los Angeles	4	2	4	1
Atlanta	1	4	3	3
Number of votes:	19	24	7	35

Use the pairwise comparison method to determine which location should be chosen.

7. Exam Review A professor is preparing an extra review session the Monday before final exams and she wants as many students as possible to be able to attend. She asks all of the students to rank different times of day in order of preference. The results are given below.

	Rankings				
Morning	4	1	4	2	3
Noon	3	2	2	3	1
Afternoon	1	3	1	4	2
Evening	2	4	3	1	4
Number of votes:	12	16	9	5	13

a. Using the plurality with elimination method, for what time of day should the professor schedule the review session?

b. Use the Borda Count method to determine the best time of day for the review.

8. Budget Proposal A committee must vote on which of three budget proposals to adopt. Each member of the committee has ranked the proposals in order of preference. The results are shown below.

	Rankings		
Proposal A	1	3	3
Proposal B	2	2	1
Proposal C	3	1	2
Number of votes:	40	9	39

a. Using the plurality system of voting, which proposal should be adopted?

b. If Proposal C is found to be invalid and is eliminated, which proposal wins using the plurality system?

c. Explain why the independence of irrelevant alternatives criterion has been violated.

d. Verify that Proposal B wins all head-to-head comparisons.

e. Explain why the Condorcet criterion has been violated.

9. Drama Department The four staff members A, B, C, and D of a college drama department use the weighted voting system {8: 5, 4, 3, 2} to make casting decisions for a play they are producing. In this voting system, voter A has a weight of 5, voter B has a weight of 4, voter C has a weight of 3, and voter D has a weight of 2. Compute the Banzhaf power index for each member of the department. Round each result to the nearest hundredth.

10. Three voters A, B, and C make decisions by using the weighted voting system {6: 5, 4, 1}. In the case of a tie, a fourth voter D casts a single vote to break the tie. For this voting scheme, determine the Banzhaf power index for each voter, including voter D.

APPENDIX | The Metric System of Measurement

International trade, or trade between nations, is a vital and growing segment of business in the world today. The opening of McDonald's restaurants around the globe is testimony to the expansion of international business.

The United States, as a nation, is dependent on world trade. And world trade is dependent on internationally standardized units of measurement. Almost all countries use the metric system as their sole system of measurement. The United States is one of only a few countries that has not converted to the metric system as its official system of measurement. The International Mathematics and Science Study compared the performances of half a million students from 41 countries at five different grade levels on tests of their mathematics and science knowledge. One area of mathematics in which the U.S. average was below the international average was measurement, largely because the units cited in the questions were metric units. Because the United States has not yet converted to the metric system, its citizens are less familiar with it.

In this Appendix we will present the metric system of measurement and explain how to convert between different units.

The basic unit of *length,* or distance, in the metric system is the **meter** (m). One meter is approximately the distance from a doorknob to the floor. All units of length in the metric system are derived from the meter. Prefixes added to the basic unit denote the length of the unit. For example, the prefix *centi-* means "one hundredth;" therefore, 1 centimeter is 1 one hundredth of a meter (0.01 m).

≈ 1 meter

kilo-	= 1 000	1 kilometer (km)	= 1 000 meters (m)
hecto-	= 100	1 hectometer (hm)	= 100 m
deca-	= 10	1 decameter (dam)	= 10 m
		1 meter (m)	= 1 m
deci-	= 0.1	1 decimeter (dm)	= 0.1 m
centi-	= 0.01	1 centimeter (cm)	= 0.01 m
milli-	= 0.001	1 millimeter (mm)	= 0.001 m

Notice that in this list 1000 is written as 1 000, with a space between the 1 and the zeros. When writing numbers using metric units, each group of three numbers is separated by a space instead of a comma. A space is also used after each group of three numbers to the right of a decimal. For example, 31,245.2976 is written 31 245.297 6 in metric notation.

QUESTION   *Which unit in the metric system is one thousandth of a meter?*

Mass and weight are closely related. *Weight* is a measure of how strongly gravity is pulling on an object. Therefore, an object's weight is less in space than on Earth's surface. However, the amount of material in the object, its *mass,* remains the same. On the surface of Earth, the terms *mass* and *weight* can be used interchangeably.

ANSWER   *The millimeter is one thousandth of a meter.*

▼ point of interest

Originally the meter (spelled *metre* in some countries) was defined as $\frac{1}{10,000,000}$ of the distance from the equator to the North Pole. Modern scientists have redefined the meter as 1,650,753.73 wavelengths of the orange-red light given off by the element krypton.

The basic unit of mass in the metric system is the **gram** (g). If a box 1 centimeter long on each side is filled with pure water, the mass of that water is 1 gram.

1 gram = the mass of water in a box that
is 1 centimeter long on each side

The units of mass in the metric system have the same prefixes as the units of length.

1 kilogram (kg)   = 1 000 grams (g)
1 hectogram (hg) = 100 g
1 decagram (dag) = 10 g
1 gram (g)   = 1 g
1 decigram (dg) = 0.1 g
1 centigram (cg) = 0.01 g
1 milligram (mg) = 0.001 g

The gram is a small unit of mass. A paperclip weighs about 1 gram. In many applications, the kilogram (1 000 grams) is a more useful unit of mass. This textbook weighs about 1 kilogram.

Weight ≈ 1 gram

QUESTION   *Which unit in the metric system is equal to 1 000 grams?*

Liquid substances are measured in units of *capacity*.

The basic unit of capacity in the metric system is the **liter** (L). One liter is defined as the capacity of a box that is 10 centimeters long on each side.

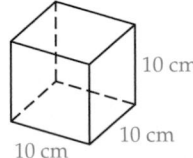

1 liter = the capacity of a box that is
10 centimeters long on each side

The units of capacity in the metric system have the same prefixes as the units of length.

1 kiloliter (kl)   = 1 000 liters (L)
1 hectoliter (hl) = 100 L
1 decaliter (dal) = 10 L
1 liter (L)   = 1 L
1 deciliter (dl) = 0.1 L
1 centiliter (cl) = 0.01 L
1 milliliter (ml) = 0.001 L

ANSWER   *The kilogram is equal to 1 000 grams.*

Converting between units in the metric system involves moving the decimal point to the right or to the left. Listing the units in order from largest to smallest will indicate how many places to move the decimal point and in which direction.

To convert 3 800 centimeters to meters, write the units of length in order from largest to smallest.

km   hm   dam   m   dm   cm   mm

2 positions

3 800 cm = 38.00 m

2 places

- Converting from cm to m requires moving 2 positions to the left.

- Move the decimal point the same number of places and in the same direction.

Convert 27 kilograms to grams.

kg   hg   dag   g   dg   cg   mg

3 positions

27 kg = 27 000 g

3 places

- Write the units of mass in order from largest to smallest.

- Converting kg to g requires moving 3 positions to the right.

- Move the decimal point the same number of places and in the same direction.

EXAMPLE 1 ■ **Convert Units in the Metric System of Measurement**

Convert.

a. 4.08 meters to centimeters   **b.** 5.93 grams to milligrams

c. 82 milliliters to liters   **d.** 9 kiloliters to liters

Solution

a. Write the units of length from largest to smallest.

km   hm   dam   (m)   dm   (cm)   mm

Converting m to cm requires moving 2 positions to the right.

4.08 m = 408 cm

b. Write the units of mass from largest to smallest.

kg   hg   dag   (g)   dg   cg   (mg)

Converting g to mg requires moving 3 positions to the right.

5.93 g = 5 930 mg

c. Write the units of capacity from largest to smallest.

kl   hl   dal   (L)   dl   cl   (ml)

Converting ml to L requires moving 3 positions to the left.

82 ml = 0.082 L

d. Write the units of capacity from largest to smallest.

(kl)   hl   dal   (L)   dl   cl   ml

Converting kl to L requires moving 3 positions to the right.

9 kl = 9 000 L

CHECK YOUR PROGRESS 1 Convert.

a. 1 295 meters to kilometers   b. 7 543 grams to kilograms

c. 6.3 liters to milliliters   d. 2 kiloliters to liters

Solution   See page S54.

Other prefixes in the metric system are becoming more common as a result of technological advances in the computer industry. For example:

tera-	=	1 000 000 000 000
giga-	=	1 000 000 000
mega-	=	1 000 000
micro-	=	0.000 001
nano-	=	0.000 000 001
pico-	=	0.000 000 000 001

A **bit** is the smallest unit of code that computers can read; it is a binary digit, either a 0 or a 1. Usually bits are grouped into bytes of 8 bits. Each byte stands for a letter, number, or any other symbol we might use in communicating information. For example, the letter W can be represented by 01010111. The amount of memory in a computer hard drive is measured in terabytes, gigabytes, and megabytes. The speed of a computer was measured in microseconds, then in nanoseconds, and then in picoseconds.

Here are a few more examples of how these prefixes are used.

The mass of Earth gains 40 Gg (gigagrams) each year from captured meteorites and cosmic dust.

The average distance from Earth to the moon is 384.4 Mm (megameters) and the average distance from Earth to the sun is 149.5 Gm (gigameters).

The wavelength of yellow light is 590 nm (nanometers).

The diameter of a hydrogen atom is about 70 pm (picometers).

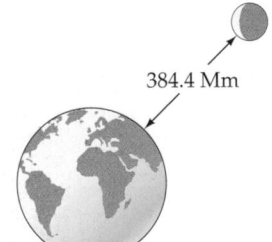

384.4 Mm

There are additional prefixes in the metric system, representing both larger and smaller units. We may hear them more and more often as computer chips hold more and more information, as computers get faster and faster, and as we learn more and more about objects in our universe and beyond that are great distances away.

Exercises

1. In the metric system, what is the basic unit of length? of liquid measure? of weight?

2. a. Explain how to convert meters to centimeters.

   b. Explain how to convert milliliters to liters.

In Exercises 3–26, name the unit in the metric system that can most conveniently be used to measure each of the following.

3. The distance from New York to London
4. The weight of a truck
5. A person's waist
6. The amount of coffee in a mug
7. The weight of a thumbtack
8. The amount of water in a swimming pool
9. The distance a baseball player hits a baseball
10. A person's hat size
11. The amount of fat in a slice of cheddar cheese
12. A person's weight
13. The maple syrup served with pancakes

14. The amount of water in a water cooler
15. The amount of vitamin C in a vitamin tablet
16. A serving of cereal
17. The width of a hair
18. A person's height
19. The amount of medication in an aspirin
20. The weight of a lawnmower
21. The weight of a slice of bread
22. The contents of a bottle of salad dressing
23. The amount of water a family uses monthly
24. The newspapers collected at a recycling center
25. The amount of liquid in a bowl of soup
26. The distance to the bank

27. **a.** Complete the table.

Metric system prefix	Symbol	Magnitude	Means multiply the basic unit by:
tera-	T	10^{12}	1 000 000 000 000
giga-	G	?	1 000 000 000
mega-	M	10^6	?
kilo-	?	?	1 000
hecto-	h	?	100
deca-	da	10^1	?
deci-	d	$\frac{1}{10}$	?
centi-	?	$\frac{1}{10^2}$	?
milli-	?	?	0.001
micro-	μ (mu)	$\frac{1}{10^6}$	?
nano-	n	$\frac{1}{10^9}$	?
pico-	p	?	0.000 000 000 001

b. How can the magnitude column in the table above be used to determine how many places to move the decimal point when converting to the basic unit in the metric system?

In Exercises 28–57, convert the given measure.

28. 42 cm = _____ mm

29. 91 cm = _____ mm

30. 360 g = _____ kg

31. 1 856 g = _____ kg

32. 5 194 ml = _____ L

33. 7 285 ml = _____ L

34. 2 m = _____ mm

35. 8 m = _____ mm

36. 217 mg = _____ g

37. 34 mg = _____ g

38. 4.52 L = _____ ml

39. 0.029 7 L = _____ ml

40. 8 406 m = _____ km

41. 7 530 m = _____ km

42. 2.4 kg = _____ g

43. 9.2 kg = _____ g

44. 6.18 kl = _____ L

45. 0.036 kl = _____ L

46. 9.612 km = _____ m

47. 2.35 km = _____ m

48. 0.24 g = _____ mg

49. 0.083 g = _____ mg

50. 298 cm = _____ m

51. 71.6 cm = _____ m

52. 2 431 L = _____ kl

53. 6 302 L = _____ kl

54. 0.66 m = _____ cm

55. 4.58 m = _____ cm

56. 243 mm = _____ cm

57. 92 mm = _____ cm

58. The Olympics a. One of the events in the summer Olympics is the 50 000-meter walk. How many kilometers do the entrants in this event walk?

    b. One of the events in the winter Olympic games is the 10 000-meter speed skating event. How many kilometers do the entrants in this event skate?

59. Gemology A carat is a unit of weight equal to 200 milligrams. Find the weight in grams of a 10-carat precious stone.

60. Sewing How many pieces of material, each 75 centimeters long, can be cut from a bolt of fabric that is 6 meters long?

61. Water Treatment An athletic club uses 800 milliliters of chlorine each day for its swimming pool. How many liters of chlorine are used in a month of 30 days?

62. Carpentry Each of the four shelves in a bookcase measures 175 centimeters. Find the cost of the shelves when the price of lumber is $15.75 per meter.

63. Consumerism The printed label from a container of milk is shown below. To the nearest whole number, how many 230-milliliter servings are in the container?

1 GAL. (3.78 L)

64. Consumerism A 1.19-kilogram container of Quaker Oats contains 30 servings. Find the number of grams in one serving of the oatmeal. Round to the nearest gram.

65. Nutrition A patient is advised to supplement her diet with 2 grams of calcium per day. The calcium tablets she purchases contain 500 milligrams of calcium per tablet. How many tablets per day should the patient take?

66. Education A laboratory assistant is in charge of ordering acid for three chemistry classes of 30 students each. Each student requires 80 milliliters of acid. How many liters of acid should be ordered? The assistant must order by the whole liter.

67. Consumerism A case of 12 one-liter bottles of apple juice costs $19.80. A case of 24 cans, each can containing 340 milliliters of apple juice, costs $14.50. Which case of apple juice costs less per milliliter?

68. Construction A column assembly is being constructed in a building. The components are shown in the diagram below. What height column must be cut?

22-cm girder
1.25-cm plate
2.4 m
Column
1.25-cm plate
20-cm concrete footing

69. Light The distance between Earth and the sun is 150 000 000 kilometers. Light travels 300 000 000 meters in 1 second. How many seconds does it take for light to reach Earth from the sun?

70. Explain why is it advantageous to have internationally standardized units of measure.

Extensions

CRITICAL THINKING

71. Business A service station operator bought 85 kl of gasoline for $38,500. The gasoline was sold for $.658 per liter. Find the profit on the 85 kl of gasoline.

72. Business For $149.50, a cosmetician buys 5 L of moisturizer and repackages it in 125-milliliter jars. Each jar costs the cosmetician $.55. Each jar of moisturizer is sold for $8.95. Find the profit on the 5 L of moisturizer.

73. Business A health food store buys nuts in 10-kilogram containers and repackages the nuts for resale. The store packages the nuts in 200-gram bags, costing $.06 each, and sells them for $2.89 per bag. Find the profit on a 10-kilogram container of nuts costing $75.

COOPERATIVE LEARNING

74. Form two debating teams. One team should argue in favor of changing to the metric system in the United States, and the other should argue against it.

SOLUTIONS TO *CHECK YOUR PROGRESS* PROBLEMS

CHAPTER 1

SECTION 1.1

CHECK YOUR PROGRESS 1, *page 2*

a. Each successive number is 5 larger than the preceding number. Thus we predict that the next number in the list is 5 larger than 25, which is 30.

b. The first two numbers differ by 3. The second and third numbers differ by 5. It appears that the difference between any two numbers is always 2 more than the preceding difference. Thus we predict that the next number will be 11 more than 26, which is 37.

CHECK YOUR PROGRESS 2, *page 3*

If the original number is 2, then $\dfrac{2 \times 9 + 15}{3} - 5 = 6$, which is

three times the original number.

If the original number is 7, then $\dfrac{7 \times 9 + 15}{3} - 5 = 21$, which is

three times the original number.

If the original number is -12, then $\dfrac{-12 \times 9 + 15}{3} - 5 = -36$,

which is three times the original number.

It appears, by inductive reasoning, that the procedure produces a number that is three times the original number.

CHECK YOUR PROGRESS 3, *page 4*

a. It appears that when the velocity of a tsunami is doubled, its height is quadrupled.

b. A tsunami with a velocity of 30 feet per second will have a height that is four times that of a tsunami with a speed of 15 feet per second. Thus, we predict a height of $4 \times 25 = 100$ feet for a tsunami with a velocity of 30 feet per second.

CHECK YOUR PROGRESS 4, *page 5*

a. Let $x = 0$. Then $\dfrac{x}{x} \neq 1$, because division by 0 is undefined.

b. Let $x = 1$. Then $\dfrac{x + 3}{3} = \dfrac{1 + 3}{3} = \dfrac{4}{3}$, whereas

$x + 1 = 1 + 1 = 2$.

c. Let $x = 3$. Then $\sqrt{x^2 + 16} = \sqrt{3^2 + 16} = \sqrt{25} = 5$, whereas $x + 4 = 3 + 4 = 7$.

CHECK YOUR PROGRESS 5, *page 6*

Let n represent the original number.
Multiply the number by 6: $6n$
Add 10 to the product: $6n + 10$

Divide the sum by 2: $\dfrac{6n + 10}{2} = 3n + 5$

Subtract 5: $3n + 5 - 5 = 3n$

The procedure always produces a number that is three times the original number.

CHECK YOUR PROGRESS 6, *page 7*

a. The conclusion is a specific case of a general assumption, so the argument is an example of deductive reasoning.

b. The argument reaches a conclusion based on specific examples, so the argument is an example of inductive reasoning.

CHECK YOUR PROGRESS 7, *page 9*

From clue 1, we know that Ashley is not the president or the treasurer. In the following chart, write X1 (which stands for "ruled out by clue 1") in the President and Treasurer columns of Ashley's row.

	Pres.	V. P.	Sec.	Treas.
Brianna				
Ryan				
Tyler				
Ashley	X1			X1

From clue 2, Brianna is not the secretary. We know from clue 1 that the president is not the youngest, and we know from clue 2 that Brianna and the secretary are the youngest members of the group. Thus Brianna is not the president. In the chart, write X2 for these two conditions. Also we know from clues 1 and 2 that Ashley is not the secretary, because she is older than the treasurer. Write an X2 in the Secretary column of Ashley's row.

S1

	Pres.	V. P.	Sec.	Treas.
Brianna	X2		X2	
Ryan				
Tyler				
Ashley	X1		X2	X1

At this point we see that Ashley must be the vice president and that none of the other members is the vice president. Thus we can update the chart as shown below.

	Pres.	V. P.	Sec.	Treas.
Brianna	X2	X2	X2	
Ryan		X2		
Tyler		X2		
Ashley	X1	✓	X2	X1

Now we can see that Brianna must be the treasurer and that neither Ryan nor Tyler is the treasurer. Update the chart as shown below.

	Pres.	V. P.	Sec.	Treas.
Brianna	X2	X2	X2	✓
Ryan		X2		X2
Tyler		X2		X2
Ashley	X1	✓	X2	X1

From clue 3, we know that Tyler is not the secretary. Thus we can conclude that Tyler is the president and Ryan must be the secretary. See the chart below.

	Pres.	V. P.	Sec.	Treas.
Brianna	X2	X2	X2	✓
Ryan	X3	X2	✓	X2
Tyler	✓	X2	X3	X2
Ashley	X1	✓	X2	X1

Tyler is the president, Ashley is the vice president, Ryan is the secretary, and Brianna is the treasurer.

SECTION 1.2

CHECK YOUR PROGRESS 1, *page 17*

sequence: $\quad$ 1 $\quad$ 14 $\quad$ 51 $\quad$ 124 $\quad$ 245 $\quad$ 426 $\quad$ 679 $\quad$ ...

first differences: $\quad$ 13 $\quad$ 37 $\quad$ 73 $\quad$ 121 $\quad$ 181 $\quad$ 253 $\quad$ ... $\quad$ (1)

second differences: $\quad$ 24 $\quad$ 36 $\quad$ 48 $\quad$ 60 $\quad$ 72 $\quad$ ... $\quad$ (2)

third differences: $\quad$ 12 $\quad$ 12 $\quad$ 12 $\quad$ 12 $\quad$ ... $\quad$ (3)

Using the method of extending the difference table, we predict that 679 is the next term in the sequence.

CHECK YOUR PROGRESS 2, *page 19*

a. Each figure after the first figure consists of a square region and a "tail." The number of tiles in the square region is n^2 and the number of tiles in the tail is $n - 1$. Thus the nth term formula for the number of tiles in the nth figure is $a_n = n^2 + n - 1$.

b. Let $n = 10$. Then $n^2 + n - 1 = (10)^2 + (10) - 1 = 109$.

c. $$n^2 + n - 1 = 419$$
$$n^2 + n - 420 = 0$$
$$(n + 21)(n - 20) = 0$$

$$n + 21 = 0 \quad \text{or} \quad n - 20 = 0$$
$$n = -21 \qquad\qquad n = 20$$

We consider only the positive result. The 20th figure will consist of 419 tiles.

CHECK YOUR PROGRESS 3, *page 21*

$$F_9 = F_8 + F_7$$
$$= 21 + 13$$
$$= 34$$

CHECK YOUR PROGRESS 4, *page 22*

a. The inequality $2F_n > F_{n+1}$ is true for $n = 3, 4, 5, 6, \ldots, 10$. Thus, by inductive reasoning, we conjecture that the statement is a true statement.

b. The equality $2F_n + 3 = F_{n+2}$ is not true for $n = 4$, because $2F_4 + 3 = 2(3) + 3 = 9$ and $F_{4+2} = F_6 = 8$. Thus the statement is a false statement.

SECTION 1.3

CHECK YOUR PROGRESS 1, *page 32*

Understand the Problem In order to go past Starbucks, Allison must walk along Third Avenue from Boardwalk to Park Avenue.

Devise a Plan Label each intersection that Allison can pass through with the number of routes to that intersection. If she can reach an intersection from two different routes, then the number of routes to that intersection is the sum of the numbers of routes to the two adjacent intersections.

Carry Out the Plan   The following figure shows the number of routes to each of the intersections that Allison could pass through. Thus there are a total of nine routes that Allison can take if she wishes to walk directly from point A to point B and pass by Starbucks.

Review the Solution   The total of nine routes seems reasonable. We know from Example 1 that if Allison can take any route, the total number of routes is 35. Requiring Allison to go past Starbucks eliminates several routes.

CHECK YOUR PROGRESS 2, *page 33*

Understand the Problem   There are several ways to answer the questions so that two answers are "false" and three answers are "true." One way is TTTFF and another is FFTTT.

Devise a Plan   Make an organized list. Try the strategy of listing a T unless doing so will produce too many T's or a duplicate of one of the previous orders in your list.

Carry Out the Plan   (Start with 3 T's in a row.)

$$
\begin{array}{ll}
\text{TTTFF} & (1) \\
\text{TTFTF} & (2) \\
\text{TTFFT} & (3) \\
\text{TFTTF} & (4) \\
\text{TFTFT} & (5) \\
\text{TFFTT} & (6) \\
\text{FTTTF} & (7) \\
\text{FTTFT} & (8) \\
\text{FTFTT} & (9) \\
\text{FFTTT} & (10)
\end{array}
$$

Review the Solution   Each entry in the list has two F's and three T's. Since the list is complete and has no duplications, we know that there are 10 ways for a student to mark two questions with "false" and the other three with "true."

CHECK YOUR PROGRESS 3, *page 34*

Understand the Problem   There are six people, and each person shakes hands with each of the other people.

Devise a Plan   Each person will shake hands with five other people (a person won't shake his or her own hand; that would be silly). Since there are six people, we could multiply 6 times 5 to get the total number of handshakes. However, this procedure would count each handshake exactly twice, so we must divide this product by 2 for the actual answer.

Carry Out the Plan   6 times 5 is 30. 30 divided by 2 is 15.

Review the Solution   Denote the people by the letters A, B, C, D, E, and F. Make an organized list. Remember that AB and BA represent the same people shaking hands, so do not list both AB and BA.

$$
\begin{array}{lllll}
\text{AB} & \text{AC} & \text{AD} & \text{AE} & \text{AF} \\
\text{BC} & \text{BD} & \text{BE} & \text{BF} \\
\text{CD} & \text{CE} & \text{CF} \\
\text{DE} & \text{DF} \\
\text{EF}
\end{array}
$$

The method of making an organized list verifies that if six people shake hands with each other there will be a total of 15 handshakes.

CHECK YOUR PROGRESS 4, *page 35*

Understand the Problem   We need to find the ones digit of 4^{200}.

Devise a Plan   Compute a few powers of 4 to see if there are any patterns. $4^1 = 4$, $4^2 = 16$, $4^3 = 64$, and $4^4 = 256$. It appears that the last digit (ones digit) of 4^{200} must be either a 4 or a 6.

Carry Out the Plan   If the exponent n is an even number, then 4^n has a ones digit of 6. If the exponent n is an odd number, then 4^n has a ones digit of 4. Because 200 is an even number, we conjecture that 4^{200} has a ones digit of 6.

Review the Solution   You could try to check the answer by using a calculator, but you would find that 4^{200} is too large to be displayed. Thus we need to rely on the patterns we have observed to conclude that 6 is indeed the ones digit of 4^{200}.

CHECK YOUR PROGRESS 5, *page 35*

Understand the Problem   We are asked to find the possible numbers that Melody could have started with.

Devise a Plan   Work backward from 18 and do the inverse of each operation that Melody performed.

Carry Out the Plan   To get 18, Melody subtracted 30 from a number, so that number was $18 + 30 = 48$. To get 48, she divided a number by 3, so that number was $48 \times 3 = 144$. To get 144, she squared a number. She could have squared either 12 or -12 to produce 144. If the number she squared was 12, then she must have doubled 6 to get 12. If the number she squared was -12, then the number she doubled was -6.

Review the Solution   We can check by starting with 6 or −6. If we do exactly as Melody did, we end up with 18. The operation that prevents us from knowing with 100% certainty which number she started with is the squaring operation. We have no way of knowing whether the number she squared was a positive number or a negative number.

CHECK YOUR PROGRESS 6, *page 36*

Understand the Problem   We need to find Diophantus's age when he died.

Devise a Plan   Read the hint and then look for clues that will help you make an educated guess. You know from the given information that Diophantus's age must be divisible by 6, 12, 7, and 2. Find a number divisible by all of these numbers and check to see if it is a possible solution to the problem.

Carry Out the Plan   All multiples of 12 are divisible by 6 and 2, but the smallest multiple of 12 that is divisible by 7 is $12 \times 7 = 84$. Thus we conjecture that Diophantus's age when he died was $x = 84$ years. If $x = 84$, then $\frac{1}{6}x = 14$, $\frac{1}{12}x = 7$, $\frac{1}{7}x = 12$, and $\frac{1}{2}x = 42$. Then $\frac{1}{6}x + \frac{1}{12}x + \frac{1}{7}x + 5 + \frac{1}{2}x + 4 = 14 + 7 + 12 + 5 + 42 + 4 = 84$. It seems that 84 years is a correct solution to the problem.

Review the Solution   After 84, the next multiple of 12 that is divisible by 7 is 168. The number 168 also satisfies all the conditions of the problem, but it is unlikely that Diophantus died at the age of 168 years or at any age older than 168 years. Hence the only reasonable solution is 84 years.

CHECK YOUR PROGRESS 7, *page 38*

Understand the Problem   We need to determine two U.S. coins that have a total value of 35¢, given that one of the coins is not a quarter.

Devise a Plan   Experiment with different coins to try to produce 35¢. After a few attempts, you should conclude that one of the coins must be a quarter. Consider that the problem may be a *deceptive problem*.

Carry Out the Plan   A total of 35¢ can be produced by using a dime and a quarter. One of the coins is a quarter, but it is also true that *one of the coins, the dime, is not a quarter*.

Review the Solution   A dime and a quarter satisfy all the conditions of the problem. No other combination of coins satisfies the conditions of the problem. Thus the only solution is a dime and a quarter.

CHECK YOUR PROGRESS 8, *page 40*

a. The maximum of the average yearly ticket prices is displayed by the tallest vertical bar in Figure 1.3. Thus the maximum of the average yearly U.S. movie theatre ticket price for the years from 1996 to 2003 was $6.03, in the year 2003.

b. Figure 1.4 indicates that in 2005, about 9% of the automobile accidents in Twin Falls were accidents involving lane changes. Thus $0.09 \cdot 4300 = 387$ of the accidents were accidents involving lane changes.

c. To estimate the average age at which women married for the first time in the year 1975, locate 1975 on the horizontal axis of Figure 1.5 and then move directly upward to the point on the green broken-line graph. The height of this point represents the average age at first marriage for women in the year 1975, and it can be estimated by moving horizontally to the vertical axis on the left. Thus the average age at first marriage for women in the year 1975 was 21 years, rounded to the nearest quarter of a year. This same procedure shows that in the year 1975, the average age at which men first married was 23.5 years, rounded to the nearest quarter of a year.

CHAPTER 2

SECTION 2.1

CHECK YOUR PROGRESS 1, *page 53*

The only months that start with the letter A are April and August. When we use the roster method, the set is given by {April, August}.

CHECK YOUR PROGRESS 2, *page 54*

The set {March, May} is the set of all months that start with the letter M.

CHECK YOUR PROGRESS 3, *page 55*

a. {0, 1, 2, 3}   b. {12, 13, 14, 15, 16, 17, 18, 19}

c. {−4, −3, −2, −1}

CHECK YOUR PROGRESS 4, *page 55*

a. False   b. True   c. True   d. True

CHECK YOUR PROGRESS 5, *page 56*

a. $\{x \mid x \in I \text{ and } x < 9\}$ b. $\{x \mid x \in N \text{ and } x > 4\}$

CHECK YOUR PROGRESS 6, *page 57*

a. $n(C) = 5$ b. $n(D) = 1$ c. $n(E) = 0$

CHECK YOUR PROGRESS 7, *page 57*

a. The sets are not equal but they both contain six elements. Thus the sets are equivalent.

b. The sets are not equal but they both contain 16 elements. Thus the sets are equivalent.

SECTION 2.2

CHECK YOUR PROGRESS 1, *page 65*

a. $M = \{0, 4, 6, 17\}$. The set of elements in $U = \{0, 2, 3, 4, 6, 7, 17\}$ but not in M is $M' = \{2, 3, 7\}$.

b. $P = \{2, 4, 6\}$. The set of elements in $U = \{0, 2, 3, 4, 6, 7, 17\}$ but not in P is $P' = \{0, 3, 7, 17\}$.

CHECK YOUR PROGRESS 2, *page 66*

a. False. The number 3 is an element of the first set but not an element of the second set. Therefore, the first set is not a subset of the second set.

b. True. The set of counting numbers is the same set as the set of natural numbers, and every set is a subset of itself.

c. True. The empty set is a subset of every set.

d. True. Each element of the first set is an integer.

CHECK YOUR PROGRESS 3, *page 67*

a. Yes, because every natural number is a whole number, and the whole numbers include 0, which is not a natural number.

b. The first set is not a proper subset of the second set because the sets are equal.

CHECK YOUR PROGRESS 4, *page 68*

Subsets with zero elements: { }

Subsets with one element: $\{a\}, \{b\}, \{c\}, \{d\}, \{e\}$

Subsets with two elements: $\{a, b\}, \{a, c\}, \{a, d\}, \{a, e\}, \{b, c\}, \{b, d\},$ $\{b, e\}, \{c, d\}, \{c, e\}, \{d, e\}$

Subsets with three elements: $\{a, b, c\}, \{a, b, d\}, \{a, b, e\}, \{a, c, d\},$ $\{a, c, e\}, \{a, d, e\}, \{b, c, d\}, \{b, c, e\}, \{b, d, e\}, \{c, d, e\}$

Subsets with four elements: $\{a, b, c, d\}, \{a, b, c, e\}, \{a, b, d, e\},$ $\{a, c, d, e\}, \{b, c, d, e\}$

Subsets with five elements: $\{a, b, c, d, e\}$

CHECK YOUR PROGRESS 5, *page 68*

a. $2^3 = 8$ **b.** $2^{15} = 32,768$ **c.** $2^{10} = 1024$

SECTION 2.3

CHECK YOUR PROGRESS 1, *page 74*

a. $D \cap E = \{0, 3, 8, 9\} \cap \{3, 4, 8, 9, 11\}$
$= \{3, 8, 9\}$

b. $D \cap F = \{0, 3, 8, 9\} \cap \{0, 2, 6, 8\}$
$= \{0, 8\}$

CHECK YOUR PROGRESS 2, *page 75*

a. $D \cup E = \{0, 4, 8, 9\} \cup \{1, 4, 5, 7\}$
$= \{0, 1, 4, 5, 7, 8, 9\}$

b. $D \cup F = \{0, 4, 8, 9\} \cup \{2, 6, 8\}$
$= \{0, 2, 4, 6, 8, 9\}$

CHECK YOUR PROGRESS 3, *page 76*

a. The set $D \cap (E' \cup F)$ can be described as "the set of all elements that are in D, and in F or not E."

b. The set $L' \cup M$ can be described as "the set of all elements that are in M or are not in L."

CHECK YOUR PROGRESS 4, *page 76*

The following Venn diagrams show that $(A \cap B)'$ is equal to $A' \cup B'$.

The white region represents $(A \cap B)$.
The shaded region represents $(A \cap B)'$.

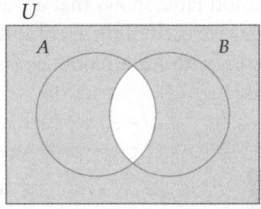

The grey shaded region below represents A'.
The diagonal patterned region below represents B'.
$A' \cup B'$ is the union of the grey shaded region and the diagonal patterned region.

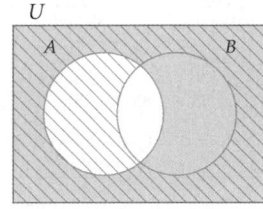

CHECK YOUR PROGRESS 5, *page 78*

The following Venn diagrams show that
$A \cup (B \cap C) = (A \cup B) \cap (A \cup C)$.

The grey shaded region represents $A \cup (B \cap C)$.

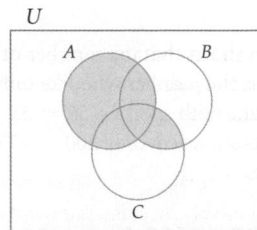

The grey shaded region below represents $A \cup B$.
The diagonal patterned region below represents $A \cup C$.
The intersection of the grey shaded region and the diagonal patterned region represents $(A \cup B) \cap (A \cup C)$.

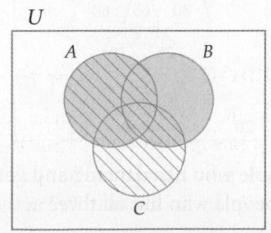

CHECK YOUR PROGRESS 6, page 79

a. Because Alex is in blood group A, not in blood group B, and is Rh+, his blood type is A+.

b. Roberto is in both blood group A and blood group B. Roberto is not Rh+. Thus Roberto's blood type is AB−.

CHECK YOUR PROGRESS 7, page 80

a. Alex's blood type is A+. The blood transfusion table shows that a person with blood type A+ can safely receive type A− blood.

b. The blood transfusion table shows that a person with type AB+ blood can safely receive each of the eight different types of blood. Thus a person with AB+ blood is classified as a universal recipient.

SECTION 2.4

CHECK YOUR PROGRESS 1, page 87

The intersection of the two sets includes the 85 students who like both volleyball and basketball.

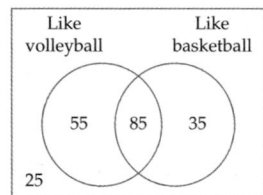

a. Because 140 students like volleyball and 85 like both sports, there must be 140 − 85 = 55 students who like only volleyball.

b. Because 120 students like basketball and 85 like both sports, there must be 120 − 85 = 35 students who like only basketball.

c. The Venn diagram shows that the number of students who like only volleyball plus the number who like only basketball plus the number who like both sports is 55 + 35 + 85 = 175. Thus of the 200 students surveyed, only 200 − 175 = 25 do not like either of the sports.

CHECK YOUR PROGRESS 2, page 88

The intersection of the three sets includes the 15 people who like all three activities.

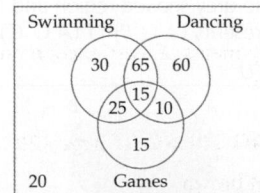

a. There are 25 people who like dancing and games. This includes the 15 people who like all three activities. Thus

there must be another 25 − 15 = 10 people who like only dancing and games. There are 40 people who like swimming and games. Thus there must be another 40 − 15 = 25 people who like only swimming and games. There are 80 people who like swimming and dancing. Thus there must be another 80 − 15 = 65 people who like only swimming and dancing. Hence 10 + 25 + 65 = 100 people who like exactly two of the three activities.

b. There are 135 people who like swimming. We have determined that 15 people like all three activities, 25 like only swimming and games, and 65 like only swimming and dancing. This means that 135 − (15 + 25 + 65) = 30 people like only swimming.

c. There are a total of 240 passengers surveyed. The Venn diagram shows that 15 + 25 + 10 + 15 + 30 + 65 + 60 = 220 passengers like at least one of the activities. Thus 240 − 220 = 20 passengers like none of the activities.

CHECK YOUR PROGRESS 3, page 90

Let B = {the set of students who play basketball}.
Let S = {the set of students who play soccer}.

$$n(B \cup S) = n(B) + n(S) - n(B \cap S)$$
$$= 80 + 60 - 24$$
$$= 116$$

Using the inclusion-exclusion principle, we see that 116 students play either basketball or soccer.

CHECK YOUR PROGRESS 4, page 90

$$n(A \cup B) = n(A) + n(B) - n(A \cap B)$$
$$852 = 785 + 162 - n(A \cap B)$$
$$852 = 947 - n(A \cap B)$$
$$n(A \cap B) = 947 - 852$$
$$n(A \cap B) = 95$$

CHECK YOUR PROGRESS 5, page 91

$$p(A \cup \text{Rh+}) = p(A) + p(\text{Rh+}) - p(A \cap \text{Rh+})$$
$$91\% = 44\% + 84\% - p(A \cap \text{Rh+})$$
$$91\% = 128\% - p(A \cap \text{Rh+})$$
$$p(A \cap \text{Rh+}) = 128\% - 91\%$$
$$p(A \cap \text{Rh+}) = 37\%$$

Thus about 37% of the U.S. population has the A antigen and is Rh+.

CHECK YOUR PROGRESS 6, page 92

a. The number 410 appears in both the column labeled "Yahoo!" and the row labeled "children." Thus the table shows that 410 children surveyed use Yahoo! as a search engine. Thus $n(Y \cap C) = 410$.

b. The set $L \cap M'$ is the set of surveyed Lycos users who are women or children. The number in this set is 325 + 40 = 365. Thus $n(L \cap M') = 365$.

c. The set $G \cap M$ represents the set of surveyed Google users who are men. The table shows that this set includes 440 people. The set $G \cap W$ represents the set of surveyed Google users who are women. The table shows that this set includes 390 people. Thus $n((G \cap M) \cup (G \cap W)) = 440 + 390 = 830$.

SECTION 2.5

CHECK YOUR PROGRESS 1, *page 99*

Write the sets so that one is aligned below the other. Draw arrows to show how you wish to pair the elements of each set. One possible method is shown in the following figure.

$$N = \{1, 2, 3, 4, \ldots, \quad n, \quad \ldots\}$$
$$D = \{1, 3, 5, 7, \ldots, 2n - 1, \ldots\}$$

In the preceding correspondence, each natural number $n \in N$ is paired with the odd number $(2n - 1) \in D$. The *general correspondence* $n \leftrightarrow (2n - 1)$ enables us to determine exactly which element of D will be paired with any given element of N, and vice versa. For instance, under this correspondence, $8 \in N$ is paired with the odd number $2 \cdot 8 - 1 = 15$ and $21 \in D$ is paired with the natural number $\frac{21 + 1}{2} = 11$. The general correspondence $n \leftrightarrow (2n - 1)$ establishes a one-to-one correspondence between the sets.

CHECK YOUR PROGRESS 2, *page 100*

One proper subset of V is $P = \{41, 42, 43, 44, \ldots, 40 + n \ldots\}$, which was produced by deleting 40 from set V. To establish a one-to-one correspondence between V and P, consider the following diagram.

$$V = \{40, 41, 42, 43, \ldots, 39 + n, \ldots\}$$
$$P = \{41, 42, 43, 44, \ldots, 40 + n, \ldots\}$$

In the above correspondence, each element of the form $39 + n$ from set V is paired with an element of the form $40 + n$ from set P. The general correspondence $(39 + n) \leftrightarrow (40 + n)$ establishes a one-to-one correspondence between V and P. Because V can be placed in a one-to-one correspondence with a proper subset of itself, V is an infinite set.

CHECK YOUR PROGRESS 3, *page 101*

The following figure shows that we can establish a one-to-one correspondence between M and the set of natural numbers N by pairing $\frac{1}{n + 1}$ of set M with n of set N.

$$M = \left\{ \frac{1}{2}, \frac{1}{3}, \frac{1}{4}, \frac{1}{5}, \ldots, \frac{1}{n + 1}, \ldots \right\}$$
$$N = \{ 1, \quad 2, \quad 3, \quad 4, \quad \ldots, \quad n, \quad \ldots\}$$

Thus the cardinality of M must be the same as the cardinality of N, which is $\aleph_0$.

CHAPTER 3

SECTION 3.1

CHECK YOUR PROGRESS 1, *page 115*

a. The sentence "Open the door." is a command. It is not a statement.

b. The word *large* is not a precise term. It is not possible to determine whether the sentence "7055 is a large number" is true or false and thus the sentence is not a statement.

c. The sentence $4 + 5 = 8$ is a false statement.

d. At this time we do not know whether the given sentence is true or false, but we know that the sentence is either true or false and that it is not both true and false. Thus the sentence is a statement.

e. The sentence $x > 3$ is a statement because for any given value of x, the inequality $x > 3$ is true or false, but not both.

CHECK YOUR PROGRESS 2, *page 117*

a. 1001 is not divisible by 7.

b. 5 is not an even number.

c. That fire engine is red.

CHECK YOUR PROGRESS 3, *page 118*

a. $\sim p \wedge r$

b. $\sim s \wedge \sim r$

c. $r \leftrightarrow q$

d. $p \rightarrow \sim r$

CHECK YOUR PROGRESS 4, *page 118*

$e \wedge \sim t$: All men are created equal and I am not trading places.

$a \vee \sim t$: I get Abe's place or I am not trading places.

$e \rightarrow t$: If all men are created equal, then I am trading places.

$t \leftrightarrow g$: I am trading places if and only if I get George's place.

CHECK YOUR PROGRESS 5, *page 119*

a. True. A conjunction is true provided both components are true.

b. True. A disjunction is true provided at least one component is true.

c. False. If both components of a disjunction are false, then the disjunction is false.

CHECK YOUR PROGRESS 6, *page 120*

a. Some bears are not brown.

b. Some math classes are fun.

c. All vegetables are green.

CHECK YOUR PROGRESS 1, *page 127*

a.

p	q	$\sim p$	$\sim q$	$p \wedge \sim q$	$\sim p \vee q$	$(p \wedge \sim q) \vee (\sim p \vee q)$	
T	T	F	F	F	T	T	Row 1
T	F	F	T	T	F	T	Row 2
F	T	T	F	F	T	T	Row 3
F	F	T	T	F	T	T	Row 4
		1	2	3	4	5	

b. p is true and q is false in row 2 of the above truth table. The truth value of $(p \wedge \sim q) \vee (\sim p \vee q)$ in row 2 is T (true).

CHECK YOUR PROGRESS 2, *page 127*

a.

p	q	r	$\sim p$	$\sim r$	$\sim p \wedge r$	$q \wedge \sim r$	$(\sim p \wedge r) \vee (q \wedge \sim r)$	
T	T	T	F	F	F	F	F	Row 1
T	T	F	F	T	F	T	T	Row 2
T	F	T	F	F	F	F	F	Row 3
T	F	F	F	T	F	F	F	Row 4
F	T	T	T	F	T	F	T	Row 5
F	T	F	T	T	F	T	T	Row 6
F	F	T	T	F	T	F	T	Row 7
F	F	F	T	T	F	F	F	Row 8
			1	2	3	4	5	

b. p is false, q is true, and r is false in row 6 of the above truth table. The truth value of $(\sim p \wedge r) \vee (q \wedge \sim r)$ in row 6 is T (true).

CHECK YOUR PROGRESS 3, *page 129*

The given statement has two simple statements. Thus you should use a standard form that has $2^2 = 4$ rows.

Step 1 Enter the truth values for each simple statement and their negations. See columns 1, 2, and 3 in the table on the right.

Step 2 Use the truth values in columns 2 and 3 to determine the truth values to enter under the "and" connective. See column 4 in the table on the right.

Step 3 Use the truth values in columns 1 and 4 to determine the truth values to enter under the "or" connective. See column 5 in the table on the right.

p	q	$\sim p$	$\vee$	$(p$	$\wedge$	$q)$
T	T	F	T	T	T	T
T	F	F	F	T	F	F
F	T	T	T	F	F	T
F	F	T	T	F	F	F
		1	5	2	4	3

The truth table for $\sim p \vee (p \wedge q)$ is displayed in column 5.

CHECK YOUR PROGRESS 4, *page 130*

p	q	p	∨	(p	∧	~q)
T	T	T	T	T	F	F
T	F	T	T	T	T	T
F	T	F	F	F	F	F
F	F	F	F	F	F	T

1 5 2 4 3

The above truth table shows that $p \equiv p \vee (p \wedge \sim q)$.

CHECK YOUR PROGRESS 5, *page 131*

Let d represent "I am going to the dance." Let g represent "I am going to the game." The original sentence in symbolic form is $\sim(d \wedge g)$. Applying one of De Morgan's laws, we find that $\sim(d \wedge g) \equiv \sim d \vee \sim g$. Thus an equivalent form of "It is not true that I am going to the dance and I am going to the game" is "I am not going to the dance or I am not going to the game."

CHECK YOUR PROGRESS 6, *page 131*

The following truth table shows that $p \wedge (\sim p \wedge q)$ is always false. Thus $p \wedge (\sim p \wedge q)$ is a self-contradiction.

p	q	p	∧	(~p	∧	q)
T	T	T	F	F	F	T
T	F	T	F	F	F	F
F	T	F	F	T	T	T
F	F	F	F	T	F	F

1 5 2 4 3

SECTION 3.3

CHECK YOUR PROGRESS 1, *page 137*

a. *Antecedent:* I study for at least 6 hours
Consequent: I will get an A on the test

b. *Antecedent:* I get the job
Consequent: I will buy a new car

c. *Antecedent:* you can dream it
Consequent: you can do it

CHECK YOUR PROGRESS 2, *page 139*

a. Because the antecedent is true and the consequent is false, the statement is a false statement.

b. Because the antecedent is false, the statement is a true statement.

c. Because the consequent is true, the statement is a true statement.

CHECK YOUR PROGRESS 3, *page 139*

p	q	[p	∧	(p	→	q)]	→	q
T	T	T	T	T	T	T	T	T
T	F	T	F	T	F	F	T	F
F	T	F	F	F	T	T	T	T
F	F	F	F	F	T	F	T	F

1 6 2 5 3 7 4

CHECK YOUR PROGRESS 4, *page 140*

a. I will move to Georgia or I will live in Houston.

b. The number is not divisible by 2 or the number is even.

CHECK YOUR PROGRESS 5, *page 141*

a. I finished the report and I did not go to the concert.

b. The square of n is 25 and n is not 5 or -5.

CHECK YOUR PROGRESS 6, *page 141*

a. Let $x = 6.5$. Then the first component of the biconditional is false and the second component of the biconditional is true. Thus the given biconditional statement is false.

b. Both components of the biconditional are true for $x > 2$, and both components are false for $x \le 2$. Because both components have the same truth value for any real number x, the given biconditional is true.

SECTION 3.4

CHECK YOUR PROGRESS 1, *page 146*

a. If a geometric figure is a square, then it is a rectangle.

b. If I am older than 30, then I am at least 21.

CHECK YOUR PROGRESS 2, *page 147*

Converse: If we are not going to have a quiz tomorrow, then we will have a quiz today.

Inverse: If we don't have a quiz today, then we will have a quiz tomorrow.

Contrapositive: If we have a quiz tomorrow, then we will not have a quiz today.

CHECK YOUR PROGRESS 3, *page 148*

a. The second statement is the inverse of the first statement. Thus the statements are not equivalent. This can also be demonstrated by the fact that the first statement is true for $c = 0$ and the second statement is false for $c = 0$.

b. The second statement is the contrapositive of the first statement. Thus the statements are equivalent.

CHECK YOUR PROGRESS 4, *page 148*

a. *Contrapositive:* If x is an odd integer, then $3 + x$ is an even integer. The contrapositive is true and so the original statement is also true.

b. *Contrapositive:* If two triangles are congruent triangles, then the two triangles are similar triangles. The contrapositive is true and so the original statement is also true.

c. *Contrapositive:* If tomorrow is Thursday, then today is Wednesday. The contrapositive is true and so the original statement is also true.

SECTION 3.5

CHECK YOUR PROGRESS 1, *page 153*

Let p represent the statement "She got on the plane." Let r represent the statement "She will regret it." Then the symbolic form of the argument is

$$\sim p \rightarrow r$$
$$\underline{\sim r}$$
$$\therefore p$$

CHECK YOUR PROGRESS 2, *page 155*

Let r represent the statement "The stock market rises." Let f represent the statement "The bond market will fall." Then the symbolic form of the argument is

$$r \rightarrow f$$
$$\underline{\sim f}$$
$$\therefore \sim r$$

The truth table for this argument is as follows:

		First premise	Second premise	Conclusion	
r	f	$r \rightarrow f$	$\sim f$	$\sim r$	
T	T	T	F	F	Row 1
T	F	F	T	F	Row 2
F	T	T	F	T	Row 3
F	F	T	T	T	Row 4

Row 4 is the only row in which all the premises are true, so it is the only row that we examine. Because the conclusion is true in row 4, the argument is valid.

CHECK YOUR PROGRESS 3, *page 156*

Let a represent the statement "I arrive before 8 A.M." Let f represent the statement "I will make the flight." Let p represent the statement "I will give the presentation." Then the symbolic form of the argument is

$$a \rightarrow f$$
$$\underline{f \rightarrow p}$$
$$\therefore a \rightarrow p$$

The truth table for this argument is as follows:

a	f	p	First premise $a \to f$	Second premise $f \to p$	Conclusion $a \to p$	
T	T	T	T	T	T	Row 1
T	T	F	T	F	F	Row 2
T	F	T	F	T	T	Row 3
T	F	F	F	T	F	Row 4
F	T	T	T	T	T	Row 5
F	T	F	T	F	T	Row 6
F	F	T	T	T	T	Row 7
F	F	F	T	T	T	Row 8

The only rows in which all the premises are true are rows 1, 5, 7, and 8. In each of these rows the conclusion is also true. Thus the argument is a valid argument.

CHECK YOUR PROGRESS 4, *page 157*
Let *f* represent "I go to Florida for spring break." Let $\sim s$ represent "I will not study." Then the symbolic form of the argument is

$$f \to \sim s$$
$$\underline{\sim f}$$
$$\therefore s$$

This argument has the form of the fallacy of the inverse. Thus the argument is invalid.

CHECK YOUR PROGRESS 5, *page 158*
Let *r* represent "I read a math book." Let *f* represent "I start to fall asleep." Let *d* represent "I drink a soda." Let *e* represent "I eat a candy bar." Then the symbolic form of the argument is

$$r \to f$$
$$f \to d$$
$$\underline{d \to e}$$
$$\therefore r \to e$$

The argument has the form of the extended law of syllogism. Thus the argument is valid.

CHECK YOUR PROGRESS 6, *page 159*
We are given the following premises:

$$\sim m \lor t$$
$$t \to \sim d$$
$$e \lor g$$
$$\underline{e \to d}$$
$$\therefore ?$$

The first premise can be written as $m \to t$, the third premise can be written as $\sim e \to g$, and the fourth premise can be written as

$\sim d \to \sim e$. Thus the argument can be expressed in the following equivalent form.

$$m \to t$$
$$t \to \sim d$$
$$\sim e \to g$$
$$\underline{\sim d \to \sim e}$$
$$\therefore ?$$

If we switch the order of the third and fourth premises, then we have the following equivalent form.

$$m \to t$$
$$t \to \sim d$$
$$\sim d \to \sim e$$
$$\underline{\sim e \to g}$$
$$\therefore ?$$

An application of the extended law of syllogism produces $m \to g$ as a valid conclusion for the argument. *Note:* Although $m \to \sim e$ is also a valid conclusion for the argument, we do not list it as our answer because it can be obtained without using all of the given premises.

SECTION 3.6

CHECK YOUR PROGRESS 1, *page 165*
The following Euler diagram shows that the argument is valid.

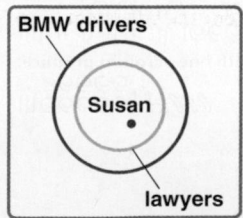

CHECK YOUR PROGRESS 2, *page 166*

From the given premises we can conclude that 7 may or may not be a prime number. Thus the argument is invalid.

CHECK YOUR PROGRESS 3, *page 167*

From the given premises we can construct two possible Euler diagrams.

 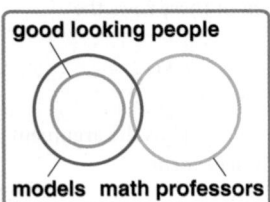

From the rightmost Euler diagram we can determine that the argument is invalid.

CHECK YOUR PROGRESS 4, *page 168*

The following Euler diagram illustrates that all squares are quadrilaterals, so the argument is a valid argument.

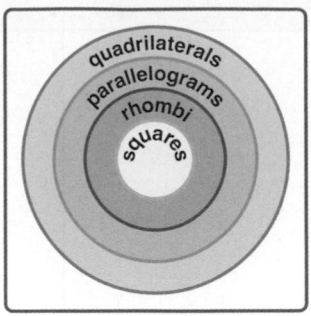

CHECK YOUR PROGRESS 5, *page 169*

The following Euler diagrams illustrate two possible cases. In both cases we see that all white rabbits like tomatoes.

 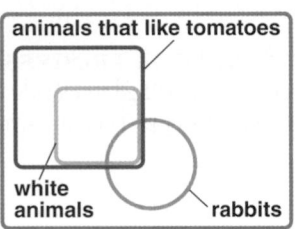

CHAPTER 4

SECTION 4.1

CHECK YOUR PROGRESS 1, *page 179*

𝕏 𝓯99∩∩∩
99∩∩∩III

CHECK YOUR PROGRESS 2, *page 179*

$(1 \times 1{,}000{,}000) + (3 \times 100{,}000) + (1 \times 10{,}000) + (4 \times 1000)$
$\qquad + (3 \times 100) + (2 \times 10) + (1 \times 6) = 1{,}314{,}326$

CHECK YOUR PROGRESS 3, *page 180*

$\begin{array}{r} 23{,}341 \\ + 10{,}562 \\ \hline \end{array}$ ∭𝓯𝓯𝓯999∩∩∩∩I
         + 𝓵99999∩∩∩∩∩∩II

∭𝓯𝓯𝓯999999∩∩∩∩∩III

Replace 10 heel bones with one scroll to produce:
∭𝓯𝓯𝓯99999∩III

which is
33,903.

CHECK YOUR PROGRESS 4, *page 180*

$\begin{array}{r} 61{,}432 \\ - 45{,}121 \\ \hline \end{array}$ ∭∭∭𝓯9999∩∩II
     −   ∭∭𝓯𝓯𝓯𝓯9∩∩I

Replace one pointing finger with 10 lotus flowers to produce:

∭∭∭𝓯𝓯𝓯𝓯𝓯𝓯𝓯𝓯9999∩∩II
−   ∭∭𝓯𝓯𝓯𝓯9∩∩I

𝓵𝓯𝓯𝓯𝓯𝓯999∩I

which is
16,311.

CHECK YOUR PROGRESS 5, *page 182*

MCDXLV = M + (CD) + (XL) + V
$\qquad = 1000 + 400 + 40 + 5 = 1445$

CHECK YOUR PROGRESS 6, *page 182*

473 = 400 + 70 + 3 = CD + LXX + III = CDLXXIII

CHECK YOUR PROGRESS 7, *page 183*

a. $\overline{\text{VII}}\text{CCLIV} = \overline{\text{VII}} + \text{CCLIV} = 7000 + 254 = 7254$

b. $8070 = 8000 + 70 = \overline{\text{VIII}} + \text{LXX} = \overline{\text{VIII}}\text{LXX}$

SECTION 4.2

CHECK YOUR PROGRESS 1, *page 187*

$17{,}325 = 10{,}000 + 7000 + 300 + 20 + 5$
$= (1 \times 10{,}000) + (7 \times 1000) + (3 \times 100) + (2 \times 10) + 5$
$= (1 \times 10^4) + (7 \times 10^3) + (3 \times 10^2) + (2 \times 10^1)$
$+ (5 \times 10^0)$

CHECK YOUR PROGRESS 2, *page 188*

$(5 \times 10^4) + (9 \times 10^3) + (2 \times 10^2) + (7 \times 10^1) + (4 \times 10^0)$
$= (5 \times 10{,}000) + (9 \times 1000) + (2 \times 100)$
$+ (7 \times 10) + (4 \times 1)$
$= 50{,}000 + 9000 + 200 + 70 + 4$
$= 59{,}274$

CHECK YOUR PROGRESS 3, *page 188*

$\begin{aligned}152 &= (1 \times 100) + (5 \times 10) + 2\\ + \ 234 &= (2 \times 100) + (3 \times 10) + 4\\ &\quad (3 \times 100) + (8 \times 10) + 6 = 386\end{aligned}$

CHECK YOUR PROGRESS 4, *page 189*

$\begin{aligned}147 &= (1 \times 100) + (4 \times 10) + \ 7\\ + \ 329 &= (3 \times 100) + (2 \times 10) + \ 9\\ &\quad (4 \times 100) + (6 \times 10) + 16\end{aligned}$

Replace 16 with $(1 \times 10) + 6$

$= (4 \times 100) + (6 \times 10) + (1 \times 10) + 6$
$= (4 \times 100) + (7 \times 10) + 6$
$= 476$

CHECK YOUR PROGRESS 5, *page 189*

$\begin{aligned}382 &= (3 \times 100) + (8 \times 10) + 2\\ - \ 157 &= (1 \times 100) + (5 \times 10) + 7\end{aligned}$

Because $7 > 2$, it is necessary to borrow by rewriting (8×10) as $(7 \times 10) + 10$.

$\begin{aligned}382 &= (3 \times 100) + (7 \times 10) + 12\\ - \ 157 &= (1 \times 100) + (5 \times 10) + \ 7\\ &\quad (2 \times 100) + (2 \times 10) + \ 5 = 225\end{aligned}$

CHECK YOUR PROGRESS 6, *page 190*

⟨⟨⧧ ⧧⧧⧧⧧⧧ ⟨⟨⧧⧧⧧⧧

$= (21 \times 60^2) + (5 \times 60) + (34 \times 1)$
$= 75{,}600 + 300 + 34 = 75{,}934$

CHECK YOUR PROGRESS 7, *page 191*

$\begin{array}{r} 3 \\ 3600\overline{)12578} \\ \underline{10800} \\ 1778 \end{array} \qquad \begin{array}{r} 29 \\ 60\overline{)1778} \\ \underline{120} \\ 578 \\ \underline{540} \\ 38 \end{array}$

Thus $12{,}578 = (3 \times 60^2) + (29 \times 60) + (38 \times 1) =$

⧧⧧⧧ ⟨⟨⧧⧧⧧⧧⧧⧧⧧⧧⧧ ⟨⟨⟨⧧⧧⧧⧧⧧⧧⧧⧧

CHECK YOUR PROGRESS 8, *page 191*

Combine the symbols for each place value.

$\begin{array}{ll} & \text{⟨⟨⟨⧧⧧} \qquad\qquad \text{⟨⟨⟨⟨⟨⧧⧧⧧⧧⧧⧧} \\ + & \text{⟨⟨⟨⟨⧧⧧⧧⧧} \qquad\qquad \text{⟨⟨⟨⟨⟨⧧⧧⧧⧧⧧⧧⧧} \\ \hline & \text{⟨⟨⟨⟨⟨⟨⟨⧧⧧⧧⧧⧧} \quad \text{⟨⟨⟨⟨⟨⟨⟨⟨⟨⟨⧧⧧⧧⧧⧧⧧⧧⧧⧧⧧⧧⧧⧧} \end{array}$

Replace ten ⧧s in the 1s' place with a ⟨.

⟨⟨⟨⟨⟨⟨⟨⧧⧧⧧⧧⧧   ⟨⟨⟨⟨⟨⟨⟨⟨⟨⟨⧧⧧⧧

Take away 60 from the ones' place and add 1 to the 60s' place.

⟨⟨⟨⟨⟨⟨⧧⧧⧧⧧⧧⧧   ⟨⟨⟨⟨⟨⧧⧧⧧

Take away 60 from the 60s' place and add 1 to the 60^2 place.

⧧   ⟨⧧⧧⧧⧧⧧⧧⧧   ⟨⟨⟨⟨⟨⧧⧧⧧

Thus

$\begin{array}{ll} & \text{⟨⟨⟨⧧⧧} \qquad\qquad \text{⟨⟨⟨⟨⟨⧧⧧⧧⧧⧧⧧} \\ + & \text{⟨⟨⟨⟨⧧⧧⧧⧧} \qquad\qquad \text{⟨⟨⟨⟨⟨⧧⧧⧧⧧⧧⧧⧧} \\ \hline \text{⧧} & \text{⟨⧧⧧⧧⧧⧧⧧⧧} \qquad\qquad \text{⟨⟨⟨⟨⟨⧧⧧⧧} \end{array}$

CHECK YOUR PROGRESS 9, *page 193*

a. $(16 \times 360) + (0 \times 20) + (1 \times 1) = 5761$

b. $(9 \times 7200) + (1 \times 360) + (10 \times 20) + (4 \times 1) = 65{,}364$

CHECK YOUR PROGRESS 10, *page 194*

$\begin{array}{r} 1 \\ 7200\overline{)11480} \\ \underline{7200} \\ 4280 \end{array} \qquad \begin{array}{r} 11 \\ 360\overline{)4280} \\ \underline{360} \\ 680 \\ \underline{360} \\ 320 \end{array} \qquad \begin{array}{r} 16 \\ 20\overline{)320} \\ \underline{20} \\ 120 \\ \underline{120} \\ 0 \end{array}$

Thus $11{,}480 = (1 \times 7200) + (11 \times 360) + (16 \times 20) + (0 \times 1)$. In Mayan numerals this is

SECTION 4.3

CHECK YOUR PROGRESS 1, *page 198*

$\begin{aligned}3156_{\text{seven}} &= (3 \times 7^3) + (1 \times 7^2) + (5 \times 7^1) + (6 \times 7^0)\\ &= (3 \times 343) + (1 \times 49) + (5 \times 7) + (6 \times 1)\\ &= 1029 + 49 + 35 + 6\\ &= 1119\end{aligned}$

CHECK YOUR PROGRESS 2, *page 199*

$\begin{aligned}111000101_{\text{two}} &= (1 \times 2^8) + (1 \times 2^7) + (1 \times 2^6) + (0 \times 2^5)\\ &\quad + (0 \times 2^4) + (0 \times 2^3) + (1 \times 2^2)\\ &\quad + (0 \times 2^1) + (1 \times 2^0)\\ &= (1 \times 256) + (1 \times 128) + (1 \times 64) + (0 \times 32)\\ &\quad + (0 \times 16) + (0 \times 8) + (1 \times 4)\\ &\quad + (0 \times 2) + (1 \times 1)\\ &= 256 + 128 + 64 + 0 + 0 + 0 + 4 + 0 + 1\\ &= 453\end{aligned}$

CHECK YOUR PROGRESS 3, *page 199*

$A5B_{twelve} = (10 \times 12^2) + (5 \times 12^1) + (11 \times 12^0)$
$= 1440 + 60 + 11$
$= 1511$

CHECK YOUR PROGRESS 4, *page 200*

$C24F_{sixteen} = (12 \times 16^3) + (2 \times 16^2) + (4 \times 16^1) + (15 \times 16^0)$
$= 49{,}152 + 512 + 64 + 15$
$= 49{,}743$

CHECK YOUR PROGRESS 5, *page 201*

a.

$1952 = 30302_{five}$

b.

$1952 = 1168_{twelve}$

CHECK YOUR PROGRESS 6, *page 202*

6	3	2	1	0_{eight}
‖	‖	‖	‖	‖
110	011	010	001	000_{two}

$63210_{eight} = 110011010001000_{two}$

CHECK YOUR PROGRESS 7, *page 202*

111	010	011	100_{two}
‖	‖	‖	‖
7	2	3	4_{eight}

$111010011100_{two} = 7234_{eight}$

CHECK YOUR PROGRESS 8, *page 203*

C	5	$A_{sixteen}$
‖	‖	‖
1100	0101	1010_{two}

$C5A_{sixteen} = 110001011010_{two}$

CHECK YOUR PROGRESS 9, *page 203*

┌── Insert a zero to
↓   make a group of four.

0101	0001	1101	0010_{two}
‖	‖	‖	‖
5	1	D	$2_{sixteen}$

$101000111010010_{two} = 51D2_{sixteen}$

CHECK YOUR PROGRESS 10, *page 204*

dabble	dabble	double	double	dabble	double
3	7	14	28	57	114

1	1	1	0	0	1	0_{two}

$1110010_{two} = 114$

SECTION 4.4

CHECK YOUR PROGRESS 1, *page 209*

$\begin{array}{r} 1\,1\quad\ 1 \\ 1\,1\,0\,0\,1_{two} \\ +\ \underline{\quad 1\,1\,0\,1_{two}} \\ 1\,0\,0\,1\,1\,0_{two} \end{array}$

CHECK YOUR PROGRESS 2, *page 210*

$\begin{array}{r} 1\,1 \\ 3\,2_{four} \\ +\ \underline{\ 1\,2_{four}} \\ 1\,1\,0_{four} \end{array}$

CHECK YOUR PROGRESS 3, *page 210*

$\begin{array}{r} 1\,2 \\ 3\,5_{seven} \\ 4\,6_{seven} \\ +\ \underline{\ 2\,4_{seven}} \\ 1\,4\,1_{seven} \end{array}$

CHECK YOUR PROGRESS 4, *page 211*

$\begin{array}{r} 1\ 1 \\ A\,C\,4_{sixteen} \\ +\ \underline{\ 6\,E\,8_{sixteen}} \\ 1\,1\,A\,C_{sixteen} \end{array}$

CHECK YOUR PROGRESS 5, *page 212*

$\begin{array}{r} 2+1 \\ \cancel{3}\,6\,5_{nine} \\ -\ \underline{1\,8\,3_{nine}} \\ \end{array}$ $\qquad$ $\begin{array}{r} 10 \\ 2\,6\,5_{nine} \\ -\ \underline{1\,8\,3_{nine}} \\ \end{array}$ $\qquad$ $\begin{array}{r} 16 \\ 2\,6\,5_{nine} \\ -\ \underline{1\,8\,3_{nine}} \\ 1\,7\,2_{nine} \end{array}$

Because $8_{nine} > 6_{nine}$, it is necessary to borrow from the 3 in the first column at the left.

Borrow 1 nine from the first column and add $9 = 10_{nine}$ to the 6 in the middle column.

$16_{nine} - 8_{nine} = 15 - 8$
$= 7$
$= 7_{nine}$

CHECK YOUR PROGRESS 6, *page 213*

$\begin{array}{r} 7\quad\ 10 \\ \cancel{8}\quad 3\quad A_{twelve} \\ -\ \underline{4\quad 6\quad 7_{twelve}} \\ 3\quad 9\quad 3_{twelve} \end{array}$

■ $A_{twelve} - 7_{twelve} = 10 - 7 = 3 = 3_{twelve}$

■ $10_{twelve} + 3_{twelve} = 13_{twelve} = 15$ $\qquad$ $15 - 6 = 9 = 9_{twelve}$

■ $7_{twelve} - 4_{twelve} = 3_{twelve}$

CHECK YOUR PROGRESS 7, *page 213*

$\begin{array}{r} 1 \\ 2\quad 1\quad 3_{four} \\ \times\ \underline{\qquad\quad 2_{four}} \\ 1\quad 0\quad 3\quad 2_{four} \end{array}$

■ $2_{four} \times 3_{four} = 12_{four}$

■ $2_{four} \times 1_{four} + 1_{four} = 3_{four}$

■ $2_{four} \times 2_{four} = 10_{four}$

CHECK YOUR PROGRESS 8, *page 215*

$$
\begin{array}{r}
2 \\
3 \quad 4_{\text{eight}} \\
\times \quad\quad 2 \quad 5_{\text{eight}} \\
\hline
2 \quad 1 \quad 4_{\text{eight}} \\
\hline
\end{array}
$$

■ $5_{\text{eight}} \times 4_{\text{eight}} = 20 = 24_{\text{eight}}$

■ $5_{\text{eight}} \times 3_{\text{eight}} + 2_{\text{eight}} = 15 + 2 = 17 = 21_{\text{eight}}$

$$
\begin{array}{r}
1 \\
3 \quad 4_{\text{eight}} \\
\times \quad\quad 2 \quad 5_{\text{eight}} \\
\hline
2 \quad 1 \quad 4_{\text{eight}} \\
7 \quad 0 \quad_{\text{eight}} \\
\hline
1 \quad 1 \quad 1 \quad 4_{\text{eight}} \\
\hline
\end{array}
$$

■ $2_{\text{eight}} \times 4_{\text{eight}} = 8 = 10_{\text{eight}}$

■ $2_{\text{eight}} \times 3_{\text{eight}} + 1_{\text{eight}} = 6 + 1 = 7 = 7_{\text{eight}}$

CHECK YOUR PROGRESS 9, *page 216*

First list a few multiples of 3_{five}.

$3_{\text{five}} \times 0_{\text{five}} = 0_{\text{five}}$

$3_{\text{five}} \times 1_{\text{five}} = 3_{\text{five}}$

$3_{\text{five}} \times 2_{\text{five}} = 11_{\text{five}}$

$3_{\text{five}} \times 3_{\text{five}} = 14_{\text{five}}$

$3_{\text{five}} \times 4_{\text{five}} = 22_{\text{five}}$

$$
\begin{array}{r}
1 \\
3_{\text{five}}\overline{)3\ 2\ 4_{\text{five}}} \\
3 \\
\hline
2
\end{array}
\qquad
\begin{array}{r}
1\ 0 \\
3_{\text{five}}\overline{)3\ 2\ 4_{\text{five}}} \\
3 \\
\hline
2 \\
0 \\
\hline
2\ 4
\end{array}
\qquad
\begin{array}{r}
1\ 0\ 4 \\
3_{\text{five}}\overline{)3\ 2\ 4_{\text{five}}} \\
3 \\
\hline
2 \\
0 \\
\hline
2\ 4 \\
2\ 2 \\
\hline
2
\end{array}
$$

Thus $324_{\text{five}} \div 3_{\text{five}} = 104_{\text{five}}$ with a remainder of 2_{five}.

CHECK YOUR PROGRESS 10, *page 216*

The divisor is 10_{two}. The multiples of the divisor are $10_{\text{two}} \times 0_{\text{two}} = 0_{\text{two}}$ and $10_{\text{two}} \times 1_{\text{two}} = 10_{\text{two}}$.

$$
\begin{array}{r}
1\ 1\ 1\ 0\ 0\ 1_{\text{two}} \\
10_{\text{two}}\overline{)1\ 1\ 1\ 0\ 0\ 1\ 1_{\text{two}}} \\
1\ 0 \\
\hline
1\ 1 \\
1\ 0 \\
\hline
1\ 0 \\
1\ 0 \\
\hline
0\ 0 \\
0 \\
\hline
0\ 1 \\
0 \\
\hline
1\ 1 \\
1\ 0 \\
\hline
1
\end{array}
$$

Thus $1110011_{\text{two}} \div 10_{\text{two}} = 111001_{\text{two}}$ with a remainder of 1_{two}.

SECTION 4.5

CHECK YOUR PROGRESS 1, *page 220*

a. Divide 9 by 1, 2, 3, ..., 9 to determine that the only natural number divisors of 9 are 1, 3, and 9.

b. Divide 11 by 1, 2, 3, ..., 11 to determine that the only natural number divisors of 11 are 1 and 11.

c. Divide 24 by 1, 2, 3, ..., 24 to determine that the only natural number divisors of 24 are 1, 2, 3, 4, 6, 8, 12, and 24.

CHECK YOUR PROGRESS 2, *page 221*

a. The only divisors of 47 are 1 and 47. Thus 47 is a prime number.

b. 171 is divisible by 3, 9, 19, and 57. Thus 171 is a composite number.

c. The divisors of 91 are 1, 7, 13, and 91. Thus 91 is a composite number.

CHECK YOUR PROGRESS 3, *page 223*

a. The sum of the digits of 341,565 is 24; therefore, 341,565 is divisible by 3.

b. The number 341,565 is not divisible by 4 because the number formed by last two digits, 65, is not divisible by 4.

c. The number 341,565 is not divisible by 10 because it does not end in 0.

d. The sum of the digits with even place-value powers is 14. The sum of the digits with odd place-value powers is 10. The difference of these sums is 4. Thus 341,565 is not divisible by 11.

CHECK YOUR PROGRESS 4, *page 224*

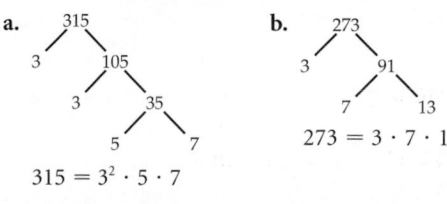

$315 = 3^2 \cdot 5 \cdot 7$

$273 = 3 \cdot 7 \cdot 13$

$1309 = 7 \cdot 11 \cdot 17$

SECTION 4.6

CHECK YOUR PROGRESS 1, *page 232*

a. The proper factors of 24 are 1, 2, 3, 4, 6, 8, and 12. The sum of these proper factors is 36. Because 24 is less than the sum of its proper factors, 24 is an abundant number.

b. The proper factors of 28 are 1, 2, 4, 7, and 14. The sum of these proper factors is 28. Because 28 equals the sum of its proper factors, 28 is a perfect number.

c. The proper factors of 35 are 1, 5, and 7. The sum of these proper factors is 13. Because 35 is larger than the sum of its proper factors, 35 is a deficient number.

CHECK YOUR PROGRESS 2, *page 232*

$2^7 - 1 = 127$, which is a prime number.

CHECK YOUR PROGRESS 3, *page 233*

The exponent $n = 61$ is a prime number and we are given that $2^{61} - 1$ is a prime number, so the perfect number we seek is $2^{60}(2^{61} - 1)$.

CHECK YOUR PROGRESS 4, *page 236*

First consider $2^{2976221}$. The base b is 2. The exponent x is 2,976,221.

$$(x \log b) + 1 = (2{,}976{,}221 \log 2) + 1$$
$$\approx 895{,}931.8 + 1$$
$$= 895{,}932.8$$

The greatest integer of 895,932.8 is 895,932. Thus $2^{2976221}$ has 895,932 digits. The number $2^{2976221}$ is not a power of 10, so the Mersenne number $2^{2976221} - 1$ also has 895,932 digits.

CHECK YOUR PROGRESS 5, *page 237*

Substituting 9 for x, 11 for y, and 4 for n in $x^n + y^n = z^n$ yields

$$9^4 + 11^4 = z^4$$
$$6561 + 14{,}641 = z^4$$
$$21{,}202 = z^4$$

The real solution of $z^4 = 21{,}202$ is $\sqrt[4]{21{,}202} \approx 12.066858$, which is not a natural number. Thus $x = 9$, $y = 11$, and $n = 4$ do not satisfy the equation $x^n + y^n = z^n$, where z is a natural number.

CHAPTER 5

SECTION 5.1

CHECK YOUR PROGRESS 1, *page 249*

a.
$$c - 6 = -13$$
$$c - 6 + 6 = -13 + 6$$
$$c = -7$$

The solution is -7.

b.
$$4 = -8z$$
$$\frac{4}{-8} = \frac{-8z}{-8}$$
$$-\frac{1}{2} = z$$

The solution is $-\frac{1}{2}$.

c.
$$22 + m = -9$$
$$22 - 22 + m = -9 - 22$$
$$m = -31$$

The solution is -31.

d.
$$5x = 0$$
$$\frac{5x}{5} = \frac{0}{5}$$
$$x = 0$$

The solution is 0.

CHECK YOUR PROGRESS 2, *page 251*

a.
$$4x + 3 = 7x + 9$$
$$4x - 7x + 3 = 7x - 7x + 9$$
$$-3x + 3 = 9$$
$$-3x + 3 - 3 = 9 - 3$$
$$-3x = 6$$
$$\frac{-3x}{-3} = \frac{6}{-3}$$
$$x = -2$$

The solution is -2.

b.
$$7 - (5x - 8) = 4x + 3$$
$$7 - 5x + 8 = 4x + 3$$
$$15 - 5x = 4x + 3$$
$$15 - 5x - 4x = 4x - 4x + 3$$
$$15 - 9x = 3$$
$$15 - 15 - 9x = 3 - 15$$
$$-9x = -12$$
$$\frac{-9x}{-9} = \frac{-12}{-9}$$
$$x = \frac{4}{3}$$

The solution is $\frac{4}{3}$.

c.
$$\frac{3x-1}{4} + \frac{1}{3} = \frac{7}{3}$$

$$12\left(\frac{3x-1}{4} + \frac{1}{3}\right) = 12\left(\frac{7}{3}\right)$$

$$12 \cdot \frac{3x-1}{4} + 12 \cdot \frac{1}{3} = 12 \cdot \frac{7}{3}$$

$$9x - 3 + 4 = 28$$

$$9x + 1 = 28$$

$$9x + 1 - 1 = 28 - 1$$

$$9x = 27$$

$$\frac{9x}{9} = \frac{27}{9}$$

$$x = 3$$

The solution is 3.

CHECK YOUR PROGRESS 3, *page 252*

a. $P = 0.05Y - 95$

$P = 0.05(1990) - 95$

$P = 99.5 - 95$

$P = 4.5$

The amount of garbage was about 4.5 pounds per day.

b.
$$P = 0.05Y - 95$$

$$5.6 = 0.05Y - 95$$

$$5.6 + 95 = 0.05Y - 95 + 95$$

$$100.6 = 0.05Y$$

$$\frac{100.6}{0.05} = \frac{0.05Y}{0.05}$$

$$2012 = Y$$

The year will be 2012.

CHECK YOUR PROGRESS 4, *page 253*

$$\boxed{\begin{array}{c}\text{\$17.50 for the first}\\\text{three lines + \$2.50}\\\text{for each additional}\\\text{line}\end{array}} = \boxed{\text{\$30}}$$

Let L = the number of lines in the ad.

$$17.50 + 2.50(L - 3) = 30$$

$$17.50 + 2.50L - 7.50 = 30$$

$$10.00 + 2.50L = 30$$

$$10.00 - 10.00 + 2.50L = 30 - 10.00$$

$$2.50L = 20$$

$$\frac{2.50L}{2.50} = \frac{20}{2.50}$$

$$L = 8$$

You can place an eight-line ad.

CHECK YOUR PROGRESS 5, *page 254*

Let n = the number of years.

$$\boxed{\begin{array}{c}\text{The 1990 population of}\\\text{Vermont plus an annual}\\\text{increase times } n\end{array}} = \boxed{\begin{array}{c}\text{The 1990 population of}\\\text{North Dakota minus an}\\\text{annual decrease times } n\end{array}}$$

$$562{,}576 + 5116n = 638{,}800 - 1370n$$

$$562{,}576 + 5116n + 1370n = 638{,}800 - 1370n + 1370n$$

$$562{,}576 + 6486n = 638{,}800$$

$$562{,}576 - 562{,}576 + 6486n = 638{,}800 - 562{,}576$$

$$6486n = 76{,}224$$

$$\frac{6486n}{6486} = \frac{76{,}224}{6486}$$

$$n \approx 12$$

$$1990 + 12 = 2002$$

The populations would be the same in 2002.

CHECK YOUR PROGRESS 6, *page 256*

a.
$$s = \frac{A + L}{2}$$

$$2 \cdot s = 2 \cdot \frac{A + L}{2}$$

$$2s = A + L$$

$$2s - A = A - A + L$$

$$2s - A = L$$

b.
$$L = a(1 + ct)$$

$$\frac{L}{a} = \frac{a(1 + ct)}{a}$$

$$\frac{L}{a} = 1 + ct$$

$$\frac{L}{a} - 1 = 1 - 1 + ct$$

$$\frac{L}{a} - 1 = ct$$

$$\frac{\frac{L}{a} - 1}{t} = \frac{ct}{t}$$

$$\frac{\frac{L}{a} - 1}{t} = c$$

$$\left(\frac{L}{a} - 1\right)\left(\frac{1}{t}\right) = c$$

$$\frac{L}{at} - \frac{1}{t} = c$$

SECTION 5.2

CHECK YOUR PROGRESS 1, *page 264*

$4.92 \div 1.5 = 3.28$

$$\frac{\$4.92}{1.5 \text{ pounds}} = \frac{\$3.28}{1 \text{ pound}} = \$3.28/\text{pound}$$

The hamburger costs $3.28 per pound.

CHECK YOUR PROGRESS 2, *page 265*

Find the difference in the hourly wage.

$\$6.75 - \$5.15 = \$1.60$

Multiply the difference in the hourly wage by 35.

$\$1.60(35) = \$56$

An employee's pay for working 35 hours and earning the California minimum wage is $56 greater.

CHECK YOUR PROGRESS 3, *page 265*

$$\frac{\$2.99}{32 \text{ ounces}} \approx \frac{\$.093}{1 \text{ ounce}} \qquad \frac{\$3.99}{48 \text{ ounces}} \approx \frac{\$.083}{1 \text{ ounce}}$$

$\$.093 > \$.083$

The more economical purchase is 48 ounces of detergent for $3.99.

CHECK YOUR PROGRESS 4, *page 267*

a. $20,000(1.3240) = 26,480$
26,480 Canadian dollars would be needed to pay for an order costing $20,000.

b. $25,000(0.8110) = 20,275$
20,275 euros would be exchanged for $25,000.

CHECK YOUR PROGRESS 5, *page 268*

a. $\dfrac{24 \text{ hours}}{1 \text{ day}} \cdot 7 \text{ days} = (24 \text{ hours})(7) = 168 \text{ hours}$

$$\frac{120 \text{ hours}}{1 \text{ week}} = \frac{120 \text{ hours}}{168 \text{ hours}} = \frac{120}{168} = \frac{5}{7}$$

The ratio is $\frac{5}{7}$.

b. $\dfrac{60 \text{ hours}}{(168 - 60) \text{ hours}} = \dfrac{60 \text{ hours}}{108 \text{ hours}} = \dfrac{60}{108} = \dfrac{5}{9}$

The ratio is 5 to 9.

CHECK YOUR PROGRESS 6, *page 269*

$6742 + 7710 = 14,452$

$$\frac{14,452}{798} \approx \frac{18.11}{1} \approx \frac{18}{1}$$

The ratio is 18 to 1.

CHECK YOUR PROGRESS 7, *page 271*

$$\frac{42}{x} = \frac{5}{8}$$

$42 \cdot 8 = x \cdot 5$

$336 = 5x$

$$\frac{336}{5} = \frac{5x}{5}$$

$67.2 = x$

The solution is 67.2.

CHECK YOUR PROGRESS 8, *page 272*

$$\frac{15 \text{ kilometers}}{2 \text{ centimeters}} = \frac{x \text{ kilometers}}{7 \text{ centimeters}}$$

$$\frac{15}{2} = \frac{x}{7}$$

$15 \cdot 7 = 2 \cdot x$

$105 = 2x$

$$\frac{105}{2} = \frac{2x}{2}$$

$52.5 = x$

The distance between the two cities is 52.5 kilometers.

CHECK YOUR PROGRESS 9, *page 273*

$$\frac{7}{5} = \frac{\$28,000}{x \text{ dollars}}$$

$$\frac{7}{5} = \frac{28,000}{x}$$

$7 \cdot x = 5 \cdot 28,000$

$7x = 140,000$

$$\frac{7x}{7} = \frac{140,000}{7}$$

$x = 20,000$

The other partner receives $20,000.

CHECK YOUR PROGRESS 10, *page 274*

$$\frac{10.1 \text{ deaths}}{1,000,000 \text{ people}} = \frac{d \text{ deaths}}{4,000,000 \text{ people}}$$

$10.1(4,000,000) = 1,000,000 \cdot d$

$40,400,000 = 1,000,000d$

$$\frac{40,400,000}{1,000,000} = \frac{1,000,000d}{1,000,000}$$

$40.4 = d$

Approximately 40 people aged 5 to 34 die from asthma each year in New York City.

SECTION 5.3

CHECK YOUR PROGRESS 1, *page 284*

a. $74\% = 0.74$

b. $152\% = 1.52$

c. $8.3\% = 0.083$

d. $0.6\% = 0.006$

CHECK YOUR PROGRESS 2, *page 284*

a. $0.3 = 30\%$

b. $1.65 = 165\%$

c. $0.072 = 7.2\%$

d. $0.004 = 0.4\%$

CHECK YOUR PROGRESS 3, *page 285*

a. $8\% = 8\left(\dfrac{1}{100}\right) = \dfrac{8}{100} = \dfrac{2}{25}$

b. $180\% = 180\left(\dfrac{1}{100}\right) = \dfrac{180}{100} = 1\dfrac{80}{100} = 1\dfrac{4}{5}$

c. $2.5\% = 2.5\left(\dfrac{1}{100}\right) = \dfrac{2.5}{100} = \dfrac{25}{1000} = \dfrac{1}{40}$

d. $66\dfrac{2}{3}\% = \dfrac{200}{3}\% = \dfrac{200}{3}\left(\dfrac{1}{100}\right) = \dfrac{2}{3}$

CHECK YOUR PROGRESS 4, *page 286*

a. $\dfrac{1}{4} = 0.25 = 25\%$

b. $\dfrac{3}{8} = 0.375 = 37.5\%$

c. $\dfrac{5}{6} = 0.83\overline{3} = 83.\overline{3}\%$

d. $1\dfrac{2}{3} = 1.66\overline{6} = 166.\overline{6}\%$

CHECK YOUR PROGRESS 5, *page 287*

$$\dfrac{\text{Percent}}{100} = \dfrac{\text{amount}}{\text{base}}$$

$$\dfrac{70}{100} = \dfrac{22,400}{B}$$

$$70 \cdot B = 100(22,400)$$

$$70B = 2,240,000$$

$$\dfrac{70B}{70} = \dfrac{2,240,000}{70}$$

$$B = 32,000$$

The Blazer cost $32,000 when it was new.

CHECK YOUR PROGRESS 6, *page 288*

$$\dfrac{\text{Percent}}{100} = \dfrac{\text{amount}}{\text{base}}$$

$$\dfrac{p}{100} = \dfrac{416,000}{1,300,000}$$

$$p \cdot 1,300,000 = 100(416,000)$$

$$1,300,000p = 41,600,000$$

$$\dfrac{1,300,000p}{1,300,000} = \dfrac{41,600,000}{1,300,000}$$

$$p = 32$$

32% of the enlisted people are over the age of 30.

CHECK YOUR PROGRESS 7, *page 289*

$$\dfrac{\text{Percent}}{100} = \dfrac{\text{amount}}{\text{base}}$$

$$\dfrac{3.5}{100} = \dfrac{A}{32,500}$$

$$3.5(32,500) = 100(A)$$

$$113,750 = 100A$$

$$\dfrac{113,750}{100} = \dfrac{100A}{100}$$

$$1137.5 = A$$

The customer would receive a rebate of $1137.50.

CHECK YOUR PROGRESS 8, *page 289*

$$PB = A$$

$$0.05(32,685) = A$$

$$1634.25 = A$$

The teacher contributes $1634.25.

CHECK YOUR PROGRESS 9, *page 290*

$$PB = A$$

$$0.03B = 14,370$$

$$\dfrac{0.03B}{0.03} = \dfrac{14,370}{0.03}$$

$$B = 479,000$$

The selling price of the home was $479,000.

CHECK YOUR PROGRESS 10, *page 290*

$$PB = A$$

$$P \cdot 90 = 63$$

$$\dfrac{P \cdot 90}{90} = \dfrac{63}{90}$$

$$P = 0.7$$

$$P = 70\%$$

You answered 70% of the questions correctly.

CHECK YOUR PROGRESS 11, *page 291*

$$PB = A$$
$$0.90(21,262) = A$$
$$19,135.80 = A$$

$$21,262 - 19,135.80 = 2126.20$$

The difference between the cost of the remodeling and the increase in value of your home is $2126.20.

CHECK YOUR PROGRESS 12, *page 293*

$$5.67 - 1.82 = 3.85$$

$$PB = A$$
$$P \cdot 1.82 = 3.85$$
$$\frac{P \cdot 1.82}{1.82} = \frac{3.85}{1.82}$$
$$P \approx 2.115$$

The percent increase in the federal debt from 1985 to 2000 was 211.5%.

CHECK YOUR PROGRESS 13, *page 295*

$$\frac{\text{Percent}}{100} = \frac{\text{amount}}{\text{base}}$$

$$\frac{3.81}{100} = \frac{A}{20,416}$$

$$3.81(20,416) = 100(A)$$
$$77,784.96 = 100A$$
$$\frac{77,784.96}{100} = \frac{100A}{100}$$
$$778 \approx A$$

$$20,416 - 778 = 19,638$$

There were 19,638 passenger car fatalities in the United States in 2003.

SECTION 5.4

CHECK YOUR PROGRESS 1, *page 307*

$$2s^2 = 6 - 4s$$
$$2s^2 + 4s = 6 - 4s + 4s$$
$$2s^2 + 4s = 6$$
$$2s^2 + 4s - 6 = 6 - 6$$
$$2s^2 + 4s - 6 = 0$$

CHECK YOUR PROGRESS 2, *page 308*

$$(n + 5)(2n - 3) = 0$$

$$n + 5 = 0 \qquad\qquad 2n - 3 = 0$$
$$n = -5 \qquad\qquad\quad 2n = 3$$
$$n = \frac{3}{2}$$

Check:

$(n + 5)(2n - 3) = 0$		$(n + 5)(2n - 3) = 0$	
$(-5 + 5)[2(-5) - 3]$	0	$\left(\frac{3}{2} + 5\right)\left(2 \cdot \frac{3}{2} - 3\right)$	0
$0(-13)$	0	$\frac{13}{2}(3 - 3)$	0
	$0 = 0$		$0 = 0$

The solutions are -5 and $\frac{3}{2}$.

CHECK YOUR PROGRESS 3, *page 309*

$$2x^2 = x + 1$$
$$2x^2 - x = x - x + 1$$
$$2x^2 - x = 1$$
$$2x^2 - x - 1 = 1 - 1$$
$$2x^2 - x - 1 = 0$$
$$(2x + 1)(x - 1) = 0$$

$$2x + 1 = 0 \qquad\qquad x - 1 = 0$$
$$2x = -1 \qquad\qquad\quad x = 1$$
$$x = -\frac{1}{2}$$

Check:

$2x^2 = x + 1$		$2x^2 = x + 1$	
$2\left(-\frac{1}{2}\right)^2$	$-\frac{1}{2} + 1$	$2(1)^2$	$1 + 1$
$2\left(\frac{1}{4}\right)$	$\frac{1}{2}$	$2(1)$	2
$\frac{1}{2} = \frac{1}{2}$		$2 = 2$	

The solutions are $-\frac{1}{2}$ and 1.

CHECK YOUR PROGRESS 4, *page 310*

$$2x^2 = 8x - 5$$
$$2x^2 - 8x + 5 = 0$$
$$a = 2, b = -8, c = 5$$
$$x = \frac{-b \pm \sqrt{b^2 - 4ac}}{2a}$$

$$x = \frac{-(-8) \pm \sqrt{(-8)^2 - 4(2)(5)}}{2(2)} = \frac{8 \pm \sqrt{64 - 40}}{4}$$

$$= \frac{8 \pm \sqrt{24}}{4} = \frac{8 \pm 2\sqrt{6}}{4} = \frac{2(4 \pm \sqrt{6})}{2(2)} = \frac{4 \pm \sqrt{6}}{2}$$

The exact solutions are $\dfrac{4 + \sqrt{6}}{2}$ and $\dfrac{4 - \sqrt{6}}{2}$.

$$\frac{4 + \sqrt{6}}{2} \approx 3.225 \qquad \frac{4 - \sqrt{6}}{2} \approx 0.775$$

To the nearest thousandth, the solutions are 3.225 and 0.775.

CHECK YOUR PROGRESS 5, *page 311*

$$z^2 = -6 - 2z$$

$$z^2 + 2z + 6 = 0$$

$$a = 1, \, b = 2, \, c = 6$$

$$z = \frac{-b \pm \sqrt{b^2 - 4ac}}{2a}$$

$$z = \frac{-(2) \pm \sqrt{(2)^2 - 4(1)(6)}}{2(1)}$$

$$= \frac{-2 \pm \sqrt{4 - 24}}{2} = \frac{-2 \pm \sqrt{-20}}{2}$$

$\sqrt{-20}$ is not a real number.

The equation has no real number solutions.

CHECK YOUR PROGRESS 6, *page 312*

$$h = 64t - 16t^2$$

$$0 = 64t - 16t^2$$

$$16t^2 - 64t = 0$$

$$16t(t - 4) = 0$$

$$16t = 0 \qquad t - 4 = 0$$
$$t = 0 \qquad\quad t = 4$$

The object will be on the ground at 0 seconds and after 4 seconds.

CHECK YOUR PROGRESS 7, *page 313*

$$h = -16t^2 + 32t + 6.5$$

$$10 = -16t^2 + 32t + 6.5$$

$$16t^2 - 32t + 3.5 = 0$$

$$a = 16, \, b = -32, \, c = 3.5$$

$$t = \frac{-b \pm \sqrt{b^2 - 4ac}}{2a}$$

$$t = \frac{-(-32) \pm \sqrt{(-32)^2 - 4(16)(3.5)}}{2(16)} = \frac{32 \pm \sqrt{800}}{32}$$

$$t = \frac{32 + \sqrt{800}}{32} \approx 1.88 \qquad t = \frac{32 - \sqrt{800}}{32} \approx 0.12$$

The solution $t \approx 0.12$ second is not reasonable. The ball hits the basket 1.88 seconds after the ball is released.

CHAPTER 6

SECTION 6.1

CHECK YOUR PROGRESS 1, *page 330*

x	$-2x + 3 = y$	(x, y)
-2	$-2(-2) + 3 = 7$	$(-2, 7)$
-1	$-2(-1) + 3 = 5$	$(-1, 5)$
0	$-2(0) + 3 = 3$	$(0, 3)$
1	$-2(1) + 3 = 1$	$(1, 1)$
2	$-2(2) + 3 = -1$	$(2, -1)$
3	$-2(3) + 3 = -3$	$(3, -3)$

CHECK YOUR PROGRESS 2, *page 331*

x	$-x^2 + 1 = y$	(x, y)
-3	$-(-3)^2 + 1 = -8$	$(-3, -8)$
-2	$-(-2)^2 + 1 = -3$	$(-2, -3)$
-1	$-(-1)^2 + 1 = 0$	$(-1, 0)$
0	$-(0)^2 + 1 = 1$	$(0, 1)$
1	$-(1)^2 + 1 = 0$	$(1, 0)$
2	$-(2)^2 + 1 = -3$	$(2, -3)$
3	$-(3)^2 + 1 = -8$	$(3, -8)$

CHECK YOUR PROGRESS 3, *page 334*

$f(z) = z^2 - z$

$f(-3) = (-3)^2 - (-3)$

$\qquad = 12$

The value of the function is 12 when $z = -3$.

CHECK YOUR PROGRESS 4, *page 334*

$N(s) = \dfrac{s^2 - 3s}{2}$

$N(12) = \dfrac{(12)^2 - 3(12)}{2}$

$\qquad = \dfrac{144 - 36}{2}$

$\qquad = 54$

A polygon with 12 sides has 54 diagonals.

CHECK YOUR PROGRESS 5, *page 336*

x	$f(x) = 2 - \dfrac{3}{4}x$	(x, y)
-3	$f(-3) = 2 - \dfrac{3}{4}(-3) = 4\dfrac{1}{4}$	$\left(-3, 4\dfrac{1}{4}\right)$
-2	$f(-2) = 2 - \dfrac{3}{4}(-2) = 3\dfrac{1}{2}$	$\left(-2, 3\dfrac{1}{2}\right)$
-1	$f(-1) = 2 - \dfrac{3}{4}(-1) = 2\dfrac{3}{4}$	$\left(-1, 2\dfrac{3}{4}\right)$
0	$f(0) = 2 - \dfrac{3}{4}(0) = 2$	$(0, 2)$
1	$f(1) = 2 - \dfrac{3}{4}(1) = 1\dfrac{1}{4}$	$\left(1, 1\dfrac{1}{4}\right)$
2	$f(2) = 2 - \dfrac{3}{4}(2) = \dfrac{1}{2}$	$\left(2, \dfrac{1}{2}\right)$
3	$f(3) = 2 - \dfrac{3}{4}(3) = -\dfrac{1}{4}$	$\left(3, -\dfrac{1}{4}\right)$

SECTION 6.2

CHECK YOUR PROGRESS 1, *page 342*

$f(x) = \dfrac{1}{2}x + 3$ $\qquad\qquad$ $f(x) = \dfrac{1}{2}x + 3$

$\quad 0 = \dfrac{1}{2}x + 3$ $\qquad\qquad$ $f(0) = \dfrac{1}{2}(0) + 3$

$-3 = \dfrac{1}{2}x$ $\qquad\qquad\qquad\qquad = 3$

$-6 = x$

The x-intercept is $(-6, 0)$. $\qquad$ The y-intercept is $(0, 3)$.

CHECK YOUR PROGRESS 2, *page 343*

$g(t) = -20t + 8000$

$g(0) = -20(0) + 8000 = 8000$

The intercept on the vertical axis is $(0, 8000)$. This means that the plane is at an altitude of 8000 feet when it begins its descent.

$\quad g(t) = -20t + 8000$

$\qquad 0 = -20t + 8000$

$-8000 = -20t$

$\quad 400 = t$

The intercept on the horizontal axis is $(400, 0)$. This means that the plane reaches the ground 400 seconds after beginning its descent.

CHECK YOUR PROGRESS 3, *page 346*

a. $(x_1, y_1) = (-6, 5), (x_2, y_2) = (4, -5)$

$m = \dfrac{y_2 - y_1}{x_2 - x_1} = \dfrac{-5 - 5}{4 - (-6)} = \dfrac{-10}{10} = -1$

The slope is -1.

b. $(x_1, y_1) = (-5, 0), (x_2, y_2) = (-5, 7)$

$m = \dfrac{y_2 - y_1}{x_2 - x_1} = \dfrac{7 - 0}{-5 - (-5)} = \dfrac{7}{0}$

The slope is undefined.

c. $(x_1, y_1) = (-7, -2), (x_2, y_2) = (8, 8)$

$m = \dfrac{y_2 - y_1}{x_2 - x_1} = \dfrac{8 - (-2)}{8 - (-7)} = \dfrac{10}{15} = \dfrac{2}{3}$

The slope is $\dfrac{2}{3}$.

d. $(x_1, y_1) = (-6, 7), (x_2, y_2) = (1, 7)$

$m = \dfrac{y_2 - y_1}{x_2 - x_1} = \dfrac{7 - 7}{1 - (-6)} = \dfrac{0}{7} = 0$

The slope is 0.

CHECK YOUR PROGRESS 4, *page 347*

For the linear function $d(t) = 50t$, the slope is the coefficient of t. Therefore, the slope is 50. This means that a homing pigeon can fly 50 miles for each 1 hour of flight time.

CHECK YOUR PROGRESS 5, *page 348*

CHECK YOUR PROGRESS 6, *page 348*

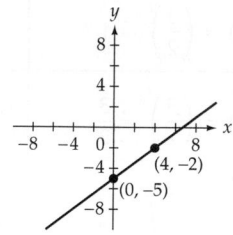

SECTION 6.3

CHECK YOUR PROGRESS 1, *page 355*

$f(a) = ma + b$
$f(a) = -3.5a + 100$

The linear function is $f(a) = -3.5a + 100$, where $f(a)$ is the boiling point of water at an altitude of a kilometers above sea level.

CHECK YOUR PROGRESS 2, *page 355*

$$y - y_1 = m(x - x_1)$$
$$y - 2 = -\frac{1}{2}[x - (-2)]$$
$$y - 2 = -\frac{1}{2}x - 1$$
$$y = -\frac{1}{2}x + 1$$

CHECK YOUR PROGRESS 3, *page 356*

$$C - C_1 = m(t - t_1)$$
$$C - 191 = 3.8(t - 50)$$
$$C - 191 = 3.8t - 190$$
$$C = 3.8t + 1$$

A linear function that models the number of calories burned is $C(t) = 3.8t + 1$.

CHECK YOUR PROGRESS 4, *page 356*

$$m = \frac{y_2 - y_1}{x_2 - x_1} = \frac{1 - 3}{4 - (-2)} = \frac{-2}{6} = -\frac{1}{3}$$
$$y - y_1 = m(x - x_1)$$
$$y - 3 = -\frac{1}{3}[x - (-2)]$$
$$y - 3 = -\frac{1}{3}x - \frac{2}{3}$$
$$y = -\frac{1}{3}x + \frac{7}{3}$$

CHECK YOUR PROGRESS 5, *page 359*

The regression equation is $y = 5.6\overline{3}x - 252.8\overline{6}$.

The estimated weight of a woman swimmer who is 63 inches tall is approximately 102 pounds.

SECTION 6.4

CHECK YOUR PROGRESS 1, *page 365*

$$a = 1, b = 0; \; -\frac{b}{2a} = -\frac{0}{2(1)} = 0$$
$$y = x^2 - 2$$
$$y = (0)^2 - 2$$
$$y = -2$$

The vertex is $(0, -2)$.

CHECK YOUR PROGRESS 2, *page 367*

a. $y = 2x^2 - 5x + 2$
$0 = 2x^2 - 5x + 2$
$0 = (2x - 1)(x - 2)$

$\quad 2x - 1 = 0 \qquad\quad x - 2 = 0$
$\qquad\quad x = \dfrac{1}{2} \qquad\qquad x = 2$

The x-intercepts are $\left(\frac{1}{2}, 0\right)$ and $(2, 0)$.

b. $y = x^2 + 4x + 4$
$0 = x^2 + 4x + 4$
$0 = (x + 2)(x + 2)$

$\quad x + 2 = 0 \qquad\quad x + 2 = 0$
$\qquad x = -2 \qquad\qquad x = -2$

The x-intercept is $(-2, 0)$.

CHECK YOUR PROGRESS 3, *page 368*

$a = 2, b = -3; -\dfrac{b}{2a} = -\dfrac{-3}{2(2)} = \dfrac{3}{4}$

$f(x) = 2x^2 - 3x + 1$

$f\left(\dfrac{3}{4}\right) = 2\left(\dfrac{3}{4}\right)^2 - 3\left(\dfrac{3}{4}\right) + 1$

$f\left(\dfrac{3}{4}\right) = -\dfrac{1}{8}$

The vertex is $\left(\dfrac{3}{4}, -\dfrac{1}{8}\right)$. The minimum value of the function is $-\dfrac{1}{8}$, the y-coordinate of the vertex.

CHECK YOUR PROGRESS 4, *page 369*

$a = -16, b = 64; -\dfrac{b}{2a} = -\dfrac{64}{2(-16)} = 2$

The ball reaches its maximum height in 2 seconds.

$s(t) = -16t^2 + 64t + 4$

$s(2) = -16(2)^2 + 64(2) + 4$

$s(2) = 68$

The maximum height of the ball is 68 feet.

CHECK YOUR PROGRESS 5, *page 370*

Perimeter: $w + l + w + l = 44$

$\qquad\qquad 2w + 2l = 44$

$\qquad\qquad w + l = 22$

$\qquad\qquad l = -w + 22$

Area: $A = lw$

$\qquad = (-w + 22)w$

$\quad A = -w^2 + 22w$

$w = -\dfrac{b}{2a} = -\dfrac{22}{2(-1)} = 11$

The width is 11 feet.

$l = -w + 22$

$l = -(11) + 22 = 11$

The length is 11 feet.

The dimensions of the rectangle with maximum area are 11 feet by 11 feet.

SECTION 6.5

CHECK YOUR PROGRESS 1, *page 378*

$g(x) = \left(\dfrac{1}{2}\right)^x$

$g(3) = \left(\dfrac{1}{2}\right)^3 = \dfrac{1}{8}$

$g(-1) = \left(\dfrac{1}{2}\right)^{-1} = \dfrac{1}{\frac{1}{2}} = 2$

$g(\sqrt{3}) = \left(\dfrac{1}{2}\right)^{\sqrt{3}} \approx \left(\dfrac{1}{2}\right)^{1.732} \approx 0.301$

CHECK YOUR PROGRESS 2, *page 380*

Because the base $\dfrac{3}{2}$ is greater than 1, f is an exponential growth function.

x	$f(x) = \left(\dfrac{3}{2}\right)^x$	(x, y)
-3	$f(-3) = \left(\dfrac{3}{2}\right)^{-3} = \dfrac{8}{27}$	$\left(-3, \dfrac{8}{27}\right)$
-2	$f(-2) = \left(\dfrac{3}{2}\right)^{-2} = \dfrac{4}{9}$	$\left(-2, \dfrac{4}{9}\right)$
-1	$f(-1) = \left(\dfrac{3}{2}\right)^{-1} = \dfrac{2}{3}$	$\left(-1, \dfrac{2}{3}\right)$
0	$f(0) = \left(\dfrac{3}{2}\right)^{0} = 1$	$(0, 1)$
1	$f(1) = \left(\dfrac{3}{2}\right)^{1} = \dfrac{3}{2}$	$\left(1, \dfrac{3}{2}\right)$
2	$f(2) = \left(\dfrac{3}{2}\right)^{2} = \dfrac{9}{4}$	$\left(2, \dfrac{9}{4}\right)$
3	$f(3) = \left(\dfrac{3}{2}\right)^{3} = \dfrac{27}{8}$	$\left(3, \dfrac{27}{8}\right)$

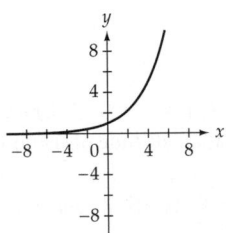

CHECK YOUR PROGRESS 3, *page 381*

x	-2	-1	0	1	2
$f(x) = e^{-x} + 2$	9.4	4.7	3	2.4	2.1

CHECK YOUR PROGRESS 4, *page 382*

$$N(t) = 1.5\left(\tfrac{1}{2}\right)^{t/193.7}$$

$$N(24) = 1.5\left(\tfrac{1}{2}\right)^{24/193.7}$$

$$\approx 1.5(0.9177) \approx 1.3766$$

After 24 hours, there are approximately 1.3766 grams of the isotope in the body.

CHECK YOUR PROGRESS 5, *page 383*

$$A(t) = 200e^{-0.014t}$$

$$A(45) = 200e^{-0.014(45)}$$

$$\approx 107$$

After 45 minutes, there are approximately 107 milligrams of aspirin in the patient's bloodstream.

CHECK YOUR PROGRESS 6, *pages 384–385*
The regression equation is $P(a) \approx 10.1468(0.8910)^a$.

The atmospheric pressure at an altitude of 24 kilometers is approximately 0.6 newton per square centimeter.

SECTION 6.6

CHECK YOUR PROGRESS 1, *page 391*

a. $2^{10} = 4x$

b. $\log_{10} 2x = 3$

CHECK YOUR PROGRESS 2, *page 392*

a. $\log_{10} 0.001 = x$
$10^x = 0.001$
$10^x = 10^{-3}$
$x = -3$
$\log_{10} 0.001 = -3$

b. $\log_5 125 = x$
$5^x = 125$
$5^x = 5^3$
$x = 3$
$\log_5 125 = 3$

CHECK YOUR PROGRESS 3, *page 392*
$\log_2 x = 6$
$2^6 = x$
$64 = x$

CHECK YOUR PROGRESS 4, *page 393*

a. $\log x = -2.1$
$10^{-2.1} = x$
$0.008 \approx x$

b. $\ln x = 2$
$e^2 = x$
$7.389 \approx x$

CHECK YOUR PROGRESS 5, *page 394*

$y = \log_5 x$
$5^y = x$

$x = 5^y$	$\tfrac{1}{25}$	$\tfrac{1}{5}$	1	5	25
y	-2	-1	0	1	2

CHECK YOUR PROGRESS 6, *page 395*

a. $S(0) = 5 + 29 \ln(0 + 1) = 5$
The average typing speed when the student first started to type was 5 words per minute.
$S(3) = 5 + 29 \ln(3 + 1) \approx 45$
The average typing speed after 3 months was about 45 words per minute.

b. $S(3) - S(0) = 45 - 5 = 40$
The typing speed increased by 40 words per minute during the 3 months.

CHECK YOUR PROGRESS 7, *page 396*
$I = 2 \cdot (12{,}589{,}254 I_0) = 25{,}178{,}508 I_0$

$$M = \log\left(\frac{I}{I_0}\right) = \log\left(\frac{25{,}178{,}508 I_0}{I_0}\right) = \log(25{,}178{,}508) \approx 7.4$$

The Richter scale magnitude of an earthquake whose intensity is twice that of the Amazonas, Brazil, earthquake is 7.4.

CHECK YOUR PROGRESS 8, *page 396*

$$\log\left(\frac{I}{I_0}\right) = 4.6$$

$$\frac{I}{I_0} = 10^{4.6}$$

$$I = 10^{4.6} I_0$$

$$I \approx 39{,}811 I_0$$

The April 29, 2003 earthquake had an intensity that was approximately 40,000 times the intensity of a zero-level earthquake.

CHECK YOUR PROGRESS 9, *page 397*

a. $\text{pH} = -\log[\text{H}^+] = -\log(2.41 \times 10^{-13}) \approx 12.6$
The cleaning solution has a pH of 12.6.

b. $\text{pH} = -\log[\text{H}^+] = -\log(5.07 \times 10^{-4}) \approx 3.3$
The cola soft drink has a pH of 3.3.

c. pH $= -\log[H^+] = -\log(6.31 \times 10^{-5}) \approx 4.2$
The rainwater has a pH of 4.2.

CHECK YOUR PROGRESS 10, *page 398*

$$pH = -\log[H^+]$$
$$10.0 = -\log[H^+]$$

$$-10.0 = \log[H^+]$$
$$10^{-10.0} = H^+$$
$$1.0 \times 10^{-10} = H^+$$

The hydronium-ion concentration of the water in the Great Salt Lake in Utah is 1.0×10^{-10} moles per liter.

CHAPTER 7

SECTION 7.1

CHECK YOUR PROGRESS 1, *page 408*

a. $6 \oplus 10 = 4$

b. $5 \oplus 9 = 2$

c. $7 \ominus 11 = 8$

d. $5 \ominus 10 = 7$

CHECK YOUR PROGRESS 2, *page 410*

The years 2008, 2012, and 2016 are leap years, so there are 3 years between the two dates with 366 days and 6 years with 365 days. The total number of days between the dates is $3 \cdot 366 + 6 \cdot 365 = 3288$. $3288 \div 7 = 469$ remainder 5, so $3288 \equiv 5 \bmod 7$. The day of the week 3288 days after Tuesday, February 12, 2008 will be the same as the day 5 days later, a Sunday.

CHECK YOUR PROGRESS 3, *page 411*

$51 + 72 = 123$, and $123 \div 3 = 41$ remainder 0, so $(51 + 72) \bmod 3 \equiv 0$.

CHECK YOUR PROGRESS 4, *page 411*

$21 - 43 = -22$, a negative number. Repeatedly add the modulus 7 to the difference until a whole number is reached.

$$-22 + 7 = -15$$
$$-15 + 7 = -8$$
$$-8 + 7 = -1$$
$$-1 + 7 = 6$$

$(21 - 43) \bmod 7 \equiv 6$.

CHECK YOUR PROGRESS 5, *page 412*

Tuesday corresponds to 2 (see the chart on page 408), so the day of the week 93 days from now is represented by $(2 + 93) \bmod 7$. Because $95 \div 7 = 13$ remainder 4, $(2 + 93) \bmod 7 \equiv 4$, which corresponds to Thursday.

CHECK YOUR PROGRESS 6, *page 412*

$33 \cdot 41 = 1353$ and $1353 \div 17 = 79$ remainder 10, so $(33 \cdot 41) \bmod 17 \equiv 10$.

CHECK YOUR PROGRESS 7, *page 414*

Substitute each whole number from 0 to 11 into the congruence.

$4(0) + 1 \not\equiv 5 \bmod 12$	Not a solution
$4(1) + 1 \equiv 5 \bmod 12$	1 is a solution.
$4(2) + 1 \not\equiv 5 \bmod 12$	Not a solution
$4(3) + 1 \not\equiv 5 \bmod 12$	Not a solution
$4(4) + 1 \equiv 5 \bmod 12$	4 is a solution.
$4(5) + 1 \not\equiv 5 \bmod 12$	Not a solution
$4(6) + 1 \not\equiv 5 \bmod 12$	Not a solution
$4(7) + 1 \equiv 5 \bmod 12$	7 is a solution.
$4(8) + 1 \not\equiv 5 \bmod 12$	Not a solution
$4(9) + 1 \not\equiv 5 \bmod 12$	Not a solution
$4(10) + 1 \equiv 5 \bmod 12$	10 is a solution.
$4(11) + 1 \not\equiv 5 \bmod 12$	Not a solution

The solutions from 0 to 11 are 1, 4, 7, and 10. The remaining solutions are obtained by repeatedly adding the modulus 12 to these solutions. So the solutions are 1, 4, 7, 10, 13, 16, 19, 22, ...

CHECK YOUR PROGRESS 8, *page 414*

In mod 12 arithmetic, $6 + 6 = 12$, so the additive inverse of 6 is 6.

CHECK YOUR PROGRESS 9, *page 415*

Solve the congruence equation $5x \equiv 1 \bmod 11$ by substituting whole number values of x less than the modulus.

$$5(1) \not\equiv 1 \bmod 11$$
$$5(2) \not\equiv 1 \bmod 11$$
$$5(3) \not\equiv 1 \bmod 11$$
$$5(4) \not\equiv 1 \bmod 11$$
$$5(5) \not\equiv 1 \bmod 11$$
$$5(6) \not\equiv 1 \bmod 11$$
$$5(7) \not\equiv 1 \bmod 11$$
$$5(8) \not\equiv 1 \bmod 11$$
$$5(9) \equiv 1 \bmod 11$$

In mod 11 arithmetic, the multiplicative inverse of 5 is 9.

SECTION 7.2

CHECK YOUR PROGRESS 1, *page 420*

Check the ISBN congruence equation.

$$0(10) + 2(9) + 0(8) + 1(7) + 1(6) + 5(5) + 5(4) + 0(3) + 2(2) + 4 \equiv ? \bmod 11$$
$$84 \equiv 7 \bmod 11$$

Because $84 \not\equiv 0 \bmod 11$, the ISBN is invalid.

CHECK YOUR PROGRESS 2, *page 421*

Check the UPC congruence equation.

$$1(3) + 3(1) + 2(3) + 3(1) + 4(3) + 2(1) + 6(3) + 5(1) + 9(3) + 3(1) + 3(3) + 9 \equiv ? \bmod 10$$
$$100 \equiv 0 \bmod 10$$

Because $100 \equiv 0 \bmod 10$, the UPC is valid.

CHECK YOUR PROGRESS 3, *page 422*

Highlight every other digit, reading from right to left:

6 0 1 1 0 1 2 3 9 1 4 5 2 3 1 7

Double the highlighted digits:

12 0 2 1 0 1 4 3 18 1 8 5 4 3 2 7

Add all the digits, treating two-digit numbers as two single digits:

$$(1 + 2) + 0 + 2 + 1 + 0 + 1 + 4 + 3 + (1 + 8) + 1 + 8 + 5 + 4 + 3 + 2 + 7 = 53$$

Because $53 \not\equiv 0 \bmod 10$, this is not a valid credit card number.

CHECK YOUR PROGRESS 4, *page 425*

a. The encrypting congruence is $c \equiv (p + 17) \bmod 26$.

A	$c \equiv (1 + 17) \bmod 26 \equiv 18 \bmod 26 \equiv 18$	Code A as R.
L	$c \equiv (12 + 17) \bmod 26 \equiv 29 \bmod 26 \equiv 3$	Code L as C.
P	$c \equiv (16 + 17) \bmod 26 \equiv 33 \bmod 26 \equiv 7$	Code P as G.
I	$c \equiv (9 + 17) \bmod 26 \equiv 26 \bmod 26 \equiv 0$	Code I as Z.
N	$c \equiv (14 + 17) \bmod 26 \equiv 31 \bmod 26 \equiv 5$	Code N as E.
E	$c \equiv (5 + 17) \bmod 26 \equiv 22 \bmod 26 \equiv 22$	Code E as V.
S	$c \equiv (19 + 17) \bmod 26 \equiv 36 \bmod 26 \equiv 10$	Code S as J.
K	$c \equiv (11 + 17) \bmod 26 \equiv 28 \bmod 26 \equiv 2$	Code K as B.
G	$c \equiv (7 + 17) \bmod 26 \equiv 24 \bmod 26 \equiv 24$	Code G as X.

Thus the plaintext ALPINE SKIING is coded as RCGZEV JBZZEX.

b. To decode, because $m = 17$, $n = 26 - 17 = 9$, and the decoding congruence is $p \equiv (c + 9) \bmod 26$.

T	$c \equiv (20 + 9) \bmod 26 \equiv 29 \bmod 26 \equiv 3$	Decode T as C.
I	$c \equiv (9 + 9) \bmod 26 \equiv 18 \bmod 26 \equiv 18$	Decode I as R.
F	$c \equiv (6 + 9) \bmod 26 \equiv 15 \bmod 26 \equiv 15$	Decode F as O.
J	$c \equiv (10 + 9) \bmod 26 \equiv 19 \bmod 26 \equiv 19$	Decode J as S.

Continuing, the ciphertext TIFJJ TFLEKIP JBZZEX decodes as CROSS COUNTRY SKIING.

CHECK YOUR PROGRESS 5, *page 426*

The encrypting congruence is $c \equiv (3p + 1) \bmod 26$.

C	$c \equiv (3 \cdot 3 + 1) \bmod 26 \equiv 10 \bmod 26 = 10$	Code C as J.
O	$c \equiv (3 \cdot 15 + 1) \bmod 26 \equiv 46 \bmod 26 \equiv 20$	Code O as T.
L	$c \equiv (3 \cdot 12 + 1) \bmod 26 \equiv 37 \bmod 26 \equiv 11$	Code L as K.
R	$c \equiv (3 \cdot 18 + 1) \bmod 26 \equiv 55 \bmod 26 \equiv 3$	Code R as C.

Continuing, the plaintext COLOR MONITOR is coded as JTKTC NTQBITC.

CHECK YOUR PROGRESS 6, *page 427*

Solve the congruence equation $c \equiv (7p + 1) \bmod 26$ for p.

$$c = 7p + 1$$
$$c - 1 = 7p \qquad \text{• Subtract 1 from each side of the equation.}$$
$$15(c - 1) = 15(7p) \qquad \text{• Multiply each side of the equation by the multiplicative inverse of 7.}$$
$$\text{Because } 7 \cdot 15 \equiv 1 \bmod 26, \text{ multiply each side by 15.}$$

$$[15(c - 1)] \bmod 26 \equiv p$$

The decoding congruence is $p \equiv [15(c - 1)] \bmod 26$.

I	$p \equiv [15(9 - 1)] \bmod 26 \equiv 120 \bmod 26 \equiv 16$	Decode I as P.
G	$p \equiv [15(7 - 1)] \bmod 26 \equiv 90 \bmod 26 \equiv 12$	Decode G as L.
H	$p \equiv [15(8 - 1)] \bmod 26 \equiv 105 \bmod 26 \equiv 1$	Decode H as A.
T	$p \equiv [15(20 - 1)] \bmod 26 \equiv 285 \bmod 26 \equiv 25$	Decode T as Y.

Continuing, the ciphertext IGHT OHGG decodes as PLAY BALL.

SECTION 7.3

CHECK YOUR PROGRESS 1, *page 433*

Check to see whether the four properties of a group are satisfied.

1. The product of two integers is always an integer, so the integers are closed with respect to multiplication.

2. The associative property of multiplication is true for integers.

3. The integers have an identity element for multiplication, namely 1.

4. Not every integer has a multiplicative inverse that is also an integer. For instance, $\frac{1}{2}$ is the multiplicative inverse of 2, but $\frac{1}{2}$ is not an integer. There is no integer that can be multiplied by 2 that gives the identity element 1.

Because property 4 is not satisfied, the integers with multiplication do not form a group.

CHECK YOUR PROGRESS 2, *page 436*

Rotate the original triangle, I, about the line of symmetry through the bottom right vertex, followed by a clockwise rotation of 240°.

Therefore, $R_r \Delta R_{240} = R_l$.

CHECK YOUR PROGRESS 3, *page 437*

$$R_r \Delta R_{240} = \begin{pmatrix} 1 & 2 & 3 \\ 2 & 1 & 3 \end{pmatrix} \Delta \begin{pmatrix} 1 & 2 & 3 \\ 3 & 1 & 2 \end{pmatrix}$$

- $1 \to 2 \to 1$. Thus $1 \to 1$.
- $2 \to 1 \to 3$. Thus $2 \to 3$.
- $3 \to 3 \to 2$. Thus $3 \to 2$.

$$= \begin{pmatrix} 1 & 2 & 3 \\ 1 & 3 & 2 \end{pmatrix} = R_l$$

CHECK YOUR PROGRESS 4, *page 438*

$E\Delta B = \begin{pmatrix} 1 & 2 & 3 \\ 2 & 1 & 3 \end{pmatrix} \Delta \begin{pmatrix} 1 & 2 & 3 \\ 3 & 1 & 2 \end{pmatrix}$. 1 is replaced by 2, which is then replaced by 1 in the second permutation. Thus 1 remains as 1. 2 is replaced by 1, which is then replaced by 3, so ultimately, 2 is replaced by 3. Finally, 3 remains as 3 in the first permutation but is replaced by 2 in the second, so ultimately 3 is replaced by 2.

The result is $\begin{pmatrix} 1 & 2 & 3 \\ 1 & 3 & 2 \end{pmatrix}$, which is C. Thus $E\Delta B = C$.

CHECK YOUR PROGRESS 5, *page 439*

$D = \begin{pmatrix} 1 & 2 & 3 \\ 3 & 2 & 1 \end{pmatrix}$ replaces 1 with 3, 2 with 2, and 3 with 1.

Reversing these, we need to replace 3 with 1, leave 2 alone, and replace 1 with 3. This is the element $\begin{pmatrix} 1 & 2 & 3 \\ 3 & 2 & 1 \end{pmatrix}$, which is D again.

Thus D is its own inverse.

CHAPTER 8

SECTION 8.1

CHECK YOUR PROGRESS 1, *page 451*

$QR + RS + ST = QT$

$28 + 16 + 10 = QT$

$54 = QT$

$QT = 54$ cm

CHECK YOUR PROGRESS 2, *page 452*

$AB + BC = AC$

$\frac{1}{4}(BC) + BC = AC$

$\frac{1}{4}(16) + 16 = AC$

$4 + 16 = AC$

$20 = AC$

$AC = 20$ ft

CHECK YOUR PROGRESS 3, *page 454*

$m\angle G + m\angle H = 127° + 53° = 180°$

The sum of the measures of $\angle G$ and $\angle H$ is 180°. Angles G and H are supplementary angles.

CHECK YOUR PROGRESS 4, *page 455*

Supplementary angles are two angles the sum of whose measures is 180°. To find the supplement, let x represent the supplement of a 129° angle.

$x + 129 = 180$

$x = 51$

The supplement of a 129° angle is a 51° angle.

CHECK YOUR PROGRESS 5, *page 456*

$m\angle a + 68° = 118°$

$m\angle a = 50°$

The measure of $\angle a$ is 50°.

CHECK YOUR PROGRESS 6, *page 457*

$m\angle b + m\angle a = 180°$

$m\angle b + 35° = 180°$

$m\angle b = 145°$

$m\angle c = m\angle a = 35°$

$m\angle d = m\angle b = 145°$

$m\angle b = 145°$, $m\angle c = 35°$, and $m\angle d = 145°$.

CHECK YOUR PROGRESS 7, *page 459*

$m\angle b = m\angle g = 124°$

$m\angle d = m\angle g = 124°$

$m\angle c + m\angle b = 180°$

$m\angle c + 124° = 180°$

$m\angle c = 56°$

$m\angle b = 124°$, $m\angle c = 56°$, and $m\angle d = 124°$.

CHECK YOUR PROGRESS 8, *page 461*

$m\angle b + m\angle d = 180°$

$m\angle b + 105° = 180°$

$m\angle b = 75°$

$m\angle a + m\angle b + m\angle c = 180°$

$m\angle a + 75° + 35° = 180°$

$m\angle a + 110° = 180°$

$m\angle a = 70°$

$m\angle e = m\angle a = 70°$

CHECK YOUR PROGRESS 9, *page 461*

Let x represent the measure of the third angle.

$x + 90° + 27° = 180°$

$x + 117° = 180°$

$x = 63°$

The measure of the third angle is 63°.

SECTION 8.2

CHECK YOUR PROGRESS 1, *page 472*

$P = a + b + c$

$P = 4\frac{3}{10} + 2\frac{1}{10} + 6\frac{1}{2}$

$P = 4\frac{3}{10} + 2\frac{1}{10} + 6\frac{5}{10}$

$P = 12\frac{9}{10}$

The total length of the bike trail is $12\frac{9}{10}$ mi.

CHECK YOUR PROGRESS 2, *page 473*

$P = 2L + 2W$

$P = 2(12) + 2(8)$

$P = 24 + 16$

$P = 40$

You will need 40 ft of molding to edge the top of the walls.

CHECK YOUR PROGRESS 3, *page 474*

$P = 4s$
$P = 4(24)$
$P = 96$

The homeowner should purchase 96 ft of fencing.

CHECK YOUR PROGRESS 4, *page 474*

$P = 2b + 2s$
$P = 2(5) + 2(7)$
$P = 10 + 14$
$P = 24$

24 m of plank is needed to surround the garden.

CHECK YOUR PROGRESS 5, *page 476*

$C = \pi d$
$C = 9\pi$

The circumference of the circle is 9π km.

CHECK YOUR PROGRESS 6, *page 476*

12 in. = 1 ft

$C = \pi d$
$C = \pi(1)$
$C = \pi$

$12C = 12\pi \approx 37.70$

The tricycle travels approximately 37.70 ft when the wheel makes 12 revolutions.

CHECK YOUR PROGRESS 7, *page 478*

$A = LW$
$A = 308(192)$
$A = 59{,}136$

59,136 cm^2 of fabric is needed.

CHECK YOUR PROGRESS 8, *page 479*

$A = s^2$
$A = 24^2$
$A = 576$

The area of the floor is 576 ft^2.

CHECK YOUR PROGRESS 9, *page 480*

$A = bh$
$A = 14(8)$
$A = 112$

The area of the patio is 112 m^2.

CHECK YOUR PROGRESS 10, *page 481*

$A = \dfrac{1}{2}bh$

$A = \dfrac{1}{2}(18)(9)$

$A = 9(9)$
$A = 81$

81 in^2 of felt is needed.

CHECK YOUR PROGRESS 11, *page 482*

$A = \dfrac{1}{2}h(b_1 + b_2)$

$A = \dfrac{1}{2} \cdot 9(12 + 20)$

$A = \dfrac{1}{2} \cdot 9(32)$

$A = \dfrac{9}{2} \cdot (32)$

$A = 144$

The area of the patio is 144 ft^2.

CHECK YOUR PROGRESS 12, *page 483*

$r = \dfrac{1}{2}d = \dfrac{1}{2}(12) = 6$

$A = \pi r^2$
$A = \pi(6)^2$
$A = 36\pi$

The area of the circle is 36π km^2.

CHECK YOUR PROGRESS 13, *page 484*

$r = \dfrac{1}{2}d = \dfrac{1}{2}(4) = 2$

$A = \pi r^2$
$A = \pi(2)^2$
$A = \pi(4)$
$A \approx 12.57$

Approximately 12.57 ft^2 of material is needed.

SECTION 8.3

CHECK YOUR PROGRESS 1, *page 494*

$\dfrac{AC}{DF} = \dfrac{CH}{FG}$

$\dfrac{10}{15} = \dfrac{7}{FG}$

$10(FG) = (15)7$
$10(FG) = 105$
$FG = 10.5$

The height *FG* of triangle *DEF* is 10.5 m.

CHECK YOUR PROGRESS 2, *page 497*

$$\frac{AO}{DO} = \frac{AB}{DC}$$

$$\frac{AO}{3} = \frac{10}{4}$$

$$4(AO) = 3(10)$$

$$4(AO) = 30$$

$$AO = 7.5$$

$$A = \frac{1}{2}bh$$

$$A = \frac{1}{2}(10)(7.5)$$

$$A = 5(7.5)$$

$$A = 37.5$$

The area of triangle *AOB* is 37.5 cm².

CHECK YOUR PROGRESS 3, *page 499*

Because two sides and the included angle of one triangle are equal in measure to two sides and the included angle of the second triangle, the triangles are congruent by the SAS Theorem.

CHECK YOUR PROGRESS 4, *page 500*

$a^2 + b^2 = c^2$	• Use the Pythagorean Theorem.
$2^2 + b^2 = 6^2$	• $a = 2, c = 6$
$4 + b^2 = 36$	
$b^2 = 32$	• Solve for b^2. Subtract 4 from each side.
$\sqrt{b^2} = \sqrt{32}$	• Take the square root of each side of the equation.
$b \approx 5.66$	• Use a calculator to approximate $\sqrt{32}$.

The length of the other leg is approximately 5.66 m.

SECTION 8.4

CHECK YOUR PROGRESS 1, *page 511*

$$V = LWH$$

$$V = 5(3.2)(4)$$

$$V = 64$$

The volume of the solid is 64 m³.

CHECK YOUR PROGRESS 2, *page 511*

$$V = \frac{1}{3}s^2h$$

$$V = \frac{1}{3}(15)^2(25)$$

$$V = \frac{1}{3}(225)(25)$$

$$V = 1875$$

The volume of the pyramid is 1875 m³.

CHECK YOUR PROGRESS 3, *page 512*

$$r = \frac{1}{2}d = \frac{1}{2}(16) = 8$$

$$V = \pi r^2 h$$

$$V = \pi(8)^2(30)$$

$$V = \pi(64)(30)$$

$$V = 1920\pi$$

$$\frac{1}{4}(1920\pi) = 480\pi$$

$$\approx 1507.96$$

Approximately 1507.96 ft³ is not being used for storage.

CHECK YOUR PROGRESS 4, *page 515*

$$r = \frac{1}{2}d = \frac{1}{2}(6) = 3$$

$$S = 2\pi r^2 + 2\pi rh$$

$$S = 2\pi(3)^2 + 2\pi(3)(8)$$

$$S = 2\pi(9) + 2\pi(3)(8)$$

$$S = 18\pi + 48\pi$$

$$S = 66\pi$$

$$S \approx 207.35$$

The surface area of the cylinder is **approximately 207.35 ft².**

CHECK YOUR PROGRESS 5, *page 515*

$$\begin{aligned}\text{Surface area of the cube} &= 6s^2 \\ &= 6(8)^2 \\ &= 6(64) \\ &= 384 \text{ cm}^2\end{aligned}$$

$$\begin{aligned}\text{Surface area of the sphere} &= 4\pi r^2 \\ &= 4\pi(5)^2 \\ &= 4\pi(25) \\ &\approx 314.16 \text{ cm}^2\end{aligned}$$

The cube has a larger surface area.

SECTION 8.5

CHECK YOUR PROGRESS 1, *page 524*

Use the Pythagorean Theorem to find the length of the hypotenuse.

$$a^2 + b^2 = c^2$$

$$3^2 + 4^2 = c^2$$

$$9 + 16 = c^2$$

$$25 = c^2$$

$$\sqrt{25} = \sqrt{c^2}$$

$$5 = c$$

$$\sin \theta = \frac{\text{opp}}{\text{hyp}} = \frac{3}{5},$$

$$\cos \theta = \frac{\text{adj}}{\text{hyp}} = \frac{4}{5},$$

$$\tan \theta = \frac{\text{opp}}{\text{adj}} = \frac{3}{4}$$

CHECK YOUR PROGRESS 2, *page 525*

$\tan 37.1° = 0.7563$

CHECK YOUR PROGRESS 3, *page 526*

We are given the measure of $\angle B$ and the hypotenuse. We want to find the length of side a. The cosine function involves the side adjacent and the hypotenuse.

$$\cos B = \frac{\text{adj}}{\text{hyp}}$$

$$\cos 48° = \frac{a}{12}$$

$$12(\cos 48°) = a$$

$$8.03 \approx a$$

The length of side a is approximately 8.03 ft.

CHECK YOUR PROGRESS 4, *page 527*

$\tan^{-1}(0.3165) \approx 17.6°$

CHECK YOUR PROGRESS 5, *page 527*

$$\theta \approx \tan^{-1}(0.5681)$$

$$\theta \approx 29.6°$$

CHECK YOUR PROGRESS 6, *page 528*

We want to find the measure of $\angle A$, and we are given the length of the side opposite $\angle A$ and the hypotenuse. The sine function involves the side opposite an angle and the hypotenuse.

$$\sin A = \frac{\text{opp}}{\text{hyp}}$$

$$\sin A = \frac{7}{11}$$

$$A = \sin^{-1}\frac{7}{11}$$

$$A \approx 39.5°$$

The measure of $\angle A$ is approximately 39.5°.

CHECK YOUR PROGRESS 7, *page 529*

Let d be the distance from the base of the lighthouse to the boat.

$$\tan 25° = \frac{20}{d}$$

$$d(\tan 25°) = 20$$

$$d = \frac{20}{\tan 25°}$$

$$d \approx 42.9$$

The boat is approximately 42.9 m from the base of the lighthouse.

SECTION 8.6

CHECK YOUR PROGRESS 1, *page 537*

$$S = (m\angle A + m\angle B + m\angle C - 180°) \cdot \left(\frac{\pi}{180°}\right) r^2$$

$$= (200° + 90° + 90° - 180°) \cdot \left(\frac{\pi}{180°}\right)(6)^2$$

$$= (200°) \cdot \left(\frac{\pi}{180°}\right) \cdot (36)$$

$$= 40\pi \text{ in}^2 \qquad \bullet \text{ Exact area}$$

$$\approx 125.66 \text{ in}^2 \qquad \bullet \text{ Approximate area}$$

CHECK YOUR PROGRESS 2, *page 541*

a. $d_E(P, Q) = \sqrt{(x_2 - x_1)^2 + (y_2 - y_1)^2}$

$$= \sqrt{[3 - (-1)]^2 + [2 - 4]^2}$$

$$= \sqrt{4^2 + (-2)^2}$$

$$= \sqrt{20} \approx 4.5 \text{ blocks}$$

$d_C(P, Q) = |x_2 - x_1| + |y_2 - y_1|$

$$= |3 - (-1)| + |2 - 4|$$

$$= |4| + |-2|$$

$$= 6 \text{ blocks}$$

b. $d_E(P, Q) = \sqrt{(x_2 - x_1)^2 + (y_2 - y_1)^2}$

$$= \sqrt{[(-1) - 3]^2 + [5 - (-4)]^2}$$

$$= \sqrt{(-4)^2 + 9^2}$$

$$= \sqrt{97} \approx 9.8 \text{ blocks}$$

$d_C(P, Q) = |x_2 - x_1| + |y_2 - y_1|$

$$= |(-1) - 3| + |5 - (-4)|$$

$$= |-4| + 9$$

$$= 4 + 9$$

$$= 13 \text{ blocks}$$

SECTION 8.7

CHECK YOUR PROGRESS 1, *page 550*

Replace each line segment with a scaled version of the generator. As you move from left to right, your first zig should be to the left.

Stage 2 of the zig-zag curve

CHECK YOUR PROGRESS 2, *page 551*

Replace each square with a scaled version of the generator.

Stage 2 of the
Sierpinski carpet

CHECK YOUR PROGRESS 3, *page 553*

a. Any portion of the box curve replicates the entire fractal, so the box curve is a strictly self-similar fractal.

b. Any portion of the Sierpinski gasket replicates the entire fractal, so the Sierpinski gasket is a strictly self-similar fractal.

CHECK YOUR PROGRESS 4, *page 554*

a. The generator of the Koch curve consists of four line segments, and the initiator consists of only one line segment. Thus the replacement ratio of the Koch curve is 4 : 1, or 4. The initiator of the Koch curve is a line segment that is 3 times as long as the replica line segments in the generator. Thus the scaling ratio of the Koch curve is 3 : 1, or 3.

b. The generator of the zig-zag curve consists of six line segments, and the initiator consists of only one line segment. Thus the replacement ratio of the zig-zag curve is 6 : 1, or 6. The initiator of the zig-zag curve is a line segment that is 4 times as long as the replica line segments in the generator. Thus the scaling ratio of the zig-zag curve is 4 : 1, or 4.

CHECK YOUR PROGRESS 5, *page 554*

a. In Example 4 we determined that the replacement ratio of the box curve is 5 and the scaling ratio of the box curve is 3. Thus the similarity dimension of the box curve is $D = \frac{\log 5}{\log 3} \approx 1.465$.

b. The replacement ratio of the Sierpinski carpet is 8 and the scaling ratio of the Sierpinski carpet is 3. Thus the similarity dimension of the Sierpinski carpet is $D = \frac{\log 8}{\log 3} \approx 1.893$.

CHAPTER 9

SECTION 9.1

CHECK YOUR PROGRESS 1, *page 572*

Because the second graph has edge AB and the first graph does not, the two graphs are not equivalent.

CHECK YOUR PROGRESS 2, *page 575*

One vertex in the graph is of degree 3, and another is of degree 5. Because not all vertices are of even degree, the graph is not Eulerian.

CHECK YOUR PROGRESS 3, *page 576*

Represent the land areas and bridges with a graph, as we did for the Königsberg bridges earlier in the section. The vertices of the resulting graph, shown at the right below, all have even degree. Thus we know that the graph has an Euler circuit. An Euler circuit corresponds to a stroll that crosses each bridge and returns to the starting point without crossing any bridge twice.

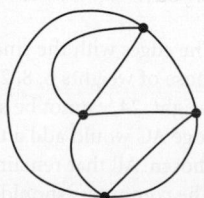

CHECK YOUR PROGRESS 4, *page 578*

Consider the campground map as a graph. A route through all the trails that does not repeat any trails corresponds to an Euler walk. Because only two vertices (A and F) are of odd degree, we know that an Euler walk exists. Furthermore, the walk must begin at A and end at F or begin at F and end at A. By trial and error, one Euler walk is A–B–C–D–E–B–G–F–E–C–A–F.

CHECK YOUR PROGRESS 5, *page 579*

The graph has seven vertices, so $n = 7$ and $n/2 = 3.5$. Several vertices are of degree less than $n/2$, so Dirac's Theorem does not apply. Still, a routing for the document may be possible. By trial and error, one such route is Los Angeles–New York–Boston–Atlanta–Dallas–Phoenix–San Francisco–Los Angeles.

CHECK YOUR PROGRESS 6, *page 581*

Represent the floor plan with a graph, as in Example 6.

A stroll passing through each doorway just once corresponds to an Euler circuit or walk. Because four vertices are of odd degree, no Euler circuit or walk exists, so it is not possible to take such a stroll.

CHECK YOUR PROGRESS 1, *page 590*

Draw a graph in which the vertices represent locations and the edges indicate available bus routes between locations. Each edge should be given a weight corresponding to the number of minutes for the bus ride.

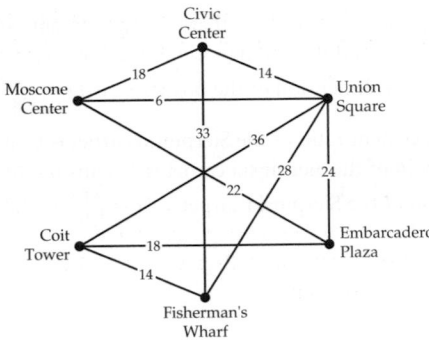

A route that visits each location and returns to the Moscone Center corresponds to a Hamiltonian circuit. Using the graph, we find that one such route is Moscone Center–Civic Center–Union Square–Fisherman's Wharf–Coit Tower–Embarcadero Plaza–Moscone Center, with a total weight of $18 + 14 + 28 + 14 + 18 + 22 = 114$. Another route is Moscone Center–Union Square–Embarcadero Plaza–Coit Tower–Fisherman's Wharf–Civic Center–Moscone Center, with a total weight of $6 + 24 + 18 + 14 + 33 + 18 = 113$. The travel time is one minute less for the second route.

CHECK YOUR PROGRESS 2, *page 592*

Starting at vertex A, the edge of smallest weight is the edge to D, with weight 5. From D, take the edge of weight 4 to C, then the edge of weight 3 to B. From B, the edge of least weight to a vertex not yet visited is the edge to vertex E (with weight 5). This is the last vertex, so we return to A along the edge of weight 9. Thus the Hamiltonian circuit is A–D–C–B–E–A, with a total weight of 26.

CHECK YOUR PROGRESS 3, *page 594*

The smallest weight appearing in the graph is 3, so we mark edge BC. The next smallest weight is 4, on edge CD. Three edges have weight 5, but we cannot mark edge BD, because it would complete a circuit. We can, however, mark edge AD. The next valid edge of smallest weight is BE, also of weight 5. No more edges can be marked without completing a circuit or adding a third edge to a vertex, so we mark the final edge, AE, to complete the Hamiltonian Circuit. In this case, the Edge-Picking Algorithm generated the same circuit as the Greedy Algorithm did in Check Your Progress 2.

CHECK YOUR PROGRESS 4, *page 598*

Represent the time between locations with a weighted graph.

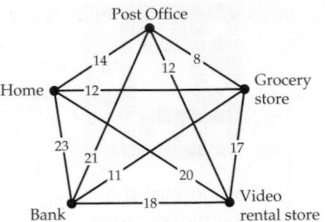

Starting at the home vertex and using the Greedy Algorithm, we first use the edge to the grocery store (of weight 12) followed by the edge of weight 8 to the post office and then the edge of weight 12 to the video rental store. The edge of next smallest weight is to the grocery store, but that vertex has already been visited, so we take the edge to the bank, with weight 18. All vertices have now been visited, so we select the last edge, of weight 23, to return home. The total weight is 73, corresponding to a total driving time of 73 minutes.

For the Edge-Picking Algorithm, we first select the edge of weight 8, followed by the edge of weight 11. Two edges have weight 12, but one adds a third edge to the grocery store vertex, so we must choose the edge from the post office to the video rental store. The next smallest weight is 14, but that edge would add a third edge to a vertex, as would the edge of weight 17. The edge of weight 18 would complete a circuit too early, so the next edge we can select is that of weight 20, the edge from home to the video rental store. The final step is to select the edge from home to the bank to complete the circuit. The resulting route is home–video rental store–Post Office–grocery store–bank–home (we could travel the same route in the reverse order) with a total travel time of 74 minutes.

CHECK YOUR PROGRESS 5, *page 599*

Represent the computer network by a graph in which the weights of the edges indicate the distances between computers.

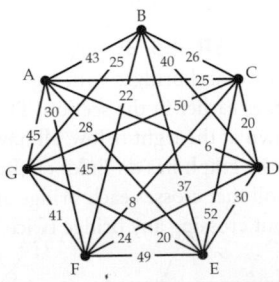

The edges with the smallest weights, which can all be chosen, are those of weights 6, 8, 20, 20, and 22. The edge of next smallest weight, 24, cannot be selected. There are two edges of weight 25; edge AC would add a third edge to vertex C, but edge BG can be chosen. All that remains is to complete the circuit with edge AE. The computers should be networked in this order: A, D, C, F, B, G, E, and back to A.

CHECK YOUR PROGRESS 1, *page 607*

First redraw the highlighted edge as shown below.

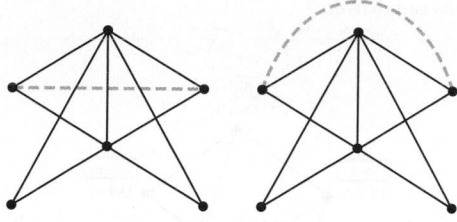

Now redraw the two lower vertices and the edges that meet there, as shown below.

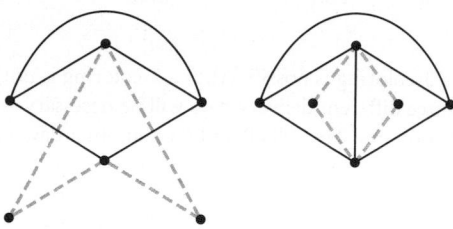

The result is a graph with no intersecting edges. Therefore, the graph is planar.

CHECK YOUR PROGRESS 2, *page 609*

The highlighted edges in the graph, considered as a subgraph, form the graph K_5. (It is upside down and slightly distorted compared with the version shown in Figure 9.17.)

CHECK YOUR PROGRESS 3, *page 612*

The graph looks similar to the Utilities Graph. Contract edges as shown below, and combine the resulting multiple edges.

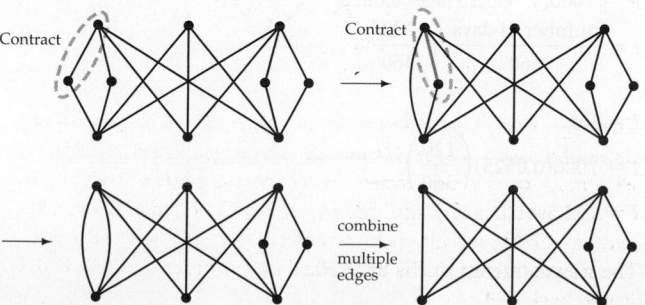

If we do the same on the right side of the graph, we are left with the Utilities Graph.

Therefore, the graph is not planar.

CHECK YOUR PROGRESS 4, *page 613*

There are 11 edges in the graph, seven vertices, and six faces (including the infinite face). Then $v + f = 7 + 6 = 13$ and $e + 2 = 11 + 2 = 13$, so $v + f = e + 2$.

CHECK YOUR PROGRESS 1, *page 619*

One possible coloring is 1-blue, 2-green, 3-red, 4-green, 5-blue, 6-red, 7-green, 8-red, 9-blue.

CHECK YOUR PROGRESS 2, *page 621*

Draw a graph on the map as in Example 2. More than two colors are required to color the resulting graph, but, by experimenting, the graph can be colored with three colors. Thus the graph is 3-colorable.

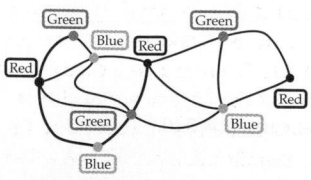

CHECK YOUR PROGRESS 3, *page 623*

There are several locations in the graph at which three edges form a triangle. Because a triangle is a circuit with an odd number of vertices, the graph is not 2-colorable.

CHECK YOUR PROGRESS 4, *page 624*

Draw a graph in which each vertex corresponds to a film and an edge joins two vertices if one person needs to view both of the corresponding films. We can use colors to represent the different times at which the films can be viewed. No two vertices connected by an edge can share the same color, because that would mean one person would have to watch two films at the same time.

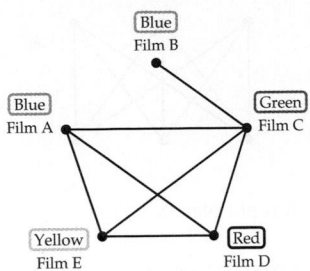

It is not possible to color the vertices with only three colors; one possible 4-coloring is shown. This means that four different time slots will be required to view the films, and the soonest all the friends can finish watching them is 4:00 A.M. A schedule can be set using the coloring in the graph. From 8 to 10, the films labeled blue, film A and film B, can be shown in two different rooms. The remaining films are represented by unique colors so will require their own viewing times. Film C can be shown from 10 to 12, film D from 12 to 2, and film E from 2 to 4.

CHECK YOUR PROGRESS 5, *page 626*

Draw a graph in which each vertex represents a deli, and an edge connects two vertices if the corresponding delis deliver to a common building. Try to color the vertices using the least number of colors possible; each color can correspond to a day of the week that the delis can deliver.

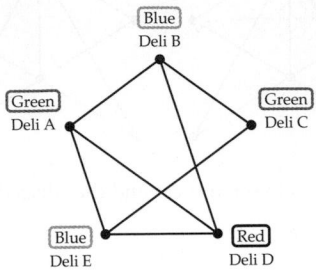

As shown, a 3-coloring is possible (but a 2-coloring is not). Therefore three different delivery days will be necessary—Delis A and C deliver on one day, delis B and E on another day, and deli D on a third day.

CHAPTER 10

SECTION 10.1

CHECK YOUR PROGRESS 1, *page 642*
$P = 500, r = 4\% = 0.04, t = 1$

$I = Prt$
$I = 500(0.04)(1)$
$I = 20$

The simple interest earned is $20.

CHECK YOUR PROGRESS 2, *page 643*
$P = 1500, r = 5.25\% = 0.0525$
$$t = \frac{4 \text{ months}}{1 \text{ year}} = \frac{4 \text{ months}}{12 \text{ months}} = \frac{4}{12}$$

$I = Prt$
$$I = 1500(0.0525)\left(\frac{4}{12}\right)$$
$I = 26.25$

The simple interest due is $26.25.

CHECK YOUR PROGRESS 3, *page 643*
$P = 700, r = 1.25\% = 0.0125, t = 5$

$I = Prt$
$I = 700(0.0125)(5)$
$I = 43.75$

The simple interest due is $43.75.

CHECK YOUR PROGRESS 4, *page 644*
$P = 7000, r = 5.25\% = 0.0525$
$$t = \frac{\text{number of days}}{360} = \frac{120}{360}$$

$I = Prt$
$$I = 7000(0.0525)\left(\frac{120}{360}\right)$$
$I = 122.5$

The simple interest due is $122.50.

CHECK YOUR PROGRESS 5, *page 645*

$$I = Prt$$

$$462 = 12,000(r)\left(\frac{6}{12}\right)$$

$$462 = 6000r$$

$$0.077 = r$$

$$r = 7.7\%$$

The simple interest rate on the loan is 7.7%.

CHECK YOUR PROGRESS 6, *page 646*

Find the interest.

$$P = 4000, \, r = 8.75\% = 0.0875, \, t = \frac{9}{12}$$

$$I = Prt$$

$$I = 4000(0.0875)\left(\frac{9}{12}\right)$$

$$I = 262.50$$

Find the maturity value.

$$A = P + I$$

$$A = 4000 + 262.50$$

$$A = 4262.50$$

The maturity value of the loan is $4262.50.

CHECK YOUR PROGRESS 7, *page 647*

$$P = 6700, \, r = 8.9\% = 0.089, \, t = 1$$

$$A = P(1 + rt)$$

$$A = 6700[1 + 0.089(1)]$$

$$A = 6700(1 + 0.089)$$

$$A = 6700(1.089)$$

$$A = 7296.30$$

The maturity value of the loan is $7296.30.

CHECK YOUR PROGRESS 8, *page 647*

$$P = 680, \, r = 6.4\% = 0.064, \, t = 1$$

$$A = P(1 + rt)$$

$$A = 680[1 + 0.064(1)]$$

$$A = 680(1 + 0.064)$$

$$A = 680(1.064)$$

$$A = 723.52$$

After 1 year, $723.52 is in the account.

CHECK YOUR PROGRESS 9, *page 648*

$$I = A - P$$

$$I = 9240 - 9000$$

$$I = 240$$

$$I = Prt$$

$$240 = 9000(r)\left(\frac{4}{12}\right)$$

$$240 = 3000r$$

$$0.08 = r$$

$$r = 8.0\%$$

The simple interest rate on the loan is 8.0%.

SECTION 10.2

CHECK YOUR PROGRESS 1, *page 656*

$$A = P(1 + rt)$$

$$A = 2000\left[1 + 0.04\left(\frac{1}{12}\right)\right]$$

$$A \approx 2006.67$$

$$A = P(1 + rt)$$

$$A \approx 2006.67\left[1 + 0.04\left(\frac{1}{12}\right)\right]$$

$$A \approx 2013.36$$

$$A = P(1 + rt)$$

$$A = 2013.36\left[1 + 0.04\left(\frac{1}{12}\right)\right]$$

$$A \approx 2020.07$$

$$A = P(1 + rt)$$

$$A = 2020.07\left[1 + 0.04\left(\frac{1}{12}\right)\right]$$

$$A \approx 2026.80$$

$$A = P(1 + rt)$$

$$A = 2026.80\left[1 + 0.04\left(\frac{1}{12}\right)\right]$$

$$A \approx 2033.56$$

$$A = P(1 + rt)$$

$$A = 2033.56\left[1 + 0.04\left(\frac{1}{12}\right)\right]$$

$$A \approx 2040.34$$

The total amount in the account at the end of 6 months is $2040.34.

CHECK YOUR PROGRESS 2, *page 659*

$r = 6\% = 0.06, n = 12, t = 2, i = \dfrac{r}{n} = \dfrac{0.06}{12} = 0.005,$

$N = nt = 12(2) = 24$

$A = P(1 + i)^N$
$A = 4000(1 + 0.005)^{24}$
$A = 4000(1.005)^{24}$
$A \approx 4000(1.127160)$
$A \approx 4508.64$

The compound amount after 2 years is approximately $4508.64.

CHECK YOUR PROGRESS 3, *page 659*

$r = 9\% = 0.09, n = 360, t = 4, i = \dfrac{r}{n} = \dfrac{0.09}{360} = 0.00025,$

$N = nt = 360(4) = 1440$

$A = P(1 + i)^N$
$A = 2500(1 + 0.00025)^{1440}$
$A = 2500(1.00025)^{1440}$
$A \approx 2500(1.4332649)$
$A \approx 3583.16$

The future amount after 4 years is approximately $3583.16.

CHECK YOUR PROGRESS 4, *page 660*

$r = 9\% = 0.09, n = 12, t = 6, i = \dfrac{r}{n} = \dfrac{0.09}{12} = 0.0075,$

$N = nt = 12(6) = 72$

$A = P(1 + i)^N$
$A = 8000(1 + 0.0075)^{72}$
$A = 8000(1.0075)^{72}$
$A \approx 8000(1.7125527)$
$A \approx 13,700.42$

$I = A - P$
$I = 13,700.42 - 8000$
$I = 5700.42$

The amount of interest earned is approximately $5700.42.

CHECK YOUR PROGRESS 5, *page 660*
The following solution utilizes the finance feature of a TI-83/84 calculator.
Press 2nd [Finance] to display the FINANCE CALC menu or press APPS ENTER.
Press ENTER to select 1: TVM Solver.
After N =, enter 10.
After I% =, enter 6.
After PV =, enter −3500.
After PMT =, enter 0.
After P/Y =, enter 2.
After C/Y =, enter 2.

Use the up arrow key to place the cursor at FV =.
Press ALPHA [Solve].
The solution is displayed to the right of FV =.

The compound amount is $4703.71.

CHECK YOUR PROGRESS 6, *page 662*

$r = 9\%, n = 2, t = 5, i = \dfrac{r}{n} = \dfrac{9\%}{2} = 4.5\% = 0.045,$

$N = nt = 2(5) = 10$

$P = \dfrac{A}{(1 + i)^N}$

$P = \dfrac{20{,}000}{(1 + 0.045)^{10}}$

$P \approx \dfrac{20{,}000}{1.552969}$

$P \approx 12{,}878.55$

$12,878.55 should be invested in the account.

CHECK YOUR PROGRESS 7, *page 663*
The following solution utilizes the finance feature of a TI-83/84 calculator.
Press 2nd [Finance] to display the FINANCE CALC menu or press APPS ENTER.
Press ENTER to select 1: TVM Solver.
After N =, enter 5400 (15 × 360).
After I% =, enter 6.
After PMT =, enter 0.
After FV =, enter 25000.
After P/Y =, enter 360.
After C/Y =, enter 360.
Use the up arrow key to place the cursor at PV =.
Press ALPHA [Solve].
The solution is displayed to the right of PV =.

$10,165.00 should be invested in the account.

CHECK YOUR PROGRESS 8, *page 664*

$r = 5\% = 0.05, n = 1, t = 17, i = \dfrac{r}{n} = \dfrac{0.05}{1} = 0.05,$

$N = nt = 1(17) = 17$

$A = P(1 + i)^N$
$A = 28{,}000(1 + 0.05)^{17}$
$A = 28{,}000(1.05)^{17}$
$A \approx 28{,}000(2.2920183)$
$A \approx 64{,}176.51$

The average new car sticker price in 2025 will be approximately $64,176.51.

CHECK YOUR PROGRESS 9, *page 664*

$r = 7\%$, $n = 1$, $t = 40$, $i = \dfrac{r}{n} = \dfrac{7\%}{1} = 7\% = 0.07$,

$N = nt = 1(40) = 40$

$P = \dfrac{A}{(1 + i)^N}$

$P = \dfrac{500{,}000}{(1 + 0.07)^{40}}$

$P \approx \dfrac{500{,}000}{14.9744578}$

$P \approx 33{,}390.19$

In 2050, the purchasing power of \$500,000 will be approximately \$33,390.19.

CHECK YOUR PROGRESS 10, *page 666*

$r = 4\% = 0.04$, $n = 4$, $t = 1$, $i = \dfrac{r}{n} = \dfrac{0.04}{4} = 0.01$,

$N = nt = 4(1) = 4$

$A = P(1 + i)^N$

$A = 100(1 + 0.01)^4$

$A = 100(1.01)^4$

$A \approx 100(1.040604)$

$A \approx 104.06$

$I = A - P$

$I = 104.06 - 100$

$I = 4.06$

The effective interest rate is 4.06%.

CHECK YOUR PROGRESS 11, *page 667*

$i = \dfrac{r}{n} = \dfrac{0.05}{4}$

$N = nt = 4(1) = 4$

$(1 + i)^N = \left(1 + \dfrac{0.05}{4}\right)^4$

≈ 1.050945

$i = \dfrac{r}{n} = \dfrac{0.0525}{2}$

$N = nt = 2(1) = 2$

$(1 + i)^N = \left(1 + \dfrac{0.0525}{2}\right)^2$

≈ 1.053189

An investment of 5.25% compounded semiannually has a higher annual yield than an investment that earns 5% compounded quarterly.

SECTION 10.3

CHECK YOUR PROGRESS 1, *page 676*

Date	Payments or Purchases	Balance Each Day	Number of Days Until Balance Changes	Unpaid Balance Times Number of Days
July 1–6		\$1024	6	\$6144
July 7–14	\$315	\$1339	8	\$10,712
July 15–21	−\$400	\$939	7	\$6573
July 22–31	\$410	\$1349	10	\$13,490
Total				\$36,919

Average daily balance $= \dfrac{\text{sum of the total amounts owed each day of the month}}{\text{number of days in the billing period}}$

$= \dfrac{36{,}919}{31} \approx \$1190.94$

$I = Prt$

$I = 1190.94(0.012)(1)$

$I \approx 14.29$

The finance charge on the August 1 bill is \$14.29.

CHECK YOUR PROGRESS 2, *page 679*

a. Down payment = Percent down $\times$ purchase price
$$= 0.20 \times 750 = 150$$

Amount financed = purchase price − down payment
$$= 750 - 150 = 600$$

Interest owed = finance rate $\times$ amount financed
$$= 0.08 \times 600 = 48$$

The finance charge is $48.

b. APR $\approx \dfrac{2Nr}{N + 1}$

$$\approx \frac{2(12)(0.08)}{12 + 1} \approx \frac{1.92}{13} \approx 0.148$$

The annual percentage rate is approximately 14.8%.

CHECK YOUR PROGRESS 3, *page 681*

Sales tax amount = sales tax rate $\times$ purchase price
$$= 0.0425 \times 1499 \approx 63.71$$

Amount financed = purchase price + sales tax amount
$$= 1499 + 63.71 = 1562.71$$

$i = \dfrac{\text{annual interest rate}}{\text{number of payments per year}} = \dfrac{0.084}{12} = 0.007$

$n = 3(12) = 36$

$PMT = A\left(\dfrac{i}{1 - (1 + i)^{-n}}\right)$

$PMT = 1562.71\left(\dfrac{0.007}{1 - (1 + 0.007)^{-36}}\right)$

$PMT \approx 49.26$

The monthly payment is $49.26.

CHECK YOUR PROGRESS 4, *page 682*

a. Sales tax = 0.0525(26,788) = 1406.37

b. Loan amount
$$= \text{purchase price} + \text{sales tax} + \text{license fee} - \text{down payment}$$
$$= 26,788 + 1406.37 + 145 - 2500$$
$$= 25,839.37$$

c. $i = \dfrac{APR}{12} = \dfrac{0.081}{12} = 0.00675$; $n = 12 \times 5 = 60$

$PMT = A\left(\dfrac{i}{1 - (1 + i)^{-n}}\right)$

$PMT = 25,839.37\left(\dfrac{0.00675}{1 - (1 + 0.00675)^{-60}}\right)$

$PMT \approx 525.17$

The monthly payment is $525.17.

CHECK YOUR PROGRESS 5, *page 683*

$i = \dfrac{APR}{12} = \dfrac{0.084}{12} = 0.007$

$A = PMT\left(\dfrac{1 - (1 + i)^{-n}}{i}\right)$

$A = 592.57\left(\dfrac{1 - (1 + 0.007)^{-24}}{0.007}\right)$

$A \approx 13,049.34$

The loan payoff is $13,049.34.

CHECK YOUR PROGRESS 6, *page 685*

Residual value = 0.40(33,395) = 13,358

Money factor $= \dfrac{\text{annual interest rate as a percent}}{2400} = \dfrac{8}{2400}$

$$\approx 0.00333333$$

Average monthly finance charge
$$= (\text{net capitalized cost} + \text{residual value}) \times \text{money factor}$$
$$= (31,900 + 13,358) \times 0.00333333$$
$$\approx 150.86$$

Average monthly depreciation
$$= \frac{\text{net capitalized cost} - \text{residual value}}{\text{term of the lease in months}}$$
$$= \frac{31,900 - 13,358}{60}$$
$$\approx 309.03$$

Monthly lease payment
$$= \text{average monthly finance charge} + \text{average monthly depreciation}$$
$$= 150.86 + 309.03$$
$$= 459.89$$

The monthly lease payment is $459.89.

SECTION 10.4

CHECK YOUR PROGRESS 1, *page 692*

($.72 per share) $\times$ (550 shares) = $396

The shareholder receives $396 in dividends.

CHECK YOUR PROGRESS 2, *page 693*

$I = Prt$

$0.82 = 51.25r(1)$ • Let I = annual dividend and P = the stock price. The time is 1 year.

$0.82 = 51.25r$

$0.016 = r$ • Divide each side of the equation by 51.25.

The dividend yield is 1.6%.

CHECK YOUR PROGRESS 3, *page 695*

a. From Table 10.2, the 52-week low is $29.43, and the 52-week high is $38.89.

Profit = selling price − purchase price
= 300($38.89) − 300($29.43)
= $11,667 − $8829 = $2838

The profit on the sale of the stock was $2838.

b. Commission = 2.1%(selling price)
= 0.021($11,667) ≈ $245.01

The broker's commission was $245.01.

CHECK YOUR PROGRESS 4, *page 696*

Use the simple interest formula to find the annual interest payments. Substitute the following values into the formula: $P = 15,000$, $r = 3.5\% = 0.035$, and $t = 1$.

$I = Prt$

$I = 15,000(0.035)(1)$

$I = 525$

Multiply the annual interest payments by the term of the bond.

$525(4) = 2100$

The total of the interest payments paid to the bondholder is $2100.

CHECK YOUR PROGRESS 5, *page 697*

a. $A - L =$ (750 million + 0.75 million
  + 1.5 million) − 1.5 million
= 750.75 million, $N = 20$ million

$\text{NAV} = \dfrac{A - L}{N} = \dfrac{750.75 \text{ million}}{20 \text{ million}} = 37.5375$

The NAV of the fund is $37.5375.

b. $\dfrac{10,000}{37.5375} \approx 266$ • Divide the amount invested by the cost per share of the fund. Round down to the nearest whole number.

You will purchase 266 shares of the mutual fund.

SECTION 10.5

CHECK YOUR PROGRESS 1, *page 703*

Down payment = 25% of 410,000 = 0.25(410,000)
= 102,500

Mortgage = selling price − down payment
= 410,000 − 102,500
= 307,500

Points = 1.75% of 307,500 = 0.0175(307,500)
= 5381.25

Total = 102,500 + 375 + 5381.25 = 108,256.25

The total of the down payment and the closing costs is $108,256.25.

CHECK YOUR PROGRESS 2, *page 704*

a. $i = \dfrac{0.07}{12} \approx 0.00583333$

$n = 25(12) = 300$

$PMT = A\left(\dfrac{i}{1 - (1 + i)^{-n}}\right)$

$PMT \approx 223,000\left(\dfrac{0.00583333}{1 - (1 + 0.00583333)^{-300}}\right)$

$PMT \approx 1576.12$

The monthly payment is $1576.12.

b. Total = 1576.12(300) = 472,836

The total of the payments over the life of the loan is $472,836.

c. Interest = 472,836 − 223,000 = 249,836

The amount of interest paid over the life of the loan is $249,836.

CHECK YOUR PROGRESS 3, *page 707*

Down payment = 0.25(295,000) = 73,750

Mortgage = 295,000 − 73,750 = 221,250

$i = \dfrac{0.0675}{12} = 0.005625$

$n = 30(12) = 360$

$PMT = A\left(\dfrac{i}{1 - (1 + i)^{-n}}\right)$

$PMT = 221,250\left(\dfrac{0.005625}{1 - (1 + 0.005625)^{-360}}\right)$

$PMT \approx 1435.02$

The monthly payment is $1435.02.

$I = Prt$
$= 221,250(0.0675)\left(\dfrac{1}{12}\right)$
≈ 1244.53

The interest paid on the first payment is $1244.53.

Principal = 1435.02 − 1244.53 = 190.49

The principal paid on the first payment is $190.49.

CHECK YOUR PROGRESS 4, *page 708*

$i = \dfrac{0.069}{12} = 0.00575$

$n = 25(12) - 4(12) = 300 - 48 = 252$

$A = PMT\left(\dfrac{1 - (1 + i)^{-n}}{i}\right)$

$A = 846.82\left(\dfrac{1 - (1 + 0.00575)^{-252}}{0.00575}\right)$

$A \approx 112,548.79$

The mortgage payoff is $112,548.79.

CHECK YOUR PROGRESS 5, *page 710*

Monthly property tax = 2332.80 ÷ 12 = 194.40
Monthly fire insurance = 450 ÷ 12 = 37.50
Total monthly payment = 1492.89 + 194.40 + 37.50 = 1724.79

The total monthly payment for mortgage, property tax, and fire insurance is $1724.79.

CHAPTER 11

SECTION 11.1

CHECK YOUR PROGRESS 1, *page 720*

The possible outcomes are {M, i, s, p}. There are four possible outcomes.

CHECK YOUR PROGRESS 2, *page 721*

a. {1, 3, 5, 7, 9}   **b.** {0, 3, 6, 9}   **c.** {8, 9}

CHECK YOUR PROGRESS 3, *page 722*

	H	T
1	1H	1T
2	2H	2T
3	3H	3T
4	4H	4T
5	5H	5T
6	6H	6T

The sample space has 12 elements:
{1H, 1T, 2H, 2T, 3H, 3T, 4H, 4T, 5H, 5T, 6H, 6T}

CHECK YOUR PROGRESS 4, *page 723*

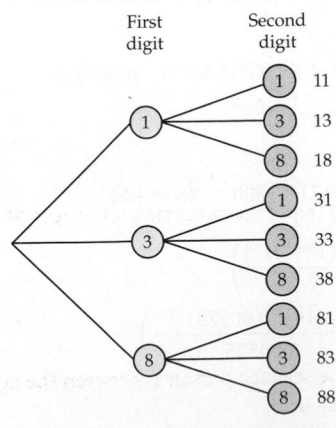

First digit   Second digit

1 → 1 → 11
1 → 3 → 13
1 → 8 → 18
3 → 1 → 31
3 → 3 → 33
3 → 8 → 38
8 → 1 → 81
8 → 3 → 83
8 → 8 → 88

CHECK YOUR PROGRESS 5, *page 724*

Any of the nine runners could win the gold medal, so $n_1 = 9$. That leaves $n_2 = 8$ runners that could win silver, and $n_3 = 7$ possibilities for bronze. By the counting principle, there are $9 \cdot 8 \cdot 7 = 504$ possible ways the medals can be awarded.

CHECK YOUR PROGRESS 6, *page 726*

a. Because a mailbox can accept more than one letter and each letter has five possible destinations, there are $5 \cdot 5 \cdot 5 = 125$ ways to place the letters.

b. Once a mailbox has a letter, it cannot be used, so there are $5 \cdot 4 \cdot 3 = 60$ different ways to place the letters.

SECTION 11.2

CHECK YOUR PROGRESS 1, *page 731*

a. $7! + 4! = (7 \cdot 6 \cdot 5 \cdot 4 \cdot 3 \cdot 2 \cdot 1) + (4 \cdot 3 \cdot 2 \cdot 1)$
$= 5040 + 24 = 5064$

b. $\dfrac{8!}{4!} = \dfrac{8 \cdot 7 \cdot 6 \cdot 5 \cdot \cancel{4!}}{\cancel{4!}} = 8 \cdot 7 \cdot 6 \cdot 5 = 1680$

CHECK YOUR PROGRESS 2, *page 732*

Because the players are ranked, the number of different golf teams possible is the number of permutations of eight players selected five at a time.

$P(8, 5) = \dfrac{8!}{(8-5)!} = \dfrac{8!}{3!} = \dfrac{8 \cdot 7 \cdot 6 \cdot 5 \cdot 4 \cdot \cancel{3!}}{\cancel{3!}}$
$= 8 \cdot 7 \cdot 6 \cdot 5 \cdot 4 = 6720$

There are 6720 possible golf teams.

CHECK YOUR PROGRESS 3, *page 733*

The order in which the cars finish is important, so the number of ways to place first, second, and third is

$P(42, 3) = \dfrac{42!}{(42-3)!} = \dfrac{42 \cdot 41 \cdot 40 \cdot \cancel{39!}}{\cancel{39!}} = 68{,}880$

There are 68,880 different ways to award the first, second, and third place prizes.

CHECK YOUR PROGRESS 4, *page 734*

a. With no restrictions, there are seven tutors available for seven hours, so the number of schedules is

$$P(7, 7) = \frac{7!}{(7 - 7)!} = \frac{7!}{0!} = 7! = 5040$$

There are 5040 possible schedules.

b. This is a multi-stage experiment; there are 3! ways to schedule the juniors and 4! ways to schedule the seniors. By the counting principle, the number of different tutoring schedules is $3! \cdot 4! = 6 \cdot 24 = 144$.

There are 144 tutor schedules.

CHECK YOUR PROGRESS 5, *page 735*

a. With $n = 8$ coins and $k_1 = 3$ (number of pennies), $k_2 = 2$ (number of nickels), and $k_3 = 3$ (number of dimes), the number of different possible stacks is

$$\frac{8!}{3! \cdot 2! \cdot 3!} = \frac{8 \cdot 7 \cdot 6 \cdot 5 \cdot 4 \cdot 3!}{3! \cdot 2! \cdot 3!} = \frac{8 \cdot 7 \cdot 6 \cdot 5 \cdot 4}{6 \cdot 2} = 560$$

There are 560 possible stacks.

b. Not including the dimes, there are $\frac{5!}{3! \cdot 2!} = 10$ ways to stack the pennies and nickels. The dimes are identical, so there is only one way to arrange the dimes together, but there are six different locations in the stack of pennies and nickels into which the dimes could be placed. By the counting principle, the total number of ways in which the stack of coins can be arranged if the dimes are together is $10 \cdot 6 = 60$.

CHECK YOUR PROGRESS 6, *page 737*

The order in which the players are chosen is not important, so the number of ways to choose 9 players from 16 is

$$C(16, 9) = \frac{16!}{9! \cdot (16 - 9)!} = \frac{16!}{9! \cdot 7!}$$

$$= \frac{16 \cdot 15 \cdot 14 \cdot 13 \cdot 12 \cdot 11 \cdot 10 \cdot 9!}{9! \cdot 7!}$$

$$= \frac{16 \cdot 15 \cdot 14 \cdot 13 \cdot 12 \cdot 11 \cdot 10}{7 \cdot 6 \cdot 5 \cdot 4 \cdot 3 \cdot 2 \cdot 1} = 11{,}440$$

There are 11,440 possible 9-player starting teams.

CHECK YOUR PROGRESS 7, *page 738*

There are $C(4, 3)$ ways for the auditor to choose three corporate tax returns and $C(6, 2)$ ways to choose two individual tax returns. By the counting principle, the total number of ways in which the auditor can choose the returns is

$$C(4, 3) \cdot C(6, 2) = \frac{4!}{3! \cdot 1!} \cdot \frac{6!}{2! \cdot 4!} = 4 \cdot 15 = 60$$

There are 60 ways to choose the tax returns.

CHECK YOUR PROGRESS 8, *page 739*

For any one suit, there are $C(13, 4)$ ways of choosing four cards. That leaves $52 - 13 = 39$ cards of other suits from which to choose the fifth card. In addition, there are four different suits we could start with. By the counting principle, the number of five-card combinations containing four cards of the same suit is

$$4 \cdot C(13, 4) \cdot 39 = 4 \cdot \frac{13!}{4! \cdot 9!} \cdot 39 = 4 \cdot 715 \cdot 39 = 111{,}540$$

There are 111,540 five-card combinations containing four cards of the same suit.

SECTION 11.3

CHECK YOUR PROGRESS 1, *page 744*
$S = \{\text{HH, HT, TH, TT}\}$

CHECK YOUR PROGRESS 2, *page 746*
The sample space for rolling a single die is $S = \{1, 2, 3, 4, 5, 6\}$. The elements in the event that an odd number will be rolled are $E = \{1, 3, 5\}$. Then

$$P(E) = \frac{n(E)}{n(S)} = \frac{3}{6} = \frac{1}{2}$$

The probability that an odd number will be rolled is $\frac{1}{2}$.

CHECK YOUR PROGRESS 3, *page 747*
The sample space is shown in Figure 11.6 on page 747. Let E be the event that the sum of the pips on the upward faces is 7; the elements of this event are

$$E = \{ \blacksquare\blacksquare, \blacksquare\blacksquare, \blacksquare\blacksquare, \blacksquare\blacksquare, \blacksquare\blacksquare, \blacksquare\blacksquare \}.$$

Then the probability of rolling a 7 is

$$P(E) = \frac{n(E)}{n(S)} = \frac{6}{36} = \frac{1}{6}$$

The probability that the sum is 7 is $\frac{1}{6}$.

CHECK YOUR PROGRESS 4, *page 748*
Let E be the event that a person between the ages of 39 and 49 is selected. Then

$$P(E) = \frac{773}{3228} \approx 0.24$$

The probability the selected person is between the ages of 39 and 49 is approximately 0.24.

CHECK YOUR PROGRESS 5, *page 749*

Make a Punnett square.

Parents	C	c
C	CC	Cc
c	Cc	cc

To be white, the child must be cc. From the table, only one of the four possible genotypes is cc, so the probability that an offspring will be white is $\frac{1}{4}$.

CHECK YOUR PROGRESS 6, *page 751*

Let E be the event of selecting a blue ball. Because there are five blue balls, there are five favorable outcomes, leaving seven unfavorable outcomes.

$$\text{Odds against } E = \frac{\text{number of unfavorable outcomes}}{\text{number of favorable outcomes}} = \frac{7}{5}$$

The odds against selecting a blue ball from the box are 7 to 5.

CHECK YOUR PROGRESS 7, *page 751*

Let E represent the event of an earthquake of magnitude 6.7 or greater in the Bay Area in the next 30 years. Then the probability of E, $P(E)$, is 0.6. The odds in favor of this event are given by

$$\text{Odds in favor} = \frac{P(E)}{1 - P(E)}$$

$$= \frac{0.6}{1 - 0.6} = \frac{0.6}{0.4} = \frac{3}{2}$$

The odds in favor of this event are 3 to 2.

SECTION 11.4

CHECK YOUR PROGRESS 1, *page 758*

Let A be the event of rolling a 7, and let B be the event of rolling an 11. From the sample space on page 721, $P(A) = \frac{6}{36} = \frac{1}{6}$ and $P(B) = \frac{2}{36} = \frac{1}{18}$. Because A and B are mutually exclusive events,

$$P(A \text{ or } B) = P(A) + P(B) = \frac{1}{6} + \frac{1}{18} = \frac{4}{18} = \frac{2}{9}$$

The probability of rolling a 7 or an 11 is $\frac{2}{9}$.

CHECK YOUR PROGRESS 2, *page 759*

Let $A = \{\text{people with a degree in business}\}$ and $B = \{\text{people with a starting salary between \$20,000 and \$24,999}\}$. Then, from the table, $n(A) = 4 + 16 + 21 + 35 + 22 = 98$, $n(B) = 4 + 16 + 3 + 16 = 39$, and $n(A \text{ and } B) = 16$. The total number of people represented in the table is 206.

$$P(A \text{ or } B) = P(A) + P(B) - P(A \text{ and } B)$$

$$= \frac{98}{206} + \frac{39}{206} - \frac{16}{206} = \frac{121}{206} \approx 0.587$$

The probability of choosing a person who has a degree in business or a starting salary between \$20,000 and \$24,999 is about 58.7%.

CHECK YOUR PROGRESS 3, *page 760*

If E is the event that a person has type A blood, then E^C is the event that the person does not have type A blood, and

$$P(E^c) = 1 - P(E) = 1 - 0.34 = 0.66$$

The probability that a person does not have type A blood is 66%.

CHECK YOUR PROGRESS 4, *page 761*

Let $E = \{\text{at least one roll of sum 7}\}$; then $E^c = \{\text{no sum of 7 is rolled}\}$. Using the table on page 721, there are 36 possibilities for each toss of the dice. Thus, $n(S) = 36 \cdot 36 \cdot 36 = 46{,}656$. For each roll of the dice, there are 30 numbers that do not total 7, so $n(E^c) = 30 \cdot 30 \cdot 30 = 27{,}000$. Then

$$P(E) = 1 - P(E^c) = 1 - \frac{27{,}000}{46{,}656} = \frac{19{,}656}{46{,}656} \approx 0.421$$

There is about a 42.1% chance of rolling a sum of 7 at least once.

CHECK YOUR PROGRESS 5, *page 763*

Let $E = \{\text{at least one \$100 bill}\}$; then $E^c = \{\text{no \$100 bills}\}$. The number of elements in the sample space is the number of ways to choose four bills from 35:

$$n(S) = C(35, 4) = \frac{35!}{4!\,(35 - 4)!} = \frac{35!}{4!\,31!} = 52{,}360$$

To count the number of ways not to choose any \$100 bills, we need to compute the number of ways to choose four \$1 bills from the 31 \$1 bills available.

$$n(E^c) = C(31, 4) = \frac{31!}{4!\,(31 - 4)!} = \frac{31!}{4!\,27!} = 31{,}465$$

$$P(E) = 1 - P(E^c) = 1 - \frac{n(E^c)}{n(S)}$$

$$= 1 - \frac{31{,}465}{52{,}360} = \frac{20{,}895}{52{,}360} \approx 0.399$$

The probability of pulling out at least one \$100 bill is about 39.9%.

SECTION 11.5

CHECK YOUR PROGRESS 1, *page 769*

Let $B = \{\text{the sum is 6}\}$ and $A = \{\text{the first die is not a 3}\}$. From the table on page 721, there are four possible rolls of the dice for which the first die is not a 3 and the sum is 6. So $P(A \text{ and } B) = \frac{4}{36} = \frac{1}{9}$. There are 30 possibilities for which the first die is not a 3, so $P(A) = \frac{30}{36} = \frac{5}{6}$. Then

$$P(B|A) = \frac{P(A \text{ and } B)}{P(A)} = \frac{\frac{1}{9}}{\frac{5}{6}} = \frac{2}{15}$$

The probability of rolling a 6 given that the first die is not a 3 is $\frac{2}{15}$.

CHECK YOUR PROGRESS 2, *page 771*

Let $A = \{$a spade is dealt first$\}$, $B = \{$a heart is dealt second$\}$, and $C = \{$a spade is dealt third$\}$. Then

$$P(A \text{ and } B \text{ and } C) = P(A) \cdot P(B|A) \cdot P(C|A \text{ and } B)$$

$$= \frac{13}{52} \cdot \frac{13}{51} \cdot \frac{12}{50} = \frac{13}{850}$$

The probability is $\frac{13}{850}$, or about 0.015.

CHECK YOUR PROGRESS 3, *page 772*

Each coin toss is independent of the others, because the probability of getting heads on any toss is not affected by the results of the other coin tosses. Let $E_1 = \{$heads on the first toss$\}$, $E_2 = \{$heads on the second toss$\}$, and $E_3 = \{$heads on the third toss$\}$. The events are independent and the probability of flipping heads is $\frac{1}{2}$, so

$$P(E_1 \text{ and } E_2 \text{ and } E_3) = P(E_1) \cdot P(E_2) \cdot P(E_3) = \frac{1}{2} \cdot \frac{1}{2} \cdot \frac{1}{2} = \frac{1}{8}$$

CHECK YOUR PROGRESS 4, *page 773*

Let D be the event that a person has the genetic defect and let T be the event that the test for the defect is positive. We are asked for $P(D|T)$, which can be calculated by

$$P(D|T) = \frac{P(D \text{ and } T)}{P(T)}$$

A tree diagram will help us compute the needed probabilities.

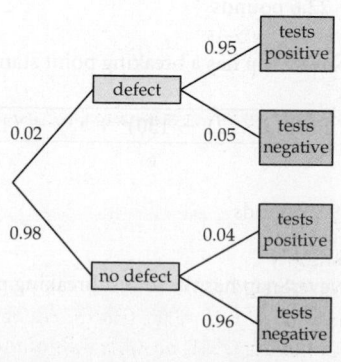

From the diagram, $P(D \text{ and } T) = P(D) \cdot P(T|D) = (0.02)(0.95)$. To compute $P(T)$ we need to combine two branches from the diagram, one corresponding to a correct positive test result when the person has the defect, and one corresponding to a false positive result when the person does not have the defect:
$P(T) = (0.02)(0.95) + (0.98)(0.04)$. Then

$$P(D|T) = \frac{P(D \text{ and } T)}{P(T)} = \frac{(0.02)(0.95)}{(0.02)(0.95) + (0.98)(0.04)} \approx 0.326$$

There is only a 32.6% chance that a person who tests positive actually has the defect.

SECTION 11.6

CHECK YOUR PROGRESS 1, *page 780*

Let S_1 be the event that the roulette ball lands on a number from 1 to 12, in which case the player wins \$10. There are 38 possible numbers, so $P(S_1) = \frac{12}{38}$. Let S_2 be the event that a number from 1 to 12 does not come up, in which case the player loses \$5. Then $P(S_2) = 1 - \frac{12}{38} = \frac{26}{38}$.

$$\text{Expectation} = P(S_1) \cdot S_1 + P(S_2) \cdot S_2$$

$$= \frac{12}{38}(10) + \frac{26}{38}(-5) = -\frac{5}{19} \approx -0.263$$

The player's expectation is about $-\$0.263$.

CHECK YOUR PROGRESS 2, *page 781*

Let S_1 be the event that the person will die within one year. Then $P(S_1) = 0.000832$ and the company must pay out \$10,000. Because the company received a premium of \$45, the actual loss is \$9955. Let S_2 be the event that the policy holder does not die during the year of the policy. Then $P(S_2) = 0.999168$ and the company keeps the premium. The expectation is

$$\text{Expectation} = P(S_1) \cdot S_1 + P(S_2) \cdot S_2$$

$$= 0.000832(-9955) + 0.999168(45)$$

$$= 36.68$$

The company's expectation is \$36.68.

CHECK YOUR PROGRESS 3, *page 782*

$$\text{Expectation} = 0.05(500,000) + 0.30(250,000) + 0.35(150,000)$$

$$+ 0.20(-100,000) + 0.10(-350,000)$$

$$= 97,500$$

The company's profit expectation is \$97,500.

CHAPTER 12

SECTION 12.1

CHECK YOUR PROGRESS 1, *page 795*

$$\bar{x} = \frac{\Sigma x}{n} = \frac{245 + 235 + 220 + 210}{4} = \frac{910}{4} = 227.5$$

The mean of the patient's blood cholesterol levels is 227.5.

CHECK YOUR PROGRESS 2, *page 796*

a. The list 14, 27, 3, 82, 64, 34, 8, 51 contains eight numbers. The median of a list of data with an even number of numbers is found by ranking the numbers and computing the mean of the two middle numbers. Ranking the numbers from smallest to largest gives 3, 8, 14, 27, 34, 51, 64, 82. The two middle numbers are 27 and 34. The mean of 27 and 34 is 30.5. Thus 30.5 is the median of the data.

b. The list 21.3, 37.4, 11.6, 82.5, 17.2 contains five numbers. The median of a list of data with an odd number of numbers is found by ranking the numbers and finding the middle number. Ranking the numbers from smallest to largest gives 11.6, 17.2, 21.3, 37.4, 82.5. The middle number is 21.3. Thus 21.3 is the median.

CHECK YOUR PROGRESS 3, *page 797*

a. In the list 3, 3, 3, 3, 3, 4, 4, 5, 5, 5, 8, the number 3 occurs more often than the other numbers. Thus 3 is the mode.

b. In the list 12, 34, 12, 71, 48, 93, 71, the numbers 12 and 71 both occur twice and the other numbers occur only once. Thus 12 and 71 are both modes for the data.

CHECK YOUR PROGRESS 4, *page 799*

Weighted mean

$$= \frac{(70 \times 1) + (55 \times 1) + (90 \times 2) + (72 \times 2) + (68 \times 2) + (85 \times 6)}{14}$$

$$= \frac{1095}{14} \approx 78.2$$

Larry's weighted mean is approximately 78.2.

CHECK YOUR PROGRESS 5, *page 801*

$$\text{Mean} = \frac{\Sigma(x \cdot f)}{\Sigma f}$$

$$= \frac{(2 \cdot 5) + (3 \cdot 25) + (4 \cdot 10) + (5 \cdot 5)}{45}$$

$$= \frac{150}{45}$$

$$= 3\frac{1}{3}$$

The mean number of bedrooms per household for the homes in the subdivision is $3\frac{1}{3}$.

SECTION 12.2

CHECK YOUR PROGRESS 1, *page 808*

Tara's largest test score is 84 and her smallest test score is 76. The range of Tara's test scores is $84 - 76 = 8$.

CHECK YOUR PROGRESS 2, *page 810*

$$\mu = \frac{5 + 8 + 16 + 17 + 18 + 20}{6} = \frac{84}{6} = 14$$

x	$x - \mu$	$(x - \mu)^2$
5	$5 - 14 = -9$	$(-9)^2 = 81$
8	$8 - 14 = -6$	$(-6)^2 = 36$
16	$16 - 14 = 2$	$2^2 = 4$
17	$17 - 14 = 3$	$3^2 = 9$
18	$18 - 14 = 4$	$4^2 = 16$
20	$20 - 14 = 6$	$6^2 = 36$
		Sum: 182

$$\sigma = \sqrt{\frac{\Sigma(x - \mu)^2}{n}} = \sqrt{\frac{182}{6}} \approx \sqrt{30.33} \approx 5.51$$

The standard deviation for this population is approximately 5.51.

CHECK YOUR PROGRESS 3, *page 811*

The rope from Trustworthy has a breaking point standard deviation of

$$s_1 = \sqrt{\frac{(122 - 130)^2 + (141 - 130)^2 + \cdots + (125 - 130)^2}{6}}$$

$$= \sqrt{\frac{1752}{6}} \approx 17.1 \text{ pounds}$$

The rope from Brand X has a breaking point standard deviation of

$$s_2 = \sqrt{\frac{(128 - 130)^2 + (127 - 130)^2 + \cdots + (137 - 130)^2}{6}}$$

$$= \sqrt{\frac{3072}{6}} \approx 22.6 \text{ pounds}$$

The rope from NeverSnap has a breaking point standard deviation of

$$s_3 = \sqrt{\frac{(112 - 130)^2 + (121 - 130)^2 + \cdots + (135 - 130)^2}{6}}$$

$$= \sqrt{\frac{592}{6}} \approx 9.9 \text{ pounds}$$

The rope from NeverSnap has the lowest breaking point standard deviation.

CHECK YOUR PROGRESS 4, *page 812*

The mean is approximately 46.577.

The population standard deviation is approximately 2.876.

L₁	L₂	L₃	1
54.2	------	------	
49.4			
49.2			
53.2			
50.0			
48.2			
49.6			
L₁(1) = 54.2			

1-Var Stats
x̄=46.57653846 ◄——— Mean
Σx=1210.99
Σx²=56618.7787
Sx=2.932960201 ◄——— Sample standard deviation
σx=2.876004095 ◄——— Population standard deviation
↓n=26

CHECK YOUR PROGRESS 5, *page 813*

In Check Your Progress 2 we found $\sigma \approx \sqrt{30.33}$. Variance is the square of the standard deviation. Thus the variance is $\sigma^2 \approx \left(\sqrt{30.33}\right)^2 = 30.33$.

SECTION 12.3

CHECK YOUR PROGRESS 1, *page 820*

$$z_{15} = \frac{15 - 12}{2.4} = 1.25 \qquad z_{14} = \frac{14 - 11}{2.0} = 1.5$$

These z-scores indicate that in comparison to her classmates, Cheryl did better on the second quiz than she did on the first quiz.

CHECK YOUR PROGRESS 2, *page 820*

$$z_x = \frac{x - \mu}{\sigma}$$

$$0.6 = \frac{70 - 65.5}{\sigma}$$

$$\sigma = \frac{4.5}{0.6} = 7.5$$

The standard deviation for this set of test scores is 7.5.

CHECK YOUR PROGRESS 3, *page 821*

a. By definition, the median is the 50th percentile. Therefore, 50% of the police dispatchers earned less than $28,288 per year.

b. Because $25,640 is the 30th percentile, $100\% - 30\% = 70\%$ of all police dispatchers made more than $25,640.

c. From parts a and b, $50\% - 30\% = 20\%$ of the police dispatchers earned between $25,640 and $28,288.

CHECK YOUR PROGRESS 4, *page 822*

$$\text{Percentile} = \frac{\text{number of data values less than 405}}{\text{total number of data values}} \cdot 100$$

$$= \frac{3952}{8600} \cdot 100$$

$$\approx 46$$

Hal's score of 405 places him at the 46th percentile.

CHECK YOUR PROGRESS 5, *page 823*

Rank the data.

7.5 9.8 10.2 10.8 11.4 11.4 12.2 12.4 12.6 12.8 13.1 14.2 14.5 15.6 16.4

The median of these 15 data values has a rank of 8. Thus the median is 12.4. The second quartile, Q_2, is the median of the data, so $Q_2 = 12.4$.

The first quartile is the median of the seven values less than Q_2. Thus Q_1 has a rank of 4, so $Q_1 = 10.8$.

The third quartile is the median of the values greater than Q_2. Thus Q_3 has a rank of 12, so $Q_3 = 14.2$.

CHECK YOUR PROGRESS 6, *page 824*

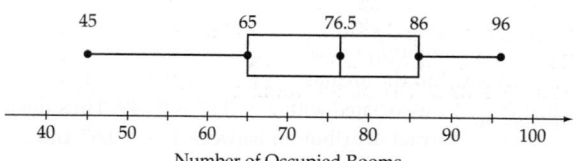

SECTION 12.4

CHECK YOUR PROGRESS 1, *page 833*

a. The percent of data in all classes with an upper bound of 25 seconds or less is the sum of the percents for the first five classes in Table 12.5. Thus the percent of subscribers who required less than 25 seconds to download the file is 30.9%.

b. The percent of data in all the classes with a lower bound of at least 10 seconds and an upper bound of 30 seconds or less is the sum of the percents in the third through sixth classes in Table 12.5. Thus the percent of subscribers who required from 10 to 30 seconds to download the file is 47.8%. The probability that a subscriber chosen at random will require from 10 to 30 seconds to download the file is 0.478.

CHECK YOUR PROGRESS 2, *page 837*

a. 0.76 pound is 1 standard deviation above the mean of 0.61 pound. In a normal distribution, 34.1% of all data lie between the mean and 1 standard deviation above the mean, and 50% of all data lie below the mean. Thus $34.1\% + 50\% = 84.1\%$ of the tomatoes weigh less than 0.76 pound.

b. 0.31 pound is 2 standard deviations below the mean of 0.61 pound. In a normal distribution, 47.7% of all data lie between the mean and 2 standard deviations below the mean, and 50% of all data lie above the mean. This gives a total of 47.7% + 50% = 97.7% of the tomatoes that weigh more than 0.31 pound. Therefore

$$(97.7\%)(6000) = (0.977)(6000) = 5862$$

of the tomatoes can be expected to weigh more than 0.31 pound.

c. 0.31 pound is 2 standard deviations below the mean of 0.61 pound and 0.91 pound is 2 standard deviations above the mean of 0.61 pound. In a normal distribution, 95.4% of all data lie within 2 standard deviations of the mean. Therefore

$$(95.4\%)(4500) = (0.954)(4500) = 4293$$

of the tomatoes can be expected to weigh from 0.31 pound to 0.91 pound.

CHECK YOUR PROGRESS 3, *page 840*
The area of the standard normal distribution between $z = -0.67$ and $z = 0$ is equal to the area between $z = 0$ and $z = 0.67$. The entry in Table 12.7 associated with $z = 0.67$ is 0.249. Thus the area of the standard normal distribution between $z = -0.67$ and $z = 0$ is 0.249 square unit.

CHECK YOUR PROGRESS 4, *page 840*
Table 12.7 indicates that the area from $z = 0$ to $z = -1.47$ is 0.429 square unit. The area to the left of $z = 0$ is 0.500 square unit. Thus the area to the left of $z = -1.47$ is $0.500 - 0.429 = 0.071$ square unit.

CHECK YOUR PROGRESS 5, *page 842*
Round z-scores to the nearest hundredth so you can use Table 12.7.

a. $z_9 = \dfrac{9 - 6.1}{1.8} \approx 1.61$

Table 12.7 indicates that 0.446 (44.6%) of the data in the standard normal distribution are between $z = 0$ and $z = 1.61$. The percent of the data to the right of $z = 1.61$ is $50\% - 44.6\% = 5.4\%$.

Approximately 5.4% of professional football players have careers of more than 9 years.

b. $z_3 = \dfrac{3 - 6.1}{1.8} \approx -1.72$ $z_4 = \dfrac{4 - 6.1}{1.8} \approx -1.17$

From Table 12.7:
$A_{1.72} = 0.457$ $A_{1.17} = 0.379$

$0.457 - 0.379 = 0.078$

The probability that a professional football player chosen at random will have a career of between 3 and 4 years is about 0.078.

SECTION 12.5

CHECK YOUR PROGRESS 1, *page 849*

x	y	x^2	xy
2.5	2.3	6.25	5.75
3.0	3.9	9.00	11.70
3.2	4.4	10.24	14.08
3.4	5.0	11.56	17.00
3.5	5.5	12.25	19.25
3.8	6.2	14.44	23.56
4.0	7.1	16.00	28.40
4.2	7.6	17.64	31.92
$\Sigma x = 27.6$	$\Sigma y = 42.0$	$\Sigma x^2 = 97.38$	$\Sigma xy = 151.66$

$n = 8$

$$a = \frac{n\Sigma xy - (\Sigma x)(\Sigma y)}{n\Sigma x^2 - (\Sigma x)^2}$$

$$= \frac{(8)(151.66) - (27.6)(42.0)}{(8)(97.38) - (27.6)^2}$$

$$\approx 3.1296$$

$$\bar{x} = \frac{\Sigma x}{n} = \frac{27.6}{8} = 3.45 \qquad \bar{y} = \frac{\Sigma y}{n} = \frac{42.0}{8} = 5.25$$

$$b = \bar{y} - a\bar{x}$$

$$= 5.25 - (3.1296)(3.45)$$

$$= -5.54712$$

$$\hat{y} = ax + b$$
$$\hat{y} \approx 3.1x - 5.5$$

CHECK YOUR PROGRESS 2, *page 850*

a. $\hat{y} = 3.1x - 5.5$
$\hat{y} = 3.1(2.7) - 5.5 \approx 2.9$

The predicted average speed of a camel with a stride length of 2.7 meters is approximately 2.9 meters per second.

b. $\hat{y} = 3.1x - 5.5$
$\hat{y} = 3.1(4.5) - 5.5 \approx 8.5$

The predicted average speed of a camel with a stride length of 4.5 meters is approximately 8.5 meters per second.

CHECK YOUR PROGRESS 3, *page 852*

From Check Your Progress 1:

$n = 8 \quad \Sigma x = 27.6 \quad \Sigma y = 42.0 \quad \Sigma x^2 = 97.38 \quad \Sigma xy = 151.66$

$$\Sigma y^2 = 2.3^2 + 3.9^2 + 4.4^2 + 5.0^2 + 5.5^2 + 6.2^2 + 7.1^2 + 7.6^2$$
$$= 241.72$$

$$r = \frac{n(\Sigma xy) - (\Sigma x)(\Sigma y)}{\sqrt{n(\Sigma x^2) - (\Sigma x)^2} \cdot \sqrt{n(\Sigma y^2) - (\Sigma y)^2}}$$

$$= \frac{8(151.66) - (27.6)(42.0)}{\sqrt{8(97.38) - (27.6)^2} \cdot \sqrt{8(241.72) - (42.0)^2}}$$

$$\approx 0.998498$$

The linear correlation coefficient, rounded to the nearest hundredth, is 1.00.

CHAPTER 13

SECTION 13.1

CHECK YOUR PROGRESS 1, *page 875*

a. The standard divisor is the sum of all the populations (251,100,000) divided by the number of representatives (20).

$$\text{Standard divisor} = \frac{251,100,000}{20} = 12,555,000$$

Country	Population	Quotient	Standard quota	Number of representatives
France	60,400,000	$\frac{60,400,000}{12,555,000} \approx 4.811$	4	5
Germany	82,400,000	$\frac{82,400,000}{12,555,000} \approx 6.563$	6	6
Italy	58,000,000	$\frac{58,000,000}{12,555,000} \approx 4.620$	4	5
Spain	40,000,000	$\frac{40,000,000}{12,555,000} \approx 3.186$	3	3
Belgium	10,300,000	$\frac{10,300,000}{12,555,000} \approx 0.820$	0	1
		Total	17	20

Because the sum of the standard quotas is 17 and not 20, we add one representative to each of the three countries with the largest decimal remainders. These are Belgium, France, and Italy. Thus the composition of the committee is France: 5, Germany: 6, Italy: 5, Spain: 3, Belgium: 1.

b. To use the Jefferson method, we must find a modified divisor such that the sum of the standard quotas is 20. This modified divisor is found by trial and error, but is always less than or equal to the standard divisor. We are using 11,000,000 for the modified standard divisor.

Country	Population	Quotient	Standard quota	Number of representatives
France	60,400,000	$\dfrac{60,400,000}{11,000,000} \approx 5.491$	5	5
Germany	82,400,000	$\dfrac{82,400,000}{11,000,000} \approx 7.491$	7	7
Italy	58,000,000	$\dfrac{58,000,000}{11,000,000} \approx 5.273$	5	5
Spain	40,000,000	$\dfrac{40,000,000}{11,000,000} \approx 3.636$	3	3
Belgium	10,300,000	$\dfrac{10,300,000}{11,000,000} \approx 0.936$	0	0
		Total	20	20

Thus the composition of the committee is France: 5, Germany: 7, Italy: 5, Spain: 3, Belgium: 0.

CHECK YOUR PROGRESS 2, *page 879*

$$\text{Relative unfairness of the apportionment} = \frac{\text{absolute unfairness of the apportionment}}{\text{average constituency of Shasta with a new representative}}$$

$$= \frac{210}{1390} \approx 0.151$$

The relative unfairness of the apportionment is approximately 0.151.

CHECK YOUR PROGRESS 3, *page 880*

Calculate the relative unfairness of the apportionment that assigns the teacher to the first grade and the relative unfairness of the apportionment that assigns the teacher to the second grade. In this case, the average constituency is the number of students divided by the number of teachers.

	First grade number of students per teacher	Second grade number of students per teacher	Absolute unfairness of apportionment
First grade receives teacher	$\dfrac{12,317}{512 + 1} \approx 24$	$\dfrac{15,439}{551} \approx 28$	$28 - 24 = 4$
Second grade receives teacher	$\dfrac{12,317}{512} \approx 24$	$\dfrac{15,439}{551 + 1} \approx 28$	$28 - 24 = 4$

If the first grade receives the new teacher, then the relative unfairness of the apportionment is

$$\text{Relative unfairness of the apportionment} = \frac{\text{absolute unfairness of the apportionment}}{\text{first grade's average constituency with a new teacher}}$$

$$= \frac{4}{24} \approx 0.167$$

If the second grade receives the new teacher, then the relative unfairness of the apportionment is

$$\begin{array}{c}\text{Relative unfairness of} \\ \text{the apportionment}\end{array} = \dfrac{\text{absolute unfairness of the apportionment}}{\text{second grade's average constituency with a new teacher}}$$

$$= \dfrac{4}{28} \approx 0.143$$

Because the smaller relative unfairness results from adding the teacher to the second grade, that class should receive the new teacher.

CHECK YOUR PROGRESS 4, *page 882*

Calculate the Huntington-Hill number for each of the classes. In this case, the population is the number of students.

First year:

$$\dfrac{2015^2}{12(12+1)} \approx 26{,}027$$

Second year:

$$\dfrac{1755^2}{10(10+1)} \approx 28{,}000$$

Third year:

$$\dfrac{1430^2}{9(9+1)} \approx 22{,}721$$

Fourth year:

$$\dfrac{1309^2}{8(8+1)} \approx 23{,}798$$

Because the second-year class has the greatest Huntington-Hill number, the new representative should represent the second year class.

SECTION 13.2

CHECK YOUR PROGRESS 1, *page 891*

To answer the question, we will make a table showing the number of second-place votes for each candy.

	Second-place votes
Caramel center	3
Vanilla center	0
Almond center	$17 + 9 = 26$
Toffee center	2
Solid chocolate	$11 + 8 = 19$

The largest number of second-place votes (26) were for almond centers. Almond centers would win second place using the plurality voting system.

CHECK YOUR PROGRESS 2, *page 895*

Using the Borda Count method, each first-place vote receives 5 points, each second-place vote receives 4 points, each third-place vote receives 3 points, and each fourth-place vote receives 2 points, and each last-place vote receives 1 point. The summary for each flavor is shown below.

Caramel:

0 first-place votes	$0 \cdot 5 =$	0
3 second-place votes	$3 \cdot 4 =$	12
0 third-place votes	$0 \cdot 3 =$	0
30 fourth-place votes	$30 \cdot 2 =$	60
17 fifth-place votes	$17 \cdot 1 =$	17
	Total	89

Vanilla:

17 first-place votes	$17 \cdot 5 =$	85
0 second-place votes	$0 \cdot 4 =$	0
0 third-place votes	$0 \cdot 3 =$	0
0 fourth-place votes	$0 \cdot 2 =$	0
33 fifth-place votes	$33 \cdot 1 =$	33
	Total	118

Almond:

8 first-place votes	$8 \cdot 5 =$	40
26 second-place votes	$26 \cdot 4 =$	104
16 third-place votes	$16 \cdot 3 =$	48
0 fourth-place votes	$0 \cdot 2 =$	0
0 fifth-place votes	$0 \cdot 1 =$	0
	Total	192

Toffee:

20 first-place votes	$20 \cdot 5 =$	100
2 second-place votes	$2 \cdot 4 =$	8
8 third-place votes	$8 \cdot 3 =$	24
20 fourth-place votes	$20 \cdot 2 =$	40
0 fifth-place votes	$0 \cdot 1 =$	0
	Total	172

Chocolate:

5 first-place votes	$5 \cdot 5 =$	25
19 second-place votes	$19 \cdot 4 =$	76
26 third-place votes	$26 \cdot 3 =$	78
0 fourth-place votes	$0 \cdot 2 =$	0
0 fifth-place votes	$0 \cdot 1 =$	0
	Total	179

Using the Borda Count method, almond centers is the first choice.

CHECK YOUR PROGRESS 3, *page 897*

	Rankings				
Italian	2	5	1	4	3
Mexican	1	4	5	2	1
Thai	3	1	4	5	2
Chinese	4	2	3	1	4
Indian	5	3	2	3	5
Number of ballots:	33	30	25	20	18

Indian food received no first place votes, so it is eliminated.

	Rankings				
Italian	2	4	1	3	3
Mexican	1	3	4	2	1
Thai	3	1	3	4	2
Chinese	4	2	2	1	4
Number of ballots:	33	30	25	20	18

In this ranking, Chinese food received the fewest first-place votes, so it is eliminated.

	Rankings				
Italian	2	3	1	2	3
Mexican	1	2	3	1	1
Thai	3	1	2	3	2
Number of ballots:	33	30	25	20	18

In this ranking, Italian food received the fewest first-place votes, so it is eliminated.

	Rankings				
Mexican	1	2	2	1	1
Thai	2	1	1	2	2
Number of ballots:	33	30	25	20	18

In this ranking, Thai food received the fewest first-place votes, so it is eliminated. The preference for the banquet food is Mexican.

CHECK YOUR PROGRESS 4, *page 899*

Do a head-to-head comparison for each of the restaurants and enter the winner in the table below. For instance, in the Sanborn's versus Apple Inn comparison, Sanborn's was favored by $31 + 25 + 11 = 67$ critics. In the Apple Inn versus Sanborn's comparison, Apple Inn was favored by $18 + 15 = 33$ critics. Therefore, Sanborn's wins this head-to-head match. The completed table is shown below.

versus	Sanborn's	Apple Inn	May's	Tory's
Sanborn's		Sanborn's	May's	Sanborn's
Apple Inn			May's	Tory's
May's				May's
Tory's				

From the table, May's has the most points, so it is the critics' choice.

CHECK YOUR PROGRESS 5, *page 901*

Do a head-to-head comparison for each of the candidates and enter the winner in the table below.

versus	Alpha	Beta	Gamma
Alpha		Alpha	Alpha
Beta			Beta
Gamma			

From this table, Alpha is the winner. However, using the Borda Count method (See Example 5), Beta is the winner. Thus the Borda Count method violates the Condorcet criterion.

CHECK YOUR PROGRESS 6, *page 903*

	Rankings		
Radiant silver	1	3	3
Electric red	2	2	1
Lightning blue	3	1	2
Number of votes:	30	27	2

Using the Borda Count method, we have

Silver:

30 first-place votes	$30 \cdot 3 =$	90
0 second-place votes	$0 \cdot 2 =$	0
29 third-place votes	$29 \cdot 1 =$	29
	Total	119

Red:

2 first-place votes	$2 \cdot 3 =$	6
57 second-place votes	$57 \cdot 2 =$	114
0 third-place votes	$0 \cdot 1 =$	0
	Total	120

Blue:

27 first-place votes	$27 \cdot 3 =$	81
2 second-place votes	$2 \cdot 2 =$	4
30 third-place votes	$30 \cdot 1 =$	30
	Total	115

Using this method, electric red is the preferred color. Now suppose we eliminate the third-place choice (lightning blue). This gives the following table.

	Rankings		
Radiant silver	1	2	2
Electric red	2	1	1
Number of votes:	30	27	2

Recalculating the results, we have

Silver:

30 first-place votes	$30 \cdot 2 = 60$
29 second-place votes	$29 \cdot 1 = 29$
	Total 89

Red:

29 first-place votes	$29 \cdot 2 = 58$
30 second-place votes	$30 \cdot 1 = 30$
	Total 88

Now radiant silver is the preferred color. By deleting an alternative, the result of the voting changed. This violates the irrelevant alternatives criterion.

SECTION 13.3

CHECK YOUR PROGRESS 1, *page 917*

a. and **b.**

Winning coalition	Number of votes	Critical voters
{A, B}	40	A, B
{A, C}	39	A, C
{A, B, C}	57	A
{A, B, D}	50	A, B
{A, B, E}	45	A, B
{A, C, D}	49	A, C
{A, C, E}	44	A, C
{A, D, E}	37	A, D, E
{B, C, D}	45	B, C, D
{B, C, E}	40	B, C, E
{A, B, C, D}	67	None
{A, B, C, E}	62	None
{A, B, D, E}	55	A
{A, C, D, E}	54	A
{B, C, D, E}	50	B, C
{A, B, C, D, E}	72	None

CHECK YOUR PROGRESS 2, *page 919*

Winning coalition	Number of votes	Critical voters
{A, B}	34	A, B
{A, C}	28	A, C
{B, C}	26	B, C
{A, B, C}	44	None
{A, B, D}	40	A, B
{A, C, D}	34	A, C
{B, C, D}	32	B, C
{A, B, C, D}	50	None

The number of times all voters are critical is 12.

$$BPI(A) = \frac{4}{12} = \frac{1}{3}$$

$$BPI(D) = \frac{0}{12} = 0$$

CHECK YOUR PROGRESS 3, *page 920*

The countries are represented as follows: B, Belgium; F, France; G, Germany; I, Italy; L, Luxembourg; N, Netherlands.

Winning coalition	Number of votes	Critical voters
{F, G, I}	12	F, G, I
{B, F, G, I}	14	F, G, I
{B, F, G, I, L}	15	F, G, I
{B, F, G, I, N}	16	None
{B, F, G, I, L, N}	17	None
{B, F, G, N}	12	B, F, G, N
{B, F, I, N}	12	B, F, I, N
{B, G, I, N}	12	B, G, I, N
{B, G, I, N, L}	13	B, G, I, N
{B, F, I, N, L}	13	B, F, I, N
{B, F, G, N, L}	13	B, F, G, N
{F, G, I, L}	13	F, G, I
{F, G, I, L, N}	15	F, G, I
{F, G, I, N}	14	F, G, I

The number of times all votes are critical is 42. The BPIs of the nations are:

$$BPI(B) = \frac{6}{42} = \frac{1}{7}$$

$$BPI(F) = \frac{10}{42} = \frac{5}{28}$$

$$BPI(G) = \frac{10}{42} = \frac{5}{28}$$

$$BPI(I) = \frac{10}{42} = \frac{5}{28}$$

$$BPI(L) = \frac{0}{42} = 0$$

$$BPI(N) = \frac{6}{42} = \frac{1}{7}$$

APPENDIX

APPENDIX

CHECK YOUR PROGRESS 1, *page 936*

a. 1 295 m = 1.295 km

b. 7 543 g = 7.543 kg

c. 6.3 L = 6 300 ml

d. 2 kl = 2 000 L

CHAPTER 1

EXERCISE SET 1.1 *page 12*

1. 28 **3.** 45 **5.** 64 **7.** $\dfrac{15}{17}$ **9.** -13 **11.** correct **13.** correct **15.** incorrect

17. no effect **19.** 150 inches **21.** The distance is quadrupled. **23.** 0.5 second **25.** inductive
27. deductive **29.** deductive **31.** inductive
In Exercises 33–39, only one possible answer is given. Your answers may vary from the given answers.

33. $x = \dfrac{1}{2}$ **35.** $x = \dfrac{1}{2}$ **37.** $x = -3$ **39.** Consider 1 and 3. $1 + 3$ is even, but $1 \cdot 3$ is odd.

41. It does not work for 121. **43.** n **45.** Maria: the utility stock; Jose: the automotive stock;
$$6n + 8$$ Anita: the technology stock; Tony: the oil stock
$$\frac{6n + 8}{2} = 3n + 4$$
$$3n + 4 - 2n = n + 4$$
$$n + 4 - 4 = n$$

47. Atlanta: stamps; Chicago: baseball cards; Philadelphia: coins; Seattle: comic books **49.** Home, bookstore, supermarket, credit
union, home; or home, credit union, supermarket, bookstore, home **51.** N, because the first letter of Nine is N. **53.** d

EXERCISE SET 1.2 *page 24*

1. 97 **3.** 329 **5.** 159 **7.** $\dfrac{3}{2}, 5, \dfrac{21}{2}, 18, \dfrac{55}{2}$ **9.** $2, 14, 36, 68, 110$ **11.** $a_n = n^2 + n - 1$

13. $a_n = 2n$ **15. a.** There are 56 cannonballs in the sixth pyramid and 84 cannonballs in the seventh pyramid.
b. The eighth pyramid has eight levels of cannonballs. The number of cannonballs in the nth level is given by the nth number in the
sequence 1, 3, 6, 10, 15, 21, 28, 36. Thus the total number of cannonballs in the eighth pyramid is $1 + 3 + 6 + 10 + 15 + 21 + 28 + 36 = 120$. **17. a.** Five cuts produce six pieces and six cuts produce 7 pieces. **b.** $a_n = n + 1$ **19. a.** 26
b. 7 **21.** $a_3 = 7, a_4 = 9, a_5 = 11$ **23.** $F_{20} = 6765, F_{30} = 832{,}040, F_{40} = 102{,}334{,}155$ **25.** n^2
27. a. 38.8 AU **b.** $38.8 - 30.6 = 8.2$ AU. The prediction is not close compared to the results obtained for the inner planets.
29. a. 154 AU **b.** Yes **31. a.** $F_n + 2F_{n+1} + F_{n+2} = F_{n+4}$ **b.** $F_n + F_{n+1} + F_{n+3} = F_{n+4}$

33. 1.615385; 1.617647; 1.617978; 1.618026. If n is an even number, then the ratio $\dfrac{F_n}{F_{n-1}}$ is slightly less than Φ.

EXERCISE SET 1.3 *page 41*

1. 195 **3.** 91 **5.** \$40 **7.** 18 **9.** $2^{12} = 4096$ **11. a.** B: 1, C: 9, D: 36, E: 84, F: 126, G: 126, H: 84
b. Region F is the fifth region from the left and region G is the fifth region from the right. For any path from A to F, the ball makes a
number of left or right turns. If the turns are reversed, right turns instead of left turns and left turns instead of right turns, then the ball
ends up in region G. Thus for each path from A to F, there is exactly one symmetrical path, about a central vertical line, from A to G. Also,
from each path from A to G, there is exactly one symmetrical path from A to F. Thus there are the same numbers of paths to both regions.
13. 28 **15.** 21 ducks, 14 pigs **17.** 12 **19.** 6 **21.** 7 **23. a.** 80,200 **b.** 151,525 **c.** 1892

25. a.   121, 484, and 676   **b.**   1331   **27.** $1\frac{1}{2}$ inches   **29. a.**   1.3 billion; 1.5 billion; 1.6 billion   **b.**   1995
c.   2002   **d.**   2001 to 2002   **31. a.**   1994   **b.**   2002   **c.**   The number of theatre admissions in 2003 was less than
the number of admissions in 2002.   **33.**   2601 tiles   **35.**   Four more sisters than brothers   **37.**   the 11th day
39.   91   **41. a.**   Place four coins on the left balance pan and the other four on the right balance pan. The pan that is the higher
contains the fake coin. Take the four coins from the higher pan and use the balance scale to compare the weight of two of these coins to the
weight of the other two. The pan that is the higher contains the fake coin. Take the two coins from the higher pan and use the balance scale
to compare the weight of one of these coins to the weight of the other. The pan that is the higher contains the fake coin. This procedure
enables you to determine the fake coin in three weighings.   **b.**   Place three of the coins on one of the balance pans and another three
coins on the other. If the pans balance, then the fake coin is one of the two remaining coins. You can use the balance scale to determine
which of the remaining coins is the fake coin because it will be lighter than the other coin. If the three coins on the left pan do not balance
with the three coins on the right pan, then the fake coin must be one of the three coins on the higher pan. Pick any two coins from these
three and place one on each balance pan. If these two coins do not balance, then the one that is the higher is the fake. If the coins balance,
then the third coin (the one that you did not place on the balance pan) is the fake. In any case, this procedure enables you to determine the
fake coin in two weighings.   **43. a.**   1600. Sally likes perfect squares.   **45. d.**   64. Each number is the cube of a term in the
sequence 1, 2, 3, 4, 5, 6.   **47. a.**   People born in 1980 will be 45 in 2025. $(2025 = 45^2)$ **b.**   2070, because people born in 2070
will be 46 in 2116. $(2116 = 46^2)$ **49.**   612   **51.**   Answers will vary.

CHAPTER 1 REVIEW EXERCISES   *page 47*

1.   deductive   [Sec 1.1]   **2.**   inductive   [Sec. 1.1]   **3.**   inductive   [Sec. 1.1]   **4.**   deductive   [Sec. 1.1]
5. $x = 0$ provides a counterexample because $0^4 = 0$ and 0 is not greater than 0.   [Sec. 1.1]   **6.** $x = 4$ provides a counterexample
because $\dfrac{(4)^3 + 5(4) + 6}{6} = 15$, which is not an even number.   [Sec. 1.1]   **7.** $x = 1$ provides a counterexample because
$[(1) + 4]^2 = 25$, but $(1)^2 + 16 = 17$.   [Sec. 1.1]   **8.**   Let $a = 1$ and $b = 1$. Then $(a + b)^3 = (1 + 1)^3 = 2^3 = 8$. However,
$a^3 + b^3 = 1^3 + 1^3 = 2$.   [Sec. 1.1]   **9. a.**   112   **b.**   479   [Sec. 1.2]   **10. a.** -72 **b.** -768 [Sec. 1.2]
11. $a_1 = 1, a_2 = 12, a_3 = 31, a_4 = 58, a_5 = 93, a_{20} = 1578$ [Sec. 1.2]   **12.** $a_1 = 3, a_2 = -6, a_3 = -39, a_4 = -108, a_5 = -225$
$a_{25} = -31{,}125$ [Sec. 1.2]   **13.** $a_n = 3n$ [Sec. 1.2]   **14.** $a_n = n^2 + 3n + 4$ [Sec. 1.2]   **15.** $a_n = n^2 + 3n + 2$
[Sec. 1.2]   **16.** $a_n = 5n - 1$ [Sec. 1.2]   **17.**   320 feet by 1600 feet   [Sec. 1.3]   **18.** $3^{15} = 14{,}348{,}907$ [Sec. 1.3]
19. 48 skyboxes   [Sec. 1.3]   **20.**   On the first trip the rancher takes the rabbit across the river. The rancher returns alone. The
rancher takes the dog across the river and returns with the rabbit. The rancher next takes the carrots across the river and returns alone. On
the final trip the rancher takes the rabbit across the river.   [Sec. 1.3]   **21.**   \$300   [Sec. 1.3]   **22.**   105   [Sec. 1.3]
23.   Answers will vary.   [Sec. 1.3]   **24.**   Answers will vary.   [Sec. 1.3]   **25.**   Michael: biology major; Clarissa: business
major; Reggie: computer science major; Ellen: chemistry major   [Sec. 1.1]   **26.**   Dodgers: drug store; Pirates: supermarket;
Tigers: bank; Giants: service station   [Sec. 1.1]   **27. a.**   Yes. Answers will vary.   **b.**   No. The countries of India, Bangladesh,
and Myanmar all share borders with each of the other two countries. Thus at least three colors are needed to color the map.   [Sec. 1.1]
28. a.   The following figure shows a route that passes over each bridge once and only once.   **b.**   No.   [Sec. 1.3]

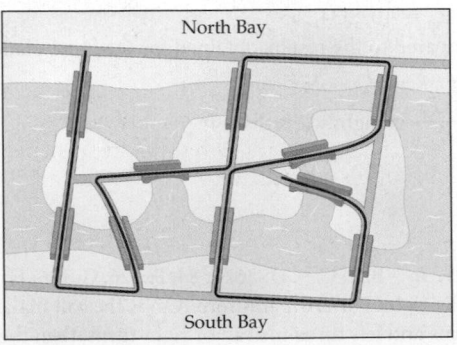

29.   1 square inch; 4 square inches; 25 square inches   [Sec. 1.3]   **30. a.** $2^{10} = 1024$ **b.** $2^{30} = 1{,}073{,}741{,}824$ [Sec. 1.2]
31.   A represents 1, B represents 9, and D represents 0.   [Sec. 1.3]   **32.**   5   [Sec. 1.3]   **33.**   10   [Sec. 1.3]
34.   1   [Sec. 1.3]   **35.**   3   [Sec. 1.3]

36. n

$4n$

$4n + 12$

$\dfrac{4n + 12}{2} = 2n + 6$

$2n + 6 - 6 = 2n$ [Sec. 1.1]

37. Each nickel is worth 5 cents. Thus 2004 nickels are worth $2004 \times 5 = 10{,}020$ cents, or \$100.20.   [Sec. 1.3]

38. a. 1970 to 1980   **b.** 5.5%   [Sec. 1.3]   **39. a.** 16 times as many   **b.** 61 times as many   [Sec. 1.3]

40. a. 2002   **b.** 2004   [Sec. 1.3]   **41.** 5005   [Sec. 1.3]   **42.** There are no narcissistic numbers.   [Sec. 1.3]

43. a. 10   **b.** yes   [Sec. 1.2]   **44. a.** 22   **b.** No. $9^9 = 387{,}420{,}489$. Thus $9^{(9^9)}$ is the product of 387,420,489 nines. At one multiplication per second, this computation would take about 12.3 years.   [Sec. 1.1/1.3]

CHAPTER 1 TEST   *page 50*

1. deductive   [Sec. 1.1]   **2.** inductive   [Sec. 1.1]   **3.** inductive   [Sec. 1.1]   **4.** deductive   [Sec. 1.1]

5. 384   [Sec. 1.2]   **6.** 1, 1, 2, 3, 5, 8, 13, 21, 34, 55   [Sec. 1.2]   **7. a.** $a_n = 4n$ **b.** $a_n = 3n + 1$ [Sec. 1.2]

8. $0, 1, -3, 6, -10,$ and -5460 [Sec. 1.2]   **9.** 131, 212, 343   [Sec. 1.2]

10. Understand the problem. Devise a plan. Carry out the plan. Review the solution.   [Sec. 1.3]   **11.** 6   [Sec. 1.3]

12. 15   [Sec. 1.3]   **13.** 3   [Sec. 1.3]   **14.** \$672   [Sec. 1.3]   **15.** 126   [Sec. 1.3]   **16.** 36   [Sec. 1.3]

17. Reynaldo is 13, Ramiro is 5, Shakira is 15, and Sasha is 7.   [Sec. 1.1]   **18.** 606   [Sec. 1.3]   **19.** $x = 4$ provides a counterexample because division by zero is undefined.   [Sec. 1.1]   **20. a.** 2002 to 2003   **b.** 250,000   [Sec. 1.3]

CHAPTER 2

EXERCISE SET 2.1   *page 61*

1. {penny, nickel, dime, quarter}   **3.** {Mercury, Mars}   **5.** {Reagan, G. H. W. Bush, Clinton, G. W. Bush}

7. $\{-5, -4, -3, -2, -1\}$ **9.** {7}   **11.** { }

In Exercises 13–19, only one possible answer is given.

13. The set of days of the week that begin with the letter T.   **15.** The set consisting of the two planets in our solar system that are closest to the sun.   **17.** The set of single-digit natural numbers.   **19.** The set of natural numbers less than or equal to 7.

21. True   **23.** False; $b \in \{a, b, c\}$, but $\{b\}$ is not an element of $\{a, b, c\}$.   **25.** False; {0} has one element, whereas $\varnothing$ has no elements.   **27.** False; the word "good" is subjective.   **29.** False; 0 is an element of the first set, but 0 is not an element of the second set.

In Exercises 31–39, only one possible answer is given.

31. $\{x \mid x \in N \text{ and } x < 13\}$ **33.** $\{x \mid x \text{ is a multiple of 5 and } 4 < x < 16\}$ **35.** $\{x \mid x \text{ is the name of a month that has 31 days}\}$ **37.** $\{x \mid x \text{ is the name of a U.S. state that begins with the letter A}\}$ **39.** $\{x \mid x \text{ is a season that starts with the letter s}\}$

41. {California, Arizona}   **43.** {California, Arizona, Florida, Texas}   **45.** {2000, 2002, 2004}   **47.** {1997, 1998}

49. {June, October, November}   **51.** {1985, 1986, 1987, 1989}   **53.** {1988, 1990, 1991, 1992, 1993, 1995, 1996}

55. 11   **57.** 0   **59.** 4   **61.** 16   **63.** 121   **65.** Neither   **67.** Both   **69.** Equivalent

71. Equivalent   **73.** Not well defined   **75.** Not well defined   **77.** Well defined   **79.** Well defined

81. Not well defined   **83.** Not well defined   **85.** $A = B$ **87.** $A \neq B$ **89.** Answers will vary; however, the set of all real numbers between 0 and 1 is one example of a set that cannot be written using the roster method.

EXERCISE SET 2.2   *page 71*

1. {0, 1, 3, 5, 8}   **3.** $U = \{0, 1, 2, 3, 4, 5, 6, 7, 8\}$ **5.** {0, 7, 8}   **7.** {0, 2, 4, 6, 8}   **9.** $\subseteq$ **11.** $\not\subseteq$

13. $\subseteq$ **15.** $\subseteq$ **17.** $\subseteq$ **19.** True   **21.** True   **23.** True   **25.** False   **27.** True

29. True   **31.** False   **33.** False   **35.** False   **37.** 18 hours   **39.** $\varnothing, \{\alpha\}, \{\beta\}, \{\alpha, \beta\}$

41. $\varnothing, \{I\}, \{II\}, \{III\}, \{I, II\}, \{I, III\}, \{II, III\}, \{I, II, III\}$ **43.** 4   **45.** 128   **47.** 2048   **49.** 1   **51. a.** 15

b. 10   **c.** Two different sets of coins can have the same value.   **53. a.** 6   **b.** 2   **c.** 4   **d.** 1

55. a. 1024   **b.** 12

57. a. {1, 2, 3} has only three elements, namely 1, 2, and 3. Because {2} is not equal to 1, 2, or 3, {2} ∉ {1, 2, 3}.   **b.** 1 is not a set, so it cannot be a subset.   **c.** The given set has the elements 1 and {1}. Because 1 ≠ {1}, there are exactly two elements in {1, {1}}.

59. a. {A, B, C}, {A, B, D}, {A, B, E}, {A, C, D}, {A, C, E}, {A, D, E}, {B, C, D}, {B, C, E}, {B, D, E}, {C, D, E}, {A, B, C, D}, {A, B, C, E}, {A, B, D, E}, {A, C, D, E}, {B, C, D, E}, {A, B, C, D, E}   **b.** {A}, {B}, {C}, {D}, {E}, {A, B}, {A, C}, {A, D}, {A, E}, {B, C}, {B, D}, {B, E}, {C, D}, {C, E}, {D, E}

EXERCISE SET 2.3   *page 83*

1. {1, 2, 4, 5, 6, 8}   **3.** {4, 6}   **5.** {3, 7}   **7.** U = {1, 2, 3, 4, 5, 6, 7, 8}   **9.** ∅   **11.** B = {1, 2, 5, 8}

13. U = {1, 2, 3, 4, 5, 6, 7, 8}   **15.** {2, 5, 8}   **17.** {1, 3, 4, 6, 7}   **19.** {2, 5, 8}

In Exercises 21–27, one possible answer is given. Your answers may vary from the given answers.

21. The set of all elements that are not in L or are in T.   **23.** The set of all elements that are in A, or are in C but not in B.

25. The set of all elements that are in T, and are also in J or not in K.   **27.** The set of all elements that are in both W and V, or are in both W and Z.   **29.**

    31.   **33.**

35. 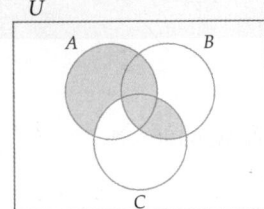   **37.** Not equal   **39.** Equal   **41.** Not equal   **43.** Not equal

45. Equal   **47.** Yellow   **49.** Cyan   **51.** Red

In Exercises 53–61, one possible answer is given. Your answers may vary from the given answers.

53. $A \cap B'$ **55.** $(A \cup B)'$ **57.** $B \cup C$ **59.** $C \cap (A \cup B)'$ **61.** $(A \cup B)' \cup (A \cap B \cap C)$

63. a.   **b.**   **c.**

65.   **67.**

See the *Student Solutions Manual* for the verification for Exercise 69.   **71.** $\{3, 9\}$ **73.** $\{2, 8\}$ **75.** $\{3, 9\}$
77. Responses will vary.   **79.**

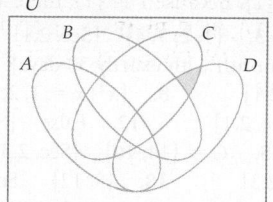

EXERCISE SET 2.4   *page 94*

1. 7   **3.** 8   **5.** 8   **7.** 12   **9.** $n(A \cup B) = 7$; $n(A) + n(B) - n(A \cap B) = 4 + 5 - 2 = 7$ **11.** 113
13. 1060   **15.**

U
A   B
6   12   11
7   3   5
25
6
C

17. a. 180   **b.** 200   **19. a.** 15%   **b.** 13%

21. a. 450   **b.** 140   **c.** 130   **23. a.** 109   **b.** 328   **c.** 104   **25. a.** 101   **b.** 370
c. 380   **d.** 373   **e.** 225   **f.** 530   **27. a.** 72   **b.** 47   **c.** 25   **d.** 0
29. a. 200   **b.** 271   **c.** 16

EXERCISE SET 2.5   *page 107*

1. a. One possible one-to-one correspondence   **b.** 6   **3.** Pair $(2n - 1)$ of D with $(3n)$ of M.   **5.** $\aleph_0$ **7.** c
between V and M is given by

$V = \{a, e, i\}$
↑ ↑ ↑
↓ ↓ ↓
$M = \{3, 6, 9\}$

9. c **11.** Equivalent   **13.** Equivalent   **15.** Let $S = \{10, 20, 30, \dots, 10n, \dots\}$. Then S is a proper subset of A. A rule
for a one-to-one correspondence between A and S is $(5n) \leftrightarrow (10n)$. Because A can be placed in a one-to-one correspondence with a proper
subset of itself, A is an infinite set.

17. Let $R = \left\{ \dfrac{3}{4}, \dfrac{5}{6}, \dfrac{7}{8}, \dots, \dfrac{2n + 1}{2n + 2}, \dots \right\}$. Then R is a proper subset of C. A rule for a one-to-one correspondence between C and R is

$\left(\dfrac{2n - 1}{2n} \right) \leftrightarrow \left(\dfrac{2n + 1}{2n + 2} \right)$. Because C can be placed in a one-to-one correspondence with a proper subset of itself, C is an infinite set.

In Exercises 19–25, let $N = \{1, 2, 3, 4, \dots, n, \dots\}$. Then a one-to-one correspondence between the given sets and the set of natural
numbers N is given by the following general correspondences.

19. $(n + 49) \leftrightarrow n$ **21.** $\left(\dfrac{1}{3^{n-1}} \right) \leftrightarrow n$ **23.** $(10^n) \leftrightarrow n$ **25.** $(n^3) \leftrightarrow n$

27. a. For any natural number n, the two natural numbers preceding $3n$ are not multiples of 3. Pair these two numbers, $3n - 2$ and
$3n - 1$, with the multiples of 3 given by $6n - 3$ and $6n$, respectively. Using the two general correspondences $(6n - 3) \leftrightarrow (3n - 2)$ and
$(6n) \leftrightarrow (3n - 1)$ (as shown below), we can establish a one-to-one correspondence between the multiples of 3 (set M) and the set K of all
natural numbers that are not multiples of 3.
$M = \{3, 6, 9, 12, 15, 18, \dots, 6n - 3, \quad 6n, \quad \dots\}$
↑ ↑
$K = \{1, 2, 4, 5, \quad 7, \quad 8, \quad \dots, 3n - 2, 3n - 1, \dots\}$
The following answers in parts b and c were produced by using the correspondences established in part a.   **b.** 302   **c.** 1800
29. The set of real numbers x such that $0 < x < 1$ is equivalent to the set of all real numbers.

CHAPTER 2 REVIEW EXERCISES   *page 110*

1. $\{0, 1, 2, 3, 4, 5, 6, 7\}$ [Sec. 2.1]   2. $\{-8, 8\}$ [Sec. 2.1]   3. $\{1, 2, 3, 4\}$ [Sec. 2.1]   4. $\{1, 2, 3, 4, 5, 6\}$ [Sec. 2.1]
5. $\{x \,|\, x \in I \text{ and } x > -6\}$ [Sec. 2.1]   6. $\{x \,|\, x \text{ is the name of a month with exactly 30 days}\}$ [Sec. 2.1]
7. $\{x \,|\, x \text{ is the name of a U.S. state that begins with the letter K}\}$ [Sec. 2.1]   8. $\{x^3 \,|\, x = 1, 2, 3, 4, \text{ or } 5\}$ [Sec. 2.1]
9. False [Sec. 2.1]   10. True [Sec. 2.1]   11. True [Sec. 2.1]   12. False [Sec. 2.1]
13. $\{6, 10\}$ [Sec. 2.3]   14. $\{2, 6, 10, 16, 18\}$ [Sec. 2.3]   15. $C = \{14, 16\}$ [Sec. 2.3]
16. $\{2, 6, 8, 10, 12, 16, 18\}$ [Sec. 2.3]   17. $\{2, 6, 10, 16\}$ [Sec. 2.3]   18. $\{8, 12\}$ [Sec. 2.3]
19. $\{6, 8, 10, 12, 14, 16, 18\}$ [Sec. 2.3]   20. $\{8, 12\}$ [Sec. 2.3]   21. Proper subset [Sec. 2.2]
22. Proper subset [Sec. 2.2]   23. Not a proper subset [Sec. 2.2]   24. Not a proper subset [Sec. 2.2]
25. $\varnothing, \{I\}, \{II\}, \{I, II\}$ [Sec. 2.2]   26. $\varnothing, \{s\}, \{u\}, \{n\}, \{s, u\}, \{s, n\}, \{u, n\}, \{s, u, n\}$ [Sec. 2.2]
27. $\varnothing$, {penny}, {nickel}, {dime}, {quarter}, {penny, nickel}, {penny, dime}, {penny, quarter}, {nickel, dime}, {nickel, quarter},
{dime, quarter}, {penny, nickel, dime}, {penny, nickel, quarter}, {penny, dime, quarter}, {nickel, dime, quarter},
{penny, nickel, dime, quarter} [Sec. 2.2]   28. $\varnothing$, {A}, {B}, {C}, {D}, {E}, {A, B}, {A, C}, {A, D}, {A, E}, {B, C}, {B, D}, {B, E},
{C, D}, {C, E}, {D, E}, {A, B, C}, {A, B, D}, {A, B, E}, {A, C, D}, {A, C, E}, {A, D, E}, {B, C, D}, {B, C, E}, {B, D, E}, {C, D, E}, {A, B, C, D},
{A, B, C, E}, {A, B, D, E}, {A, C, D, E}, {B, C, D, E}, {A, B, C, D, E} [Sec. 2.2]   29. $2^4 = 16$ [Sec. 2.2]
30. $2^{26} = 67{,}108{,}864$ [Sec. 2.2]   31. $2^{15} = 32{,}768$ [Sec. 2.2]   32. $2^7 = 128$ [Sec. 2.2]

33.
[Sec. 2.3]

34.
[Sec. 2.3]

35.
[Sec. 2.3]

36.
[Sec. 2.3]

37. Equal [Sec. 2.3]

38. Not equal [Sec. 2.3]   39. Not equal [Sec. 2.3]   40. Not equal [Sec. 2.3]
41. $(A \cup B)' \cap C$ or $C \cap (A' \cap B')$ [Sec. 2.3]   42. $(A \cap B) \cup (B \cap C')$ [Sec. 2.3]

43.
[Sec. 2.3]

44.
[Sec. 2.3]

45. 391 [Sec. 2.4]

46. a. 42   b. 31   c. 20   d. 142 [Sec. 2.4]
47. One possible one-to-one correspondence between
$\{1, 3, 6, 10\}$ and $\{1, 2, 3, 4\}$ is given by
$\{1, 3, 6, 10\}$
$\updownarrow \updownarrow \updownarrow \updownarrow$
$\{1, 2, 3, 4\}$ [Sec. 2.5]

48. $\{x \,|\, x > 10 \text{ and } x \in N\} = \{11, 12, 13, 14, \ldots, n + 10, \ldots\}$
Thus a one-to-one correspondence between the sets is given by
$\{11, 12, 13, 14, \ldots, n + 10, \ldots\}$
$\updownarrow \updownarrow \updownarrow \updownarrow \qquad \updownarrow$
$\{2, 4, 6, 8, \ldots, 2n, \ldots\}$ [Sec. 2.5]

49. One possible one-to-one correspondence between
the sets is given by
$\{3, 6, 9, \ldots, 3n, \ldots\}$
$\updownarrow \updownarrow \updownarrow \qquad \updownarrow$
$\{10, 100, 1000, \ldots, 10^n, \ldots\}$ [Sec. 2.5]

50. In the following figure, the line from E that passes through $\overline{AB}$ and $\overline{CD}$ illustrates a method of establishing a one-to-one correspondence between $\{x \mid 0 \le x \le 1\}$ and $\{x \mid 0 \le x \le 4\}$.

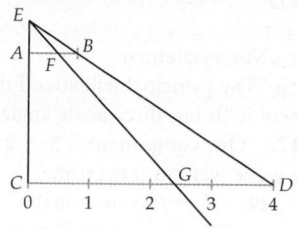

[Sec. 2.5]

51. A proper subset of A is $S = \{10, 14, 18, \ldots, 4n + 6, \ldots\}$. A one-to-one correspondence between A and S is given by
$$A = \{6, \ 10, 14, 18, \ \ldots, 4n + 2, \ldots\}$$
$$\updownarrow \quad \updownarrow \ \updownarrow \ \updownarrow \qquad \quad \updownarrow$$
$$S = \{10, 14, 18, 22, \ldots, 4n + 6, \ldots\}$$
Because A can be placed in a one-to-one correspondence with a proper subset of itself, A is an infinite set. [Sec. 2.5]

52. A proper subset of B is $T = \left\{ \dfrac{1}{2}, \dfrac{1}{4}, \dfrac{1}{8}, \dfrac{1}{16}, \ldots, \dfrac{1}{2^n}, \ldots \right\}$. A one-to-one correspondence between B and T is given by
$$B = \left\{ 1, \dfrac{1}{2}, \dfrac{1}{4}, \dfrac{1}{8}, \ \ldots, \dfrac{1}{2^{n-1}}, \ldots \right\}$$
$$\quad \updownarrow \ \updownarrow \ \updownarrow \ \updownarrow \qquad \quad \updownarrow$$
$$T = \left\{ \dfrac{1}{2}, \dfrac{1}{4}, \dfrac{1}{8}, \dfrac{1}{16}, \ldots, \ \dfrac{1}{2^n}, \ \ldots \right\}$$
Because B can be placed in a one-to-one correspondence with a proper subset of itself, B is an infinite set. [Sec. 2.5]

53. 5 [Sec. 2.1] **54.** 10 [Sec. 2.1] **55.** 2 [Sec. 2.1] **56.** 5 [Sec. 2.1] **57.** $\aleph_0$ [Sec. 2.5]
58. $\aleph_0$ [Sec. 2.5] **59.** c [Sec. 2.5] **60.** c [Sec. 2.5] **61.** $\aleph_0$ [Sec. 2.5] **62.** $\aleph_0$ [Sec. 2.5]
63. $\aleph_0$ [Sec. 2.5] **64.** c [Sec. 2.5] **65.** c [Sec. 2.5] **66.** c [Sec. 2.5] **67.** $\aleph_0$ [Sec. 2.5]
68. c [Sec. 2.5]

CHAPTER 2 TEST *page 112*

1. $\{2, 3, 5, 7, 8, 9, 10\}$ [Sec. 2.1/2.3] **2.** $\{2, 9, 10\}$ [Sec. 2.1/2.3] **3.** $\{1, 2, 4, 5, 6, 7, 9, 10\}$ [Sec. 2.1/2.3]
4. $\{2, 9, 10\}$ [Sec. 2.1/2.3] **5.** $\{1, 2, 3, 4, 6, 9, 10\}$ [Sec. 2.1/2.3] **6.** $\{5, 7, 8\}$ [Sec. 2.1/2.3]
7. $\{x \mid x \in W \text{ and } x < 7\}$ [Sec. 2.1] **8.** $\{x \mid x \in I \text{ and } -3 \le x \le 2\}$ [Sec. 2.1] **9. a.** 4
b. $\aleph_0$ **c.** $\aleph_0$ **d.** c [Sec. 2.1/2.5] **10. a.** Equivalent **b.** Equivalent [Sec. 2.5]
11. a. Neither **b.** Equivalent [Sec. 2.5]
12. $\varnothing, \{a\}, \{b\}, \{c\}, \{d\}$ **13.** $2^{21} = 2,097,152$ [Sec. 2.2] **14. a.** False **b.** True
$\{a, b\}, \{a, c\}, \{a, d\}, \{b, c\}, \{b, d\}, \{c, d\}$ **c.** False **d.** True [Sec. 2.1/2.2/2.5]
$\{a, b, c\}, \{a, b, d\}, \{a, c, d\}, \{b, c, d\}$
$\{a, b, c, d\}$ [Sec. 2.2]
15. a. **b.** **16.** $B \cup (A \cap C)$ [Sec. 2.3]

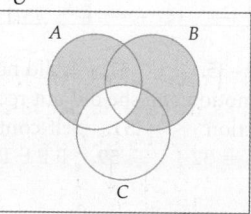

[Sec. 2.3]

17. 541 [Sec. 2.4] **18. a.** 232 **b.** 102 **c.** 857 **d.** 79 [Sec. 2.4]
19. $\{5, 10, 15, 20, 25, \ldots, \ 5n, \ \ldots\}$ **20.** $\{3, 6, \ 9, 12, \ldots, 3n, \ldots\}$
$\quad \ \updownarrow \ \updownarrow \ \ \updownarrow \ \ \updownarrow \ \ \updownarrow \qquad \quad \updownarrow$ $\qquad \updownarrow \ \ \updownarrow \ \ \ \updownarrow \ \ \ \updownarrow \qquad \quad \updownarrow$
$\{0, 1, \ 2, \ 3, \ 4, \ \ldots, n - 1, \ldots\}$ $\{6, 12, 18, 24, \ldots, 6n, \ldots\}$
$\quad (5n) \leftrightarrow (n - 1)$ [Sec. 2.5] $\quad (3n) \leftrightarrow (6n)$ [Sec. 2.5]

CHAPTER 3

EXERCISE SET 3.1   *page 123*

1. Statement   **3.** Statement   **5.** Not a statement   **7.** Statement   **9.** Not a statement
11. One component is "The principal will attend the class on Tuesday." The other component is "The principal will attend the class on Wednesday."   **13.** One component is "A triangle is an acute triangle." The other component is "It has three acute angles."
15. One component is "I ordered a salad." The other component is "I ordered a cola."   **17.** One component is $5 + 2 > 6$. The other component is $5 + 2 = 6$.   **19.** The Giants did not lose the game.   **21.** The game went into overtime.
23. $w \rightarrow t$; conditional   **25.** $s \rightarrow r$; conditional   **27.** $l \leftrightarrow a$; biconditional   **29.** $d \rightarrow f$; conditional
31. $m \vee c$; disjunction   **33.** The tour goes to Italy and the tour does not go to Spain.   **35.** If we go to Venice, then we will not go to Florence.   **37.** We will go to Florence if and only if we do not go to Venice.   **39.** All cats have claws.
41. Some classic movies were not first produced in black and white.   **43.** Some of the numbers were even numbers.
45. Some irrational numbers can be written as terminating decimals.   **47.** Some cars do not run on gasoline.
49. Some items are not on sale.   **51.** True   **53.** True   **55.** True   **57.** True   **59.** True   **61.** True
63. True   **65.** $p \rightarrow q$, where p represents "you can count your money" and q represents "you don't have a billion dollars."
67. $p \rightarrow q$, where p represents "you do not learn from history" and q represents "you are condemned to repeat it."
69. $p \rightarrow q$, where p represents "people concentrated on the really important things in life" and q represents "there'd be a shortage of fishing poles."   **71.** $p \leftrightarrow q$, where p represents "an angle is a right angle" and q represents "its measure is 90°."
73. $p \rightarrow q$, where p represents "two sides of a triangle are equal in length" and q represents "the angles opposite those sides are congruent."   **75.** $p \rightarrow q$, where p represents "it is a square" and q represents "it is a rectangle."

EXERCISE SET 3.2   *page 135*

1. True   **3.** False   **5.** False   **7.** False   **9.** False   **11. a.** If p is false, then $p \wedge (q \vee r)$ must be a false statement.   **b.** For a conjunctive statement to be true, it is necessary that all components of the statement be true. Because it is given that one of the components (p) is false, $p \wedge (q \vee r)$ must be a false statement.

p	q	13.	15.	17.
T	T	T	F	F
T	F	F	T	T
F	T	T	F	T
F	F	T	F	T

p	q	r	19.	21.	23.	25.	27.
T	T	T	F	T	T	T	F
T	T	F	F	T	F	T	T
T	F	T	F	T	F	T	T
T	F	F	F	T	F	T	F
F	T	T	F	F	T	T	F
F	T	F	F	F	F	T	F
F	F	T	F	T	T	F	T
F	F	F	T	T	F	T	F

See the *Student Solutions Manual* for the solutions to Exercises 29–35.   **37.** It did not rain and it did not snow.   **39.** She did not visit either France or Italy.   **41.** She did not get a promotion and she did not receive a raise.   **43.** Tautology
45. Tautology   **47.** Tautology   **49.** Self-contradiction   **51.** Self-contradiction   **53.** Not a self-contradiction
55. The symbol $\leq$ means "less than or equal to."   **57.** $2^5 = 32$ **59.** F F F T T T F T F F F T F F F F

EXERCISE SET 3.3   *page 144*

1. *Antecedent:* I had the money   **3.** *Antecedent:* they had a guard dog
Consequent: I would buy the painting   *Consequent:* no one would trespass on their property
5. *Antecedent:* I change my major   **7.** True   **9.** True   **11.** True   **13.** False
Consequent: I must reapply for admission

p	q	15.	17.
T	T	T	T
T	F	T	T
F	T	T	T
F	F	T	T

p	q	r	19.	21.	23.
T	T	T	T	T	T
T	T	F	T	F	T
T	F	T	T	T	T
T	F	F	T	T	T
F	T	T	T	T	T
F	T	F	T	F	T
F	F	T	T	T	T
F	F	F	T	T	T

25. She cannot sing or she would be perfect for the part. **27.** Either x is not an irrational number or x is not a terminating decimal. **29.** The fog must lift or our flight will be cancelled. **31.** They offered me the contract and I didn't accept. **33.** Pigs have wings and they still can't fly. **35.** She traveled to Italy and she didn't visit her relatives. **37.** False **39.** True **41.** False **43.** True **45.** True **47.** $p \to v$ **49.** $t \to {\sim}v$ **51.** $({\sim}t \land p) \to v$ **53.** Not equivalent **55.** Not equivalent **57.** Equivalent **59.** If a number is a rational number, then it is a real number. **61.** If a number is a repeating decimal, then it is a rational number. **63.** If an animal is a Sauropod, then it is herbivorous.

EXERCISE SET 3.4   *page 150*

1. If we take the aerobics class, then we will be in good shape for the ski trip. **3.** If the number is an odd prime number, then it is greater than 2. **5.** If he has the talent to play a keyboard, then he can join the band. **7.** If I was able to prepare for the test, then I had the textbook. **9.** If you ran the Boston marathon, then you are in excellent shape. **11. a.** If I quit this job, then I am rich. **b.** If I were not rich, then I would not quit this job. **c.** If I would not quit this job, then I would not be rich. **13. a.** If we are not able to attend the party, then she did not return soon. **b.** If she returns soon, then we will be able to attend the party. **c.** If we are able to attend the party, then she returned soon. **15. a.** If a figure is a quadrilateral, then it is a parallelogram. **b.** If a figure is not a parallelogram, then it is not a quadrilateral. **c.** If a figure is not a quadrilateral, then it is not a parallelogram. **17. a.** If I am able to get current information about astronomy, then I have access to the Internet. **b.** If I do not have access to the Internet, then I will not be able to get current information about astronomy. **c.** If I am not able to get current information about astronomy, then I don't have access to the Internet. **19. a.** If we don't have enough money for dinner, then we took a taxi. **b.** If we did not take a taxi, then we will have enough money for dinner. **c.** If we have enough money for dinner, then we did not take a taxi. **21. a.** If she can extend her vacation for at least two days, then she will visit Kauai. **b.** If she does not visit Kauai, then she could not extend her vacation for at least two days. **c.** If she cannot extend her vacation for at least two days, then she will not visit Kauai. **23. a.** If two lines are parallel, then the two lines are perpendicular to a given line. **b.** If two lines are not perpendicular to a given line, then the two lines are not parallel. **c.** If two lines are not parallel, then the two lines are not both perpendicular to a given line. **25.** Not equivalent **27.** Equivalent **29.** Not equivalent **31.** If $x = 7$, then $3x - 7 \neq 11$. The original statement is true. **33.** If $|a| = 3$, then $a = 3$. The original statement is false. **35.** If $a + b = 25$, then $\sqrt{a + b} = 5$. The original statement is true. **37.** $p \to q$ **39. a. and b.** Answers will vary. **41.** If you can dream it, then you can do it. **43.** If I were a dancer, then I would not be a singer. **45.** A conditional statement and its contrapositive are equivalent. They always have the same truth values. **47.** The Hatter is telling the truth.

EXERCISE SET 3.5   *page 162*

1. $r \to c$
   $\underline{\quad r \quad}$
   $\therefore c$

3. $g \to s$
   $\underline{\quad {\sim}g \quad}$
   $\therefore {\sim}s$

5. $s \to i$
   $\underline{\quad s \quad}$
   $\therefore i$

7. ${\sim}p \to {\sim}a$
   $\underline{\quad a \quad}$
   $\therefore p$

9. Invalid **11.** Invalid **13.** Valid **15.** Invalid **17.** Invalid **19.** Invalid **21.** Valid **23.** Valid

25. $h \to r$ / $\sim h$ / $\therefore \sim r$ Invalid
27. $\sim b \to d$ / $b \vee d$ / $\therefore b$ Invalid
29. $c \to t$ / t / $\therefore c$ Invalid
31. Valid argument; modus tollens
33. Invalid argument; fallacy of the inverse
35. Valid argument; law of syllogism   **37.** Valid argument; modus ponens   **39.** Valid argument; modus tollens
See the *Student Solutions Manual* for the solutions to Exercises 41–45.   **47.** q **49.** it is not a theropod   **51.** Valid

EXERCISE SET 3.6 *page 171*

1. Valid **3.** Valid **5.** Valid **7.** Valid **9.** Invalid **11.** Invalid **13.** Invalid
15. Valid **17.** Valid **19.** Invalid **21.** All Reuben sandwiches need mustard. **23.** 1001 ends with a 5.
25. Some horses are grey. **27. a.** Invalid **b.** Invalid **c.** Invalid **d.** Invalid **e.** Valid **f.** Valid
29.

1	2
2	1
3	4
8	4

CHAPTER 3 REVIEW EXERCISES *page 174*

1. Not a statement [Sec. 3.1] **2.** Statement [Sec. 3.1] **3.** Statement [Sec. 3.1] **4.** Statement [Sec. 3.1]
5. Not a statement [Sec. 3.1] **6.** Statement [Sec. 3.1] **7.** $m \wedge b$; conjunction [Sec. 3.1]
8. $d \to e$; conditional [Sec. 3.1] **9.** $g \leftrightarrow d$; biconditional [Sec. 3.1] **10.** $t \to s$; conditional [Sec. 3.1]
11. No dogs bite. [Sec. 3.1] **12.** Some desserts at the Cove restaurant are not good. [Sec. 3.1] **13.** Some winners do not receive a prize. [Sec. 3.1] **14.** All cameras use film. [Sec. 3.1] **15.** Some of the students received an A. [Sec. 3.1]
16. Nobody enjoyed the story. [Sec. 3.1] **17.** True [Sec. 3.1] **18.** True [Sec. 3.1] **19.** True [Sec. 3.1]
20. True [Sec. 3.1] **21.** True [Sec. 3.1] **22.** True [Sec. 3.1] **23.** False [Sec. 3.2]
24. False [Sec. 3.2/3.3] **25.** True [Sec. 3.2] **26.** True [Sec. 3.2/3.3] **27.** True [Sec. 3.2/3.3]
28. False [Sec. 3.2/3.3]

p	q	29. [Sec. 3.2/3.3]	30. [Sec. 3.2/3.3]	31. [Sec. 3.2/3.3]	32. [Sec. 3.2/3.3]
T	T	T	F	F	T
T	F	T	F	F	T
F	T	T	T	F	F
F	F	F	F	F	T

p	q	r	33. [Sec. 3.2/3.3]	34. [Sec. 3.2/3.3]	35. [Sec. 3.2/3.3]	36. [Sec. 3.2/3.3]
T	T	T	T	F	F	T
T	T	F	T	T	F	T
T	F	T	T	T	T	T
T	F	F	F	T	T	T
F	T	T	T	F	F	F
F	T	F	T	F	F	T
F	F	T	T	T	F	T
F	F	F	T	T	F	T

37. Bob passed the English proficiency test or he did not register for a speech course. [Sec. 3.2] **38.** It is not true that Ellen went to work this morning or she took her medication. [Sec. 3.2] **39.** It is not the case that Wendy will not go to the store this afternoon and she will be able to prepare her fettuccine al pesto recipe. [Sec. 3.2] **40.** It is not the case that Gina did not enjoy the movie or she enjoyed the party. [Sec. 3.2/3.3] See the *Student Solutions Manual* for solutions to Exercises 41–44.
45. Self-contradiction [Sec. 3.2] **46.** Tautology [Sec. 3.2/3.3] **47.** Tautology [Sec. 3.2/3.3]
48. Tautology [Sec. 3.2/3.3] **49.** *Antecedent:* he has talent **50.** *Antecedent:* I had a credential
Consequent: he will succeed [Sec. 3.3] *Consequent:* I could get the job [Sec. 3.3]
51. *Antecedent:* I join the fitness club **52.** *Antecedent:* I will attend
Consequent: I will follow the exercise program [Sec. 3.3] *Consequent:* it is free [Sec. 3.3]
53. She is not tall or she would be on the volleyball team. [Sec. 3.3] **54.** He cannot stay awake or he would finish the report. [Sec. 3.3] **55.** Rob is ill or he would start. [Sec. 3.3] **56.** Sharon will not be promoted or she closes the deal. [Sec. 3.3] **57.** I get my paycheck and I do not purchase a ticket. [Sec. 3.3] **58.** The tomatoes will get big and you did not provide plenty of water. [Sec. 3.3] **59.** You entered Cleggmore University and you did not have a high score on the SAT exam. [Sec. 3.3] **60.** Ryan enrolled at a university and he did not enroll at Yale. [Sec. 3.3] **61.** False [Sec. 3.3]
62. True [Sec. 3.3] **63.** True [Sec. 3.3] **64.** False [Sec. 3.3] **65.** False [Sec. 3.3]
66. False [Sec. 3.3] **67.** If a real number has a nonrepeating, nonterminating decimal form, then the real number is irrational. [Sec. 3.4] **68.** If you are a politician, then you are well known. [Sec. 3.4] **69.** If I can sell my condominium, then I can buy the house. [Sec. 3.4] **70.** If a number is divisible by 9, then the number is divisible by 3. [Sec. 3.4]
71. a. *Converse:* If $x > 3$, then $x + 4 > 7$. **b.** *Inverse:* If $x + 4 \leq 7$, then $x \leq 3$. **c.** *Contrapositive:* If $x \leq 3$, then $x + 4 \leq 7$. [Sec. 3.4] **72. a.** *Converse:* If the recipe can be prepared in less than 20 minutes, then the recipe is in this book.
b. *Inverse:* If the recipe is not in this book, then the recipe cannot be prepared in less than 20 minutes. **c.** *Contrapositive:* If the recipe cannot be prepared in less than 20 minutes, then the recipe is not in this book. [Sec. 3.4] **73. a.** *Converse:* If $(a + b)$ is divisible by 3, then a and b are both divisible by 3. **b.** *Inverse:* If a and b are not both divisible by 3, then $(a + b)$ is not divisible by 3. **c.** *Contrapositive:* If $(a + b)$ is not divisible by 3, then a and b are not both divisible by 3. [Sec. 3.4]
74. a. *Converse:* If they come, then you built it. **b.** *Inverse:* If you do not build it, then they will not come.
c. *Contrapositive:* If they do not come, then you did not build it. [Sec. 3.4] **75. a.** *Converse:* If it has exactly two parallel sides, then it is a trapezoid. **b.** *Inverse:* If it is not a trapezoid, then it does not have exactly two parallel sides.
c. *Contrapositive:* If it does not have exactly two parallel sides, then it is not a trapezoid. [Sec. 3.4] **76. a.** *Converse:* If they returned, then they liked it. **b.** *Inverse:* If they do not like it, then they will not return. **c.** *Contrapositive:* If they do not return, then they did not like it. [Sec. 3.4] **77.** $q \rightarrow p$, the converse of the original statement [Sec. 3.4] **78.** $p \rightarrow q$, the original statement [Sec. 3.4] **79.** If x is an odd prime number, then $x > 2$. [Sec. 3.4] **80.** If the senator attends the meeting, then she will vote on the motion. [Sec. 3.4] **81.** If their manager contacts me, then I will purchase some of their products. [Sec. 3.4] **82.** If I can rollerblade, then Ginny can rollerblade. [Sec. 3.4] **83.** Valid [Sec. 3.5]
84. Valid [Sec. 3.5] **85.** Invalid [Sec. 3.5] **86.** Valid [Sec. 3.5] **87.** Valid argument; disjunctive syllogism [Sec. 3.5] **88.** Valid argument; law of syllogism [Sec. 3.5] **89.** Invalid argument; fallacy of the inverse [Sec. 3.5] **90.** Valid argument; disjunctive syllogism [Sec. 3.5] **91.** Valid argument; modus tollens [Sec. 3.5]
92. Invalid argument; fallacy of the inverse [Sec. 3.5] **93.** Valid [Sec. 3.6] **94.** Invalid [Sec. 3.6]
95. Invalid [Sec. 3.6] **96.** Valid [Sec. 3.6]

CHAPTER 3 TEST *page 176*

1. a. Not a statement **b.** Statement [Sec. 3.1] **2. a.** All trees are green. **b.** Some of the kids had seen the movie. [Sec. 3.1] **3. a.** False **b.** True [Sec. 3.1] **4. a.** False **b.** True [Sec. 3.2/3.3]

p	q	**5.** [Sec. 3.2/3.3]
T	T	T
T	F	T
F	T	T
F	F	T

p	q	r	**6.** **[Sec. 3.2/3.3]**
T	T	T	F
T	T	F	T
T	F	T	F
T	F	F	F
F	T	T	F
F	T	F	T
F	F	T	T
F	F	F	F

7. It is not the case that Elle ate breakfast or took a lunch break.   [Sec. 3.2]

8. A tautology is a statement that is always true.   [Sec. 3.2]   **9.** $\sim p \lor q$ [Sec. 3.3]

10. a. False   **b.** False   [Sec. 3.2/3.3]   **11. a.** *Converse:* If $x > 4$, then $x + 7 > 11$.   **b.** *Inverse:* If $x + 7 \leq 11$, then $x \leq 4$.   **c.** *Contrapositive:* If $x \leq 4$, then $x + 7 \leq 11$.   [Sec. 3.4]

12. $p \to q$
$\underline{p \qquad}$
$\therefore q$ [Sec. 3.5]

13. $p \to q$
$\underline{q \to r}$
$\therefore p \to r$ [Sec. 3.5]

14. Valid   [Sec. 3.5]   **15.** Invalid   [Sec. 3.5]

16. Invalid argument; the argument is a fallacy of the inverse.   [Sec. 3.5]   **17.** Valid argument; the argument is a disjunctive syllogism.   [Sec. 3.5]   **18.** Invalid argument, as shown by an Euler diagram.   [Sec. 3.6]   **19.** Invalid argument, as shown by an Euler diagram.   [Sec. 3.6]   **20.** Invalid argument; the argument is a fallacy of the converse.   [Sec. 3.5]

CHAPTER 4

EXERCISE SET 4.1   *page 185*

1. ∩∩∩∩|||||| **3.** 9||| **5.** ⌡⌡99999∩∩∩∩∩|||||||| **7.** ⌡⌡⌡⌡⌡99999||

9. ⌡⌡⌡⌡⌡⌡⌡⌡⌡99999999   **11.** ⌡⌡⌡⌡⌡99||| **13.** 2134   **15.** 845   **17.** 1232

19. 221,011   **21.** 65,769   **23.** 5,122,406   **25.** 94   **27.** 666   **29.** 32   **31.** 56   **33.** 650

35. 1409   **37.** 1240   **39.** 840   **41.** 9044   **43.** 11,461   **45.** CLVII   **47.** DXLII

49. MCXCVII   **51.** DCCLXXXVII   **53.** DCLXXXIII   **55.** $\overline{\text{V}}$DCCCXCVIII   **57.** 504   **59.** 203

61. 595   **63.** 2484   **65. a. and b.** Answers will vary.

EXERCISE SET 4.2   *page 196*

1. $(4 \times 10^1) + (8 \times 10^0)$ **3.** $(4 \times 10^2) + (2 \times 10^1) + (0 \times 10^0)$ **5.** $(6 \times 10^3) + (8 \times 10^2) + (0 \times 10^1) + (3 \times 10^0)$

7. $(1 \times 10^4) + (0 \times 10^3) + (2 \times 10^2) + (0 \times 10^1) + (8 \times 10^0)$ **9.** 456   **11.** 5076   **13.** 35,407

15. 683,040   **17.** 76   **19.** 395   **21.** 2481   **23.** 27   **25.** 3363   **27.** 10,311   **29.** 23

31. 97   **33.** 72,133   **35.** 2,171,466   **37.** ≪≪≪⟨⟨   **39.** ⟨⟨ ⟨⟨⟨⟨⟨⟨⟨

41. ⟨ ≪≪⟨⟨⟨⟨ ≪≪⟨⟨⟨⟨⟨⟨⟨   **43.** ⟨⟨ ≪≪≪≪≪⟨⟨⟨⟨⟨ ≪≪⟨⟨⟨⟨   **45.** ⟨⟨⟨⟨⟨ ≪≪≪≪⟨⟨⟨⟨⟨ ≪≪≪⟨⟨⟨⟨⟨

47. ⟨ ⟨⟨⟨⟨⟨⟨⟨⟨   **49.** ⟨ ⟨⟨⟨⟨⟨⟨ ⟨⟨⟨   **51.** ⟨⟨ ≪≪≪≪≪⟨⟨⟨ ⟨⟨⟨⟨⟨

53. 194   **55.** 1803   **57.** 14,492   **59.** 36,103   **61.** —   **63.** ··   **65.** ····

67. ·   **69. a. and b.** Answers will vary.

EXERCISE SET 4.3   *page 205*

1. 73   **3.** 61   **5.** 718   **7.** 485   **9.** 181   **11.** 2032_{five} **13.** 12540_{six} **15.** 22886_{nine}
17. 111111011100_{two} **19.** $1B7_{twelve}$ **21.** 13   **23.** 27   **25.** 100   **27.** 139   **29.** 41
31. 90   **33.** 1338   **35.** 26_{eight} **37.** 23033_{four} **39.** 24_{five} **41.** 2446_{nine} **43.** 126_{eight}
45. $7C_{sixteen}$ **47.** 11101010_{two} **49.** 312_{eight} **51.** $151_{sixteen}$ **53.** 1011111011110011_{two}
55. $1011101001011001111_{two}$ **57.** Answers will vary.   **59.** 54
61.   **63.**   **65.** 256   **67. a. and b.** Answers will vary.

EXERCISE SET 4.4   *page 218*

1. 332_{five} **3.** 6562_{seven} **5.** 1001000_{two} **7.** 1271_{twelve} **9.** $D036_{sixteen}$ **11.** 1124_{six} **13.** 241_{five}
15. 6542_{eight} **17.** 1111_{two} **19.** 1111001_{two} **21.** $411A_{twelve}$ **23.** 384_{nine} **25.** 523_{six}
27. 1201_{three} **29.** 45234_{eight} **31.** 1010100_{two} **33.** 14207_{eight} **35.** 321222_{four} **37.** $3A61_{sixteen}$
39. 33_{four} **41.** Quotient 33_{four}; remainder 0_{four} **43.** Quotient 1223_{six}; remainder 1_{six}
45. Quotient 1110_{two}; remainder 0_{two} **47.** Quotient $A8_{twelve}$; remainder 3_{twelve} **49.** Quotient 14_{five}; remainder 11_{five}
51. Eight   **53. a.** 629   **b.** $384 = 110000000_{two}$; $245 = 11110101_{two}$ **c.** 1001110101_{two}
d. 629   **e.** Same   **55. a.** 6422   **b.** $247 = 11110111_{two}$; $26 = 11010_{two}$ **c.** 1100100010110_{two} **d.** 6422
e. Same   **57.** Base seven.   **59.** In a base one numeration system, 0 would be the only numeral, and the place values
would be $1^0, 1^1, 1^2, 1^3, \ldots$, each of which equals 1. Thus 0 is the only number you could write using a base one numeration system.
61. M = 1, A = 4, S = 3, and O = 0

EXERCISE SET 4.5   *page 228*

1. 1, 2, 4, 5, 10, 20   **3.** 1, 5, 13, 65   **5.** 1, 41   **7.** 1, 2, 5, 10, 11, 22, 55, 110   **9.** 1, 5, 7, 11, 35, 55, 77, 385
11. Composite   **13.** Prime   **15.** Prime   **17.** Prime   **19.** Composite   **21.** 2, 3, 5, 6, and 10
23. 3   **25.** 2, 3, 4, 6, and 8   **27.** 2, 5, and 10   **29.** $2 \cdot 3^2$ **31.** $2^3 \cdot 3 \cdot 5$ **33.** $5^2 \cdot 17$
35. 2^{10} **37.** $2^3 \cdot 3 \cdot 263$ **39.** $2 \cdot 3^2 \cdot 1013$ **41.** 2, 3, 5, 7, 11, 13, 17, 19, 23, 29, 31, 37, 41, 43, 47, 53, 59, 61, 67, 71,
73, 79, 83, 89, 97, 101, 103, 107, 109, 113, 127, 131, 137, 139, 149, 151, 157, 163, 167, 173, 179, 181, 191, 193, 197, 199
43. 3 and 5, 5 and 7, 11 and 13, 17 and 19, 29 and 31, 41 and 43, 59 and 61, 71 and 73, 101 and 103, 107 and 109, 137 and 139, 149 and
151, 179 and 181, 191 and 193, 197 and 199   **45.** 311 and 313, or 347 and 349   In Exercise 47, parts a–f, only one
possible sum is given.   **47. a.** $24 = 5 + 19$ **b.** $50 = 3 + 47$ **c.** $86 = 3 + 83$ **d.** $144 = 5 + 139$
e. $210 = 11 + 199$ **f.** $264 = 7 + 257$ **49.** Yes   **51.** Yes   **53.** No   **55.** Yes   **57.** Yes
59. Yes   **61.** No   **63.** Yes   **65. a.** $n = 3$ **b.** $n = 4$ **67.** To determine whether a given number is
divisible by 17, multiply the ones digit of the given number by 5. Find the difference between this result and the number formed by
omitting the ones digit from the given number. Keep repeating this procedure until you obtain a small final difference. If the final
difference is divisible by 17, then the given number is divisible by 17. If the final difference is not divisible by 17, then the given number
is not divisible by 17.   **69.** 12   **71.** 8   **73.** 24

EXERCISE SET 4.6   *page 240*

1. Abundant   **3.** Deficient   **5.** Deficient   **7.** Abundant   **9.** Deficient   **11.** Deficient
13. Abundant   **15.** Abundant   **17.** Prime   **19.** Prime   **21.** $2^{126}(2^{127} - 1)$ **23.** 6
25. 420,921   **27.** 2,098,960   **29.** $9^5 + 15^5 = 818{,}424$. Because $15^5 < 818{,}424$ and $16^5 > 818{,}424$, we know there is no
natural number z such that $z^5 = 9^5 + 15^5$.   **31. a.** False. For instance, if $n = 11$, then $2^{11} - 1 = 2047 = 23 \cdot 89$.   **b.** False.
Fermat's Last Theorem was the last of Fermat's theories (conjectures) that other mathematicians were able to establish.   **c.** True
d. Conjecture.   **33. a.** $12^7 - 12 = 35{,}831{,}796$, which is divisible by 7.   **b.** $8^{11} - 8 = 8{,}589{,}934{,}584$, which is divisible by
11.   **35.** $8128 = 1^3 + 3^3 + 5^3 + \cdots + 13^3 + 15^3$.   See the *Student Solutions Manual* for the verifications in Exercise 37.
39. The first five Fermat numbers formed using $m = 0, 1, 2, 3$, and 4 are all prime numbers. In 1732, Euler discovered that the sixth
Fermat number 4,294,967,297, formed using $m = 5$, is not a prime number because it is divisible by 641.

CHAPTER 4 REVIEW EXERCISES   *page 242*

1. ⦚⦚⦚⦚⧫⧫⧫⧫⧫⧫999∩∩IIIII   [Sec. 4.1]   **2.** ⦚⦚⦚⧫⦚⦚⧫⧫⧫∩∩∩III   [Sec. 4.1]

3. 223,013 [Sec. 4.1]   **4.** 221,354 [Sec. 4.1]   **5.** 349 [Sec. 4.1]   **6.** 774 [Sec. 4.1]   **7.** 9640 [Sec. 4.1]
8. 92,444 [Sec. 4.1]   **9.** DLXVII [Sec. 4.1]   **10.** DCCCXXIII [Sec. 4.1]   **11.** MMCDLXXXIX. [Sec. 4.1]
12. MCCCXXXV [Sec. 4.1]   **13.** $(4 \times 10^2) + (3 \times 10^1) + (2 \times 10^0)$ [Sec. 4.2]
14. $(4 \times 10^5) + (5 \times 10^4) + (6 \times 10^3) + (3 \times 10^2) + (2 \times 10^1) + (7 \times 10^0)$ [Sec. 4.2]   **15.** 5,038,204 [Sec. 4.2]
16. 387,960 [Sec. 4.2]   **17.** 801 [Sec. 4.2]   **18.** 1603 [Sec. 4.2]   **19.** 76,441 [Sec. 4.2]
20. 87,393 [Sec. 4.2]   **21.** ⟨𝖳𝖳 𝖳 [Sec. 4.2]   **22.** ⟨𝖳𝖳𝖳𝖳𝖳𝖳𝖳𝖳 ▲ [Sec. 4.2]

23. 𝖳𝖳𝖳 ⟨⟨𝖳𝖳𝖳𝖳𝖳𝖳𝖳 𝖳𝖳𝖳 [Sec. 4.2]   **24.** 𝖳𝖳𝖳𝖳𝖳 ⟨⟨𝖳 ⟨⟨𝖳 [Sec. 4.2]

25. 194 [Sec. 4.2]   **26.** 267 [Sec. 4.2]   **27.** 2178 [Sec. 4.2]   **28.** 6580 [Sec. 4.2]
29. ⋯ (dots) [Sec. 4.2]   **30.** ≡ (dots) [Sec. 4.2]   **31.** ― (dots) [Sec. 4.2]   **32.** ― (dots) [Sec. 4.2]   **33.** 29 [Sec. 4.3]

34. 146 [Sec. 4.3]   **35.** 227 [Sec. 4.3]   **36.** 286 [Sec. 4.3]   **37.** 1153_{six} [Sec. 4.3]
38. 640_{eight} [Sec. 4.3]   **39.** 458_{nine} [Sec. 4.3]   **40.** $B62_{twelve}$ [Sec. 4.3]   **41.** 34_{eight} [Sec. 4.3]
42. 124_{eight} [Sec. 4.3]   **43.** $38D_{sixteen}$ [Sec. 4.3]   **44.** $754_{sixteen}$ [Sec. 4.3]   **45.** 10101_{two} [Sec. 4.3]
46. 1100111010_{two} [Sec. 4.3]   **47.** 1001010_{two} [Sec. 4.3]   **48.** 110001110010_{two} [Sec. 4.3]
49. 423_{six} [Sec. 4.4]   **50.** 1240_{eight} [Sec. 4.4]   **51.** 536_{nine} [Sec. 4.4]   **52.** 1113_{four} [Sec. 4.4]
53. 16412_{eight} [Sec. 4.4]   **54.** 324203_{five} [Sec. 4.4]   **55.** Quotient 11100_{two}; remainder 1_{two} [Sec. 4.4]
56. Quotient 21_{four}; remainder 3_{four} [Sec. 4.4]   **57.** $3^2 \cdot 5$ [Sec. 4.5]   **58.** $2 \cdot 3^3$ [Sec. 4.5]
59. $3^2 \cdot 17$ [Sec. 4.5]   **60.** $3 \cdot 5 \cdot 19$ [Sec. 4.5]   **61.** Composite [Sec. 4.5]   **62.** Composite [Sec. 4.5]
63. Composite [Sec. 4.5]   **64.** Composite [Sec. 4.5]   **65.** Perfect [Sec. 4.6]   **66.** Deficient [Sec. 4.6]
67. Abundant [Sec. 4.6]   **68.** Abundant [Sec. 4.6]   **69.** $2^{60}(2^{61} - 1)$ [Sec. 4.6]   **70.** $2^{1278}(2^{1279} - 1)$ [Sec. 4.6]
71. 368 [Sec. 4.1]   **72.** 513 [Sec. 4.1]   **73.** 1162 [Sec. 4.1]   **74.** 3003 [Sec. 4.1]   **75.** 410 [Sec. 4.3]
76. 277 [Sec. 4.3]   **77.** 1041 [Sec. 4.3]   **78.** 1616 [Sec. 4.3]   **79.** A base ten number is divisible by 3 provided
the sum of the digits of the number is divisible by 3. [Sec. 4.5]   **80.** A number is divisible by 6 provided the number is divisible by
2 and by 3. [Sec. 4.5]   **81.** Every composite number can be written as a unique product of prime numbers (disregarding the order
of the factors). [Sec. 4.5]   **82.** Zero [Sec. 4.6]   **83.** 39,751 [Sec. 4.6]   **84.** 895,932 [Sec. 4.6]

CHAPTER 4 TEST   *page 244*

1. ⧫⧫⧫9∩∩IIIII [Sec. 4.1]   **2.** 4263 [Sec. 4.1]   **3.** 1447 [Sec. 4.1]   **4.** MMDCIX [Sec. 4.1]
5. $(6 \times 10^4) + (7 \times 10^3) + (4 \times 10^2) + (8 \times 10^1) + (5 \times 10^0)$ [Sec. 4.2]   **6.** 530,284 [Sec. 4.2]
7. 37,274 [Sec. 4.2]   **8.** 𝖳𝖳 ⟨⟨⟨⟨𝖳 ⟨𝖳𝖳𝖳𝖳𝖳 [Sec. 4.2]   **9.** 1305 [Sec. 4.2]   **10.** (dots) [Sec. 4.2]

11. 854 [Sec. 4.3]   **12. a.** 4144_{eight} **b.** $12B0_{twelve}$ [Sec. 4.3]   **13.** 100101110111_{two} [Sec. 4.3]
14. $AB7_{sixteen}$ [Sec. 4.3]   **15.** 112_{five} [Sec. 4.4]   **16.** 313_{eight} [Sec. 4.4]   **17.** 11100110_{two} [Sec. 4.4]
18. Quotient 61_{seven}; remainder 3_{seven} [Sec. 4.4]   **19.** $2 \cdot 5 \cdot 23$ [Sec. 4.5]   **20.** Composite [Sec. 4.5]
21. a. No   **b.** Yes   **c.** No [Sec. 4.5]   **22. a.** Yes   **b.** No   **c.** No [Sec. 4.5]
23. Abundant [Sec. 4.6]   **24.** $2^{16}(2^{17} - 1)$ [Sec. 4.6]

CHAPTER 5

EXERCISE SET 5.1   *page 258*

1. An equation expresses the equality of two mathematical expressions. An equation contains an equals sign. An expression does not.
3. Substitute the solution back into the original equation and confirm the equality.   **5.** 12   **7.** 22   **9.** −8

11. -20 **13.** 8 **15.** -1 **17.** 1 **19.** $-\dfrac{1}{3}$ **21.** $\dfrac{2}{3}$ **23.** -2 **25.** 4 **27.** 2

29. 2 **31.** $\dfrac{1}{4}$ **33.** -2 **35.** 4 **37.** 8 **39.** 1 **41.** -32 **43.** $16,859.34

45. 1350 inches **47.** 60 feet **49.** 1952 **51.** 168 feet **53.** 18.6 degrees Celsius **55.** 175
57. $22,000 **59. a.** $2395 **b.** $4694 **61.** $117.75 **63. a.** 163,000 kilograms **b.** 1930 kilograms
65. $12.50 **67.** 1280 horizontal pixels **69.** more than 16 minutes but not over 17 minutes **71.** $b = P - a - c$

73. $R = \dfrac{E}{I}$ **75.** $r = \dfrac{I}{Pt}$ **77.** $C = \dfrac{5}{9}(F - 32)$ **79.** $t = \dfrac{A - P}{Pr}$ **81.** $f = \dfrac{T + gm}{m}$ **83.** $S = C - Rt$

85. $b_2 = \dfrac{2A}{h} - b_1$ **87.** $h = \dfrac{S}{2\pi r} - r$ **89.** $y = 2 - \dfrac{4}{3}x$ **91.** $x = \dfrac{y - y_1}{m} + x_1$ **93.** 0

95. Every real number is a solution. **97.** $x = \dfrac{d - b}{a - c}$. $a \neq c$ or the denominator equals zero and the expression is undefined.

EXERCISE SET 5.2 *page 276*

1. Examples will vary. **3.** The purpose is to allow currency from one country to be converted into the currency of another country. **5.** Explanations will vary. **7.** The cross-products method is a shortcut for multiplying each side of the proportion by the least common multiple of the denominators. **9.** 23 miles per gallon **11.** 12.5 meters per second
13. 400 square feet per gallon **15.** 272,160 kilograms **17.** A 24-ounce jar of mayonnaise for $2.09
19. $16.50 per hour **21. a.** Australia **b.** 850 more people per square mile **23.** 60,374 krona
25. 434,834 pesos **27.** For each state, the ratio is 3.125 to 1. **29.** 13:1 or 13 to 1. There is one faculty member for every 13 students at Syracuse University. **31.** University of Connecticut **33.** No **35.** 17.14 **37.** 25.6
39. 20.83 **41.** 2.22 **43.** 13.71 **45.** 39.6 **47.** 0.52 **49.** 6.74 **51.** $45,000
53. 5.5 milligrams **55.** 24 feet; 15 feet **57.** 160,000 people **59.** 63,000 miles **61.** 11.25 grams.
Explanations will vary. **63. a.** True **b.** True **c.** True **d.** False
65. a.–c. Explanations will vary.

EXERCISE SET 5.3 *page 297*

1. Answers will vary. **3.** 3 **5.** Employee B's salary is now the highest because Employee B had the highest initial salary, and the percent raises were the same for all employees. **7.** 0.5; 50% **9.** $\dfrac{2}{5}$; 0.4 **11.** $\dfrac{7}{10}$; 70% **13.** 0.55; 55%

15. $\dfrac{5}{32}$; 0.15625 **17. a.** 73 fans **b.** More fans approved. **c.** 7%; 100% − 73% − 20% = 7%

19. $26.6 billion **21.** 23.7% **23. a.** $1381 **b.** $1628 **25. a.** 48.2 hours
b. 33.6 hours **c.** 3.4 hours **27. a.** 1998 to 2000 **b.** 2004 to 2006 **c.** More slowly
29. a. Arizona: 118,153; California: 625,041; Colorado: 165,038; Maryland: 142,718; Massachusetts: 246,833; Minnesota: 229,543; New Hampshire: 51,714; New Jersey: 229,543; Vermont: 17,274; Virginia: 185,900 **b.** New Hampshire; California
c. More than half **d.** Massachusetts: 7.5%; New Jersey: 5.5%; Virginia: 5.2% **e.** 5.3% **f.** The rate is 10 times the percent. **31. a.** 900% **b.** 60% **c.** 1500% **d.** Explanations will vary. **33. a.** home health aides
b. software engineers (applications) **c.** 63,200 people **d.** 320,580 people **e.** computer support specialists
f. The percent increases are based on different original employment figures. **g.** Answers will vary. **35.** Less than
37. 39 months **39. a.** 10,700,000 TV households; 62,800,000 TV households **b.** 5,900,000 TV households; 53,600,000 TV households **c.** 2.5 people **d.** Answers will vary.

EXERCISE SET 5.4 *page 316*

1. The Principle of Zero Products states that if the product of two factors is zero, then one of the two factors equals zero. A second-degree equation must be written in standard form so that the variable expression is equal to zero. Then, when the variable expression is factored, the Principle of Zero Products can be used to set each factor equal to zero. **3.** Answers will vary. **5.** -2 and 5

7. $\dfrac{1 + \sqrt{5}}{2}$ and $\dfrac{1 - \sqrt{5}}{2}$; -0.618 and 1.618 **9.** $3 + \sqrt{13}$ and $3 - \sqrt{13}$; -0.606 and 6.606 **11.** 0 and 2

13. $\dfrac{1 + \sqrt{17}}{2}$ and $\dfrac{1 - \sqrt{17}}{2}$; -1.562 and 2.562 **15.** $\dfrac{2 + \sqrt{14}}{2}$ and $\dfrac{2 - \sqrt{14}}{2}$; -0.871 and 2.871

17. $2 + \sqrt{11}$ and $2 - \sqrt{11}$; -1.317 and 5.317 **19.** $-\dfrac{3}{2}$ and 6   **21.** No real number solutions   **23.** -4 and $\dfrac{1}{4}$

25. $-\dfrac{1}{2}$ and $\dfrac{4}{3}$ **27.** $1 + \sqrt{5}$ and $1 - \sqrt{5}$; -1.236 and 3.236 **29.** 0.75 second and 3 seconds

31. $T = 0.5(1)^2 + 0.5(1) = 1$; $T = 0.5(2)^2 + 0.5(2) = 3$; $T = 0.5(3)^2 + 0.5(3) = 6$; $T = 0.5(4)^2 + 0.5(4) = 10$; 10 rows
33. a. 240 feet   **b.** 30 miles per hour   **35.** 5.51 seconds   **37.** 244.10 feet   **39.** No   **41.** 1.74 seconds
and 10.76 seconds   **43.** 71 cents   **45.** If the discriminant is not a perfect square, the radical expression in the quadratic
formula will not simplify to a whole number.   **47.** $-12a$ and $-4a$ **49.** $-\dfrac{b}{2}$ and $-b$ **51.** $-y$ and $\dfrac{3}{2}y$

53. $b^2 - 4ac = b^2 - 4(1)(-1) = b^2 + 4$. If $b^2 - 4ac \geq 0$, then the equation has real number solutions. Because $b^2 \geq 0$ for all real
numbers b, $b^2 + 4 \geq 4$ for all real numbers b. Therefore, the equation has real number solutions regardless of the value of b.

CHAPTER 5 REVIEW EXERCISES   *page 320*

1. 4 [Sec. 5.1]   **2.** $\dfrac{1}{8}$ [Sec. 5.1]   **3.** -2 [Sec. 5.1]   **4.** $\dfrac{10}{3}$ [Sec. 5.2]   **5.** No real number

solutions [Sec. 5.4]   **6.** -5 and 6 [Sec. 5.4]   **7.** $2 + \sqrt{3}$ and $2 - \sqrt{3}$ [Sec. 5.4]   **8.** $\dfrac{1 + \sqrt{13}}{2}$ and

$\dfrac{1 - \sqrt{13}}{2}$ [Sec. 5.4]   **9.** $y = -\dfrac{4}{3}x + 4$ [Sec. 5.1]   **10.** $t = \dfrac{f - v}{a}$ [Sec. 5.1]   **11.** 2450 feet [Sec. 5.1]

12. 3 seconds [Sec. 5.1]   **13.** 60°C [Sec. 5.1]   **14.** 39 minutes [Sec. 5.1]   **15.** 28.4 miles per gallon [Sec. 5.2]

16. $\dfrac{1}{4}$ [Sec. 5.2]   **17.** $1260 [Sec. 5.1]   **18. a.** New York, Chicago, Philadelphia, Los Angeles, Houston

b. 21,596 more people per square mile [Sec. 5.2]   **19. a.** $15:1$, 15 to 1. There are 15 students for every one faculty member at
the university.   **b.** Grand Canyon University, Arizona State University   **c.** Embry-Riddle Aeronautical University, Northern
Arizona University, and University of Arizona [Sec. 5.2]   **20.** Department A: $105,000; Department B: $245,000 [Sec. 5.2]
21. 7.5 tablespoons [Sec. 5.2]   **22. a.** No   **b.** $41:9$ **c.** $1,828.6 billion   **d.** $490.6 billion [Sec. 5.2]
23. a. 51.0%   **b.** Less than [Sec. 5.3]   **24.** 735,000 people [Sec. 5.3]   **25.** 69.0% [Sec. 5.3]
26. a. 83.3%   **b.** 100%   **c.** 50% [Sec. 5.3]   **27.** 16.4% [Sec. 5.3]   **28. a.** Ages 9–10
b. Ages 15–16   **c.** 46.5%; less than   **d.** 7230 boys   **e.** 549,400 young people [Sec. 5.3]
29. 1 second and 5 seconds [Sec. 5.4]   **30.** 0.5 second and 1.5 seconds [Sec. 5.4]

CHAPTER 5 TEST   *page 324*

1. 14 [Sec. 5.1]   **2.** 10 [Sec. 5.1]   **3.** $\dfrac{21}{4}$ [Sec. 5.2]   **4.** 3 and 9 [Sec. 5.4]

5. $\dfrac{2 + \sqrt{7}}{3}$ and $\dfrac{2 - \sqrt{7}}{3}$ [Sec. 5.4]   **6.** $y = \dfrac{1}{2}x - \dfrac{15}{2}$ [Sec. 5.1]   **7.** $F = \dfrac{9}{5}C + 32$ [Sec. 5.1]

8. 2.5 minutes [Sec. 5.1]   **9.** 10 days [Sec. 5.1]   **10.** 54.8 miles per hour [Sec. 5.2]   **11.** 843 acres [Sec. 5.1]
12. a. 2.727, 2.905, 2.777, 2.808, 2.901, 2.904   **b.** Ty Cobb, Rogers Hornsby, Joe Jackson, Tris Speaker, Ted Williams,

Billy Hamilton [Sec. 5.2]   **13.** $\dfrac{4}{7}$ [Sec. 5.2]   **14.** $112,500 and $67,500 [Sec. 5.2]   **15.** 2.75 pounds [Sec. 5.2]

16. a. Miami-Dade   **b.** 9420 violent crimes [Sec. 5.2]   **17.** 14.4% [Sec. 5.3]   **18. a.** 20.6%
b. Between 2004 and 2005   **c.** 39.1% [Sec. 5.3]   **19. a.** 20%   **b.** 1.6 million working farms
c. Answers will vary. [Sec. 5.3]   **20.** 0.2 second and 1.6 seconds [Sec. 5.4]

CHAPTER 6

EXERCISE SET 6.1 *page 338*

1.

3.

5.

7.

9.

11.

13.

15.

17.

19.

21.

23.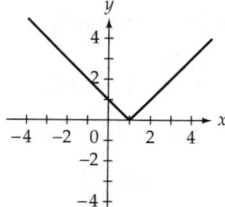

25. 3 **27.** 3 **29.** 10 **31.** 0 **33. a.** 16 meters **b.** 20 feet
35. a. 100 feet **b.** 68 feet **37. a.** 1087 feet per second **b.** 1136 feet per second
39. a. 10% **b.** 40%

41.

43.

45.

47.

49.

51.

53.

55.

57. 48 square units **59.** No. A function cannot have different elements in the range corresponding to one element in the domain.
61. 2 **63.** 17 **65.** $x = 0$

EXERCISE SET 6.2   *page 350*

1. $(2, 0), (0, -6)$ **3.** $(6, 0), (0, -4)$ **5.** $(-4, 0), (0, -4)$ **7.** $(4, 0), (0, 3)$ **9.** $\left(\dfrac{9}{2}, 0\right), (0, -3)$

11. $(2, 0), (0, 3)$ **13.** $(1, 0), (0, -2)$ **15.** $\left(\dfrac{30}{7}, 0\right)$; At $\dfrac{30}{7}$°C the cricket stops chirping.   **17.** The intercept on the

vertical axis is $(0, -15)$. This means that the temperature of the object is -15°F before it is removed from the freezer. The intercept on the horizontal axis is $(5, 0)$. This means that it takes 5 minutes for the temperature of the object to reach 0°F.   **19.** -1

21. $\dfrac{1}{3}$ **23.** $-\dfrac{2}{3}$ **25.** $-\dfrac{3}{4}$ **27.** Undefined   **29.** $\dfrac{7}{5}$ **31.** 0 **33.** $-\dfrac{1}{2}$ **35.** Undefined

37. The slope is 40, which means the motorist was traveling at 40 miles per hour.   **39.** The slope is 0.25, which means the tax rate for an income range of \$29,050 to \$70,350 is 25%.   **41.** The slope is approximately 343.9, which means the runner traveled at a rate of 343.9 meters per minute.   **43.**

45.

47.

49.

51.

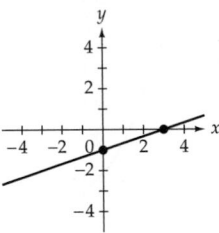

53. Line A represents the distance traveled by Lois in x hours, line B represents the distance traveled by Tanya in x hours, and line C represents the distance between them in x hours.   **55.** No   **57.** 7   **59.** 2   **61.** It rotates the line counterclockwise.
63. It raises the line on the rectangular coordinate system.   **65.** No. A vertical line through $(4, 0)$ does not have a y-intercept.

EXERCISE SET 6.3   *page 360*

1. $y = 2x + 5$ **3.** $y = -3x + 4$ **5.** $y = -\dfrac{2}{3}x + 7$ **7.** $y = -3$ **9.** $y = x + 2$ **11.** $y = -\dfrac{3}{2}x + 3$

13. $y = \dfrac{1}{2}x - 1$ **15.** $y = -\dfrac{5}{2}x$ **17.** $R(x) = -\dfrac{3}{5}x + 545$; 485 rooms   **19.** $D(t) = 415t$; 1867.5 miles

21. $N(x) = -20x + 230{,}000$; 60,000 cars   **23. a.** $y = 0.56x + 41.71$ **b.** 89
25. a. $y = 42.50x + 2613.76$ **b.** 3209 thousand students   **27. a.** $y = -1.35x + 106.98$ **b.** 46°F
29. Answers will vary. For example, $(0, 3), (1, 2),$ and $(3, 0)$.   **31.** 7   **33.** No. The three points do not lie on a straight line.   **35.** 3°. The car is climbing.

EXERCISE SET 6.4   *page 372*

1. $(0, -2)$ **3.** $(0, -1)$ **5.** $(0, 2)$ **7.** $(0, -1)$ **9.** $\left(\dfrac{1}{2}, -\dfrac{9}{4}\right)$ **11.** $\left(\dfrac{1}{4}, -\dfrac{41}{8}\right)$

13. $(0, 0), (2, 0)$ **15.** $(-2, 0), \left(-\dfrac{3}{4}, 0\right)$ **17.** $\left(-1 + \sqrt{2}, 0\right), \left(-1 - \sqrt{2}, 0\right)$ **19.** None

21. $\left(2 + \sqrt{5}, 0\right), \left(2 - \sqrt{5}, 0\right)$ **23.** $\left(-\dfrac{1}{2}, 0\right), (3, 0)$ **25.** Minimum: 2   **27.** Maximum: -3

29. Minimum: -3.25 **31.** Maximum: $\dfrac{9}{4}$ **33.** c   **35.** 150 feet   **37.** 100 lenses

39. 24.36 feet   **41.** Yes   **43.** 141.6 feet   **45. a.** 41 miles per hour   **b.** 33.658 miles per gallon

47. 7   **49.** 4

EXERCISE SET 6.5   *page 386*

1. a. 9   **b.** 1   **c.** $\dfrac{1}{9}$ **3. a.** 16   **b.** 4   **c.** $\dfrac{1}{4}$ **5. a.** 1   **b.** $\dfrac{1}{8}$ **c.** 16

7. a. 7.3891   **b.** 0.3679   **c.** 1.2840   **9. a.** 54.5982   **b.** 1   **c.** 0.1353

11. a. 16   **b.** 16   **c.** 1.4768   **13. a.** 0.1353   **b.** 0.1353   **c.** 0.0111

15.   **17.**   **19.**   **21.**

23.

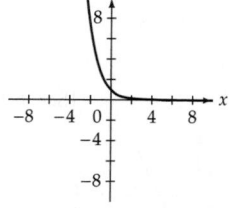

25. $11,202.50   **27.** $3210.06   **29.** 5.2 micrograms   **31.** $F(n) = 440(2^{n/12})$

33. $y = 8000(1.1066^t)$; 552,200,000 automobiles   **35.** $y = 100(0.99^t)$ **37. a.** $y = 4.959(1.063^x)$ **b.** 12.4 milliliters

39. a. 5.9 billion people   **b.** 7.2 billion people   **c.** The maximum population that Earth can support is 70.0 billion people.

EXERCISE SET 6.6   *page 400*

1. $\log_7 49 = 2$ **3.** $\log_5 625 = 4$ **5.** $\log 0.0001 = -4$ **7.** $\log x = y$ **9.** $3^4 = 81$

11. $5^3 = 125$ **13.** $4^{-2} = \dfrac{1}{16}$ **15.** $e^y = x$ **17.** 4   **19.** 2   **21.** -2 **23.** 6   **25.** 9

27. $\dfrac{1}{7}$ **29.** $\dfrac{1}{9}$ **31.** 1   **33.** 316.23   **35.** 7.39   **37.** 2.24   **39.** 14.39

41.   **43.**   **45.**   **47.** 79%

49. 65 decibels   **51.** 1.35   **53.** 6.8   **55.** $794{,}328{,}235 I_0$ **57.** 100 times as strong   **59.** 6.0 parsecs

61. 7805.5 billion barrels   **63.** $x = \dfrac{10^{0.47712}}{10^{0.30103}} = 10^{0.17609} \approx 1.5$; $\log x = 0.17609$ **65.** Answers will vary.

CHAPTER 6 REVIEW EXERCISES   *page 403*

1.

[Sec. 6.1]

2.

[Sec. 6.1]

3.

[Sec. 6.1]

4.

[Sec. 6.1]

5.

[Sec. 6.1]

6.

[Sec. 6.1]

7.

[Sec. 6.1]

8.

[Sec. 6.1]

9.

[Sec. 6.1]

10.

[Sec. 6.1]

11.

[Sec. 6.1]

12.

[Sec. 6.1]

13.

[Sec. 6.5]

14.

[Sec. 6.5]

15.

[Sec. 6.5]

16.

[Sec. 6.6]

17. -13 [Sec. 6.1]   **18.** 13 [Sec. 6.1]   **19.** $-\dfrac{1}{2}$ [Sec. 6.1]

20. -21 [Sec. 6.1]   **21.** 4 [Sec. 6.5]   **22.** $\dfrac{4}{9}$ [Sec. 6.5]   **23.** 15.78 [Sec. 6.5]   **24. a.** 113.1 cubic inches

b. 7238.2 cubic centimeters [Sec. 6.1]   **25. a.** 133 feet   **b.** 133 feet [Sec. 6.1]

26. a. 5%   **b.** 36.7% [Sec. 6.1]   **27.** $(-5, 0), (0, 10)$ [Sec. 6.2]   **28.** $(12, 0), (0, -9)$ [Sec. 6.2]
29. $(5, 0), (0, -3)$ [Sec. 6.2]   **30.** $(6, 0), (0, 8)$ [Sec. 6.2]   **31.** The intercept on the vertical axis is $(0, 25,000)$. This means that the value of the truck was $25,000 when it was new. The intercept on the horizontal axis is $(5, 0)$. This means that after 5 years the truck will be worth $0. [Sec. 6.2]   **32.** 5 [Sec. 6.2]   **33.** $\dfrac{5}{2}$ [Sec. 6.2]   **34.** 0 [Sec. 6.2]

35. Undefined [Sec. 6.2]   **36.** The slope is -0.6, which means that the revenue from home video rentals is decreasing $600,000,000 annually. [Sec. 6.2]   **37.**

[Sec. 6.2]

38.

[Sec. 6.2]

39. $y = 2x + 7$ [Sec. 6.3]   **40.** $y = x - 5$ [Sec. 6.3]   **41.** $y = \dfrac{2}{3}x + 3$ [Sec. 6.3]   **42.** $y = \dfrac{1}{4}x$ [Sec. 6.3]

43.

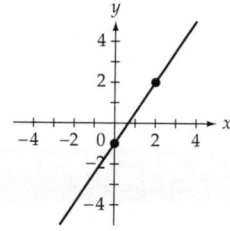

[Sec. 6.2]

44. a. $f(x) = 25x + 100$ **b.** $900 [Sec. 6.3]

45. a. $A(p) = -25,000x + 10,000$ **b.** 10,750 gallons [Sec. 6.3]   **46. a.** $y = 0.16204x - 0.12674$ **b.** 25 [Sec. 6.3]
47. $(-1, 3)$ [Sec. 6.4]   **48.** $\left(-\dfrac{3}{2}, \dfrac{11}{2}\right)$ [Sec. 6.4]   **49.** $(1, 2)$ [Sec. 6.4]   **50.** $(-2.5, -7.25)$ [Sec. 6.4]

51. $(4, 0), (-5, 0)$ [Sec. 6.4]   **52.** $\left(-1 + \sqrt{2}, 0\right), \left(-1 - \sqrt{2}, 0\right)$ [Sec. 6.4]   **53.** $\left(-\dfrac{1}{2}, 0\right), (-4, 0)$ [Sec. 6.4]

54. None [Sec. 6.4]   **55.** 5, maximum [Sec. 6.4]   **56.** $-\dfrac{15}{2}$, minimum [Sec. 6.4]

57. -5, minimum [Sec. 6.4]   **58.** $\dfrac{1}{8}$, maximum [Sec. 6.4]   **59.** 125 feet [Sec. 6.4]

60. 2000 CD-RWs [Sec. 6.4]   **61.** $12,297.11 [Sec. 6.5]   **62.** 7.94 milligrams [Sec. 6.5]

63. 3.36 micrograms [Sec. 6.5]   **64. a.** $H(n) = 6\left(\dfrac{2}{3}\right)^{n}$ **b.** 0.79 foot [Sec. 6.5]   **65. a.** $N = 250.2056(0.6506)^{t}$
b. 19 thousand people [Sec. 6.5]   **66.** 5 [Sec. 6.6]   **67.** -4 [Sec. 6.6]   **68.** -1 [Sec. 6.6]
69. 6 [Sec. 6.6]   **70.** 64 [Sec. 6.6]   **71.** 1.4422 [Sec. 6.6]   **72.** 12.1825 [Sec. 6.6]
73. 251.1886 [Sec. 6.6]   **74.** 43.7 parsecs [Sec. 6.6]   **75.** 140 decibels [Sec. 6.6]

CHAPTER 6 TEST   *page 406*

1. -21 [Sec. 6.1]   **2.** $\dfrac{1}{9}$ [Sec. 6.5]   **3.** 3 [Sec. 6.6]   **4.** 36 [Sec. 6.6]

5.

[Sec. 6.1]

6.

[Sec. 6.1]

7.

[Sec. 6.5]

8.

[Sec. 6.6]

9. $\dfrac{3}{5}$ [Sec. 6.2]   **10.** $y = \dfrac{2}{3}x + 3$ [Sec. 6.3]   **11.** $(-3, -10)$ [Sec. 6.4]

12. $(-4, 0), (2, 0)$ [Sec. 6.4]   **13.** $\dfrac{49}{4}$, maximum   [Sec. 6.4]   **14.** The vertical intercept is $(0, 250)$. This means that the plane starts 250 miles from its destination. The horizontal intercept is $(2.5, 0)$. This means that it takes the plane 2.5 hours to reach its destination.   [Sec. 6.2]   **15.** 148 feet   [Sec. 6.4]   **16.** 3.30 grams   [Sec. 6.5]   **17.** 2.0 times as great   [Sec. 6.6]   **18.** $y = -1.5x + 740$ [Sec. 6.3]   **19. a.** $y = 40.5x + 659$ **b.** 983 pounds   [Sec. 6.3]   **20.** 2.5 meters   [Sec. 6.6]

CHAPTER 7

EXERCISE SET 7.1   *page 416*

1. 8   **3.** 12   **5.** 2   **7.** 4   **9.** 4   **11.** 7   **13.** 11   **15.** 7   **17.** 0300
19. 0400   **21.** 2000   **23.** 2100   **25.** 3   **27.** 6   **29.** True   **31.** False   **33.** True
35. False   **37.** True   **39.** Possible answers are 2, 8, 14, 20, 26, 32, 38, ...   **41.** 3   **43.** 3   **45.** 2
47. 10   **49.** 3   **51.** 3   **53.** 5   **55.** 4   **57.** 3   **59.** 7   **61.** 2   **63. a.** 6 o'clock
b. 5 o'clock   **65. a.** Tuesday   **b.** Monday   **67.** Saturday   **69.** Friday   **71.** 1, 4, 7, 10, 13, 16, . . .
73. 1, 6, 11, 16, 21, 26, . . .   **75.** 0, 2, 4, 6, 8, 10, 12, . . .   **77.** No solutions   **79.** 0, 2, 4, 6, 8, 10, 12, . . .
81. No solutions   **83.** 5, 7   **85.** 3, 3   **87.** 5, 3   **89.** 6   **91.** 6   **93.** 2
97. 11:00   **99.** 4

EXERCISE SET 7.2   *page 429*

1. No   **3.** No   **5.** Yes   **7.** 9   **9.** 7   **11.** 3   **13.** 0   **15.** 6   **17.** 7
19. 5   **21.** 1   **23.** 7   **25.** 3   **27.** Yes   **29.** Yes   **31.** Yes   **33.** No   **35.** No
37. Yes   **39.** BPZMM UCASMBMMZA   **41.** UF'E M SUDX   **43.** VWLFNV DQG VWRQHV   **45.** AGE OF
ENLIGHTENMENT   **47.** FRIEND IN NEED   **49.** DANGER WILL ROBINSON   **51.** FORTUNE COOKIE
53. PHQ ZLOOLQJWR EHOLHYH ZKDW WKHB ZLVK   **55.** JUSQD UT LURNUR   **57.** PODONNQN NSBQK
59. TURN BACK THE CLOCK   **61.** BARREL OF MONKEYS   **63.** Because the check digit is simply the sum of the first
10 digits mod 9, the same digits in a different order will give the same sum and hence the same check digit.

EXERCISE SET 7.3   *page 442*

1. a. Yes   **b.** No   **3. a.** Yes   **b.** No   **5.** Yes   **7.** Yes   **9.** No; property 4 fails.   **11.** Yes
13. Yes   **15.** No; property 4 fails.   **17.** Yes   **19.** R_l **21.** R_{120} **23.** R_{120} **25.** R_r

27. R_l **29.** $I = \begin{pmatrix} 1 & 2 & 3 & 4 \\ 1 & 2 & 3 & 4 \end{pmatrix}, R_{90} = \begin{pmatrix} 1 & 2 & 3 & 4 \\ 2 & 3 & 4 & 1 \end{pmatrix}, R_{180} = \begin{pmatrix} 1 & 2 & 3 & 4 \\ 3 & 4 & 1 & 2 \end{pmatrix}, R_{270} = \begin{pmatrix} 1 & 2 & 3 & 4 \\ 4 & 1 & 2 & 3 \end{pmatrix}, R_v = \begin{pmatrix} 1 & 2 & 3 & 4 \\ 4 & 3 & 2 & 1 \end{pmatrix},$

$R_h = \begin{pmatrix} 1 & 2 & 3 & 4 \\ 2 & 1 & 4 & 3 \end{pmatrix}, R_r = \begin{pmatrix} 1 & 2 & 3 & 4 \\ 3 & 2 & 1 & 4 \end{pmatrix}, R_l = \begin{pmatrix} 1 & 2 & 3 & 4 \\ 1 & 4 & 3 & 2 \end{pmatrix}$ **31.** R_r **33.** R_{90} **35.** I **37.** D

39. E **41.** B **43.** $\begin{pmatrix} 1 & 2 & 3 & 4 \\ 1 & 2 & 3 & 4 \end{pmatrix}, \begin{pmatrix} 1 & 2 & 3 & 4 \\ 1 & 2 & 4 & 3 \end{pmatrix}, \begin{pmatrix} 1 & 2 & 3 & 4 \\ 1 & 3 & 2 & 4 \end{pmatrix}, \begin{pmatrix} 1 & 2 & 3 & 4 \\ 1 & 3 & 4 & 2 \end{pmatrix}, \begin{pmatrix} 1 & 2 & 3 & 4 \\ 1 & 4 & 2 & 3 \end{pmatrix}, \begin{pmatrix} 1 & 2 & 3 & 4 \\ 1 & 4 & 3 & 2 \end{pmatrix},$

$\begin{pmatrix} 1 & 2 & 3 & 4 \\ 2 & 1 & 3 & 4 \end{pmatrix}, \begin{pmatrix} 1 & 2 & 3 & 4 \\ 2 & 1 & 4 & 3 \end{pmatrix}, \begin{pmatrix} 1 & 2 & 3 & 4 \\ 2 & 3 & 1 & 4 \end{pmatrix}, \begin{pmatrix} 1 & 2 & 3 & 4 \\ 2 & 3 & 4 & 1 \end{pmatrix}, \begin{pmatrix} 1 & 2 & 3 & 4 \\ 2 & 4 & 1 & 3 \end{pmatrix}, \begin{pmatrix} 1 & 2 & 3 & 4 \\ 2 & 4 & 3 & 1 \end{pmatrix}, \begin{pmatrix} 1 & 2 & 3 & 4 \\ 3 & 1 & 2 & 4 \end{pmatrix}, \begin{pmatrix} 1 & 2 & 3 & 4 \\ 3 & 1 & 4 & 2 \end{pmatrix},$

$\begin{pmatrix} 1 & 2 & 3 & 4 \\ 3 & 2 & 1 & 4 \end{pmatrix}, \begin{pmatrix} 1 & 2 & 3 & 4 \\ 3 & 2 & 4 & 1 \end{pmatrix}, \begin{pmatrix} 1 & 2 & 3 & 4 \\ 3 & 4 & 1 & 2 \end{pmatrix}, \begin{pmatrix} 1 & 2 & 3 & 4 \\ 3 & 4 & 2 & 1 \end{pmatrix}, \begin{pmatrix} 1 & 2 & 3 & 4 \\ 4 & 1 & 2 & 3 \end{pmatrix}, \begin{pmatrix} 1 & 2 & 3 & 4 \\ 4 & 1 & 3 & 2 \end{pmatrix}, \begin{pmatrix} 1 & 2 & 3 & 4 \\ 4 & 2 & 1 & 3 \end{pmatrix}, \begin{pmatrix} 1 & 2 & 3 & 4 \\ 4 & 2 & 3 & 1 \end{pmatrix},$

$\begin{pmatrix} 1 & 2 & 3 & 4 \\ 4 & 3 & 1 & 2 \end{pmatrix}, \begin{pmatrix} 1 & 2 & 3 & 4 \\ 4 & 3 & 2 & 1 \end{pmatrix}$ **45.** $\begin{pmatrix} 1 & 2 & 3 & 4 \\ 2 & 1 & 3 & 4 \end{pmatrix}$ **47.** $\begin{pmatrix} 1 & 2 & 3 & 4 \\ 3 & 1 & 4 & 2 \end{pmatrix}$ **49.** $\begin{pmatrix} 1 & 2 & 3 & 4 \\ 4 & 3 & 2 & 1 \end{pmatrix}$ **51.** d

53. c **55.** Answers will vary.   **57.** Yes   **59. a. and b.** Answers will vary.   **c.** Values of n that are prime

61. a.   **b.** Yes   **c.** 1   **d.** 1 is its own inverse; 2 and 5 are inverses; 3 and 4 are inverses.

$\oplus$	1	2	3	4	5
1	1	2	3	4	5
2	2	3	4	5	1
3	3	4	5	1	2
4	4	5	1	2	3
5	5	1	2	3	4

CHAPTER 7 REVIEW EXERCISES   *page 446*

1. 2 [Sec. 7.1]   **2.** 2 [Sec. 7.1]   **3.** 5 [Sec. 7.1]   **4.** 6 [Sec. 7.1]   **5.** 9 [Sec. 7.1]
6. 4 [Sec. 7.1]   **7.** 11 [Sec. 7.1]   **8.** 7 [Sec. 7.1]   **9.** 3 [Sec. 7.1]   **10.** 4 [Sec. 7.1]
11. True [Sec. 7.1]   **12.** False [Sec. 7.1]   **13.** False [Sec. 7.1]   **14.** True [Sec. 7.1]   **15.** 2 [Sec. 7.1]
16. 4 [Sec. 7.1]   **17.** 0 [Sec. 7.1]   **18.** 3 [Sec. 7.1]   **19.** 8 [Sec. 7.1]   **20.** 3 [Sec. 7.1]
21. 7 [Sec. 7.1]   **22.** 5 [Sec. 7.1]   **23. a.** 2 o'clock   **b.** 6 o'clock [Sec. 7.1]   **24.** Monday [Sec. 7.1]
25. 3, 7, 11, 15, 19, 23, ... [Sec. 7.1]   **26.** 7, 16, 25, 34, 43, 52, ... [Sec. 7.1]   **27.** 0, 5, 10, 15, 20, 25, 30, ... [Sec. 7.1]
28. 4, 15, 26, 37, 48, 59, 70, ... [Sec. 7.1]   **29.** 2, 3 [Sec. 7.1]   **30.** 5, 7 [Sec. 7.1]   **31.** 6 [Sec. 7.1]
32. 2 [Sec. 7.1]   **33.** 6 [Sec. 7.2]   **34.** 6 [Sec. 7.2]   **35.** 2 [Sec. 7.2]   **36.** 1 [Sec. 7.2]
37. No [Sec. 7.2]   **38.** Yes [Sec. 7.2]   **39.** No [Sec. 7.2]   **40.** No [Sec. 7.2]   **41.** THF AOL MVYJL IL
DPAO FVB [Sec. 7.2]   **42.** NLYNPW LWW AWLYD [Sec. 7.2]   **43.** GOOD LUCK TOMORROW [Sec. 7.2]
44. THE DAY HAS ARRIVED [Sec. 7.2]   **45.** UVR YX NDU PGVU [Sec. 7.2]   **46.** YOU PASSED
THE TEST [Sec. 7.2]   **47.** Yes [Sec. 7.3]   **48.** Yes [Sec. 7.3]   **49.** No, properties 1, 3, and 4 fail. [Sec. 7.3]
50. Yes [Sec. 7.3]   **51.** R_{240} [Sec. 7.3]   **52.** R_l [Sec. 7.3]   **53.** R_r [Sec. 7.3]   **54.** R_{270} [Sec. 7.3]
55. R_{180} [Sec. 7.3]   **56.** R_r [Sec. 7.3]   **57.** There are only four distinct ways to place the rectangle in the
reference rectangle. [Sec. 7.3]   **58.** $\begin{pmatrix} 1 & 2 & 3 & 4 \\ 1 & 2 & 3 & 4 \end{pmatrix}, \begin{pmatrix} 1 & 2 & 3 & 4 \\ 3 & 4 & 1 & 2 \end{pmatrix}, \begin{pmatrix} 1 & 2 & 3 & 4 \\ 2 & 1 & 4 & 3 \end{pmatrix}, \begin{pmatrix} 1 & 2 & 3 & 4 \\ 4 & 3 & 2 & 1 \end{pmatrix}$ [Sec. 7.3]
59. Yes [Sec. 7.3]   **60.** Answers will vary. [Sec. 7.3]   **61.** Answers will vary. [Sec. 7.3]   **62.** A [Sec. 7.3]
63. A [Sec. 7.3]   **64.** $\begin{pmatrix} 1 & 2 & 3 & 4 & 5 \\ 3 & 4 & 1 & 5 & 2 \end{pmatrix}$ [Sec. 7.3]   **65.** $\begin{pmatrix} 1 & 2 & 3 & 4 & 5 \\ 3 & 5 & 1 & 4 & 2 \end{pmatrix}$ [Sec. 7.3]

CHAPTER 7 TEST   *page 448*

1. a. 3   **b.** 5 [Sec. 7.1]   **2. a.** 0200   **b.** 1300 [Sec. 7.1]   **3. a.** True   **b.** False [Sec. 7.1]
4. 4 [Sec. 7.1]   **5.** 6 [Sec. 7.1]   **6.** 8 [Sec. 7.1]   **7. a.** 6 o'clock   **b.** 5 o'clock [Sec. 7.1]
8. 5, 14, 23, 32, 41, 50, ... [Sec. 7.1]   **9.** 1, 3, 5, 7, 9, 11, ... [Sec. 7.1]   **10.** 4, 2 [Sec. 7.1]   **11.** 5 [Sec. 7.2]
12. 0 [Sec. 7.2]   **13.** Yes [Sec. 7.2]   **14.** BOZYBD LKMU [Sec. 7.2]   **15.** NEVER QUIT [Sec. 7.2]
16. a. Yes   **b.** No [Sec. 7.3]   **17.** No, Property 4 fails; many elements do not have an inverse. [Sec. 7.3]
18. a. R_t **b.** R_r [Sec. 7.3]   **19.** $\begin{pmatrix} 1 & 2 & 3 \\ 1 & 3 & 2 \end{pmatrix}$ [Sec. 7.3]   **20.** $\begin{pmatrix} 1 & 2 & 3 & 4 \\ 2 & 4 & 1 & 3 \end{pmatrix}$ [Sec. 7.3]

CHAPTER 8

EXERCISE SET 8.1   *page 464*

1. $\angle O$, $\angle AOB$, and $\angle BOA$ **3.** 40°, acute   **5.** 30°, acute   **7.** 120°, obtuse   **9.** Yes   **11.** No
13. A 28° angle   **15.** An 18° angle   **17.** 14 cm   **19.** 28 ft   **21.** 30 m   **23.** 86°   **25.** 71°
27. 30°   **29.** 36°   **31.** 127°   **33.** 116°   **35.** 20°   **37.** 20°   **39.** 20°   **41.** 141°
43. 106°   **45.** 11°   **47.** $m\angle a = 38°$, $m\angle b = 142°$ **49.** $m\angle a = 47°$, $m\angle b = 133°$ **51.** 20°   **53.** 47°
55. $m\angle x = 155°$, $m\angle y = 70°$ **57.** $m\angle a = 45°$, $m\angle b = 135°$ **59.** $90° - x$ **61.** 60°   **63.** 35°
65. 102°   **67.** The three angles form a straight angle. The sum of the measures of the angles of a triangle is 180°.
69. Zero dimensions; one dimension; one dimension; one dimension; two dimensions   **71.** 360°   **73.** $\angle AOC$ and $\angle BOC$
are supplementary angles; therefore, $m\angle AOC + m\angle BOC = 180°$. Because $m\angle AOC = m\angle BOC$, by substitution,
$m\angle AOC + m\angle AOC = 180°$. Therefore, $2(m\angle AOC) = 180°$, and $m\angle AOC = 90°$. Hence $\overline{AB} \perp \overline{CD}$.

EXERCISE SET 8.2   *page 486*

1.

W

L

3. a. Perimeter is not measured in square units.   **b.** Area is measured in square units.
5. Heptagon   **7.** Quadrilateral   **9.** Isosceles   **11.** Scalene   **13.** Right   **15.** Obtuse
17. a. 30 m   **b.** 50 m²   **19. a.** 16 cm   **b.** 16 cm²   **21. a.** 40 km   **b.** 100 km²
23. a. 40 ft   **b.** 72 ft²   **25. a.** 8π cm; 25.13 cm   **b.** 16π cm²; 50.27 cm²   **27. a.** 11π mi; 34.56 mi
b. 30.25π mi²; 95.03 mi²   **29. a.** 17π ft; 53.41 ft   **b.** 72.25π ft²; 226.98 ft²   **31.** $29\frac{1}{2}$ ft   **33.** $10\frac{1}{2}$ mi
35. 68 ft   **37.** 20 in.   **39.** 214 yd   **41.** 10 mi   **43.** 2 packages   **45.** 144 m²   **47.** 9 in.
49. 10 in.   **51.** 8 m   **53.** 96 m²   **55.** 607.5 m²   **57.** 2 bags   **59.** 2 qt   **61.** 20 tiles
63. $40   **65.** $34   **67.** 120 ft²   **69.** 13.19 ft   **71.** 1256.6 ft²   **73.** 94.25 ft   **75.** 144π in²
77. 113.10 in²   **79.** 266,281 km   **81.** $8r^2 - 2\pi r^2$ **83.** 4 times as large   **85.** $(a + 4)$ by $(a - 4)$
87. a. 18 cm; 8 cm²   **b.** 20 cm; 16 cm²   **c.** 32 cm; 64 cm²

EXERCISE SET 8.3   *page 502*

1. $\frac{1}{2}$ **3.** $\frac{3}{4}$ **5.** 7.2 cm   **7.** 3.3 m   **9.** 12 m   **11.** 12 in.   **13.** 56.3 cm²   **15.** 18 ft
17. 16 m   **19.** $14\frac{3}{8}$ ft   **21.** 15 m   **23.** 8 ft   **25.** 13 cm   **27.** 35 m
29. Yes, SAS Theorem   **31.** Yes, SSS Theorem   **33.** Yes, ASA Theorem   **35.** No   **37.** Yes, SAS Theorem
39. No   **41.** No   **43.** 13 in.   **45.** 11.4 cm   **47.** 8.7 ft   **49.** 7.9 m   **51.** 7.4 m   **53.** 21.6 mi
55. 24 in.   **57.** Yes. Explanations will vary.

EXERCISE SET 8.4   *page 518*

1. 840 in³   **3.** 15 ft³   **5.** 4.5π cm³; 14.14 cm³   **7.** 94 m²   **9.** 56 m²   **11.** 96π in²; 301.59 in²
13. 34 m³   **15.** 15.625 in³   **17.** 36π ft³   **19.** 8143.01 cm³   **21.** 75π in³   **23.** 120 in³   **25.** 7.80 ft³
27. 6416 cm²   **29.** 13.5 in²   **31.** 50.27 in²   **33.** 2.88π m²   **35.** 874.15 in²   **37.** 832 m²
39. 8.5 in.   **41.** 3 ft   **43.** 3217 ft²   **45.** 881.22 cm²   **47.** 1.67 m³   **49.** 115.43 cm³
51. 4580.44 cm³   **53.** 19 m²   **55.** 622.65 m²   **57.** 19,405.66 m²   **59.** 888.02 ft³
61. 95,000 L   **63.** 79.17 g   **65.** $4860   **67.** $V = \frac{2}{3}\pi r^3$; $SA = 3\pi r^2$

69. Surface area of the sphere $= 4\pi r^2$. Surface area of the side of the cylinder $= 2\pi rh = 2\pi r(2r) = 4\pi r^2$.
71. a. Doubled $+ 4WH$ **b.** Quadrupled   **c.** 8 times as large   **d.** Quadrupled

EXERCISE SET 8.5   *page 530*

1. a. $\dfrac{a}{c}$ **b.** $\dfrac{b}{c}$ **c.** $\dfrac{b}{c}$ **d.** $\dfrac{a}{c}$ **e.** $\dfrac{a}{b}$ **f.** $\dfrac{b}{a}$

3. $\sin\theta = \dfrac{5}{13}$, $\cos\theta = \dfrac{12}{13}$, $\tan\theta = \dfrac{5}{12}$ **5.** $\sin\theta = \dfrac{24}{25}$, $\cos\theta = \dfrac{7}{25}$, $\tan\theta = \dfrac{24}{7}$

7. $\sin\theta = \dfrac{8}{\sqrt{113}}$, $\cos\theta = \dfrac{7}{\sqrt{113}}$, $\tan\theta = \dfrac{8}{7}$ **9.** $\sin\theta = \dfrac{1}{2}$, $\cos\theta = \dfrac{\sqrt{3}}{2}$, $\tan\theta = \dfrac{1}{\sqrt{3}}$

11. 0.6820   **13.** 1.4281   **15.** 0.9971   **17.** 1.9970   **19.** 0.8878   **21.** 0.8453
23. 0.8508   **25.** 0.6833   **27.** 38.6°   **29.** 41.1°   **31.** 21.3°   **33.** 38.0°
35. 72.5°   **37.** 0.6°   **39.** 66.1°   **41.** 29.5°   **43.** 841.79 ft   **45.** 13.6°   **47.** 29.14 ft
49. 52.92 ft   **51.** 13.59 ft   **53.** 1056.63 ft   **55.** 29.58 yd   **57.** No. Explanations will vary.

59. $\dfrac{\sqrt{5}}{3}$ **61.** $\dfrac{\sqrt{7}}{3}$ **63.** $\sqrt{1-a^2}$

EXERCISE SET 8.6   *page 544*

1. a. Through a given point not on a given line, exactly one line can be drawn parallel to the given line.   **b.** Through a given point not on a given line, there are at least two lines parallel to the given line.   **c.** Through a given point not on a given line, there exist no lines parallel to the given line.   **3.** Carl Friedrich Gauss   **5. a.** The sum equals 180°.   **b.** The sum is less than 180°.   **c.** The sum is greater than 180° but less than 540°.   **7.** Imaginary geometry
9. A geodesic is a curve on a surface such that for any two points of the curve the portion of the curve between the points is the shortest path on the surface that joins these points.   **11.** An infinite saddle surface   **13.** π square units
15. 1,370,000 mi^2 **17.** $d_E(P, Q) = \sqrt{49} = 7$ blocks, $d_C(P, Q) = 7$ blocks
19. $d_E(P, Q) = \sqrt{89} \approx 9.4$ blocks, $d_C(P, Q) = 13$ blocks   **21.** $d_E(P, Q) = \sqrt{72} \approx 8.5$ blocks, $d_C(P, Q) = 12$ blocks
23. $d_E(P, Q) = \sqrt{37} \approx 6.1$ blocks, $d_C(P, Q) = 7$ blocks   **25.** $d_C(P, Q) = 7$ blocks   **27.** $d_C(P, Q) = 5$ blocks
29. $d_C(P, Q) = 5$ blocks   **31.** A city distance may be associated with more than one Euclidean distance. For example, if $P = (0, 0)$ and $Q = (2, 0)$, then the city distance between the points is 2 blocks and the Euclidean distance is also 2 blocks. However, if $P = (0, 0)$ and $Q = (1, 1)$, then the city distance between the points is still 2 blocks, but the Euclidean distance is $\sqrt{2}$ blocks.

33.

35.

37. $4n$

39. a.

b.

41. a. 10   **b.** 3

EXERCISE SET 8.7   *page 558*

1. Stage 2 —— ——   —— ——

Stage 3 – – – –   – – – –

3.

Stage 2

5.
Stage 2

7.
Stage 2

9. Stage 3   Stage 4

11. 0.631   **13.** 1.465   **15.** 2.000   **17.** 2.000

19. 1.613   **21. a.** Sierpinski carpet, 1.893; Variation 2, 1.771; Variation 1, 1.465   **b.** The Sierpinski carpet
23. The binary tree fractal is not a strictly self-similar fractal.

CHAPTER 8 REVIEW EXERCISES   *page 563*

1. $m\angle x = 22°; m\angle y = 158°$ [Sec. 8.1]   **2.** 24 in. [Sec. 8.3]   **3.** 240 in^3 [Sec. 8.4]   **4.** 68° [Sec. 8.1]
5. 220 ft^2 [Sec. 8.4]   **6.** 40π m^2 [Sec. 8.4]   **7.** 44 cm [Sec. 8.1]   **8.** 19° [Sec. 8.1]   **9.** 27 in^2 [Sec. 8.2]
10. 96 cm^3 [Sec. 8.4]   **11.** 14.14 m [Sec. 8.2]   **12.** $m\angle a = 138°; m\angle b = 42°$ [Sec. 8.1]
13. a 148° angle [Sec. 8.1]   **14.** 39 ft^3 [Sec. 8.4]   **15.** 95° [Sec. 8.1]   **16.** 8 cm [Sec. 8.2]
17. 288π mm^3 [Sec. 8.4]   **18.** 21.5 cm [Sec. 8.2]   **19.** 4 cans [Sec. 8.4]   **20.** 208 yd [Sec. 8.2]
21. 90.25 m^2 [Sec. 8.2]   **22.** 276 m^2 [Sec. 8.2]   **23.** Carl Friedrich Gauss [Sec. 8.6]
24. The triangles are congruent by the SAS theorem. [Sec. 8.3]   **25.** 9.75 ft [Sec. 8.3]
26. $\sin\theta = \dfrac{5\sqrt{89}}{89}, \cos\theta = \dfrac{8\sqrt{89}}{89}, \tan\theta = \dfrac{5}{8}$ [Sec. 8.5]   **27.** $\sin\theta = \dfrac{\sqrt{3}}{2}, \cos\theta = \dfrac{1}{2}, \tan\theta = \sqrt{3}$ [Sec. 8.5]
28. 25.7° [Sec. 8.5]   **29.** 29.2° [Sec. 8.5]   **30.** 53.8° [Sec. 8.5]   **31.** 1.9° [Sec. 8.5]   **32.** 100.1 ft [Sec. 8.5]
33. 153.2 mi [Sec. 8.5]   **34.** 56.0 ft [Sec. 8.5]   **35.** Nikolai Lobachevsky [Sec. 8.6]
36. Spherical geometry or elliptical geometry [Sec. 8.6]   **37.** Hyperbolic geometry [Sec. 8.6]
38. Lobachevskian or hyperbolic geometry [Sec. 8.6]   **39.** Riemannian or spherical geometry [Sec. 8.6]
40. 120π in^2 [Sec. 8.6]   **41.** $\dfrac{25\pi}{3}$ ft^2 [Sec. 8.6]   **42.** $d_E(P, Q) = 5$ blocks, $d_C(P, Q) = 7$ blocks [Sec. 8.6]
43. $d_E(P, Q) = \sqrt{113} \approx 10.6$ blocks, $d_C(P, Q) = 15$ blocks [Sec. 8.6]
44. $d_E(P, Q) = \sqrt{37} \approx 6.1$ blocks, $d_C(P, Q) = 7$ blocks [Sec. 8.6]
45. $d_E(P, Q) = \sqrt{89} \approx 9.4$ blocks, $d_C(P, Q) = 13$ blocks [Sec. 8.6]   **46. a.** P and Q **b.** P and R [Sec. 8.6]

47.

Stage 0 ————————

Stage 1

Stage 2 ⌃⌃⌃ [Sec. 8.7]

48.

Stage 2   [Sec. 8.7]

49. $\dfrac{\log 5}{\log 4} \approx 1.161$ [Sec. 8.7]

50. 1 [Sec. 8.7]

CHAPTER 8 TEST   *page 566*

1. 169.65 m³ [Sec. 8.4]   **2.** 6.8 m [Sec. 8.2]   **3.** a 58° angle [Sec. 8.1]   **4.** 3.14 m² [Sec. 8.2]

5. 150° [Sec. 8.1]   **6.** $m\angle a = 45°$; $m\angle b = 135°$ [Sec. 8.1]   **7.** 5.0625 ft² [Sec. 8.2]   **8.** 448π cm³ [Sec. 8.4]

9. $1\frac{1}{5}$ ft [Sec. 8.3]   **10.** 90° and 50° [Sec. 8.1]   **11.** 125° [Sec. 8.1]   **12.** 32 m² [Sec. 8.2]

13. 25 ft [Sec. 8.3]   **14.** 113.10 in² [Sec. 8.2]   **15.** The triangles are congruent by the SAS theorem. [Sec. 8.3]

16. 7.55 cm [Sec. 8.3]   **17.** $\sin\theta = \frac{4}{5}$, $\cos\theta = \frac{3}{5}$, $\tan\theta = \frac{4}{3}$ [Sec. 8.5]   **18.** 127 ft [Sec. 8.5]

19. 103.87 ft² [Sec. 8.2]   **20.** 780 in³ [Sec. 8.4]   **21. a.** Through a given point not on a given line, exactly one line can be drawn parallel to the given line.   **b.** Through a given point not on a given line, there exist no lines parallel to the given line. [Sec. 8.6]   **22. a.** 1   **b.** 3 [Sec. 8.6]   **23.** A great circle of a sphere is a circle on the surface of the sphere whose center is at the center of the sphere. [Sec. 8.6]   **24.** 80π ft² ≈ 251.3 ft² [Sec. 8.6]

25. $d_E(P, Q) = \sqrt{82} \approx 9.1$ blocks, $d_C(P, Q) = 10$ blocks [Sec. 8.6]   **26.** 16 [Sec. 8.6]

27.

Stage 2   [Sec. 8.7]

28.

Stage 2   [Sec. 8.7]

29. Replacement ratio: 2; scale ratio: 2; similarity dimension: 1 [Sec. 8.7]

30. Replacement ratio: 3; scale ratio: 2; similarity dimension: $\frac{\log 3}{\log 2} \approx 1.585$ [Sec. 8.7]

CHAPTER 9

EXERCISE SET 9.1   *page 583*

1. a. 6   **b.** 7   **c.** 6   **d.** Yes   **e.** No   **3. a.** 6   **b.** 4   **c.** 4   **d.** Yes   **e.** Yes

5.

7.

9. a. No   **b.** 3   **c.** Ada   **d.** A loop would correspond to a friend speaking to himself or herself.

11. Equivalent   **13.** Not equivalent   **15.** The graph on the right has a vertex of degree 4 and the graph on the left does not.

17. a. D–A–E–B–D–C–E–D   **19. a.** Not Eulerian   **b.** A–E–A–D–E–D–C–E–C–B–E–B

21. a. Not Eulerian   **b.** No   **23. a.** Not Eulerian   **b.** E–A–D–E–G–D–C–G–F–C–B–F–A–B–E–F

25. a.

b. Yes

27. Yes   **29.** Yes, but the hamster cannot return to its starting point.   **31.** Yes; you will always return to the starting room.

33. A–B–C–D–E–G–F–A   **35.** A–B–E–C–H–D–F–G–A

37. Springfield–Greenfield–Watertown–Riverside–Newhope–Midland–Springfield each room once and returns to the starting room without visiting any room twice

39. A route through the museum that visits

41. Euler circuit

43. There is not an Euler circuit or an Euler walk; there is a Hamiltonian circuit.

45. a.

(many possible answers)

b.

(many possible answers)

c.

(many possible answers)

EXERCISE SET 9.2   *page 601*

1. A–B–E–D–C–A, total weight 31; A–D–E–B–C–A, total weight 32   **3.** A–D–C–E–B–F–A, total weight 114; A–C–D–E–B–F–A, total weight 158   **5.** A–D–B–C–F–E–A   **7.** A–C–E–B–D–A   **9.** A–D–B–F–E–C–A
11. A–C–E–B–D–A   **13.** Louisville–Evansville–Bloomington–Indianapolis–Lafayette–Fort Wayne–Louisville
15. Louisville–Evansville–Bloomington–Indianapolis–Lafayette–Fort Wayne–Louisville   **17.** Tokyo–Seoul–Beijing–Hong Kong–Bangkok–Tokyo   **19.** Tokyo–Seoul–Beijing–Hong Kong–Bangkok–Tokyo   **21.** Home–pharmacy–pet store–farmers' market–shopping mall–home; home–pharmacy–pet store–shopping mall–farmers' market–home
23. Home state–task B–task D–task A–task C–home state; Edge–Picking Algorithm gives the same sequence.

25.   **27.**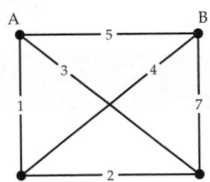

EXERCISE SET 9.3   *page 615*

1.   **3.**   **5.**   **7.**

See the *Student Solutions Manual* for the solutions to Exercises 9–15.   **17.** 5 faces, 5 vertices, 8 edges
19. 2 faces, 8 vertices, 8 edges   **21.** 5 faces, 10 vertices, 13 edges   **23.** 9
25.   **27.**   **29.** Euler's Formula cannot be satisfied.

31. a.

b. The number of vertices in the dual graph is equal to the number of faces in the original graph, and the number of faces in the dual graph is equal to the number of vertices in the original graph.   **c.** The dual of the dual is equivalent to the original graph.

 EXERCISE SET 9.4   *page 628*

1.

3.

5.

7.

9.

11.

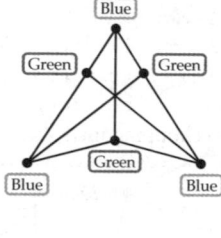

13. Not 2-colorable   **15.**   **17.** 3   **19.** 4   **21.** 3   **23.** 2 time slots

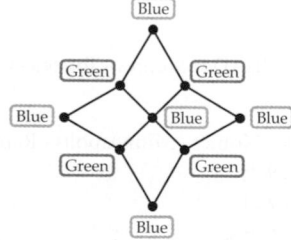

25. 5 days: group 1, group 2, groups 3 and 5, group 4, group 6   **27.** 3 days: films 1 and 4, films 2 and 6, films 3 and 5

29.

31.

33. a.

b.

c.

d.

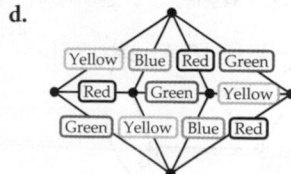

e. Answers will vary.

CHAPTER 9 REVIEW EXERCISES *page 634*

1. a. 8   **b.** 4   **c.** All vertices have degree 4.   **d.** Yes [Sec. 9.1]   **2. a.** 6   **b.** 7
c. 1, 1, 2, 2, 2, 2, 2   **d.** No [Sec. 9.1]   **3.**   **4. a.** No   **b.** 4

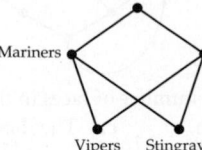

[Sec. 9.1]

c. 110, 405   **d.** 105 [Sec. 9.1]   **5.** Equivalent [Sec. 9.1]   **6.** Equivalent [Sec. 9.1]
7. a. E–A–B–C–D–B–E–C–A–D   **b.** Not possible [Sec. 9.1]   **8. a.** Not possible   **b.** Not possible [Sec. 9.1]
9. a. and b. F–A–E–C–B–A–D–B–E–D–C–F [Sec. 9.1]   **10. a.** B–A–E–C–A–D–F–C–B–D–E

b. Not possible [Sec. 9.1]   **11.** Yes   **12.** Yes; no [Sec. 9.1]

[Sec. 9.1]

13. A–B–C–E–D–A [Sec. 9.1]   **14.** A–D–F–B–C–E–A [Sec. 9.1]

15.

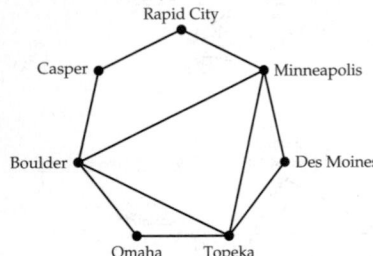

Casper–Rapid City–Minneapolis–Des Moines–Topeka–Omaha–Boulder–Casper
[Sec. 9.1]

16. Casper–Boulder–Topeka–Minneapolis–Boulder–Omaha–Topeka–Des Moines–Minneapolis–Rapid City–Casper   [Sec. 9.1]
17. A–D–F–E–B–C–A [Sec. 9.2]   **18.** A–B–E–C–D–A [Sec. 9.2]
19. A–D–F–E–C–B–A [Sec. 9.2]   **20.** A–B–E–D–C–A [Sec. 9.2]

21.

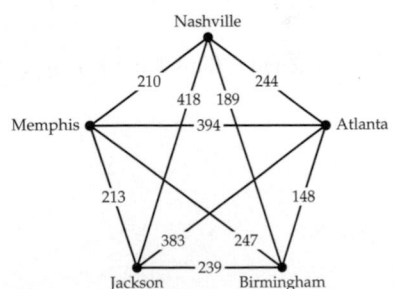

Memphis–Nashville–Birmingham–Atlanta–Jackson–Memphis   [Sec. 9.2]

22. A–E–B–C–D–A [Sec. 9.2]   **23.**

[Sec. 9.3]

24.

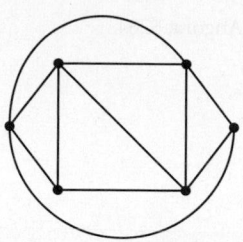

See the *Student Solutions Manual* for the solutions to Exercises 25–26.

[Sec. 9.3]

27. 5 vertices, 8 edges, 5 faces [Sec. 9.3]   **28.** 14 vertices, 16 edges, 4 faces [Sec. 9.3]   **29.** Requires 4 colors [Sec. 9.4]

30. Requires 4 colors

31. 2-colorable

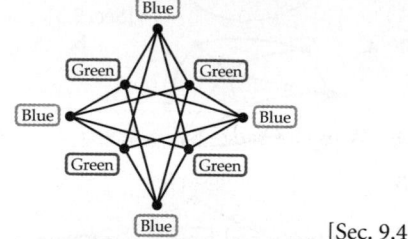

[Sec. 9.4]

[Sec. 9.4]

32. Not 2-colorable [Sec. 9.4]   **33.** 3 [Sec. 9.4]   **34.** 5 [Sec. 9.4]
35. 3 time slots: Budget and Planning, Marketing and Executive, Sales and Research

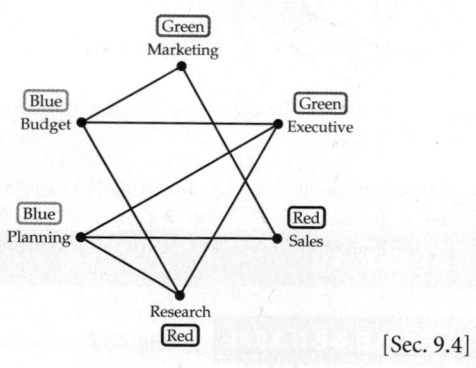

[Sec. 9.4]

CHAPTER 9 TEST   *page 638*

1. a. No   **b.** Monique   **c.** 0   **d.** No [Sec. 9.1]   **2.** Equivalent [Sec. 9.1]   **3. a.** No
b. A–B–E–A–F–D–C–F–B–C–E–D [Sec. 9.1]   **4.** No

[Sec. 9.1]

5. a. See page 579.   **b.** A–G–C–D–F–B–E–A [Sec. 9.1]

6. a.

Bancroft, Angora, Chester, Elmwood, Davenport with edge values 48, 98, 42, 32, 52, 90, 76, 84, 36, 106

b. Angora–Elmwood–Chester–Bancroft–Davenport–Angora; $284

c. Yes [Sec. 9.2]   **7.** A–E–D–B–C–F–A [Sec. 9.2]

8.

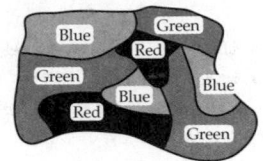

Graph with vertices C, D, B, A, E, F

[Sec. 9.3]

See the *Student Solutions Manual* for the solution to Exercise 9.

10. a. 6
b. 7
c. $v = 12$, $f = 7$, $e = 17$; $12 + 7 = 17 + 2$ [Sec. 9.3]

11. a.

b. 3   **c.**

Blue, Green, Red, Green, Blue, Red, Blue, Green [Sec. 9.4]

12.

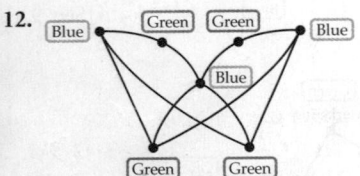

Blue, Green, Green, Blue, Blue, Green, Green [Sec. 9.4]

CHAPTER 10

EXERCISE SET 10.1 *page 651*

1. Divide the number of months by 12.   **3.** I is the interest, P is the principal, r is the interest rate, and t is the time period.
5. $560   **7.** $227.50   **9.** $202.50   **11.** $16.80   **13.** $159.60   **15.** $125   **17.** $168
19. $15,667.50   **21.** $7390.80   **23.** $2864.40   **25.** 7.5%   **27.** 10.5%   **29.** 9.3%   **31.** $161
33. $78   **35.** $18   **37.** $7406   **39.** $5730.40   **41.** $804.75   **43.** 10.2%   **45.** 10%
47. $133.32   **49.** The ordinary method. The lender benefits.   **51.** There are fewer days in September than there are in August.   **53. a.** $5, $10, $15, $20, $25   **b.** $30   **c.** $35   **d.** $40   **e.** $45
f. Multiply the interest due by 8.   **g.** Twice as large   **h.** Three times as large

EXERCISE SET 10.2 *page 669*

1. $2739.99   **3.** $852.88   **5.** $20,836.54   **7.** $12,575.23   **9.** $3532.86   **11.** $5450.09
13. $2213.84   **15.** $13,625.23   **17.** $14,835.46   **19.** $41,210.44   **21.** $7641.78   **23.** $3182.47
25. $10,094.57   **27.** $11,887.58   **29.** $3583.16   **31.** $8188.40   **33.** $391.24   **35.** $18,056.35
37. $11,120.58   **39. a.** $450   **b.** $568.22   **c.** $118.22   **41. a.** $20,528.54   **b.** $20,591.79
c. $63.25   **43. a.** $1698.59   **b.** $1716.59   **c.** $18.00   **45. a.** $10,401.63   **b.** $3401.63

47. $9612.75   **49. a.** $67,228.19   **b.** $94,161.98   **51.** $6789.69   **53.** $4651.73   **55.** $56,102.07
57. $12,152.77   **59.** $2495.45   **61.** 7.40%   **63.** 7.76%   **65.** 8.44%   **67.** 6.10%
69. $2.68, $3.58, $6.41   **71.** $3.60, $4.82, $8.63   **73.** $12.04, $16.12, $28.86   **75.** $368,012.03, $492,483.12,
$881,962.25   **77.** $25,417.46   **79.** $25,841.90   **81.** $53,473.96   **83. a.** 4.0%, 4.04%, 4.06%, 4.07%, 4.08%
b. increase   **85.** 3.04%   **87.** 6.25% compounded semiannually   **89.** 5.8% compounded quarterly
91. 10%   **93.** $561.39

EXERCISE SET 10.3   *page 686*

1. $1.48   **3.** $152.32   **5.** $335.87   **7.** $15.34   **9.** $5.00   **11.** $26.93   **13.** 13.5%
15. 19.2%   **17.** $34.59   **19. a.** $696.05   **b.** $174.01   **c.** $88.46   **21. a.** $68,569.73
b. $13,713.95   **c.** $641.17   **23.** $874.88   **25.** $571.31   **27. a.** $621.19   **b.** $4372.12
29. $13,575.25   **31.** $3472.57   **33. a.** $22,740   **b.** $101.90   **c.** $161.25   **d.** $263.15
35. a. $21,100   **b.** 0.003375   **c.** $121.84   **d.** $169.44   **e.** $291.28   **37.** The monthly payment for the
loan is *PMT*. The interest rate per period, *i*, is the annual interest rate divided by 12. The term of the loan, *n*, is the number of years of the
loan times 12. Substitute these values into the Payment Formula for an APR Loan and solve for *A*, the selling price of the car. The selling
price of the car is $9775.72.   **39. a.** $168.48   **b.** $2669   **c.** $11,391.04

EXERCISE SET 10.4   *page 699*

1. $382.50   **3.** $535.50   **5.** 2.51%   **7.** 1.83%   **9. a.** $8.73   **b.** $67.50   **c.** 3,750,600 shares
d. Decrease   **e.** $22.59   **11.** 50 shares   **13. a.** Profit of $290   **b.** $78.66   **15. a.** Profit of $9096
b. $472.33   **17.** $252   **19.** $840   **21.** $22.50   **23.** 714 shares   **25.** 240 shares   **27.** The no-load
fund's value ($2800.57) is $2.05 greater than the load fund's value ($2798.52).

EXERCISE SET 10.5   *page 711*

1. $64,500; $193,500   **3.** $5625   **5.** $99,539   **7.** $34,289.38   **9.** $974.37   **11.** $2155.28
13. a. $1088.95   **b.** $392,022   **c.** $240,022   **15.** $174,606   **17.** Interest: $1407.38; principal: $495.89
19. Interest: $1347.68; principal: $123.62   **21.** $112,025.49   **23.** $61,039.75   **25.** $1071.10   **27.** $2022.50
29. a. $330.57   **b.** $140,972.40   **31. a.** $390.62   **b.** $178,273.20   **33.** $125,000   **35.** $212,065
37. No   **39.** You pay less total interest on a 15-year mortgage loan.

CHAPTER 10 REVIEW EXERCISES   *page 715*

1. $61.88 [Sec. 10.1]   **2.** $782 [Sec. 10.1]   **3.** $90 [Sec. 10.1]   **4.** $7218.40 [Sec. 10.1]
5. 7.5% [Sec. 10.1]   **6.** $3654.90 [Sec. 10.2]   **7.** $11,609.72 [Sec. 10.2]   **8.** $7859.52 [Sec. 10.2]
9. $200.23 [Sec. 10.2]   **10.** $10,683.29 [Sec. 10.2]   **11. a.** $11,318.23   **b.** $3318.23 [Sec. 10.2]
12. $19,225.50 [Sec. 10.2]   **13.** 1.1% [Sec. 10.4]   **14.** $9000 [Sec. 10.4]   **15.** $2.31 [Sec. 10.2]
16. $43,650.68 [Sec. 10.2]   **17.** 6.06% [Sec. 10.2]   **18.** 5.4% compounded semiannually [Sec. 10.2]
19. $431.16 [Sec. 10.3]   **20.** $6.12 [Sec. 10.3]   **21. a.** $259.38   **b.** 12.9% [Sec. 10.3]
22. a. $36.03   **b.** 12.9% [Sec. 10.3]   **23.** $45.41 [Sec. 10.3]   **24. a.** $10,092.69   **b.** $2018.54
c. $253.01 [Sec. 10.3]   **25.** $704.85 [Sec. 10.3]   **26. a.** $540.02   **b.** $12,196.80 [Sec. 10.3]
27. a. $29,450   **b.** $181.80   **c.** $224.17   **d.** $436.42 [Sec. 10.3]   **28. a.** Profit of $5325
b. $256.10 [Sec. 10.4]   **29.** 200 shares [Sec. 10.4]   **30.** $99,041 [Sec. 10.5]
31. a. $1659.11   **b.** $597,279.60   **c.** $341,479.60 [Sec. 10.5]   **32. a.** $1396.69
b. $150,665.74 [Sec. 10.5]   **33.** $2658.53 [Sec. 10.5]

CHAPTER 10 TEST   *page 717*

1. $108.28 [Sec. 10.1]   **2.** $202.50 [Sec. 10.1]   **3.** $8408.89 [Sec. 10.1]   **4.** 9% [Sec. 10.1]
5. $7340.87 [Sec. 10.2]   **6.** $312.03 [Sec. 10.2]   **7. a.** $15,331.03   **b.** $4831.03 [Sec. 10.2]
8. $21,949.06 [Sec. 10.2]   **9.** 1.2% [Sec. 10.4]   **10.** $1900 [Sec. 10.4]   **11.** $612,184.08 [Sec. 10.2]

12. 6.40% [Sec. 10.2]   **13.** 4.6% compounded semiannually [Sec. 10.2]   **14.** $7.79 [Sec. 10.3]   **15. a.** $48.56
b. 16.6% [Sec. 10.3]   **16.** $60.61 [Sec. 10.3]   **17. a.** loss of $4896   **b.** $226.16 [Sec. 10.4]
18. 208 shares [Sec. 10.4]   **19. a.** $6985.94   **b.** $1397.19   **c.** $174.62 [Sec. 10.3]
20. $60,083.50 [Sec. 10.5]   **21. a.** $1530.69   **b.** $221,546.46 [Sec. 10.5]   **22.** $2595.97 [Sec. 10.5]

CHAPTER 11

EXERCISE SET 11.1   *page 728*

1. {0, 2, 4, 6, 8}   **3.** {Monday, Tuesday, Wednesday, Thursday, Friday, Saturday, Sunday}
5. {HH, TT, HT, TH}   **7.** {1H, 2H, 3H, 4H, 5H, 6H, 1T, 2T, 3T, 4T, 5T, 6T}
9. $\{S_1E_1D_1, S_1E_1D_2, S_1E_2D_1, S_1E_2D_2, S_1E_3D_1, S_1E_3D_2, S_2E_1D_1, S_2E_1D_2, S_2E_2D_1, S_2E_2D_2, S_2E_3D_1, S_2E_3D_2\}$
11. {ABCD, ABDC, ACBD, ACDB, ADBC, ADCB}   **13.** {AA BB CC, AA BC CB, AB BA CC, AC BA CB, AC BB CA, AB BC CA}
15. 12   **17.** 4^{20} **19.** 7000   **21.** 90   **23.** 18   **25.** 62   **27.** 24   **29.** 15   **31.** 13^4
33. 1   **35.** Answers will vary.   **37.** 150; 25   **39.** Answers will vary.

EXERCISE SET 11.2   *page 740*

1. 40,320   **3.** 362,760   **5.** 120   **7.** 40,320   **9.** 120   **11.** $n = 7$ **13.** 6720   **15.** 181,440
17. 1   **19.** 40,320   **21.** 3360   **23.** $\dfrac{1}{720}$ **25.** 36   **27.** 1   **29.** 525   **31.** $\dfrac{60}{143}$
33. $\dfrac{360}{1001}$ **35.** 2880   **37.** 21   **39.** 792   **41.** 1   **43.** No   **45.** 120   **47.** 43,680
49. 35   **51.** 455   **53.** 16!   **55.** 28   **57.** 30   **59.** 252   **61.** 21   **63.** 9
65. 48,620   **67.** 7,484,400   **69.** 45,360   **71.** 735,471   **73.** 48   **75.** 4512   **77.** 103,776
79. Answers will vary.   **81.** $x^5 + 5x^4y + 10x^3y^2 + 10x^2y^3 + 5xy^4 + y^5$

EXERCISE SET 11.3   *page 753*

1. {HHH, HHT, HTH, HTT, THH, THT, TTH, TTT}
3. {Nov. 1, Nov. 2, Nov. 3, Nov. 4, Nov. 5, Nov. 6, Nov. 7, Nov. 8, Nov. 9, Nov. 10, Nov. 11, Nov. 12, Nov. 13, Nov. 14}
5. {Alaska, Alabama, Arizona, Arkansas}   **7.** {BBB, BBG, BGB, BGG, GBB, GBG, GGB, GGG}   **9.** {BGG, BGB, GGB, GGG}
11. {BBG, BGB, BGG, GBB, GBG, GGB, GGG}   **13.** $\dfrac{1}{2}$ **15.** $\dfrac{7}{8}$ **17.** $\dfrac{1}{4}$ **19.** $\dfrac{1}{8}$ **21.** $\dfrac{11}{16}$ **23.** $\dfrac{1}{12}$
25. $\dfrac{1}{4}$ **27.** $\dfrac{5}{36}$ **29.** $\dfrac{1}{36}$ **31.** 0   **33.** $\dfrac{1}{6}$ **35.** $\dfrac{1}{2}$ **37.** $\dfrac{1}{6}$ **39.** $\dfrac{1}{2}$ **41.** $\dfrac{1}{13}$
43. $\dfrac{3}{13}$ **45.** $\dfrac{1267}{3228}$ **47.** $\dfrac{804}{3228}$ **49.** $\dfrac{150}{3228}$ **51.** $\dfrac{26}{425}$ **53.** $\dfrac{18}{425}$ **55.** $\dfrac{58}{293}$ **57.** $\dfrac{36}{293}$
59. 1 to 14   **61.** $\dfrac{1}{4}$ **63.** 0   **65.** Answers will vary.   **67.** $\dfrac{1}{3}$ **69.** $\dfrac{3}{10}$ **71.** $\dfrac{8}{13}$ **73.** 1 to 4
75. 3 to 5   **77.** 11 to 9   **79.** 1 to 8   **81.** 1 to 3   **83.** $\dfrac{3}{11}$ **85. a.** 7 to 50   **b.** $\dfrac{7}{57}$ **87.** $\dfrac{3}{8}$
89. Answers will vary.   **91.** $\dfrac{1}{108,290}$

EXERCISE SET 11.4   *page 764*

1. Answers will vary.   3. $\dfrac{2}{13}$ 5. $\dfrac{1}{9}$ 7. 0.6   9. 0.2   11. $\dfrac{7}{10}$ 13. $\dfrac{4}{5}$ 15. $\dfrac{5}{18}$

17. $\dfrac{1}{2}$ 19. $\dfrac{11}{18}$ 21. $\dfrac{4}{13}$ 23. $\dfrac{3}{13}$ 25. $\dfrac{3}{4}$ 27. $\dfrac{1150}{3179}$ 29. $\dfrac{1170}{3179}$ 31. 0.96

33. 2499 in 2500   35. $\dfrac{5}{6}$ 37. $\dfrac{11}{12}$ 39. $\dfrac{12}{13}$ 41. $\dfrac{15}{16}$ 43. 42.1%   45. 36.1%   47. 54.5%

49. 55.3%   51. 88.8%   53. 20.4%   55. No   57. 100%   59. Answers will vary.

EXERCISE SET 11.5   *page 775*

1. Answers will vary.   3. $P(A\,|\,B) = 0.625$; $P(B\,|\,A) \approx 0.357$ 5. $P(A\,|\,B) \approx 0.389$; $P(B\,|\,A) \approx 0.115$ 7. $\dfrac{179}{864}$

9. $\dfrac{557}{921}$ 11. 0.30   13. 0.15   15. $\dfrac{5}{18}$ 17. $\dfrac{1}{5}$ 19. 0.050   21. 0.127   23. $\dfrac{6}{1045}$

25. $\dfrac{3}{1045}$ 27. $\dfrac{13}{102}$ 29. $\dfrac{8}{5525}$ 31. 0.000484   33. 0.001424   35. Independent

37. Not independent   39. $\dfrac{25}{1296}$ 41. $\dfrac{1}{72}$ 43. $\dfrac{1}{4}$ 45. $\dfrac{1}{16}$ 47. $\dfrac{1}{216}$ 49. $\dfrac{1}{169}$ 51. $\dfrac{1}{16}$

53. $\dfrac{1}{16}$ 55. a. $\dfrac{1}{32}$ b. $\dfrac{13}{425}$ 57. a. $\dfrac{100}{4913}$ b. $\dfrac{1}{51}$ 59. 0.46   61. 0.11

63. a. $\dfrac{1}{8}$ b. $\dfrac{1}{4}$ c. $\dfrac{3}{8}$

EXERCISE SET 11.6   *page 783*

1. 49.5   3. −5 cents   5. 52 cents   7. −11 cents   9. $64   11. −$204.41   13. More than $42.60
15. $39,100   17. $20,250   19. −0.017 cent   21. 7   23. 7   25. Red dice

CHAPTER 11 REVIEW EXERCISES   *page 788*

1. {11, 12, 13, 21, 22, 23, 31, 32, 33} [Sec. 11.1]   2. {26, 28, 62, 68, 82, 86} [Sec. 11.1]   3. {HHHH, HHHT, HHTH, HHTT, HTHH, HTHT, HTTH, HTTT, THHH, THHT, THTH, THTT, TTHH, TTHT, TTTH, TTTT} [Sec. 11.1]
4. {7A, 8A, 9A, 7B, 8B, 9B} [Sec. 11.1]   5. 72 [Sec. 11.1]   6. 10,000 [Sec. 11.1]   7. 6000 [Sec. 11.1]
8. 64 [Sec. 11.1]   9. 5040 [Sec. 11.2]   10. 40,296 [Sec. 11.2]   11. 1260 [Sec. 11.2]

12. 151,200 [Sec. 11.2]   13. 336 [Sec. 11.2]   14. $\dfrac{60}{143}$ [Sec. 11.2]   15. 5040 [Sec. 11.2]

16. 5040 [Sec. 11.2]   17. 2520 [Sec. 11.2]   18. 180 [Sec. 11.2]   19. 495 [Sec. 11.2]
20. 60 [Sec. 11.2]   21. 3,268,760 [Sec. 11.2]   22. 165 [Sec. 11.2]   23. 660 [Sec. 11.2]

24. 282,240 [Sec. 11.2]   25. 624 [Sec. 11.2]   26. $\dfrac{1}{4}$ [Sec. 11.3]   27. $\dfrac{3}{8}$ [Sec. 11.3]

28. 0.56 [Sec. 11.3]   29. 0.37 [Sec. 11.3]   30. 0.85 [Sec. 11.3]   31. $\dfrac{1}{9}$ [Sec. 11.3]   32. $\dfrac{17}{18}$ [Sec. 11.4]

33. $\dfrac{1}{6}$ [Sec. 11.4]   34. $\dfrac{5}{9}$ [Sec. 11.4]   35. $\dfrac{2}{9}$ [Sec. 11.5]   36. $\dfrac{1}{6}$ [Sec. 11.5]   37. $\dfrac{3}{4}$ [Sec. 11.4]

38. $\dfrac{4}{13}$ [Sec. 11.4]   39. $\dfrac{12}{13}$ [Sec. 11.4]   40. $\dfrac{2}{3}$ [Sec. 11.5]   41. 5 to 31 [Sec. 11.3]

42. 1 to 3 [Sec. 11.3]   43. $\dfrac{5}{9}$ [Sec. 11.3]   44. $\dfrac{1}{2}$ [Sec. 11.3]   45. 0.036 [Sec. 11.4]

46. $\dfrac{173}{1000}$ [Sec. 11.4]   47. $\dfrac{5}{8}$ [Sec. 11.3]   48. 1 to 5 [Sec. 11.3]   49. $\dfrac{7}{16}$ [Sec. 11.5]

50. $\dfrac{646}{1771}$ [Sec. 11.5]   **51.** $\dfrac{7}{253}$ [Sec. 11.5]   **52.** 0.37 [Sec. 11.3]   **53.** 0.62 [Sec. 11.4]

54. 0.07 [Sec. 11.3]   **55.** 0.47 [Sec. 11.5]   **56.** 0.29 [Sec. 11.5]   **57.** $\dfrac{1}{216}$ [Sec. 11.5]

58. 0.60 [Sec. 11.5]   **59.** 0.16 [Sec. 11.5]   **60.** $\dfrac{175}{256}$ [Sec. 11.5]   **61.** 0.648 [Sec. 11.5]

62. 0.029 [Sec. 11.5]   **63.** 0.135 [Sec. 11.4]   **64.** −50 cents [Sec. 11.6]   **65.** 25 cents [Sec. 11.6]
66. −37.5 cents [Sec. 11.6]   **67.** About 5.4 [Sec. 11.6]   **68.** $295.36 [Sec. 11.6]   **69.** $760.60 [Sec. 11.6]
70. $11,000 [Sec. 11.6]

CHAPTER 11 TEST   *page 791*

1. {A2, D2, G2, K2, A3, D3, G3, K3, A4, D4, G4, K4} [Sec. 11.1]   **2.** 72 [Sec. 11.1]   **3.** 5040 [Sec. 11.2]
4. About 1.09×10^{10} [Sec. 11.2]   **5.** 116,280 [Sec. 11.2]   **6.** $\dfrac{7}{12}$ [Sec. 11.3]   **7.** Yes [Sec. 11.5]

8. $\dfrac{1}{17}$ [Sec. 11.3]   **9.** 0.72 [Sec. 11.4]   **10.** 1 to 7 [Sec. 11.3]   **11.** 0.635 [Sec. 11.5]

12. 0.466 [Sec. 11.5]   **13.** $\dfrac{1}{2}$ [Sec. 11.3]   **14.** $38,350 [Sec. 11.6]

CHAPTER 12

EXERCISE SET 12.1   *page 803*

1. 7; 7; 7   **3.** 22; 14; no mode   **5.** 18.8; 8.1; no mode   **7.** 192.4; 190; 178   **9.** 0.1; −3; −5   **11. a.** Yes.
The mean is computed by using the sum of all the data.   **b.** No. The median is not affected unless the middle value, or one of the
two middle values, in a data set is changed.   **13.** ≈38; 35; 35   **15. a.** Answers will vary.   **b.** Answers will vary.
17. ≈82.9   **19.** 82   **21.** 2.5   **23.** ≈6.1 points; 5 points; 2 points and 5 points   **25.** ≈7.2; 7; 7
27. 64°   **29.** −6°F   **31.** 92   **33. a.** ≈0.275   **b.** ≈0.273   **c.** No   **35.** 81
37. $d_1 = d_2$

$$r_1 = \frac{d_1}{t_1} \qquad r_2 = \frac{d_2}{t_2} = \frac{d_1}{t_2}$$

$$t_1 = \frac{d_1}{r_1} \qquad t_2 = \frac{d_1}{r_2}$$

$$r = \frac{d_1 + d_2}{t_1 + t_2} = \frac{d_1 + d_1}{t_1 + t_2} = \frac{2d_1}{t_1 + t_2}$$

$$= \frac{2d_1}{\dfrac{d_1}{r_1} + \dfrac{d_1}{r_2}} = \frac{2d_1}{d_1\left(\dfrac{1}{r_1} + \dfrac{1}{r_2}\right)}$$

$$= \frac{2}{\dfrac{1}{r_1} + \dfrac{1}{r_2}} \cdot \left(\frac{r_1 r_2}{r_1 r_2}\right) = \frac{2r_1 r_2}{r_1 + r_2}$$

39. Yes. Joanne has a smaller average for the first month and the second month, but she has a larger average for both months combined.

EXERCISE SET 12.2   *page 815*

1. 84°F   **3.** 21; 8.2; 67.1   **5.** 3.3; 1.3; 1.7   **7.** 52; 17.7; 311.6   **9.** 0; 0; 0   **11.** 23; 8.3; 69.6
13. Opinions will vary. However, many climbers would consider rope B to be safer because of its small standard deviation.
15. The students in the college statistic course because the range of weights is greater.   **17. a.** 30.1; 10.1   **b.** 15.6; 6.5
c. Winning scores; winning scores   **19. a.** 44.9; 9.3   **b.** 42.8; 7.7   **c.** National League; National League

21. 54.8 years; 6.2 years   **23. a.** Answers will vary.   **b.** The population standard deviation remains the same.
25. a. 0   **b.** Yes   **c.** No

EXERCISE SET 12.3   *page 828*

1. a. ≈ 0.87 **b.** ≈ 1.74 **c.** ≈ -2.17 **d.** 0.0   **3. a.** ≈ -0.32 **b.** ≈ 0.21 **c.** ≈ 1.16
d. ≈ -0.95 **5. a.** ≈ -0.67 **b.** 147.78 mm Hg   **7. a.** ≈ 0.72 **b.** ≈ 112.16 mg/dl   **9.** The score in
part a.   **11.** $\approx$59th percentile   **13.** 6396 students   **15. a.** 50%   **b.** 12%   **c.** 38%
17. $Q_1 = 5, Q_2 = 10, Q_3 = 26$ **19.**

The ERAs in the National League tend to be smaller than the ERAs in the American League. Also, the range of the ERAs is larger for the National League.

21.

The median salary for men was approximately as high as the highest salary for women. The lowest salary for men was approximately the median salary for women.

23. a. $\mu = 0, \sigma = 1$ **b.** $\mu = 0, \sigma = 1$ **c.** $\mu = 0, \sigma = 1$

EXERCISE SET 12.4   *page 844*

1. Greater   **3. a.** 95.4%   **b.** 15.9%   **c.** 81.8%   **5. a.** 81.8%   **b.** 0.15%   **7. a.** 1272 vehicles
b. 12 vehicles   **9.** 0.433 square unit   **11.** 0.468 square unit   **13.** 0.130 square unit   **15.** 0.878 square unit
17. 0.097 square unit   **19.** 0.013 square unit   **21.** 0.926 square unit   **23.** 0.997 square unit   **25.** $z = 0.84$
27. $z = -0.90$ **29.** $z = 0.35$ **31. a.** 30.9%   **b.** 33.4%   **33. a.** 13.6%   **b.** 35.2%
35. a. 10.6%   **b.** 98.8%   **37. a.** 0.106   **b.** ≈ 0.460 **39. a.** ≈ 0.749 **b.** 0.023
41. Answers will vary.   **43.** True   **45.** True   **47.** False   **49.** False   **51.** True
53. a. They are identical.   **b.** The area of the region is the same with or without the vertical boundary at $z = 1$.
55. -0.84 and 0.84 **57.** For any positive constant k, the probability that a random variable will take on a value within k standard
deviations of the mean is at least $1 - \dfrac{1}{k^2}$. According to Chebyshev's Theorem, a minimum of 75% of the data in any data set must lie
within 2 standard deviations of the mean.

EXERCISE SET 12.5   *page 857*

1. a. b   **b.** c   **3. a.**

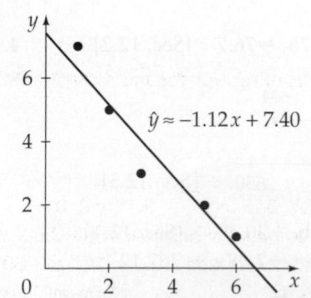

$\hat{y} \approx -1.12x + 7.40$

b. $n = 5, \Sigma x = 17, \Sigma y = 18, \Sigma x^2 = 75,$
$(\Sigma x)^2 = 289, \Sigma xy = 42$
c. $a = -\dfrac{48}{43} \approx -1.12, b = \dfrac{318}{43} \approx 7.40$
d. See the graph in part a.
e. Yes
f. $y \approx 3.6$
g. $r \approx -0.96$

5. $\hat{y} \approx 2.01x + 0.56; r \approx 0.96$ **7.** $\hat{y} \approx -0.72x + 9.23; r \approx -0.96$ **9.** $\hat{y} \approx 1.66x + 2.25; r \approx 0.99$
11. a. $\hat{y} \approx -0.328x + 50270.994$ **b.** $40,431 **c.** $r \approx -0.99$ **d.** As the number of miles the car is driven increases, the value of the car decreases. **13. a.** $\hat{y} \approx x + 15.6$ **b.** $\approx 25.6\%$ **15. a.** $r \approx 0.99$ **b.** Yes, at least for the years 1998 to 2003. The correlation coefficient is very close to 1, which indicates a near perfect linear correlation.
17. a. $r \approx 0.96$ **b.** Yes. The median income of men rose as the median income of women rose. **19. a.** $r = 1.00$ **b.** The data display a perfect linear relationship. **c.** $\hat{y} = 1.8x + 32$ **d.** 95°F **e.** Interpolation
21. Yes. The linear correlation coefficient is $r \approx 0.98$. **23. a.** $\hat{y} \approx 0.98x + 15.45$ **b.** In situations in which one or two of the y data values are suspected of being off by a considerable amount due to experimental error.

CHAPTER 12 REVIEW EXERCISES   *page 863*

1. 14.7; 14; 12 [Sec. 12.1] **2.** The mode [Sec. 12.1] **3.** Answers will vary. [Sec. 12.1] **4. a.** Median
b. Mode **c.** Mean [Sec. 12.1] **5.** 1331.125 feet; 1223.5 feet; 1200 feet; 462 feet [Sec. 12.1/12.2]
6. 36 miles per hour [Sec. 12.1] **7.** ≈ 3.10 [Sec. 12.1] **8. a.** 1.25 **b.** The 89th percentile [Sec. 12.4]
9. ≈ 3.16; ≈ 10.00 [Sec. 12.2] **10.** $5.008; $4.885; $\approx $0.679 [Sec. 12.1/12.2] **11. a.** The second student's mean is
5 points higher than the first student's mean. **b.** They are the same. [Sec. 12.1/12.2] **12. a.** ≈ -1.73
b. ≈ 0.58 [Sec. 12.3] **13.**

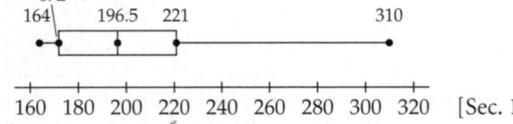

14. a. 8 **b.** 40 **c.** 8
[Sec. 12.4]

[Sec. 12.3]

15. a. 40% **b.** 0.34 [Sec. 12.4] **16.** Yes. $r \approx 0.997$, which is greater than 0.9. [Sec 12.5] **17. a.** $y = 12.9x + 8.15$
b. $y = -4.5x + 71$ **c.** Greater than [Sec. 12.5] **18.** No. No information is given about how the scores are distributed
below the mean. [Sec. 12.4] **19. a.** 0.933 **b.** 0.309 [Sec. 12.4] **20. a.** 21.2% **b.** 95.4% [Sec. 12.4]
21. a. 6.7% **b.** 64.5% **c.** 78.8% [Sec. 12.4] **22.** 93.15 million miles [Sec. 12.1]
23. a.

b. $n = 5, \Sigma x = 67, \Sigma y = 25, \Sigma x^2 = 921, (\Sigma x)^2 = 4489, \Sigma xy = 310$
c. $a \approx -1.08, b \approx 19.44$
d. See the graph in part a.
e. Yes
f. ≈ 10.8
g. $r \approx -0.95$ [Sec. 12.5]

24. a. $r \approx 0.999$ **b.** $\hat{y} \approx 0.07x + 0.29$ **c.** 13.94 inches [Sec. 12.5]
25. a. $\hat{y} \approx 0.018x + 0.0005$ **b.** Yes. $r \approx 0.999$, which is very close to 1. **c.** 1.80 seconds [Sec. 12.5]
26. a. $\hat{y} \approx 13.67x + 108.24, r \approx 0.998$ **b.** 108.24 [Sec. 12.5]

CHAPTER 12 TEST   *page 867*

1. 9.1; 9; 7 [Sec. 12.1] **2.** 82.2 [Sec. 12.1] **3.** 24; ≈ 8.76; ≈ 76.7 [Sec. 12.2] **4. a.** ≈ 1.18
b. ≈ -0.49 [Sec. 12.3] **5.**

439.5
413   462   523   634

400   450   500   550   600   650 [Sec. 12.3]

6. a. 33%
b. 40% [Sec. 12.4]

7. a. 47.7% **b.** 15.9% [Sec. 12.4] **8. a.** 10.6% **b.** 20.3% [Sec. 12.4]
9. Yes. $r \approx -0.99$. Therefore $|-0.99| > 0.9$ [Sec. 12.5] **10. a.** $\hat{y} \approx -7.98x + 767.12$
b. 57 calories [Sec. 12.5]

CHAPTER 13

EXERCISE SET 13.1   *page 884*

1. To calculate the standard divisor, divide the total population p by the number of items to apportion n.   **3.** The standard quota for a state is the whole number part of the quotient of the state's population divided by the standard divisor.   **5. a.** 0.273
b. 0.254   **c.** Salinas   **7.** Seaside Malls   **9. a.** 646,952; There is one representative for every 646,952 citizens in the U.S.
b. Underrepresented; The average constituency is greater than the standard divisor.   **c.** Overrepresented; The average constituency is less than the standard divisor.   **11. a.** 37.10; There is one new nurse for every 37.10 beds.   **b.** Sharp: 7; Palomar: 10; Tri-City: 8; Del Raye: 5; Rancho Verde: 7; Bel Aire: 11   **c.** Sharp: 7; Palomar: 10; Tri-City: 8; Del Raye: 5; Rancho Verde: 7; Bel Aire: 11
d. They are identical.   **13.** The population paradox occurs when the population of one state is increasing faster than that of another state, yet the first state still loses a representative.   **15.** The Balinski-Young Impossibility Theorem states that any apportionment method will either violate the quota rule or will produce paradoxes such as the Alabama paradox.   **17. a.** Yes
b. No   **c.** Yes   **19. a.** Boston: 2; Chicago: 20   **b.** Yes. Chicago lost a vice president while Boston gained one.
21. a. Sixth grade   **b.** Sixth grade; same   **23.** Valley   **25. a.** They are the same.   **b.** Using the Jefferson method, the humanities division gets one less computer and the sciences division gets one more computer compared with using the Webster method.   **27.** The Jefferson and Webster methods   **29.** The Huntington-Hill method   **31.** Answers will vary.

33. Del Mar: 3; Wheatly: 7; West: 5; Mountain View: 7   **35. a.** $\dfrac{P_A}{a+1}$ **b.** $\dfrac{P_B}{b}$ **c.** $\dfrac{\frac{P_B}{b} - \frac{P_A}{a+1}}{\frac{P_A}{a+1}}$ **d.** $\dfrac{\frac{P_A}{a} - \frac{P_B}{b+1}}{\frac{P_B}{b+1}}$

e. $\dfrac{\frac{P_A}{a} - \frac{P_B}{b+1}}{\frac{P_B}{b+1}} < \dfrac{\frac{P_B}{b} - \frac{P_A}{a+1}}{\frac{P_A}{a+1}}$ **f.** $\dfrac{(P_B)^2}{b(b+1)} < \dfrac{(P_A)^2}{a(a+1)}$

EXERCISE SET 13.2   *page 904*

1. A majority means that a choice receives more than 50% of the votes. A plurality means that the choice with the most votes wins. It is possible to have a plurality without a majority when there are more than two choices.   **3.** If there are n choices in an election, each voter ranks the choices by giving n points to the voter's first choice, $n - 1$ points to the voter's second choice, and so on, with the voter's least favorite choice receiving 1 point. The choice with the most points is the winner.   **5.** In the pairwise comparison voting method, each choice is compared one-on-one with each of the other choices. A choice receives 1 point for a win, 0.5 point for a tie, and 0 points for a loss. The choice with the greatest number of points is the winner.   **7.** No; no   **9. a.** Al Gore   **b.** No
c. George Bush   **11. a.** 35   **b.** 18   **c.** Scooby Doo   **13.** Go to a theater   **15.** Bugs Bunny
17. Elaine Garcia   **19.** Blue and white   **21.** Raymond Lee   **23. a.** Buy new computers for the club.   **b.** Pay for several members to travel to a convention.   **c.** Pay for several members to travel to a convention.   **d.** Answers will vary.
25. *Return of the Jedi*   **27.** There is a tie between the panther and the bobcat.   **29.** Blue and white   **31.** No
33. Yes   **35.** No   **37. a.** Stephen Hyde   **b.** Stephen Hyde received the fewest number of first-place votes.
c. John Lorenz   **d.** The candidate that wins all head-to-head matches does not win the election.   **e.** John Lorenz
f. The candidate winning the original election (Stephen Hyde) did not remain the winner in a recount in which a losing candidate withdrew from the race.   **39.** Medin is president, Jen is vice president, Andrew is secretary, and Hector is treasurer.
41. The Borda Count method

EXERCISE SET 13.3   *page 922*

1. a. 6   **b.** 4   **c.** 3   **d.** 6   **e.** No   **f.** A and C   **g.** 15   **h.** 6   **3.** 0.60, 0.20, 0.20
5. 0.50, 0.30, 0.10, 0.10   **7.** 0.36, 0.28, 0.20, 0.12, 0.04   **9.** 1.00, 0.00, 0.00, 0.00, 0.00, 0.00   **11.** 0.44, 0.20, 0.20, 0.12,
0.04   **13. a.** Exercise 9   **b.** Exercises 3, 5, 6, 9, and 12   **c.** None   **d.** Exercise 8   **15.** 0.33, 0.33, 0.33
17. a. {12: 1, 1, 1, 1, 1, 1, 1, 1, 1, 1, 1, 1}   **b.** Yes   **c.** Yes   **d.** Divide the vote power, 1, by the quota, 12.
19. Dictator: A; dummies: B, C, D, E   **21.** None   **23. a.** 0.60, 0.20, 0.20   **b.** Answers will vary.
25. a. 0.33, 0.33, 0.33   **b.** This system has the same effect as a one-person, one-vote system.

27. a. 11 and 14 **b.** 15 and 16 **c.** No **29.** Yes **31.** In the weighted system, all voters have equal weight and the quota is equal to 50% of the sum of the weights rounded up to the nearest whole number, or a strict majority. **33.** Answers will vary. **35. a.** $BPI(29) \approx 0.0855$, $BPI(27) \approx 0.081$, $BPI(13) \approx 0.0422$, $BPI(12) \approx 0.039$, $BPI(10) \approx 0.0326$, $BPI(7) \approx 0.0229$, $BPI(4) \approx 0.0131$ **b.** 6.5 times

CHAPTER 13 REVIEW EXERCISES *page 927*

1. a. 0.098 **b.** 0.194 **c.** High Desert **2.** Morena Valley **3. a.** Health: 7; business: 18; engineering: 10; science: 15 **b.** Health: 6; business: 18; engineering: 10; science: 16 **c.** Health: 7; business: 18; engineering: 10; science: 15 [Sec. 13.1] **4. a.** Newark: 9; Cleveland: 6; Chicago: 11; Philadelphia: 4; Detroit: 5 **b.** Newark: 9; Cleveland: 6; Chicago: 11; Philadelphia: 4; Detroit: 5 **c.** Newark: 9; Cleveland: 6; Chicago: 11; Philadelphia: 4; Detroit: 5 [Sec. 13.1] **5. a.** No. None of the offices loses a new printer. **b.** Yes. Office A drops from two new printers to only one new printer. [Sec. 13.1] **6. a.** *A*: 2; *B*: 5; *C*: 3; *D*: 16; *E*: 2. No. None of the centers lose an automobile. **b.** No. None of the centers lose an automobile. [Sec. 13.1] **7. a.** Los Angeles: 9; Newark: 2 **b.** Yes. Newark loses a computer file server. [Sec. 13.1] **8. a.** *A*: 10; *B*: 3; *C*: 21 **b.** Yes. The population of region B grew at a higher rate than the population of region A, yet region B lost an inspector to region A. [Sec. 13.1] **9.** Yes [Sec. 13.1] **10.** Yes [Sec. 13.1] **11. a.** A **b.** B [Sec. 13.1] **12. a.** Shannon M. **b.** Hannah A. **c.** Hannah A. won all head-to-head comparisons, but lost the overall election. **d.** Hannah A. **e.** Hannah A. received a majority of the first-place votes, but lost the overall election. [Sec. 13.2] **13. a.** Hannah A. **b.** Cynthia L., a losing candidate, withdrew from the race and caused a change in the overall winner of the election. [Sec. 13.2] **14.** The monotonicity criterion was violated because the only change was that the supporter of a losing candidate changed his or her vote to support the original winner, but the original winner did not win the second vote. [Sec. 13.2] **15. a.** 18 **b.** 18 **c.** Yes **d.** A and C **e.** 15 **f.** 6 [Sec. 13.3] **16. a.** 35 **b.** 35 **c.** Yes **d.** A **e.** 31 **f.** 10 [Sec. 13.3] **17.** 0.60, 0.20, 0.20 [Sec. 13.3] **18.** 0.20, 0.20, 0.20, 0.20, 0.20 [Sec. 13.3] **19.** 0.42, 0.25, 0.25, 0.08 [Sec. 13.3] **20.** 0.62, 0.14, 0.14, 0.05, 0.05 [Sec. 13.3] **21.** Dictator: A; dummies: B, C, D, E [Sec. 13.3] **22.** Dummy: D [Sec. 13.3] **23.** 0.50, 0.125, 0.125, 0.125, 0.125 [Sec. 13.3] **24. a.** Manuel Ortega **b.** No **c.** Crystal Kelley [Sec. 13.2] **25. a.** Vail **b.** Aspen [Sec. 13.2] **26.** A. Kim [Sec. 13.2] **27.** Snickers [Sec. 13.2] **28.** A. Kim [Sec. 13.2] **29.** Snickers [Sec. 13.2]

CHAPTER 13 TEST *page 931*

1. Spring Valley **2. a.** Sales: 17; advertising: 4; service: 11; manufacturing: 53 **b.** Sales: 17; advertising: 4; service: 10; manufacturing: 54; no [Sec. 13.1] **3. a.** Cedar Falls $\approx$ 77,792; Lake View $\approx$ 70,290 **b.** Cedar Falls [Sec. 13.1] **4. a.** 33 **b.** 26 **c.** No **d.** A and C **e.** 31 **f.** 10 [Sec. 13.3] **5. a.** Aquafina **b.** No **c.** Evian [Sec. 13.2] **6.** New York [Sec. 13.2] **7. a.** Afternoon **b.** Noon [Sec. 13.2] **8. a.** Proposal A **b.** Proposal B **c.** Eliminating a losing choice changed the outcome of the vote. **e.** Proposal B won all head-to-head comparisons but lost the vote when all the choices were on the ballot. [Sec. 13.2] **9.** 0.42, 0.25, 0.25, 0.08 [Sec. 13.3] **10.** 0.40, 0.20, 0.20, 0.20 [Sec. 13.3]

APPENDIX

APPENDIX *page 936*

1. Meter, liter, gram **3.** Kilometer **5.** Centimeter **7.** Gram **9.** Meter **11.** Gram **13.** Milliliter **15.** Milligram **17.** Millimeter **19.** Milligram **21.** Gram **23.** Kiloliter **25.** Milliliter **27. a.** Column 2: k, c, m; column 3: 10^9, 10^3, 10^2, $\dfrac{1}{10^3}$, $\dfrac{1}{10^{12}}$; column 4: 1 000 000 000, 10, 0.1, 0.01, 0.000 001, 0.000 000 001 **b.** Answers will vary. **29.** 910 **31.** 1.856 **33.** 7.285 **35.** 8 000 **37.** 0.034 **39.** 29.7 **41.** 7.530 **43.** 9 200 **45.** 36 **47.** 2 350 **49.** 83 **51.** 0.716 **53.** 6.302 **55.** 458 **57.** 9.2 **59.** 2 grams **61.** 24 liters **63.** 16 servings **65.** 4 tablets **67.** The case containing 12 one-liter bottles **69.** 500 seconds **71.** $17,430 **73.** $66.50

A Brief History of Mathematics

From the beginning to 4000 B.C.

There is very little evidence to create a definitive picture of mathematics prior to 4000 B.C. Early humans were more focused on survival than on counting possessions. Much of the suppositions about early mathematics are based on findings by anthropologists who study existing primitive cultures. For instance, there are clans in Australia that count only to two. Any quantity beyond that is many. Some South American clans count to higher numbers but do so by using only the words for one and two. For instance, four is two-two and five is one-two-two. Generally these clans use many for numbers beyond eight. Historians suspect that early human cultures had the same math abilities as these clans.

4000 to 300 B.C.

Counting days was an important function to early communities. As hunters and gatherers banded together to form tribes, the passage of time was important for planting crops and preparing for changes in the seasons. Around 4000 B.C. the Egyptians had created a calendar. This is significant in the history of mathematics because it is the first record of humans organizing number concepts.

By 3000 B.C. there is evidence arithmetic had evolved and was used by merchants. The Rhind papyrus, written around 1650 B.C., contained methods for working with fractions and solving equations. In some sense, it is an example of a mathematics textbook.

Rhind papyrus

Prior to 600 B.C., mathematics was prescriptive. That is, there were procedures for doing certain calculations or solving some equations. The procedures were based on "this works for this type of problem" and not on underlying principles or logic that could be applied to a broad class of problems. Then, around 600 B.C., the merchant Thales of Miletus, who had studied Egyptian geometry and Babylonian astronomy, concluded that certain facts could be deduced from other facts. He is generally regarded as the first person to use logical reasoning as a way of doing mathematics. Thales was one of the Seven Sages of Greece and is credited with the saying "Know thyself."

Aristotle

The creation of Plato's Academy around 385 B.C. provided a place where scholars could meet and discuss problems from many fields and in particular mathematics. One of the scholars to study at Plato's Academy was Aristotle. Although Aristotle contributed to many areas of science and philosophy, his work on logic laid the foundation for modern mathematics.

300 B.C. to A.D. 200

Euclid used the principles of logic as stated by Aristotle to write the *Elements*, certainly one of the most important works of mathematics in all of history. This book established mathematics as a discipline of reasoning that required mathematical theorems to have irrefutable arguments to confirm their validity.

Euclid

Approximately a generation after Euclid, Archimedes applied some of the theorems of geometry to mathematics and to physics. He gave us the approximation $\pi \approx \frac{22}{7}$ and the Archimedean screw, a device still used in some parts of the world to lift water from a canal onto land to irrigate farms.

Claudius Ptolemy used the geometry of Euclid to write what is now called the *Almagest*, a complete account of Greek astronomy. This book established that a real-world situation (for instance, the orbits of planets) could be described by a mathematical model.

Archimedes

200 to 1000

Egyptian and Babylonian mathematics were presented in words. Then, around A.D. 250, Diophantes of Alexandria wrote a series of 13 books called *Arithmetica*. The major focus of these books was algebra and the solutions of equations. The importance of *Arithmetica* to modern mathematics is that he changed from a verbal description of mathematics to a symbolic one. For instance, he would write $\Delta^Y \theta$ which, in our modern notation, is $9x^2$. In his book, Diophantes stated some of rules of solving equations such as "add the same term to each side of an equation."

After the first publication of the major works we have discussed, other scholars would translate, annotate, or amplify the concepts contained in these works. Hypatia is the first known woman to undertake such a task. She lectured at the Museum of Alexandria, the most prestigious school of ancient Egypt, and wrote commentaries on the *Elements*, the *Almagest*, and *Arithmetica*.

Hypatia